Proceedings

21st Annual IEEE Symposium on Logic in Computer Science

LICS 2006

Proceedings

21st Annual IEEE Symposium on Logic in Computer Science

LICS 2006

12-15 August 2006 • Seattle, Washington

Sponsored by
IEEE Computer Society
Technical Committee on Mathematical Foundations of Computing

With support from
Cadence
IBM
Microsoft Research
NEC
the John von Neumann Minerva Center for Development of Reactive Systems
US National Science Foundation

IEEE Computer Society
IEEE
Los Alamitos, California
Washington • Tokyo

IEEE Computer Society Order Number P2631
ISBN-13: 0-7695-2631-7
ISBN-10: 0-7695-2631-4
ISSN 1043-6871

Additional copies may be ordered from:

IEEE Computer Society
Customer Service Center
10662 Los Vaqueros Circle
P.O. Box 3014
Los Alamitos, CA 90720-1314
Tel: + 1 800 272 6657
Fax: + 1 714 821 4641
http://computer.org/cspress
csbooks@computer.org

IEEE Service Center
445 Hoes Lane
P.O. Box 1331
Piscataway, NJ 08855-1331
Tel: + 1 732 981 0060
Fax: + 1 732 981 9667
http://shop.ieee.org/store/
customer-service@ieee.org

IEEE Computer Society
Asia/Pacific Office
Watanabe Bldg., 1-4-2
Minami-Aoyama
Minato-ku, Tokyo 107-0062
JAPAN
Tel: + 81 3 3408 3118
Fax: + 81 3 3408 3553
tokyo.ofc@computer.org

Individual paper REPRINTS may be ordered at: reprints@computer.org

Editorial production by Lisa O'Conner
Cover graphic design by Alvy Ray Smith
Cover art production by Joe Daigle/Studio Productions
Printed in the United States of America by The Printing House

IEEE Computer Society

IEEE

IEEE Computer Society
Conference Publishing Services
http://www.computer.org/proceedings/

Table of Contents

LICS 2006

Participant Meeting in FLoC 2006

▶Session 3: Pushdown Systems

▶Invited Talk

▶Session 4: Logics of Programs

▶Session 5: Proof Theory

▶Session 6: Model Theory

▶ Invited Talk

▶ Session 7: Temporal Logics and Automata

▶ Session 8: Lambda Calculus

▶ Keynote Session: Celebrating Birth Centennial of Kurt Gődel

▶ Invited Talk

▶Session 9: Timed and Stochastic Systems

▶Session 10: Verification

▶Session 11: Approximations

List of Short Presentations

Foreword

This volume contains the proceedings of the Twenty-First Annual IEEE Symposium on Logic in Computer Science (LICS 2006). LICS is an annual international forum on topics that lie at the intersection of computer science and mathematical logic. LICS 2006 is scheduled for August 12–15, 2006 in Seattle, USA, as one of the participating meetings in the Fourth Federated Logic Conference (FLoC 2006).

This volume contains 39 contributed papers that were selected from 152 submissions. The high quality of the submissions received this year and the broad spectrum of topics they covered attest to the vitality of our subject and bode well for the future of LICS. At the same time, the high quality of the submissions and the constraints of the conference made the final decisions quite difficult. Each paper was initially reviewed by four members of the program committee. In many cases, the committee members chose to consult additional reviewers whose names are listed later. The program committee did not meet in person, but carried out extensive electronic discussion over a period of two weeks.

This volume also contains either abstracts or papers corresponding to invited talks. This year, LICS also has a special session to celebrate the birth centennial of Kurt Gődel. In keeping with the LICS tradition, we also solicited abstracts for short presentations on relevant and ongoing research. The program includes 8 such presentations.

An important and pleasant task of the program committee was the selection of the best student paper for the Kleene Award. From a strong pool of several excellent student papers, the committee selected the paper "Context Semantics, Linear Logic and Computational Complexity" by Ugo Dal Lago as the winner of the 2006 Kleene Award for Best Student Paper. On behalf of the committee, I would like to extend my warmest congratulations to the author.

I wish to thank all the authors who submitted papers for consideration, and the invited speakers. On behalf of the LICS community, let me also thank all the members of the LICS 2006 Program Committee and the additional reviewers for their hard work in reading and evaluating the papers.

Special thanks go to Margus Veanes for his effort as LICS 2006 Conference Chair, Tom Ball and Jakob Rehoff for their efforts as FLoC 2006 Conference Co-Chairs, Moshe Vardi for his guidance as FLoC 2006 General Chair, Stephan Kreutzer and Nicole Schweikardt for their help as LICS Publicity Co-Chairs, and Philip Scott for his work as LICS Workshops Chair.

I am grateful to Andrei Voronkov for allowing the use of EasyChair conference management software and for providing excellent support throughout the review process.

Finally, I wish to acknowledge and thank the financial support provided by Cadence, IBM, Microsoft Research, NEC, the John von Neumann Minerva Center for Development of Reactive Systems, and US National Science Foundation.

The conclusion of LICS 2006 marks the end of the tenure of Phokion Kolaitis as LICS General Chair. On behalf of the entire LICS community, I would like to express my gratitude to Phokion for his leadership, guidance, and counsel during the past three years.

Rajeev Alur

University of Pennsylvania

LICS 2006 Program Chair

Conference Organization

Program Chair

Rajeev Alur, *University of Pennsylvania*

Program Committee

Luca Aceto, *Reykjavik Univ., Iceland and Aalborg University, Denmark*
Christel Baier, *University of Bonn, Germany*
Maria Luisa Bonet, *Polytechnic University of Catalunya, Spain*
Flavio Corradini, *University of Camarino, Italy*
Victor Dalmau, *University Pompeu Fabra, Spain*
Thomas Eiter, *TU Vienna, Austria*
Kousha Etessami, *University of Edinburgh, UK*
Amy Felty, *University of Ottawa, Canada*
Cedric Fournet, *Microsoft Research, UK*
Patrice Godefroid, *Bell Labs, USA*
Jason Hickey, *California Institute of Technology, USA*
Radha Jagadeesan, *DePaul University, USA*
Leonid Libkin, *University of Toronto, Canada*
Patrick Lincoln, *SRI, USA*
Yoram Moses, *Technion, Israel*
George Necula, *University of California at Berkeley, USA*
Joel Ouaknine, *Oxford University, UK*
Davide Sangiorgi, *University of Bologna, Italy*
Mahesh Viswanathan, *University of Illinois at Urbana-Champaign, USA*
Thomas Wilke, *University of Kiel, Germany*

Conference Chair

Magus Veanes, *Microsoft Research, Redmond, USA*

Workshops Chair

Philip J. Scott, *University of Ottawa, Canada*

Publicity Co-Chairs

Stephan Kreutzer and Nicole Schweikardt, *Humboldt-University, Berlin, Germany*

General Chair

Phokion G. Kolaitis, *IBM Almaden Research Center and University of California, Santa Cruz, USA*

Organizing Committee

Samson Abramsky
Rajeev Alur
Franz Baader
Andrei Broder
Samuel Buss
Edmund Clarke
Amy Felty
Hal Gabow
Lauri Hella
Radhakrishnan Jagadeesan
Alan Jeffrey
Phokion Kolaitis (chair)
Stephan Kreutzer
Johann Makowsky
John Mitchell
Mogens Nielsen
Prakash Panangaden
Femke van Raamsdonk
Philip Scott
Nicole Schweikardt
Magus Veanes
Andrei Voronkov

Advisory Board

Robert Constable
Yuri Gurevich
Claude Kirchner
Dexter Kozen
Ursula Martin
Albert Meyer
Leszek Pacholski
Vaughan Pratt
Andre Scedrov
Dana S. Scott
Moshe Y. Vardi
Glynn Winskel

List of Reviewers

Klaus Aehlig
Amal Ahmed
Alessandro Aldini
Luca de Alfaro
Thorsten Altenkirch
Andrew Appel
Krzysztof Apt
Ofer Arieli
Argimiro Arratia
David Aspinall
Robert Atkey
Albert Atserias
Serge Autexier
Jeremy Avigad
Arnon Avron
Matthias Baaz
Jos Baeten
Patrick Baillot
Steffen van Bakel
Paolo Baldan
Pablo Barcelo
Howard Barringer
Gilles Barthe
Michael Benedikt
Nick Benton
Maria Rita Di Berardini
Josh Berdine
Ulrich Berger
Dietmar Bergwanger
Marco Bernardo
Nathalie Bertrand
Dietmar Berwanger
Karthik Bhargavan
Achim Blumensath
Bernard Boigelot
Maria Paola Bonacina
Michele Boreale
Johannes Borgstrom
Ahmed Bouajjani
Patricia Bouyer
Julian Bradfield
Aaron R. Bradley
Franck van Breugel
Roberto Bruni
Kai Brunnler
Glenn Bruns
Veronique Bruyre
Andrei Bulatov
Tevfik Bultan
Guillaume Burel
Diletta Romana Cacciagrano
Venanzio Capretta
Felice Cardone
Franck Cassez
Luca Cattani
Pavol Cerny
Iliano Cervesato
Evan Chang
Krishnendu Chatterjee
Swarat Chaudhuri
Marsha Chechik
Hubie Chen
Adam Chlipala
Corina Cirstea
Anders Claesson
Bob Coecke
Byron Cook
Stefania Costantini
James Cussens
Mads Dam
Ferruccio Damiani
Dennis Dams
Rene David
Rowan Davies
Anuj Dawar
Stephane Demri
Josee Desharnais
Damien Doligez
Carmel Domshlak
Gilles Dowek
Govert van Drimmelen
Bruno Dutertre
Roy Dyckhoff
Uwe Egly
Zoltan Esik
Juan Luis Esteban
Tomas Feder
Yossi Feinberg
Marcelo Fiore
Martin Fraenzle
Sybille Froeschle
David de Frutos
Kenetsu Fujita
Murdoch Gabbay
Nicola Galesi
Ricard Gavalda
Dan Ghica
Hugo Gimbert
Omer Gimenez
Lluis Godo
Massimiliano Goldwurm
Valentin Goranko
Daniele Gorla
Alexey Gotsman
Georg Gottlob
Jean Goubault-Larrecq
Gianluigi Greco
Benjamin Gregoire
Marcus Groesser
Martin Grohe
Vineet Gupta
Arie Gurfinkel
Peter Habermehl
Matthew Hague
Joseph Halpern
Michael R. Hansen
Matthew Harren
Masahito Hasegawa
Hugo Herbelin
Claudio Hermida
Pascal Hitzler
C. A. R. Hoare
Michael Huth
Hans Huttel
Giovambattista Ianni
Anna Ingolfsdottir
Petr Jancar
Peter Jeavons
Alan Jeffrey
Ranjit Jhala
Marcin Jurdzinski
Detlef Kaehler
Lukasz Kaiser
Andrew Kennedy
Delia Kesner
Claude Kirchner
Felix Klaedtke
Joachim Klein
Bartek Klin
Phokion Kolaitis
Eryk Kopczynski
Alexei Kopylov
Dexter Kozen
Christoph Kreitz
Stephan Kreutzer
Andrei Krokhin
Ralf Kuesters
Orna Kupferman
Hirohiko Kushida
Dietrich Kuske

Gerardo Lafferriere
Ugo Dal Lago
Jim Laird
Benoit Larose
Soren Lassen
James Leifer
Alexander Leitsch
Jean-Jacques Levy
Jordi Levy
Paul Blain Levy
Alexei Lisitsa
Christoph Loeding
Markus Lohrey
Etienne Lozes
Chris Lynch
Rupak Majumdar
Stefano Mancini
Jean-Yves Marion
Nicolas Markey
Miklos Maroti
Maarten Marx
Hasegawa Masahito
Andrea Masini
Richard Mayr
Igor Melatti
John Mark Mercer
Emanuela Merelli
Massimo Merro
Stefan Milius
Eugenio Moggi
Stefan Monnier
Carroll Morgan
Mohammad Reza Mousavi
Markus Mueller-Olm
Supratik Mukhopadhyay
Gopalan Nadathur
Kedar Namjoshi
Aleksandar Nanevski
Shiva Nejati
Uwe Nestmann
Roberto Nieuwenhuis
Damian Niwinski
Aleksey Nogin
Gethin Norman
Karim Nour
Jan Obdrzalek
Peter O'Hearn
Luke Ong
Jaap van Oosten
Martin Otto
Sam Owre
Luca Padovani
Catuscia Palamidessi
Paritosh Pandya
Luca Paolini
David Parker
Matthew Parkinson
Madhusudan Parthasarathy
Corina Pasareanu
Benjamin Pierce
Adolfo Piperno
Marco Pistore
Toniann Pitassi
Nir Piterman
Andrew Pitts
Randy Pollack
Damien Pous
Rosario Pugliese
Shaz Qadeer
Alexander Rabinovich
Jean-Francois Raskin
Michael Rathjens
Jason Reed
Laurent Regnier
Simona Ronchi Della Rocca
Benjamin Rossman
Sasha Rubin
Albert Rubio
Andrey Rybalchenko
Amr Sabry
Gernot Salzer
Ulrike Sattler
Francesco Scarcello
Mark Schaefer
Klaus-Dieter Schewe
Manfred Schmidt-Schauss
Alan Schmitt
Henning Schnoor
Ulrich Schoepp
Carsten Schuermann
Thomas Schwentick
Philip Scott
Luc Segoufin
Peter Selinger
Olivier Serre
Natarajan Shankar
Steven Shapiro
Alex Simpson
Pawel Sobocinski
Jeremy Sproston
Jiri Srba
Katherine StJohn
Martin Steffen
Mark-Oliver Stehr
Ben Steinberg
Colin Stirling
Lutz Strassburger
Howard Straubing
Jan Strecek
Aaron Stump
Carolyn Talcott
Tachio Terauchi
Luca Tesei
Pascal Tesson
Hayo Thielecke
Alwen Tiu
Anthony Widjaja To
Carlo Toffalori
Jacobo Toran
Ashutosh Trivedi
Stephen Tse
Pawel Urzyczyn
Daniele Varacca
Moshe Vardi
Helmut Veith
Ramesh Viswanathan
Vladimeros Vladimerou
Fer-Jan de Vries
Benjamin Wack
Klaus Wagner
Stephen Weeks
Stephanie Weirich
Vicky Weissman
Benjamin Werner
Pierre Wolper
James Worrell
Hongseok Yang
Mihalis Yannakakis
Sergio Yovine
Lotfi Zadeh
Gianluigi Zavattaro
Artur Zawlocki
Steve Zdancewic

Plenary Talk

Formal Verification of Infinite State Systems Using Boolean Methods*

Randal E. Bryant
Carnegie Mellon University
School of Computer Science
Pittsburgh, PA 15213 USA
Randy.Bryant@cs.cmu.edu

Abstract

The UCLID project seeks to develop formal verification tools for infinite-state systems having a degree of automation comparable to that of model checking tools for finite-state systems. The UCLID modeling language describes systems where the state variables are Booleans, integers, and functions mapping integers to integers or Booleans. The verifier supports several forms of verification for proving safety properties. They rely on a decision procedure that translates a quantifier-free formula into an equi-satisfiable Boolean formula and then applies a Boolean satisfiability solver. UCLID has successfully verified a number of hardware designs and protocols.

Most successful automated formal verification tools are based on a bit-level model of computation, where a set of Boolean state variables encodes the system state. Using powerful inference engines, such as Binary Decision Diagrams (BDDs) and Boolean satisfiability (SAT) checkers, symbolic model checkers and similar tools can analyze all possible behaviors of very large, finite-state systems.

For many hardware and software systems, we would like to go beyond bit-level models to handle systems that are truly infinite state, or that are better modeled as infinite-state systems. Examples include programs manipulating integer data, concurrency protocols involving arbitrary numbers of processes, and systems containing buffers where the sizes are described parametrically.

Historically, much of the effort in verifying such systems involved automated theorem provers, requiring considerable guidance and expertise on the part of the user. We would like to devise approaches for these more expressive system models that retain the desirable features of model checking, such as the high degree of automation and the ability to generate counterexamples.

We have developed UCLID [1], a prototype verifier for infinite-state systems. The UCLID modeling language extends that of SMV [9], a bit-level model checker, to include state variables that are integers, as well as functions mapping integers to integers and integers to Booleans. Functional state variables can be used to define array and memory structures, including arrays of identical processes, FIFO buffers, and content-addressable memories.

System operation is defined in UCLID in terms of the initial values and next-state functions of the state variables. Integer operations include linear arithmetic and relational operations. Functions can be defined using uninterpreted function symbols, as well as via a restricted form of lambda expression. The underlying logic is reasonably expressive, yet it still permits a decision procedure that translates the formula into propositional logic and then uses a SAT solver [7].

UCLID supports multiple forms of verification, requiring different levels of sophistication in the handling of quantifiers. All styles verify that a safety property of the form $\forall \mathcal{X} P(s)$ holds for some set of system states s, where $\mathcal{X}$ denotes a set of integer *index variables*. Index variables can be used to express universal properties for all elements in an array of identical processes, all entries in a FIFO buffer, etc.

The simplest form of *bounded property checking* allows the user to determine that property $\forall \mathcal{X} P(s)$ holds for all states reachable within a fixed number of steps k from an initial state. Verifying such a property can be done by direct application of the decision procedure. In practice, the effort required to verify such a property grows exponentially in k, limiting the verification to around 10–20 steps. However, it provides a useful debugging tool. In our experience, most errors are detected by this approach.

Of course, it is important to verify that properties hold for all reachable states of the system. Unfortunately, the standard fixed-point methods for bit-level model checking do not work for infinite-state systems. In many cases, the system will not reach a fixed point within a bounded number of steps. Even for those that do, checking convergence is

*This research was supported by the Semiconductor Research Corporation, Contract RID 1029.001

undecidable, and our efforts to implement incomplete methods for this task have had limited success [2].

To prove that property $\forall \mathcal{X} P(s)$ holds for all reachable states s, UCLID supports *inductive invariant* checking, where the user provides an invariant Q such that Q holds for all initial states, Q implies P, and any successor for a state satisfying Q must also satisfy Q. This latter condition requires proving the validity of a formula containing existentially quantified index variables. Although this problem is undecidable for our logic, we have successfully implemented an incomplete approach using quantifier instantiation [8].

A more automated technique is to derive an inductive invariant via *predicate abstraction* [4]. Predicate abstraction operates much like the fixed-point methods of symbolic model checking, but using the concretization and abstraction operations of abstract interpretation [3] on each step. We have generalized predicate abstraction to handle the indexed predicates supported by UCLID [6]. Each step requires quantifier elimination to eliminate the current state variables, much like the relational product step of symbolic model checking. We implement this step by performing SAT enumeration on the translated Boolean formula.

As a final level of automation, we can automatically discover a set of relevant predicates for predicate abstraction based on the property P and the next-state expressions for the state variables [5].

We have successfully verified a number of systems with UCLID, including out-of-order microprocessors, distributed cache protocols, and distributed synchronization protocols.

References

[1] R. E. Bryant, S. K. Lahiri, and S. A. Seshia. Modeling and verifying systems using a logic of counter arithmetic with lambda expressions and uninterpreted functions. In E. Brinksma and K. G. Larsen, editors, *Computer-Aided Verification (CAV '02)*, LNCS 2404, pages 78–92, 2002.

[2] R. E. Bryant, S. K. Lahiri, and S. A. Seshia. Convergence testing in term-level bounded model checking. In *Correct Hardware Design and Verification Methods (CHARME '03)*, LNCS, September 2003.

[3] P. Cousot and R. Cousot. Abstract interpretation : a unified lattice model for the static analysis of programs by construction or approximation of fixpoints. In *Principles of Programming Languages (POPL '77)*, pages 238–252, 1977.

[4] S. Graf and H. Saïdi. Construction of abstract state graphs with PVS. In O. Grumberg, editor, *Computer-Aided Verification (CAV '97)*, LNCS 1254, pages 72–83, 1997.

[5] S. K. Lahiri and R. E. Bryant. Indexed predicate discovery for unbounded system verification. In *Computer-Aided Verification (CAV '04)*, LNCS 3114, pages 135–147, 2004.

[6] S. K. Lahiri and R. E. Bryant. Indexed predicate abstraction. *ACM Transactions on Computational Logic*, To appear.

[7] S. K. Lahiri and S. A. Seshia. The UCLID decision procedure. In *Computer-Aided Verification (CAV '04)*, LNCS 3114, pages 475–478, 2004.

[8] S. K. Lahiri, S. A. Seshia, and R. E. Bryant. Modeling and verification of out-of-order microprocessors in UCLID. In M. D. Aagaard and J. W. O'Leary, editors, *Formal Methods in Computer-Aided Design (FMCAD '02)*, LNCS 2517, pages 142–159, 2002.

[9] K. McMillan. *Symbolic Model Checking*. Kluwer Academic Publishers, 1992.

Session 1:
Complexity and Decidability

Two-Variable Logic on Words with Data*

Mikołaj Bojańczyk Anca Muscholl Thomas Schwentick Luc Segoufin Claire David
Warsaw University LIAFA, Paris VII Dortmund University INRIA, Paris XI LIAFA, Paris VII

***Abstract*— In a *data word* each position carries a label from a finite alphabet and a data value from some infinite domain. These models have been already considered in the realm of semistructured data, timed automata and extended temporal logics.**

It is shown that satisfiability for the two-variable first-order logic $FO^2(\sim,<,+1)$ is decidable over finite and over infinite data words, where $\sim$ is a binary predicate testing the data value equality and $+1,<$ are the usual successor and order predicates. The complexity of the problem is at least as hard as Petri net reachability. Several extensions of the logic are considered, some remain decidable while some are undecidable.

I. Introduction

Finding decidable logics for models that handle data values is an important problem in several areas that need algorithmic procedures for property validation. Examples can be found in both program verification and database management. In this paper we reconsider a data model that was investigated both in verification (related to timed languages [1] and extended temporal logics [4]) and in XML reasoning [16]. As in these papers, data values are modeled by an infinite alphabet, consisting of a finite and an infinite part. The logic can address the finite part directly, while the infinite part can only be tested for equality. As a first step, this paper considers simple models: words, both finite and infinite.

Our main result is that the satisfiability problem for two variable first-order logic extended by equality tests for data values – $FO^2(\sim,<,+1)$ for short – is decidable over word models. When more variables are permitted, or when a linear order on the data values is available, or when more than two equivalence relations are present, the logic becomes undecidable.

Following [1], a data word is a finite sequence of positions having each a label over some finite alphabet together with a data value over some infinite alphabet. The logic admits the equality test $x \sim y$, which is satisfied if both positions carry the same data value. Moreover, there are two navigational predicates on strings: the linear order $<$ and the successor relation $+1$. (With only two variables, the successor $+1$ cannot be defined in terms of the order $<$.) As usual we also have a unary predicate corresponding to each letter of the finite alphabet.

Perhaps surprisingly, we show that the satisfiability problem for $FO^2(\sim,<,+1)$ is closely related to the well known problem of reachability for Petri nets. More precisely we show that languages formed by the projection onto the finite alphabet of word models definable by an $FO^2(\sim,<,+1)$ sentence are recognized by multicounter automata (which are equivalent to Petri nets [7]). The converse is also true, modulo an erasing inverse morphism. Moreover, the correspondences are effective. We give a 2EXPTIME reduction of satisfiability for $FO^2(\sim,<,+1)$ to emptiness for multicounter automata which is known to be decidable [11], [14]. For the opposite direction we provide a PTIME reduction from emptiness for multicounter automata to satisfiability for $FO^2(\sim,<,+1)$. Since there is no known elementary upper bound for emptiness for multicounter automata (see e.g. [5]), finding the exact complexity of satisfiability for $FO^2(\sim,<,+1)$ formulas is a hard question.

The decidability of $FO^2(\sim,<,+1)$ immediately implies the decidability of $EMSO^2(\sim,<,+1)$. Here $EMSO^2$ stands for the closure of FO^2 under existential quantification of sets of nodes. Without data values, $EMSO^2(+1)$ has the same expressive power as MSO. In this sense the decidability of $EMSO^2(\sim,<,+1)$ can be seen as an extension of the classical decidability result of monadic second-order logic over strings.

We also show that the satisfiability problem for $FO^2(\sim,<,+1)$ remains decidable over data ω-words. In this case we no longer recognize the string projection of definable languages but we show that, again using emptiness of multicounter automata, it is decidable whether an $FO^2(\sim,<,+1)$ formula is satisfied in a data ω-word whose string projection is ultimately periodic.

We then show that our decision procedure works even when the logic is extended by predicates ± 1 and $+2$, $+3$, ... Here ± 1 is a binary predicate,

*Work supported by the French-German cooperation programme PROCOPE, the EU-TMR network GAMES and Polish MNII grant 4 T11C 042 25

which relates two positions if they have the same data value, but all positions between them have a different data value. The $+k$ binary predicate, on the other hand, generalizes the successor predicate $+1$ to the kth successor.

The paper is organized as follows. The main result – a decision procedure for satisfiability of $FO^2(\sim,<,+1)$– is presented in Section III. In the proof, a concept of data automaton is introduced. There are two steps: first we show in Section IV that each language definable in $FO^2(\sim,<,+1)$ can be recognized by a data automaton; then we show in Section V how emptiness for data automata can be decided using multicounter automata. The reduction from reachability of multicounter automata to satisfiability of $FO^2(\sim,<,+1)$ is shown in Section VI. In Section VII, we extend the main decidability result: first by adding new predicates, second by considering ω-words. In Section VIII, we show that the logic becomes undecidable when: a) three variables are allowed (even without the order $<$); or b) a linear order on data values is included. Finally, we conclude with a discussion of the results. Because of space limitation some proofs are missing and are available only in the full version of this paper.

Related work. Automata on finite strings of data values (without labels) were introduced in [18], [9]. They used registers to store data values and data values could be compared wrt. equality. In [16] register automata and pebble automata over such words were studied. Several versions of these automata (one-way/two-way, deterministic/nondeterministic/alternating) were compared. Most of the results were negative however, i.e., most models are undecidable. Register automata have been also considered by Bouyer et al. [1] in the context of timed languages. However, the automata considered therein have a limited expressive power and cannot test data equality on arbitrary two positions (they are one-way automata). In particular the string projection of any language recognized by their automata is regular. As mentioned above, this is not the case for the logic considered in this paper.

In [4] an extension of LTL was given which can manipulate data values using a *freeze* operator. Their decidable fragment is incomparable to $FO^2(\sim,<,+1)$ as it can only process the word left-to-right, but can express properties that $FO^2(\sim,<,+1)$ cannot.

Restricting first-order logic to its two-variable fragment is a classical idea when looking for decidability [8]. Over graphs or over any relational structures, first-order logic is undecidable, while its two-variable fragment is decidable [15]. This does not imply anything on the decidability of $FO^2(\sim,<,+1)$, since the equivalence relation, the successor relation and the order $<$ cannot be axiomatized with only two variables. A recent paper generalized the result of [15] in the presence of one or two equivalence relations [10]. Again this does not apply to our context as we also have the order and the successor relation. However [10] also showed that FO^2 with *three* equivalence relations, without any other structure, is undecidable. This implies immediately that we cannot extend the decidability result to data words with more than two data parts.

In the context of XML reasoning we considered $FO^2(\sim,+1)$ over unranked ordered data trees [2] and showed the decidability of the satisfiability question. In this context, the predicate $+1$ stands for two successor predicates, one for the vertical axis and one for the horizontal one. As data words are special cases of data trees, this implies the decidability of $FO^2(\sim,+1)$ over words. The complexity for data trees is in 3NEXPTIME but it becomes 2NEXPTIME when restricted to data words. This should be contrasted with the complexity of satisfiability of $FO^2(\sim,<,+1)$ which is not known to be elementary.

On strings over a finite alphabet (without data values), the $FO^2(<,+1)$ fragment of first-order logic is very well understood. A characterization in terms of temporal logic says that it is equivalent to LTL restricted to the unary operators F, G, X and their past counterparts [6]. In terms of automata, $FO^2(<)$ is equivalent to partially-ordered, two-way deterministic finite automata [17], while in terms of algebra the logic corresponds to the semigroup variety DA [19]. The satisfiability question is NEXPTIME-complete in [6] (using an arbitrary number of unary predicates).

II. PRELIMINARIES

Let Σ be a finite alphabet of *labels* and D an infinite set of *data values*. A **data word** $w = w_1 \cdots w_n$ is a finite sequence over $\Sigma \times D$, i.e., each w_i is of the form (a_i, d_i) with $a_i \in \Sigma$ and $d_i \in D$. A **data language** is a set of data words, for some Σ. The idea is that the alphabet Σ is accessed directly, while data values can only be tested for equality. This amounts to considering words over Σ endowed with an equivalence relation on the set of positions. The string $\mathrm{str}(w) = a_1 \cdots a_n$ is called the **string projection** of A. The **marked string projection** $\mathrm{mstr}(w) = (a_1, b_1) \cdots (a_n, b_n) \in (\Sigma \times$

$\{0,1\})^*$ of w adds a new coordinate, where $b_i = 1$ on all positions i with the same data value as $i-1$. For a language of data words L, we write $\mathrm{str}(L)$ for $\{\mathrm{str}(w) \mid w \in L\}$ and $\mathrm{mstr}(L)$ for $\{\mathrm{mstr}(w) \mid w \in L\}$.

A **class** is a maximal set of positions in a data word with the same data value. For a class with positions $i_1 < \cdots < i_k$ the **class string** is $a_{i_1} \cdots a_{i_k}$ and the **marked class string** is $(a_{i_1}, b_{i_1}) \cdots (a_{i_k}, b_{i_k})$, with the b_i as above.

Data words can be seen as models for first-order logic, where the carrier of the model is the set of positions in the word. Let $\mathrm{FO}(\sim, <, +1)$ be first-order logic with the following atomic predicates: $x \sim y$, $x < y$, $x = y + 1$, and a predicate $a(x)$ for every $a \in \Sigma$. The interpretation of $a(x)$ is that the label in position x is a. The order $<$ and successor $+1$ are interpreted in the usual way. Two positions satisfy $x \sim y$ if they have the same data value. We write $L(\varphi)$ for the set of data words that satisfy the formula φ. A formula satisfied by some data word is **satisfiable**.

We write FO^k for formulas using at most k variables. Note that the following examples use 2 variables only.

Example: We present here a formula φ such that $\mathrm{str}(L(\varphi))$ is exactly the set of all words over $\{a, b\}$ that contain the same number of a's and b's.

- The formula φ_a says all a's are in different classes:

$$\varphi_a = \forall x \forall y (x \neq y \ \wedge a(x) \wedge a(y)) \rightarrow x \not\sim y \ .$$

Similarly we define φ_b.
- The formula $\psi_{a,b}$ says each class with an a also contains a b:

$$\psi_{a,b} = \forall x \exists y \big(a(x) \rightarrow (b(y) \wedge x \sim y)\big) \ .$$

Similarly we define $\psi_{b,a}$.
- Hence, in a data word satisfying $\varphi = \varphi_a \wedge \varphi_b \wedge \psi_{a,b} \wedge \psi_{b,a}$ the numbers of a and b-labeled positions are equal.

This can be easily extended to describe data words with an equal number of a's, b's and c's, hence a language with a non-context-free string projection.

Example: For $a \in \Sigma$ the formula below is satisfied precisely by the first a which has an a in a different class on its left, i.e., the first a in the second a-class.

$$\begin{gathered} a(x) \wedge \exists y \ (y < x \ \wedge \ a(y) \ \wedge \ x \not\sim y) \wedge \\ \forall y \ (y < x \ \wedge \ a(y)) \rightarrow \\ [x \not\sim y \wedge \forall x \ \big((x < y \ \wedge \ a(x)\big) \rightarrow \ x \sim y)] \end{gathered}$$

Note how in this example the variable x is reused.

III. Decidability of $\mathrm{FO}^2(\sim,<,+1)$

The main result of this paper is:

Theorem 1 *Satisfiability of* $\mathrm{FO}^2(\sim,<,+1)$ *over data word models is decidable.*

The basic idea of the proof of Theorem 1 is to compute for each formula φ a multicounter automaton that recognizes $\mathrm{str}(L(\varphi))$. As an intermediate step, we use a new type of finite automaton that works over data words, called a data automaton (these will be defined in Section IV). Theorem 1 follows immediately from the following three statements.

Proposition 2 Every language definable in $\mathrm{FO}^2(\sim,<,+1)$ is recognized by an effectively obtained data automaton.

Proposition 3 From each data automaton we can compute a multicounter automaton recognizing the string projection of its recognized language.

Theorem 4 *[11], [14] Emptiness of multicounter automata is decidable.*

Proposition 2 is shown in Section IV, and Proposition 3 is shown in Section V. Regarding complexity, satisfiability of a $\mathrm{FO}^2(\sim,<,+1)$ formula is reduced in 2ExpTime to the emptiness of a multicounter automaton of doubly exponential size.

IV. Data automata

In this section we define *data automata*[1], a means to define data languages, and show that they can recognize all languages of data words definable in $\mathrm{FO}^2(\sim,<,+1)$.

A **data automaton** $\mathcal{D} = (\mathcal{A}, \mathcal{B})$ consists of

- a nondeterministic letter-to-letter string transducer $\mathcal{A}$ (the **base automaton**) with input alphabet $\Sigma \times \{0,1\}$, for some Σ and some output alphabet Γ (letter-to-letter means that each transition reads and writes exactly one symbol), and
- a nondeterministic string automaton $\mathcal{B}$ (the **class automaton**) with input alphabet Γ.

A data word $w = w_1 \cdots w_n \in (\Sigma \times D)^*$ is accepted by $\mathcal{D}$ if there is an *accepting* run of $\mathcal{A}$ on the marked string projection of w, yielding an output string $b_1 \cdots b_n$, such that, for *each class* $\{x_1, \ldots, x_k\} \subseteq \{1, \ldots, n\}$, $x_1 < \cdots < x_k$, the class automaton accepts $b_{x_1}, \ldots, b_{x_k}$.

[1]Our data automata differ from what is called data automaton in [1], which are essentially 1-way automata with one register.

As an example, consider the property: "w has at least two classes with an a". The data automaton for this property works as follows. The base automaton nondeterministically chooses two positions with an a and outputs 1 on each of them and 0 everywhere else. If there are no such two positions it rejects. The class automaton checks that each class contains at most one 1, thus verifying that the two positions were chosen from different classes. We call below *renaming* a letter-to-letter morphism, that is a morphism defined as $h : \Sigma \to \Sigma'$, where Σ, Σ' are alphabets.

Lemma 5 Languages recognized by data automata are closed under union, intersection, and renaming.

Proof. Closure under union and intersection is obtained using the usual product construction. Closure under renaming is obtained using the nondeterminism of the base automaton. □

The same cannot be said about negation. Indeed, if we were to have effective closure under negation, then all data languages defined by monadic second-order logic could be effectively translated into data automata, as we show that data automata recognize all of $\mathrm{EMSO}^2(\sim, <, +1)$. This would be a contradiction, since we show that emptiness of data automata is decidable, while satisfiability is undecidable for monadic second-order logic [16] (even for first-order logic, see Proposition 20).

The following lemma presents a family of data languages recognizable by data automata which will be used later in the proof.

Lemma 6 For any given regular language $L \subseteq (\Sigma \times \{0, 1\})^*$, there is a data automaton accepting all data strings w, for which each marked class string belongs to L.

Proof. The base automaton just copies its input $\Sigma \times \{0, 1\}$ and the class automaton checks membership in L. □

One can also verify if *some* marked class string belongs to L: for each position i, the base automaton nondeterministically chooses to either output the input symbol a_i or a special symbol $\perp$. It accepts, if it outputs at least one non-$\perp$ symbol. The class automaton accepts the language $L \cup \perp^*$.

A. Reduction to data automata

The goal of this section is to prove Proposition 2, i.e. to transform a formula of $\mathrm{FO}^2(\sim,<,+1)$ into an equivalent data automaton of doubly exponential size. The transformation is done in two steps, first we rewrite the given formula into "intermediate normal form", and then we show that the normal form can be recognized by data automata. Each step gives an exponential blowup.

In the first step, we transform $\mathrm{FO}^2(\sim,<,+1)$ formulas into an intermediate normal form (we denote as *type* below any conjunction of unary predicates or their negations):

Definition 7 A formula is said to be in **intermediate normal form** if it is of the form $\exists R_1 \cdots R_m \ (\theta_1 \wedge \cdots \wedge \theta_n)$, where $\exists R_1 \cdots R_m$ quantifies over unary predicates (sets of positions) and each θ_i is of one of the following kinds:

(1) $\forall x \forall y \quad [\rho(x,y) \wedge \alpha(x) \wedge \beta(y) \wedge \delta(x,y)] \to \gamma(x,y)$
(2) $\forall x \exists y \quad \alpha(x) \to [\beta(y) \wedge \delta(x,y) \wedge \epsilon(x,y)]$
(3) $\forall x \forall y \quad \psi$

where

- α and β are types,
- $\rho(x,y) = (x \neq y+1 \wedge y \neq x+1 \wedge x \neq y)$,
- $\delta(x,y)$ is $x \sim y$ or $x \not\sim y$,
- $\gamma(x,y)$ is $x < y$, $x > y$, or *ff*, and
- $\epsilon(x,y)$ is $x+1 < y$, $x+1 = y$, $x = y$, $x = y+1$ or $x > y+1$,
- ψ is a quantifier free formula in DNF that doesn't use $\sim$.

Here, $x+1 < y$ is an abbreviation for $x < y \wedge x+1 \neq y$.

Formally speaking, a formula in intermediate normal form is a normal form of $\mathrm{EMSO}^2(\sim, <, +1)$, the extension of $\mathrm{FO}^2(\sim,<,+1)$ by existential monadic second-order predicates quantification in front of $\mathrm{FO}^2(\sim,<,+1)$ formulas. Note that as far as satisfiability is concerned $\mathrm{FO}^2(\sim,<,+1)$ and $\mathrm{EMSO}^2(\sim, <, +1)$ are equivalent.

Lemma 8 Every formula of $\mathrm{FO}^2(\sim,<,+1)$ can be effectively transformed into an equivalent formula in intermediate normal form of exponential size, with exponentially many unary predicates R_i.

Proof. The overall idea is classical: we reduce the quantifier depth to 2, then we add unary predicates that color certain distinguished positions, resp. classes containing distinguished positions. These additional colors are then used to simplify the formulas.

The formal proof proceeds in three steps.

Step 1: Scott normal form
The first step is classical for two variable logics (see e.g. [8]). It says that each $\mathrm{FO}^2(\sim,<,+1)$

formula φ is equivalent with respect to satisfiability to a (linear size) formula φ' in *Scott Normal Form*,

$$\forall x \forall y\ \chi \wedge \bigwedge_i \forall x \exists y\ \chi_i,$$

where χ and each χ_i are quantifier-free. The signature of φ' is an extension of the signature of φ by (linearly many) unary predicates. Furthermore, a data word satisfies φ if and only if it can be extended by additional predicates to a word satisfying φ'. The additional unary predicates are the relations R_i which are existentially quantified by the formula. The additional predicates state which subformulas are satisfied at a given position.

Hence, φ is equivalent to a formula of the form

$$\exists R_1 \cdots \exists R_m (\forall x \forall y\ \chi \wedge \bigwedge_i \forall x \exists y\ \chi_i).$$

Step 2: Dealing with $\forall x \forall y\ \chi$.
In the second step we show that the formula $\forall x \forall y\ \chi$ can be replaced by a formula

$$\exists R_1 \cdots \exists R_m \bigwedge_i \theta_i \quad \wedge \quad \bigwedge_{i=1,2,3} \forall x \exists y\ \xi_i$$

where the ξ_i are again quantifier-free and each θ_i is of the form (1) (from Definition 7). Moreover, the number of θ_i is exponential.

To this end, we first rewrite $\forall x \forall y\ \chi$ into the following form:

$$\begin{array}{lrcl} \forall x \forall y & (\quad y = x+1 & \rightarrow & \psi_{y=x+1}(x,y) \\ & \wedge \quad x = y+1 & \rightarrow & \psi_{x=y+1}(x,y) \\ & \wedge \quad x = y & \rightarrow & \psi_{x=y}(x,y) \\ & \wedge \quad \rho(x,y) & \rightarrow & \psi_{\rho}(x,y)) \end{array}$$

where the ψ formulas are quantifier-free and use only $\sim$, $<$ and the unary predicates. They have the same size as χ. Over the (linearly ordered) models considered in this paper this is logically equivalent to:

$$\begin{array}{l} \forall x \forall y \ (\rho(x,y) \rightarrow \psi_\rho(x,y)) \\ \wedge\ \forall x \exists y \ (\neg R_{\text{last}}(x) \rightarrow (y = x+1 \ \wedge \psi_{y=x+1})) \\ \wedge\ \forall x \exists y \ (\neg R_{\text{first}}(x) \rightarrow (x = y+1 \ \wedge \psi_{x=y+1})) \\ \wedge\ \forall x \exists y \ ((x = y \ \wedge \psi_{x=y})) \end{array}$$

Here, we assume that R_{first} and R_{last} are two extra predicates marking the first and last position of the word, respectively. They can easily be enforced by a formula of the form (3). The last three conjuncts give rise to ξ_1, ξ_2, ξ_3 and we are left with the first conjunct $\forall x \forall y\ (\rho(x,y) \rightarrow \psi_\rho(x,y))$. We turn ψ_ρ into CNF (with an exponential blow-up) and rewrite it as

$$\bigwedge_{\alpha,\beta} (\alpha(x) \wedge \beta(y)) \rightarrow \psi(x,y)$$

where α, β are types occurring in ψ_ρ, and $\psi(x,y)$ is a quantifier-free formula using only $<$ and $\sim$. Finally, we rewrite the formula $\psi(x,y)$ into the form:

$$\psi(x,y) = (x \sim y \rightarrow \gamma_1(x,y)) \wedge (x \not\sim y \rightarrow \gamma_2(x,y))$$

where $\gamma_1(x,y)$ and $\gamma_2(x,y)$ are $x < y$, $x > y$, *ff* or *tt*.

Step 3: Dealing with $\bigwedge_i \forall x \exists y\ \chi_i$.

In the last step, we show that each formula $\forall x \exists y\ \chi$ can be rewritten into an equivalent formula $\exists R'_1 \cdots \exists R'_n \bigwedge_i \theta_i$ with θ_i of type (2) or (3) in Definition 7. Moreover, the size of θ_i and the number n of additional predicates are both polynomial.

First, χ can be written as a disjunction (of exponential size)

$$\bigvee_j (\alpha_j(x) \rightarrow \beta_j(y) \wedge \delta_j(x,y) \wedge \epsilon_j(x,y)),$$

where the $\alpha_j, \beta_j, \delta_j, \epsilon_j$ are of corresponding forms as in (2). It only remains to eliminate the disjunction. To this end, we add for each conjunct above a new unary predicate $R_{\chi,j}$ with the intended meaning that $R_{\chi,j}$ holds at a position x if there is a y such that $\alpha_j(x) \wedge \beta_j(y) \wedge \delta_j(x,y) \wedge \epsilon_j(x,y)$ holds. Formally, we rewrite each $\forall x \exists y\ \chi$ as

$$\begin{array}{l} \exists R_{\chi,1}\ R_{\chi,2} \cdots (\forall x \quad \bigvee_i R_{\chi,i}(x)) \ \wedge \\ \bigwedge_j \forall x \exists y \ (\alpha_j(x) \wedge R_{\chi,j}(x) \rightarrow \\ \qquad (\beta_j(y) \wedge \delta_j(x,y) \wedge \epsilon_j(x,y))) \ . \end{array}$$

By putting together the obtained formulas we get a formula in intermediate normal form. □

We are now ready for the second step, where the intermediate normal form is transformed into a data automaton, thus completing the proof of Proposition 2. Since data automata are closed under renaming and intersection, it suffices to consider just the conjuncts θ in Definition 7. Note that the Cartesian product gives an exponential blowup.

Lemma 9 Every conjunct θ of a formula in intermediate normal form can be recognized by a data automaton with constantly many states.

Proof. The formula θ may be in one of the three forms (1), (2) or (3) from Definition 7. The case of formula of the form (3) is no problem as it can easily be checked using the base automaton. We consider first the case of (1):

$$\forall x \forall y \ [(\rho(x,y) \ \wedge \ \alpha(x) \ \wedge \ \beta(y) \ \wedge \ \delta(x,y)) \rightarrow \gamma(x,y)]$$

The proof uses the data automaton for marking a fixed number of classes, say k for some constant k. We explain this technique first. The base automaton uses the output alphabet $\Gamma_k = \{\bot, (1,1), \ldots, (k,1), (1,0), \ldots, (k,0)\}$. It guesses, for each position i an output symbol $b_i \in \Gamma_k$. It makes sure that, for each j, at most once the symbol $(j,1)$ is chosen. The class automaton accepts then all strings of the form $\bot^*$ and $(l,1)(l,0)^*$, for some l. In this way, it is ensured that, for each class, always the output symbol $\bot$ is chosen or the first output symbol is $(l,1)$ and all others are $(l,0)$, for some l. As each $(j,1)$ is used at most once, it can not happen that two classes share the same $(j,0)$ (and $(j,1)$) symbols. Thus, the base automaton can assume, for each position, to which of the $\leq k$ classes it belongs.

It remains to perform a case analysis on the formulas δ, γ and ϵ.

In the case where $\delta(x,y)$ is $x \sim y$ the formula θ gives a regular condition that must be satisfied by each class. Thanks to Lemma 6, we can use that class automaton to verify θ.

If $\delta(x,y)$ is $x \not\sim y$ there are three subcases.

- $\gamma(x,y) = \mathit{ff}$ means that the data string may not have an α- and a β-position which are not adjacent (or identical) and in different classes. It is easy to see that the formula evaluates to false if both α and β appear in the string and there are at least 4 classes with an α or at least 4 classes with a β.
  Thus, it is sufficient that the base automaton selects (at most) 6 classes, using the technique explained above, and tests that (a) neither α nor β occur outside these 6 classes and (b) within the 6 classes θ holds.
- $\gamma(x,y) = x < y$. In this case only two classes are involved.
  Let Lst_α be the *position* of the rightmost α in the string and Llst_α be the position of the rightmost α that is in a different class than Lst_α. Using this notation, θ holds if and only if w (a) has no β up to position $\mathrm{Llst}_\alpha - 2$; and (b) the β-positions between $\mathrm{Llst}_\alpha - 1$ and $\mathrm{Lst}_\alpha - 2$ are in the same class as Lst_α.
  Thus, the base automaton simply guesses the two classes containing Lst_α and Llst_α and tests that (a) and (b) hold.
- The case where $\gamma(x,y)$ is $x > y$ is analogous.

It remains to consider formulas θ of type (2):

$$\forall x \exists y \quad \alpha(x) \rightarrow \left[\beta(y) \ \wedge \ \delta(x,y) \ \wedge \ \epsilon(x,y)\right]$$

As before, the difficult case is when $\delta(x,y)$ is $x \not\sim y$. If $\epsilon(x,y)$ is one of $x+1=y$, $x=y$, $x=y+1$ then θ can be verified by the base automaton. Otherwise $\epsilon(x,y)$ is $x+1<y$ or $x>y+1$. We describe the case of $x+1<y$, the other being analogous.

In this case, θ expresses that each α-position needs a β-position in a different class to its right (but not as its right neighbor). Since every α-position before $\mathrm{Llst}_\beta - 2$ is guaranteed to have such a β-witness in a different class, it suffices to require the following properties: a) from position $\mathrm{Lst}_\beta - 1$ on, the data word contains no α; and b) all α's between $\mathrm{Llst}_\beta - 1$ and $\mathrm{Lst}_\beta - 2$ are not in the same class as Lst_β. This involves checking 2 classes and can be handled analogously as the cases above.

As for the size, it is easy to check that the base and class automata have a number of states bounded by a constant. The number of transitions is bounded by the number of types (if we allow also type negations in the transitions, the number of transitions is also bounded by a constant). □

We would like to note that the converse of Proposition 2 does not hold. There are two reasons for this. First, a data automaton can verify arbitrary regular properties of classes, which cannot be done with first-order logic. For instance, no $\mathrm{FO}^2(\sim,<,+1)$ formula captures the language: "each class is of even length". This problem can be solved by adding a prefix of monadic second-order existential quantification. However, even with such a prefix, it is difficult to write a formula that describes accepting runs of data automata. The problem is that describing runs of the class automata requires comparing successive positions in the same class, which need not be successive positions in the word. That is why we consider a new predicate ± 1, called the **class successor**, which is true for two successive positions in a same class of the data word. The following result easily follows from Proposition 2 and the obvious extension of its proof to include $\mathrm{EMSO}^2(\sim,<,+1,\pm 1)$:

Proposition 10 A language is recognized by a data automaton iff it is definable in $\mathrm{EMSO}^2(\sim,<,+1,\pm 1)$.

Proof. It is easy to extend the proof of Proposition 2 to the logic $\mathrm{EMSO}^2(\sim,<,+1,\pm 1)$. The other direction follows immediately from the classical simulation of automata in $\mathrm{EMSO}^2(+1)$. □

By translating a formula into a data automaton and then back again into a formula, we can obtain a certain normal form for $\mathrm{EMSO}^2(\sim,<,+1,\pm 1)$. In the normal form, the formulas verify the correctness of transitions in an accepting run. In particular, the order $<$ is not used.

Remark: Using the same idea of the proof of Proposition 2 one could show the following normal form for $\mathrm{EMSO}^2(\sim,<,+1)$. Each formula of $\mathrm{EMSO}^2(\sim,<,+1)$ is equivalent to one where the FO part is a Boolean combination of simple formulas of the form (where α and β are types):

(a) θ is does not use $\sim$ (i.e., an $\mathrm{FO}^2(<,+1)$ formula).
(b) Each class contains at most one occurrence of α.
(c) In each class, all occurrences of α occur strictly before all occurrences of β.
(d) In each class with at least one occurrence of α, there must be a β, too.
(e) If x is not in the same class at its successor then it is of type α.

V. Recognizing the Projection by Multicounter Automata

In this section, we show that the string projection of a language recognized by a data automaton can be recognized by a multicounter automaton.

We first introduce multicounter automata. An ϵ-free **multicounter automaton** is a finite automaton extended by a finite set $C = \{1,\ldots,n\}$ of counters. It can be described as a tuple $(Q,\Sigma,C,\delta,q_I,F)$. The set of states Q, finite alphabet Σ, initial state $q_I \in Q$ and final states $F \subseteq Q$ are as in a usual finite automaton. The transition relation δ is more involved – it is a finite subset of $Q \times \Sigma \times (\mathit{dec}^*(i)\, \mathit{inc}^*(i))_{i\in C} \times Q$.

The idea is that in each step, the automaton can change its state and modify the counters, by incrementing or decrementing them, according to the current state and the current letter on the input. In a step, the automaton can apply to each counter $i \in C$ a sequence of decrements, followed by a sequence of increments. Whenever it tries to decrement a counter of value zero the computation stops. Besides this, the transition of a multicounter automaton does not depend on the value of the counters. In particular, it cannot test whether a counter is exactly zero. Nevertheless, by decrementing a counter k times and incrementing it again afterward it can test whether the value of that counter is at least k.

A **configuration** of such an automaton is a tuple $c = (q,(c_i)_{i\in C}) \in Q \times \mathbb{N}^n$, where q is the current state and c_i is the value of the counter i. A transition

$$(q,a,(\mathit{dec}^{k_i}(i)\mathit{inc}^{l_i}(i))_{i\in C},q') \in \delta$$

can be applied if the current state is q, the current letter is a and for every counter $i \in C$, the value c_i is at least k_i. The successor configuration is $d = (q',(c(i)-k_i+l_i)_{i\in C})$. A **run** over a word w is a sequence of configurations that is consistent with the transition function δ. The acceptance condition is given by a subset R of the counters C and the final states. A run is **accepting** if it starts in the state q_I with all counters empty and ends in a configuration where all counters in R are empty and the state is final.

The key idea in the reduction from data automata to multicounter automata, is that acceptance can be expressed using the Shuffle(L) operation defined below.

Definition 11 A word $v \in (\Sigma \times \{0,1\})^*$ is a **marked shuffle** of n words $u_1,\ldots,u_n$ if its positions can be colored with n colors so that we have:

1) for every i, the positions colored with color i – read from left to right – give the word u_i,
2) a position of v is labeled by a symbol from $\Sigma \times \{1\}$ iff its predecessor position has the same color (neighborhood condition).

We write Shuffle(L) for the set of marked shuffles of words from a language $L \subseteq \Sigma^*$.

Proposition 12 Let $\mathcal{D} = (\mathcal{A},\mathcal{B})$ be a data automaton. The string projection $\mathrm{str}(L(\mathcal{D}))$ is recognized by a multicounter automaton of size $O(|\mathcal{A}||\mathcal{B}|)$.

Proof. By definition of data automata, a word

$$v = (a_1,m_1)\cdots(a_n,m_n) \in (\Sigma \times \{0,1\})^*$$

belongs to the marked string projection $\mathrm{mstr}(L(\mathcal{D}))$ if and only if it there is an accepting run of the base automaton on v with output $b_1\cdots b_n$ such that $(b_1,m_1)\cdots(b_n,m_n)$ is a marked shuffle of the language accepted by the class automaton. We will show in Proposition 13 that the set of such words $(b_1,m_1)\cdots(b_n,m_n)$ is recognized by a multicounter automaton $\mathcal{M}$ of same size as $\mathcal{B}$.

Thus, it is sufficient to compose $\mathcal{M}$ with a nondeterministic transducer which, on input $a_1\cdots a_n$, outputs a string $(a_1,m_1)\cdots(a_n,m_n)$, where each $m_i \in \{0,1\}$ is guessed independently, and which simulates $\mathcal{A}$. We obtain a multicounter automaton which on input $a_1\cdots a_n$ constructs a string $(a_1,m_1)\cdots(a_n,m_n)$ which is read by $\mathcal{A}$ and whose output in turn is the input for $\mathcal{M}$. □

Thus it remains to prove the following proposition which is an adaptation of Lemma (IV.6) in [7], where the result is shown for the usual shuffle operation (i.e., without marking explicitly the positions where the coloring changes).

Proposition 13 If $L \subseteq \Sigma^*$ is regular then Shuffle(L) is recognized by a multicounter automaton of size bounded by the size of an NFA recognizing L.

VI. Lower bounds

In this section we show that satisfiability for $\mathrm{FO}^2(\sim,<,+1)$ is at least as hard as non-emptiness of multicounter automata. The best lower bound known for the latter problem is EXPSPACE [12] and no elementary upper bound is known.

Theorem 14 *Emptiness of multicounter automata can be reduced in* PTIME *to the satisfiability problem of* $\mathrm{FO}^2(\sim,<,+1)$.

Proof sketch. Without loss of generality we assume that the multicounter has a one-letter input alphabet, no states (also known as vector addition system) and it accepts when *all* counters are empty. This can be done by adding one counter per states. Given a multicounter automaton $\mathcal{A}$, we construct a $\mathrm{FO}^2(\sim,<,+1)$ formula whose models are exactly (the encodings of) the accepting runs of the automaton.

Let $C = \{1,\ldots,n\}$ be the counters of the automaton, and let δ be its transition relation. We define Σ to be $D_1, I_1, \ldots, D_n, I_n$, and \$. An occurrence of D_i (I_i) codes a decrement (an increment) of counter i. The idea is to use data values to make sure that each decrement matches a previous increment. We encode a transition $t = (dec(i)^{k_i} inc(i)^{l_i})_{i \in C} \in \delta$ by a data word $\mathrm{enc}(t) = D_1^{k_1} I_1^{l_1} \cdots D_n^{k_n} I_n^{l_n}$ \$ where each occurrence of I_i have a new data value while each occurrence of D_i has the data value of the matching increment of the counter.

We can now check in $\mathrm{FO}^2(\sim,<,+1)$ that the string projection belongs to $\{\mathrm{enc}(t) \mid t \in \delta\}^*$. This is expressible in $\mathrm{FO}^2(<,+1)$ by a formula whose size is polynomial in δ. Then we enforce by an $\mathrm{FO}^2(\sim,<,+1)$ formula that each class string is either \$ or $I_k D_k$ for some k.

□

VII. Decidable extensions

A. More successors

It is often useful to be able to express in the logic the existence of a given pattern in the string, e.g. the existence of two positions x and y such that x and y are in the same class and the substring between x and y is *abc*. This does not seem to be expressible in $\mathrm{FO}^2(\sim,<,+1)$. This kind of property becomes immediately expressible in the presence of the predicates $+k$ for any $k \in \mathbb{N}$, where $x = y + k$ has the obvious meaning. We denote by $\mathrm{FO}^2(\sim,<,+\omega)$ the logic extending $\mathrm{FO}^2(\sim,<,+1)$ with all predicates $+k$. It turns out that this does not affect the decidability of the logic. The proof follows the lines of the of the proof for $\mathrm{FO}^2(\sim,<,+1)$ and will appear in the full version of the paper.

Theorem 15 *Satisfiability of* $\mathrm{FO}^2(\sim,<,+\omega)$ *is decidable.*

B. Infinite words

Another extension which is useful in the context of verification is the case of data ω-words, i.e., infinite length data strings. In this section we show the following result.

Theorem 16 *It is decidable whether a sentence of* $\mathrm{FO}^2(\sim,<,+1)$ *has a data* ω*-word model.*

The proof is along very similar lines as that of Theorem 1 but slightly departs as it does not reason about the string projection $\mathrm{str}(L(\varphi))$. Instead, the basic idea is to show that each satisfiable formula $\varphi \in \mathrm{FO}^2(\sim,<,+1)$ has a *simple* model of a given shape and that it is decidable whether a formula has a simple model. A data ω-word x is called **simple** if $\mathrm{mstr}(x)$ is of the form $u \cdot v^\omega$ for some finite words u and v over Σ.

As an intermediate step we use data ω-automata which are defined in analogy to data automata. We only mention the differences here. A **data** ω**-automaton** $(\mathcal{A}, \mathcal{B}_f, \mathcal{B}_i)$ consists of (1) a **base automaton** $\mathcal{A}$ which is a Büchi letter-to-letter transducer with output over some alphabet Γ, (2) a **finitary class automaton** $\mathcal{B}_f$ which is a finite string automaton over Γ and 3) an **infinitary class automaton** $\mathcal{B}_i$, which is another Büchi automaton over Γ. A data ω-word w is accepted if the base automaton has an accepting run over the marked string projection of w with output $b_1 b_2 \cdots$ such that for every finite class $i_1 < \cdots < i_k$, $b_{i_1} \cdots b_{i_k}$ is accepted by $\mathcal{B}_f$; similarly, for every infinite class $i_1 < i_2 < \cdots$, the ω-string $b_{i_1} b_{i_2} \cdots$ is accepted by $\mathcal{B}_i$.

Theorem 16 follows immediately from the following propositions.

Proposition 17 Every data ω-language definable in $\mathrm{FO}^2(\sim,<,+1)$ is recognized by some data ω-automaton.

Proof sketch. The proof follows exactly the lines of the proof of Proposition 2. Actually, the reduction to intermediate normal form is literally identical, as the proof of Lemma 8 does not assume finiteness. For the transformation of the intermediate normal form into a data ω-automaton, it suffices again to consider just the conjuncts θ since data ω-automata are closed under renaming, union and intersection.

Thus, it only remains to show that every conjunct θ of a formula in intermediate normal form can be recognized by a data ω-automaton.

This statement can be shown by a similar case analysis as in the proof of Lemma 9. □

Proposition 18 If a data ω-automaton accepts any ω-string it also accepts some simple ω-string.

Proof sketch. Let w be a (data) ω-string accepted by a data ω-automaton $(\mathcal{A}, \mathcal{B}_f, \mathcal{B}_i)$. Let $r = (r_{\mathcal{A}}, r_{\mathcal{B}_f}, r_{\mathcal{B}_i})$ be an accepting run for w that we view as functions from position to states. We call a position in w which is in a different class than its successor a **border position**. If w contains only finitely many border positions we can find u and v analogously as for classical (non-data) ω-automata. We only have to make sure that u contains all border positions. We thus assume in the following that there are infinitely many border positions in w.

A class c **overlaps** a position x if c contains positions $y < x$ and $z > x$. We say the class is **q-open** at x if $r_{\mathcal{B}_i}$ or $r_{\mathcal{B}_f}$ assigns the state q to the last position of c occurring before x. For a border position x of w, and for each state q, let m_q denote the number of q-open classes of w overlapping x.

The construction of u and v is based on the fact that there exist two border positions $x < x'$ of w such that:

(1) $r_{\mathcal{A}}(x) = r_{\mathcal{A}}(x')$ and $r_{\mathcal{A}}(y) \in F$, for some y, $x < y \leq x'$.
(2) For each $q \in \mathcal{B}_f$ and each q-open class c of w overlapping x there is a position $x < y_c \leq x'$ of c with $r_{\mathcal{A}}(y_c)$ accepting for $\mathcal{B}_f$.
(3) For each $q \in \mathcal{B}_i$ and each q-open class c of w overlapping x there is a position y_c, $x < y_c \leq x'$ with $r_{\mathcal{B}}(y_c)$ accepting for $\mathcal{B}_i$.
(4) for each q, $m_q(x) = m_q(x') = 0$ or $0 < m_q(x) \leq m_q(x')$.

Let w_u and w_v be the data subwords of w from positions 1 to x and from $x+1$ to x', respectively. Let $u = \mathrm{mstr}((w_u))$ and $v = \mathrm{mstr}((w_v))$. The proof is completed by showing how to choose the data values for uv^ω in order to get the desired data ω-word. □

Proposition 19 It is decidable whether a data ω-automaton accepts some simple ω-string.

Proof sketch. We construct a multicounter automaton which tests, for a string uv whether it can be marked and extended by data values and a (partial) run such that conditions (1) - (4) above are satisfied with x the last position of u and x' the last position of v. If this automaton accepts some string uv we can conclude that uv^ω is the string projection of an ω-string accepted by E. Otherwise, it can be shown that E accepts no data string at all, in particular it accepts no simple string. □

VIII. Undecidable extensions

In this section we show that many immediate extensions yields undecidability. In the context of XML, nodes in the document may have several different attributes which are accessed via the query languages. Equality tests between node attributes could be simulated using several equivalence relations. For instance checking that the nodes x and y agree on attribute a could be written as $x \sim_a y$. However, very recently Kieroński and Otto [10] showed that two-variable logic with 3 equivalence relations and some unary relations is undecidable.

Extending the model by allowing more variables, even three, also gives undecidability.

Proposition 20 Satisfiability of $\mathrm{FO}^3(\sim,+1)$ is undecidable.

Note that this implies the undecidability of $\mathrm{FO}^3(\sim,<)$, since the relation $+1$ is definable from $<$ if three variables are allowed.

Proof sketch. We reduce Post's Correspondence Problem (PCP) to the satisfiability of $\mathrm{FO}^3(\sim,+1)$. An instance of PCP consists of a finite number of pairs (u_i, v_i) of words from Σ^* and the question is whether there exists a non-empty, finite sequence of indexes $i_0, \ldots, i_n$ such that $u_{i_0}u_{i_1}\cdots u_{i_n} = v_{i_0}v_{i_1}\cdots v_{i_n}$.

Given an instance I of PCP, let $\Sigma' = \Sigma \cup \overline{\Sigma}$ be the alphabet consisting of two disjoint copies of Σ.

Consider a solution $i_0, \ldots, i_n$ such that $w = u_{i_0}u_{i_1}\cdots u_{i_n} = v_{i_0}v_{i_1}\cdots v_{i_n}$. We encode w by a data word $\hat{w} \in (\Sigma' \times D)^*$ satisfying the following:

- The string projection $\mathrm{str}(\hat{w})$ is $u_{i_0}\overline{v_{i_0}}\cdots u_{i_n}\overline{v_{i_n}}$. In particular, the sequence of letters from Σ is w and the sequence of letters from $\overline{\Sigma}$ is $\overline{w}$.
- Each data value appears exactly twice, once associated with a letter of Σ and once associated with the same letter in $\overline{\Sigma}$. Moreover, if a data value of $\hat{w}$ occurs at position i within w then its second occurrence must be at the same position i within $\overline{w}$.

It is possible to construct a formula φ of $\mathrm{FO}^3(\sim,+1)$ such that w is a solution of I iff $\hat{w}$ is a model of φ. □

Another possible extension is to suppose that there is a linear order on the data values and to include in the logic an extra binary predicate $\prec$ such that $x \prec y$ if the data value of x is smaller than the one of y. Unfortunately this yields undecidability even for FO^2.

Proposition 21 Satisfiability of $\mathrm{FO}^2(\sim,\prec,+1,<)$ is undecidable.

IX. Discussion

We have shown that satisfiability of $\mathrm{FO}^2(\sim,<,+1)$ over data words is decidable. Actually we have shown that the stronger logic $\mathrm{EMSO}^2(\sim,<,+1,\pm1)$ is decidable over such models.

In the absence of data values, $\mathrm{FO}^2(+1,<)$ has several equivalent characterizations, for instance it corresponds to the fragment of LTL that uses only unary temporal predicates. Still in the absence of data values, $\mathrm{EMSO}^2(+1,<)$ has the same expressive power as MSO. In a sense the decidability of $\mathrm{EMSO}^2(\sim,<,+1)$ can be seen as an extension of classical decidability result of MSO over strings.

An interesting side result is the connection between $\mathrm{FO}^2(\sim,<,+1)$ and multicounter automata (and therefore Petri nets). Indeed, if we project out the data values, the languages defined by $\mathrm{FO}^2(\sim,<,+1)$ formulas are recognized by multicounter automata. The converse is also true modulo an erasing inverse morphism. It would be interesting to understand better the connection between the two formalisms. Because of the connection with Petri nets pinpointing the complexity of satisfiability is likely to be difficult.

Our reduction from the decidability of $\mathrm{FO}^2(\sim,<,+1)$ to emptiness multicounter automata, is 2NExpTime. We do not know whether this is optimal or not.

When only one of the two predicates $+1$ and $<$ is present we can show that the decision problem is elementary. It is NExpTime-complete for $\mathrm{FO}^2(\sim,<)$ and in 2NExpTime for $\mathrm{FO}^2(\sim,+1)$. In [2] we studied in more details the logic $\mathrm{FO}^2(\sim,+1)$ and proved that it is decidable over unranked ordered trees. We inferred from this result many interesting consequences for XML reasoning. Whether $\mathrm{FO}^2(\sim,<,+1)$ is decidable over trees is still an open question which was shown in [2] to be at least as hard as checking emptiness of multicounter automata over trees (stated as an open question in [3]).

References

[1] P. Bouyer, A. Petit and D. Thérien. An algebraic approach to data languages and timed languages. *Inf. Comput.*, 182(2): 137-162 (2003).

[2] M. Bojańczyk, C. David, A. Muscholl, T. Schwentick, and L. Segoufin. Two-Variable Logic on Data Trees and XML Reasoning. To appear in PODS'06.

[3] P. de Groote, B. Guillaume, and S. Salvati. Vector Addition Tree Automata. In *LICS'04*, pp. 64-73, 2004.

[4] S. Demri, R. Lazic, D. Nowak. On the Freeze Quantifier in Constraint LTL: Decidability and Complexity. In *TIME'05*, 2005.

[5] J. Esparza and M. Nielsen. Decidability Issues for Petri Nets - a survey. *Elektronische Informationsverarbeitung und Kybernetik*, 30(3): 143-160 (1994).

[6] K. Etessami, M.Y. Vardi, and Th. Wilke. First-Order Logic with Two Variables and Unary Temporal Logic. *Inf. Comput.*, 179(2): 279-295 (2002).

[7] J. L. Gischer. Shuffle Languages, Petri Nets, and Context-Sensitive Grammars. *Commun. ACM*, 24(9):597-605 (1981).

[8] E. Grädel and M. Otto. On Logics with Two Variables. *Theor. Comp. Sci.*, 224:73-113 (1999).

[9] M. Kaminski and N. Francez. Finite memory automata. *Theor. Comp. Sci.*, 134(2):329-363 (1994).

[10] E. Kieroński and M. Otto. Small Substructures and Decidability Issues for First-Order Logic with Two Variables. Preprint. 2005.

[11] S.R. Kosaraju. Decidability of reachability in vector addition systems. In *STOC'84*, pp. 267-281. 1984.

[12] R.J. Lipton. The reachability problem requires exponential space. Dep. of Comp.Sci., Research report 62, Yale University, 1976.

[13] M. Marx. First order paths in ordered trees. In *ICDT'05*, 2005.

[14] E. Mayr. An algorithm for the general Petri net reachability problem. *SIAM J. of Comp.*, 13:441-459 (1984).

[15] M. Mortimer. On languages with two variables. *Zeitschr. f. math. Logik u. Grundlagen d. Math.*, 21(1975), pp. 135-140.

[16] F. Neven, Th. Schwentick, and V. Vianu. Finite state machines for strings over infinite alphabets. *ACM Trans. Comput. Log.*, 15(3): 403-435 (2004).

[17] Th. Schwentick, D. Thérien, and H. Vollmer. Partially-Ordered Two-Way Automata: A New Characterization of DA. In *Developments in Language Theory (DLT'01)*, pp. 239-250, 2001.

[18] Y. Shemesh, N. Francez. Finite-State Unification Automata and Relational Languages In *Inf. Comput.*, 114(2): 192-213 (1994)

[19] D. Thérien and Th. Wilke. Over Words, Two Variables Are as Powerful as One Quantifier Alternation. In *STOC'98*, pp. 234-240, 1998.

LTL with the Freeze Quantifier and Register Automata

Stéphane Demri *
LSV, CNRS & ENS Cachan & INRIA Futurs, France

Ranko Lazić †
Department of Computer Science, University of Warwick, UK

Abstract

Temporal logics, first-order logics, and automata over data words have recently attracted considerable attention. A data word is a word over a finite alphabet, together with a datum (an element of an infinite domain) at each position. Examples include timed words and XML documents. To refer to the data, temporal logics are extended with the freeze quantifier, first-order logics with predicates over the data domain, and automata with registers or pebbles.

We investigate relative expressiveness and complexity of standard decision problems for LTL with the freeze quantifier (LTL$^{\downarrow}$), 2-variable first-order logic (FO^2) over data words, and register automata. The only predicate available on data is equality. Previously undiscovered connections among those formalisms, and to counter automata with incrementing errors, enable us to answer several questions left open in recent literature.

We show that the future-time fragment of LTL$^{\downarrow}$ which corresponds to FO^2 over finite data words can be extended considerably while preserving decidability, but at the expense of non-primitive recursive complexity, and that most of further extensions are undecidable. We also prove that surprisingly, over infinite data words, LTL$^{\downarrow}$ without the 'until' operator, as well as nonemptiness of one-way universal register automata, are undecidable even when there is only 1 register.

1. Introduction

Being able to store a value in some register/variable and to test it later in a different context, is a common feature of many recently studied logical formalisms. The following are the most prominent examples:

Timed logics. The freeze quantifier in timed logics was introduced in the logic TPTL (e.g. [2]), where the formula $x \cdot \phi(x)$ binds the variable x to the time t of the current state. Depending on the semantics, x is interpreted as a real number or a natural number and the formula is semantically equivalent to $\phi(t)$.

Hybrid logics. In [13], the formula $\downarrow_x \phi(x)$ holds whenever $\phi(x)$ holds in the variant Kripke structure where the propositional variable x is interpreted as a singleton containing exactly the current state.

Modal logics. Predicate λ-abstraction is presented in [11] to solve the problem of interpreting constants in first-order modal logics: $\langle \lambda x \cdot \mathtt{F}\ P(x) \rangle(c)$ states that the current value of the constant c satisfies the predicate P eventually in the future.

Logics with forgettable past. In [15], `Now` ϕ holds whenever ϕ holds in a linear structure in which the origin is updated to the current position (ϕ may contain past-time operators). Equivalently, the register containing the position of the origin of time is assigned the current position.

Interestingly, the same general mechanism is central to the notion of register automata [14, 26, 6, 21], which recognise words over infinite alphabets. Indeed, a letter can be stored in a register and tested later against the current letter. Similarly, in Alur-Dill timed automata (e.g. [1]), resetting a clock c to 0 is equivalent to storing the current time as the time when c was last reset.

The ability to store and test is powerful, since many problems are undecidable in its presence [14, 1, 6, 8, 17]. However, searching for decidable fragments or subproblems, and determining their complexity, is well-motivated by the fact that logical and automata formalisms with such features are helpful for querying semi-structured data [21, 7, 3], verifying timed systems [2, 1], model checking constrained automata [8], and verifying dynamic systems with resources [17], quoting a few examples.

In this paper, we consider logics and automata over finite and infinite data words. In a data word, at each index, there is a letter from a finite alphabet Σ, and an element of an infinite domain D. As in [14, 26, 21, 7, 4, 8, 17], elements of D can only be compared for equality, so it is equivalent and simpler to define a data word as a word over Σ

* Supported by the ACI "Sécurité et Informatique" CORTOS.

† Supported by an invited professorship from ENS Cachan, and by grants from the EPSRC (GR/S52759/01) and the Intel Corporation. Also affiliated to the Mathematical Institute, Serbian Academy of Sciences and Arts, Belgrade.

equipped with an equivalence relation on its indices: $i \sim j$ iff the elements of D at indices i and j are equal. In common with [7, 4], we take this latter approach. To be able to consider languages of words over Σ obtained by projecting data words, we do not eliminate the finite alphabets from the definition of data words, although such eliminations are possible by encodings as in [14, 26, 21, 8].

We study linear temporal logic extended by the freeze quantifier (LTL$^{\downarrow}$). The formula $\downarrow_r \phi$ holds at an index i of a data word iff ϕ holds with i stored in the register r. Within the scope of the freeze quantifier $\downarrow_r$, the atomic formula $\uparrow_r \sim$ is true at an index j iff $i \sim j$, i.e. the data value at the index in r is equal to the data value at the current index.

LTL$^{\downarrow}$ is the core of Constraint LTL with the freeze quantifier [8], and of the linear temporal logics with predicate λ-abstraction [17]. Moreover, Repeating Hybrid LTL considered in [12] is exactly the fragment of LTL$^{\downarrow}$ with the temporal operators $\mathtt{X}$, $\mathtt{X}^{-1}$, $\mathtt{F}$ and $\mathtt{F}^{-1}$.

We show that the first-order logic with 2 variables $\mathrm{FO}^2(\sim, <, +1)$ studied in [7, 4] is equivalent to a natural fragment of LTL$^{\downarrow}$ with only 1 register. That extends the equivalence between $\mathrm{FO}^2(<, +1)$ and unary LTL in the setting without data values [10]. In [4], satisfiability for $\mathrm{FO}^2(\sim, <, +1)$ is proved decidable and as hard as reachability for Petri nets, over finite and over infinite data words.

The automata formalism we consider is register automata (RA) over data words. As in LTL$^{\downarrow}$, an RA can store the current data word index in a register r, and subsequently test whether the index in r is in the same class of $\sim$ as the current index. Over finite data words, essentially the same automata were studied in [14, 26, 21], and one-way nondeterministic RA are a subclass of data automata [6, 5]. We consider two-way alternating RA, as well as subclasses obtained by restricting directionality and/or control. In contrast to finite automata on words over finite alphabets, a number of separation results for such subclasses were obtained in [14, 21]. For infinite data words, we focus on weak parity RA, a subclass of both Büchi and co-Büchi RA.

The second expressiveness result in the paper is a translation in logarithmic space from sentences of LTL$^{\downarrow}$ to equivalent RA. For the future fragment, one-way RA are sufficient.

The central part of the paper consists of a systematic investigation of decidability and complexity of standard decision problems for fragments of LTL$^{\downarrow}$ and classes of RA. Most of the results are based on surprising translations to and from counter automata (CA), where we consider both standard (Minsky) CA whose computations are exact, and faulty (Incrementing) CA whose computations may contain errors which increase one or more counters.

We show that, over finite and infinite data words, with only 1 register, satisfiability for the future fragment of LTL$^{\downarrow}$, as well as nonemptiness of one-way alternating RA, are reducible in polynomial space to nonemptiness of Incrementing CA. In the finitary case, that gives us decidability of the former two problems. The only decidable fragment of LTL$^{\downarrow}$ previously known is the flat fragment in [8], in which use of the freeze quantifier is heavily restricted. Interestingly, the translation from one-way alternating RA to Incrementing CA consists of broadly similar steps as the translation from one-way alternating timed automata to faulty channel machines in [24].

For the next main result, we first adapt the recent results in [27, 24] on faulty channel machines to obtain that finitary [resp. infinitary] nonemptiness of Incrementing CA is not primitive recursive [resp. Π_1^0-hard]. Then, through encoding runs of Incrementing CA as data words, we obtain that, even with only 1 register, finitary [resp. infinitary] satisfiability for the future fragment of LTL$^{\downarrow}$ without the $\mathtt{U}$ operator, as well as nonemptiness of one-way universal RA (equivalently, nonuniversality of one-way nondeterministic RA), are not primitive recursive [resp. Π_1^0-hard].

By translating from Minsky CA instead of Incrementing CA, we show that several other satisfiability problems for fragments of LTL$^{\downarrow}$ and nonemptiness problems for classes of RA are Σ_1^0-hard over finite data words, and Σ_1^1-hard over infinite data words.

Taken together, the decision problem results in this paper provide a tighter demarkation of the decidability border than was known in the literature, in terms of finite versus infinite data words, the number of registers, sets of temporal operators, and automata directionality and control. We answer several questions posed in [14, 21, 12, 8, 17]. In particular, the undecidability result for nonemptiness of one-way universal RA with only 1 register shows that it is impossible to extend the developments in [14] to infinite words, which was a challenge posed in that paper.

Along the way, we obtain several other results, including a characterisation of projections onto the finite alphabet of languages of sentences from the future fragment of LTL$^{\downarrow}$ with 1 register. Surprisingly, the characterisation is the same with or without the $\mathtt{U}$ operator.

More detailed comparisons with related work can be found throughout the paper.

Sections 2 and 3 contain the definitions, and warm-up results on closure properties of register automata and on nonemptiness of counter automata. The results on relative expressiveness are in Section 4. The central part of the paper is in Sections 5 and 6, which are mainly on decidability and complexity of decision problems.

2. Preliminaries

2.1. LTL over data words

LTL$^{\downarrow}(\sim; \mathcal{O})$ will denote the linear temporal logic with the freeze quantifier, the predicate $\sim$, and temporal operators in the set $\mathcal{O}$. Each formula is over a finite alphabet Σ. Atomic propositions a are elements of Σ, r ranges over $\mathbb{N} \setminus \{0\}$, and $\mathtt{O}$ ranges over $\mathcal{O}$.

$$\phi ::= \top \mid a \mid \uparrow_r\sim \mid \neg\phi \mid \phi \wedge \phi \mid \mathtt{O}(\phi, \ldots, \phi) \mid \downarrow_r \phi$$

An occurence of $\uparrow_r\sim$ within the scope of some freeze quantifier $\downarrow_r$ is bound by it; otherwise, it is free. A sentence is a formula with no free occurence of any $\uparrow_r\sim$.

We consider the set $\{\mathtt{X}, \mathtt{X}^{-1}, \mathtt{F}, \mathtt{F}^{-1}, \mathtt{U}, \mathtt{U}^{-1}\}$ of temporal operators, and its subsets. As $\mathtt{F}\phi$ is equivalent to $\top\mathtt{U}\phi$, $\mathtt{F}$ can be omitted from any set which contains $\mathtt{U}$, and the same is true for $\mathtt{F}^{-1}$ and $\mathtt{U}^{-1}$. As usual, we regard $\mathtt{G}$ and $\mathtt{G}^{-1}$ as abbreviations for $\neg\mathtt{F}\neg$ and $\neg\mathtt{F}^{-1}\neg$.

Let $\mathrm{LTL}^{\downarrow}_n(\sim; \mathcal{O})$ be the fragment of $\mathrm{LTL}^{\downarrow}(\sim; \mathcal{O})$ with n registers, i.e. where $r \in \{1, \ldots, n\}$.

Models of $\mathrm{LTL}^{\downarrow}(\sim; \mathcal{O})$ are *data words.* A data word σ over a finite alphabet Σ is a nonempty word in $\Sigma^{<\omega}$ or Σ^{ω}, together with an interpretation of $\sim$ as an equivalence relation on word indices. We write $|\sigma|$ for the length of the word, $\sigma(i)$ for its letters where $0 \leq i < |\sigma|$, and $\sim^{\sigma}$ for the interpretation of $\sim$. Let $\Sigma^{<\omega}(\sim)$ and $\Sigma^{\omega}(\sim)$ denote the sets of all such finite and infinite (respectively) data words. For a data word σ, let $\mathrm{str}(\sigma)$ be the underlying word in $\Sigma^{\leq\omega}$.

A *register valuation* v for a data word σ is a finite partial map from $\mathbb{N} \setminus \{0\}$ to the indices of σ. An undefined register value in an atomic formula will make the latter false. Undefined register values will be used for initial automata states. The satisfaction relation $\models$ is defined as follows. Temporal operators are interpreted as in LTL, so we show only one. We also omit the Boolean cases.

$$\begin{aligned}
\sigma, i \models_v a &\overset{\text{def}}{\Leftrightarrow} \sigma(i) = a \\
\sigma, i \models_v \uparrow_r\sim &\overset{\text{def}}{\Leftrightarrow} r \in \mathrm{dom}(v) \text{ and } v(r) \sim^{\sigma} i \\
\sigma, i \models_v \mathtt{X}\phi &\overset{\text{def}}{\Leftrightarrow} i + 1 < |\sigma| \text{ and } \sigma, i+1 \models_v \phi \\
\sigma, i \models_v \downarrow_r \phi &\overset{\text{def}}{\Leftrightarrow} \sigma, i \models_{v[r \mapsto i]} \phi
\end{aligned}$$

2.2. First-order logic over data words

As defined in [4], $\mathrm{FO}(\sim, <, +1, \ldots, +m)$ denotes first-order logic over data words, in which variables range over word indices. We use variable names $x_0, x_1, \ldots$ The predicates $x_i < x_j$ and $x_i = x_j + k$ are interpreted as expected. Each formula has an alphabet Σ, and it may contain unary predicates $P_a(x_i)$ which are satisfied by a data word iff the letter at index x_i is a. When we write $\phi(x_{i_1}, \ldots, x_{i_N})$, it means that at most $x_{i_1}, \ldots, x_{i_N}$ occur free in ϕ.

$\mathrm{FO}^n(\sim, <, +1, \ldots, +m)$ has variables $x_0, \ldots, x_{n-1}$.

2.3. Register automata

Suppose Q is a finite set of locations, and $n \in \mathbb{N}$. The set $\Phi(Q, n)$ of all *transition formulae* with respect to Q and n is defined as follows, where $r \in \{1, \ldots, n\}$ and $q \in Q$:

$$\begin{aligned}
\varphi ::= {} & \top \mid \bot \mid \uparrow_r\sim \mid \uparrow_r\not\sim \mid \mathtt{beg} \mid \mathtt{nbeg} \mid \mathtt{end} \mid \mathtt{nend} \mid \\
& \varphi \wedge \varphi \mid \varphi \vee \varphi \mid \downarrow_r \varphi \mid \langle q, 1\rangle \mid \langle q, -1\rangle
\end{aligned}$$

A transition formula is *locationless* iff it has no subformula of the form $\langle q, o\rangle$. Otherwise, it is *locationful.* For any locationless transition formula φ, let $\bar{\varphi}$ denote its dual, obtained by replacing any atomic subformula by its negation, and interchanging $\wedge$ and $\vee$.

A two-way alternating *register automaton* $\mathcal{A}$ is a tuple $\langle \Sigma, Q, q_I, n, \delta, \rho\rangle$ such that:

- Σ is a finite alphabet;
- Q is a finite set of locations;
- $q_I \in Q$ is the initial location;
- $n \in \mathbb{N}$ is the number of registers (given in unary);
- $\delta : Q \times \Sigma \to \Phi(Q, n)$ is the transition function;
- $\rho : Q \to \mathbb{N}$ specifies ranks such that, whenever $\langle q', o\rangle$ is a subformula of $\delta(q, a)$, we have $\rho(q') \leq \rho(q)$.

Suppose $\sigma \in \Sigma^{\leq\omega}(\sim)$. To define runs of $\mathcal{A}$ over σ, we first define a state of $\mathcal{A}$ for σ to be a triple $\langle i, q, v\rangle$ where i is an index of σ, q is a location of $\mathcal{A}$, and v is a register valuation for σ.

Next, we interpret the transition function δ by means of a satisfaction relation $S \models_v^{\sigma,i} \varphi$ where S is a finite set of states for σ and φ is a transition formula. The cases for Boolean constants and operators are standard, and treatments of dual clauses are as expected:

$$\begin{aligned}
S \models_v^{\sigma,i} \uparrow_r\sim &\overset{\text{def}}{\Leftrightarrow} v(r) \sim^{\sigma} i \text{ and } v(r) \text{ is defined} \\
S \models_v^{\sigma,i} \mathtt{beg} &\overset{\text{def}}{\Leftrightarrow} i = 0 \\
S \models_v^{\sigma,i} \mathtt{end} &\overset{\text{def}}{\Leftrightarrow} i = |\sigma| - 1 \\
S \models_v^{\sigma,i} \downarrow_r \varphi &\overset{\text{def}}{\Leftrightarrow} S \models_{v[r \mapsto i]}^{\sigma,i} \varphi \\
S \models_v^{\sigma,i} \langle q, o\rangle &\overset{\text{def}}{\Leftrightarrow} \langle i + o, q, v\rangle \in S
\end{aligned}$$

Now, a run of $\mathcal{A}$ of length $0 < \kappa \leq \omega$ over σ is a directed acyclic graph G consisting of:

- for each $0 \leq j < \kappa$, a finite set $G(j)$ (called a level) of states of $\mathcal{A}$ for σ, and
- for each j with $j+1 < \kappa$, an edge relation $\to_j$ between $G(j)$ and $G(j+1)$,

such that:

(i) $G(0) = \{\langle 0, q_I, \emptyset\rangle\}$, where $\emptyset$ is the empty register valuation;

(ii) for any j with nonempty $G(j)$, we have $j + 1 < \kappa$, $G(j+1) = \bigcup_{\langle i,q,v\rangle \in G(j)} S_{\langle i,q,v\rangle}$ where each $S_{\langle i,q,v\rangle}$ is some minimal set satisfying $S_{\langle i,q,v\rangle} \models_v^{\sigma,i} \delta(q, \sigma(i))$, and $\langle i, q, v\rangle \to_j \langle i', q', v'\rangle$ iff $\langle i', q', v'\rangle \in S_{\langle i,q,v\rangle}$.

Observe that, as a consequence of (ii), any finite run is complete, in the sense that its last level $G(\kappa - 1)$ is necessarily empty. Note also that, in any valid run, for every $\langle i, q, v\rangle$ in any level, some $S_{\langle i,q,v\rangle}$ as in (ii) must exist.

Along any path π of a run, the location ranks are non-increasing. Therefore, if π is infinite, the location ranks eventually have the same value, which we denote by $\rho(\pi)$. A data word is accepted iff it has a run such that, for each infinite path π, $\rho(\pi)$ is even. [1]

An automaton as above is one-way iff it contains no transition subformula of the form $\langle q, -1\rangle$. For one-way automata, any successor state of a state $\langle i, q, v\rangle$ is of the form $\langle i + 1, q, v\rangle$. Over a finite data word σ, any run of a one-way automaton is finite. Hence, σ is accepted iff it has a run, i.e. the ranking function ρ is irrelevant.

An automaton is nondeterministic (i.e. existential) iff any transition subformula which is a conjunction of locationful formulae is of the form $(\varphi \vee \varphi') \wedge (\bar{\varphi} \vee \varphi'')$ where φ is locationless. For nondeterministic automata, any successor set of any state has size at most 1. Thus, any run is a sequence of states.

An automaton is universal iff any transition subformula which is a disjunction of locationful formulae is of the form $(\varphi \wedge \varphi') \vee (\bar{\varphi} \wedge \varphi'')$ where φ is locationless. For universal automata, any state has at most one successor set. Thus, any data word has at most one run.

An automaton is deterministic iff it is both nondeterministic and universal.

The classes of register automata above will be denoted by d*C*RA($\sim$), where $d \in \{1, 2\}$ and $C \in \{\mathrm{A, N, U, D}\}$ specify any restrictions on directionality and control. Let d*C*RA$_n(\sim)$ denote the subclass with n registers.

Note 1 The definition of register automata above is suited to the uses in this paper, and has similarities with definitions in [6, 5, 16, 23]. Thus, it differs in some technical details from the definition of register automata in [14, 26, 21]. With the latter definition, in any state, the registers contain mutually distinct data values (or the default value $\sharp$), and the previous data value is always held in a register. It can be checked that, for any automaton with $n + 1$ registers in the sense of [14, 26, 21], we can construct an equivalent automaton with $n + 1$ registers and an equivalent alternating automaton with n registers in the sense of this paper.

2.4. Counter automata

A *counter automaton* (CA), with ε transitions and zero testing, is a tuple $\langle \Sigma, Q, q_I, n, \delta, F\rangle$ where Σ is a finite alphabet, Q is a finite set of locations, q_I is the initial location, $n \in \mathbb{N}$ is the number of counters (given in unary), $\delta \subseteq Q \times (\Sigma \uplus \{\varepsilon\}) \times L \times Q$ is the transition relation over the instruction set $L = \{\mathtt{inc}, \mathtt{dec}, \mathtt{ifzero}\} \times \{1, \ldots, n\}$, and $F \subseteq Q$ is the set of accepting locations.

A counter valuation is a function $\{1, \ldots, n\} \to \mathbb{N}$. An error-free run over $w \in \Sigma^{<\omega}$ [resp. $w \in \Sigma^{\omega}$] is a finite [resp. infinite] sequence $\langle q_0, v_0\rangle \xrightarrow{w_0, l_0} \langle q_1, v_1\rangle \xrightarrow{w_1, l_1} \cdots$ observing the standard interpretation of the instructions ($\langle \mathtt{dec}, c\rangle$ can be performed only if c is nonzero), where $q_0 = q_I$, $v_0, v_1, \ldots$ are counter valuations, v_0 assigns 0 to each counter, and $w = w_0 w_1 \ldots$.

A finite run is accepting iff it ends with an accepting location. An infinite run is accepting iff it contains an accepting location infinitely often.

A *Minsky* CA has error-free runs. For Minsky CA, finitary nonemptiness is in Σ^0_1, and infinitary nonemptiness is in Σ^1_1. Already with 2 counters, infinitary nonemptiness is Σ^1_1-hard [2, Lemma 8], and finitary nonemptiness of deterministic Minsky CA is Σ^0_1-hard [19].

An *Incrementing* CA is defined as a Minsky CA except that its runs may contain errors which increase one or more counters. Formally, for counter valuations v and $v_\dagger$, we write $v \leq v_\dagger$ iff, for all c, $v(c) \leq v_\dagger(c)$. Runs of Incrementing CA are defined by replacing the relation $\xrightarrow{w,l}$ with the following: $\langle q, v\rangle \xrightarrow{w,l}_\dagger \langle q', v'\rangle$ iff there exist $v_\dagger$ and $v'_\dagger$ such that $v \leq v_\dagger$, $\langle q, v_\dagger\rangle \xrightarrow{w,l} \langle q', v'_\dagger\rangle$, and $v'_\dagger \leq v'$. When it is clear from the context that we are considering an Incrementing CA, we may write simply $\xrightarrow{w,l}$ instead of $\xrightarrow{w,l}_\dagger$.

Theorem 2 *For Incrementing CA, finitary nonemptiness is decidable and not primitive recursive;*[2] *infinitary nonemptiness is* Π^0_1*-complete.*

Proof. Decidability of finitary nonemptiness follows from the decidability of the coverability problem for Reset Petri nets [9] by reversing the computations, and non-primitive recursiveness from an adaptation of the result of [27]. Π^0_1-completeness of infinitary nonemptiness follows by adapting the proof of [24, Theorem 2], and by Π^0_1 membership of the recurrent-state problem for Insertion Channel Machines with Emptiness Testing [25]. □

2.5. Languages and decision problems

For an LTL$^{\downarrow}(\sim; \mathcal{O})$ sentence ϕ over an alphabet Σ, let $\mathrm{L}^{\alpha}_{\Sigma}(\phi) = \{\sigma \in \Sigma^{\alpha}(\sim) : \sigma, 0 \models \phi\}$.

For an FO($\sim, <, +1$) sentence ϕ over an alphabet Σ, let $\mathrm{L}^{\alpha}_{\Sigma}(\phi) = \{\sigma \in \Sigma^{\alpha}(\sim) : \sigma \models \phi\}$.

For a register automaton $\mathcal{A}$ whose alphabet is Σ, let $\mathrm{L}^{<\omega}(\mathcal{A})$ [resp. $\mathrm{L}^{\omega}(\mathcal{A})$] denote the set of all finite [resp. infinite] data words over Σ accepted by $\mathcal{A}$.

[1] Recall that we consider only nonempty data words. It is straightforward to extend the definitions to enable acceptance of the empty data word, but that is not necessary in this paper.

[2] Recall the Ritchie-Cobham property [22, page 297]: a decision problem (i.e. a set) is primitive recursive iff it is solvable in primitive recursive time/space.

For a counter automaton $\mathcal{C}$ whose alphabet is Σ, let $\mathrm{L}^{<\omega}(\mathcal{C})$ [resp. $\mathrm{L}^{\omega}(\mathcal{C})$] denote the set of all finite [resp. infinite] words over Σ accepted by $\mathcal{C}$.

The decision problems of *satisfiability* for a logical fragment, and *nonemptiness* for a class of automata, are defined as usual in terms of the languages above. A problem is *finitary* or *infinitary*, which specifies word length.

A sentence or register automaton is said to be *equivalent* to another one iff they are over the same alphabet and have the same finitary and infinitary languages.

3. Closure properties

Proposition 3 *Over finite and over infinite data words, and for any $d \in \{1, 2\}$, dDRA$_n(\sim)$ and dARA$_n(\sim)$ are closed under complement, and dNRA$_n(\sim)$ is dual to dURA$_n(\sim)$.*

Proof. It can be shown that the dual automaton recognises the complement language, by adapting complementation of alternating automata and using determinacy of weak parity games (see [18]). □

Proposition 4 *Over finite and over infinite data words:*

(a) Each automata class $1\mathcal{C}$RA$(\sim)$ is closed under intersection and union. For intersections of universal or alternating automata, and for unions of nondeterministic or alternating automata, the maximum of the two numbers of registers suffices. Otherwise, their sum suffices.

(b) 2URA$(\sim)$ is closed under intersection, 2NRA$(\sim)$ is closed under union, and 2ARA$(\sim)$ is closed under intersection and union. The maximum of the two numbers of registers suffices.

Proof. By branching and product constructions. □

4. Expressiveness

Suppose $m \geq 1$. We write $\mathtt{X}^m$ [resp. $\mathtt{X}^{-m}$] to denote the temporal operator made of $m \geq 1$ successive operators $\mathtt{X}$ [resp. $\mathtt{X}^{-1}$]. The operators $\mathtt{X}^m\mathtt{F}$ and $\mathtt{X}^{-m}\mathtt{F}^{-1}$ are defined analogously. Let $\mathcal{O}_m$ denote the following set of temporal operators: $\{\mathtt{X}, \mathtt{X}^{-1}, \ldots, \mathtt{X}^m, \mathtt{X}^{-m}, \mathtt{X}^{m+1}\mathtt{F}, \mathtt{X}^{-(m+1)}\mathtt{F}^{-1}\}$.

An $\mathrm{LTL}_1^{\downarrow}(\sim; \mathcal{O}_m)$ formula is said to be *simple* iff any occurrence of a temporal operator is immediately preceded by $\downarrow_1$ (and there are no other occurences of $\downarrow_1$).

Example 5 Since the Boolean operators and the freeze quantifier commute, the simple fragment of $\mathrm{LTL}_1^{\downarrow}(\sim; \mathcal{O}_1)$ can express $\downarrow_1 \mathtt{F}$, $\downarrow_1 \mathtt{G}$ and $\downarrow_1 \mathtt{XG}$. Hence, there is a simple formula in $\mathrm{LTL}_1^{\downarrow}(\sim; \mathcal{O}_1)$ equivalent to the 'nonces' sentence $\mathtt{G} \downarrow_1 \mathtt{XG}\neg \uparrow_1\sim$ which states that no class of $\sim$ contains more than one element.

An $\mathrm{LTL}_1^{\downarrow}(\sim; \mathcal{O}_m)$ sentence ϕ is said to be equivalent to an $\mathrm{FO}^2(\sim, <, +1, \ldots, +m)$ formula $\phi'(x_j)$ iff they are over the same alphabet Σ and, for every $\sigma \in \Sigma^{\leq\omega}(\sim)$ and index i of σ, we have $\sigma, i \models_{\emptyset} \phi \Leftrightarrow \sigma \models_{[x_j \mapsto i]} \phi'(x_j)$.

Proposition 6 *(a) For any simple $\mathrm{LTL}_1^{\downarrow}(\sim; \mathcal{O}_m)$ sentence, an equivalent $\mathrm{FO}^2(\sim, <, +1, \ldots, +m)$ formula is computable in logspace.*

(b) For any $\mathrm{FO}^2(\sim, <, +1, \ldots, +m)$ formula $\phi(x_j)$, an equivalent simple $\mathrm{LTL}_1^{\downarrow}(\sim; \mathcal{O}_m)$ formula is computable in pspace.

Proof. First, we introduce some convenient notation. Let $\mathtt{O}^0 = \downarrow_1$, $\mathtt{O}^k = \downarrow_1 \mathtt{X}^k$ for $k \in \{-m, \ldots, -1, 1, \ldots, m\}$, $\mathtt{O}^{m+1} = \downarrow_1 \mathtt{X}^{m+1}\mathtt{F}$, and $\mathtt{O}^{-(m+1)} = \downarrow_1 \mathtt{X}^{-(m+1)}\mathtt{F}^{-1}$. For $j \in \{0, 1\}$, let

$$\begin{aligned}
\chi_0^j &\stackrel{\text{def}}{=} x_{1-j} = x_j \\
\chi_k^j &\stackrel{\text{def}}{=} x_{1-j} = x_j + k \; (1 \leq k \leq m) \\
\chi_{-k}^j &\stackrel{\text{def}}{=} x_j = x_{1-j} + k \; (1 \leq k \leq m) \\
\chi_{m+1}^j &\stackrel{\text{def}}{=} x_j < x_{1-j} \wedge \textstyle\bigwedge_{1 \leq k \leq m} \neg x_{1-j} = x_j + k \\
\chi_{-(m+1)}^j &\stackrel{\text{def}}{=} x_{1-j} < x_j \wedge \textstyle\bigwedge_{1 \leq k \leq m} \neg x_j = x_{1-j} + k
\end{aligned}$$

(The equality predicate can be expressed using $<$.)

We have (a) by the following translations T_j which map simple $\mathrm{LTL}_1^{\downarrow}(\sim; \mathcal{O}_m)$ formulae to $\mathrm{FO}^2(\sim, <, +1, \ldots, +m)$ formulae. Any sentence ϕ will be equivalent to $T_j(\phi)$ which will contain at most x_j free. T_j are defined by structural recursion, by encoding the semantics of simple formulae into first-order logic, and by recycling variables (to use only two variables). The Boolean clauses are omitted.

$$T_j(a) \stackrel{\text{def}}{=} P_a(x_j) \qquad T_j(\uparrow_1\sim) \stackrel{\text{def}}{=} x_{1-j} \sim x_j$$
$$T_j(\mathtt{O}^k\psi) \stackrel{\text{def}}{=} \exists x_{1-j}(\chi_k^j \wedge T_{1-j}(\psi))$$

For (b), we proceed by adapting the proof of [10, Theorem 1]. We define recursively translations T'_j from $\mathrm{FO}^2(\sim, <, +1, \ldots, +m)$ formulae $\phi(x_j)$ to equivalent simple $\mathrm{LTL}_1^{\downarrow}(\sim; \mathcal{O}_m)$ sentences. The cases of Boolean operators and one-variable atomic formulae are straightforward. The remaining case is when $\phi(x_j)$ is of the form

$$\exists x_{1-j}\, \beta(\alpha_1(x_0, x_1), \ldots, \alpha_L(x_0, x_1),$$
$$\xi_1(x_j), \ldots, \xi_N(x_j), \zeta_1(x_{1-j}), \ldots, \zeta_M(x_{1-j}))$$

where β is a Boolean formula, and each $\alpha_i(x_0, x_1)$ is a $\sim$, $<$ or $+k$ atomic formula. Now, for any $-(m+1) \leq k \leq m+1$ and $\bowtie \in \{\sim, \not\sim\}$, let $\alpha_i^{k,\bowtie}$ denote the truth value of $\alpha_i(x_0, x_1)$ under the assumption $\chi_k^j \wedge x_j \bowtie x_{1-j}$. Also, for any $X \subseteq \{1, \ldots, N\}$, let $\xi_i^X = \top$ if $i \in X$, and $\xi_i^X = \bot$ otherwise. $T'_j(\phi(x_j))$ is then computed as

$$\textstyle\bigvee_{-(m+1) \leq k \leq m+1} \bigvee_{\bowtie \in \{\sim, \not\sim\}} \bigvee_{X \subseteq \{1, \ldots, N\}}$$
$$(\textstyle\bigwedge_{i \in \{1, \ldots, N\}} T'_j(\xi_i(x_j)) \Leftrightarrow \xi_i^X) \wedge$$
$$\mathtt{O}^k(\uparrow_1\bowtie \wedge\, \beta(\alpha_1^{k,\bowtie}, \ldots, \alpha_L^{k,\bowtie},$$
$$\xi_1^X, \ldots, \xi_N^X, T'_{1-j}(\zeta_1(x_{1-j})), \ldots, T'_{1-j}(\zeta_M(x_{1-j})))$$

The size of the equivalent simple $\mathrm{LTL}_1^{\downarrow}(\sim;\mathcal{O}_m)$ formula is exponential in $|\phi|$, because the length of the stack of recursive calls is linear and generalized conjunctions and disjunctions have at most exponentially many arguments. For the same reasons, polynomial space is sufficient for the computation. □

Corollary 7 *Over finite and over infinite data words, simple $LTL_1^{\downarrow}(\sim;\mathcal{O}_m)$ satisfiability is logspace reducible to $FO^2(\sim,<,+1,\ldots,+m)$ satisfiability, and there is a pspace reduction in the reverse direction.*

We now turn to translating temporal formulae to register automata.

Theorem 8 *For any $LTL_n^{\downarrow}(\sim;\mathtt{X},\mathtt{X}^{-1},\mathtt{U},\mathtt{U}^{-1})$ sentence, an equivalent automaton in $2ARA_n(\sim)$ is constructible in logspace. For formulae with only future-time operators, the automata are one-way.*

Proof. By a standard logspace reduction, we can assume that ϕ over an alphabet Σ is a sentence in $\mathrm{LTL}_n^{\downarrow}(\sim;\mathtt{X},\mathtt{X}^{-1},\mathtt{U},\mathtt{U}^{-1})$ extended by the duals $\bot,\vee,\bar{\mathtt{X}},\bar{\mathtt{X}}^{-1},\bar{\mathtt{U}},\bar{\mathtt{U}}^{-1}$ of $\top,\wedge,\mathtt{X},\mathtt{X}^{-1},\mathtt{U},\mathtt{U}^{-1}$ (respectively), and that ϕ is in negation normal form, i.e. such that $\neg$ occurs only in front of atomic formulae.

To construct an equivalent $\mathcal{A}_\phi^\Sigma = \langle\Sigma,Q,n,q_I,\delta,\rho\rangle$ in $2\mathrm{ARA}_n(\sim)$, let $Q = \mathrm{cl}(\phi)$, where $\mathrm{cl}(\phi)$ is the set of all subformulae of ϕ, and let $q_I = \phi$.

The transition function is defined as follows. It is homomorphic for $\top$, $\bot$, $\wedge$ and $\vee$ formulae, and the clauses for $\bar{\mathtt{U}}$, $\mathtt{U}^{-1}$ and $\bar{\mathtt{U}}^{-1}$ are similar to the clause for $\mathtt{U}$.

$$\begin{aligned}
\delta(b,a) &= \text{truth value of } b=a\\
\delta(\neg b,a) &= \text{truth value of } b\neq a\\
\delta(\uparrow_r\sim,a) &= \uparrow_r\sim\\
\delta(\neg\uparrow_r\sim,a) &= \uparrow_r\not\sim\\
\delta(\mathtt{X}\psi,a) &= \langle\psi,1\rangle\\
\delta(\bar{\mathtt{X}}\psi,a) &= \mathtt{end}\vee\langle\psi,1\rangle\\
\delta(\mathtt{X}^{-1}\psi,a) &= \langle\psi,-1\rangle\\
\delta(\bar{\mathtt{X}}^{-1}\psi,a) &= \mathtt{beg}\vee\langle\psi,-1\rangle\\
\delta(\psi\mathtt{U}\psi',a) &= \delta(\psi',a)\vee(\delta(\psi,a)\wedge\langle\psi\mathtt{U}\psi',1\rangle)\\
\delta(\downarrow_r\psi,a) &= \downarrow_r\delta(\psi,a)
\end{aligned}$$

To complete the construction, for every $\psi\in\mathrm{cl}(\phi)$, let $\rho(\psi) = 2\times|\psi|+1$ if the outermost construct in ψ is $\mathtt{U}$, and let $\rho(\psi) = 2\times|\psi|$ otherwise. As required, we have that, whenever $\langle q',o\rangle$ is a subformula of $\delta(q,a)$, $\rho(q')\leq\rho(q)$.

Showing $\mathrm{L}_\Sigma^{\leq\omega}(\phi) = \mathrm{L}^{\leq\omega}(\mathcal{A}_\phi^\Sigma)$ is routine. □

Example 9 Let $\phi = \mathtt{G}\downarrow_1\mathtt{XG}\neg\uparrow_1\sim$ be the nonces sentence. Recalling that $\mathtt{G}\psi$ is equivalent to $\bot\bar{\mathtt{U}}\psi$, the transition formulae $\delta(\mathtt{G}\psi,a)$ in the construction of Theorem 8 simplify to $\delta(\psi,a)\wedge(\mathtt{end}\vee\langle\mathtt{G}\psi,1\rangle)$. Figure 1 represents the resulting one-way register automaton. The forks are read as conjunctions, and edge labels $\mathtt{nend}$ and $\uparrow_1\sim$ as implication premises. Thus, the edges from location $\mathtt{G}\neg\uparrow_1\sim$ represent the transition formula

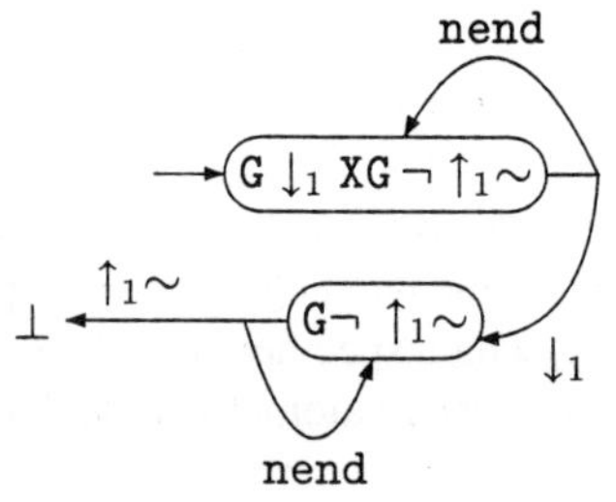

Figure 1. A one-way universal RA

$$(\uparrow_1\sim\Rightarrow\bot)\wedge(\mathtt{nend}\Rightarrow\langle\mathtt{G}\neg\uparrow_1\sim,1\rangle)$$

or equivalently $\uparrow_1\not\sim\wedge(\mathtt{end}\vee\langle\mathtt{G}\neg\uparrow_1\sim,1\rangle)$. The rank of location ϕ is larger than the rank of location $\mathtt{G}\neg\uparrow_1\sim$, and both are even. Observe that the automaton is universal, as it does not contain a disjunction between locationful transition subformulae.

5. Upper complexity bounds

The following warm-up theorem contains basic membership results. In some cases, they will be matched by the hardness results in Section 6.

Theorem 10 *Over finite data words, satisfiability for $LTL^{\downarrow}(\sim;\mathtt{X},\mathtt{X}^{-1},\mathtt{U},\mathtt{U}^{-1})$ and nonemptiness for $2ARA(\sim)$ are in Σ_1^0. Over infinite data words, satisfiability for $LTL^{\downarrow}(\sim;\mathtt{X},\mathtt{X}^{-1},\mathtt{U},\mathtt{U}^{-1})$ and nonemptiness for $2ARA(\sim)$ are in Σ_1^1, and nonemptiness for $2NRA(\sim)$ is in Σ_2^0.*

Proof. For encoding runs of alternating automata, we use the following observation: a run is accepting iff, at infinitely many levels we have that, for each state of odd rank, all its successors at some subsequent level have strictly smaller ranks. We also note that, for any finite data word, any automaton has finitely many states. □

In [26], finitary nonemptiness for $1\mathrm{NRA}(\sim)$ was shown to be in NP, but their proof does not carry over to the definition of register automata in this paper: see Note 1 and Theorem 14.

Theorem 11 *Finitary nonemptiness and infinitary nonemptiness for $1NRA(\sim)$ are in* PSPACE.

Proof. By a logspace reduction to satisfiability for CLTL($\mathbb{N}, =$), which is PSPACE-complete [8]. □

By Corollary 7 and [4], finitary and infinitary satisfiability for simple $\text{LTL}_1^{\downarrow}(\sim; \mathtt{X}, \mathtt{X}^{-1}, \mathtt{XXF}, \mathtt{X}^{-1}\mathtt{X}^{-1}\mathtt{F}^{-1})$ are reducible to reachability for Petri nets. The latter problem is decidable, so the former also are. It is not known whether reachability for Petri nets is elementary.

It was shown in [14, Appendix A] that, over finite data words, for $\mathcal{A}$ in $1\text{NRA}_1(\sim)$ and $\mathcal{A}'$ in $1\text{NRA}(\sim)$, containment of $\mathcal{A}'$ in $\mathcal{A}$ is decidable.[3] By Theorem 2 and Proposition 3, the result in [14, Appendix A] is subsumed by the following theorem. The proofs in [14, Appendix A] and of Theorem 2 both involve well-quasi-orders.

Theorem 12 *For $\mathcal{A}$ in $1ARA_1(\sim)$ and $\mathcal{A}'$ in $1NRA(\sim)$, finitary [resp. infinitary] nonemptiness of the intersection of $\mathcal{A}$ and $\mathcal{A}'$ is pspace reducible to finitary [resp. infinitary] nonemptiness of an Incrementing CA.*

Proof. Suppose that $\mathcal{A} = \langle \Sigma, Q, q_I, 1, \delta, \rho \rangle$ and $\mathcal{A}' = \langle \Sigma', Q', q_I', n, \delta', \rho' \rangle$. We can assume $\Sigma = \Sigma'$.

We first consider finitary nonemptiness. Suppose $\sigma \in \Sigma^{<\omega}(\sim)$, $0 \leq i < |\sigma|$, and G and G' are partial runs of $\mathcal{A}$ and $\mathcal{A}'$ (respectively) up to ith level. Any element of $G(i)$ is of the form $\langle i, q, v \rangle$, and $G'(i)$ is either a singleton $\{\langle i, q', v' \rangle\}$ or empty.

Observe that the intersection of $\mathcal{A}$ and $\mathcal{A}'$ is nonempty iff, from some such $\langle \sigma, i, G(i), G'(i) \rangle$, an empty $(i+1)$th level is reachable. Moreover, it suffices to consider G such that, whenever $\langle i, q, [1 \mapsto j] \rangle, \langle i, q, [1 \mapsto j'] \rangle \in G(i)$, $j \sim^\sigma j'$ and $\langle i, q, [1 \mapsto j] \rangle \to_i \langle i+1, q', [1 \mapsto j''] \rangle$, we have $\langle i, q, [1 \mapsto j'] \rangle \to_i \langle i+1, q', [1 \mapsto j''[j'/j]] \rangle$, where $j''[j'/j] = j''$ if $j'' \neq j$, and $j[j'/j] = j'$.

Now, quadruples $\langle \sigma, i, G(i), G'(i) \rangle$ as above will be represented by *configurations*, which are tuples of the form

$$\langle c, Q_u, q', E, f, \varphi_b, \varphi_e \rangle$$

where c is a function from $\mathcal{P}^+(Q)$ (the set of all nonempty subsets of Q) to $\mathbb{N}$, $Q_u \in \mathcal{P}(Q)$, $q' \in Q'$ or $q' = \emptyset$, E is an equivalence relation on a subset of $\{1, \ldots, n\}$, f is a function from classes of E to $\mathcal{P}(Q)$, $\varphi_b \in \{\mathtt{beg}, \mathtt{nbeg}\}$, and $\varphi_e \in \{\mathtt{end}, \mathtt{nend}\}$.

A configuration $\langle c, Q_u, q', E, f, \varphi_b, \varphi_e \rangle$ represents a quadruple $\langle \sigma, i, G(i), G'(i) \rangle$ as above iff:

- for any $Q^\dagger \in \mathcal{P}^+(Q)$, $c(Q^\dagger)$ is the number of classes S of $\approx$ such that $\pi_2(S) = Q^\dagger$ and $\pi_3(S)$ is not in the same class of $\sim^\sigma$ as any $v'(r)$ as below, where $\approx$ is the equivalence relation on the set of all $\langle i, q, v \rangle \in G(i)$ with $v \neq \emptyset$ defined by

$$\langle i, q_1, [1 \mapsto j_1] \rangle \approx \langle i, q_2, [1 \mapsto j_2] \rangle \Leftrightarrow j_1 \sim^\sigma j_2$$

  and π_k is kth-component tuple projection;
- $Q_u = \{q : \langle i, q, \emptyset \rangle \in G(i)\}$;
- if $G'(i) = \emptyset$ then $q' = \emptyset$, otherwise we have $G'(i) = \{\langle i, q', v' \rangle\}$, $r_1 \, E \, r_2$ iff $r_1, r_2 \in \text{dom}(v')$ and $v'(r_1) \sim^\sigma v'(r_2)$, and $f(\bar{r}) = Q^\dagger$ if there exists a class S of $\approx$ such that $\pi_2(S) = Q^\dagger$ and $\pi_3(S)$ is in the same class of $\sim^\sigma$ as $v'(r)$, otherwise $f(\bar{r}) = \emptyset$;
- $\varphi_b = \mathtt{beg}$ iff $i = 0$, and $\varphi_e = \mathtt{end}$ iff $i = |\sigma| - 1$.

For φ a transition formula in $\mathcal{A}$, $\varphi_b \in \{\mathtt{beg}, \mathtt{nbeg}\}$, $\varphi_e \in \{\mathtt{end}, \mathtt{nend}\}$, $\bowtie \in \{\sim, \not\sim\}$, and $Q^=, Q^{\neq} \in \mathcal{P}(Q)$, we write $\varphi \rightsquigarrow_{\bowtie}^{\varphi_b, \varphi_e} Q^=, Q^{\neq}$ iff there exist $\sigma \in \Sigma^{<\omega}(\sim)$, $0 \leq i < |\sigma|$, a partial function v_1 from $\{1\}$ to $\{0, \ldots, i-1\}$, and a minimal S such that $S \models_{v_1}^{\sigma, i} \varphi$, $\varphi_b = \mathtt{beg}$ iff $i = 0$, $\varphi_e = \mathtt{end}$ iff $i = |\sigma| - 1$, $v_1(1) \bowtie^\sigma i$,

$$\begin{aligned} Q^= &= \{q : \langle i+1, q, [1 \mapsto i] \rangle \in S\} \\ Q^{\neq} &= \{q : \langle i+1, q, [1 \mapsto j] \rangle \in S \wedge j \neq i\} \end{aligned}$$

Observe that it suffices to consider σ with $|\sigma| \leq 3$.

Similarly, for φ' a transition formula in $\mathcal{A}'$, $\varphi_b \in \{\mathtt{beg}, \mathtt{nbeg}\}$, $\varphi_e \in \{\mathtt{end}, \mathtt{nend}\}$, $R_1, R_2 \subseteq \{1, \ldots, n\}$, and $q' \in Q'$, we write $\varphi' \rightsquigarrow_{R_1}^{\varphi_b, \varphi_e} q', R_2$ iff there exist $\sigma \in \Sigma^{<\omega}(\sim)$, $0 \leq i < |\sigma|$, a partial function v_1' from $\{1, \ldots, n\}$ to $\{0, \ldots, i-1\}$, and a minimal S such that $S \models_{v_1'}^{\sigma, i} \varphi'$, $\varphi_b = \mathtt{beg}$ iff $i = 0$, $\varphi_e = \mathtt{end}$ iff $i = |\sigma| - 1$, $R_1 = \{r : v_1'(r) \sim^\sigma i\}$, and $S = \{\langle i+1, q', v_2' \rangle\}$ with $R_2 = \{r : i = v_2'(r)\}$. Whenever the above is satisfied with $S = \emptyset$, we write $\varphi' \rightsquigarrow_{R_1}^{\varphi_b, \varphi_e} \emptyset$. Observe that, in any case, it suffices to consider σ with $|\sigma| \leq 3$.

We are now ready to begin constructing an Incrementing CA $\mathcal{C}$ with the alphabet Σ. $\mathcal{C}$ will have $2 \times (2^{|Q|} - 1)$ counters, which we denote by $c(Q^\dagger)$ and $\hat{c}(Q^\dagger)$ for $Q^\dagger \in \mathcal{P}^+(Q)$. The locations, initial location, transition relation and accepting locations are constructed so that $\mathcal{C}$ performs the following:

(1) A configuration $\langle c, Q_u, q', E, f, \varphi_b, \varphi_e \rangle$ is kept in each state of $\mathcal{C}$. Initially, $Q_u = \{q_I\}$, $q' = q_I'$, $E = f = \emptyset$, $\varphi_b = \mathtt{beg}$, and φ_e is chosen (nondeterministically, by ε transitions).

(2) At this point, $\mathcal{C}$ performs an $a \in \Sigma$ transition, chooses

$$C \in \{Q^\dagger : c(Q^\dagger) > 0\} \cup \{\bar{r} : q' \neq \emptyset \wedge r \, E \, r\} \cup \{\not\sim\}$$

which specifies whether the current index is regarded as belonging to a class represented in the current configuration, and proceeds to compute a successor configuration $\langle \hat{c}, \hat{Q}_u, \hat{q}', \hat{E}, \hat{f}, \hat{\varphi}_b, \hat{\varphi}_e \rangle$.

The successor configurations will represent exactly quadruples $\langle \sigma, i+1, G(i+1), G'(i+1) \rangle$ such that the current configuration represents $\langle \sigma, i, G(i), G'(i) \rangle$, and either $C = \pi^2(S)$ for some class S of $\approx$ whose register values are in the class of i and where the register values in $G'(i)$ are not in the class of i, or C consists

[3] The exact statement allows $\mathcal{A}$ to have 2 registers, but see Note 1.

of those registers whose values in $G'(i)$ are in the class of i, or $C = \not\sim$ and there are no register values in $G(i)$ or $G'(i)$ which are in the class of i.

(3) If $q' = \emptyset$, then $\hat{q}' = \emptyset$. Otherwise, let $R_1 = \emptyset$ if $C = Q^\dagger$ or $C = \not\sim$, and $R_1 = C$ if $C = \bar{r}$. $\mathcal{C}$ then chooses a completion of $\delta'(q', a) \rightsquigarrow_{R_1}^{\varphi_b, \varphi_e}$: either $\hat{q}', R_2$ or $\emptyset$.

- If $\hat{q}', R_2$ was chosen, $\mathcal{C}$ obtains $\hat{E}$ from E by making the registers in $R_1 \cup R_2$ related only to each other.
- Otherwise, $\hat{q}' = \emptyset$.

An auxiliary $Q^\sim \in \mathcal{P}(Q)$ is initialised to $\emptyset$. At the end of (6), $Q^\sim$ will be equal to $\{q : \langle i+1, q, [1 \mapsto j]\rangle \in G(i+1) \wedge j \sim i\}$.

(4) While there exists $Q^\dagger \in \mathcal{P}^+(Q)$ such that $c(Q^\dagger) > 0$, $\mathcal{C}$ chooses and processes a successor set from each location in $Q^\dagger$ with respect to a and C:

- If $C = Q^\dagger$, $\mathcal{C}$ chooses, for each $q \in Q^\dagger$, $Q_q^=$ and $Q_q^{\neq}$ with $\delta(q, a) \rightsquigarrow_{\sim}^{\varphi_b, \varphi_e} Q_q^=, Q_q^{\neq}$. $Q^\sim$ is then updated to $Q^\sim \cup \bigcup_{q \in Q^\dagger} Q_q^= \cup Q_q^{\neq}$, and C to $\not\sim$.
- Otherwise, $\mathcal{C}$ chooses, for each $q \in Q^\dagger$, $Q_q^=$ and $Q_q^{\neq}$ with $\delta(q, a) \rightsquigarrow_{\not\sim}^{\varphi_b, \varphi_e} Q_q^=, Q_q^{\neq}$. $Q^\sim$ is then updated to $Q^\sim \cup \bigcup_{q \in Q^\dagger} Q_q^=$, and if $\bigcup_{q \in Q^\dagger} Q_q^{\neq} \neq \emptyset$, $\hat{c}(\bigcup_{q \in Q^\dagger} Q_q^{\neq})$ is incremented.

Now, $c(Q^\dagger)$ is decremented, and (4) is repeated.

(5) For each $q \in Q_u$, $\mathcal{C}$ chooses $Q_q^=$ and $Q_q^{\neq}$ such that $\delta(q, a) \rightsquigarrow_{\not\sim}^{\varphi_b, \varphi_e} Q_q^=, Q_q^{\neq}$. $Q^\sim$ is then updated to $Q^\sim \cup \bigcup_{q \in Q_u} Q_q^=$, and $\hat{Q}_u$ is set to $\bigcup_{q \in Q_u} Q_q^{\neq}$.

(6) For each $\bar{r}$ such that $f(\bar{r}) \neq \emptyset$, $\mathcal{C}$ chooses and processes a successor set from each location in $f(\bar{r})$ with respect to a and C:

- If $C = \bar{r}$, $\mathcal{C}$ chooses, for each $q \in f(\bar{r})$, $Q_q^=$ and $Q_q^{\neq}$ with $\delta(q, a) \rightsquigarrow_{\sim}^{\varphi_b, \varphi_e} Q_q^=, Q_q^{\neq}$. $Q^\sim$ is then updated to $Q^\sim \cup \bigcup_{q \in f(\bar{r})} Q_q^= \cup Q_q^{\neq}$.
- Otherwise ($R_1 = \emptyset$), $\mathcal{C}$ chooses, for each $q \in f(\bar{r})$, $Q_q^=$ and $Q_q^{\neq}$ with $\delta(q, a) \rightsquigarrow_{\not\sim}^{\varphi_b, \varphi_e} Q_q^=, Q_q^{\neq}$. $Q^\sim$ is then updated to $Q^\sim \cup \bigcup_{q \in f(\bar{r})} Q_q^=$. If $\hat{q}' \neq \emptyset$ and $\bar{r} \not\subseteq R_2$, then $\hat{f}(\bar{r} \setminus R_2)$ is set to $\bigcup_{q \in f(\bar{r})} Q_q^{\neq}$. Otherwise, and if $\bigcup_{q \in f(\bar{r})} Q_q^{\neq} \neq \emptyset$, $\hat{c}(\bigcup_{q \in f(\bar{r})} Q_q^{\neq})$ is incremented.

(7) If $\hat{q}' \neq \emptyset$ and $R_1 \cup R_2 \neq \emptyset$, $\hat{f}(R_1 \cup R_2)$ is set to $Q^\sim$. Otherwise, and if $Q^\sim \neq \emptyset$, $\hat{c}(Q^\sim)$ is incremented.

(8) If $\hat{c}(Q^\dagger) = 0$ for each $Q^\dagger \in \mathcal{P}^+(Q)$, $\hat{Q}_u = \emptyset$, and $\hat{q}' = \emptyset$, $\mathcal{C}$ stops at an accepting location if $\varphi_e = \text{end}$, or goes to a location from which it accepts all nonempty words if $\varphi_e = \texttt{nend}$. Otherwise, and if $\varphi_e = \texttt{nend}$, then $\hat{\varphi}_b$ is set to $\texttt{nbeg}$, $\hat{\varphi}_e$ is chosen, $\langle c, Q_u, q', E, f, \varphi_b, \varphi_e\rangle$ is replaced by $\langle \hat{c}, \hat{Q}_u, \hat{q}', \hat{E}, \hat{f}, \hat{\varphi}_b, \hat{\varphi}_e\rangle$, and $\mathcal{C}$ repeats from (2).

Now, suppose the intersection of $\mathcal{A}$ and $\mathcal{A}'$ contains a finite data word σ. Let G and G' be runs of $\mathcal{A}$ and $\mathcal{A}'$ (respectively) over σ. As above, the levels of G and G' are represented by some configurations $\langle c_i, Q_u^i, q_i', E_i, f_i, \varphi_b^i, \varphi_e^i\rangle$ for $i = 0, \ldots, |\sigma| - 1$. By the construction of $\mathcal{C}$, it has an error-free accepting finite run, such that the configurations whenever (2) is begun are exactly $\langle c_i, Q_u^i, q_i', E_i, f_i, \varphi_b^i, \varphi_e^i\rangle$ for $i = 0, \ldots, |\sigma| - 1$.

Conversely, suppose $\mathcal{C}$ has an accepting finite run. Let $\langle \tilde{c}_i, \tilde{Q}_u^i, \tilde{q}_i', \tilde{E}_i, \tilde{f}_i, \tilde{\varphi}_b^i, \tilde{\varphi}_e^i\rangle$ for $i = 0, \ldots, k-1$ be the configurations whenever (2) is begun. By the construction of $\mathcal{C}$, it has an error-free accepting finite run. More precisely, the configurations whenever (2) is begun are some $\langle c_i, Q_u^i, q_i', E_i, f_i, \varphi_b^i, \varphi_e^i\rangle$ for $i = 0, \ldots, k-1$ such that, for each i, we have $c_i \sqsubseteq \tilde{c}_i$, $Q_u^i = \tilde{Q}_u^i$, $q_i' = \tilde{q}_i'$, $E_i = \tilde{E}_i$, $f_i(\bar{r}) \subseteq \tilde{f}_i(\bar{r})$ for all $\bar{r}$, $\varphi_b^i = \tilde{\varphi}_b^i$ and $\varphi_e^i = \tilde{\varphi}_e^i$, where $c_i \sqsubseteq \tilde{c}_i$ iff there exists an injection

$$\iota : \{\langle Q^\dagger, j\rangle : Q^\dagger \in \mathcal{P}^+(Q) \wedge j \in \{1, \ldots, c_i(Q^\dagger)\}\} \rightarrow \{\langle \tilde{Q}^\dagger, j\rangle : \tilde{Q}^\dagger \in \mathcal{P}^+(Q) \wedge j \in \{1, \ldots, \tilde{c}_i(\tilde{Q}^\dagger)\}\}$$

such that, whenever $\iota(\langle Q^\dagger, j\rangle) = \langle \tilde{Q}^\dagger, \tilde{j}\rangle$, we have $Q^\dagger \subseteq \tilde{Q}^\dagger$. It follows that $\mathcal{A}$ and $\mathcal{A}'$ have runs G and G' (respectively) over a finite data word σ of length k, whose levels are represented by the configurations $\langle c_i, Q_u^i, q_i', E_i, f_i, \varphi_b^i, \varphi_e^i\rangle$.

To complete the proof for finitary nonemptiness, polynomial space suffices for the construction of $\mathcal{C}$ because: the number of counters is exponential in $|Q|$; each branching or iteration in $\mathcal{C}$ is at most polynomial in $|\Sigma|$ or $|Q'|$, or exponential in $|Q|$ or n, and their nesting is bounded by a constant; for each of the relations $\varphi \rightsquigarrow_{\bowtie}^{\varphi_b, \varphi_e} Q^=, Q^{\neq}$, $\varphi' \rightsquigarrow_{R_1}^{\varphi_b, \varphi_e} q', R_2$ and $\varphi' \rightsquigarrow_{R_1}^{\varphi_b, \varphi_e} \emptyset$, membership is in PSPACE.

Infinitary nonemptiness is handled in the same way, except that the construction is extended in order to transform alternating weak parity acceptance into nondeterministic Büchi acceptance, similarly as in the proof of [20, Theorem 5.1]. □

Corollary 13 *Finitary [resp. infinitary] satisfiability for* $LTL_1^\downarrow(\sim; \mathtt{X}, \mathtt{U})$ *is pspace reducible to finitary [resp. infinitary] nonemptiness of Incrementing CA.*

Proof. By Theorems 8 and 12. □

6. Lower complexity bounds

The following result matches PSPACE membership shown in Theorem 11, even for deterministic automata.

Theorem 14 *Finitary nonemptiness and infinitary nonemptiness for 1DRA($\sim$) are* PSPACE*-hard.*

Proof. By reducing from QBF. □

By [4] and Corollary 7, reachability for Petri nets is PTIME reducible to finitary and infinitary satisfiability for simple $\mathrm{LTL}_1^{\downarrow}(\sim; \mathtt{X}, \mathtt{X}^{-1}, \mathtt{XXF}, \mathtt{X}^{-1}\mathtt{X}^{-1}\mathtt{F}^{-1})$. The former problem is EXPSPACE-hard, so the latter also are.

We now turn to hardness results for fragments of $\mathrm{LTL}^{\downarrow}(\sim; \mathtt{X}, \mathtt{X}^{-1}, \mathtt{U}, \mathtt{U}^{-1})$ without the simplicity restriction, and for register automata which are not one-way and nondeterministic.

The following shows that the problems in Theorem 12 in Corollary 13 are also not easier than nonemptiness of Incrementing CA (see Theorem 2), already for nonemptiness of universal automata and with F instead of U.

Theorem 15 *In both finitary and infinitary cases, nonemptiness of Incrementing CA is logspace reducible to satisfiability for $\mathrm{LTL}_1^{\downarrow}(\sim; \mathtt{X}, \mathtt{F})$ and nonemptiness for 1URA$_1(\sim)$.*

Proof. For the finitary case, suppose $\mathcal{C} = \langle \Sigma, Q, q_I, n, \delta, F\rangle$ is an Incrementing CA. Let $L = \{\mathtt{inc}, \mathtt{dec}, \mathtt{ifzero}\} \times \{1, \ldots, n\}$, and $\hat{\Sigma} = Q \times (\Sigma \cup \{\varepsilon\}) \times L \times Q$. For any $\sigma \in \hat{\Sigma}^{<\omega}(\sim)$, where $\mathrm{str}(\sigma) = \langle q_0, w_0, l_0, q'_0\rangle\langle q_1, w_1, l_1, q'_1\rangle \cdots$, let $\bar{\sigma} = w_0 w_1 \cdots$.

To ensure that $\sigma \in \hat{\Sigma}^{<\omega}(\sim)$ corresponds to a run of $\mathcal{C}$, we constrain the equivalence relation $\sim^\sigma$. Firstly, there must not be two $\langle \mathtt{inc}, c\rangle$ transitions, or two $\langle \mathtt{dec}, c\rangle$ transitions (with the same c) in the same class. For an $\langle \mathtt{ifzero}, c\rangle$ transition to be correct, whenever it is preceded by $\langle \mathtt{inc}, c\rangle$, there must be an intermediate $\langle \mathtt{dec}, c\rangle$ in the same class. Incrementing errors may occur because a $\langle \mathtt{dec}, c\rangle$ transition may be preceded by no $\langle \mathtt{inc}, c\rangle$ in the same class. Such a $\langle \mathtt{dec}, c\rangle$ transition corresponds to a faulty decrement which leaves c unchanged. Now, it is easy to check that, for any run of $\mathcal{C}$, there is a run which differs at most in counter values and whose only incrementing errors are such faulty decrements.

More precisely, $w \in \Sigma^{<\omega}$ is accepted by $\mathcal{C}$ iff $w = \bar{\sigma}$ for some $\sigma \in \hat{\Sigma}^{<\omega}(\sim)$ which satisfies the following, where $\mathrm{str}(\sigma) = \langle q_0, w_0, l_0, q'_0\rangle\langle q_1, w_1, l_1, q'_1\rangle \cdots$:

(1) for each i, $\langle q_i, w_i, l_i, q'_i\rangle \in \delta$;

(2) $q_0 = q_I$, and for each $i > 0$, $q'_{i-1} = q_i$;

(3) for the maximum i, $q'_i \in F$;

(4) there are no c and $i < j$ such that $l_i = l_j = \langle \mathtt{inc}, c\rangle$ and $i \sim^\sigma j$;

(5) there are no c and $i < j$ such that $l_i = l_j = \langle \mathtt{dec}, c\rangle$ and $i \sim^\sigma j$;

(6) for any c and i such that $l_i = \langle \mathtt{inc}, c\rangle$, it is not the case that, there is $j > i$ with $l_j = \langle \mathtt{ifzero}, c\rangle$ but there is no $k > i$ with $l_k = \langle \mathtt{dec}, c\rangle$ and $i \sim^\sigma k$;

(7) there are no c and $i < j < k$ such that $l_i = \langle \mathtt{inc}, c\rangle$, $l_j = \langle \mathtt{ifzero}, c\rangle$, $l_k = \langle \mathtt{dec}, c\rangle$ and $i \sim^\sigma k$;

An $\mathrm{LTL}_1^{\downarrow}(\sim; \mathtt{X}, \mathtt{F})$ sentence over $\hat{\Sigma}$ which expresses the conjunction of (1)–(7) can be constructed from $\mathcal{C}$ in logarithmic space. (1)–(3) are straightforward. Among (4)–(7), the most interesting is (7), and the rest can be expressed similarly. Note how (6) and (7) were formulated to avoid using the U operator. The following sentence expresses (7):

$$\begin{aligned}\neg \textstyle\bigvee_{c=1}^{n} \mathtt{F}\left(\bigvee_{q,w,q'} \langle q, w, \langle \mathtt{inc}, c\rangle, q'\rangle\right) \wedge \\ \downarrow_1 \mathtt{XF}\left(\bigvee_{q,w,q'} \langle q, w, \langle \mathtt{ifzero}, c\rangle, q'\rangle\right) \wedge \\ \mathtt{XF}\left(\bigvee_{q,w,q'} \langle q, w, \langle \mathtt{dec}, c\rangle, q'\rangle\right) \wedge \uparrow_1 \sim\end{aligned}$$

A 1URA$_1(\sim)$ automaton which accepts exactly those $\sigma \in \hat{\Sigma}^{<\omega}(\sim)$ which satisfy (1)–(7) can also be constructed in logarithmic space. By Propositions 3 and 4, it suffices, for each of (1)–(7), to construct in logarithmic space a 1NRA$_1(\sim)$ automaton which accepts a data word iff it fails the condition. In fact, (6) and (7) can be treated together, and this automaton is the most interesting. It makes sure that σ has a run iff it contains an $\langle \mathtt{inc}, c\rangle$ instruction, followed by no occurence of $\langle \mathtt{dec}, c\rangle$ in the same class until $\langle \mathtt{ifzero}, c\rangle$ occurs. Formally, it has locations $\{0, 1, \ldots, n\}$ where 0 is initial, and the following transition function. (As the automaton is one-way, we omit the offsets of 1.)

$$\begin{aligned}(0, \langle q, w, \langle \mathtt{inc}, c\rangle, q'\rangle) &\mapsto 0 \vee \downarrow_1 c \\ (0, \langle q, w, l, q'\rangle) &\mapsto 0, \text{ otherwise} \\ (c, \langle q, w, \langle \mathtt{dec}, c\rangle, q'\rangle) &\mapsto \uparrow_1 \not\sim \wedge\, c \\ (c, \langle q, w, \langle \mathtt{ifzero}, c\rangle, q'\rangle) &\mapsto \top \\ (c, \langle q, w, l, q'\rangle) &\mapsto c, \text{ otherwise}\end{aligned}$$

The infinitary case is obtained similarly, where (3) is replaced by:

(3') for infinitely many i, $q_i \in F$, and for infinitely many i, $w_i \neq \varepsilon$. □

Corollary 16 *Over finite and over infinite words, the following sets of languages are the same:*

(i) of the form $\mathrm{L}(\mathcal{C})$*, where* $\mathcal{C}$ *is an Incrementing CA;*

(ii) of the form $f(\mathrm{str}(\mathrm{L}(\phi)))$*, where* f *is a string homomorphism and* ϕ *is an* $\mathrm{LTL}_1^{\downarrow}(\sim; \mathtt{X}, \mathtt{F})$ *sentence;*

(iii) of the form $f(\mathrm{str}(\mathrm{L}(\phi)))$*, where* f *is a string homomorphism and* ϕ *is an* $\mathrm{LTL}_1^{\downarrow}(\sim; \mathtt{X}, \mathtt{U})$ *sentence.*

Proof. By the proofs of Corollary 13 and Theorem 15. □

Our final result shows that it is impossible, without causing Σ_1^0 or Σ_1^1 hardness (see Section 2.4), to extend the problems in Theorem 12 in Corollary 13 by adding backward transitions, the $\mathtt{F}^{-1}$ operator, or one more register, even if we restrict to nonemptiness of universal automata and replace $\mathtt{U}$ with $\mathtt{F}$. The result should also be compared with Theorem 10.

The theorem below is stronger than [12, Corollary 1] and [8, Theorem 3], which showed Σ_1^1-hardness of infinitary satisfiability for $\mathrm{LTL}_2^{\downarrow}(\sim; \mathtt{X}, \mathtt{X}^{-1}, \mathtt{F}, \mathtt{F}^{-1})$ and $\mathrm{LTL}_2^{\downarrow}(\sim; \mathtt{X}, \mathtt{U})$. Also, together with Proposition 3, it implies [21, Theorem 5.1] where finitary nonuniversality for 1NRA($\sim$) was shown undecidable. Undecidability of finitary nonemptiness for $2\mathrm{DRA}_1(\sim)$ was shown in [7, Section 7.3], using a different encoding.

Theorem 17 *In both finitary and infinitary cases, nonemptiness of Minsky CA is logspace reducible to satisfiability for $LTL_1^{\downarrow}(\sim; \mathtt{X}, \mathtt{F}, \mathtt{F}^{-1})$ and $LTL_2^{\downarrow}(\sim; \mathtt{X}, \mathtt{F})$, and nonemptiness for $1URA_2(\sim)$. In the finitary [resp. infinitary] case, we also have a logspace reduction to nonemptiness of $2DRA_1(\sim)$ [resp. $2URA_1(\sim)$].*

Proof. The reductions to problems with $\mathtt{F}^{-1}$ or backward transitions use encodings as in the proof of Theorem 15. The reductions to problems with 2 registers use encodings similar to that in [17, Section 4]. □

7. Concluding remarks

A summary of the results in this paper on the complexity of satisfiability for fragments of $\mathrm{LTL}^{\downarrow}(\sim; \mathtt{X}, \mathtt{X}^{-1}, \mathtt{U}, \mathtt{U}^{-1})$ can be found in boldface in the table below. The remaining entries were shown in [12, 8]. R \ PR means decidable and not primitive recursive, and 'co.' abbreviates 'complete'.

	$\mathrm{SAT}^{<\omega}$		SAT^{ω}	
registers	1	2	1	2
$\mathtt{X}, \mathtt{F}$	**R \ PR**	**Σ_1^0-co.**	**Π_1^0-co.**	**Σ_1^1-co.**
$\mathtt{X}, \mathtt{U}$	**R \ PR**	Σ_1^0-co.	**Π_1^0-co.**	Σ_1^1-co.
$\mathtt{X}, \mathtt{F}, \mathtt{F}^{-1}$	**Σ_1^0-co.**	**Σ_1^0-co.**	**Σ_1^1-co.**	Σ_1^1-co.

We are grateful to Claire David, Massimo Franceschet, Marcin Jurdziński, Anca Muscholl, David Nowak, Joël Ouaknine, Philippe Schnoebelen and Luc Segoufin for helpful discussions.

References

[1] R. Alur and D. Dill. A theory of timed automata. *TCS*, 126:183–235, 1994.

[2] R. Alur and T. Henzinger. A really temporal logic. *JACM*, 41(1):181–204, 1994.

[3] M. Bojańczyk, C. David, A. Muscholl, T. Schwentick, and L. Segoufin. Two-variable on Data Trees and XML reasoning. In *PODS*, 2006.

[4] M. Bojańczyk, A. Muscholl, T. Schwentick, L. Segoufin, and C. David. Two-variable logic on words with data. In *LICS*. IEEE, 2006.

[5] P. Bouyer. A logical characterization of data languages. *IPL*, 84(2):75–85, 2002.

[6] P. Bouyer, A. Petit, and D. Thérien. An algebraic approach to data languages and timed languages. *I & C*, 182(2):137–162, 2003.

[7] C. David. Mots et données infinies. Master's thesis, LIAFA, 2004.

[8] S. Demri, R. Lazić, and D. Nowak. On the freeze quantifier in constraint LTL: decidability and complexity. Technical Report 05-3, LSV, 2005. Extended abstract appeared in Proc. of TIME'05.

[9] C. Dufourd, A. Finkel, and P. Schnoebelen. Reset nets between decidability and undecidability. In *ICALP*, volume 1443 of *LNCS*, pages 103–115. Springer, 1998.

[10] K. Etessami, M. Vardi, and T. Wilke. First-order logic with two variables and unary temporal logic. *I & C*, 179(2):279–295, 2002.

[11] M. Fitting. Modal logic between propositional and first-order. *JLC*, 12(6):1017–1026, 2002.

[12] T. French. Quantified propositional temporal logic with repeating states. In *TIME-ICTL*, pages 155–165. IEEE, 2003.

[13] V. Goranko. Hierarchies of modal and temporal logics with references pointers. *JoLLI*, 5:1–24, 1996.

[14] M. Kaminski and N. Francez. Finite-memory automata. *TCS*, 134(2):329–363, 1994.

[15] F. Laroussinie, N. Markey, and P. Schnoebelen. Temporal logic with forgettable past. In *LICS*, pages 383–392. IEEE, 2002.

[16] S. Lasota and I. Walukiewicz. Alternating timed automata. In *FOSSACS*, volume 3441 of *LNCS*, pages 250–265. Springer, 2005.

[17] A. Lisitsa and I. Potapov. Temporal logic with predicate λ-abstraction. In *TIME*, pages 147–155. IEEE, 2005.

[18] C. Löding and W. Thomas. Alternating automata and logics over infinite words. In *IFIP TCS*, volume 1878 of *LNCS*, pages 521–535. Springer, 2000.

[19] M. Minsky. *Computation, Finite and Infinite Machines*. Prentice Hall, 1967.

[20] S. Miyano and T. Hayashi. Alternating finite automata on ω-words. *TCS*, 32:321–330, 1984.

[21] F. Neven, T. Schwentick, and V. Vianu. Finite state machines for strings over infinite alphabets. *ACM TOCL*, 5(3):403–435, 2004.

[22] P. Odifreddi. *Classical Recursion Theory II*, volume 143. Elsevier, 1999.

[23] J. Ouaknine and J. Worrell. On the decidability of metric temporal logic. In *LICS*, pages 188–197, 2005.

[24] J. Ouaknine and J. Worrell. On metric temporal logic and faulty Turing machines. In *FOSSACS*, volume 3921 of *LNCS*, pages 217–230. Springer, 2006.

[25] J. Ouaknine and J. Worrell. Personal communication, March 2006.

[26] H. Sakamoto and D. Ikeda. Intractability of decision problems for finite-memory automata. *TCS*, 231(2):297–308, 2000.

[27] P. Schnoebelen. Verifying lossy channel systems has non-primitive recursive complexity. *IPL*, 83(5):251–261, 2002.

Fixed-Parameter Hierarchies inside PSPACE

Guoqiang Pan
Department of Computer Science
Rice University
gqpan@cs.rice.edu

Moshe Y. Vardi
Department of Computer Science
Rice University and Microsoft Research
vardi@cs.rice.edu

Abstract

Treewidth measures the "tree-likeness" of structures. Many NP-complete problems, e.g., propositional satisfiability, are tractable on bounded-treewidth structures. In this work, we study the impact of treewidth bounds on QBF, a canonical PSPACE-complete problem. This problem is known to be fixed-parameter tractable if both the treewidth and alternation depth are taken as parameters. We show here that the function bounding the complexity in the parameters is provably nonelementary (assuming P is different than NP). This yields a strict hierarchy of fixed-parameter tractability inside PSPACE. As a tool for proving this result, we first prove a similar hierarchy for model checking QPTL, quantified propositional temporal logic. Finally, we show that QBF, restricted to instances with a slowly increasing ($\log^*$) treewidth, is still PSPACE-complete.

1. Introduction

Considerable attention has been dedicated recently, cf. [5], to the complexity-theoretic analysis of *constraint satisfaction*, a problem of great significance in computer science, see [6]. In particular, a focus on of this attention has been to identify tractable classes of this problem, which is NP-complete in general. A particular way to study constraint satisfaction problems is to focus on their *parametrized complexity* [8], where we analyze the complexity in terms of both the problem-instance size n and and a parameter k that relates to some property of the problem. Typically, this approach is used to capture the intuition that problems hard in the classical sense might have tractable classes, here represented as problems with a small k. The class of *fixed-parameter tractable (FPT)* problems are those that can be solved in time $f(k)\mathsf{poly}(n)$, where f is any computable function. We typically use parameterized complexity to study problems that are intractable in the classical setting, so under the usual assumptions, $f(k)$ is at least exponential. A popular parameter for structural problems is that of *treewidth*, which measures how close a structure is to being a tree (trees have treewidth 1) [15]. Many NP-complete problems, for example, Boolean satisfiability, are FPT with respect to the treewidth w, specifically $2^w n$ [7, 10].

A very recent focus of inquiry has been on *quantified* constraint satisfaction [2, 12], which is PSPACE-complete in general. It is natural to ask whether such problems exhibit fixed-parameter tractability under structural restrictions such as bounded treewidth. On one hand, it is shown in [12] that quantified constraint satisfaction remains PSPACE-hard under restrictions less restrictive than treewidth (for example, acyclic QCSP is still PSPACE-complete). On the other hand, [2] showed that quantified constraint satisfaction is FPT when treewidth, alternation depth, and domain size are all taken as parameters.

Our focus here is on investigating the complexity of quantified constraint satisfaction, specifically, *quantified Boolean formulas* (QBF), with respect to the treewidth parameter[1]. (Quantified CSP with constant domain size can be reduced to QBF with only a constant factor – logarithmic in the domain size – increase in width.) A careful analysis of the results in [2] shows that the parametric bound $f(d, w)$, where d is the alternation depth and w is the treewidth, grows nonelementarily in d; that is, the function consists of a tower of exponential that grows linearly with d. We show here that this nonelementary growth is unavoidable. Specifically, we show that, under the assumption that P is different than NP, the parametric function $f(d, n)$ must be a tower of exponentials of height almost d. This yields a strict hierarchy of parametrized complexity inside PSPACE.

The nonelementary growth of the parametrized bound suggests that QBF is not FPT with respect to treewidth alone. We prove a result that gets quite close to this; we show that QBF, restricted to instances with a slowly increasing ($\log^*$) treewidth, is still PSPACE-complete. This leaves open a small gap, which is the hardness of QBF under the assumption of bounded treewidth.

We prove our results via a technical detour of QPTL model checking. QPTL is a quantified propositional temporal logic, introduced in [16]. It is a monadic second-order logic, so its model-checking problem is closely related to the model-checking problem for the monadic second-order

[1] In [3], a modified notion of treewidth is introduced for quantified constraint satisfaction, while our focus here is on the standard notion.

logic of words, studied in [11]. It is known that while satisfiability for monadic second-order logic is nonelementarily decidable [14], its model checking problem is PSPACE-complete. Classical automata-theoretic techniques, cf. [1], entail that the model-checking problem for monadic second-order logic is FPT, where formula size is taken as the parameter. It is shown in [11] that the nonelementary lower-bound technique of [14] can be "telescoped down" to prove a nonelementary lower bound for the parametrized bound (assuming that P is different than NP). Analogously to [11], we show that the nonelementary satisfiability lower-bound for QPTL [16] can be telescoped down to yield a nonelementary lower bound for the parametrized bound (assuming that P is different than NP). The advantage of using QPTL rather than monadic second-order logic is that the latter contains both first- and second-order quantifiers, while QPTL has only second-order quantifiers. This enables us to get more refined results than those in [11], getting an FPT hierarchy in terms of alternation depth, rather than formula size.

A second advantage of using QPTL is that its model-checking problem can be reduced to QBF satisfiability, while maintaining a bounded *pathwidth*. (Pathwidth measures how close a structure is to being a path; it is a stricter measure than treewidth). Thus, the FPT complexity hierarchy result for QPTL model checking can be transferred to a similar hierarchy for QBF satisfiability.

The approach in [11] relies on the assumption that P is different than NP, so we can use it only to show that QBF for small-treewidth formulas is NP-hard. To show that QBF of small-treewidth is PSPACE-hard, we have to go beyond QPTL model checking to QPTL model-checking games, which embed quantifier alternation in the word being model checked. This built-in alternation enables us to go from NP-hardness to PSPACE-hardness, by showing that quantified satisfiability for the set of formulas with treewidth in $O(\log^*(n))$ is PSPACE-complete.

The paper is organized as follows. In Section 2, we provide basic definitions for QPTL, the tiling problem, and QBF. In Section 3, we establish a parametrized complexity hierarchy for QPTL model checking, via a reduction from tiling. In Section 4, we present a reduction from QPTL model checking to QBF, and show similar hierarchy for QBF. In Section 5, we present model-checking games and use them to prove PSPACE-completeness of small-width QBF.

2. Background

2.1. QPTL

Definition 2.1. Given a set P of propositions, the set of formulas of QPTL is the smallest set satisfying the following: Every proposition in P is a formula in QPTL; if φ and ψ are formulas in QPTL, then $(\varphi \wedge \psi)$, $(\neg\varphi)$, $X\varphi$, $F\varphi$, and $(\exists p)\varphi$ are formulas in QPTL; we use X^n as shorthand for a sequence of n X operators, $G\varphi$ as shorthand for $\neg F \neg\varphi$, and $(\forall p)\varphi$ as shorthand for $\neg(\exists p)\neg\varphi$.

We interpret QPTL formulas on finite words. A finite word model π for QPTL is a word of length n over 2^P, that is, a mapping $\pi : [0 \ldots n-1] \rightarrow 2^P$, where n is the size of the model, and P is a set of propositions (which needs to contain the free propositions in the formula we are interpreting). All propositional connectives have their standard meaning. Since we are considering semantics for finite-word models, the temporal operators X and F need to consider the finiteness of the model, and so do the quantifiers. We use $\pi, i \models \varphi$ to mean the word model π at position i satisfies the formula φ. (The standard notation of $\pi \models \varphi$ now becomes a shorthand for $\pi, 0 \models \varphi$.) Of course, $\models$ is only defined when $0 \leq i < |\pi|$. The formal semantics of QPTL on a finite word model follows:

- $\pi, i \models p$ iff $p \in \pi(i)$,
- $\pi, i \models \neg\varphi$ iff $\pi, i \not\models \varphi$,
- $\pi, i \models \varphi \wedge \psi$ iff $\pi, i \models \varphi$ and $\pi, i \models \psi$,
- $\pi, i \models X\varphi$ iff $i < |\pi| - 1$ and $\pi, i+1 \models \varphi$,
- $\pi, i \models F\varphi$ iff there exists some $i \leq j < |\pi|$, where $\pi, j \models \varphi$,
- $\pi, i \models (\exists q)\varphi$ iff there is a set $Q \subseteq [0 \ldots |\pi| - 1]$ of positions, such that $\pi[q \mapsto Q], i \models \varphi$, where $p \in \pi[q \mapsto Q](i)$ iff either $p \neq q$ and $p \in \pi(i)$, or $p = q$ and $i \in Q$.

Each QPTL formula φ defines a language which is the set of all πs where $\pi, 0 \models \varphi$.

Definition 2.2. The finite model-checking problem for QPTL is defined as: given a model π and a formula φ, where π is defined on a vocabulary that includes the free variables of φ, does $\pi \models \varphi$ hold?

Here, we only consider QPTL formulas in prenex normal form, where a formula can be written as $(Q_1 p_1)(Q_2 p_2) \ldots (Q_k p_k)\varphi$, each Q_i is $\exists$ or $\forall$, and φ is quantifier free. The logic can be stratified into bounded-alternation layers as follows:

1. The set $\Sigma_0^{QPTL} = \Pi_0^{QPTL}$ includes the quantifier-free formulas in QPTL.
2. If φ is in Σ_k^{QPTL} or Π_{k-1}^{QPTL}, then $(\exists p)\varphi$ is in Σ_k^{QPTL}.
3. If φ is in Π_k^{QPTL} or Σ_{k-1}^{QPTL}, then $(\forall p)\varphi$ is in Π_k^{QPTL}.

The sets Σ_k^{QPTL} and Π_k^{QPTL} split QPTL into fragments where Σ_k^{QPTL} (Π_k^{QPTL}) represents the existential (universal) formulas with *alternation depth k*.

While all the QPTL formulas constructed in this paper should be in prenex normal form, we do, for simplicity of presentation, apply quantifiers to sub-formulas and later compose them with other sub-formulas. Still, we never put quantified sub-formulas under temporal operators, which allows all formulas we built to be converted to prenex normal form with a simple renaming and lifting of quantifiers without increase in either size or alternation depth. In Section 4 and 5, we also assume the QPTL formula is in negation normal form, which means that negation is applied only to atomic propositions.

2.2. Tiling Systems

Definition 2.3. A *tiling system* is a tuple $T = (D, H, V)$, where D is a finite set of *tiles*, $H \subseteq D \times D$ and $V \subseteq D \times D$ are, respectively, the *horizontal* and *vertical* adjacency relations. A *tiling problem* is the tuple (T, w, h, I), where w and h are natural numbers, and I is an *initial constraint* (see below). The tiling problem (T, w, h, I) has a solution iff there exists a mapping $F : [1 \dots w] \times [1 \dots h] \to D$, where the following requirements are satisfied:

- For all $1 \leq i < w$ and $1 \leq j \leq h$, $(F(i,j), F(i+1,j)) \in H$, and for all $1 \leq i \leq w$ and $1 \leq j < h$, $(F(i,j), F(i,j+1)) \in V$.
- F satisfies the initial constraint I.

Each position (i,j), where $i \in [1..w]$, $j \in [1..h]$, is called a *cell* with row i and column j.

The tiling problem is useful in representing a number of natural complexity classes. The most well known of which is the case where $h = w$ (*square tiling*), w is written in unary, and the initial condition I is empty. This version have been shown to be NP-complete by Lewis [13]. Here, we consider a constant tiling system T. This is possible because tiling systems encode runs of Turing machines, so a T that corresponds to a universal Turing machine can be used. Still, to maintain NP-completeness where we use a constant T, we need to use a different initial condition, namely, the first row needs to be fixed to a particular sequence of tiles I, where $F(1,j) = I(j)$ for $1 \leq j \leq w$ (which encodes the initial tape of the Turing machine). This allows polynomial-sized computations of Turing automaton to be encoded with the tiling problem.

Theorem 2.4. [13] There is a tiling system T (corresponding to universal Turing machines) such that The tiling-problem (T, w, h, I), where $h = w$, and I defines the first row of the tiling, is NP-complete.

In the following, we concern ourselves only with this NP-complete variant, which we denote as (T, w, I). Given a tiling F, we name the corresponding solution checking problem, in absence of the initial condition, as the *tiling check* problem, where we check whether F satisfies the horizontal and vertical relations. We also assume we can separate the tile set into two parts D' and D'', where D' does not appear on the first row, and D'' only appears on the first row. Only tiles in D'' can appear in I. This allows us to use quantifiers to guess the non-initial part of the tiling. Since $w = |I|$, and T is fixed, the size of the tiling problem is defined as $|I|$, which is the same as the size of w in unary.

2.3. QBF

Quantified Boolean formula (QBF) extends propositional logic by introducing quantifiers over the Boolean domain $\{0, 1\}$. We write formulas in QBF in prenex normal form $\psi = (Q_1 p_1)(Q_2 p_2) \dots (Q_k p_k)\psi'$, where the Qs are quantifiers, the ps are propositions, and ψ' is a propositional formula, which we call the *matrix*. By bounding the number of alternations, QBF can be stratified into classes Σ_k^{QBF} and Π_k^{QBF}, where k is the number of alternations, and a formula is in Σ_k^{QBF} if its outermost quantifier is $\exists$ and contains k alternations and in Π_k^{QBF} if its outermost quantifier is $\forall$ and contains k alternations. The complexity hierarchy of deciding these formula classes corresponds the *polynomial hierarchy* [18]. Here, we consider the case where the matrix ψ' is restricted to CNF, so the innermost universal quantifier block introduces no additional complexity. In other words, we only consider the classes Σ_k^{QBF} where k is odd and Π_k^{QBF} where k is even.

The *width* of a QBF formula is defined as the width of the *interaction graph* of its CNF matrix. The interaction graph is defined with the set of propositions as vertices, and the co-occurrence (in the same clause) relation between propositions as edges.

Definition 2.5. (Robertson and Seymour [15]) Let $G = (V, E)$ be a graph. A *tree (path)-decomposition* of G is a pair $(T, \mathcal{X})$ where $T = (I, F)$ is a tree (path) with node set I and edge set F, and $\mathcal{X} = \{X_i \mid i \in I\}$ is a family of subsets of V, one for each node of T, such that

- $\bigcup_{i \in I} X_i = V$,
- for every edge $(v, w) \in E$, there is an $i \in I$ with $\{v, w\} \subseteq X_i$, and
- for all $i, j, k \in I$, if j is on the path from i to k in T, then $X_i \cap X_k \subseteq X_j$.

The *width* of a tree (path)-decomposition is $\max_{i \in I}|X_i| - 1$. The *treewidth (pathwidth)* of a graph G, denoted by $tw(G)$ ($pw(G)$), is the minimum width over all possible tree (path) decompositions of G.

Bounded pathwidth is clearly a more restrictive concept than bounded treewidth, since a path-decomposition can be used without change as a tree-decomposition. In other words, for all graphs G, $tw(G) \leq pw(G)$. Thus, any complexity lower-bound result proved for bounded pathwidth also applies to bounded treewidth. In this paper, all constructions have bounded pathwidth.

3. Complexity of finite model-checking problem for QPTL

Our goal is to study the complexity of the finite model-checking problem for QPTL. First, we define the non-elementary tower function g: $g(0, n) = n$, $g(k+1, n) =$

$2^{g(k,n)}$. The inverse of g would be the $\log^k$ function: $\log^1(n) = \log n$, $\log^{k+1}(n) = \log(\log^k(n))$. Finally, the $\log^*$ function is defined by: $k = \log^*(n)$ iff k is the least natural number such that $g(k,1) \geq n$.

3.1. Upper Bound

In [16], the satisfiability problem of QPTL is studied, i.e., for a given QPTL formula φ, whether there exists a model π such that $\pi \models \varphi$. While their analysis of QPTL is over infinite words, the automata-theoretic approach can be used to analyze QPTL also over finite words (in fact, that was the origin this approach, cf. [1]). The following lemma characterizes QPTL over finite words.

Lemma 3.1. Given a QPTL formula φ in Σ_k^{QPTL}, there exists a non-deterministic finite automaton of size $g(k, |\varphi|)$ that accepts the same language as φ.

Theorem 3.2. (Analogous to Theorem 4.1, [16]) The satisfiability problem for Σ_k^{QPTL}, where $k \geq 1$, is complete for $NSPACE(g(k-1, |\varphi|))$.

In contrast to the satisfiability problem, under a finite semantics, the model-checking problem has elementary complexity.

Theorem 3.3. The finite model-checking problem for QPTL is PSPACE-complete.

A usual parametrization of model-checking problems is to take the formula size and alternation depth as the parameter and the size of the model as the size of the problem.

Theorem 3.4. The finite model-checking problem for a formula φ in Σ_k^{QPTL} on a finite word model of size n has time complexity $O(g(k, |\varphi|)n)$.

3.2. Lower Bound

For the lower bound, we proceed by connecting the complexity of QPTL model checking on finite word models to the NP-completeness of the tiling problem. In the following, we write poly($\cdot$) as the class of polynomially-bounded functions.

Theorem 3.5. Assuming $P \neq NP$, there exists a constant $c > 0$ such that for every $h(\cdot)$ in poly($\cdot$), model checking for Σ_k^{QPTL} on models of size $|\pi|$, where $k > 2$, cannot be done in time $g(k-1, c|\varphi|)h(|\pi|)^2$.

The rest of this section is dedicated to the proof of Theorem 3.5. We start with an overview of the proof.

For a tiling problem (T, w, I), if we are given a tiling F satisfying I, we can reduce the tiling-check problem to QPTL model checking as follows: The tiling F is converted to a word F_w, and the tiling problem (T, w, I) is converted to a QPTL formula $\varphi'_{T,w}$. Note that the initial condition I is not checked by the formula, but instead, encoded in the model. In the following, when our concern is the formula, we use (T, w) to denote the relevent part of the tiling problem. We want $F_w \models \varphi'_{T,w}$ iff F is a solution for (T, w). Writing F in word form requires concatenating the rows of F into a word of length w^2. We order the rows from w to 1 for technical reasons. To convert (T, w) to $\varphi'_{T,w}$, we need to state row and column constraints using small QPTL formulas. Once we reduced the tiling-check problem to the finite model-checking problem for QPTL, going to the tiling (decision) problem is just a small step, using existential quantifiers to state the existence of a tiling. We add an additional existential quantifier block on the outside of $\varphi'_{T,w}$ for all the propositions that actually represent non-initial tiles, and call the resulting formula $\varphi_{T,w}$. Since now the actual tiling is quantified out in the formula, the interpretation of the propositions that correspond to non-initial tiles in the word model no longer affect the decision procedure, so the word model can contain an arbitrary mapping from cells after the first row to non-initial tiles, and the mapping from cells in the first row to initial tiles is based on I. We call such a model $\pi_{w,I}$. Thus, $\pi_{w,I} \models \varphi_{T,w}$ iff (T, w, I) has a solution. Assuming the reduction is polynomial, this particular model-checking problem is NP-hard, while fixed-parameter tractable. Assuming $P \neq NP$, a lower-bound can be shown for the function in the parameter.

The idea of using short formulas to describe very long "yardsticks" go back to the early 1970s, cf. [17, 14, 16]. The idea of "telescoping" such constructions down, using extremely short formulas to describe short yarsticks, enabling one to prove nonelementary bounds inside PSPACE, is due to [11].

We give here the proof for Theorem 3.5, under the following assumptions on the reduction. Later, we describe in detail each step in the construction of $\pi_{w,I}$ and $\varphi_{T,w}$ and show that the assumptions hold.

1. $\pi_{w,I} \models \varphi_{T,w}$ iff (T, w, I) have a solution.
2. The word $\pi_{w,I}$ has size polynomial in w.
3. The formulas $\varphi_{T,w}$ are in Σ_k^{QPTL} and are small enough so that there exists a constant $c > 0$ where $g(k-1, c|\varphi_{T,w}|)$ is in poly(w).
4. The construction of $\pi_{w,I}$ and $\varphi_{T,w}$ from (T, w, I) can be performed in time polynomial in w.

Proof. Choose $h(\cdot)$ in poly($\cdot$). Assume that we have a model-checking algorithm with time complexity $g(k-1, c|\varphi|)h(|\pi|)$ for Σ_k^{QPTL}, where c is small enough to apply Assumption 3. We use this algorithm to give a polynomial algorithm for tiling, which by Theorem 2.4, is NP-complete. We are given inputs w and I (where $w = |I|$). Based on Assumption 2 and 4, we can construct $\pi_{w,I}$ in time and space polynomial in w. Based on Assumption 3, we can construct a formula $\varphi_{T,w} \in \Sigma_k^{QPTL}$, where $g(k-1, c|\varphi_{T,w}|)$ is in poly(w), and by Assumption 4, the time taken for the construction is in poly(w). Then, by Assumption 1, the

[2] In the proof of Theorem 4.2, we need to refer to the actual value of this constant, and call it c_{QPTL}

model-checking algorithm can be applied, which takes time $g(k-1, c|\varphi_{T,w}|)h(|\pi_{w,I}|)$, which by Assumptions 2 and 3, is in poly(w). So, if we have an algorithm for the finite model-checking problem that does better than the lower-bound, then there exists a polytime algorithm for an NP-complete problem. □

Here, readers would note that there is an exponential gap between the lower bound in Theorem 3.5 and the upper bound in Theorem 3.4. The gap can be closed by strengthening the $P \neq NP$ assumption as follows.

Corollary 3.6. Assuming NP cannot be solved in sub-exponential time, then there exists a constant $c > 0$ such that model checking for Σ_k^{QPTL} on models of size $|\pi|$, where $k > 2$, cannot be done in time $g(k, c|\varphi|)h(|\pi|)$ where $h(\cdot)$ is in poly($\cdot$).

For space reasons, we will only point out when we use Assumption 3, i.e., when $g(k-1, c|\varphi|)$ is polynomially bounded in w, we can always choose a smaller c' such that $g(k-1, c'|\varphi|)$ is sub-polynomial in w. In turn, $g(k, c'|\varphi|)$ is sub-exponential in w, leading to the tiling problem being solved in time sub-exponential in w.

3.2.1 Constructing the Tagged Model $\pi_{w,I}$

To facilitate easier check of row and column constraints on the word model $\pi_{w,I}$, we add annotation in the form of tags. The tags mark the column number of each cell, since we want to write the tiling in row major order. Our technique is based on a combination of techniques from [16, 11]. While both approaches allow checking of very large models by small formulas, they use different logics[3] and different constructions to assert relations between two positions that are very distant in the word model. The approach in [16] used counters that are implicitly encoded using alternation; in contrast, the approach in [11] used explicit tags[4]. Using explicit tags allows us to simplify construction of the QPTL formula, since we can now check arbitrary-sized models (unlike the counter-based approach, where the model needs to align on exact tower-of-exponentials boundaries), while at the same time maintain the alternation depth low.

Definition 3.7. A *tag of level h* is defined with the alphabet $\Sigma = \{0, 1, \langle 1\rangle, \langle /1\rangle, \ldots, \langle h\rangle, \langle /h\rangle\}$. We denote the set of tags of level h with parameter n by $\mathsf{tags}_h(n)$. Each tag represents a mapping that can be inductively defined as follows: A tag $t \in \mathsf{tags}_1(n)$ is a mapping $\{0\ldots n-1\} \rightarrow \{0, 1\}$. A tag $t \in \mathsf{tags}_{h+1}(n)$ is a mapping $\mathsf{tags}_h(n) \rightarrow \{0, 1\}$. Tags are written as words on Σ. For $t \in \mathsf{tags}_1(n)$, t is a bracketed n-bit sequence, i.e., a word of form $\langle 1\rangle\{0|1\}^n\langle /1\rangle$, where $t(i)$ is the $(i+1)$-th bit after $\langle 1\rangle$. For $t \in \mathsf{tags}_{h+1}(n)$, t is a bracketed sequence of tags in $\mathsf{tags}_h(n)$ and a corresponding bit for each tag, i.e., $\langle h+1\rangle(t'\{0|1\})^*\langle /h+1\rangle$, where each t' is a tag in $\mathsf{tags}_h(n)$. Since t is a total function, every possible tag of level h appear exactly once in a tag of level $h+1$. Every tag $t' \in \mathsf{tags}_h(n)$ that appears inside t is called a *sub-tag* of t. For every sub-tag $t' \in \mathsf{tags}_h(n)$ in a tag $t \in \mathsf{tags}_{h+1}(n)$, the bit that appears directly after the t' is the mapped value of the t'. Equality on tags is defined as the (unordered) equality on the underlying mappings.

For example, a tag in $\mathsf{tags}_2(1)$ is $\langle 2\rangle\langle 1\rangle 0\langle /1\rangle 0\ \langle 1\rangle 1\langle /1\rangle 1\langle /2\rangle$, which maps the sub-tag $\langle 1\rangle 0\langle /1\rangle \in \mathsf{tags}_1(1)$ to 0 and the sub-tag $\langle 1\rangle 1\langle /1\rangle \in \mathsf{tags}_1(1)$ to 1.

We now consider the size of tags.

Lemma 3.8. There are $g(h, n)$ different tags in $\mathsf{tags}_h(n)$.

The construction we use for tags is similar to that used in [11]. One important difference is that our construction requires each tag in $\mathsf{tags}_h(n)$ to be a complete mapping, where the one in [11] allowed partial maps. Our approach trades a larger tag size for better alternation efficiency.

First, we consider the size blowup in tags for our construction. We only need to provide a very relaxed bound for our final result:

Lemma 3.9. The size $s_h(n)$ of a tag in $\mathsf{tags}_h(n)$, for $n > 2$, is at most $g(h-1, 2n)$.

Our goal is to use tags to address the column for each tile. This introduces an blowup in the size of $\pi_{w,I}$ and we want to maintain polynomial size in w. Thus, the size of each tag need to be polynomial in w. We use the following lemma:

Lemma 3.10. For a given w and $h \leq \log^*(w) - 2$, there exists $n > 2$ such that:

- There are at least w distinct tags in $\mathsf{tags}_h(n)$.
- The size of each individual tag in $\mathsf{tags}_h(n)$ is at most w.

Definition 3.11. We define a mapping $\mathsf{tag}_{h,n} : N \rightarrow \mathsf{tags}_h(n)$ by induction. For the base case, $\mathsf{tag}_{1,n}(x) := \langle 1\rangle bit_{n-1}(x)\ldots bit_0(x)\langle /1\rangle$, where $bit_i(x)$ extracts the value of the ith bit of x. For the inductive case, $\mathsf{tag}_{h,n}(x) := \langle h\rangle \mathsf{tag}_{h-1,n}(g(h-1,n)-1)bit_{g(h-1,n)-1}(x)\ldots \mathsf{tag}_{h-1,n}(0)bit_0(x)\langle /h\rangle$. In other words, $\mathsf{tag}_{h,n}(x)$ is a tagged binary number, which maps every $\mathsf{tag}_{h-1,n}(y)$ to the yth bit of x.

Next, we describe the tagged word model $\pi_{w,I}$. The construction is with respect to a parameter $k > 2$ (which is the k of Theorem 3.5). We build the word using tags of level $h = k - 1$. The vocabulary of the word model is $\Sigma = \Sigma_h \cup D \cup \{\mathsf{r}\}$, where D is the set of tiles of T. We use r as a row marker. Given a tiling problem of size w, choose n where $g(h, n-1) < w \leq g(h, n)$. In other words, $n = \lceil \log^h(w) \rceil$. Now $\pi_{w,I}$ is the concatenation of

[3] In [16], QPTL is used, but on infinite models. In [11], monadic second-order logic is used, although second-order quantifiers are only used to "quantify-out the model", i.e., to check the existence of solutions. The base constructions only use first-order logic on linearly ordered structures.

[4] The tags can be seen as a form of counters, except that they only have to be checked for equality instead of "counting" anything.

$w-1$ blank rows and one initial row. The blank rows use an arbitrary non-initial tile $d_0 \in D$ (In the formula, we guess a tiling via quantification, so the use of d_0 here is purely as a placeholder.):

$$row_{blank} := \mathsf{tag}_{h,n}(0)d_0\mathsf{tag}_{h,n}(1)d_0 \ldots \mathsf{tag}_{h,n}(w-1)d_0\mathsf{r}$$

The initial row is the same as defined by I:

$$row_{init} := \mathsf{tag}_{h,n}(0)I(1)\mathsf{tag}_{h,n}(1)I(2) \ldots \mathsf{tag}_{h,n}(w-1)I(w)\mathsf{r}$$

Finally $\pi_{w,I} := (row_{blank})^{w-1}row_{init}$.

For ease of the construction we use in Section 5, we concatenate the rows in inverted order, where the first row is at the end of the word.

Lemma 3.12. For every k, the length of the word $\pi_{w,I}$ is polynomial in w, and $\pi_{w,I}$ can be generated in time polynomial in w. In addition, the polynomial functions do not depend on k.

Lemma 3.12 shows that Assumption 2 and 4 for Theorem 3.5 above hold.

3.2.2 Tag Comparison Using QPTL

Next we describe how to use QPTL formulas to check equality of tags, which we use to check the vertical constraints of tilings. The formula we build uses a set P of propositions. For any letter $d \in \Sigma$, we have a corresponding proposition p_d, where in the word model π, we have $\pi, i \models \mathsf{p}_d$ iff d is the ith letter in π. Other propositions in P are used to mark sets of locations in the word model; we call them *markers*. Since we often want to mark a single position, most occurrences of these propositions are restricted to be singletons. A pair of such singleton markers outline a subword by pointing to the beginning and ending positions of the subword. Given two markers p and q, the subword is denoted by $\pi_{[p,q]}$.

In the following construction, we use formula templates as follows: $\psi(p) := \psi'$ defines a template ψ with parameter p based on ψ', which is a QPTL formula. An instantiation $\psi(q)$ is a copy of ψ', where all free occurrences of p are replaced with q.

Lemma 3.13. Given $h \geq 1$ and $n \geq 1$, one can construct a formula $\varphi_{h,n}(p,p',q,q') \in \Sigma_h^{QPTL}$ of length linear in $h+n$ such that if $\pi \models \varphi_{h,n}(p,p',q,q')$, then

1. p, p', q, and q' are each true at exactly one position in the model;
2. The subwords $\pi_{[p,p']}$ and $\pi_{[q,q']}$ are equal tags in $\mathsf{tags}_h(n)$;
3. The subword $\pi_{[p,p']}$ appears before the subword $\pi_{[q,q']}$.

Proof. In the following, we first construct the formula $\varphi_{h,n}$, and then show that it satisfies the requirements in the lemma. We proceed with an inductive construction:

We present some basic templates to state some commonly used relationships for propositions. First, define $\mathsf{sing}(p)$ to assert that the proposition p is a singleton where $\mathsf{sing}(p) := Fp \wedge G(p \rightarrow XG\neg p)$. We also need to state that a proposition r is never true strictly inside a subword $\pi_{[p,q]}$ where $\mathsf{notbetween}(p,q,r) := G(p \rightarrow XG(XFq \rightarrow \neg r))$. We also need to state that two positions, both i letters away from singleton markers p and q, assert a proposition r where $\mathsf{same}^i(p,q,r) := G(p \rightarrow X^i r) \wedge G(q \rightarrow X^i r)$.

Now we construct the base case, where $\pi_{[p,p']}$ and $\pi_{[q,q']}$ mark tags in $\mathsf{tags}_1(n)$. In order to check equality, we need to state the following:

- The markers only appear once: $\mathsf{sing}(p) \wedge \mathsf{sing}(p') \wedge \mathsf{sing}(q) \wedge \mathsf{sing}(q')$.
- The range defined by the markers does not contain multiple tags at level 1: $\mathsf{notbetween}(p,p',\mathsf{p}_{\langle 1\rangle}) \wedge \mathsf{notbetween}(q,q',\mathsf{p}_{\langle 1\rangle})$.
- The markers point to the correct symbols: $G(p \rightarrow \mathsf{p}_{\langle 1\rangle}) \wedge G(p' \rightarrow \mathsf{p}_{\langle /1\rangle}) \wedge G(q \rightarrow \mathsf{p}_{\langle 1\rangle}) \wedge G(q \rightarrow \mathsf{p}_{\langle /1\rangle})$.
- The markers appear in the correct order: $G(p \rightarrow XFp') \wedge G(p' \rightarrow XFq) \wedge G(q \rightarrow XFq')$.
- The bit strings are the same: $\bigwedge_{1\leq i\leq n}(\mathsf{same}^i(p,q,\mathsf{p}_1) \vee \mathsf{same}^i(p,q,\mathsf{p}_0))$.
- $\varphi_{1,n}(p,p',q,q')$ is the conjunction of all the formula above.

By construction, $\varphi_{1,n}(p,p',q,q')$ is a formula in Σ_1^{QPTL} with size linear in n.

For the inductive case, we need to check whether two tags in $\mathsf{tags}_h(n)$ are equal. We need to check that all (internal) tags in $\mathsf{tags}_{h-1}(n)$ have matching values. We state the following:

- We still need to the same format checks as the first four entries in $\varphi_{1,n}(p,p',q,q')$, except all the references to $\langle 1\rangle$ and $\langle /1\rangle$ are changed to references to a tag of appropriate depth. We name this formula $\mathsf{format}_h(p,p',q,q')$.
- We use a proposition b to mark all starting positions of sub-tags in $\mathsf{tags}_{h-1}(n)$ that appear in $\pi_{[t,t']}$. $\mathsf{insidemarker}_h(t,t',b) := G(Ft \rightarrow \neg b) \wedge G(t' \rightarrow G\neg b) \wedge G(\neg \mathsf{p}_{\langle h-1\rangle} \rightarrow \neg b) \wedge G(t \rightarrow G((Ft' \wedge \mathsf{p}_{\langle h-1\rangle}) \rightarrow b))$
- Given (singleton) markers r, r', s, s', we can state that the pair of tags they point to map to the same value: $\mathsf{idmap}^h(r,r',s,s') := \varphi_{h-1,n}(r,r',s,s') \rightarrow (\mathsf{same}^1(r',s',\mathsf{p}_0) \vee \mathsf{same}^1(r',s',\mathsf{p}_1))$.
- We now define a formula to assert the equivalence of tags $\pi_{[p,p']}$ and $\pi_{[q,q']}$. For the meaning of the formula defined as checktags, see proof below. $\mathsf{checktags}_h(p,p',q,q') := (\exists b,b')(\forall r,r',s,s')(\mathsf{insidemarker}_h(p,p',b) \wedge \mathsf{insidemarker}_h(q,q',b') \wedge ((G(r \rightarrow b) \wedge G(s \rightarrow b')) \rightarrow \mathsf{idmap}_h(r,r',s,s')))$. Note $\mathsf{idmap}_h(r,r',s,s')$ is true whenever r' or s' does not point to the end of a tag in $\mathsf{tags}_h(n)$.

- $\varphi_{h,n}(p, p', q'q') := \mathsf{format}_h(p, p', q, q') \wedge \mathsf{checktags}_h(p, p', q, q')$.

Since in $\varphi_{h,n}$ the iterative part $\varphi_{h-1,n}$ appears under negation, and the quantifier prefix for the $\varphi_{h,n}$ outside $\varphi_{h-1,n}$ is $\exists\forall$, $\varphi_{h,n}$ in Σ_h^{QPTL} and of size linear in $h+n$.

Now we proceed to show that the construction is correct:

Claim 3.14. $\pi_{[p,p']}$ and $\pi_{[q,q']}$ are identical tags iff $\varphi_{h,n}(p, p', q, q')$. □

3.2.3 Constructing $\varphi_{T,w}$

Next, by using $\varphi_{k-1,n}(p, p', q, q')$ we construct a formula $\varphi'_{T,w}$ in Σ_k^{QPTL} to check that an annotated model is a tiling for the tiling problem (T, w) with size $w \leq g(k-1, n)$.

- Every position in the word has exactly one symbol: $\varphi_D := G(\bigwedge_{s\in\Sigma}(\mathsf{p}_s \rightarrow \bigwedge_{t\neq s}\neg\mathsf{p}_t)) \wedge G(\bigvee_{s\in\Sigma}\mathsf{p}_s)$.
- Horizontal constraints are observed: Define $\varphi_H := (\forall s, s', t, t')((\mathsf{sing}(s) \wedge \mathsf{sing}(s') \wedge \mathsf{sing}(t) \wedge \mathsf{sing}(t') \wedge G(s \rightarrow \mathsf{p}_{\langle k-1\rangle}) \wedge G(s' \rightarrow \mathsf{p}_{\langle /k-1\rangle}) \wedge G(t \rightarrow \mathsf{p}_{\langle k-1\rangle}) \wedge G(t' \rightarrow \mathsf{p}_{\langle /k-1\rangle}) \wedge G(s \rightarrow Fs') \wedge G(s' \rightarrow Ft) \wedge G(t \rightarrow Ft') \wedge \mathsf{notbetween}(s, s', \mathsf{p}_{\langle k-1\rangle}) \wedge \mathsf{notbetween}(s', t, \mathsf{p}_{\langle k-1\rangle}) \wedge \mathsf{notbetween}(s', t, \mathsf{p}_r) \wedge \mathsf{notbetween}(t, t', \mathsf{p}_{\langle k-1\rangle})) \rightarrow \bigvee_{\langle d,d'\rangle\in H}(G(s' \rightarrow X\mathsf{p}_d) \wedge G(t' \rightarrow X\mathsf{p}_{d'})))$. This checks for every pair of tags $\pi_{[s,s']}$ and $\pi_{[t,t']}$, if $\pi_{[s,s']}$ appears before $\pi_{[t,t']}$, and there is no row marker or other tag markers that appear between $\pi_{[s,s']}$ and $\pi_{[t,t']}$, then the symbol that appears after $\pi_{[s,s']}$ and the symbol that appears after $\pi_{[t,t']}$ are consecutive symbols on the same row, and need to satisfy the horizontal constraint.
- Vertical constraints are observed: Define $\varphi_V := (\forall s, s', t, t')((\varphi_{k-1,n}(s, s', t, t') \wedge G(s' \rightarrow (F(\mathsf{p}_r \wedge Ft) \wedge \neg F(\mathsf{p}_r \wedge XF(\mathsf{p}_r \wedge Ft))))) \rightarrow \bigvee_{\langle d,d'\rangle\in V}(G(s' \rightarrow X\mathsf{p}_{d'}) \wedge G(t' \rightarrow X\mathsf{p}_d)))$. We know from Lemma 3.13 that $\varphi_{k-1,n}(s, s', t, t')$ checks whether $\pi_{[s,s']}$ and $\pi_{[t,t']}$ are identical tags in $\mathsf{tags}_{k-1}(n)$. In φ_V, we first check that the pair of tags are identical, i.e., they mark the same column; then we check that the pair of tags has exactly one row marker appearing between them, i.e., they are in consecutive rows; finally, we check that the tiles that appear after the pair of tags satisfy the vertical constraint.
- The formula for checking whether the model is a solution is $\varphi'_{T,w} := \varphi_D \wedge \varphi_H \wedge \varphi_V$.

For $k \geq 2$, $\varphi'_{T,w}$ is a formula in Π_{k-1}^{QPTL}, since the occurrence of $\varphi_{k-1,n}$ in $\varphi'_{T,w}$ is negative, and the quantifier block of $\varphi'_{T,w}$ outside $\varphi_{k-1,n}$ is universal.

Given a tiling problem T and a mapping F, F is a solution for (T, w) iff $F_w \models \varphi'_{T,w}$. To check whether (T, w, I) has a solution, we take $\varphi_{T,w} = (\exists\mathsf{p}_{d_0})(\exists\mathsf{p}_{d_1})\ldots(\exists\mathsf{p}_{d_m})\varphi'_{T,w}$.

Lemma 3.15. Given a tiling instance (T, w, I), and an integer $k \geq 2$, we can generate in time $O(k + \log^{k-1}(w))$ a Σ_k^{QPTL} formula $\varphi_{T,w}$ of size $O(k + \log^{k-1}(w))$ such that $\pi_{w,I} \models \varphi_{T,w}$ iff (T, w, I) have a solution, and the coefficient in $O(k + \log^{k-1}(w))$ is independent from k.

Lemma 3.15 allows us to meet Assumption 1 needed for Theorem 3.5. We now show that we can also satisfy Assumption 3 and 4 of Theorem 3.5.

Lemma 3.16. There exists a constant $c > 0$ such that for every $k > 2$, the formula $\varphi_{T,w}$ is small enough so that $g(k-1, c|\varphi_{T,w}|)$ is in $\mathsf{poly}(w)$, and $\varphi_{T,w}$ can be constructed in time polynomial in w.

4. The complexity of low-width QBF

We now come back to the decision problem of bounded-width QBF. A variant of this problem is studied in [2] in the context of quantified constraint satisfaction and an FPT algorithm is given, where both the width and the alternation depth are taken as parameters. The function f given in the algorithm is non-elementary. We prove here that, under complexity-theoretic assumptions, the function in the parameter is indeed non-elementary.

4.1. Parameterized complexity of bounded-width QBF

Theorem 4.1. Satisfiability for Σ_k^{QBF} formulas of treewidth at most w can be solved in time $O(g(k, w)|\varphi|)$.

Proof. The result follows by a careful analysis of the algorithm in [2], counting the number of distinct trees generated by the algorithm. □

The algorithm presented in [2] is an extension of the decision procedure for bounded-width propositional formulas, which can be decided in $O(2^w|\varphi|)$ time [7, 10]. Unfortunately, it is unlikely that bounded-width QBF enjoys the same kind of tractability:

Theorem 4.2. Assuming $P \neq NP$, there exists a $c > 0$ such that for every $h(\cdot)$ in $\mathsf{poly}(\cdot)$, satisfiability for bounded-pathwidth formula ψ in Σ_k^{QBF}, where k is an odd number > 2, of pathwidth at most w cannot be solved in time $g(k-1, cw)h(|\psi|)$.

Proof. We combine Theorem 3.5 above with a translation from QPTL finite model checking to QBF satisfiability to show the lower bound. In Theorem 4.5 that follows, we show that for every QPTL formula $\varphi \in \Sigma_k^{QPTL}$, with odd k, and every word model π, we can construct a QBF formula $\psi = \varphi_{Q,\pi}$ of pathwidth at most $2|\varphi| - 1$ and alternation depth k such that $\models \psi$ iff $\pi \models \varphi$. Also, ψ is of size $O(|\varphi||\pi|)$, so there is a constant c' such that the construction takes time at most $c'|\varphi||\pi|$ and $|\psi| \leq c'|\varphi||\pi|$. Consider

$c = c_{QPTL}/2$. For every $k > 2$ and for every polynomially bounded function $f'(\cdot)$, we have that $g(k-1, c(2|\varphi| - 1))f'(|\varphi|) < g(k-1, c_{QPTL}|\varphi|)$ for large enough $|\varphi|$. This is because $g(k-1, c(2|\varphi| - 1)) = g(k-1, c_{QPTL}|\varphi| - c_{QPTL}/2)$, which is far smaller than $g(k-1, c_{QPTL}|\varphi|)$. For example, for every positive constant d, $g(2,x)/g(2,x-d)$ is not polynomially bounded on x. Now, suppose we can decide the satisfiability of ψ in time $g(k-1, cw)h(|\psi|)$, we can use it to decide the truth of $\pi \models \varphi$ through deciding ψ in time $g(k-1, c_{QPTL}|\varphi|)h'(|\pi|)$, with a polynomial $h'(\cdot)$. First, the time taken to solve the model checking of φ on π through QBF is $g(k-1, c(2|\varphi|-1))h(c'|\varphi||\pi|) + c'|\varphi||\pi| \leq g(k-1, c(2|\varphi|-1))(h(c'|\varphi||\pi|) + c'|\varphi||\pi|)$. Because $h(\cdot)$ is polynomial, there exist polynomial functions $f'(\cdot)$ and $h'(\cdot)$ such that $h(c'|\varphi||\pi|) + c'|\varphi||\pi| \leq f'(|\varphi|)h'(|\pi|)$. Also, from our assumption, $g(k-1, c(2|\varphi|-1))f'(\varphi) \leq g(k-1, c_{QPTL}(|\varphi|))$ for large enough $|\varphi|$. Thus, $g(k-1, c(2|\varphi|-1))h(c'|\varphi||\pi|) + c'|\varphi||\pi| \leq g(k-1, c_{QPTL}|\varphi|)h'(|\pi|)$ for large enough $|\varphi|$. This contradicts with Theorem 3.5 under the same $P \neq NP$ assumption. □

Note we have the similar one-exponential gap between the upper and lower bound, and it can be closed in the same way as the bounds for QPTL model checking. A direct consequence is that low-width QBF can not be solved with an FPT algorithm with an elementary blowup in the parameters k and w, where k is the alternating depth and w is the width.

Definition 4.3. The class of $\log^*$-pathwidth QBF is the set of QBF formulas ψ that have pathwidth $O(\log^*(|\psi|))$.

Theorem 4.4. The class of $\log^*$-pathwidth QBF is NP-hard.

Proof. NP-hardness is by a reduction from the NP-hard tiling problem. For a tiling instance (T, w, I), We first use the construction in Section 3 to encode it as a QPTL model-checking instance, then use the translation presented for Theorem 4.5 below to translate it to a QBF instance. For the first step of the construction, take the alternation depth k to be the least odd number $\geq \log^*(w) - 2$ (in other words, k is either $\log^*(w) - 2$ or $\log^*(w) - 1$). Because $k - 1 \geq \log^*(w) - 3$, we have that $\log^{k-1}(w) \leq 16$. By Lemma 3.15, the size of the QPTL formula $\varphi_{T,w}$ is $O(k + \log^{k-1}(w)) = O(k)$. By Lemma 3.12, the model $\pi_{w,I}$ has size $h(w)$ for some polynomial function h. Now we use Theorem 4.5 to translate the finite model-checking problem $\pi_{w,I} \models \varphi_{T,w}$ to a QBF instance $\psi = \varphi_{Q,\pi_{w,I},T,w}$ that has size $|\psi| = O(|\varphi_{T,w}||\pi_{w,I}|) = O(k \times h(w))$ and pathwidth at most $2|\varphi_{T,w}| - 1$. Since $k = O(\log^*(w))$, $O(k \times h(w))$ is polynomial in w. Similarly, the pathwidth of ψ is at most $2|\varphi_{T,w}| - 1$, which is in $O(k) = O(\log^*(w))$ and in turn, $O(\log^*(|\psi|))$ (since $|\psi|$ is polynomial in w). Thus, the family of $\log^*$-pathwidth QBF problems is $NP - hard$. □

In contrast, propositional satisfiability problems that have $O(\log(|\psi|))$ pathwidth are still in P [9].

4.2. Translating QPTL finite model checking to QBF

Theorem 4.5. Given a formula φ in Σ_k^{QPTL} (for odd k) that is in negation normal form and a finite word model π, we can generate in time $O(|\varphi||\pi|)$ a formula $\varphi_{Q,\pi}$ in Σ_k^{QBF} of size $O(|\varphi||\pi|)$ and pathwidth at most $2|\varphi| - 1$, such that $\pi \models \varphi$ iff $\models \varphi_{Q,\pi}$.

Proof. We perform the following translation from QPTL to QBF. Consider the QPTL formula $\varphi = (\exists x_{1,1}) \ldots (\forall x_{2,1}) \ldots (\exists x_{k,1}) \ldots \varphi'$. We first construct a propositional model π_Q such that $\pi_Q \models \varphi_Q$ iff $\pi \models \varphi$. We can then eliminate the propositional model by describing it as a conjunction of unit literals and conjoining with φ_Q (this does not increase the width of the formula). We establish the correspondence between $\pi \models \varphi$ and $\pi_Q \models \varphi_Q$ inductively.

The base case is when φ is quantifier free. A propositional model π_Q can capture all information encoded in the word model π: For each free proposition q of φ we create $|\pi|$ Boolean propositions $p_{q,i}$, $0 \leq i < |\pi|$, defined by $\pi_Q(p_{q,i}) = 1$ iff $q \in \pi(i)$. We refer to this set of Boolean propositions as P_Q.

We write $\mathsf{sub}(\varphi)$ for the set of sub-formulas of φ, and $\mathsf{sub}'(\varphi)$ for the set of non-atomic sub-formulas of φ, in other words, $\mathsf{sub}'(\varphi) = \mathsf{sub}(\varphi) - \{q, \neg q | q \text{ is a proposition defined in } \varphi\}$. With each ψ in $\mathsf{sub}'(\varphi)$, we associate $|\pi|$ new propositions $p_{\psi,i}$. Essentially, we use a propositional encoding of accepting runs of the automaton constructed in [19] (adapted to finite words). The formula φ_Q can be encoded in CNF form by unrolling the formula onto the structure as follows. (For ease of understanding, clause groups for closely related propositions are written using the $\leftrightarrow$ operator.)

- In the following, whenever $\psi = a$ or $\psi = \neg a$, substitute $p_{a,i}$ or $\neg p_{a,i}$ for $p_{\psi,i}$.
- $\psi = X\psi'$: $C_\psi := (\neg p_{\psi,|\pi|-1}) \wedge \bigwedge_{0 \leq i < |\pi|-1} (p_{\psi,i} \leftrightarrow p_{\psi',i+1})$
- $\psi = F\psi'$: $C_\psi := (p_{\psi,|\pi|-1} \leftrightarrow p_{\psi',|\pi|-1}) \wedge \bigwedge_{0 \leq i < |\pi|-1} (p_{\psi,i} \leftrightarrow (p_{\psi,i+1} \vee p_{\psi',i}))$ (because $\pi, i \models F\psi$ iff $\pi, i \models \psi$ or $\pi, i+1 \models F\psi$.)
- $\psi = G\psi'$: $C_\psi := (p_{\psi,|\pi|-1} \leftrightarrow p_{\psi',|\pi|-1}) \wedge \bigwedge_{0 \leq i < |\pi|-1} (p_{\psi,i} \leftrightarrow (p_{\psi,i+1} \wedge p_{\psi',i}))$ (Because $\pi, i \models G\psi$ iff $\pi, i \models \psi$ and $\pi, i+1 \models G\psi$.)
- $\psi = \psi' \wedge \psi''$: $C_\psi := \bigwedge_{0 \leq i < |\pi|} p_{\psi,i} \leftrightarrow (p_{\psi',i} \wedge p_{\psi'',i})$
- $\psi = \psi' \vee \psi''$: $C_\psi := \bigwedge_{0 \leq i < |\pi|} p_{\psi,i} \leftrightarrow (p_{\psi',i} \vee p_{\psi'',i})$

Now, we have $\varphi'_Q := p_{\varphi,0} \wedge \bigwedge_{\psi \in \mathsf{sub}'(\varphi)} C_\psi$ in CNF with $O(|\pi||\varphi|)$ clauses. We proceed to quantify out the propositions that correspond to valuations of subformulas in $\mathsf{sub}'(\varphi) = \{\psi_1, \psi_2 \ldots \psi_m\}$. Thus, π_Q define exactly the set of propositions we need to interpret $\varphi_Q := (\exists p_{\psi_1,0}) \ldots (\exists p_{\psi_m,|\pi|-1})\varphi'_Q$. φ_Q is in turn the *QBF translation* of φ.

Claim 4.6. If φ is quantifier free, then $\pi \models \varphi$ iff $\pi_Q \models \varphi_Q$.

We use QBF quantifiers to simulate QPTL quantifiers inductively. Assume we can translate ψ to ψ_Q in QBF. The inductive case is:

- $\varphi = (\exists x)\psi$: Take $\varphi_Q = (\exists p_{x,0}) \dots (\exists p_{x,|\pi|-1})\psi_Q$
- $\varphi = (\forall x)\psi$: Take $\varphi_Q = (\forall p_{x,0}) \dots (\forall p_{x,|\pi|-1})\psi_Q$

Clearly, φ_Q is in prenex normal form. The following claims are immediate.

Claim 4.7. $\pi \models \varphi$ iff $\pi_Q \models \varphi_Q$.

Claim 4.8. The matrix of $\varphi_{Q,\pi}$ have pathwidth at most $2|\varphi| - 1$.

Not only is the translation width efficient, it is also alternation efficient as well, in that

- For $\varphi \in \Sigma_i^{QPTL}$ where i is even, $\varphi_{Q,\pi} \in \Sigma_{i+1}^{QBF}$.
- For $\varphi \in \Sigma_i^{QPTL}$ where i is odd, $\varphi_{Q,\pi} \in \Sigma_i^{QBF}$.

The construction of $\varphi_{Q,\pi}$ can be performed in time linear to its size, i.e., $O(|\varphi||\pi|)$. In summary, the formula $\varphi_{Q,\pi}$ we constructed meets all the requirements posed by Theorem 4.5. □

5. PSPACE-hardness for $\log^*$-pathwidth QBF

In section 3 and 4, we showed that unlike propositional satisfiability, QBF is hard even when the width is greatly limited (to $\log^*(n)$). To keep the low-width version as hard as tiling (NP), $\log^*(n)$ alternations are needed. Our goal is to increase the hardness of the low-width class beyond NP. One would expect $O(n)$ alternations to be needed to capture PSPACE. We move therefore from model checking to model-checking games in order to boost the alternation depth, while keeping the formulas small.

We would like to show the following improvement over Theorem 4.4:

Theorem 5.1. The decision problem for the class of $\log^*$-pathwidth QBF is PSPACE-complete.

Proof. The problem is trivially in PSPACE. For PSPACE-hardness, we start from a PSPACE-complete tiling-game problem and combine two translation results to achieve a polynomial reduction. Given a tiling-game instance (T, w, I), we use Theorem 5.5 to convert it into a QPTL model-checking game $(\pi_{w,I}, \varphi_{T,w,G}, G)$. The model $\pi_{w,I}$ and the play order G have size polynomial in w, and $\varphi_{T,w,G}$ has size $O(\log^*(w))$. Then, by applying Theorem 5.3, we convert the QPTL model-checking game $(\pi_{w,I}, \varphi_{T,w,G}, G)$ to a QBF formula $\psi = \varphi_{Q,\pi_{w,I},w,G}$ that has size polynomial in $|\pi_{w,I}|$, $|G|$, and $|\varphi_{T,w,G}|$. In turn, $|\psi|$ is polynomial in w. Also, ψ have pathwidth at most $2|\varphi_{T,w,G}| - 1$, which is in $O(\log^*(w))$, and in turn, $O(\log^*(|\psi|))$. Thus, the family of $\log^*$-pathwidth QBF problems is PSPACE-complete. □

5.1. Model-checking games

First, we extend finite model checking for QPTL to a two-player game. Instead of being given a model to check, two players (the Constructor and the Spoiler) play a game to update a model for a specific formula. The Constructor's goal is to satisfy the formula in the resulting model, under opposition by the Spoiler.

Definition 5.2. A *finite model-checking game* for QPTL is defined as follows: A finite-word model is a map $\pi : [0 \dots n-1] \to 2^P$. The input to the game is a formula φ (which uses both the propositions in π as well as two distinguished propositions $\mathsf{p}_\exists$ and $\mathsf{p}_\forall$), a word model π, the number m of rounds, and a *play order* G. The play order G labels each position $0 \dots n-1$ in the model π either with a *round number*, which is an integer between 0 and $m-1$, or leaves it unlabelled. Thus, for each round number i, we have a set G_i of positions in the model defined by $G_i = \{d | G(d) = i\}$. Two players, the Constructor and the Spoiler, attempt to update π under the play order G. The play order is processed in increasing round order i. If i is even, the Constructor updates π^i to π^{i+1} (with $\pi^0 = \pi$) on every position d in G_i by choosing a new assignment $x_d \in 2^P$ and updating π^i with x_d. In summary, $\pi^{i+1} = \pi^i[d_1 \mapsto x_{d_1}][d_2 \mapsto x_{d_2}] \dots [d_k \mapsto x_{d_k}]$, where $G_i = \{d_1, \dots, d_k\}$. Here, $\pi[d \mapsto x](i) = \pi(i)$ if $d \neq i$ and $\pi[d \mapsto x](d) = x$. If i is odd, the Spoiler performs the update instead of the Constructor. The model π^m is extended onto the distinguished propositions $\mathsf{p}_\exists$ and $\mathsf{p}_\forall$ to become π', where $\mathsf{p}_\exists \in \pi'(d)$ only if $G(d)$ is even, and $\mathsf{p}_\forall \in \pi'(d)$ only if $G(d)$ is odd. π' is a winning model for the Constructor iff $\pi' \models \varphi$. The Constructor wins a model-checking game iff given π, G, m, and φ, he has a strategy to make the resulting model π' winning, and we write it as $\pi \models_G \varphi$.

The *finite model-checking game* for QPTL is a conservative extension of the finite model-checking problem on QPTL, since given an empty G, it is exactly the finite model-checking problem for QPTL. We can use a translation similar to that of Section 4 to convert QPTL model-checking games to QBF.

Theorem 5.3. Given a QPTL model-checking game (π, φ, G), we can construct in polynomial time a QBF formula $\varphi_{Q,\pi,G}$ such that $\pi \models_G \varphi$ iff $\models \varphi_{Q,\pi,G}$. The size of $\varphi_{Q,\pi,G}$ is polynomial in $|\varphi|$, $|\pi|$, and $|G|$, and the pathwidth of $\varphi_{Q,\pi,G}$ is at most $2|\varphi| - 1$.

5.2. Reducing tiling games to model-checking games

In Section 3, we showed that we can reduce the tiling problem (T, w, I) to a QPTL finite model-checking problem with model size in $\mathsf{poly}(w)$ and formula size in $O(k + \log^k(w))$. This result is combined with that of Theorem 4.4 to show that QBF formulas of $\log^*(n)$ width is NP-hard.

The ideal result would be to show PSPACE-completeness, i.e., restricting QBF to $\log^*(n)$ width does not reduce its complexity. To do that, we need a tiling problem that is PSPACE-complete and has a polynomial number of cells. This requires inherent alternation in the problem in the form of a game. We use the following model of the tiling game:

Definition 5.4. A *tiling game* uses a tiling system T and is played on a board with h rows and w columns with an initial condition I. Two players, the Constructor, and the Spoiler plays by tiling alternating rows, starting with the Constructor on row 1. The resulting tiling F is a winning tiling for the Constructor if one of the following holds:

1. The tiling F is a solution for the tiling problem (T, h, w, I).
2. The smallest j such that $(F(i, j-1), F(i, j)) \notin V$ or $(F(i-1, j), F(i, j)) \notin H$ is even.

The second condition states that the Spoiler is the first to produce a failing tile. The Constructor wins the game (T, h, w, I) iff he has a strategy to force a winning tiling.

A unary, square version of the tiling game (T, w, I), where $h = w$ and I specifies the first row, like most variants of square tiling games [4], is PSPACE-complete. We use finite model-checking games for QPTL to encode tiling games. The construction of the model $\pi_{w,I}$ from w is the same as in section 3.2.1. The play order G have w rounds, where each round G_{i-1} for $1 \leq i \leq w$ contains the set of positions in $\pi_{w,I}$ that corresponds to the cells (i, x) for $1 < x \leq w$. The formula is constructed as follows. Condition 1 is encoded by the $\varphi'_{T,w}$ of section 3.2.3. To encode condition 2, we guess the first position where the Spoiler made a failing play using a new variable e (and auxiliary variables e_D, e_H, and e_V). The following checks need to be performed. First, we check that e is a singleton and on a cell that is played by the Spoiler. Second, we check the tiling against the constraints. But, now the requirement for a correct tiling is reduced; the tiling is not necessarily a solution, as errors can occur on rows after the error marker e. Since we use an inverted row-major order, the correctness checks are not applied on positions before e in the word model, i.e., whenever Fe holds. Third, we check that an actual error occurred on the error marker. There are three types of errors, guessed by the variables e_D, e_H, and e_V. 1) The player chooses an assignment that does not correspond to a tile, i.e., more than one of p_ds or none of the p_ds are assigned to true. 2) The horizontal constraint is violated. 3) The vertical constraint is violated.

Theorem 5.5. Given a tiling game (T, w, I), we can construct in polynomial time a QPTL model-checking game $(\pi_{w,I}, \varphi_{T,w,G}, G)$ such that the Constructor wins the tiling game (T, w, I) iff $\pi_{w,I} \models_G \varphi_{T,w,G}$, the model $\pi_{w,I}$ and the play order G have size polynomial in w, and the formula $\varphi_{T,w,G}$ has size $O(\log^*(w))$.

Acknowledgements

Supported in part by NSF grants CCR-9988322, CCR-0124077, CCR-0311326, and ANI-0216467, by BSF grant 9800096, and by Texas ATP grant 003604-0058-2003. Part of this work was done while the second author was visiting the Isaac Newton Institute for Mathematical Science, as part of a Special Programme on Logic and Algorithms.

References

[1] J. Büchi. Weak second-order arithmetic and finite automata. *Zeit. Math. Logik und Grundl. Math.*, 6:66–92, 1960.

[2] H. Chen. Quantified constraint satisfaction and bounded treewidth. In R. L. de Mántaras and L. Saitta, editors, *ECAI*, pages 161–165. IOS Press, 2004.

[3] H. Chen and V. Dalmau. From pebble games to tractability: An ambidextrous consistency algorithm for quantified constraint satisfaction. In *CSL 2005*, pages 232–247, 2005.

[4] B. Chlebus. Domino-tiling games. *J. Comp. Sys. Sci.*, 32:374–392, 1986.

[5] N. Creignou, S. Khanna, and M. Sudan. Complexity classifications of Boolean constraint satisfaction problems. *Monographs on Discrete Applied Mathematics*, 2001.

[6] R. Dechter. *Constraint Processing*. Morgan Kaufmman, 2003.

[7] R. Dechter and J. Pearl. Tree clustering for constraint networks. *Artificial Intelligence*, pages 353–366, 1989.

[8] R. Downey and M. Fellows. *Parametrized Complexity*. Springer-Verlag, 1999.

[9] A. Ferrara, G. Pan, and M. Vardi. Treewidth in verification: Local vs. global. In *LPAR 2005*, pages 489–503, 2005.

[10] E. Freuder. Complexity of k-tree structured constraint satisfaction problems.

[11] M. Frick and M. Grohe. The complexity of first-order and monatic second-order logic revisited. In *LICS'02*, pages 215–224, 2002.

[12] G. Gottlob, G. Greco, and F. Scarcello. The complexity of quantified constraint satisfaction problems under structural restrictions. In *IJCAI 05*, pages 150–155, 2005.

[13] H. Lewis. Complexity of solvable cases of the decision problem for the predicate calculus. In *FOCS 1978*, pages 35–47, 1978.

[14] A. Meyer. Weak monadic second order theory of successor is not elementary-recursive. In *Logic Colloquium, Lecture Notes in Mathematics 453*. Springer-Verlag, 1975.

[15] N. Robertson and P. Seymour. Graph minors. ii. algorithmic aspects of treewidth. *J. of Algorithms*, 7:309–322, 1986.

[16] A. Sistla, M. Vardi, and P. Wolper. The complementation problem for Büchi automana with applications to temporal logic. *Theo. Comp. Sci.*, 49:217–237, 1987.

[17] L. Stockmeyer. *The complexity of decision problems in automate theory and logic*. PhD thesis, Dept. of Elec. Eng., MIT, 1974.

[18] L. Stockmeyer. The polynomial hierarchy. *Theo. Comp. Sci.*, 3:1 – 22, 1976.

[19] M. Vardi and P. Wolper. Reasoning about infinite computations. *Information and Computation*, 15:1 – 37, 1994.

The Boundedness Problem for Monadic Universal First-Order Logic

Martin Otto
Fachbereich Mathematik
Technische Universität Darmstadt
64289 Darmstadt, Germany

Abstract

We consider the monadic boundedness problem for least fixed points over FO *formulae as a decision problem: Given a formula $\varphi(X, x)$, positive in X, decide whether there is a uniform finite bound on the least fixed point recursion based on φ. Few fragments of* FO *are known to have a decidable boundedness problem; boundedness is known to be undecidable for many fragments. We here show that monadic boundedness is decidable for purely universal* FO *formulae without equality in which each non-recursive predicate occurs in just one polarity (e.g., only negatively). The restrictions are shown to be essential: waving either the polarity constraint or allowing positive occurrences of equality, the monadic boundedness problem for universal formulae becomes undecidable. The main result is based on a model theoretic analysis involving ideas from modal and guarded logics and a reduction to the monadic second-order theory of trees.*

1 Introduction

Consider a formula $\varphi(X, x) \in$ FO that is positive in the monadic second-order variable X and with a single free first-order variable x. Over corresponding structures $\mathfrak{A}$ such φ defines an operation on subsets,

$$\begin{array}{rcl} F_\varphi^{\mathfrak{A}} \colon \mathcal{P}(A) & \longrightarrow & \mathcal{P}(A) \\ P & \longmapsto & \{a \in A \colon \mathfrak{A} \models \varphi[P, a]\}. \end{array}$$

Due to positivity in X, this operation is monotone w.r.t. $\subseteq$, and hence has a least fixed point $(\mu_X\varphi)^{\mathfrak{A}}$, which is also attained as the limit of the monotone sequence of its stages $X^\alpha[\mathfrak{A}]$ generated by iteration of $F_\varphi^{\mathfrak{A}}$ on $\emptyset$.

When is this recursion uniformly finitely bounded, and hence the least fixed point uniformly definable by a finite iteration of φ? We say that $\varphi(X, x)$ is bounded iff there is $n \in \mathbb{N}$ such that $X^{n+1}[\mathfrak{A}] = X^n[\mathfrak{A}] (= (\mu_X\varphi)^{\mathfrak{A}})$ for all $\mathfrak{A}$. We consider the *boundedness problem* as a decision problem $\mathsf{Bdd}(\mathcal{F})$, for formulae φ from a fixed syntactic fragment $\mathcal{F} \subseteq$ FO.

$\mathsf{Bdd}(\mathcal{F})$	given $\varphi = \varphi(X, x) \in \mathcal{F}$, decide if φ is bounded

This decision problem has originally been considered in particular for the query language Datalog with a view to query optimisation [1, 13, 9, 11, 12]. However, the overwhelmingly negative picture w.r.t. decidability there has largely defeated initial hopes that bounded (i.e., spurious) recursion could be systematically detected and eliminated.

But similar concerns arise also for instance in connection with temporal fixed point logics like the μ-calculus, cf. Theorem 2 below, or other fixed point formalisms. Because of the model theoretic link between boundedness and FO definability of the least fixed point, there is also a connection with circumscription, which is of interest in artificial intelligence [17, 16]. By the Barwise-Moschovakis theorem [5] (cf. Theorem 6 below), φ is bounded if, and only if, $\mu_X\varphi$ is FO definable. So, for circumscriptions based on FO formulae that are positive in the target predicate, FO definability of this target predicate is the same as boundedness.

Overall however, very few fragments of FO are known to have a decidable boundedness problem. Quite to the contrary, boundedness is known to be undecidable for many fragments. Among the scarce decidability results, the following result of Cosmadakis, Gaifman, Kanellakis, Vardi [9] stands out.

Theorem 1. *Boundedness is decidable for monadic Datalog. I.e.,* Bdd *is decidable for positive existential* FO *formulae in monadic recursion variables X, as well as for systems of such.*

Another decidability result that is important for our considerations is the following from [19] (cf. the modal variant of Theorem 6 below).

Theorem 2. Bdd(ML), *the boundedness problem for the modal fragment of* FO *is decidable. More generally, one* *can decide for formulae of the μ-calculus whether they are equivalent to plain modal formulae.*

Undecidability results for Bdd abound; we mention some. See [12] for (i), [11] for (ii), and [14] for (iii). For (iv) and (v) compare section 3.2 below.

Theorem 3. $\mathsf{Bdd}(\mathcal{F})$ *is undecidable for the following fragments $\mathcal{F}$ of* FO*:*

(i) *$\mathcal{F}$: positive existential formulae in a binary recursive predicate X.*

(ii) *$\mathcal{F}$: existential formulae in a monadic recursive predicate if negation (or even just inequality) is allowed.*

(iii) *$\mathcal{F}$: formulae in a monadic recursive predicate using just two distinct first-order variables.*

(iv) *$\mathcal{F}$: universal formulae in a monadic recursive predicate, negative in all non-recursive predicates but allowing positive occurrences of equality.*

(v) *$\mathcal{F}$: universal* FO *formulae in a monadic recursive predicate, if some of the non-recursive relations can occur both positively and negatively.*

In a way, therefore, few natural fragments remain that would be candidates for a decidable boundedness problem. Among the most obvious are: the guarded fragment (still open) and the universal fragment of FO (settled here). The present investigation shows that monadic boundedness is decidable for purely universal FO formulae without (positive occurrences of) equality in which each non-recursive predicate occurs in just one polarity. As the boundedness issue is obviously invariant under swapping relations for their complements in the underlying relational structures, we may w.l.o.g. restrict attention to the case where all non-recursive predicates (and equality) only appear negatively, denoted by $\mathcal{F}(\forall, -)$ in the following.

Main Theorem $\mathsf{Bdd}(\mathcal{F}(\forall, -))$ *is decidable. I.e., boundedness is decidable for monadic recursion over purely universal* FO *formulae that are purely negative in all non-recursive predicates and equality (or, by extension, universal formulae in which each predicate letter occurs in just one polarity).*

The restrictions expressed in the theorem are essential. The decidability result obtained provides a counterpart to the one expressed in Theorem 1. Note, however, that the logical "dual" of the decidability result in Theorem 1 would concern boundedness for *greatest* fixed points of universal formulae, rather than least fixed points. Conversely, our main theorem proves, by duality, decidability of the boundedness problem for greatest fixed points of purely positive, purely existential formulae.

Organisation. In the following section, we review the basic definitions and discuss the model theoretic connection between boundedness and definability of the fixed point (Barwise–Moschovakis theorem). Section 3 focuses on boundedness for the universal fragment of FO and introduces a normal form for universal fixed points; we also contrast our decidability result with undecidability proofs for less restricted classes of universal formulae. In section 4 we prepare the reduction argument underlying our main result by collecting the relevant facts about decidability of boundedness for systems in the modal fragment; we also give a new model theoretic argument for decidability there. The main technical contribution in section 5 provides the reduction from the restricted universal case to the modal case (based on an intuitive intermediate stage that is motivated by a formalisation in the guarded fragment). We conclude with some remarks on ramifications and open problems in section 6.

2 Preliminaries

2.1 Boundedness

Consider fixed point recursion in systems for simultaneous least fixed points. (Even when we are ultimately interested in boundedness for single formulae rather than systems, the reductions applied take us to systems.)

An *admissible system* is given by a tuple of FO formulae $\bar{\varphi} = (\varphi_1, \dots, \varphi_k)$ in a relational vocabulary τ and monadic second-order variables $\bar{X} = (X_1, \dots, X_k)$, where each φ_i is of the form

$$\varphi_i(\bar{X}, x) \in \text{FO}, \quad \text{positive in each } X_j.$$

Over any τ-structure $\mathfrak{A}$ associate with this system the monotone operator on $(\mathcal{P}(A))^k$

$$\bar{P} = (P_i)_{1\leqslant i\leqslant k} \longmapsto \quad a \in A \colon \mathfrak{A} \models \varphi_i[\bar{P}, a] \quad {}_{1\leqslant i\leqslant k}.$$

The simultaneous least fixed point of this operator is denoted $\bar{\varphi}^\infty[\mathfrak{A}]$; its components $(\bar{\varphi}^\infty[\mathfrak{A}])_i$. The least fixed point $\bar{\varphi}^\infty$ is also the limit $\bar{X}^\infty$ of the monotone sequence of stages $\bar{X}^\alpha[\mathfrak{A}] = \bar{X}^\alpha = (X_1^\alpha, \dots, X_k^\alpha)$ inductively defined over the given $\mathfrak{A}$ according to

$$\begin{aligned} X_i^0 &= \emptyset \\ X_i^{\alpha+1} &= \quad a \in A \colon \mathfrak{A} \models \varphi_i[\bar{P}, a] \\ X_i^\lambda &= \quad {}_{\alpha<\lambda} X_i^\alpha \text{ for limit } \lambda. \end{aligned}$$

The *closure ordinal* $\gamma[\bar{\varphi}, \mathfrak{A}]$ of $\bar{\varphi}$ in $\mathfrak{A}$ is the least α such that $\bar{X}^\alpha[\mathfrak{A}] = \bar{\varphi}^\infty[\mathfrak{A}]$.

Observation 4. *Over ω-saturated $\mathfrak{A}$, the closure ordinal for any first-order least fixed point is bounded by ω.*

Note that all finite stages X_i^n, for $n \in \mathbb{N}$, are uniformly FO definable. We write φ^n for the formula that defines the n-th stage of φ, which is obtained inductively by substituting φ^{n-1} for X in $\varphi(X, x)$.

Definition 5. The admissible system $\bar{\varphi} = (\varphi_1, \ldots, \varphi_k)$ is *bounded* if for some $n \in \mathbb{N}$, $\gamma[\bar{\varphi}, \mathfrak{A}] \leqslant n$ for all $\mathfrak{A}$. This notion naturally relativise to restricted classes C of structures $\mathfrak{A}$; we speak of boundedness of $\bar{\varphi}$ over C in this sense.

Unboundedness as generalised satisfiability. It is useful to think of unboundedness as a satisfiability issue in the following sense. $\varphi(X, x)$ is unbounded iff $\varphi^{n+1}(x) \wedge \neg\varphi^n(x)$ is satisfiable for all $n \in \mathbb{N}$. It is not hard to see that, for fragments satisfying some mild closure properties, SAT($\mathcal{F}$) is reducible to Bdd($\mathcal{F}$).

Boundedness in finite model theory. For many natural fragments of FO, boundedness (over all structures) coincides with boundedness over the class of all finite structures. This is easily seen for fragments that are closed under positive substitution, negation and conjunction and that have the finite model property. Closure under positive substitution implies that the finite stages X^n in the fixed point generation are themselves definable by formulae φ^n in the given fragment $\mathcal{F}$; closure under conjunction and negation provide the formulae $\varphi^{n+1} \wedge \neg\varphi^n$ within $\mathcal{F}$. For such fragments unboundedness (in infinite structures) implies unboundedness over finite structures, by an appeal to the finite model property. This applies in particular to the modal, guarded and two-variable fragments.

For the existential and universal fragments, one can argue similarly, but invoking the finite model property for the $\exists^*\forall^*$ fragment of FO (the Bernays–Schönfinkel class of the classical decision problem, see [8]) for $\varphi^{n+1} \wedge \neg\varphi^n$.

2.2 The BarwiseMoschovakis Theorem

The following is an adaptation of a well-known classical theorem [5], which links boundedness to FO definability of the fixed point. The non-obvious part, (iii) $\Rightarrow$ (i), is based on a compactness argument using ω-saturated structures $\mathfrak{A}$, applying Observation 4.

Theorem 6 (Barwise-Moschovakis). *For admissible $\bar{\varphi}$, the following are equivalent:*
(i) *$\bar{\varphi}$ is bounded.*
(ii) *$(\bar{\varphi}^\infty)$ is uniformly* FO *definable over all $\mathfrak{A}$.*
(iii) *$(\bar{\varphi}^\infty[\mathfrak{A}])$ is* FO *definable for each $\mathfrak{A}$.*

The statement of the theorem relativises to elementary classes. It also relativises to fragments $\mathcal{F} \subseteq$ FO with the property that the finite stages of admissible systems over $\mathcal{F}$ are themselves $\mathcal{F}$-definable. Natural fragments of this kind are, for instance, the universal or the existential fragments of FO, the k-variable fragments FO^k, the guarded fragment GF and modal logic ML. For the latter, for instance, we have that an admissible system $\bar{\varphi}$ of modal formulae is bounded if, and only if, its least fixed point is definable in modal logic (over each individual Kripke structure).

Status in finite model theory. As discussed in the previous section, the boundedness problem coincides with its finite model theory version for several 'good' fragments, including the universal fragment. For the finite model theory (fmt) version of the Barwise–Moschovakis theorem, however, one also needs to link definability of the fixed point over all finite structures to boundedness over all finite structures, and hence (for a 'good' fragment) to boundedness and therefore definability of the fixed point over all structures. For the existential positive fragment, a strong form of the finite model theory version of the Barwise–Moschovakis theorem was proved by Ajtai and Gurevich: a Datalog query is FO definable if, and only if, the program is bounded. This result has recently been put in a new context, by major new results on the fmt version of the classical preservation theorem that links preservation under homomorphisms to positive existential definability, by Rossmann [21] and Atserias, Dawar and Kolaitis [4]. These fmt versions show that FO definability of the fixed point of a positive existential recursion implies its positive existential definability, due to preservation of the fixed point under homomorphisms in finite structures. By duality, Rossmann's theorem similarly implies that FO definability for a universal equality-free recursion that is negative in all non-recursive predicates implies its universal FO definability, in all finite structures.

For the existential fragment, one can show directly that existential FO definability of the fixed point over all finite structures implies its definability (by the same existential formula) over all structures, again by use of the finite model property of the $\exists^*\forall^*$ fragment. It is unclear, though, whether also for the universal fragment, universal definability of the fixed point in all finite structures implies its definability over all structures.

3 Universal FO

The formulae of the universal fragment of FO are generated from atomic and negated atomic formulae by conjunction, disjunction and universal quantification.

3.1 Moschovakis normal form

The following normal form for universal formulae $\varphi(X, x)$ that are positive in the second-order variable X is an adaptation of the normal form of [18], Chapter 4B.

Proposition 7 (Moschovakis).
Let $\varphi(X, x)$ positive in X and purely universal. Then there is a formula $\tilde{\varphi}(X, x)$ of the form

$$\tilde{\varphi}(X, x) = \forall \mathbf{y}\ \theta(x, \mathbf{y}) \rightarrow \delta(X, \mathbf{y}) \ ,$$

where θ is quantifier free and does not contain X, and where δ is a disjunction of atoms Xy_j for some $y_j \in \mathbf{y}$

such that

$$\neg\forall x Xx \models \forall x\ \varphi(X,x) \leftrightarrow \tilde{\varphi}(X,x)\ .$$

If φ is purely negative in all non-recursive predicates and in $=$, then θ can be chosen purely positive (in all predicates and in $=$).

Proof. We sketch the key steps in the inductive proof.

For $\varphi = Xz$, let $\tilde{\varphi} := \forall y(y = z \rightarrow Xy)$.

For $\varphi = R\mathbf{z}$, let $\tilde{\varphi} := \forall y\ \neg R\mathbf{z} \rightarrow Xy$. Here equivalence with φ relies on the existence of elements outside X.

The universal quantification step is trivial. The interesting inductive steps are for $\wedge$ and $\vee$:
Consider $\varphi = \varphi_1(X,\mathbf{z}) * \varphi_2(X,\mathbf{z})$, where $* \in \{\wedge,\vee\}$. Assume that $\tilde{\varphi}_i = \forall \mathbf{y}^{(i)}\ \theta_i(\mathbf{x},\mathbf{y}^{(i)}) \rightarrow \delta_i(X,\mathbf{y}^{(i)})$ is as desired for φ_i, w.l.o.g. with disjoint $\mathbf{y}^{(i)}$. Let $\tilde{\varphi}$ be the following, where $\bar{*}$ is the dual of $*$:

$$\forall \mathbf{y}^{(1)}\forall \mathbf{y}^{(2)} \quad \begin{array}{l} \theta_1(\mathbf{z},\mathbf{y}^{(1)})\ \bar{*}\ \theta_2(\mathbf{z},\mathbf{y}^{(2)}) \\ \rightarrow\ \delta_1(X,\mathbf{y}^{(1)}) \vee \delta_2(X,\mathbf{y}^{(2)}) \end{array} .$$

In both cases ($* = \wedge$ or $* = \vee$) it is clear that $\varphi(X,\mathbf{z}) \models \tilde{\varphi}(X,\mathbf{z})$. It remains to establish, that, whenever X is not the full universe, then $\tilde{\varphi}$ implies φ.

Consider first the case of $* = \vee$. We look at a model of ψ, and suppose for instance that $\forall \mathbf{y}^{(1)}\ \theta_1(\mathbf{y}^{(1)}) \rightarrow \delta_1(X,\mathbf{y}^{(1)})$ does not hold true. We therefore find an interpretation for $\mathbf{y}^{(1)}$ such that $\theta_1 \wedge \neg\delta_1$; fixing any such interpretation for $\mathbf{y}^{(1)}$, ψ becomes equivalent to $\forall \mathbf{y}^{(2)}\ \theta_2(\mathbf{y}^{(2)}) \rightarrow \delta_2(X,\mathbf{y}^{(2)})$, as it should.

Consider now the case of $* = \wedge$. Again, we look at a model of ψ, in which there are elements outside X. We need to show that, for instance, this implies that $\theta_1(\mathbf{y}^{(1)}) \rightarrow \delta_1(X,\mathbf{y}^{(1)})$. Instantiate the universally quantified $\mathbf{y}^{(2)}$ in ψ by a tuple consisting of components not in X; this makes δ_2 false. Then ψ implies that $\theta_1(\mathbf{y}^{(1)}) \rightarrow \delta_1(X,\mathbf{y}^{(1)})$, as desired. □

The normal form given in [18] goes further in also eliminating the disjunctions in δ in favour of existential quantification in the prefix; this is not desirable here.

3.2 Limits for decidability

The following is in marked contrast with our main decidability result.

Theorem 8. Bdd *is undecidable for monadic recursion w.r.t. purely universal formulae in which all non-recursive predicates occur only negatively, but equality may occur positively.*

The proof follows a general pattern established in [14] and in [15] for several other undecidable cases of the monadic boundedness problem, via reduction of the tiling problem [7]. A domino system is a finite structure $\mathfrak{D} = (D, R_H, R_V)$ consisting of tile types $d \in D$ with two adjacency relations R_H and R_V that specify when two tile types fit in horizontally or vertically adjacent positions in tiling.

Formally a $\mathfrak{D}$-tiling of $n \times n$ is a homomorphism from the $n \times n$ grid structure $\mathfrak{G}_n$ to $\mathfrak{D}$. Here

$$\begin{array}{rcl} \mathfrak{G}_n & = & (\{0,\ldots,n-1\}^2, H, V) \\ \text{with}\ H & = & \{((i,j),(i+1,j)) \colon i+1, j < n\}, \\ V & = & \{((i,j),(i,j+1)) \colon i, j+1 < n\}. \end{array}$$

Intuitively, a $\mathfrak{D}$-tiling of $n \times n$ corresponds to a placement of tile types on the nodes of the $n \times n$ grid such that horizontally and vertically adjacent tiles respect the adjacency constraints given by R_H and R_V, respectively. We also refer to a corresponding expansion of $\mathfrak{G}_n$ by colours $(P_d)_{d\in D}$ as a $\mathfrak{D}$-tiling of $n \times n$.

Theorem 9 (Berger). *The following problem is undecidable: Given a tiling system $\mathfrak{D}$, decide whether $\mathfrak{D}$ admits tilings of size n for arbitrarily large $n \in \mathbb{N}$.*

We now want to associate with a given $\mathfrak{D}$ a formula $\varphi_{\mathfrak{D}} = \varphi(X,x)$, positive in X, purely universal and with only negative occurrences of the relations H, V (binary) and P_d (unary) for $d \in D$, such that $\varphi_{\mathfrak{D}}$ is unbounded iff $\mathfrak{D}$ admits arbitrarily large tilings. Consider firstly an auxiliary sentence φ_0 which is the conjunction of the following:

$$\forall y \quad {}_{d\neq d'} \neg(P_d y \wedge P_{d'} y)$$

$$\forall y_1 \forall y_2 \neg\ Hy_1y_2 \wedge \quad {}_{(d,d')\notin R_H}(P_d y_1 \wedge P_{d'} y_2)$$

$$\forall y_1 \exists y_2 \neg\ Vy_1y_2 \wedge \quad {}_{(d,d')\notin R_V}(P_d y_1 \wedge P_{d'} y_2)$$

$$\forall y y_1 y_2\ (Hyy_1 \wedge Hyy_2) \rightarrow y_1 = y_2$$

$$\forall y y_1 y_2\ (Vyy_1 \wedge Vyy_2) \rightarrow y_1 = y_2$$

$$\forall y \forall y_1 \forall y_2 \forall z_1 \forall z_2 \quad \begin{array}{r} (Hyy_1 \wedge Vy_1z_1 \wedge Vyy_2 \wedge Hy_2z_2) \\ \rightarrow z_1 = z_2 \end{array}$$

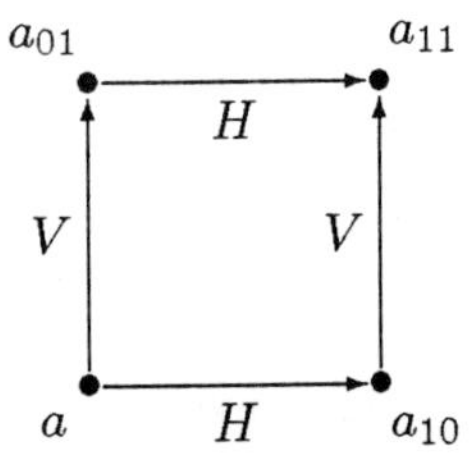

$\varphi = \varphi_{\mathfrak{D}}$ will be of the form $\varphi(X,x) = \varphi_0 \wedge \varphi_1(X,x)$ with static part φ_0 as given above. Clearly φ is unbounded iff φ_1 is unbounded in models of φ_0. Models of φ_0 are H-V-graphs in which H and V are the graphs of partial functions that commute where defined, and in which each node carries at most one colour P_d in such a way that the colours of adjacent nodes respect the tiling constraints.

φ_1 is set up so as to ensure that (in models of φ_0) the recursion on $\varphi_1(X, x)$ has closure ordinal n on $\mathfrak{D}$-tilings of $\mathfrak{G}_n$, and that any structure on which φ_1 has a non-trivial $(n+1)$-st stage, embeds $\mathfrak{G}_n$ and hence establishes the existence of a $\mathfrak{D}$-tiling of $n \times n$.

The formalisation of φ_1 uses the following abbreviations (corresponding to positive quantifier-free definitions):

$$\begin{array}{lcl} \dot{H} & := & (x, y)\colon Hxy \wedge \quad {}_{d \in D} P_d y\}, \\ \dot{V} & := & (x, y)\colon Vxy \wedge \quad {}_{d \in D} P_d y\}. \end{array}$$

$$\begin{array}{lcl} \text{Put } \varphi_1(X, x) := & & \forall y(\dot{H}xy \rightarrow Xy) \\ & \vee & \forall y(\dot{V}xy \rightarrow Xy) \\ & \vee & \forall y \forall z\ (\dot{H}xy \wedge \dot{V}yz) \rightarrow Xz \\ & \vee & \forall y \forall z\ (\dot{V}xy \wedge \dot{H}yz) \rightarrow Xz\ . \end{array}$$

Obviously $\varphi_{\mathfrak{D}} := \varphi_0 \wedge \varphi_1(X, x)$ is purely negative in H, V and the P_d, but uses equality positively (in φ_0).

It is obvious that $\gamma[\varphi_{\mathfrak{D}}, \mathfrak{A}] = n$ for a $\mathfrak{D}$-tiling $\mathfrak{A} = (\mathfrak{G}_n, (P_d))$ of $n \times n$. It remains to show that conversely, unboundedness of $\varphi_{\mathfrak{D}}$ implies that $\mathfrak{D}$ has tilings of arbitrarily large $n \times n$ grids.

Lemma 10. *Let $\mathfrak{A} \models \varphi_0$, $X^i[\mathfrak{A}]$ the stages of $\varphi_{\mathfrak{D}}$ on $\mathfrak{A}$. Let $\dot{\mathfrak{A}}$ be $\mathfrak{A}$ with H and V replaced by $\dot{H}$ and $\dot{V}$, respectively. Let $a \notin X^n[\mathfrak{A}]$. Then there is a homomorphism $h\colon \mathfrak{G}_{n+1} \longrightarrow \dot{\mathfrak{A}}$ with $h(0,0) = a$. It follows that there is a $\mathfrak{D}$-tiling of $\mathfrak{G}_n$ if $\gamma[\varphi_{\mathfrak{D}}, \mathfrak{A}] > n$.*

Proof. The main claim is proved by induction. Note that $a \notin X^n[\mathfrak{A}]$ implies that a has $\dot{H}$-, $\dot{V}$- and $(\dot{V} \circ \dot{H})$- and $(\dot{H} \circ \dot{V})$-successors a_{10}, a_{01}, a_{11} and a'_{11} that are not in $X^{n-1}[\mathfrak{A}]$. φ_0 forces $a_{11} = a'_{11}$. By the inductive hypothesis there are homomorphisms $h_i\colon \mathfrak{G}_n \longrightarrow \dot{\mathfrak{A}}$ with $h_1(0,0) = a_{10}$, $h_2(0,0) = a_{01}$ and $h_3(0,0) = a_{11}$.

φ_0 now also forces $h_1(0,1)$ (the V-successor of a_{10}) to be the same as $h_2(1,0)$ (the H-successor of a_{01}) and $h_3(0,0)$. Similarly, $h_1(i, j+1) = h_2(i+1, j) = h_3(i,j)$ for all i, j where defined. But this implies that these three homomorphisms can be combined consistently to obtain the desired homomorphism h by putting $h(0,0) := a$, $h(i+1, j) := h_1(i,j)$, $h(i, j+1) := h_2(i,j)$ and $h(i+1, j+1) := h_3(i,j)$ (whichever righthand sides are defined). □

Instead of equality one can introduce an extra binary relation $\approx$ which, by purely universal axioms, can be forced to be a congruence w.r.t. H, V and the P_d. However, these axioms will necessarily involve $\approx$ and the predicates H, V, P_d in both polarities. In other words, we may trade the restriction on polarities for avoidance of equality.

Theorem 11. Bdd *is undecidable for monadic recursion w.r.t. purely universal formulae without equality.*

4 Boundedness in modal logic

We regard modal logic as a fragment $\mathrm{ML} \subseteq \mathrm{FO}$ in the usual way. In a vocabulary σ consisting of binary relations E_i and unary predicates P_j, the formulae of $\mathrm{ML}[\sigma]$ are generated as the closure of the atomic formulae P_j under booleans and modal quantification $\langle E_i \rangle$ and $[E_i]$. In FO terms, $(\langle E_i \rangle \varphi)(x)$ is $\exists y\ E_i xy \wedge \varphi(y)$, and dually $([E_i]\varphi)(x)$ is $\forall y\ E_i xy \rightarrow \varphi(y)$.

We consider admissible systems in a tuple of monadic recursive predicates $\bar{X}$. The modal version of the Barwise–Moschovakis theorem provides the means to decide boundedness, ultimately via reduction to the MSO theory of the ω-branching tree, which is decidable by Rabin's well known theorem. We outline the chain of model theoretic arguments underlying this reduction.

Due to bisimulation invariance and the Löwenheim–Skolem theorem, it suffices to consider the behaviour of systems in ML over countable tree structures.

Let σ be a relational type consisting of binary predicates E_i (for labelled edges) and unary predicates P_j (for colouring or labelling vertices). A *tree structure* of type σ is a rooted directed tree w.r.t. $E := \quad E_i$ with disjoint E_i (no multiple edge labels).

For a tree structure $\mathfrak{A}, \lambda$ with root λ and $\ell \geqslant 1$ we let $A{\restriction}\ell \subseteq A$ denote the initial segment consisting of all nodes up to depth ℓ. Some related terminology:

(a) $A' \subseteq A$ is called *initial* in $\mathfrak{A}, \lambda$ if it contains the root λ and is connected.

(b) $A' \subseteq A$ is called *bounded* if $A' \subseteq A{\restriction}\ell$ for some $\ell \in \mathbb{N}$.

(c) $A' \subseteq A$ is called *path-finite* if it contains no infinite paths.

Note that, while properties (a) and (c) are MSO definable, property (b) is not.

Definition 12. Call a formula $\psi(x) \in \mathrm{MSO}$ *tree-local* if there is some $\ell \in \mathbb{N}$ such that for all countable tree structures $\mathfrak{A}$ and for all initial subsets $A' \supseteq A{\restriction}\ell$:

$$\mathfrak{A}, \lambda \models \psi \quad \Leftrightarrow \quad \mathfrak{A}{\restriction}A', \lambda \models \psi.$$

The following is a straightforward consequence of the combination of the modal variant of Theorem 6 and the expressive completeness of ML for bisimulation invariant properties that are ℓ-local for some ℓ [6, 20].

Lemma 13. *The following are equivalent for admissible systems $\bar{\varphi} \in \mathrm{ML}$:*

(i) *$\bar{\varphi}$ bounded.*

(ii) *$\bar{\varphi}^{\infty}$ tree-local.*

(iii) *$\bar{\varphi}^{\infty}$ ML-definable.*

Theorem 14. $\mathsf{Bdd}(\mathrm{ML})$ *is decidable via reduction to the* MSO *theory of the ω-branching tree $\mathfrak{T}_{\omega}$. Similarly for* *boundedness of modal systems over* MSO *definable classes of trees.*

The proof of correctness for the intended reduction involves a regular version of König's lemma that allows us to "apply König's lemma" in the context of the ω-branching tree, its infinite branching notwithstanding.

A *regular* expansion of $\mathfrak{T}_\omega$ is one that realises only finitely many isomorphism types of subtrees.

Lemma 15. *The following are equivalent for initial subsets D in regular expansions $(\mathfrak{T}_\omega, D)$:*

(i) *D is path-finite.*

(ii) *D is bounded.*

Proof. For (i) $\Rightarrow$ (ii) one shows that one can inductively choose an infinite path within an unbounded D. Starting from the root, select a successor node in D such that D is unbounded in restriction to the subtree rooted in that node. This is always possible, as there are only finitely many isomorphism types of subtrees rooted in the available successor nodes. So D cannot be bounded in each of those without being bounded in the father node. □

Let

$$\psi(Z) := \forall \bar{I}\ \psi_0(\bar{I}) \rightarrow \quad_{i} \left(\varphi(\bar{I})_i^{\infty} \leftrightarrow \varphi(\bar{I}{\restriction}Z)_i^{\infty}\right)$$

be an MSO formula that says (of an initial subset Z of $\mathfrak{T}_\omega$) that for all interpretations of countable tree structures of type suitable for $\bar{\varphi}$, the evaluation of the fixed point produces the same outcome at the root whether $\bar{\varphi}$ is evaluated in the whole structure or in the initial substructure induced on Z. Here $\psi_0(\bar{I})$ collects the obvious FO conditions on unary predicates $\bar{I}$ to encode an interpretation of a countable tree structure of the appropriate type within $\mathfrak{T}_\omega$ in the natural way. The intended interpretations are such that all nodes at depth ℓ in the interpreted tree are represented by depth ℓ nodes in $\mathfrak{T}_\omega$. This compatibility with depth is crucial for the reduction; it is for this reason that we work with the ω-branching tree rather than the binary tree.

Lemma 16. *The following are equivalent:*

(i) *$\bar{\varphi}$ bounded.*

(ii) *for some $\ell \in \mathbb{N}$ and for $D = T_\omega{\restriction}\ell$: $\mathfrak{T}_\omega, \lambda \models \psi[D]$.*

(iii) *$\mathfrak{T}_\omega, \lambda \models \exists Z\ Z$ initial and path-finite $\wedge\ \psi(Z)$.*

(iv) *there is some regular expansion $(\mathfrak{T}_\omega, D)$ of $\mathfrak{T}_\omega$ with an initial, path-finite D, such that $\mathfrak{T}_\omega, \lambda \models \psi[D]$.*

Note that (iii) is decidable, as part of the MSO theory of $\mathfrak{T}_\omega$, thus proving the theorem.

Proof. (i) $\Rightarrow$ (ii) $\Rightarrow$ (iii) are clear. (iii) $\Rightarrow$ (iv) is a well known fact about MSO: any MSO formula satisfiable in some tree model has a regular tree model. (iv) $\Rightarrow$ (i) follows with Lemma 15. □

5 From modal to universal boundedness

Consider boundedness for an equality-free universal formula $\varphi(X, x)$, positive in X, and with all other predicates of one polarity only. W.l.o.g. assume that φ is in Moschovakis normal form (see Proposition 7) and purely negative in all predicates other than X.

$$\begin{aligned}\varphi(X, x) &= \forall \mathbf{y} \quad {}_{i}\,\theta_i(x, \mathbf{y}) \rightarrow \delta(X, \mathbf{y}) \\ &\equiv \quad {}_{i=1}^{k} \forall \mathbf{y}\ \theta_i(x, \mathbf{y}) \rightarrow \delta(X, \mathbf{y}) \ ,\end{aligned}$$

the θ_i conjunctions of relational atoms (and not involving X), δ a disjunction over X-atoms in variables $\mathbf{y}$.

Intuitively we treat the θ_i as if they were relational guards (in the sense of the guarded fragment, [3]). To this end, we use new relation symbols R_i, whose intended interpretations are the relations defined by θ_i. We may also assume w.l.o.g. that all these R_i have the same arity $m + 1$ where m is the arity of $\mathbf{y}$. Let τ be the original vocabulary of φ, τ^θ its extension by these R_i.

With τ-structures $\mathfrak{A}$ we associate corresponding expansions to τ^θ-structures $\mathfrak{A}^\theta := (\mathfrak{A}, \bar{R})$ by R_i defined by θ_i according to

$$R_i^{\mathfrak{A}} := \{\mathbf{a} = (a_0, a_1, \ldots, a_m) \in A^{m+1} : \mathfrak{A} \models \theta_i[\mathbf{a}]\}.$$

Over these expansions

$$\varphi(X, x) \equiv \quad {}_{i=1}^{k} \forall \mathbf{y}\ R_i x \mathbf{y} \rightarrow \delta(X, \mathbf{y}) \ .$$

5.1 Unfoldings and tree representations

The following technique of switching between tree representations and relational structures is similar to the one used in [10].

Let the vocabulary of φ be τ, and τ^θ its extension by the R_i as introduced above. For tree representations of τ^θ structures we use a vocabulary $\sigma[\tau^\theta]$ consisting of the following unary and binary predicates:

- for each τ^θ-structure $\mathfrak{B}$ of size up to $m + 1$ and an enumeration of these elements as $\mathbf{b} = (b_0, \ldots, b_m)$, a unary predicate P_β associated with the isomorphism type β of $(\mathfrak{B}, \mathbf{b})$ (or, equivalently, the quantifier-free type of $\mathbf{b}$ in $\mathfrak{B}$);
- for each $\rho \subseteq \{0, \ldots, m\} \times \{0, \ldots, m\}$ that is the graph of a partial function, a binary relation E_ρ. We include $\rho = \emptyset$.

With $\mathfrak{A}^\theta$ and a suitable tuple $\mathbf{a} \in A^{m+1}$ we associate

- a transition system $K(\mathfrak{A}^\theta)$ of type $\sigma[\tau^\theta]$, with distinguished node $\lambda = \mathbf{a}$,
- the tree unfolding $T(\mathfrak{A}^\theta, \mathbf{a})$ of $K(\mathfrak{A}^\theta)$, which is a $\sigma[\tau^\theta]$ tree structure with root $\lambda = \mathbf{a}$.

Conversely, we associate with every $\sigma[\tau^\theta]$ tree structure T satisfying some weak FO definable consistency conditions outlined below:

- a tree-like τ^θ-structure $\mathfrak{B}(T)$,
  of which T is a tree decomposition.

In particular, the tree unfolding of $\mathfrak{A}^\theta$ from $\mathbf{a}$:

- $(\mathfrak{A}^\theta)^* := \mathfrak{B}(T(\mathfrak{A}^\theta, \mathbf{a}))$.

The transition system: The nodes of $K(\mathfrak{A}^\theta)$ are those $(m+1)$-tuples of $\mathfrak{A}^\theta$ that are in one of the relations R_i (i.e., that satisfy one of the θ_i), plus all $(m+1)$-tuples of the form $(a, \dots, a)$ representing single elements. A node $\mathbf{a}$ is in P_β, if β is the quantifier-free type of $\mathbf{a}$ in $\mathfrak{A}^\theta$. Transitions are labelled with labels ρ to indicate identities between components of different tuples. $(\mathbf{a}, \mathbf{a}') \in E_\rho$ for $\rho = \{(i,j) \colon a_i = a'_j\}$. Note that $\rho = \emptyset$ is admitted, and applies to any two nodes corresponding to disjoint tuples; between any two nodes of $K(\mathfrak{A}^\theta)$ there is a transition.

The trees: $T(\mathfrak{A}^\theta, \mathbf{a})$ is the usual bisimilar unfolding of $K(\mathfrak{A}^\theta)$ into a tree structure, rooted in node $\mathbf{a}$.

Let $C^* = \{T(\mathfrak{A}^\theta, \mathbf{a}) \colon \mathfrak{A}$ a τ-structure $\}$ be the class of all $\sigma[\tau^\theta]$ trees obtained in this manner.

All $T \in C^*$ satisfy some local and FO definable consistency criteria Cons related to the node labels and transition labels. These enforce, for $(u, u') \in E_\rho$, $u \in P_\beta$, $u' \in P_{\beta'}$, the obvious local compatibility conditions between the quantifier-free types β and β' w.r.t. the identification encoded in ρ. For instance, for ρ such that $i_1, \dots, i_k \in \mathrm{dom}(\rho)$, the following is in Cons:

$$\forall y_1 \forall y_2 \; E_\rho y_1 y_2 \longrightarrow \quad \bigwedge \Phi(y_1, y_2) \ ,$$

where Φ is the set of all formulae $P_\beta y_1 \wedge P_{\beta'} y_2$ for pairs β, β' for which $\rho \colon \beta \restriction \{i_1, \dots, i_k\} \simeq \beta' \restriction \{\rho(i_1), \dots, \rho(i_k)\}$.

The class C^*, however, is not even MSO definable. A crucial property of $T \in C^*$ is their homogeneity which stems from the fact that in $K(\mathfrak{A}^\theta)$ every node is reachable from every other one. For the tree unfolding this implies that the sibling subtrees at any two nodes are set-wise isomorphic.

Relational structures from trees: With every tree $T \models$ Cons associate a relational structure $\mathfrak{B}(T)$ as follows. Each node $u \in P_\beta$ of T gives rise to a relational structure $\mathfrak{B}_u$ of size up to $(m+1)$ according to the isomorphism type encoded in β. $\mathfrak{B}(T)$ is obtained from the disjoint union of the $\mathfrak{B}_u$ for $u \in T$, with identifications according to ρ between $\mathfrak{B}_u$ and $\mathfrak{B}_{u'}$ for $(u, u') \in E_\rho$. More formally, let $(u, i) \in T \times \{0, \dots, m\}$ be the element of the disjoint union of the $\mathfrak{B}_u$ that corresponds to the i-th element of $\mathfrak{B}_u$. Let then $\approx$ be the symmetric and transitive closure of the binary relation consisting of the pairs $((u,i),(u',i'))$ for $(u,u') \in E_\rho$ and $(i,i') \in \rho$. The universe of $\mathfrak{B}(T)$ is the quotient of the disjoint union of the $\mathfrak{B}_u$ w.r.t. $\approx$. Cons is such that $\approx$ is compatible with the relational information in the individual $\mathfrak{B}_u$.

It is important to note that the interpretation of the relations R_i over $\mathfrak{B}(T)$ is *not* in general the one that would be defined by the θ_i over the τ-reduct of $\mathfrak{B}(T)$. In general one only has that

$$(*) \quad \mathfrak{B}(T) \models \forall \mathbf{z}(R_i \mathbf{z} \rightarrow \theta_i(\mathbf{z})),$$

due to positivity of the θ_i and the construction of $\mathfrak{B}(T)$.

Remark: T provides a tree decomposition of width m of $\mathfrak{B}(T)$; the patches of this tree decomposition are guarded in the extended vocabulary τ^θ.

For a tree unfolding $(\mathfrak{A}^\theta)^* := \mathfrak{B}(T(\mathfrak{A}^\theta, \mathbf{a}))$ let $\pi \colon (\mathfrak{A}^\theta)^* \rightarrow \mathfrak{A}^\theta$ be the natural projection.

We denote as $\mathfrak{A}^*$ the τ-reduct of $(\mathfrak{A}^\theta)^*$.

Lemma 17. *$\pi \colon (\mathfrak{A}^\theta)^* \rightarrow \mathfrak{A}^\theta$ preserves the stages of the fixed point generation for φ in the sense that for all α: $X^\alpha[\mathfrak{A}^*] = \pi^{-1}\ X^\alpha[\mathfrak{A}]$.*

Proof. The claim is clear for $\alpha = 0$; also limit stages are trivial. So consider a successor step. Let $\pi(c^*) = c$. We show that

$$\mathfrak{A}^* \models \varphi[X^\alpha[\mathfrak{A}^*], c^*] \quad \text{iff} \quad \mathfrak{A} \models \varphi[X^\alpha[\mathfrak{A}], c],$$

assuming that $X^\alpha[\mathfrak{A}^*] = \pi^{-1}\ X^\alpha[\mathfrak{A}]$.

Let $\mathfrak{A}^* \models \varphi[X^\alpha, c^*]$ and let $\mathfrak{A} \models \theta_i[c, \mathbf{c}]$. By construction of $\mathfrak{A}^*$ there is $\mathbf{c}^* \in \pi^{-1}(\mathbf{c})$ such that $\mathfrak{A}^* \models \theta_i[c^*, \mathbf{c}^*]$. So $\mathfrak{A}^* \models \delta[X^\alpha, \mathbf{c}^*]$ and hence $\mathfrak{A} \models \delta[X^\alpha, \mathbf{c}]$. It follows that $\mathfrak{A} \models \varphi[X^\alpha, c]$.

Conversely, let $\mathfrak{A} \models \varphi[X^\alpha, c]$ and $\mathfrak{A}^* \models \theta_i[c^*, \mathbf{c}^*]$. Then $\mathfrak{A} \models \theta_i[c, \mathbf{c}]$ for $\mathbf{c} := \pi(\mathbf{c}^*)$, as π is a homomorphism. It follows that $\mathfrak{A} \models \delta[X^\alpha, \mathbf{c}]$ and thus $\mathfrak{A}^* \models \delta[X^\alpha, \mathbf{c}^*]$ by the inductive hypothesis. So $\mathfrak{A}^* \models \varphi[X^\alpha, c^*]$. □

5.2 A translation into modal logic

We want to capture the generation of the least fixed point of φ over $\mathfrak{A}^*$ in terms of the associated tree $T(\mathfrak{A}^\theta, \mathbf{a})$. A modal system $\bar{\varphi}(\bar{X})$ for $\bar{X} = (X_0, \dots, X_m)$ can serve this purpose. A system rather than recursion in a single predicate variable X is necessary, as each node in the tree stands for an $(m+1)$-tuple. The intended meaning of $u \in X_j^\alpha$ will be that the j-th component of this tuple is in X^α. Correspondingly, $\bar{\varphi}$ is of the form $\bar{\varphi}(\bar{X}) = \varphi_0(\bar{X}), \dots, \varphi_m(\bar{X})$.

Recall that $\varphi(X, x)$ is the conjunction of the following, for $1 \leqslant i \leqslant k$:

$$\forall y_1 \dots \forall y_m \; \theta_i(x, y_1, \dots, y_m) \rightarrow \delta(X, y_1, \dots, y_m) \ .$$

$\varphi_j(\bar{X})$ has, for each $1 \leqslant i \leqslant k$ and each quantifier-free τ^θ-type $\beta = \beta(x_0, \dots, x_m)$ such that $\beta \models \theta_i$ the conjunct

$$\underset{\rho(j)=0}{[E_\rho]}\ P_\beta \rightarrow \delta(\bar{X})$$

where $\delta(\bar{X})$ is the disjunction of those X_s for which Xy_s is a disjunct in $\delta(X, \mathbf{y})$.

The following correspondence between φ and $\bar{\varphi}$ is based on a correspondence between the individual stages, using Lemma 17.

Recall that $\mathcal{C}^*$ is the class of tree structures $T(\mathfrak{A}^\theta, \mathbf{a})$ that represent unfoldings $\mathfrak{A}^*$ of τ-structures $\mathfrak{A}$. With a node u of $T(\mathfrak{A}^\theta, \mathbf{a})$ we associate the tuple $\mathbf{b} = \pi(u) \in A^{m+1}$: this is the tuple $\mathbf{b}$ which, as an element of $K(\mathfrak{A}^\theta)$, gives rise to u in the tree unfolding, or the last node in the path u. We also denote the j-th component b_j of this tuple $\mathbf{b}$ by $\pi_j(u)$, thus regarding π_j as a map $\pi_j \colon T(\mathfrak{A}^\theta, \mathbf{a}) \rightarrow A$ for $j \leqslant m$.

Lemma 18. *Consider the stages $(X_j^\alpha)_{j \leqslant m}$ of the fixed point generation for system $\bar{\varphi}$ over $T(\mathfrak{A}^\theta, \mathbf{a})$ and the stages X^α in the generation of the fixed point for φ over $\mathfrak{A}$. Then, for all α, the (X_j^α) represent X^α:*

$$X_j^\alpha = \ u \in T(\mathfrak{A}^\theta, \mathbf{a}) \colon \pi_j(u) \in X^\alpha \ .$$

It follows that φ is bounded iff $\bar{\varphi}$ is bounded over $\mathcal{C}^*$.

Proof. As $\bar{\varphi}$ is modal, and since $T(\mathfrak{A}^\theta, \mathbf{a}) = T(K(\mathfrak{A}^\theta), \mathbf{a})$ is bisimilar to $K(\mathfrak{A}^\theta)$, we may prove the correspondence between φ on $\mathfrak{A}$ and $\bar{\varphi}$ on $K(\mathfrak{A}^\theta)$, where is becomes:

$$X_j^\alpha = \ \mathbf{b} \in K(\mathfrak{A}^\theta) \colon b_j \in X^\alpha \ .$$

We write K for $K = K(\mathfrak{A}^\theta)$ for the rest of this proof.

The claim for the stages $(X_j^\alpha)_{j \leqslant m}$ of $\bar{\varphi}$ over K and the stages X^α of φ over $\mathfrak{A}$ is proved by induction on α. Consider the successor step from α to $\alpha + 1$ and assume the claim for α.

Let $\mathbf{b} \in X_j^{\alpha+1}$, i.e., $K, \mathbf{b} \models \varphi_j[\bar{X}^\alpha]$. To show that $b_j \in X^{\alpha+1}$ in $\mathfrak{A}$, we need to establish that, for all $\mathbf{b}' = (b_j, b_1', \dots, b_m')$ such that $\mathfrak{A} \models \theta_i[\mathbf{b}']$ also $\mathfrak{A}, \mathbf{b}' \models \delta[X^\alpha]$. $\mathfrak{A} \models \theta_i[\mathbf{b}']$ implies that $\mathbf{b}'$ is a node of K, contained in some P_β for which $\beta \models \theta_i$, and $(\mathbf{b}, \mathbf{b}') \in E_\rho$ for some ρ with $\rho(j) = 0$. For these β and ρ, therefore, φ_j has the conjunct $[E_\rho](P_\beta \rightarrow \delta(\bar{X}))$, and $K, \mathbf{b} \models \varphi_j[\bar{X}^\alpha]$ implies that $K, \mathbf{b}' \models \delta[\bar{X}^\alpha]$. It follows that $\mathfrak{A}, \mathbf{b}' \models \delta[X^\alpha]$.

Conversely, let $\mathbf{b} \in K$ and $b_j \in X^{\alpha+1}$. Then $\mathfrak{A} \models \varphi[X^\alpha, b_j]$ implies that $\mathbf{b} \in X_j^{\alpha+1}$ as follows. Consider a conjunct $[E_\rho](P_\beta \rightarrow \delta(\bar{X}))$ in φ_j, where $\beta \models \theta_i$. Then $(\mathbf{b}, \mathbf{b}') \in E_\rho$ implies that $b_j = b_0'$, and $\mathbf{b}' \in P_\beta$ implies that $\mathfrak{A} \models \theta_i[\mathbf{b}']$. Therefore, $\mathfrak{A} \models \varphi[X^\alpha, b_j]$ implies, as $\mathfrak{A} \models \theta_i[\mathbf{b}']$, that $\mathfrak{A} \models \delta[X^\alpha, \mathbf{b}']$. Therefore $K, \mathbf{b}' \models \delta[\bar{X}^\alpha]$. We thus get $K, \mathbf{b} \models \varphi_j[\bar{X}^\alpha]$ and $\mathbf{b} \in X_j^{\alpha+1}$. □

This reduction, however, does not yield decidability directly as the class $\mathcal{C}^*$ of relevant tree structures is *not* MSO definable. We must therefore extend the class $\mathcal{C}^*$ of actual tree representations to a wider class $\mathcal{C} \supseteq \mathcal{C}^*$ that is MSO definable and still supports a correspondence as in the lemma. The lemma implies

$$\varphi \text{ unbounded} \quad \Rightarrow \quad \bar{\varphi} \text{ unbounded over } \mathcal{C}$$

for any $\mathcal{C} \supseteq \mathcal{C}^*$. Crucial for the choice of $\mathcal{C}$ is that it is tight enough to make the converse true as well.

5.3 Monotonicity and admissible trees

Consider an arbitrary tree $T \models \text{Cons}$ and the associated τ-structure $\mathfrak{B}(T)$ represented by T. It is clear from the construction of $\mathfrak{B}(T)$ that there is a translation from MSO over $\mathfrak{B}(T)$ into MSO over T. Essentially this amounts to a translation $\psi \mapsto \hat{\psi}$ such that $\mathfrak{B}(T) \models \psi \Leftrightarrow T \models \hat{\psi}$. Some care has to be taken w.r.t. first- and second-order free variables, though. Consider for instance a formula $\psi(X, x)$. An instantiation by $P \subseteq \mathfrak{B}(T)$ is represented in T by a tuple $\bar{P} = (P_0, \dots, P_m)$ of subsets of T, where

$$P_j = \{u \in T \colon u_j \in P\} \subseteq T,$$

u_j the j-th component of the tuple represented in $\mathfrak{B}_u$. Similarly, w.r.t. its first-order variable x, ψ translates into a tuple of formulae $\hat{\psi}_j$ such that $\hat{\psi}_j$ expresses of $u \in T$ whether ψ is true of u_j.

So in this case (with just one free variable of each type), $\hat{\psi}$ is of the form $\ \hat{\psi}_j(\bar{X}, y)\ _{0 \leqslant j \leqslant m}$ and such that for all j:

$$\mathfrak{B}(T) \models \psi[P, u_j] \quad \text{iff} \quad T \models \hat{\psi}_j[\bar{P}, u].$$

The availability of MSO quantification in this translation is essential even for the translation of FO formulae ψ, since the set of nodes of T in which a given element of $\mathfrak{B}(T)$ is represented can only be defined in MSO. This is because the same element can be carried along (E_ρ)-paths of arbitrary lengths. For instance, in order to check whether $\psi(x) = \exists y Rxy$ is true of some x, which is represented as the i-th component of $u \in T$, $\hat{\psi}_i$ needs to involve checking all nodes u' reachable from u on paths labelled $\rho_1 \dots \rho_k$ such that $i \in \text{dom}(\rho_k \circ \dots \circ \rho_1)$.

Lemma 19. *There is an effective translation of $\varphi(X, x)$ into $(\hat{\varphi}_j(\bar{X}, x))_{0 \leqslant j \leqslant m}$ such that for all $P \subseteq \mathfrak{B}(T)$, represented by $\bar{P}$ over T, and for $0 \leqslant j \leqslant m$:*

$$\mathfrak{B}(T) \models \varphi[P, u_j] \quad \textit{iff} \quad T \models \hat{\varphi}_j[\bar{P}, u].$$

Similarly, for the fixed points:

$$\mathfrak{B}(T) \models \varphi^\infty[u_j] \quad \textit{iff} \quad T \models (\hat{\varphi})_j^\infty[u].$$

Due to (negative) monotonicity of φ in the non-recursive predicates, the evaluation of the fixed point w.r.t. $\bar{\varphi}$ in T will in general result in an overestimate for the fixed point of φ over $\mathfrak{B}(T)$. More generally, for any $P \subseteq \mathfrak{B}(T)$ and its representation $\bar{P}$ over T, by $(*)$ in section 5.1,

$$(**) \quad T \models \forall x \; \hat{\varphi}_j(\bar{X}, x) \rightarrow (\bar{\varphi})_j(\bar{X}, x) \; .$$

Definition 20. Call a tree T *admissible for* φ if T is consistent (cf. local FO conditions Cons) and $\hat{\varphi}_j^\infty = \bar{\varphi}_j^\infty$ on T for $j = 0, \ldots, m$. Let C_φ be the class of trees that are admissible for φ.

Observation 21. C_φ *is* MSO *definable.*

Lemma 22. φ *is bounded iff* $\bar{\varphi}$ *is bounded over* C_φ.

Proof. $C_\varphi \supseteq C^*$ follows from Lemma 18. The tree structure $T(\mathfrak{A}^\theta, \mathrm{a})$ underlying $\mathfrak{A}^*$ provides a faithful representation of the fixed point generation of φ (over $\mathfrak{A}$ or $\mathfrak{A}^*$, see Lemma 17) in terms of $\bar{\varphi}$. It follows that $\bar{\varphi}$ is unbounded over C_φ if φ is unbounded.

Consider φ that is bounded by $n \in \mathbb{N}$. By the definition of C_φ, the results of the fixed points w.r.t. $\bar{\varphi}$ and the faithful translation $\hat{\varphi}$ of φ on $T \in C_\varphi$ are the same. By monotonicity $(**)$, $\bar{\varphi}$ can only *over*estimate individual stages, which means that $\gamma[\bar{\varphi}, T] \leqslant \gamma[\hat{\varphi}, T] = \gamma[\varphi, \mathfrak{B}(T)] \leqslant n$. So $\bar{\varphi}$ is bounded over C_φ. □

This finishes the proof of the main theorem, since boundedness of the modal system $\bar{\varphi}$ over the MSO definable class C_φ is decidable by Theorem 14.

6 Summary

Decidability of $\mathsf{Bdd}(\mathcal{F}(\forall, -))$ has been shown by model theoretic methods, involving a reduction to the boundedness problem for modal systems over some suitable MSO definable class of trees. Both the modal system and the class over which its boundedness is checked depend on the input formula $\varphi(X, x) \in \mathcal{F}(\forall, -)$, and the ultimate target in the reduction is a satisfiability issue in the MSO theory of the ω-branching tree.

As a result of this approach we cannot expect to extract good complexity bounds. The complexity of $\mathsf{Bdd}(\mathcal{F}(\forall, -))$ remains to be determined.

Applicability of the reduction seems to depend, in a rather subtle way, on the very special monotonicity properties involved in universal quantifications in which the only role that the (exclusively negative) occurrences of non-recursive predicates play is that of restricting the scope of the universal quantifiers, as in universal guarded quantification.

Among the obvious ramifications, therefore, that can be treated in an analogous fashion are systems of $\mathcal{F}(\forall, -)$ formulae in monadic recursive predicates, and universal formulae of the guarded fragment in arbitrary arities.

It remains open whether binary purely universal recursion – with otherwise the same constraints on polarities and equality – has a decidable boundedness problem.

The present investigation covers recursion in monadic recursive predicates (or higher arity but then guarded universal rather than arbitrary universal quantification would seem to be essential).

In the wider picture, major open issues concern the boundedness problem for the full guarded fragment, as well as the monadic boundedness problem for larger fragments or all of FO on the class of structures of tree-width k, for fixed k. In both cases, suitable reductions to the MSO theory of trees could possibly provide a route to decidability proofs.

References

[1] S. Abiteboul, R. Hull, and V. Vianu. *Foundations of Databases.* Addison-Wesley, 1995.

[2] M. Ajtai and Y. Gurevich. Datalog vs. first-order logic. *Journal of Computer and System Sciences*, 49, pages 562–588, 1994.

[3] H. Andréka, J. van Benthem, and I. Németi. Modal languages and bounded fragments of predicate logic. *Journal of Philosophical Logic*, 27, pages 217–274, 1998.

[4] A. Atserias, A. Dawar, and P. Kolaitis. On preservation under homomorphisms and unions of conjunctive queries. In *Proc. 23rd Symp. on Principles of Database Systems*, pages 319–329, 2004.

[5] J. Barwise and Y. Moschovakis. Global inductive definability. *Journal of Symbolic Logic*, 43(3), pages 521–534, 1978.

[6] J. van Benthem. *Modal Logic and Classical Logic.* Bibliopolis, Naples, 1985.

[7] R. Berger. *The Undecidability of the Domino Problem*, volume 66 of *Memoirs of the AMS.* American Mathematical Society, 1966.

[8] E. Börger, E. Grädel, and Y. Gurevich. *The Classical Decision Problem.* Springer-Verlag, 1997.

[9] S. Cosmadakis, H. Gaifman, P. Kanellakis, and M. Vardi. Decidable optimization problems for database logic programs. In *Proc. 20th ACM Symp. on Theory of Computing*, pages 477–490, 1988.

[10] E. Grädel, C. Hirsch, and M. Otto. Back and forth between guarded and modal logics. *ACM Transactions on Computational Logic*, 3, pages 418–463, 2002.

[11] H. Gaifman, H. Mairson, Y. Sagiv, and M. Vardi. Undecidable optimization problems for database logic problems. *Journal of the ACM*, 40(3), pages 683–713, 1993.

[12] G. Hillebrand, P. Kanellakis, H. Mairson, and M. Vardi. Undecidable boundedness problems for datalog programs. *Journal of Logic Programming*, 25(2), pages 163–190, 1995.

[13] P. Kanellakis. *Elements of Relational Database Theory*. In J. van Leeuwen, editor, *Handbook of Theoretical Computer Science*, volume B, pages 1073–1157. MIT Press/Elsevier, 1990.

[14] P. Kolaitis and M. Otto. On the boundedness problem for two-variable first-order logic. In *Proc. 13th IEEE Symp. on Logic in Computer Science*, pages 513–524, 1998.

[15] P. Kolaitis and M. Otto. On the boundedness problem for fragments of first-order logic: Undecidability results. *unpublished draft*.

[16] P. Kolaitis and C. Papadimitriou. Some computational aspects of circumscription. *Journal of the ACM*, 37, pages 1–14, 1990.

[17] J. McCarthy. Circumscription - a form of nonmonotonic reasoning. *Artificial Intelligence*, 13, pages 27–39, 1980.

[18] Y. Moschovakis. *Elementary Induction on Abstract Structures*. North Holland, 1974.

[19] M. Otto. Eliminating recursion in the μ-calculus. In *Proc. 16th Symp. on Theoretical Aspects of Computer Science*, volume 1563 of LNCS, pages 531–540, 1999.

[20] M. Otto. Modal and guarded characterisation theorems over finite transition systems. *Annals of Pure and Applied Logic*, 130, pages 173–205, 2004.

[21] B. Rossmann. Existential positive types and preservation under homomorphisms. In *Proc. 20th IEEE Symp. on Logic in Computer*, pages 467–476, 2005.

Session 2:
Concurrency

A Congruence Rule Format for Name-Passing Process Calculi from Mathematical Structural Operational Semantics

(Extended Abstract)

Marcelo Fiore* and Sam Staton†
Computer Laboratory, University of Cambridge

Abstract

We introduce a mathematical structural operational semantics that yields a congruence result for bisimilarity and is suitable for investigating rule formats for name-passing systems. Indeed, we instantiate this general abstract model theory in a framework of nominal sets and extract from it a GSOS-like rule format for name-passing process calculi for which the associated notion of behavioural equivalence — given by a form of open bisimilarity — is a congruence.

Introduction

A significant strand of research in semantics concerns defining and establishing properties of formats for operational rules [2]. By moving away from a particular syntax and semantics one can simultaneously study a whole class of calculi, becoming instead concerned with the intrinsic nature of the kinds of system that the formats allow.

In this vein, the present work provides an analysis of the congruence properties of bisimilarity for name-passing systems, with the π-calculus [13] being the paradigmatic example. Specifically we ask: What is a name-passing process calculus, and when is its behavioural equivalence a congruence? As we proceed to explain, we tackle these questions from a model-theoretic perspective, merging a series of strands in semantics research.

Background. A starting point for models of the π-calculus is the work of Fiore, Moggi and Sangiorgi [6] and of Stark [18], where a domain equation is solved in a functor category $\mathcal{D}^{\mathbb{I}}$, for a category of domains $\mathcal{D}$. The crucial ingredient of this semantic universe is that it is parameterised by finite sets of names (intuitively those available to a process at any one time) subject to the mode of variation given by injective renamings, so that the model embodies the well-known invariance property of bisimilarity under injective renaming.

An abstract treatment of the GSOS rule format and of bisimilarity congruences was later provided by the mathematical operational semantics of Turi and Plotkin [20]. Given a model $(\mathcal{M}, \Sigma, B)$ as follows

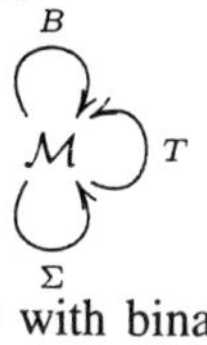

(1)

where $\mathcal{M}$ is a category with binary products, Σ is a signature endofunctor with free term monad T and B is a behaviour endofunctor, they introduced natural transformations of the form

$$\Sigma\big((-) \times B(-)\big) \Longrightarrow BT(-) : \mathcal{M} \to \mathcal{M} \qquad (2)$$

as an abstract notion of operational rule, explaining how such rules induce liftings of the monad T to the category of B-coalgebras by structural recursion and giving conditions under which this yields a compositional semantics. In particular, when the monad T is freely generated by an algebraic signature Σ on the universe of sets, they established that a family of rules in the GSOS format [4] for a first-order process calculus corresponds to a natural transformation as in (2) where $B(-) = \mathcal{P}_{\mathrm{f}}(-)^A$, for $\mathcal{P}_{\mathrm{f}}$ the covariant finite powerset functor and A a set of actions.

The first step needed to put name-passing systems within this framework was to give an algebraic treatment of binding operators. This, amongst other things, was achieved by Fiore, Plotkin and Turi [7] by shifting from the universe of sets to the universe $\mathbf{Set}^{\mathbb{F}}$ of sets parameterised by finite sets of variables (intuitively those that may be free in a term) subject to the mode of variation given by arbitrary variable renamings, so that the model embodies the well-known properties of substitution.

Thus in this model-theoretic study of name-passing process calculi two different, but closely related, natural semantic universes arise: a category $\mathcal{M} = \mathbf{Set}^{\mathbb{I}}$ for behaviour, that supports a behaviour endofunctor B, and another category $\mathcal{S} = \mathbf{Set}^{\mathbb{F}}$ for syntax, that supports algebraic signatures Σ for binding operators inducing free term monads T on $\mathcal{S}$. The aforementioned framework of mathematical operational semantics is thus not directly applicable. Importantly, however, as Fiore and Turi [9] realised, the two universes are related by an adjunction, leading to the following

*Research partially supported by an EPSRC Advanced Research Fellowship.
†Research partially supported by EPSRC grant GR/T22049/01.

situation

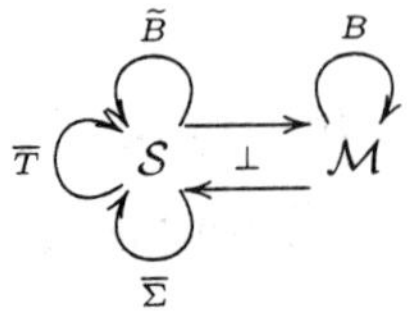

(3)

where $\widetilde{B}$ is obtained by shifting B from $\mathcal{M}$ to $\mathcal{S}$ by pre and post composition with the left and right adjoints respectively. Intuitively, $\widetilde{B}$ is a version of B for behaviour embodying the extra structure imposed by the category $\mathcal{S}$, which in the case under consideration amounts to closure under arbitrary renamings. It follows that abstract rules for the model $(\mathcal{S}, \overline{\Sigma}, \widetilde{B})$, given by natural transformations

$$\overline{\Sigma}((-) \times \widetilde{B}(-)) \Longrightarrow \widetilde{B}\overline{T}(-) : \mathcal{S} \to \mathcal{S} \ , \qquad (4)$$

induce a semantics for which $\widetilde{B}$-bisimulation is a congruence.

The notion of $\widetilde{B}$-bisimulation that arises amounts to what we call *wide-open* bisimulation; *viz.*, the version of open bisimulation that does not take account of distinctions [16, Sec. 3], and so is less discriminating than open bisimilarity [16, Sec. 7]. Wide-open bisimilarity has been considered by various authors, under different names; *e.g.* [14, 5, 9, 8].

Contributions. In the present work, we continue this line of investigation.

In aiming to extract a concrete rule format from the abstract rules (4) one faces the problem of devising syntax for the shifted-behaviour endofunctor—a difficult task due to the nature of the right adjoint. Rather than following this direction here, our first step is to instead develop a model theory that lies in between that of (1–2) and (3–4). Indeed, we consider models of the following kind

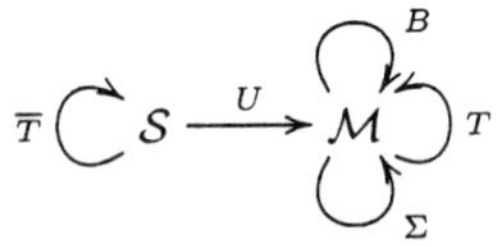

(5)

where $\overline{T}$ is a lifting of T, and develop a mathematical operational semantics for abstract rules of the form

$$\Sigma\big(U(-) \times BU(-)\big) \Longrightarrow BTU(-) : \mathcal{S} \to \mathcal{M} \qquad (6)$$

The way to think about this framework is as a model of syntax and behaviour in which the syntax, and consequently the rules, carry extra structure. In the context of this paper, the extra structure amounts to an operation of name substitution which is essential for modelling name communication.

The framework (5–6) clearly extends (1–2). Moreover, (5) fits within (3) whenever $\overline{\Sigma}$ and $\overline{T}$ restrict from $\mathcal{S}$ to $\mathcal{M}$ and, in this case, if U preserves binary products, the abstract rules (6) can actually be regarded as a subclass of the abstract rules (4), all of which happens in our example.

Our next step is to move away from semantic universes based on functor (more specifically, presheaf) categories (in which stages are explicitly indexed) and instead work in more convenient (sheaf) subcategories. Indeed, we take (5) with $\mathcal{M}$ the universe **Nom** of nominal sets and $\mathcal{S}$ a universe **NomSub** of nominal substitutions over it. Nominal sets have been championed by Gabbay, Pitts and others (*e.g.* [10]) as a convenient setting in which to handle various aspects of syntax with variable binding. Nominal substitutions are a novel contribution of this paper; they provide a natural extension of nominal sets, supporting the operation of name substitution. Thus, we explore the abstract GSOS rule format (6) from a practical, concrete point of view for the case $\mathcal{S} = \mathbf{NomSub}$ and $\mathcal{M} = \mathbf{Nom}$. In this context, signature endofunctors will arise from algebraic binding signatures. As for behaviour, a key observation is that for relations that are closed under name substitutions, the usual notions of early, late, and ground (as in [17]) bisimulation coincide. Hence we are able to work with ground bisimulation, which admits a reasonably simple behavioural model.

In order to give a concrete representation to abstract rules of the form (6), we introduce a syntactic notion of rule structure. This can be seen as the same concrete notion of rule that has been used, though in a slightly informal fashion, to define systems such as the π-calculus (*e.g.* as in [13]). Subsequently, we provide conditions on rule structures leading to a GSOS-like format that gives rise to abstract rules. For name-passing process calculi defined using rule structures satisfying our conditions, wide-open bisimilarity is a congruence.

Related work. Our work is novel in that we extract a concrete rule format from a model theory for name-passing. However, several authors have tackled congruence formats for name passing from an operational point of view. Weber and Bloom [21] introduced a rule format for name passing where they take a restriction operator and a structural congruence as primitive. Bernstein [3] has encoded the π-calculus rules within her framework, but the bisimilarity there is unusual in that it does not contain α-equivalence. More recently, and relevant, Ziegler, Miller and Palamidessi [22] have reformulated the tyft/tyxt format within a formal system (fold-nabla [12]) with a special quantifier for new names, introduced a notion of congruence in that setting, and established a congruence result for open bisimilarity.

Future research. In this paper we give an interpretation of rule structures in terms of abstract rules in the model, but it might be worthwhile to interpret rule structures in a formal system, such as nominal logic [15] and/or the logic fold-nabla [12].

Concerning the possibilities on rule formats that this work opens up, it would be interesting to investigate extensions to our concrete format that are complete with respect to the model theory (that is, where every abstract rule arises from a family of concrete ones), and to further provide concrete formats for abstract rules of the form (4).

An immediate problem for achieving completeness is that the concrete format that we present here involves only positive premises, whereas Turi and Plotkin [20] have shown that abstract rules (2) over **Set** account for rules with both positive and negative premises. We have found that by restricting attention to natural transformations that are suitably monotone one is able to capture the positive nature of the rules. Even for this restricted model, it seems that, for a completeness result, our concrete format needs to be further extended to allow rules equipped with suitable freshness assumptions on names.

It would also be interesting to adapt the model to account for open bisimulation and/or to see how the framework of Klin [11], which accounts for equivalences other than bisimilarity, extends to the name-passing case. More speculatively, we would like to extend the model theory, and the rule format, to be relevant for data-passing systems such as the applied pi calculus [1].

1. Mathematical operational semantics

We develop a mathematical operational semantics for rules that carry extra structure, establishing the congruence of behavioural equivalence.

Mathematical universe. We consider the following universe of discourse

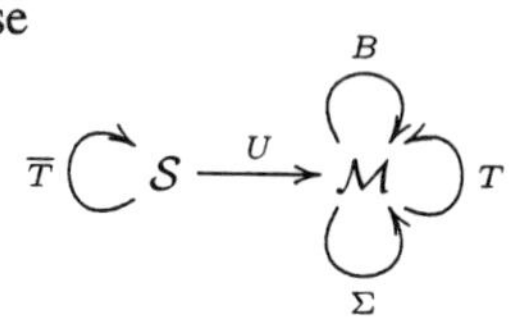

of categories and functors between them, where T is the free monad on the endofunctor Σ and where $\overline{T}$ is a monad lifting of T along U. Recall that a *monad lifting* of a monad S on $\mathcal{C}$ along a functor $F : \mathcal{D} \longrightarrow \mathcal{C}$ is a monad $\overline{S}$ on $\mathcal{D}$ together with a natural isomorphism $\lambda : SF \xrightarrow{\sim} F\overline{S}$ that defines a monad functor $(F, \lambda) : (\mathcal{D}, \overline{S}) \longrightarrow (\mathcal{C}, S)$ in the sense of Street [19]. When $SF = F\overline{S}$ and $\lambda = \mathrm{id}$, the monad lifting is said to be *strict*.

Operational models and bisimulation. A (U, BU)-*dialgebra* (occasionally referred to as a U-*structured* B-*coalgebra*) is an object X of $\mathcal{S}$ equipped with a B-coalgebra structure $UX \to BUX$ on UX in $\mathcal{M}$. These are operational models to be thought as abstract transition systems carrying extra structure. We let (U, BU)-**dialg** be the category of (U, BU)-dialgebras and homomorphisms (*viz.*, maps between the underlying objects that are compatible with the coalgebra structure).

A U-*structured* B-*bisimulation (relation)* between two (U, BU)-dialgebras, (X, h) and (Y, k), is a (jointly mono) span $X \leftarrow R \to Y$ in $\mathcal{S}$ such that there is a B-coalgebra structure $UR \to BUR$ on UR lifting the span to the category of (U, BU)-dialgebras.

We say that a U-structured B-bisimulation between two (U, BU)-dialgebras is *final* if every other U-structured B-bisimulation between them factors through it uniquely. Whenever it exists, the final U-structured B-bisimulation is called U-*structured* B-*bisimilarity*.

Congruence of bisimilarity. For a monad S, to be thought of as describing algebraic structure, an S-*congruence* between two S-algebras (X, x) and (Y, y) is a span $X \leftarrow R \to Y$ for which there exists an S-algebra structure lifting the span to the category of S-algebras.

The following result describes a setting in which structured bisimilarity is a congruence.

Theorem 1.1 *Let $\overline{S}$ be a monad lifting of a monad S on $\mathcal{S}$ along the forgetful functor $F : (U, BU)$-**dialg** $\longrightarrow \mathcal{S}$. Consider (U, BU)-dialgebras (X, h) and (Y, k), and let $SX \leftarrow R \to SY$ be a span in $\mathcal{S}$.*

If the span $F\overline{S}(X, h) \xleftarrow{\sim} SX \leftarrow R \to SY \xrightarrow{\sim} F\overline{S}(Y, k)$ is a U-structured B-bisimilarity between $\overline{S}(X, h)$ and $\overline{S}(Y, k)$ then the span $SX \leftarrow R \to SY$ is an S-congruence, where SX and SY are considered with their respective free algebra structures.

Abstract rules and operational semantics. We assume that $\mathcal{M}$ has binary products, and define an *abstract operational rule* as a natural transformation as follows:

$$\rho : \Sigma\big(U(-) \times BU(-)\big) \Longrightarrow BTU(-) : \mathcal{S} \to \mathcal{M} \qquad (7)$$

Note that for $\mathcal{S} = \mathcal{M}$, $U = \mathrm{Id}$, and $T = \overline{T}$ this notion, and the following result, specialise to those of Turi and Plotkin [20].

Theorem 1.2 *For every B-coalgebra $h : UX \to BUX$ there exists a unique B-coalgebra $h^\sharp : TUX \to BTUX$ such that the diagram*

$$\begin{array}{ccccc}
\Sigma TUX & \xrightarrow{\Sigma(\mathrm{id}, h^\sharp)} & \Sigma(TUX \times BTUX) & \xrightarrow{\sim} & \Sigma(U\overline{T}X \times BU\overline{T}X) \\
\downarrow{\scriptstyle \sigma_{UX}} & & \downarrow & & \downarrow{\scriptstyle \rho_{\overline{T}X}} \\
 & & BTTUX & \xrightarrow{\sim} & BTU\overline{T}X \\
 & & \downarrow{\scriptstyle B\mu_{UX}} & & \\
TUX & \xrightarrow{h^\sharp} & BTUX & & \\
\uparrow{\scriptstyle \eta_{UX}} & & \uparrow{\scriptstyle B\eta_{UX}} & & \\
UX & \xrightarrow[h]{} & BUX & &
\end{array}$$

commutes, where σ denotes the free Σ-algebra structure, and η and μ respetively denote the unit and multiplication of the monad T. Further, the mapping defined by

$$\overline{T}^{\rho}(X, h) = (\overline{T}X, U\overline{T}X \xrightarrow{\sim} TUX \xrightarrow{h^\sharp} BTUX \xrightarrow{\sim} BU\overline{T}X)$$

*extends to a strict monad lifting $\overline{T}^{\rho}$ of $\overline{T}$ along the forgetful functor (U, BU)-**dialg** $\to \mathcal{S}$.*

Thus, the monad $\overline{T}^{\rho}$, which is actually lifted from $\overline{T}$ via structural recursion, associates to each operational model $UX \to BUX$ a behavioural interpretation $U\overline{T}X \to BU\overline{T}X$ of the monadic structure as specified by the operational rule ρ.

Corollary 1.3 *Assume that $\mathcal{S}$ has an initial object 0, and that U preserves it. If it exists, the U-structured B-bisimilarity $\overline{T}0 \leftarrow E \to \overline{T}0$ on the operational model $U\overline{T}0 \to BU\overline{T}0$ (arising from the unique map $U0 \to BU0$) is a $\overline{T}$-congruence on $\overline{T}0$. Consequently, the span $T0 \xleftarrow{\sim} U\overline{T}0 \leftarrow UE \to U\overline{T}0 \xrightarrow{\sim} T0$ is a T-congruence on* *the initial* Σ*-algebra* $T0$.

Adjoint mathematical universes. The mathematical universes of discourse in the examples at hand (see [9] and Section 2 below) support plenty of further structure. For the purpose of the development here we highlight the following: (i) the category $\mathcal{S}$ has binary products; (ii) the endofunctor Σ on $\mathcal{M}$ arises as the restriction of an endofunctor $\overline{\Sigma}$ on $\mathcal{S}$, and $\overline{T}$ is the free monad on $\overline{\Sigma}$; (iii) the functor U preserves binary products and has a right adjoint, say $V : \mathcal{M} \to \mathcal{S}$ (so that the categories (U, BU)-**dialg** and VBU-**coalg** are isomorphic). Thus we have the following adjoint situation

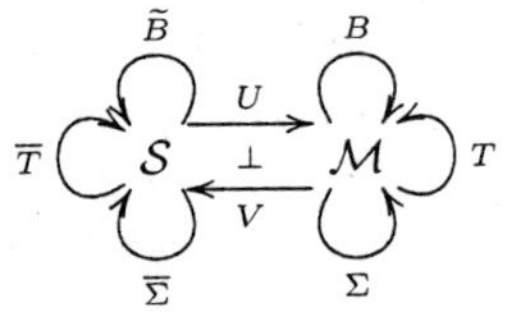

where $\widetilde{B} = VBU$. Hence, one can consider, as did Fiore and Turi [9], abstract rules of the form

$$\overline{\Sigma}((-) \times \widetilde{B}(-)) \Longrightarrow \widetilde{B}\overline{T}(-) : \mathcal{S} \to \mathcal{S} \qquad (8)$$

as in the setting of Turi and Plotkin [20].

The following result relates the operational semantics advocated here based on rules of the form (7) to the more general one with rules of the form (8).

Theorem 1.4 *Every* ρ *as in (7) induces a* $\overline{\rho}$ *of the form (8) such that the monad liftings* $\overline{T}^{\rho}$ *and* $\overline{T}^{\overline{\rho}}$ *of the monad* $\overline{T}$ *respectively to* (U, BU)-**dialg** *and to* $\widetilde{B}$-**coalg** *are isomorphic.*

Indeed, for $X \in \mathcal{S}$, one lets $\overline{\rho}_X$ be the right adjunct of the composite $U\overline{\Sigma}(X \times VBUX) \xrightarrow{\sim} \Sigma(UX \times UVBUX) \xrightarrow{\Sigma(\mathrm{id}\times\varepsilon_{BUX})} \Sigma(UX\times BUX) \xrightarrow{\rho_X} BTUX \xrightarrow{\sim} BU\overline{T}X$, where ε denotes the counit of the adjunction $U \dashv V$.

2. Abstract syntax

We develop a theory of binding signatures suitable for name-passing systems. We investigate models for the signatures and consider how morphisms between model categories relate different kinds of model.

2.1. Signatures and their models

Binding signatures. The syntax of the π-calculus is built from various operators. For instance, the input phrase $c(a).P$, which will be written $\mathsf{inp}(c, \langle a\rangle P)$, has one name parameter c and one term parameter P with name a bound; the output phrase $\bar{c}d.P$ will be written $\mathsf{out}(c, d, P)$, it has two name parameters c, d, and one term parameter P with no names bound. We will also use the restriction phrase $\nu a.P$, written $\mathsf{res}(\langle a\rangle P)$, with one term parameter with a name bound in it; and the parallel phrase $P|Q$, written $\mathsf{par}(P, Q)$, which has two term parameters, neither with any names bound.

The following notion of signature, already used by Fiore and Turi [9], can be seen as an extension of that of Fiore, Plotkin and Turi [7] to allow name parameters, or alternatively as a restricted form of nominal-logic signature as introduced by Pitts [15].

Definition 2.1 *A* binding signature Σ *consists of a finite set* OP_Σ *of operators together with, for each operator* $\mathrm{op} \in \mathrm{OP}_\Sigma$, *a* name-arity $\mathrm{ar_n(op)} \in \mathbb{N}$ *and a* term-arity $\mathrm{ar_t(op)} \in \mathbb{N}$. *To each* $j \in [1, \mathrm{ar_t(op)}]$ *is associated a* binding depth $\mathrm{bdep_{op}}(j) \in \mathbb{N}$.

Note for instance that for the fragment of the π-calculus recalled above we have a signature Σ_π with operators $\mathrm{OP}_{\Sigma_\pi} = \{\mathsf{inp}, \mathsf{out}, \mathsf{res}, \mathsf{par}\}$; arities are assigned as follows.

op	$\mathrm{ar_n(op)}$	$\mathrm{ar_t(op)}$	dep
inp	1	1	$\mathrm{bdep}_{\mathsf{inp}}(1) = 1$
out	2	1	$\mathrm{bdep}_{\mathsf{out}}(1) = 0$
res	0	1	$\mathrm{bdep}_{\mathsf{res}}(1) = 1$
par	0	2	$\mathrm{bdep}_{\mathsf{par}}(j) = 0 \quad (j = 1, 2)$

Signature models. Signatures for name-passing admit interpretation in a variety of categories.

Definition 2.2 *A* model category *(for binding signatures) is a category* C *with (i) finite products and coproducts, (ii) a distinguished object* $\mathcal{N}_C \in C$ *representing names, and (iii) an endofunctor* $[\mathcal{N}]_C$ *on* C *representing name binding.*

Definition 2.3 *A* model *for a binding signature* Σ *in a model category* C *is an algebra for the endofunctor* Σ_C *on* C *given as follows.*

$$\Sigma_C(-) = \coprod_{\mathrm{op}\in\mathrm{OP}_\Sigma}\left(\mathcal{N}_C{}^{\mathrm{ar_n(op)}} \times \prod_{j\in\mathrm{ar_t(op)}} [\mathcal{N}]_C{}^{\mathrm{bdep_{op}}(j)}(-)\right)$$

In particular, for the π-calculus fragment introduced above, we have the following endofunctor.

$$\begin{aligned}\Sigma_{\pi,C}(-) = {} & \mathcal{N}_C \times [\mathcal{N}]_C(-) + \mathcal{N}_C \times \mathcal{N}_C \times (-) \\ & + \quad [\mathcal{N}]_C(-) \quad + \quad (-) \times (-)\end{aligned}$$

Typically, and this is the case in all our examples, C is cartesian closed and has colimits of ω-chains that are preserved by $[\mathcal{N}]_C$; thus the free monad T_C on Σ_C can be constructed in the usual fashion to provide a free model for the signature. A model for Σ in C can be equivalently given by an algebra for the monad T_C.

Raw syntax. Fixing a set $\mathtt{N}$ of name meta-variables, we can consider the model category $\mathbf{Set}_\mathtt{N} = \mathbf{Set}$ with name object $\mathcal{N}_{\mathbf{Set}_\mathtt{N}} = \mathtt{N}$ and with abstraction endofunctor $[\mathcal{N}]_{\mathbf{Set}_\mathtt{N}} = \mathtt{N} \times (-)$. Then for any set X the set $T_{\mathbf{Set}_\mathtt{N}}X$ contains all raw Σ-terms with name variables from $\mathtt{N}$ and term variables from X, where α-equivalent terms are not identitifed.

Notation. Elements $(\mathtt{a}, \mathtt{x})$ of $[\mathcal{N}]_{\mathbf{Set}_\mathtt{N}}\mathtt{X}$ will be written suggestively as $\langle\mathtt{a}\rangle\mathtt{x}$, even though no α-equivalence is imposed on them.

2.2. Abstract syntax with variable binding

We give two examples of model categories capturing syntax up-to α-equivalence. The first one is the model of nominal sets of Gabbay and Pitts [10]; the second one is an extension of the former which is a sheaf subcategory of the model of Fiore, Plotkin and Turi [7].

2.2.1. Nominal sets

We briefly review and set notation for the theory of nominal sets.

Nominal sets. Throughout the paper we fix an infinite countable set $\mathcal{N}$ of names. Recall that a left action of the symmetric group $\mathsf{Sym}(\mathcal{N})$ on $\mathcal{N}$ is a set X equipped with a function $\bullet_X : \mathsf{Sym}(\mathcal{N}) \times X \to X$ (written infix) which is such that for any element $x \in X$ we have $\mathrm{id}_{\mathcal{N}} \bullet_X x = x$ and, for any $\sigma, \tau \in \mathsf{Sym}(\mathcal{N})$, that $(\tau\sigma) \bullet_X x = \tau \bullet_X (\sigma \bullet_X x)$.

A finite set of names $C \subseteq_{\mathrm{f}} \mathcal{N}$ is said to support an element x of a $\mathsf{Sym}(\mathcal{N})$-action $(X, \bullet_X)$ if every permutation $\sigma \in \mathsf{Sym}(\mathcal{N})$ that fixes every element of C also fixes x. A *nominal set* is a $\mathsf{Sym}(\mathcal{N})$-action in which every element has finite support. We let $\mathbf{Nom}$ be the category of nominal sets and equivariant functions, *i.e.* functions compatible with the actions.

Notation. For names $a, b \in \mathcal{N}$ be write $[a \leftrightarrow b]$ for the permutation on $\mathcal{N}$ that swaps a and b and fixes the other names. The expression "$a\#x$", that stands for "a is fresh for x", means that there is a support of x that does not contain a.

Constructions. The category $\mathbf{Nom}$ has colimits and finite limits, and the functor $|-| : \mathbf{Nom} \to \mathbf{Set}$ that forgets the $\mathsf{Sym}(\mathcal{N})$-action structure preserves them. So, in particular, sums and products are inherited from $\mathbf{Set}$.

The set $\mathcal{N}$ of names has nominal-set structure; the action is given by evaluation, *i.e.* $\sigma \bullet_{\mathcal{N}} a = \sigma(a)$. For any nominal set X we have the nominal set $[\mathcal{N}]X$ of the names abstracted in X. The carrier set is the quotient

$$[\mathcal{N}]X = (\mathcal{N} \times X)/{\sim_{[\mathcal{N}]X}}$$

where $(a, x) \sim_{[\mathcal{N}]X} (a', x')$ if for any $b \in \mathcal{N}$ such that $b\#x$ and $b\#x'$ we have $[b \leftrightarrow a] \bullet_X x = [b \leftrightarrow a'] \bullet_X x'$. We write $\langle a \rangle x$ for the equivalence class $(a, x)_{[\mathcal{N}]X}$. The $\mathsf{Sym}(\mathcal{N})$-action of $[\mathcal{N}]X$ is inherited from that of the product.

These constructions make $\mathbf{Nom}$ into a model category.

Syntax up-to α-equivalence. For any binding signature Σ and nominal set X, the nominal set $T_{\mathbf{Nom}}X$ contains all Σ-terms with name variables from $\mathcal{N}$ and term variables from X; here, α-equivalent terms are identified in accordance with the intrinsic notion of α-equivalence in X. Indeed, a $T_{\mathbf{Nom}}$-algebra is a model of the nominal-logic signature underlying Σ, in the sense of Pitts [15].

2.2.2. Nominal substitutions

While nominal sets support actions of bijective renamings useful for modelling α-equivalence, to give semantics to name communication it is necessary to further consider arbitrary name substitutions.

Definition 2.4 *A* nominal substitution *is a nominal set X together with an equivariant function* $\mathsf{sub}_X : \mathcal{N} \times [\mathcal{N}]X \to X$ *that satisfies the following four axioms, where, for clarity, we write $[b/a]x$ for $\mathsf{sub}_X(b, \langle a \rangle x)$.*

1. *Identity:* $[a/a]x = x$.
2. *Weakening:* $[b/a]x = x$, *whenever* $a\#x$.
3. *Contraction:* $[c/b][b/a]x = [c/b][c/a]x$.
4. *Permutation:* $[d/b][c/a]x = [c/a][d/b]x$, *whenever* $c \neq b \neq a \neq d$.

(Note that by definition of $[\mathcal{N}]X$ we have that $[b/a]x = [b/z][a \leftrightarrow z]x$, whenever $z\#x$.)

A homomorphism of nominal substitutions is an equivariant function between the underlying nominal sets that respects the nominal substitution. Thus we have a category $\mathbf{NomSub}$ of nominal substitutions. This category is complete and cocomplete, and the forgetful functor $\mathbf{NomSub} \to \mathbf{Nom}$ preserves limits and colimits. The object $\mathcal{N}$ of names in $\mathbf{Nom}$ has a unique nominal-substitution structure, while for any nominal substitution X the nominal set $[\mathcal{N}]X$ has a nominal-substitution structure such that for $x \in X$ and $a, b, c \in \mathcal{N}$ with $a \neq c \neq b$ we have $[b/a]\langle c \rangle x = \langle c \rangle [b/a]x$. In this way the endofunctor $[\mathcal{N}]$ on $\mathbf{Nom}$ is lifted along the forgetful functor $\mathbf{NomSub} \to \mathbf{Nom}$.

Thus $\mathbf{NomSub}$ is a model category and we are also able to consider syntax there. In fact, the syntax thus obtained is as in the model category $\mathbf{Nom}$, but equipped with a name-substitution action (see the following subsection).

Explicit name substitutions. For every signature Σ there is an extended signature Σ^{sub} which is the same as Σ but has one extra operator: the substitution operator sub, that takes one name parameter and one term parameter with a name bound in it. For any model category $\mathcal{C}$, we write $\Sigma^{\mathsf{sub}}_{\mathcal{C}}$ for the endofunctor on $\mathcal{C}$ generated by the signature Σ^{sub}. We further write $T^{\mathsf{sub}}_{\mathcal{C}}$ for the free monad on $\Sigma^{\mathsf{sub}}_{\mathcal{C}}$, when it exists.

In the particular case of the model category $\mathbf{NomSub}$, we have a natural transformation $\Sigma^{\mathsf{sub}}_{\mathbf{NomSub}} \to \Sigma_{\mathbf{NomSub}}$ which evaluates the explicit substitutions using the notion internal to nominal substitutions. This induces a monad functor $T_{\mathbf{NomSub}} \to T^{\mathsf{sub}}_{\mathbf{NomSub}}$, and hence, in particular, morphisms $T^{\mathsf{sub}}_{\mathbf{NomSub}}X \to T_{\mathbf{NomSub}}X$ natural for X in $\mathbf{NomSub}$.

2.3. Morphisms of model categories

By considering morphisms between model categories we are able to relate the different models of syntax.

Definition 2.5 *A morphism $(F, f, \phi) : \mathcal{D} \to \mathcal{C}$ between model categories is given by a product-preserving functor $F : \mathcal{D} \to \mathcal{C}$ together with a morphism $f : \mathcal{N}_{\mathcal{C}} \to F(\mathcal{N}_{\mathcal{D}})$ in $\mathcal{C}$ and a natural transformation $\phi : [\mathcal{N}]_{\mathcal{C}}\, F \to F\, [\mathcal{N}]_{\mathcal{D}}$.*

For any binding signature Σ, such a morphism induces a natural transformation $\Sigma_{\mathcal{C}}F \to F\Sigma_{\mathcal{D}}$. If the free monads on

$\Sigma_{\mathcal{C}}$ and $\Sigma_{\mathcal{D}}$ exist then they induce, by structural recursion, a monad functor $(\mathcal{D}, T_{\mathcal{D}}) \to (\mathcal{C}, T_{\mathcal{C}})$.

We now use this framework to explain how raw syntax is quotiented by α-equivalence.

Instantiating raw syntax. We fix a set $\mathtt{N}$ of name meta-variables and consider an instantiation function $I : \mathtt{N} \to \mathcal{N}$ sending name meta-variables to names. We have a morphism of model categories $\mathbf{NomSub} \to \mathbf{Set}_{\mathtt{N}}$ given by the forgetful functor $|-| : \mathbf{NomSub} \to \mathbf{Set}$ together with the function $I : \mathtt{N} \to |\mathcal{N}|$ and the natural transformation $\mathtt{N} \times |-| \to |\mathcal{N}| \times |-| \twoheadrightarrow |[\mathcal{N}](-)|$. Thus for any binding signature we have an induced monad functor $T_{\mathbf{NomSub}} \to T_{\mathbf{Set}_{\mathtt{N}}}$, and so for any nominal substitution X we have a function $T_{\mathbf{Set}_{\mathtt{N}}}|X| \to |T_{\mathbf{NomSub}}X|$ that in fact converts terms of raw syntax into terms of abstract syntax up-to α-equivalence.

Lifting syntax from Nom to NomSub. For any morphism $(F, f, \phi) : \mathcal{D} \to \mathcal{C}$ of model categories, if the functor F preserves coproducts and f and ϕ are isomorphisms then the induced natural transformation $\Sigma_{\mathcal{C}} F \to F \Sigma_{\mathcal{D}}$ is an isomorphism. If, in addition, the free monads on $\Sigma_{\mathcal{C}}$ and $\Sigma_{\mathcal{D}}$ exist and F has a right adjoint then the further induced natural transformation $T_{\mathcal{C}} F \to F T_{\mathcal{D}}$ is also an isomorphism. That is, $T_{\mathcal{D}}$ is a monad lifting of $T_{\mathcal{C}}$ along F.

We can apply this to relate models in $\mathbf{Nom}$ with models in $\mathbf{NomSub}$. Indeed, a morphism $\mathbf{NomSub} \to \mathbf{Nom}$ of model categories is given by the forgetful functor $|-| : \mathbf{NomSub} \to \mathbf{Nom}$ together with the identities $\mathcal{N}_{\mathbf{Nom}} = |\mathcal{N}_{\mathbf{NomSub}}|$ and $[\mathcal{N}]_{\mathbf{Nom}} |-| = |[\mathcal{N}]_{\mathbf{NomSub}}(-)|$. Moreover, $|-|$ has a right adjoint and so for any binding signature Σ we have isomorphisms $\Sigma_{\mathbf{Nom}}|X| \xrightarrow{\sim} |\Sigma_{\mathbf{NomSub}} X|$ and $T_{\mathbf{Nom}}|X| \xrightarrow{\sim} |T_{\mathbf{NomSub}} X|$ natural for X in $\mathbf{NomSub}$.

3. Behavioural models of name-passing

We introduce coalgebraic models for both ground and wide-open bisimulation.

3.1. Ground bisimulation

We study ground bisimulation, *viz.* bisimulation for which the only relevant input transitions are those involving fresh data.

Deterministic ground behaviour. We introduce an endofunctor on $\mathbf{Nom}$ for deterministic ground behaviour:

$$
\begin{array}{rlll}
L_{\mathrm{g}}(-) = & & \mathcal{N} \times [\mathcal{N}](-) & \text{(input)} \\
& + & \mathcal{N} \times \mathcal{N} \times (-) & \text{(output)} \\
& + & \mathcal{N} \times [\mathcal{N}](-) & \text{(bound output)} \\
& + & (-) & \text{(silent action)}
\end{array}
$$

Thus an L_{g}-coalgebra is a nominal set of states together with an equivariant function assigning to each state either: an input (in) behaviour (*i.e.* a channel name and a resumption state with one name bound); an output (out) behaviour, with the output data paired rather than bound; or a bound output (bout) or silent (tau) behaviour.

Ground behaviour. We introduce non-determinism into the model by interpreting the theory of (finite-)join semi-lattices in the category $\mathbf{Nom}$. For any nominal set X, we write $\mathcal{P}_{\mathrm{f}}X$ for the carrier of the free join semi-lattice on X. This free construction is a monad lifting of the free join semi-lattice monad on $\mathbf{Set}$ (whose underlying functor is the covariant finite powerset) along the forgetful functor $\mathbf{Nom} \to \mathbf{Set}$.

We thus define an endofunctor B_{g} on $\mathbf{Nom}$ for (non-deterministic) *ground behaviour*:

$$B_{\mathrm{g}} = \mathcal{P}_{\mathrm{f}} L_{\mathrm{g}} \quad .$$

In the remainder of this subsection we put this theory in a more concrete perspective.

Nominal transition systems. We start by introducing a notion of nominal transition system. First, for each nominal set N we have a nominal set of labels over N:

$$Lab(N) \;=\; N \times N \;+\; N \times N \;+\; N \times N \;+\; 1 \quad .$$

The components of this sum correspond respectively to input action (written $c(z)$), output action ($\bar{c}d$), bound output action ($\bar{c}(z)$), and silent action (τ). For any label $l \in Lab(N)$ the binding names $\mathsf{bn}(l)$ and free names $\mathsf{fn}(l)$ are defined as usual: $\mathsf{bn}(c(z)) = \mathsf{bn}(\bar{c}(z)) = \{z\}$ and $\mathsf{bn}(\bar{c}d) = \mathsf{bn}(\tau) = \emptyset$; whilst $\mathsf{fn}(c(z)) = \mathsf{fn}(\bar{c}(z)) = \{c\}$, $\mathsf{fn}(\bar{c}d) = \{c, d\}$, and $\mathsf{fn}(\tau) = \emptyset$.

Definition 3.1 *A* ground transition system *is a nominal set X together with an equivariant relation $\longrightarrow \subseteq X \times Lab(\mathcal{N}) \times X$ for which binding names are always fresh; i.e., if $x \xrightarrow{l} x'$ then $\mathsf{bn}(l)\#x$.*

Every B_{g}-coalgebra (X, h) induces a ground transition system with carrier the underlying nominal set X and with transition relation $\longrightarrow_h \subseteq X \times Lab(\mathcal{N}) \times X$ given as follows.

If $\mathsf{in}(c, \langle z \rangle x') \in h(x)$ and $z\#x$ then $x \xrightarrow{c(z)}_h x'$.

If $\mathsf{out}(c, d, x') \in h(x)$ then $x \xrightarrow{\bar{c}d}_h x'$.

If $\mathsf{bout}(c, \langle z \rangle x') \in h(x)$ and $z\#x$ then $x \xrightarrow{\bar{c}(z)}_h x'$.

If $\mathsf{tau}(x') \in h(x)$ then $x \xrightarrow{\tau}_h x'$.

Note that this transition relation is finite-branching, up to renaming of bound names.

Ground bisimulation. We consider ground bisimulations in the sense of Sangiorgi [17, Def. 2.1] that are closed under bijective renamings.

Definition 3.2 *A* ground bisimulation *between two ground transition systems $(X, \longrightarrow)$ and $(X', \longrightarrow')$ is an equivariant relation $R \subseteq X \times X'$ such that the following holds: for any $(x, x') \in R$ and any label $l \in Lab(\mathcal{N})$ such that*

$\mathsf{bn}(l)\#(x,x')$, (i) if $x \xrightarrow{l} y$ then there is $y' \in X'$ such that $x' \xrightarrow{l}{}' y'$ and $(y,y') \in R$, and (ii) if $x' \xrightarrow{l}{}' y'$ then there is $y \in X$ such that $x \xrightarrow{l} y$ and $(y,y') \in R$.

Proposition 3.3 *An equivariant relation between the carriers of two B_g-coalgebras is a B_g-bisimulation if and only if it is a ground bisimulation between the induced ground transition systems.*

3.2. Wide-open bisimulation

Operational models. We consider the operational models given by structured B_g-coalgebras with respect to the forgetful functor $|-| : \mathbf{NomSub} \to \mathbf{Nom}$; that is, B_g-coalgebras together with a name-substitution action on their carrier.

Interestingly, this notion of operational model has essentially appeared before, though in a different guise. Indeed, to give a structured B_g-coalgebra is to give an $\mathcal{N}$-LTS in the sense of Cattani and Sewell [5, Def. 3.4] that additionally satisfies an image finiteness condition, and for which the carrier presheaf preserves pullbacks of injections. We explored correspondences of this kind in [8].

Wide-open bisimulation. The associated notion of behavioural equivalence, *viz.* structured B_g-bisimulation, has a simple description as a form of open bisimulation.

Definition 3.4 *Let X and Y be nominal substitutions. A wide-open bisimulation between ground transition systems on the nominal sets $|X|$ and $|Y|$ is a ground bisimulation $R \subseteq |X| \times |Y|$ that is substitution closed in the sense that, for any $a, b \in \mathcal{N}$, $x \in X$, $y \in Y$, if $x\,R\,y$ then $[b/a]x\,R\,[b/a]y$.*

Proposition 3.5 *The notions of B_g-bisimulation relation between structured B_g-coalgebras (X, h) and (Y, k) and of wide-open bisimulation between the induced ground transition systems $(|X|, \longrightarrow_h)$ and $(|Y|, \longrightarrow_k)$ coincide.*

Furthermore, wide-open bisimilarity is characterised as the structured B_g-bisimilarity.

4. Operational rules for name-passing

We proceed to give concrete rules for name-passing systems that have been extracted from abstract ones. Recall then from Sections 2 and 3 that for every binding signature Σ we obtain a mathematical universe as follows

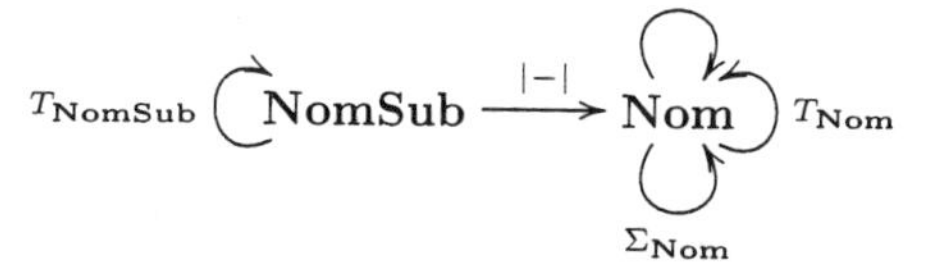

$$T_{\mathbf{NomSub}} \mathrel{\reflectbox{$\circlearrowright$}} \mathbf{NomSub} \xrightarrow{|-|} \mathbf{Nom} \mathrel{\overset{B_\mathrm{g}}{\underset{\Sigma_{\mathbf{Nom}}}{\circlearrowright}}} T_{\mathbf{Nom}} \qquad (9)$$

(which is in fact an adjoint mathematical universe).

Following the mathematical operational semantics of Section 1, an abstract rule is a natural transformation of the form:

$$\Sigma_{\mathbf{Nom}}\big(|-| \times B_\mathrm{g}\,|-|\big) \implies B_\mathrm{g} T_{\mathbf{Nom}}|-| \qquad (10)$$

between functors $\mathbf{NomSub} \to \mathbf{Nom}$.

(We stress that rules merely arising from the model $(\mathbf{Nom}, \Sigma_{\mathbf{Nom}}, B_\mathrm{g})$ are not expressive enough, crucially to support name communication.)

4.1. Concrete rules

We introduce rule structures as a formalisation of the usual, concrete notion of rule.

Informal presentation. Systems such as the π-calculus involve rules of the form

$$\frac{\mathsf{x}_1 \xrightarrow{l_1} \mathsf{y}_1 \quad \mathsf{x}_2 \xrightarrow{l_2} \mathsf{y}_2 \quad \cdots}{\mathsf{op}(\mathsf{c}, \langle \mathsf{a}\rangle\mathsf{x}, \ldots) \xrightarrow{l} t} \quad \begin{array}{l} \text{— premises} \\[1.5em] \text{— conclusion} \end{array}$$

where op is an operator of a binding signature; a, c are name meta-variables; $\mathsf{x}, \mathsf{x}_j, \mathsf{y}_j$ are term meta-variables; l, l_j are labels (for input, output, bound output, and silent actions) involving name meta-variables; and where t is a compound term built out of operators from the signature together with name and term meta-variables.

For first examples consider the π-calculus rules for input and scope closure.

$$(input) \; \frac{\rule{1em}{0.4pt}}{\mathsf{inp}(\mathsf{c}, \langle \mathsf{a}\rangle\mathsf{x}) \xrightarrow{\mathsf{c}(\mathsf{a})} \mathsf{x}}$$

$$(close) \; \frac{\mathsf{x} \xrightarrow{\bar{\mathsf{c}}(\mathsf{a})} \mathsf{y} \quad \mathsf{x}' \xrightarrow{\mathsf{c}(\mathsf{a})} \mathsf{y}'}{\mathsf{par}(\mathsf{x}, \mathsf{x}') \xrightarrow{\tau} \mathsf{res}(\langle \mathsf{a}\rangle\mathsf{par}(\mathsf{y}, \mathsf{y}'))}$$

While the terms of the language are considered up-to α-equivalence, it makes little sense to consider α-equivalence in the rules themselves. Indeed, rules are templates where no actual binding takes place. In the terminology of Section 2: rules are built of raw syntax.

Note also that rules may involve renamings in the right hand side of the conclusion; consider for instance the π-calculus rule for communication.

$$(com) \; \frac{\mathsf{x} \xrightarrow{\bar{\mathsf{c}}\mathsf{d}} \mathsf{y} \quad \mathsf{x}' \xrightarrow{\mathsf{c}(\mathsf{a})} \mathsf{y}'}{\mathsf{par}(\mathsf{x}, \mathsf{x}') \xrightarrow{\tau} \mathsf{par}(\mathsf{y}, [\mathsf{d}/\mathsf{a}]\mathsf{y}')}$$

For this reason explicit substitutions (as in Section 2.2.2) are needed.

Formal rule structures. Rule structures for a binding signature Σ are defined as follows.

Definition 4.1 *Let $\mathtt{N}$ and $\mathtt{X}$ be finite sets, and write $Lab(\mathtt{N})$ for the set of labels over $\mathtt{N}$.*

1. *A rule structure over $(\mathtt{N}, \mathtt{X})$ is a finite set of premises over $(\mathtt{N}, \mathtt{X})$ together with a conclusion over $(\mathtt{N}, \mathtt{X})$.*

2. *A premise over $(\mathtt{N}, \mathtt{X})$ is a triple in $\mathtt{X} \times Lab(\mathtt{N}) \times \mathtt{X}$; the components are referred to as the source, the label, and the target of the premise.*

3. A conclusion *over* $(\mathtt{N},\mathtt{X})$ *is a triple in*

$$\Sigma_{\mathbf{Set}_\mathtt{N}}\mathtt{X} \times Lab(\mathtt{N}) \times T^{\mathsf{sub}}_{\mathbf{Set}_\mathtt{N}}\mathtt{X}$$

The components are again referred to as the source, the label, and the target of the conclusion.

Interpretation of rules. In Section 4.3 we explain how a rule structure induces an operational semantics. For the time being, we suggest that a rule be used to define a transition system by induction in the usual way, subject to two conventions about how the rule can be instantiated: (i) Names, when instantiated, must be as distinct as the corresponding name meta-variables are in the rule. (ii) Binding data on the conclusion label must be fresh for the conclusion source.

These two conventions are to be thought of as side conditions that are implicit in every rule. For instance, consider the π-calculus rules for mismatch and parallel transition.

$$(mm)\ \frac{\mathtt{x} \xrightarrow{\tau} \mathtt{y}}{\mathsf{mm}(\mathtt{c},\mathtt{d},\mathtt{x}) \xrightarrow{\tau} \mathtt{y}} \qquad (par)\ \frac{\mathtt{x} \xrightarrow{\bar{\mathtt{c}}(\mathtt{a})} \mathtt{y}}{\mathsf{par}(\mathtt{x},\mathtt{x}') \xrightarrow{\bar{\mathtt{c}}(\mathtt{a})} \mathsf{par}(\mathtt{y},\mathtt{x}')}$$

Convention (i) eliminates the need for the usual side condition $\mathtt{c} \neq \mathtt{d}$ on the rule *(mm)*; convention (ii) covers the usual side condition $\mathtt{a} \notin \mathsf{fn}(\mathtt{x}')$ in rule *(par)*.

On the other hand, because of these conventions, some duplication in the rules may be necessary. For instance, to attain the usual output behaviour it is necessary to split the usual rule in two:

$$(out\text{-}eq)\ \frac{-}{\mathsf{out}(\mathtt{c},\mathtt{c},\mathtt{x}) \xrightarrow{\bar{\mathtt{c}}\mathtt{c}} \mathtt{x}} \qquad (out\text{-}neq)\ \frac{-}{\mathsf{out}(\mathtt{c},\mathtt{d},\mathtt{x}) \xrightarrow{\bar{\mathtt{c}}\mathtt{d}} \mathtt{x}}$$

One can envisage a notion of rule structure with explicit side conditions from which a finite family of rule structures in the form of Definition 4.1 can be derived, but we will not dwell on that here.

4.2. Rule format for name-passing

We introduce conditions on rule structures explicitly designed to capture concrete rules that give rise to abstract rules, and hence to guarantee that wide-open bisimilarity is a congruence for the induced transition systems.

Throughout this section we fix a rule structure $\mathtt{R}$ over $(\mathtt{N},\mathtt{X})$, with premise set Prem and conclusion with source

$$\underline{\mathtt{op}}\left((\underline{\mathtt{c}}_i)_{i\in[1,\mathrm{ar_n}(\underline{\mathtt{op}})]}, \left(\langle\underline{\mathtt{a}}^j_k\rangle_{k\in[1,\mathrm{bdep}_{\underline{\mathtt{op}}}(j)]}\underline{\mathtt{x}}_j\right)_{j\in[1,\mathrm{ar_t}(\underline{\mathtt{op}})]}\right),$$

label $\underline{\mathtt{l}}$, and target $\underline{\mathtt{tar}}$. (We distinguish entities appearing in the conclusion by underlining them.)

Conditions on rule structures. In Figure 1 we present conditions that we expect to hold of rule structures. Conditions (1–2) are the conditions of the GSOS format [4] considered in this context. Conditions (3–9) relate to the freshness of the names that appear in binding position. To specify these conditions formally it is necessary to formalise the notions of bound and free names that are implicit in rule structures.

Associating names to variables. From here on we assume that Conditions (1–2) hold of $\mathtt{R}$. We then assign to each term meta-variable $\mathtt{x} \in \mathtt{X}$ the set $\mathtt{BN}(\mathtt{x}) \subseteq \mathtt{N}$ of name meta-variables that are binding in $\mathtt{x}$. For instance, in the *(input)* rule above, $\mathtt{BN}(\mathtt{x}) = \{\mathtt{a}\}$, and in the *(par)* rule, $\mathtt{BN}(\mathtt{x}) = \mathtt{BN}(\mathtt{x}') = \emptyset$, while $\mathtt{BN}(\mathtt{y}) = \{\mathtt{a}\}$.

To define BN we use the fact that since Conditions (1–2) are satisfied we have a bijection

$$\mathtt{X} \cong [1,\mathrm{ar_t}(\underline{\mathtt{op}})] + \coprod_{j\in[1,\mathrm{ar_t}(\underline{\mathtt{op}})]} \{(\mathtt{x},\mathtt{l},\mathtt{y}) \in \mathrm{Prem} \mid \mathtt{x} = \underline{\mathtt{x}}_j\}$$

whose inverse maps $j \in [1,\mathrm{ar_t}(\underline{\mathtt{op}})]$ to $\underline{\mathtt{x}}_j$, and $\mathsf{inj}_j(\mathtt{x},\mathtt{l},\mathtt{y})$ to $\mathtt{y}$. Now:

- For $j \in [1,\mathrm{ar_t}(\underline{\mathtt{op}})]$ we let
$$\mathtt{BN}(\underline{\mathtt{x}}_j) = \left\{\underline{\mathtt{a}}^j_k \;\middle|\; k \in [1,\mathrm{bdep}_{\underline{\mathtt{op}}}(j)]\right\} .$$
- For $(\mathtt{x},\mathtt{l},\mathtt{y}) \in \mathrm{Prem}$ we let
$$\mathtt{BN}(\mathtt{y}) = \mathtt{BN}(\mathtt{x}) \cup \mathsf{bn}(\mathtt{l}) .$$

Finally, we write $\mathtt{BN}(\underline{\mathtt{src}},\mathrm{Prem}) \subseteq \mathtt{N}$ for the set

$$\mathtt{BN}(\underline{\mathtt{src}},\mathrm{Prem}) = \bigcup_{\mathtt{x}\in\mathtt{X}} \mathtt{BN}(\mathtt{x})$$

of all name meta-variables that appear in binding position in the conclusion source or the premise labels.

We now associate to each variable $\mathtt{x} \in \mathtt{X}$ a set $\mathtt{FN}(\mathtt{x}) \subseteq \mathtt{N}$, which approximates (from the point of view of the rule) the names which appear free when the variable $\mathtt{x}$ is instantiated. To do this we first define the set $\mathtt{FN}(\underline{\mathtt{src}},\mathrm{Prem}) \subseteq \mathtt{N}$ that approximates the names that will be free in the conclusion source when it is instantiated.

$$\mathtt{FN}(\underline{\mathtt{src}},\mathrm{Prem}) = \left\{\underline{\mathtt{c}}_i \;\middle|\; i \in [1,\mathrm{ar_n}(\underline{\mathtt{op}})]\right\} \cup \bigcup_{(\mathtt{x},\mathtt{l},\mathtt{y})\in\mathrm{Prem}} \mathsf{fn}(\mathtt{l}) \setminus \mathtt{BN}(\mathtt{x})$$

Finally, for any $\mathtt{x} \in \mathtt{X}$, we let

$$\mathtt{FN}(\mathtt{x}) = \mathtt{FN}(\underline{\mathtt{src}},\mathrm{Prem}) \cup \mathtt{BN}(\mathtt{x}) .$$

The function FN extends to compound terms with explicit substitutions. For $\mathtt{t} \in T^{\mathsf{sub}}_{\mathbf{Set}_\mathtt{N}}\mathtt{X}$ with

$$\mathtt{t} = \mathtt{op}\left(\begin{array}{l}(\mathtt{c}_i)_{i\in[1,\mathrm{ar_n}(\mathtt{op})]}, \\ \left(\langle\mathtt{a}^j_k\rangle_{k\in[1,\mathrm{bdep}_{\mathtt{op}}(j)]}\mathtt{t}_j\right)_{j\in[1,\mathrm{ar_t}(\mathtt{op})]}\end{array}\right)$$

we define $\mathtt{FN}(\mathtt{t}) \subseteq \mathtt{N}$ by

$$\mathtt{FN}(\mathtt{t}) = \{\mathtt{c}_i \mid i \in [1,\mathrm{ar_n}(\mathtt{op})]\} \cup \bigcup\left\{\begin{array}{l}\mathtt{FN}(\mathtt{t}_j) \setminus \\ \left\{\mathtt{a}^j_k \mid k \in [1,\mathrm{bdep}_{\mathtt{op}}(j)]\right\}\end{array} \;\middle|\; j \in [1,\mathrm{ar_t}(\mathtt{op})]\right\}$$

As an example, consider the *(close)* rule above: $\mathtt{FN}(\underline{\mathtt{src}},\mathrm{Prem}) = \{\mathtt{c}\}$, while $\mathtt{BN}(\mathtt{y}) = \mathtt{BN}(\mathtt{y}') = \{\mathtt{a}\}$, and so $\mathtt{FN}(\mathtt{y}) = \mathtt{FN}(\mathtt{y}') = \{\mathtt{a},\mathtt{c}\}$. However, $\mathtt{FN}(\underline{\mathtt{tar}}) = \{\mathtt{c}\}$.

For the *(com)* rule above, we have $\mathtt{FN}(\underline{\mathtt{src}},\mathrm{Prem}) = \mathtt{FN}(\mathtt{y}) = \{\mathtt{c},\mathtt{d}\}$, while $\mathtt{BN}(\mathtt{y}') = \{\mathtt{a}\}$ and so $\mathtt{FN}(\mathtt{y}') = \{\mathtt{a},\mathtt{c},\mathtt{d}\}$. However, $\mathtt{FN}(\underline{\mathtt{tar}}) = \{\mathtt{c},\mathtt{d}\}$.

GSOS-like conditions:

1. Every term meta-variable appears exactly once in the conclusion source and the premise targets.
2. The source of every premise appears in the conclusion source.

Conditions relating to name binding:

3. For each term meta-variable in the conclusion source, the binding names are distinct.
$$\forall j \in [1, \mathrm{ar_t}(\underline{\mathtt{op}})],\ k, k' \in [1, \mathrm{bdep}_{\underline{\mathtt{op}}}(j)].\quad \underline{\mathtt{a}}^j_k = \underline{\mathtt{a}}^j_{k'} \implies k = k'$$
4. No free names bind in the conclusion source.
$$\forall j \in [1, \mathrm{ar_t}(\underline{\mathtt{op}})],\ k \in [1, \mathrm{bdep}_{\underline{\mathtt{op}}}(j)].\quad \underline{\mathtt{a}}^j_k \notin \mathtt{FN}(\underline{\mathtt{src}}, \mathrm{Prem})$$
5. For each premise, binding names in the label are fresh for the source.
$$\forall (\mathtt{x}, \mathtt{l}, \mathtt{y}) \in \mathrm{Prem}.\ \mathsf{bn}(\mathtt{l}) \cap \mathtt{FN}(\mathtt{x}) = \emptyset$$
6. Free names of the conclusion label are free.
$$\mathsf{fn}(\underline{\mathtt{l}}) \subseteq \mathtt{FN}(\underline{\mathtt{src}}, \mathrm{Prem})$$
7. Bound names of the conclusion label are fresh.[1]
$$\mathsf{bn}(\underline{\mathtt{l}}) \cap \mathtt{FN}(\underline{\mathtt{src}}, \mathrm{Prem}) = \emptyset$$
8. No names become unbound in the induced transition.
$$\mathtt{FN}(\underline{\mathtt{tar}}) \subseteq \mathtt{FN}(\underline{\mathtt{src}}, \mathrm{Prem}) \cup \mathsf{bn}(\underline{\mathtt{l}})$$
9. The conclusion target is well-formed.
$$\mathtt{WF}(\underline{\mathtt{tar}})$$

Figure 1. Conditions on rule structures.

Well-formed conclusion targets. Condition (9) asserts that the predicate WF holds of the conclusion target. Informally, this predicate requires that a binding variable is not used to bind in one term in the conclusion source and in a different term in the conclusion target. For instance, consider a strange operator taking two term parameters, the first one with a binder, and the following rule structure.

$$(\mathit{strange})\ \frac{-}{\mathsf{strange}(\langle \mathtt{a}\rangle \mathtt{x}, \mathtt{x}') \xrightarrow{\tau} \mathsf{res}(\langle \mathtt{a}\rangle \mathsf{par}(\mathtt{x}, \mathtt{x}'))}$$

Here the scope of the binder a in the conclusion target encompasses both x and x′, but was previously only binding in x; thus the conclusion target is not well-formed.

Formally, the predicate WF is defined by induction on the structure of the set $T^{\mathsf{sub}}_{\mathbf{Set_N}}\mathtt{X}$, as follows.

- For $\mathtt{x} \in \mathtt{X}$, we always let $\mathtt{WF}(\mathtt{x})$.
- For $\mathtt{t} = \mathsf{op}\left(\begin{array}{l} (\mathtt{c}_i)_{i \in [1, \mathrm{ar_n}(\mathsf{op})]}, \\ \left(\langle \mathtt{a}^j_k \rangle_{k \in [1, \mathrm{bdep_{op}}(j)]} \mathtt{t}_j \right)_{j \in [1, \mathrm{ar_t}(\mathsf{op})]} \end{array} \right)$,
  we let $\mathtt{WF}(\mathtt{t})$ if: for all $j \in [1, \mathrm{ar_t}(\mathsf{op})]$ we have $\mathtt{WF}(\mathtt{t}_j)$ and, furthermore, for all $k \in [1, \mathrm{bdep_{op}}(j)]$, if $\mathtt{a}^j_k \in \mathtt{BN}(\underline{\mathtt{src}}, \mathrm{Prem})$ then for all x appearing in $\mathtt{t}_j$ we have $\mathtt{a}^j_k \in \mathtt{FN}(\mathtt{x})$.

Necessity of conditions. If one of Conditions (1–6) or (8--9) is violated then wide-open bisimilarity need not be a congruence for the induced transition system.[1] The reasons suggested by Bloom *et. al.* [4, App. A] justify Conditions (1–2). Conditions (3–6) and (8–9) are important because they disallow testing of name freshness. For instance, consider the construct if-fresh, which takes one name parameter and one term parameter with a binder, with semantics given by the rule structure

$$(\mathit{if\text{-}fresh})\ \frac{\mathtt{x} \xrightarrow{\tau} \mathtt{y}}{\mathsf{if\text{-}fresh}(\mathtt{c}, \langle \mathtt{c}\rangle \mathtt{x}) \xrightarrow{\tau} \mathtt{y}}$$

which violates Condition (4). If the if-fresh construct was allowed, the semantics in the nominal framework would be that if $a\#\langle b\rangle P$ then $\mathsf{if\text{-}fresh}(a, \langle b\rangle P)$ performs all the τ transitions of $[a \leftrightarrow b]P$, because in that case $\langle b\rangle P = \langle a\rangle [a \leftrightarrow b]P$. Thus the context $\mathsf{if\text{-}fresh}(a, \langle b\rangle \mathsf{tau}(-))$ would distinguish the π-calculus term nil from the bisimilar term $\mathsf{mm}(a, b, \mathsf{nil})$.

4.3. From concrete to abstract rules

Our aim in this section is to derive from a rule structure an abstract rule, *i.e.* a natural transformation of the form (10). To do this we consider all the possible instantiations of the rule structure.

Instantiations. For a nominal substitution X, an *instantiation* I of the rule structure R is a pair of functions $(I_{\mathrm{n}} : \mathtt{N} \to |\mathcal{N}|, I_{\mathrm{t}} : \mathtt{X} \to |X|)$ such that I_{n} is injective.

Archetypal parameter. To each instantiation I we assign an *archetypal parameter*

$$I(\underline{\mathtt{src}}, \mathrm{Prem}) \in \Sigma_{\mathbf{Nom}}(|X| \times B_{\mathrm{g}}\,|X|)$$

This is to be thought of as a simultaneous instantiation of both the conclusion source and of the premises.

First, for each $j \in [1, \mathrm{ar_t}(\underline{\mathtt{op}})]$, we instantiate the premises with source $\underline{\mathtt{x}}_j$, by defining $I(\mathrm{Prem}[j]) \in B_{\mathrm{g}}\,|X|$.

$$\begin{aligned} &I(\mathrm{Prem}[j]) \\ &= \{\mathsf{in}(I_{\mathrm{n}}(\mathtt{c}), \langle I_{\mathrm{n}}(\mathtt{a})\rangle I_{\mathrm{t}}(\mathtt{y})) \mid (\underline{\mathtt{x}}_j, \mathtt{c}(\mathtt{a}), \mathtt{y}) \in \mathrm{Prem}\} \\ &\quad \cup \{\mathsf{out}(I_{\mathrm{n}}(\mathtt{c}), I_{\mathrm{n}}(\mathtt{d}), I_{\mathrm{t}}(\mathtt{y})) \mid (\underline{\mathtt{x}}_j, \bar{\mathtt{c}}\mathtt{d}, \mathtt{y}) \in \mathrm{Prem}\} \\ &\quad \cup \{\mathsf{bout}(I_{\mathrm{n}}(\mathtt{c}), \langle I_{\mathrm{n}}(\mathtt{a})\rangle I_{\mathrm{t}}(\mathtt{y})) \mid (\underline{\mathtt{x}}_j, \bar{\mathtt{c}}(\mathtt{a}), \mathtt{y}) \in \mathrm{Prem}\} \\ &\quad \cup \{\mathsf{tau}(I_{\mathrm{t}}(\mathtt{y})) \mid (\underline{\mathtt{x}}_j, \tau, \mathtt{y}) \in \mathrm{Prem}\} \end{aligned}$$

[1] Condition (7), though sensible, is not strictly necessary for our main result (Theorem 4.4); rules violating it do not induce any transitions.

Now the archetypal parameter $I(\underline{\texttt{src}}, \mathrm{Prem})$ is given by

$$\underline{\texttt{op}}\left(\begin{array}{l}(I_{\mathrm{n}}(\underline{\texttt{c}}_i))_{i\in[1,\mathrm{ar}_{\mathrm{n}}(\underline{\texttt{op}})]}\,,\\ \left(\begin{array}{l}\langle I_{\mathrm{n}}(\underline{\texttt{a}}^j_k)\rangle_{k\in[1,\mathrm{bdep}_{\underline{\texttt{op}}}(j)]}\\ \quad (I_{\mathrm{t}}(\underline{\texttt{x}}_j), I(\mathrm{Prem}[j]))\end{array}\right)_{j\in[1,\mathrm{ar}_{\mathrm{t}}(\underline{\texttt{op}})]}\end{array}\right)$$

Archetypal result. To each instantiation I we assign an *archetypal result* $I(\underline{\texttt{l}}, \underline{\texttt{tar}}) \in L_{\mathrm{g}}T_{\mathbf{Nom}}|X|$. This is to be thought of as a simultaneous instantiation of both the conclusion label and of the conclusion target.

First, we consider how to instantiate the conclusion target. By instantiating raw syntax into abstract syntax (as in Section 2.3) and then evaluating explicit substitutions (as in Section 2.2.2), we have a function

$$T^{\mathsf{sub}}_{\mathbf{Set}_{\mathbb{N}}}\mathtt{X} \to \left|T^{\mathsf{sub}}_{\mathbf{NomSub}}X\right| \to |T_{\mathbf{NomSub}}X| \stackrel{\sim}{\to} T_{\mathbf{Nom}}|X|$$

and we let $I(\underline{\texttt{tar}}) \in T_{\mathbf{Nom}}|X|$ be the image of this function on the conclusion target $\underline{\texttt{tar}}$.

Now the archetypal result is dependent on the kind of conclusion label, as follows:

for $\underline{\texttt{l}} = \mathsf{c(a)}$, $I(\underline{\texttt{l}}, \underline{\texttt{tar}}) = \mathsf{in}(I_{\mathrm{n}}(\mathsf{c}), \langle I_{\mathrm{n}}(\mathsf{a})\rangle I(\underline{\texttt{tar}}))$;
for $\underline{\texttt{l}} = \bar{\mathsf{c}}\mathsf{d}$, $I(\underline{\texttt{l}}, \underline{\texttt{tar}}) = \mathsf{out}(I_{\mathrm{n}}(\mathsf{c}), I_{\mathrm{n}}(\mathsf{d}), I(\underline{\texttt{tar}}))$;
for $\underline{\texttt{l}} = \bar{\mathsf{c}}\mathsf{(a)}$, $I(\underline{\texttt{l}}, \underline{\texttt{tar}}) = \mathsf{bout}(I_{\mathrm{n}}(\mathsf{c}), \langle I_{\mathrm{n}}(\mathsf{a})\rangle I(\underline{\texttt{tar}}))$;
for $\underline{\texttt{l}} = \tau$, $I(\underline{\texttt{l}}, \underline{\texttt{tar}}) = \mathsf{tau}(I(\underline{\texttt{tar}}))$.

Abstract rules. The archetypal parameter of an instantiation represents the smallest parameter that should be considered with that instantiation. The same instantiation, however, is also adequate for overspecified parameters; *i.e.* those that more than fulfill the premises. Formally, thus, we say that an instantiation I is *adequate* for a parameter

$$s = \underline{\texttt{op}}\left(\begin{array}{l}(I_{\mathrm{n}}(\underline{\texttt{c}}_i))_{i\in[1,\mathrm{ar}_{\mathrm{n}}(\underline{\texttt{op}})]}\,,\\ \left(\langle I_{\mathrm{n}}(\underline{\texttt{a}}^j_k)\rangle_{k\in[1,\mathrm{bdep}_{\underline{\texttt{op}}}(j)]}\,(I_{\mathrm{t}}(\underline{\texttt{x}}_j), \beta_j)\right)_{j\in[1,\mathrm{ar}_{\mathrm{t}}(\underline{\texttt{op}})]}\end{array}\right)$$

in $\Sigma_{\mathbf{Nom}}(|X| \times B_{\mathrm{g}}|X|)$ if $I(\mathrm{Prem}[j]) \subseteq \beta_j$ for all $j \in \mathrm{ar}_{\mathrm{t}}(\underline{\texttt{op}})$ and $I_{\mathrm{n}}(\mathsf{bn}(\underline{\texttt{l}}))\#s$.

Thus for every parameter $s \in \Sigma_{\mathbf{Nom}}(|X| \times B_{\mathrm{g}}|X|)$ we have a set $[\![\mathrm{R}]\!]_X(s) \subseteq L_{\mathrm{g}}T_{\mathbf{Nom}}|X|$ of possible results:

$$[\![\mathrm{R}]\!]_X(s) = \{I(\underline{\texttt{l}}, \underline{\texttt{tar}}) \mid I \text{ is an adequate instantiation for } s\}$$

The collection of adequate instantiations is typically not finite. However, we have the following result.

Lemma 4.2 *The set $[\![\mathrm{R}]\!]_X(s)$ is finite.*

Thus the mapping $s \mapsto [\![\mathrm{R}]\!]_X(s)$ yields a function as follows:

$$[\![\mathrm{R}]\!]_X : \Sigma_{\mathbf{Nom}}(|X| \times B_{\mathrm{g}}|X|) \to B_{\mathrm{g}}T_{\mathbf{Nom}}|X| \quad .$$

Theorem 4.3 *The family $\{[\![\mathrm{R}]\!]_X\}_{X\in\mathbf{NomSub}}$ is a natural family of equivariant functions.*

The collection of natural transformations (10) pointwise inherits a join semi-lattice structure from B_{g}, allowing the extension of the theory to finite sets of rules.

Theorem 4.4 *For a name-passing system defined by a finite set of rule structures for a binding signature Σ, each satisfying Conditions (1–9), wide-open bisimilarity on the ground transition system induced by the syntactic operational model $T_{\mathbf{Nom}}\emptyset \to B_{\mathrm{g}}T_{\mathbf{Nom}}\emptyset$ is a congruence.*

References

[1] M. Abadi and C. Fournet. Mobile values, new names, and secure communication. In *Proc. POPL'01*, 2001.

[2] L. Aceto, W. Fokkink, and C. Verhoef. Structural operational semantics. In *Handbook of Process Algebra*, chapter 1.3, pages 197–292. Elsevier, 1999.

[3] K. L. Bernstein. A congruence theorem for structural operational semantics of higher-order languages. In *Proc. LICS'98*, pages 153–164, 1998.

[4] B. Bloom, S. Istrail, and A. R. Meyer. Bisimulation can't be traced. *J. ACM*, 42(1):232–268, 1995.

[5] G. L. Cattani and P. Sewell. Models for name-passing processes: interleaving and causal. *Inform. and Comput.*, 190(2):136–178, 2004.

[6] M. P. Fiore, E. Moggi, and D. Sangiorgi. A fully abstract model for the π-calculus. *Inform. and Comput.*, 179(1):76–117, 2002.

[7] M. P. Fiore, G. D. Plotkin, and D. Turi. Abstract syntax and variable binding. In *Proc. LICS'99*, pages 193–202, 1999.

[8] M. P. Fiore and S. Staton. Comparing operational models of name-passing process calculi. *Inform. and Comput.*, 204(4):524–560, 2006.

[9] M. P. Fiore and D. Turi. Semantics of name and value passing. In *Proc. LICS'01*, pages 93–104, 2001.

[10] M. J. Gabbay and A. M. Pitts. A new approach to abstract syntax involving binders. *Formal Aspect. Comput.*, 13(3–5):341–363, 2002.

[11] B. Klin. From bialgebraic semantics to congruence formats. In *Proc. SOS'04*, ENTCS, pages 3–37, 2005.

[12] D. Miller and A. Tiu. A proof theory for generic judgments. *ACM Trans. Comput. Logic*, 6(4):749–783, 2005.

[13] R. Milner, J. Parrow, and D. Walker. A calculus of mobile processes (II). *Inform. and Comput.*, 100(1):41–77, 1992.

[14] J. Parrow and B. Victor. The Update calculus. In *Proc. AMAST'97*, volume 1349 of *LNCS*, 1997.

[15] A. M. Pitts. Nominal logic, a first order theory of names and binding. *Inform. and Comput.*, 186(2):165–193, 2003.

[16] D. Sangiorgi. A theory of bisimulation for the pi-calculus. *Acta Inform.*, 33(1):69–97, 1996.

[17] D. Sangiorgi. Lazy functions and mobile processes. In *Essays in honour of Robin Milner*. MIT Press, 2000.

[18] I. Stark. A fully abstract domain model for the π-calculus. In *Proc. LICS'96*, pages 36–42, 1996.

[19] R. Street. The formal theory of monads. *J. Pure Appl. Algebra*, 2:149–168, 1972.

[20] D. Turi and G. Plotkin. Towards a mathematical operational semantics. In *Proc. LICS'97*, pages 280–291, 1997.

[21] S. Weber and B. Bloom. Metatheory of the π-calculus. Technical Report TR96-1564, Cornell University, 1996.

[22] A. Ziegler, D. Miller, and C. Palamidessi. A congruence format for name-passing calculi. In *Proc. SOS'05*, 2005.

On the Expressiveness of Linearity vs Persistence in the Asychronous Pi-Calculus

Catuscia Palamidessi
INRIA and LIX École Polytechnique
catuscia@lix.polytechnique.fr

Vijay Saraswat
IBM TJ Watson Research Lab
vijay@saraswat.org

Frank D. Valencia
CNRS and LIX École Polytechnique
frank.valencia@lix.polytechnique.fr

Björn Victor
Dept. of Information Technology, Uppsala Univ.
bjorn.victor@it.uu.se

Abstract

We present an expressiveness study of linearity and persistence of processes. We choose the π-calculus, one of the main representatives of process calculi, as a framework to conduct our study. We consider four fragments of the π-calculus. Each one singles out a natural source of linearity/persistence also present in other frameworks such as Concurrent Constraint Programming (CCP), Linear CCP, and several calculi for security. The study is presented by providing (or proving the non-existence of) encodings among the fragments, a processes-as-formulae interpretation and a reduction from Minsky machines.

1 Introduction

Several process calculi such as CCS, CSP, the π-calculus [15] and Linear CCP [8, 23] have an obvious source of *linearity*: Messages (or *senders*) are consumed upon being received. For example, in the π-calculus, the system

$$\overline{x}\langle z\rangle \mid x(y).P \mid x(y).Q \tag{1}$$

represents a message with a datum z, tagged with x, that can be *consumed* by either $x(y).P$ or $x(y).Q$. The system can evolve into either (a) $P\{z/y\} \mid x(y).Q$ or (b) $x(y).P \mid Q\{z/y\}$.

Nevertheless, there are other process calculi which follow a different pattern: Messages cannot be consumed; they are *persistent* rather than linear. One of the most prominent representatives of such calculi is Concurrent Constraint Programming (CCP) [22]. In this framework all messages, more precisely items of information, are accumulated in a global store. The messages in the store can be read but, unlike in Linear CCP, they cannot be consumed, i.e., the store is persistent.

Several other frameworks using a persistent store can be found in the context of calculi for analyzing and describing security protocols. For instance, Crazzolara and Winskel's SPL [7], the Spi Calculus variants by Fiore and Abadi [9] and by Amadio et al [1], and the calculus of Boreale and Buscemi [4] are all operationally defined in terms of configurations containing items of information (messages) which cannot be consumed during evolution. The idea is that the persistent store models an attacker's ability to see and remember every message that has been in transit.

A legitimate question is whether such persistence restricts the systems that we can specify, model or reason about in the framework. For instance, whether CCP can specify the kind of systems that can be described in Linear CCP. Analogously, in the context of the above-mentioned calculi for security, e.g. in SPL, one may wonder if not allowing the attacker to remove messages from the network may rule out the specification of a possible attack to a given protocol. (Note that the claims of extra expressivity of Linear CCP over CCP in [2, 8] are based on discrimination introduced by divergence that is ignored by the standard notion of weak bisimulation.)

There is another source of linearity in (1): *Receivers* can also be consumed. For example, in the case in which $x(y).P$ evolves into $P\{z/y\}$. Persistent receivers arise, e.g. in the notion of *omega receptiveness* [20] where the input of a name is always available—but always with the same continuation. In the π-calculus persistent receivers are used, for instance, to model functions, objects, higher-order communications, or procedure definitions. Notice that the situation in this case is somehow dual to the persistent outputs case and begs the same kind of question: If we require inputs to be persistent, do we restrict the kind of systems we can specify?

Now, in the above situations we have that either messages or receivers are persistent. One can further consider the complementary case in which both messages and re-

1043-6871/06 $20.00 © 2006 IEEE

ceivers are persistent. In the context of CCP, such a restriction would correspond to CCP with universally-quantified persistent ask operations. In the context of calculi for security, persistent receivers can be used to specify protocols where principals are willing to run an unbounded number of times (and persistent messages to model the fact that every message can be remembered by the spy). In fact, the approach of specifying protocols in a persistent setting, with an unbounded number of sessions, has been explored in [3] by using a classic logic Horn clause representation of protocols (rather than a linear logic one).

In this paper, we present our expressiveness study of linearity and persistence in a well-established framework, namely the *asynchronous π-calculus*. This way our study (and its applications) benefits from standard and well-investigated reasoning techniques and notions of equivalence. Furthermore the linear/persistent features of the above calculi are naturally captured in this framework. Linear messages are represented as asynchronous *outputs*, and linear receivers as *input* processes. Persistent messages (and receivers) can simply be specified using the *replication* operator of the calculus which creates an unbounded number of copies of a given process.

We consider four sub-languages of the asynchronous polyadic π-calculus, each capturing one of the above sources of linearity/persistence. Namely, the polyadic asynchronous π-calculus (π), the *persistent-input* π (PIπ) defined as π but inputs must be replicated, *persistent-output* defined dually, i.e. outputs rather than inputs must be replicated (POπ), and finally *persistent* π defined as π but with all inputs and outputs replicated (Pπ). We conduct our study by providing (or proving the non-existence of) encodings among the fragments, a processes-as-formulae interpretation and a reduction from Minsky machines.

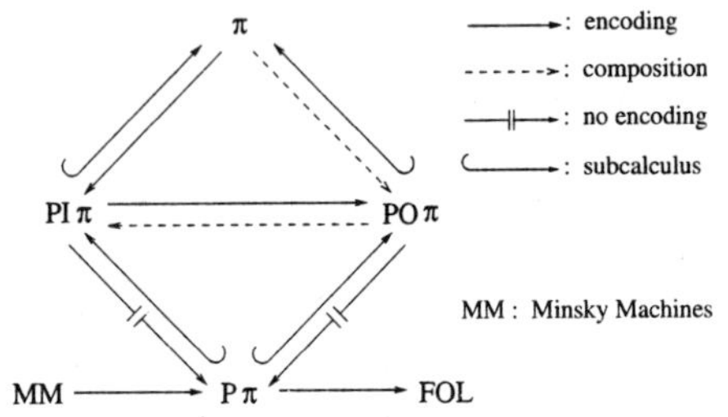

Figure 1. The hierarchy of linearity vs persistence.

Contributions. We provide encodings, homomorphic w.r.t. parallel composition, from π into PIπ and POπ capturing the behaviour of the source processes. These encodings are, respectively, fully abstract w.r.t. weak barbed congruence and weak barbed congruence restricted to encoded contexts. In contrast, we show that it is impossible to provide such encodings from π into Pπ. Intuitively this means that we need one source of linearity, i.e. either on inputs (PIπ) or outputs (POπ) to capture the behaviour of arbitrary π processes via full-abstraction. Despite the impossibility result for Pπ we also prove that Pπ is in fact Turing-powerful by encoding Minsky machines. Figure 1 illustrates these expressiveness results (a dashed arrow means that the encoding is obtained via composition).

	Pπ	POπ	PIπ
0	yes	yes	no
1	?	no	no
2	no	no	no

Table 1. Decidability of barbed congruence for the n-adic ($n = 0, 1, 2$) persistent calculi.

Furthermore, we consider sub-languages of the above π-calculi with restricted arity (i.e., the maximum number of names that can be sent in a single communication) and classify them according to the decidability of barbed congruence and their arity. Interestingly, we state that barbed congruence is undecidable for the zero-adic version of PIπ, the monadic version of POπ and the bi-adic version of Pπ. We also show that barbed congruence is decidable for the zero-adic versions of Pπ and PIπ. We leave open the corresponding decidability question for the monadic version of Pπ. Table 1 summarizes these decidability results.

We also show that Pπ admits a processes-as-formulae compositional interpretation, building on the translation of π to linear logic in [13, 23] and the logical characterization of CCP languages [11, 12]. Specifically, we characterize the standard π-calculus notion of barbed observability (for Pπ) as entailment in First-Order Logic (FOL). Indeed, Pπ can be seen as a CCP language over the Gentzen constraint system (without function symbols), with persistent universal asks [22]. Furthermore, we exploit classic FOL results by Bernays, Schönfinkel and Gödel to identify classes of *infinite-state* processes with meaningful mobile behaviour for which barbed reachability is decidable.

Our expressiveness results bear witness to the generality of the persistent store assumption in CCP and calculi for security. Moreover, the processes-as-formulae interpretation of POπ has interesting applications. In particular, the decidability results for barbed reachability for Pπ may be beneficial for analyzing protocols in which principals (represented as replicated input processes) are willing to run unboundedly many times, as those studied in [3] .

Due to space limitations most proofs will be omitted. They can be found in the extended version of this paper [18].

$$\text{COM: } \overline{x}\langle\vec{z}\rangle \mid x(\vec{y}).P \longrightarrow P\{\vec{z}/\vec{y}\} \quad \text{if } |\vec{z}| = |\vec{y}|$$

$$\text{PAR: } \frac{P \longrightarrow P'}{P \mid Q \longrightarrow P' \mid Q} \qquad \text{RES: } \frac{P \longrightarrow P'}{(\nu x)P \longrightarrow (\nu x)P'}$$

$$\text{STRUCT: } \frac{P \equiv P' \longrightarrow Q' \equiv Q}{P \longrightarrow Q}$$

Table 2. Reduction Rules.

2 The Calculi

Here we define the calculi we study. We first recall the (polyadic) *asynchronous π-calculus* here referred to as π. The other calculi are defined as syntactic restrictions of π.

2.1 Asynchronous Pi Calculus: π

We presuppose a countable set of *names*, ranged over by $x, y, \ldots$, and for each name x, a *co-name* $\overline{x}$. We use $l, l', \ldots$ to range over names and co-names. We use $\vec{x}$ to denote a finite sequence of names $x_1 x_2 \ldots x_n$ of size $|\vec{x}\,| = n$. The π *processes* are given by the following syntax:

$$P, Q, \ldots := 0 \mid \overline{x}\langle\vec{z}\rangle \mid x(\vec{y}).P \mid (\nu x)P \mid P \mid Q \mid !P$$

requiring that no name may occur more than once in $\vec{y}$.

Intuitively, an *output* $\overline{x}\langle\vec{z}\rangle$ represents a particle tagged with a name x indicating that can be received by an *input process* $x(\vec{y}).P$ which behaves, upon receiving $\vec{z}$, as $P\{\vec{z}/\vec{y}\}$. Furthermore, $x(\vec{y}).P$ binds the names $\vec{y}$ in P. The other binder is the *restriction* $(\nu x)P$ which declares a name x private to P. The *parallel composition* $P \mid Q$ means P and Q running in parallel. The *replication* $!P$ means $P \mid P \mid \ldots$, i.e., $!P$ represents a *persistent resource*.

We use the standard notations $bn(Q)$ for the *bound names* in Q, and $fn(Q)$ for the *free names* in Q, and write $(\nu x_1 \ldots x_n)P$ to denote $(\nu x_1) \ldots (\nu x_n)P$. We let σ range over non-capturing substitutions of names on processes.

The *reduction* $\longrightarrow$ is the least binary relation on processes satisfying the rules in Table 2. We use $\longrightarrow^*$ to denote the reflexive, transitive closure of $\longrightarrow$. The reductions are quotiented by the *structural congruence* relation $\equiv$.

Definition 2.1. *Let $\equiv$ be the smallest congruence over processes satisfying α-equivalence, the commutative monoid laws for composition with 0 as identity, the replication law $!P \equiv P \mid !P$, the restriction laws $(\nu x)0 \equiv 0$, $(\nu x)(\nu y)P \equiv (\nu y)(\nu x)P$ and the extrusion law: $(\nu x)(P \mid Q) \equiv P \mid (\nu x)Q$ if $x \notin fn(P)$.*

We conclude the description of π by recalling some process equivalences we shall use throughout the paper. First we recall a basic notion of observation in the π-calculus.

Definition 2.2. *Define $P \downarrow_{\overline{x}}$ iff $\exists \vec{z}, \vec{y}, R : P \equiv (\nu\vec{z})(\overline{x}\langle\vec{y}\rangle \mid R)$ and x is not in $\vec{z}$. Similarly, $P \downarrow_x$ iff $\exists \vec{z}, \vec{y}, Q, R : P \equiv (\nu\vec{z})(x(\vec{y}).Q \mid R)$ and x is not $\vec{z}$. Furthermore, $P \Downarrow_l$ iff $\exists Q : P \longrightarrow^* Q \downarrow_l$.*

Intuitively, given $l = x$ ($l = \overline{x}$) we say that l, a *barb*, can be *observed* at P, written $P \downarrow_l$, iff P can perform an input (output) on channel x. However, in the context of the *asynchronous* π-calculus in defining the process equivalences it is standard to restrict the observables to be the output barbs; i.e., barbs of the form $\overline{x}$ [21].

We begin with a basic π process equivalence, sometimes referred to as *barbed correspondence* [17], which equates processes iff they exhibit the same barbs. In what follows we prefer to refer to this equivalence as *output equivalence* since we only consider output barbs. Recall that a process *context* C is an expression with a hole $[\cdot]$ such that placing a process in the hole produces a process term.

Definition 2.3 (Output Equivalence, Output Congruence). *We say that P and Q are* output equivalent, *written $P \overset{\circ}{\simeq} Q$ iff for every x, $P \Downarrow_{\overline{x}} \Leftrightarrow Q \Downarrow_{\overline{x}}$. We say that P and Q are* output congruent, *written $P \simeq Q$, iff for every process context C, $C[P] \overset{\circ}{\simeq} C[Q]$.*

We now recall the notion of (weak) barbed bisimilarity.

Definition 2.4 (Barbed Bisimilarity, Barbed Congruence). *A* (weak) barbed bisimulation *is a symmetric relation $\mathcal{R}$ satisfying the following: $(P, Q) \in \mathcal{R}$ implies that:*

1. *$P \longrightarrow P'$ then $\exists Q' : Q \longrightarrow^* Q' \wedge (P', Q') \in \mathcal{R}$.*
2. *$P \downarrow_{\overline{x}}$ then $Q \Downarrow_{\overline{x}}$.*

We say that P and Q are (weak) barbed bisimilar, *written $P \overset{\circ}{\approx} Q$, iff $(P, Q) \in \mathcal{R}$ for some barbed bisimulation $\mathcal{R}$. Furthermore,* (weak) barbed congruence $\approx$ *is defined as: $P \approx Q$ iff for every process context $C[\cdot]$, $C[P] \overset{\circ}{\approx} C[Q]$.*

2.2 (Semi) Persistent Subcalculi of π

The Persistent-Output Calculus: POπ. The *persistent-output* calculus POπ arises as from π by requiring all outputs to be replicated. In fact for POπ processes, $\longrightarrow$ can equivalently be defined as in Table 2 with COM replaced with the rule below. The new rule reflects the *linear-input* and *persistent-output* nature of POπ.

$$!\overline{x}\langle\vec{z}\rangle \mid x(\vec{y}).P \longrightarrow !\overline{x}\langle\vec{z}\rangle \mid P\{\vec{z}/\vec{y}\} \quad \text{if } |\vec{z}| = |\vec{y}|$$

The Persistent-Input Calculus: PIπ. The PIπ calculus results from π by requiring all input processes to be replicated. The relation $\longrightarrow$ for PIπ can be equivalently defined as in Table 2 with COM replaced with the rule

$$\overline{x}\langle\vec{z}\rangle \mid !x(\vec{y}).P \longrightarrow P\{\vec{z}/\vec{y}\} \mid !x(\vec{y}).P \quad \text{if } |\vec{z}| = |\vec{y}|$$

The Persistent Calculus: Pπ. Finally, we have the *persistent* calculus Pπ where output and input processes must be replicated. The relation $\longrightarrow$ for Pπ can be equivalently defined as in Table 2 with COM replaced with the rule

$$!\overline{x}\langle\vec{z}\rangle \mid !x(\vec{y}).P \longrightarrow P\{\vec{z}/\vec{y}\} \mid !\overline{x}\langle\vec{z}\rangle \mid !x(\vec{y}).P \text{ if } |\vec{z}| = |\vec{y}|$$

The next proposition reflects the duality of PIπ and POπ.

Proposition 2.5. *The following monotone properties hold:*

1. *If P is a* POπ *process,* $P \longrightarrow Q$ *and* $P \downarrow_{\overline{x}}$ *then* $Q \downarrow_{\overline{x}}$.
2. *If P is a* PIπ *process* $P \longrightarrow Q$ *and* $P \downarrow_x$ *then* $Q \downarrow_x$.
3. *If P is a* Pπ *process,* $P \longrightarrow Q$ *and* $P \downarrow_l$ *then* $Q \downarrow_l$.

2.3 Calculi Conventions and their Equivalences

We will work with fragments of the various calculi in terms of arity.

Definition 2.6. *Define the* arity *of P,* $\mathcal{A}(P)$*, as* $\mathcal{A}(\overline{x}\langle\vec{y}\rangle) = |\vec{y}|$, $\mathcal{A}(x(\vec{y}).Q) = max(|\vec{y}|, \mathcal{A}(Q))$, $\mathcal{A}(Q \mid R) = max(\mathcal{A}(Q), \mathcal{A}(R))$, $\mathcal{A}((\nu x)Q) = \mathcal{A}(!Q) = \mathcal{A}(Q)$.

Given $\Sigma \in \{\pi, \text{PO}\pi, \text{PI}\pi, \text{P}\pi\}$*, the k-adic (version of)* Σ*,* Σ^k *is defined as* Σ *except that its processes have arity less or equal to k. We decree that* $\Sigma^\omega = \Sigma$.

Convention 2.7. *Henceforth* **Calc** *denote the set of calculi* $\{\pi^k, \text{P}\pi^k, \text{PI}\pi^k, \text{PO}\pi^k \mid k \in \mathbb{N} \cup \{\omega\}\}$.

Let us now specialize our equivalences and reduction relation to the various calculi.

Definition 2.8. *Let* $\Sigma \in$ **Calc**. *Define* $P \stackrel{\circ}{\simeq}^{\Sigma} Q$ $(P \stackrel{\bullet}{\approx}^{\Sigma} Q)$ *iff P and Q are* Σ *processes and* $P \stackrel{\circ}{\simeq} Q$ $(P \stackrel{\bullet}{\approx} Q)$*. Also, define* $P \simeq^{\Sigma} Q$ $(P \approx^{\Sigma} Q)$ *iff P and Q are* Σ *processes and for every* Σ *context C,* $C[P] \stackrel{\circ}{\simeq}^{\Sigma} C[Q]$ $(C[P] \stackrel{\bullet}{\approx}^{\Sigma} C[Q])$*. Finally, define* $P \longrightarrow_{\Sigma} Q$ *iff P and Q are* Σ *processes and* $P \longrightarrow Q$.

Notice that reduction, modulo $\equiv$, is invariant wrt the processes of a given calculus $\Sigma \in$ **Calc**, i.e., if $P \in \Sigma$ and $P \longrightarrow Q$ then there exists $Q' \in \Sigma$ such that $Q' \equiv Q$.

In what follows when no confusion arises we omit the indices from process relations.

3 Encodings and their properties

In the following sections we provide, or under reasonable conditions demonstrate the impossibility of the existence of, encodings $[\![\cdot]\!]$ from the terms of a given language into the terms of another.

The following condition is particularly appropriate in the context of distributed systems. It describes encodings preserving the parallel topology of the source system.

Definition 3.1. *An encoding* $[\![\cdot]\!]$ *is a* homomorphism w.r.t. parallel composition *iff* $[\![P \mid Q]\!] = [\![P]\!] \mid [\![Q]\!]$*. Homomorphism w.r.t the other operators is defined analogously.*

The following notions describe some criteria used in the literature for the correctness of encodings (see e.g., [17]).

Definition 3.2. *Let* $\Sigma, \Sigma' \in$ **Calc**, *and* $\bowtie \in \{\stackrel{\bullet}{\approx}, \approx, \stackrel{\circ}{\simeq}, \simeq\}$*. Let* $[\![\cdot]\!] : \Sigma \rightarrow \Sigma'$ *be an* encoding *(i.e., a map of* Σ *terms into* Σ' *terms). The encoding is* sound *wrt* $\bowtie$ *iff* $[\![P]\!] \bowtie^{\Sigma'} [\![Q]\!]$ *implies* $P \bowtie^{\Sigma} Q$*. The encoding is* complete *wrt* $\bowtie$ *iff* $P \bowtie^{\Sigma} Q$ *implies* $[\![P]\!] \bowtie^{\Sigma'} [\![Q]\!]$*. The encoding is* fully abstract *wrt* $\bowtie$ *iff it is both sound and complete wrt* $\bowtie$ *. Finally,* $[\![\cdot]\!]$ *is* ideal *wrt* $\bowtie$ *iff* $[\![P]\!] \bowtie^{\pi} P$.

Intuitively, given a chosen equivalence, full abstraction says that the encoding reflects (soundness) and preserves (completeness) equivalence of source terms. Full abstraction is a useful criterion for the correctness of an encoding wrt a given equivalence when ideal encodings may not exist. Notice that the criterion of being ideal is stronger than that of being fully abstract.

4 On the Expressiveness of Pπ

In this section we study the expressiveness of the persistent calculus Pπ. We first prove that it is *impossible* to provide a *sound* encoding, homomorphic wrt parallel composition, from π into Pπ. This holds for all the equivalences under consideration in this paper—see Definition 3.2.

Despite the above impossibility result, we prove that Pπ is Turing powerful. We also show Pπ processes can compositionally be encoded as FOL formulae. We illustrate how *mobility* in Pπ can be naturally simulated in FOL and state the characterization of barbed reachability as FOL entailment. We use the characterization and classic FOL theorems to prove decidability results for meaningful classes of infinite-state mobile Pπ processes.

4.1 Impossibility of encoding π into Pπ

Key to our impossibility result is establishing the property $P \mid P \approx P$ for arbitrary Pπ processes P. Consider $P = (\nu z)!\overline{x}\langle z\rangle$. P may be viewed as a generator of a single private name broadcast on x while $P \mid P$ may be viewed as a generator of two different privates names broadcast on x. Therefore, it may not be immediate than $P \mid P$ should be barbed congruent to P in Pπ . In fact, the property would not hold if we had the mismatch operator $[x \neq y]Q$ whose intended meaning is that Q will be executed iff x and y are different names [21], as the following example illustrates:

Example 4.1. Take $R = !x(y).!x(y').[y \neq y']!\overline{t}$ and $Q = (\nu z)!\overline{x}\langle z\rangle$. One can verify that $(R \mid Q) \not\Downarrow_{\overline{t}}$ but $(R \mid Q \mid Q) \Downarrow_{\overline{t}}$.

The following monotonicity property, which also does not hold in the presence of mismatch, is very useful for our results:

Proposition 4.2. *For any name substitution σ, $P \longrightarrow Q$ implies $P\sigma \longrightarrow Q\sigma$.*

Now, the first interesting result for $\mathrm{P}\pi$ is that output congruence and barbed congruence (restricted to $\mathrm{P}\pi$ contexts) coincide. The result is a corollary of the following lemma whose proof basically rests on showing that $\mathrm{P}\pi$ is confluent.

Lemma 4.3. $\overset{\circ}{\simeq}^{\mathrm{P}\pi} = \dot{\approx}^{\mathrm{P}\pi}$.

Corollary 4.4. $\simeq^{\mathrm{P}\pi} = \approx^{\mathrm{P}\pi}$.

We now proceed to prove the Duplication Lemma below. First we need the following Context Lemma whose proof is similar to Lemma 2.1.19 in [21].

Lemma 4.5 (Context Lemma). *$P \approx^{\mathrm{P}\pi} Q$ if for every $\mathrm{P}\pi$ process T and name substitution σ,*

$$T \mid P\sigma \dot{\approx}^{\mathrm{P}\pi} T \mid Q\sigma.$$

Lemma 4.6 (Duplication Lemma). *For every $P \in \mathrm{P}\pi$, $P \mid P \approx^{\mathrm{P}\pi} P$.*

Proof. From Corollary 4.3 we can freely replace $\approx$ with $\simeq$. The proof proceeds by induction on the size of P. The proof of $P = (\nu x)R$ is particularly interesting and it uses Proposition 4.2 and Lemmas 4.3 and 4.5. The other cases are easier. See [18] for details. □

The following proposition can be proven from the above lemmata, and analysis of the reduction of $!P$ in arbitrary contexts.

Proposition 4.7. *For every $\mathrm{P}\pi$ process P, $!P \approx^{\mathrm{P}\pi} P$.*

We now have all what we need to prove the following impossibility result.

Theorem 4.8 (Impossibility of Sound Encodings). *Let $\bowtie \in \{\dot{\approx}, \approx, \overset{\circ}{\simeq}, \simeq\}$. There is no encoding $[\![\cdot]\!] : \pi \longrightarrow \mathrm{P}\pi$, homomorphic wrt parallel composition, such that for all $P, Q \in \pi$, $[\![P]\!] \bowtie^{\mathrm{P}\pi} [\![Q]\!]$ implies $P \bowtie^{\pi} Q$.*

Proof. Notice $\overset{\circ}{\simeq}^{\pi}$ contains all the other process equivalences of the form $\bowtie^{\pi}$ while $\approx^{\mathrm{P}\pi}$ is contained in every process equivalence of the from $\bowtie^{\mathrm{P}\pi}$. Then, it suffices to show that there are P, Q such that $[\![P]\!] \approx^{\mathrm{P}\pi} [\![Q]\!]$ but $P \not\overset{\circ}{\simeq}^{\pi} Q$ with $[\![\cdot]\!]$ being homomorphic wrt parallel composition. Take $P = R \mid R$ and $Q = R$ where $R = \overline{x} \mid x.x.\overline{t}$. Clearly, $P \not\overset{\circ}{\simeq}^{\pi} Q$ since $P \Downarrow_{\overline{t}}$ but $Q \not\Downarrow_{\overline{t}}$. From Lemma 4.6 and homomorphism wrt parallel composition we obtain $[\![P]\!] = [\![R]\!] \mid [\![R]\!] \approx^{\mathrm{P}\pi} [\![R]\!] = [\![Q]\!]$ as wanted. □

4.2 FOL Characterization of $\mathrm{P}\pi$

In this section we give a characterization of $\mathrm{P}\pi$ in first-order logic by providing a compositional translation of $\mathrm{P}\pi$ processes into logical formulae, following the translation of π into linear logic [23, Table 2], and the well-known embedding of intuitionistic logic in linear logic through the "of course" modality "!". In particular we shall identify barbed reachability in $\mathrm{P}\pi$ as logical consequence.

We assume the reader is familiar with basic notations and concepts of first-order logic. We presuppose a first-order language $\mathcal{L}$ whose non-logical symbols include predicates of the form $\mathtt{out}^k$ where $k \geq 0$ denotes the arity of the predicate. We omit this arity index if it is understood from the context. Given two FOL formulae F and G over $\mathcal{L}$, we write $F \models G$ iff the implication formula $(F \Rightarrow G)$ is *logically valid*. If $F \models G$ we say that G is a *logical consequence* of F.

The following proposition simplifies the kind of $\mathrm{P}\pi$ processes we need to consider in the translation.

Definition 4.9. *A $\mathrm{P}\pi$ process is said to be* minimal *iff it can be generated by the following syntax:*

$$P, Q, \ldots := 0 \mid !\overline{x}\langle\vec{y}\rangle \mid !x(\vec{y}).P \mid (\nu x)P \mid P \mid Q.$$

Hence minimal processes are those $\mathrm{P}\pi$ processes where replication only appears immediately before input and output processes. For example, $!(\nu x)P$ is not minimal.

Definition 4.10. *Let $m(\cdot) : \mathrm{P}\pi \longrightarrow \mathrm{P}\pi$ be the map into minimal processes given as $m(!0) = m(0) = 0$, $m(!\overline{x}\langle\vec{z}\rangle) = !\overline{x}\langle\vec{z}\rangle$, $m(!x(\vec{y}).Q) = !x(\vec{y}).m(Q)$, $m(!(P \mid Q)) = m(P \mid Q) = m(P) \mid m(Q)$ and $m(!(\nu x)P) = m((\nu x)P) = (\nu x)m(P)$.*

Proposition 4.11. *For every $P \in \mathrm{P}\pi$, $m(P) \approx^{\mathrm{P}\pi} P$.*

Proof. From Proposition 4.7. □

Therefore, we can freely restrict ourselves to minimal processes. The following encoding compositionally translates minimal processes into formulae.

Definition 4.12. *Let $[\![\cdot]\!] : \mathrm{P}\pi \rightharpoonup \mathrm{FOL}$ be the partial map from minimal $\mathrm{P}\pi$ terms into FOL formulae given by:*

$$\begin{aligned} [\![0]\!] &= \mathtt{true} \\ [\![!\overline{x}\langle\vec{z}\rangle]\!] &= \mathtt{out}(x, \vec{z}) \\ [\![!x(\vec{y}).P]\!] &= \forall\vec{y}(\mathtt{out}(x, \vec{y}) \Rightarrow [\![P]\!]) \\ [\![P \mid Q]\!] &= [\![P]\!] \wedge [\![Q]\!] \\ [\![(\nu x)P]\!] &= \exists x [\![P]\!] \end{aligned}$$

Intuitively, the above encoding $[\![\cdot]\!]$ is meant to capture in logic terms how computation proceeds in $\mathrm{P}\pi$. In particular it has the following property: P will perform an output iff that output is a logical consequence of $[\![P]\!]$. Notice that existential quantification corresponds to restriction, which can simulate *name extrusion* as illustrated below. Also notice that in the translation the two binders of $\mathrm{P}\pi$, input and restriction, are translated into universal and existential quantifiers (resp), hence reflecting an elegant duality.

Example 4.13 (Name Extrusion in FOL). The process $P = (\nu z)(!\overline{x}\langle z\rangle \mid !z(u).\overline{u})$ *creates a name* z, broadcasts it to the outside on x, and waits on it for a message u from the outside. So, $R = Q \mid P$, with $Q = x(y).\overline{y}\langle t\rangle$, can perform the output $\overline{t}$, i.e., $R \Downarrow_{\overline{t}}$. Consider the FOL translation in Definition 4.12. We have

$$[\![R]\!] = \forall y(\mathtt{out}(x,y) \Rightarrow \mathtt{out}(y,t)) \wedge \exists z(\mathtt{out}(x,z) \wedge \forall u\, \mathtt{out}(z,u) \Rightarrow \mathtt{out}(u)).$$

which is logically equivalent to

$$F = \exists z(\forall y(\mathtt{out}(x,y) \Rightarrow \mathtt{out}(y,t)) \wedge \mathtt{out}(x,z) \wedge \forall u\, \mathtt{out}(z,u) \Rightarrow \mathtt{out}(u)).$$

Now, since $\mathtt{out}(z,t)$ is a logical consequence of $\forall y(\mathtt{out}(x,y) \Rightarrow \mathtt{out}(y,t)) \wedge \mathtt{out}(x,z)$, we have $F \models \exists z\, \mathtt{out}(z,t) \wedge \forall u\, \mathtt{out}(z,u) \Rightarrow \mathtt{out}(u)$ from which we obtain $F \models \mathtt{out}(t)$.

Roughly speaking, the logical step to (4.13) corresponds to using the Structural Equivalence to move a restriction to outermost position (Definition 2.1). The other steps involve Modus Ponens which corresponds to applying rule COM. □

The lemma below, which can be proven using induction on length of the derivation, states that $\mathrm{P}\pi$ reduction corresponds to logical consequence.

Lemma 4.14. *If* $P \longrightarrow_{\mathrm{P}\pi} Q$ *then* $[\![P]\!] \models [\![Q]\!]$.

The following theorem states the characterization of barbed observability in terms of logical consequence. It is related to a similar characterization in [23, Theorem 2.6]. Recall that $\mathcal{A}(P)$ denotes the arity of P (see Definition 2.6) and that from Proposition 4.11, up-to barbed congruence for $\mathrm{P}\pi$, we can confine our attention to minimal processes.

Theorem 4.15 (FOL Characterization of Barbs). *Let* $[\![\cdot]\!] : \mathrm{P}\pi \rightharpoonup \mathrm{FOL}$ *be the map in Definition 4.12. Let* P *be a minimal* $\mathrm{P}\pi$ *process. Then*

$$P \Downarrow_{\overline{x}} \text{ if and only if } [\![P]\!] \models \exists \vec{z}\, \mathtt{out}(x,\vec{z})$$

for some $\vec{z}$ *such that* $|\vec{z}| \leq \mathcal{A}(P)$.

Proof. The proof of the "only-if" direction uses Lemma 4.14. The proof of the "if" direction, the most difficult case, uses a normal form representation of the target formulae. Such normal forms simplifies the analysis of how the formulae on the right-hand of $\models$ could have been deduced from $[\![P]\!]$. See [18]. □

Remark 4.16. Theorem 4.15 reveals an interesting correspondence between restriction and existential quantification. Intuitively, it holds because we do not have operators than can make use of the fact that two names are different. It would not hold if we had mismatch with the natural translation $[\![[x \neq y]P]\!] = (x \neq y) \Rightarrow [\![P]\!]$. E.g., $(\nu xy)[x \neq y]\overline{t}$ can perform $\overline{t}$ while from $\exists xy(x \neq y) \Rightarrow \mathtt{out}(t)$ we cannot conclude $\mathtt{out}(t)$. For more on this issue see [18].

Applications. The following results are meant to illustrate applications of our FOL characterization. We use classic results from FOL to prove decidability results for barb reachability and barbed congruence.

Decidable $\mathrm{P}\pi$ Classes. The following lemma identifies several classes of $\mathrm{P}\pi$ processes whose barb-reachability problem is decidable. These classes include classes of *infinite-state* processes with name mobility (extrusion). The reachability question is relevant for safety properties stating that a given undesired output will never be performed.

Lemma 4.17. *Let* $[\![\cdot]\!] : \mathrm{P}\pi \rightharpoonup \mathrm{FOL}$ *be the map in Definition 4.12. Given* P *and* z*, the question whether* $P \Downarrow_{\overline{z}}$ *is decidable if* P *belongs to one of the following classes:*

1. $\{R \mid [\![R]\!] \Leftrightarrow \forall\vec{x}\exists\vec{y}F\}$ *(Bernays-Schönfinkel's class).*
2. $\{R \mid [\![R]\!] \Leftrightarrow \forall\vec{x}\exists uw\forall\vec{y}F\}$ *(Gödel's class).*
3. $\{R \mid R \equiv R'$ *for some R' s.t.* $|fn(R') \cup bn(R')| \leq 2\}$ *(Two-Variables Class).*
4. $\mathrm{P}\pi^0$ *(Persistent CCS-like Class).*

where F *is a quantifier-free formula.*

Proof. By reducing the question, with the help of Proposition 4.11, Theorem 4.15, to the validity of a formula which is in the class of either Bernays-Schönfinkel, Gödel, two-variables, or Monadic FOL formulae without function symbols. All these classes of formulae are decidable [5]. See [18] for details. □

Decidable Classes with Mobility. Let us illustrate briefly the name extrusion capabilities of the "mobile" classes in the above lemma. Recall that input and restriction binders are translated into universal and existential quantifiers, respectively. Hence an alternation of inputs and restrictions corresponds to alternation of universal and existential quantifiers. For instance, take $Q = !x(y).(\nu z)!\overline{y}\langle z\rangle$. Notice that Q has an input-restriction alternation and $[\![Q]\!]$ has an universal-existential alternation as it is equivalent to $\forall y\exists z(\mathtt{out}(x,y) \Rightarrow \mathtt{out}(y,z))$.

Consequently, Bernays-Schönfinkel's class allows *providers of new names* like the process Q above, i.e, processes that upon request, say on a channel x, can output private names in a given return channel y. It is worth pointing out that this class is closed under parallel composition.

So Q composed with a process R in the class, remains in the class: e.g. R could be a process $!\overline{x}\langle r\rangle \mid !r(z).Q'$ requesting from Q a fresh name.

Nevertheless, in general the Bernays-Schönfinkel's class does not allow processes with inputs on private names as the $P = (\nu z)(!\overline{x}\langle z\rangle \mid !z(u).!\overline{u})$ in our name-extrusion example (Example 4.13). However, the Gödel class allows such processes only if the number of such inputs on private names is less than three.

The third class allows processes which can be rewritten (by re-using bound names wherever possible) with only two names. E.g., P and Q above belong to the class since $P \equiv (\nu z)(!\overline{x}\langle z\rangle \mid !z(x).!\overline{x})$ and $Q \equiv !x(u).(\nu x)!\overline{u}\langle x\rangle$.

Decidability Result for Barbed Congruence. It is easy to adapt the results [6] to prove that (weak) barbed congruence is *undecidable* for the zero-adic version of the π, in our notation π^0. In contrast, here we prove that (weak) barbed congruence is decidable for the zero-adic version of Pπ, Pπ^0. The proof, which can be found in [18], uses the FOL reasoning.

The following theorem states the decidability of all the equivalences under consideration for Pπ^0. It should be noticed that the decidability result for $\simeq$ involves the use of FOL reasoning to characterize a finite set of contexts which is sufficient for verifying the congruence (see [18]).

Theorem 4.18 (Decidable Equivalences of Pπ^0). *Let* $\Sigma =$ Pπ^0. *Given* P, Q *in* Σ *and* $\bowtie \in \{\mathring{\simeq}, \simeq, \dot{\approx}, \approx\}$, *the question whether* $P \bowtie^{\Sigma} Q$ *is decidable.*

4.3 Turing Expressiveness of Pπ

In Section 4.1 we proved that there is no sound encoding, homomorphic wrt parallel, from π into Pπ. In this section we show that despite such an impossibility result Pπ is Turing-powerful. We do this by encoding two-counter machines, also called Minsky machines, which are known to be Turing-powerful [16].

Minsky Machines. A *two-counter Minsky machine* is an imperative program consisting of a sequence of labelled instructions $I_1; \ldots; I_k$ which modify the values of two non-negative counters c_0 and c_1. The instructions, using counters c_n for $n \in \{0, 1\}$, are of three kinds: L_i : `halt`, L_i : $c_n := c_n + 1$; `goto` L_j, and L_i : `if` $c_n =$ 0 `then goto` L_j^1 `else` $c_n := c_n - 1$; `goto` L_j^2. The Minsky machine starts at L_s and halts if control reaches the location of a `halt` instruction. A Minsky machine $M(v_0, v_1)$ computes the value n if it halts with $c_0 = n$.

Encoding Minsky Machines. Our encoding of a given Minsky machine M with start location L_s and initial counter values v_0, v_1 into Pπ, $[\![M_s(v_0, v_1)]\!]$, is given below, with the encoding of non-negative numbers in counter c, $(\![n]\!)_c$. The counter values are encoded in a standard fashion (similar to the persistent lists in [14]), and each location L_i corresponds to a fresh name l_i over which the current counter values are passed. Where ever $\overline{l_j}\langle c, c_{n\oplus 1}\rangle$ appears, order the objects correctly based on n ($\oplus$ denotes addition modulo 2).

$$
\begin{array}{lll}
[\![M_s(v_0, v_1)]\!] & = (\nu c_0, c_1)((\![v_0]\!)_{c_0} \mid (\![v_1]\!)_{c_1} \mid !\overline{l_s}\langle c_0, c_1\rangle & \\
 & \quad \mid \prod_{1 \le i \le k} [\![I_i]\!]) & \text{where } M = I_1; \ldots; I_k \\
[\![L_i : \texttt{halt}]\!] & = !l_i(c_0, c_1).!\overline{halt}\langle c_0\rangle & \\
\multicolumn{3}{l}{[\![L_i : c_n := c_n + 1;\ \texttt{goto}\ L_j]\!]} \\
 & = !l_i(c_0, c_1).(\nu c)(S(c, c_n) \mid !\overline{l_j}\langle c, c_{n\oplus 1}\rangle) & \\
\multicolumn{3}{l}{[\![L_i : \texttt{if}\ c_n = 0\ \texttt{then goto}\ L_j^1\ \texttt{else}\ c_n := c_n - 1;\ \texttt{goto}\ L_j^2]\!]} \\
 & = !l_i(c_0, c_1).(\nu s, z)(!\overline{c_n}\langle s, z\rangle \mid & \\
 & \quad !z.!\overline{l_j^1}\langle c_0, c_1\rangle \mid !s(c).!\overline{l_j^2}\langle c, c_{n\oplus 1}\rangle) & \\
(\![0]\!)_c & = Z(c) & \\
(\![n]\!)_c & = (\nu p)((\![n-1]\!)_p \mid S(c, p)) & \text{for } n > 0 \\
Z(c) & = !c(s, z).!\overline{z} & \text{(zero)} \\
S(c, p) & = !c(s, z).!\overline{s}\langle p\rangle & \text{(successor)}
\end{array}
$$

In the encoding, because of the persistent nature of Pπ, all states which have been triggered can always be "re-executed". The encoding of (persistent) counter values uses private channels for signalling successor and zero values, and incremented values are created at private locations. Thus the operations on the counters in one state have no effect on the values encoded in another state – the encoding is free of side-effects.

For example, consider the encoding of the if-then-else instruction. The counter values at the previous enabled location are received over l_i; the counter c_n is asked for its value and will respond on *one* of the fresh names s and z. If it responds on z, location l_j^1 is triggered with the current counter values; if it responds on s, indicating it is a successor value, then location l_j^2 is triggered with the predecessor of c_n (which is received over s) and the other counter value.

Theorem 4.19. *A Minsky machine* $M_s(v_0, v_1)$ *computes the value* n *iff* $[\![M_s(v_0, v_1)]\!] \mid !halt(c).Dec_n(c) \Downarrow \overline{yes}$ *where*

$$
\begin{array}{ll}
Dec_0(c) = (\nu s, z)(!\overline{c}\langle s, z\rangle \mid !z.!\overline{yes}) & \\
Dec_i(c) = (\nu s, z)(!\overline{c}\langle s, z\rangle \mid !s(p).Dec_{i-1}(p)) & \textit{for } i > 0
\end{array}
$$

Applications. In the previous sections we proved that all equivalences and barb reachability problems are decidable for Pπ^0. Here we state, on the contrary, that all these problems are undecidable for Pπ.

As a direct consequence of the encoding of two-counter machines, we get undecidability of barbed reachability:

Lemma 4.20. *Given* P *in* Pπ *and a name* x, *the question whether* $P \Downarrow_{\overline{x}}$ *is undecidable.*

From the above lemma and a series of reductions (see [18]) we get the following results.

Theorem 4.21 (Undecidable Equivalences of Pπ). *Let* $\Sigma =$ Pπ. *Given* P, Q *in* Σ *and* $\bowtie \in \{\mathring{\simeq}, \simeq, \dot{\approx}, \approx\}$, *the question whether* $P \bowtie^{\Sigma} Q$ *is undecidable.*

Remark 4.22. In fact, the above undecidability results (Lemma 4.20 and Theorem 4.21) apply already to $\mathrm{P}\pi^2$—they are all obtained from reductions of the Halting Problem for Minsky Machines which were encoded using only the $\mathrm{P}\pi^2$ fragment of $\mathrm{P}\pi$. We leave open the corresponding decidability questions for $\mathrm{P}\pi^1$—recall that all the corresponding questions are decidable for $\mathrm{P}\pi^0$ (Theorem 4.18).

5 Expressiveness of Semi-Persistent Calculi

Here we study the expressiveness of the semi-persistent calculi $\mathrm{PI}\pi$ and $\mathrm{PO}\pi$ by means of encodings from π.

Encoding Linearity. Consider the π system:

$$S = \overline{x}\langle u\rangle \mid \overline{x}\langle w\rangle \mid x(y).\overline{y}\langle m\rangle \mid x(y).\overline{y}\langle n\rangle \qquad (2)$$

An encoding from π into a semi-persistent calculus will be a homomorphism that on S takes the form

$$[\![S]\!] = [\![\overline{x}\langle u\rangle]\!] \mid [\![\overline{x}\langle w\rangle]\!] \mid [\![x(y).\overline{y}\langle m\rangle]\!] \mid [\![x(y).\overline{y}\langle n\rangle]\!]$$

Intuitively, to capture the linear communication nature of π, the encoding would evolve into a process that behaves either as (a) $[\![\overline{u}\langle m\rangle]\!] \mid [\![\overline{w}\langle n\rangle]\!]$ or as (b) $[\![\overline{w}\langle m\rangle]\!] \mid [\![\overline{u}\langle n\rangle]\!]$. Notice that in each case an output and input (prefix) are consumed.

The obvious problem is that in the semi-persistent calculi either input or outputs are persistent. Let us first discuss the encoding of π into $\mathrm{PO}\pi$.

From π into $\mathrm{PO}\pi$. A convenient approach is to view (the *encoding* of) input processes as agents competing for the data of (the *encoding* of) an output which must become unavailable upon being received by the successful agent.

A naive solution is to have the above-mentioned competing agents send a private channel r on which the output data would be received; e.g., $[\![x(\vec{y}).P]\!] = (\nu r)(!\overline{x}\langle r\rangle \mid r(\vec{y}).[\![P]\!])$. The encoded outputs must wait for the private channel on which they send their data; e.g., $[\![\overline{x}\langle\vec{z}\rangle]\!] = x(r).!\overline{r}\langle\vec{z}\rangle$. Now, a problem is then that, e.g., the two encoded outputs in (2) may get the private channel of only one of the encoded inputs, thus making it impossible for the other encoded input to get u or w. So one of the encoded outputs will be consumed and the other will be unable to react with other encoded inputs.

The above observation suggests that encoded outputs should also send a secret channel s on which they get a encoded input's secret channel. We could then try

$$\begin{array}{rcl} [\![\overline{x}\langle\vec{z}\rangle]\!] & = & (\nu s)(!\overline{x}\langle s\rangle \mid s(r).!\overline{r}\langle\vec{z}\rangle) \\ [\![x(\vec{y}).P]\!] & = & x(s).(\nu r)(!\overline{s}\langle r\rangle \mid r(\vec{y}).[\![P]\!]) \end{array} \qquad (3)$$

with $[\![0]\!] = 0$ and $[\![\cdot]\!]$ being homomorphic w.r.t all other operators. This solves the above problem, but it creates the dual one. E.g., one of the two encoded inputs in (2) will successfully get the data but the other will be unable to react with another encoded output. It would then seem that we need a more involved protocol to solve the problem.

From π to $\mathrm{PI}\pi$ and from $\mathrm{PI}\pi$ to $\mathrm{PO}\pi$. The above-mentioned problem of an encoded input being unable to react with other encoded outputs would disappear if such an input was replicated; i.e., if a copy becomes unable to react, we can always try another one. Recall that inputs are always replicated in $\mathrm{PI}\pi$. Thus, an encoding of π into $\mathrm{PO}\pi$ may arise from an encoding of π into $\mathrm{PI}\pi$ composed with the encoding in (3). Let us then give the latter encoding first.

5.1 Encoding π into $\mathrm{PI}\pi$: Forwarders

To make a replicated-input behave as a resource that provides a service only once one may suggest: $[\![x(\vec{y}).P]\!] = (\nu l)(\overline{l} \mid !x(\vec{y}).!l.[\![P]\!])$ and $[\![\overline{x}\langle\vec{z}\rangle]\!] = \overline{x}\langle\vec{z}\rangle$. The idea is that the encoded input has a private "lock" l which is activated only once. So, even if the input is replicated, its continuation can be executed only once. Unfortunately the prefix $!x(\vec{y})$ may act as a "sink" consuming several outputs. Nevertheless, a suitable combination of this "lock" idea with a forwarding mechanism leads us to the following encoding:

Definition 5.1. *The encoding* $[\![\cdot]\!] : \pi \to \mathrm{PI}\pi$ *is a homomorphism for parallel composition, restriction and replication, otherwise is defined as* $[\![0]\!] = 0, [\![\overline{x}\langle\vec{z}\rangle]\!] = \overline{x}\langle\vec{z}\rangle$ *and*

$$[\![x(\vec{y}).P]\!] = (\nu\, t\, f)(\overline{t} \mid !x(\vec{y}).(\nu\, l\,)(\overline{l} \mid !t.!l.([\![P]\!] \mid !\overline{f}) \mid !f.!l.\overline{x}\langle\vec{y}\rangle))$$

where $t, f, l \notin fn(P) \cup \{x, \vec{y}\}$.

Intuitively, an encoded input behaves thus: It creates two flags t and f, and then always waits for messages on x. The first time it receives a message $\overline{x}\langle z\rangle$, it consumes $\overline{t}$. It then creates the lock l—we will comment on the need of this lock below. This way only the $!t.!l$-branch is activated and the message is accepted by executing $[\![P]\!]\{\vec{z}/\vec{y}\}$ and activating $\overline{f}$. For every subsequent message $\overline{x}\langle u\rangle$ the input gets, only the $!f.!l$-branch is opened, and hence $\overline{x}\langle\vec{u}\rangle$ is forwarded.

Notice that if we did not use the lock l, then a "dangling" f-branch $!f.\overline{x}\langle\vec{z}\rangle$, resulting after having received the first message $\overline{x}\langle\vec{z}\rangle$, could be opened by an $\overline{f}$. This would cause $\overline{x}\langle z\rangle$ to be forwarded but this message must be consumed.

Properties of $[\![\cdot]\!] : \pi \to \mathrm{PI}\pi$. Our encoding is ideal w.r.t barbed congruence. The proof uses a fundamental property of asynchronous π: Forwarders are barbed congruent to the null process [10]; i.e. $!x(\vec{y}).\overline{x}\langle\vec{y}\rangle \approx 0$.

Lemma 5.2. *Let* $[\![\cdot]\!] : \pi \to \mathrm{PI}\pi$ *be the encoding in Definition 5.1. For every* P, $[\![P]\!] \approx^{\pi} P$ *holds.*

From the above lemma, we get full abstraction w.r.t barbed congruence.

Theorem 5.3. *(Full Abstraction) Let* $[\![\cdot]\!] : \pi \longrightarrow \mathrm{PI}\pi$ *as in Definition 5.1. For every* P, Q*:* $P \approx Q$ *iff* $[\![P]\!] \approx^{\mathrm{PI}\pi} [\![Q]\!]$.

Application. Using the above encoding we can prove that barbed congruence for the zero-adic version of $\mathrm{PI}\pi$, $\mathrm{PI}\pi^0$, is undecidable. This is to be contrasted with the decidability of $\mathrm{P}\pi^0$ shown in the previous section. The results follows from the full-abstraction theorem above and the undecidability of barbed congruence for π^0 which can be proven as that of weak bisimilarity for π^0 in [6].

Theorem 5.4. *Let* $\Sigma = \mathrm{PI}\pi^0$*. Given* $P, Q \in \Sigma$*, the question whether* $P \approx^{\Sigma} Q$ *is undecidable.*

5.2 Encoding π into $\mathrm{PO}\pi$ via composition

We can now use the above encoding of π into $\mathrm{PI}\pi$ to get an encoding of π into $\mathrm{PO}\pi$ by composing it with the following encoding from $\mathrm{PI}\pi$ into $\mathrm{PO}\pi$.

Definition 5.5. *The encoding* $f = [\![\cdot]\!] : \mathrm{PI}\pi \longrightarrow \mathrm{PO}\pi$ *is a homomorphism for parallel composition, restriction, and replication, otherwise is defined as* $[\![0]\!] = 0$*, and*

$$\begin{aligned}[\![\overline{x}\langle\vec{z}\rangle]\!] &= (\nu s)(!\overline{x}\langle s\rangle \mid s(r).!\overline{r}\langle\vec{z}\rangle) \\ [\![!x(\vec{y}).P]\!] &= !x(s).(\nu r)(!\overline{s}\langle r\rangle \mid r(\vec{y}).[\![P]\!])\end{aligned}$$

where $s, r \notin fn(P) \cup \{x, z\}$*. Let* g *be* $[\![\cdot]\!] : \pi \longrightarrow \mathrm{PI}\pi$ *in Definition 5.1. The encoding* $[\![\cdot]\!] : \pi \longrightarrow \mathrm{PO}\pi$ *is the composite function* $f \circ g$*.*

Properties of $[\![\cdot]\!] : \pi \longrightarrow \mathrm{PO}\pi$**.** Let us state the main properties of $[\![\cdot]\!] : \pi \longrightarrow \mathrm{PO}\pi$ given in Definition 5.5. Because of this encoding maps a linear output into a replicated one with the same barb, the encoding does not enjoy the property of being ideal wrt barbed congruence. Notice that replicated inputs were not a problem since the standard barb congruence for π does not observe inputs barbs. However, the following proposition states that the encoding is fully-abstract w.r.t. (weak) barbed bisimilarity.

Proposition 5.6. *For* $[\![\cdot]\!] : \pi \longrightarrow \mathrm{PO}\pi$ *in Definition 5.5 we have:* $P \mathrel{\dot{\approx}} Q$ *iff* $[\![P]\!] \mathrel{\dot{\approx}}^{\mathrm{PO}\pi} [\![Q]\!]$

Nevertheless, due to the compositional definition of $[\![\cdot]\!]$, we can give a stronger correspondence result which takes into account weak barbed congruence. Assume that $[\![\cdot]\!] : \pi \longrightarrow \mathrm{PO}\pi$ in Definition 5.5 is extended to process contexts: We decree that $[\![[\cdot]]\!] = [\cdot]$. Define $[\![P]\!] \approx^{\mathrm{PO}\pi}_{[\cdot]} [\![Q]\!]$ iff for every π context C, $[\![C]\!][[\![P]\!]] \mathrel{\dot{\approx}}^{\mathrm{PO}\pi} [\![C]\!][[\![Q]\!]]$.

Theorem 5.7 (Full-Abstraction wrt Encoded Contexts)**.** *Let* $[\![\cdot]\!] : \pi \longrightarrow \mathrm{PO}\pi$ *be the encoding given in Definition 5.5. The following holds:* $P \approx Q$ *iff* $[\![P]\!] \approx^{\mathrm{PO}\pi}_{[\cdot]} [\![Q]\!]$

Remark 5.8. Intuitively, $[\![\cdot]\!] : \pi \longrightarrow \mathrm{PO}\pi$ in Definition 5.5 simulates an atomic communication (i.e., interaction between an output and input process) with a protocol of finer communications in which each of the participant waits at some stage for a message from another—this is not the case for $[\![\cdot]\!] : \pi \longrightarrow \mathrm{PI}\pi$ in Definition 5.1 since encoded outputs do not wait for any message. Thus one can envisage a malicious context which does not behave according to the protocol. This is the same kind of problem of the encodings of the polyadic into the monadic π-calculus. In fact, the following construction is a counter-example to full-abstraction w.r.t. barbed congruence: Take $P = x.x.0$ and $Q = x.0 \mid x.0$. Clearly, $P \approx Q$. Let $C_t = !\overline{x}\langle n\rangle \mid !\overline{x}\langle m\rangle \mid !n(r\,t\,f).!m(r'\,t'\,f').!\overline{t}$. Verify that $(C_t \mid [\![Q]\!]) \Downarrow_{\overline{t}}$ but $(C_t \mid [\![P]\!]) \not\Downarrow_{\overline{t}}$. Hence, $[\![P]\!] \not\approx [\![Q]\!]$.

Nevertheless following the work of [19, 24], we believe we can provide a type system in order to give a stronger correspondence for the encoding. The type system would allow contexts that may not behave as dictated by the protocol but do not interfere either. However, this is out of the scope of this paper.

Applications. Obviously, the undecidability of barbed congruence for $\mathrm{PO}\pi$ follows from its sub-calculus $\mathrm{P}\pi$. However, we left open the (un)-decidability of $\mathrm{P}\pi^1$. As an application, we use the encoding $[\![\cdot]\!] : \pi \longrightarrow \mathrm{PO}\pi$ in Definition 5.5 to prove the next undecidability result (see [18]).

Theorem 5.9. *Let* $\Sigma = \mathrm{PO}\pi^1$*. Given* $P, Q \in \Sigma$*, the question of whether* $P \approx^{\Sigma} Q$ *is undecidable.*

So all in all we have shown undecidability for barbed congruence for $\mathrm{PI}\pi^0$, $\mathrm{PO}\pi^1$, and $\mathrm{P}\pi^2$. However, in contrast to $\mathrm{PI}\pi^0$ and like $\mathrm{P}\pi^0$, barbed congruence for $\mathrm{PO}\pi^0$ is decidable as shown below.

From $\mathrm{PO}\pi^0$ **into** $\mathrm{P}\pi^0$**.** We conclude this section by proving the decidability of barbed congruence for $\mathrm{PO}\pi^0$ by encoding it into its subcalculus $\mathrm{P}\pi^0$. This encoding also gives us a FOL characterization for $\mathrm{PO}\pi^0$.

Definition 5.10. *The encoding* $[\![\cdot]\!] : \mathrm{PO}\pi^0 \longrightarrow \mathrm{P}\pi^0$ *is a homomorphism for parallel composition, restriction, and replication, otherwise is defined as* $[\![0]\!] = 0$*,* $[\![!\overline{x}]\!] = !\overline{x}$ *and* $[\![x.P]\!] = !x.[\![P]\!]$*.*

Notice that linear inputs are interpreted as replicated ones. The following result states that in the context of $\mathrm{PO}\pi^0$ this interpretation is ideal wrt barbed congruence.

Proposition 5.11. *Let* $[\![\cdot]\!] : \mathrm{PO}\pi^0 \longrightarrow \mathrm{P}\pi^0$ *be the encoding in Definition 5.10. We have* $[\![P]\!] \approx^{\mathrm{PO}\pi^0} P$*.*

From the above proposition and the decidability $\approx$ for $\mathrm{P}\pi^0$ (Theorem 4.18) we obtain the following:

Corollary 5.12. *Let* $\Sigma = \mathrm{PO}\pi^0$*. Given* $P, Q \in \Sigma$*, the question of whether* $P \approx^{\Sigma} Q$ *is decidable.*

Furthermore using the above encoding and lemma and the processes-as-formulae FOL interpretation of Pπ (Definition 4.12) we conclude that $\mathrm{PO}\pi^0$ can be interpreted likewise. E.g., $x.P$ and $(\nu x)P$ are compositionally interpreted as the formulae $\mathtt{out}(x) \Rightarrow [\![P]\!]$ and $\exists x[\![P]\!]$, respectively, where $[\![P]\!]$ is the interpretation of P.

Corollary 5.13. *Let $f : \mathrm{P}\pi \rightarrow \mathrm{FOL}$ as in Definition 4.12, $g : \mathrm{PO}\pi^0 \rightarrow \mathrm{P}\pi^0$ in Definition 5.10 and $m : \mathrm{P}\pi \rightarrow \mathrm{P}\pi$ in Definition 4.10. Let $P \in \mathrm{PO}\pi^0$ and $[\![P]\!] = (f \circ m \circ g)(P)$:*

$$P \Downarrow_{\overline{x}} \text{ if and only if } [\![P]\!] \models \mathtt{out}(x).$$

6 Future Work

We presented an expressiveness study of linearity and persistence of processes. In this study, however, we did not consider the issue of divergence. E.g., the encoding of π into PIπ introduces divergent computations which are ignored by the equivalence we chose in this paper, i.e., weak barbed bisimilarity. It would be interesting to provide an analogous study in which the discrimination power of divergence is taken into consideration.

The encoding of π into POπ here provided is fully-abstract w.r.t. to barbed congruence restricted to encoded contexts. We conjecture that a fully-abstract encoding of π into POπ w.r.t to barbed congruence cannot exist. A similar conjecture can be stated about the existence of encodings which simulate an atomic communication with a protocol of finer communications in which each participant waits at some stage for a message from another. In fact several works in the π-calculus literature use such kind of encodings, thus studying such conjectures could be relevant for the process calculi community.

We have studied the expressiveness of Pπ by encoding Minsky Machines. A more insightful approach could be to encode the λ-calculus into Pπ as witnessed by the extensive work on translations of this canonical calculus of computable functions into the π-calculus [21].

We also showed that barbed observability for Pπ can be characterized as FOL entailment. The characterization was fundamental to state positive decidability results for infinite-state Pπ processes. By building on the translation of π to linear logic in [13, 23] we should be able to characterize barbed observability for all the π sub-calculi here studied as entailment in linear logic. The resulting characterizations may provide us with useful reasoning techniques for the π-calculus from linear logic.

References

[1] R. Amadio, D. Lugiez, and V. Vanackere. On the symbolic reduction of processes with cryptographic functions. *Theoretical Computer Science*, 290, 2003.

[2] E. Best, F. de Boer, and C. Palamidessi. Partial order and sos semantics for linear constraint programs. In *Proc. of Coordination'97*, volume 1282 of *LNCS*, 1997.

[3] B. Blanchet. From linear to classical logic by abstract interpretation. *Information Processing Letters*, 95(5), 2005.

[4] M. Boreale and M. Buscemi. A framework for the analysis of security protocols. In *Proc. CONCUR'02*, volume 2421 of *LNCS*, 2002.

[5] E. Börger, E. Grädel, and Y. Gurevich. *The Classical Decision Problem*. Springer-Verlag, 1997.

[6] N. Busi, M. Gabbrielli, and G. Zavattaro. Comparing recursion, replication and iteration in process calculi. In *Proc. ICALP'04*, volume 3142 of *LNCS*, 2004.

[7] F. Crazzolara and G. Winskel. Events in security protocols. In *Proc. CCS 2001*. ACM Press, 2001.

[8] F. Fages, P. Ruet, and S. Soliman. Linear concurrent constraint programming: operational and phase semantics. *Information and Computation*, 2001.

[9] M. Fiore and M. Abadi. Computing symbolic models for verifying cryptographic protocols. In *Proc. CSFW-14*. IEEE, 2001.

[10] K. Honda and N. Yoshida. On reduction-based process semantics. *Theoretical Computer Science*, 151(2):437–486, 1995.

[11] P. Lincoln and V. Saraswat. Proofs as concurrent processes: A logical interpretation of concurrent constraint programming. Technical report, Xerox PARC, 1991.

[12] N. P. Mendler, P. Panangaden, P. J. Scott, and R. A. G. Seely. A logical view of concurrent constraint programming. *Nordic J. of Computing*, 2(2):181–220, 1995.

[13] D. Miller. The pi-calculus as a theory in linear-logic. In *Proc. of Workshop on Extensions to Logic Programming*, volume 660 of *LNCS*, 1992.

[14] R. Milner. *Communicating and Mobile Systems: the π-calculus*. Cambridge University Press, 1999.

[15] R. Milner, J. Parrow, and D. Walker. A calculus of mobile processes, Part I + II. *Information and Computation*, 100(1):1–77, 1992.

[16] M. Minsky. *Computation: Finite and Infinite Machines*. Prentice-Hall, 1967.

[17] U. Nestmann. What is a 'good' encoding of guarded choice? *Information and Computation*, 156:287–319, 2000.

[18] C. Palamidessi, V. Saraswat, F. Valencia, and B. Victor. On the expressiveness of linearity and persistence in the asynchronous π-calculus. Technical report, LIX, Ecole Polytechnique, 2006. http://www.lix.polytechnique.fr/~fvalenci.

[19] P. Quaglia and D. Walker. On encoding pπ in mπ. In *Proc. FSTTCS'98*, volume 1530 of *LNCS*, 1998.

[20] D. Sangiorgi. The name discipline of uniform receptiveness. *Theoretical Computer Science*, 221(1–2):457–493, 1999.

[21] D. Sangiorgi and D. Walker. *The π-calculus: A Theory of Mobile Processes*. Cambridge University Press, 2001.

[22] V. Saraswat. *Concurrent Constraint Programming*. The MIT Press, Cambridge, MA, 1993.

[23] V. Saraswat and P. Lincoln. Higher-order linear concurrent constraint programming. Technical report, Xerox PARC, 1992.

[24] N. Yoshida. Graph types for monadic mobile processes. In *Proc. FSTTCS'96*, volume 1180 of *LNCS*, 1996.

Saturated Semantics for Reactive Systems *

Filippo Bonchi
University of Pisa

Barbara König
University of Duisburg-Essen

Ugo Montanari
University of Pisa

Abstract

The semantics of process calculi has traditionally been specified by labelled transition systems (LTS), but with the development of name calculi it turned out that reaction rules (i.e., unlabelled transition rules) are often more natural. This leads to the question of how behavioural equivalences (bisimilarity, trace equivalence, etc.) defined for LTS can be transferred to unlabelled transition systems. Recently, in order to answer this question, several proposals have been made with the aim of automatically deriving an LTS from reaction rules in such a way that the resulting equivalences are congruences. Furthermore these equivalences should agree with the standard semantics, whenever one exists.

In this paper we propose saturated semantics, based on a weaker notion of observation and orthogonal to all the previous proposals, and we demonstrate the appropriateness of our semantics by means of two examples: logic programming and a subset of the open π-calculus. Indeed, we prove that our equivalences are congruences and that they coincide with logical equivalence and open bisimilarity respectively, while equivalences studied in previous works are strictly finer.

1 Introduction

The operational semantics of process calculi is usually given in terms of transition systems labelled with actions, which, when visible, represent both observations and interactions with the external world. The abstract semantics is given in terms of behavioural equivalences, which depend on the action labels and on the amount of branching structure considered. Behavioural equivalences are often congruences with respect to the operations of the language, and this property expresses the compositionality of the abstract semantics.

A simpler approach, inspired by classical formalisms like λ-calculus, Petri nets, term and graph rewriting, and pioneered by the Chemical Abstract Machine [3], defines operational semantics by means of *structural axioms* and *reaction rules*. Process calculi representing complex systems, in particular those able to generate and communicate names, are often defined in this way, since structural axioms give a clear idea of the intended structure of the states while reaction rules, which are often non-conditional, give a direct account of the possible steps. Transitions caused by reaction rules, however, are not labelled, since they represent evolutions of the system without interactions with the external world. Thus reduction semantics in itself is neither abstract nor compositional. To enhance the expressiveness of reduction semantics, Leifer and Milner proposed in [12] a systematic method for deriving bisimulation congruences from reduction rules. The main idea is the following: a process p can do a move with label $C[-]$ and become p' iff $C[p] \rightsquigarrow p'$. This definition was inspired by the work of Sewell [20]. Also, the approach of observing contexts imposed on agents at each step was introduced in [16], yielding the notion of *dynamic bisimilarity*.

Leifer and Milner introduced also the categorical notions of relative pushout (RPO) and idem relative pushout (IPO) in order to specify a/the minimal context that allows the state to react with a given rule. This construction leads to labelled transition systems (LTS) that use only contexts generated by IPOs, and not all contexts, as labels, and thus are smaller than in the latter case. Bisimilarity on this LTS is a congruence under rather restrictive conditions. A generalisation to reactive systems over G-categories has been proposed by Sassone and Sobociński [19, 18]. Recently other extensions to open systems and to weak semantics were introduced in [10] and in [4] respectively. The approach has been applied to bigraphs [14] and DPO graph rewriting [6].

The above constructions start from actionless reduction rules and have fundamental motivations in terms of minimality of basic definitions. However in most interactive systems some notion of observation is built in, and it is difficult to derive the corresponding semantics purely by using contexts, as testified by the lack of results where the ordinary semantics of a process description language is derived from reduction rules. For instance, Milner and Sangiorgi in [15] introduced the notion of *barbed bisimulation*, where only reactions are considered, but where states are labelled by

*Research partially supported by the DFG project SANDS, the IST 2004-16004 SENSORIA, and the MIUR PRIN 2005015824 ART.

barbs (potential interactions with the environment). Even considering only labelled transitions, the RPO/IPO paradigm can be used to add relevant experiments to a transition system for which bisimilarity is not a congruence. In this line, Ferrari, Montanari and Tuosto in [8] considered a fragment of the π-calculus where name fusions are contexts and where IPO constructions add the transitions with the minimal fusions needed by the symbolic transition system [17] of the open π-calculus. But the resulting abstract semantics is strictly finer than open bisimilarity.

Another interesting interpretation of the RPO/IPO construction is in terms of models of computation tailored to the needs of the general server-to-client bindings required by the new web service applications. When a new service is discovered, not only the service must adapt to the client, e.g. accepting a list of parameters, but also the client must sometimes adapt to the server, in order to establish the connection. Moreover, the minimal possible adaptation should be sought, in order to minimise the possible degradation. Suitable modelling of the details of the negotiation may lead to formalisations able to take advantage of the semantic properties guaranteed by the RPO/IPO constructions. The above symmetrical server-client adaptation reminds us of the unification step of logic programming, where a goal and a clause adapt reciprocally in the most general way. Quite interestingly, in the observational view of logic programming [5] the label of a goal reduction is exactly the instantiation of the goal imposed by the unification step, as required by the RPO/IPO construction.

In this paper our aim is, as in the ordinary case, to derive a bisimilarity congruence from given reduction rules. However we introduce in the transition system *all* context-labelled transitions which make a state and a rule match. We call the resulting equivalences *saturated*. Saturated equivalences are coarser than ordinary ones and have nice properties, e.g., they are trivially congruences, but the LTS is infinite-branching in more cases. Here we develop a *semi-saturated* technique that allows to compute saturated equivalences without considering all matching contexts. In fact, if we call Alice the player choosing the move and Bob the player choosing a matching reply, we prove that if Alice chooses an IPO move and Bob replies with any matching move, the resulting equivalence is again the saturated one, even if the moves to be considered are usually much less. In order to apply this technique we require less restrictive conditions than for the ordinary equivalences: instead of requiring the existence of all redex RPOs we need only redex IPOs, i.e., we allow several local minima.

Indeed we show that in some relevant cases saturated equivalences are exactly what we want, while ordinary equivalences are too fine. In the paper we discuss two important cases: logic programming and π-calculus.

We model logic programming in a way similar to [5]. It turns out that saturated trace congruence coincides with the ordinary logic semantics of logic programming, while the ordinary trace congruence yields a finer semantics, know in the logic programming community as S-semantics [7]. Interestingly enough, a goal (i.e. a conjunction of atomic goals) and the head of a clause must adapt in two different ways: both must be instantiated, but in addition the head must be ($\wedge$-)composed with other formulas which stay idle in the reduction. We are able to obtain both adaptations at the same time within our approach, without resorting to an infinite number of rules, as it is usually the case for the ordinary construction, since agents are normally forced to be closed. In fact in our encoding we will have only one rule for each Horn clause. Several authors (see for instance [10]) consider the restriction to closed agents a big limitation of the label derivation approaches.

For the π-calculus we refer to the above mentioned paper [8], where the RPO/IPO approach yields the symbolic transition system of a fragment of the calculus. Again, while ordinary bisimilarity congruence yields a finer semantics, the saturated bisimilarity congruence yields the ordinary semantics of open π-calculus.

The main contribution of the paper is the appreciation of saturated equivalences (bisimilarity and trace). Saturated bisimilarity (in the sense of all contexts) was already known in the literature [12], but it was dismissed as not promising. In this paper we show an alternative definition which considers fewer contexts and we exhibit two important examples where saturated equivalences yield the most natural notions. Our alternative definition works under weaker conditions than those required in [12]. The construction proposed for logic programming is original and, in our opinion, particularly interesting because, at our knowledge, it is the only example in the literature of reactive systems, where the rules are both instantiated and contextualised.

Structure of the paper. In Section 2, we first review Leifer and Milner's theory of reactive systems, and then we recall some basic concepts of logic. In Section 3, we introduce the main theoretical contributions of the paper, and in Sections 4 and 5 we apply our results to logic programming and to open π-calculus. Throughout the paper, we will use as running example the reactive semantics of CCS [13] with the reaction rule $a.P \mid \overline{a}.Q \rightsquigarrow P \mid Q$.

2 Background

Reactive Systems. Here we summarise the theory of reactive systems proposed in [12] to derive labelled transition systems and bisimulation congruences from a given reaction semantics. The theory is centred on the concepts of *term*, *context* and *reaction rules*: contexts are arrows of a category, terms are arrows having as domain 0 (a special object that denotes no holes), and reaction rules are pairs of terms.

Definition 1 (Reactive System). *A reactive system* $\mathbb{C}$ *consists of:*

1. *a category* $\mathbf{C}$
2. *a distinguished object* $0 \in |\mathbf{C}|$
3. *a composition-reflecting subcategory* $\mathbf{D}$ *of* reactive contexts
4. *a set of pairs* $\mathcal{R} \subseteq \bigcup_{I \in |\mathbf{C}|} \mathbf{C}(0, I) \times \mathbf{C}(0, I)$ *of* reaction rules.

The reactive contexts are those in which a reaction can occur. By composition-reflecting we mean that $d; d' \in \mathbf{D}$ implies $d, d' \in \mathbf{D}$.

Note that the rules have to be ground, i.e., left-hand and right-hand sides have to be terms without holes and, moreover, with the same codomain. Having ground rules is a simplification often made, but there is some work which tries to overcome this constraint [10].

From reaction rules one generates the reaction relation by closing them under all reactive contexts. Formally the *reaction relation* is defined by taking $p \rightsquigarrow q$ if there is $\langle l, r \rangle \in \mathcal{R}$ and $d \in \mathbf{D}$ such that $p = l; d$ and $q = r; d$.

Thus the behaviour of a reactive system is expressed as an unlabelled transition system. On the other hand many useful behavioural equivalences are only defined for LTSs. In order to obtain an LTS, we can plug a term p into some context $C[-]$ and observe if a reaction occurs. In this case we have that $p \xrightarrow{C[-]}$. Categorically speaking this means that $p; C[-]$ matches $l; d$ for some rule $\langle l, r \rangle \in \mathcal{R}$ and some reactive context d. This situation is formally depicted by diagram (i) in Figure 1: a commuting diagram like this is called a *redex square*.

Definition 2 (context transition system). *The* context transition system *(CTS for short) is defined as follows:*

- *states: arrows* $p : 0 \to I$ *in* $\mathbf{C}$*, for arbitrary* I*;*
- *transitions:* $p \xrightarrow{C[-]}_C q$ *iff* $C[p] \rightsquigarrow q$.

Note that this labelled transition system is often infinite-branching since all contexts that allow reactions may occur as labels. Another problem of *CTS* is that it has redundant transitions. For example, consider the term $a.0$ of CCS. The observer can put this term into the context $\overline{a}.0 \mid -$ and observe a reaction. This correspond to the transition $a.0 \xrightarrow{\overline{a}.0|-}_C 0|0$. However we also have $a.0 \xrightarrow{p|\overline{a}.0|-}_C p \mid 0 \mid 0$ as a transition, yet p does not contribute to the reaction. Hence we need a notion of "minimal context that allows a reaction". Leifer and Milner define idem pushouts (IPOs) to capture this notion.

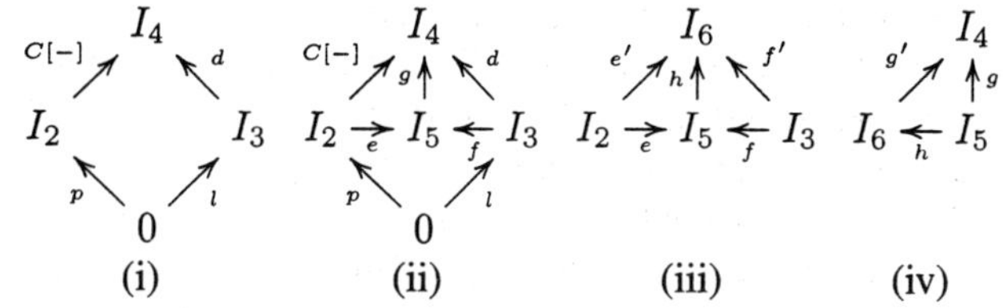

Figure 1. Redex Square and RPO

Definition 3 (RPO). *Let the diagrams in Figure 1 be in some category* $\mathbf{C}$*. Let (i) be a commuting diagram. Any tuple* $\langle I_5, e, f, g \rangle$ *which makes (ii) commute is called a* candidate *for (i). A* relative pushout (RPO) *is the smallest such candidate. More formally, it satisfies the universal property that given any other candidate* $\langle I_6, e', f', g' \rangle$*, there exists a unique mediating morphism* $h : I_5 \to I_6$ *such that (iii) and (iv) commute.*

Definition 4 (IPO). *A commuting square such as diagram (i) of Figure 1 is called* idem pushout (IPO) *if* $\langle I_4, c, d, id_{I_4} \rangle$ *is its RPO.*

Definition 5 (redex RPOs). *A* reactive system *has* redex RPOs *if every redex square has an RPO.*

Definition 6 (IPO-Labelled Transition System). *The* IPO-labelled transition system *(ILTS for short) is defined as follows:*

- *states:* $p : 0 \to I$ *in* $\mathbf{C}$*, for arbitrary* I*;*
- *transitions:* $p \xrightarrow{C[-]}_I r; d$ *iff* $d \in \mathbf{D}$*,* $\langle l, r \rangle \in \mathcal{R}$ *and the diagram (i) in Figure 1 is an IPO.*

In other words, if inserting p into the context $C[-]$ matches $l; d$, and $C[-]$ is the "smallest" such context (according to the IPO condition), then p transforms to $r; d$ with label $C[-]$, where r is the reduct of l.

Bisimilarity on *ILTS* is referred to as *standard bisimilarity* (denoted by $\sim_{IPO}$), and Leifer and Milner have shown that if the reactive system has redex RPOs, then it is a congruence (i.e., it is preserved under all contexts).

It can be easily shown that bisimilarity over *CTS* is a congruence as well. In this paper we will focus on this bisimilarity, which will be called *saturated bisimilarity* (denoted by $\sim_{SAT}$). In [12], it is referred to as $\sim_4$, and the authors show that $\sim_{IPO} \subseteq \sim_{SAT}$.

Logic Programming. As an application domain for saturated semantics we will now introduce logic programming and semantic equivalences of logic formulas.

A *logic signature* Γ is a pair (Σ, Π), where Σ is a set of *function symbols* and Π is a set of *predicate symbols* with an associated arity. As usual, given a set X of variables, we denote by $T_\Sigma(X)$ the free Σ-algebra over X. A *term* over X is an element of $T_\Sigma(X)$. Given a term t, $Var(t)$ is the smallest set of variables X such that $t \in T_\Sigma(X)$. An *atomic formula* over X has the form $P(t_1, \ldots, t_n)$ where P is a predicate with arity n, and $t_1, \ldots, t_n$ are terms over X. A *formula* is a finite conjunction of atomic formulas: $a_1 \wedge \cdots \wedge a_n$ where $\wedge$ is associative and it has the *empty formula* $\Box$ as unit. Note that in the standard definition $\wedge$ is also commutative, but to simplify our construction, as it is the case in Prolog, we do not consider it to be commutative (however the resulting behaviour is the same).

If X and Y are sets of variables, a *substitution* from X to Y is a function $\sigma : X \to T_\Sigma(Y)$. If t is a term over X and σ a substitution from X to Y, then the term over Y, obtained by simultaneously substituting in t all the occurrences of the variables in X with their image under σ, is called the application of σ to t and written $t; \sigma$ (or $\sigma(t)$). If σ is a substitution from X to Y, and σ' from Y to Z, then $\sigma; \sigma'$ from X to Z is defined by applying σ' to each image of the variables in X under σ. Given $\sigma : X \to T_\Sigma(Y)$ and $X' \subseteq X$ the *restriction* of σ to X', written $\sigma \upharpoonright X'$, is the substitution $\sigma' : X' \to T_\Sigma(Y)$ acting as σ on X'.

A substitution σ is *more general* than σ' if there exists a substitution θ such that $\sigma' = \sigma; \theta$. Two substitutions ψ and ϕ *unify* if there exists a substitution σ such that $\psi; \sigma = \phi; \sigma$, in this case σ is a *unifier* of ψ and ϕ. It is well-known that if ψ and ϕ unify, then there exists a unifier that is more general than all the others, called the *most general unifier* (*mgu* for short). It is also well-known that an *mgu* is the coequalizer in the category of substitutions [9], and in [5] it is shown that the *mgu* of substitutions with disjoint sets of variables corresponds to a pushout (this will be detailed later).

A *logic program* is a finite collection of *Horn clauses*, i.e., expressions of the form $h :- b$ where h is an atomic formula called the *head* of a clause, and b is a formula called the *body*. Rules in Table 1 define the operational semantics of logic programming. A goal $g = a_1 \wedge \cdots \wedge a_n$ reacts with a clause $c = h :- b$ if a_i, an atomic formula of the goal g, unifies with $\rho(h)$ (where ρ substitutes the variables of h with fresh variables not appearing in g). Let σ be the *mgu* of a_i and $\rho(h)$, then g reacts and becomes $g' = \sigma(a_1) \wedge \cdots \wedge \sigma(a_{i-1}) \wedge \sigma(b) \wedge \sigma(a_{i+1}) \wedge \cdots \wedge \sigma(a_n)$. A *refutation* of g is a derivation $g \Rightarrow_{\sigma_1} g_2 \Rightarrow_{\sigma_2} \cdots \Rightarrow_{\sigma_n} g_n$ ending with the empty formula (i.e. $g_n = \Box$). In this case $\sigma = \sigma_1; \ldots; \sigma_n \upharpoonright Var(g)$ is a *computed answer substitution* of g.

Now, given a logic program, when are two goals equivalent? First note that we already have an LTS, but bisimulation is quite uninteresting in this case because we would like to consider as equivalent two goals with different branching behaviour. Here the interesting point is if, and when, two goals can be refuted. The first naive equivalence that comes to mind is: g_1 can be refuted iff g_2 can be refuted. This equivalence is however not a congruence.

$$\frac{h :- b \in P \quad \sigma = mgu(a, \rho(h))}{P \Vdash a \Rightarrow_\sigma \sigma(\rho(b))}$$

where ρ renames to globally fresh names

$$\frac{P \Vdash g \Rightarrow_\sigma f}{P \Vdash g_1 \wedge g \wedge g_2 \Rightarrow_\sigma \sigma(g_1) \wedge f \wedge \sigma(g_2)}$$

Table 1. Operational rules for SLD-resolution

Logic equivalence (denoted by $\simeq_L$) equates g_1 and g_2 if and only if, for any ground substitution σ, $\sigma(g_1)$ is refuted iff $\sigma(g_2)$ is refuted. In [7], *S-equivalence* (denoted by $\simeq_S$) is proposed: g_1 and g_2 have the same set of computed answer substitutions. Another interesting equivalence is *correct answer equivalence* (denoted by $\simeq_C$) that equates two goals iff they have the same set of correct answer substitutions (defined as follows). Let $\xrightarrow{\sigma}$ be the transition system defined by changing the premise of the first rule of Table 1: we do not require anymore that σ is the mgu, but only that it unifies a and $\rho(h)$ i.e, $\sigma(a) = \sigma(\rho(h))$. If $g \xrightarrow{\sigma_1} g_2 \xrightarrow{\sigma_2} \ldots \xrightarrow{\sigma_n} \Box$ we say that $\sigma = \sigma_1; \ldots; \sigma_n \upharpoonright Var(g)$ is a *correct answer substitution* of g. In other words σ is a correct answer substitution of g iff $\sigma(g)$ is a logical consequence of the program.

In [5], it is shown that, if we work with an infinite set of function symbols, $g_1 \simeq_L g_2$ iff $g_1 \simeq_C g_2$.

The following example shows that S-equivalence is somehow too detailed and that logic equivalence is more abstract.

Example 1. *Consider the following program, where y is a variable and a is a constant:*

$$P(y) :- \Box \qquad P(a) :- \Box \qquad Q(y) :- \Box$$

Now consider the goals $P(x)$ and $Q(x)$. They are refuted by any ground substitution, which means that they are logic equivalent (and also correct answer equivalent). However, they are not S-equivalent: in fact the set of computed answer substitutions for $P(x)$ is $\{\epsilon, [a/x]\}$, while the computed answer substitutions for $Q(x)$ are $\{\epsilon\}$.

3 Saturated Semantics

In Section 2 we have shown that given a reactive system one can define two LTSs: the *CTS*, where the labels are all contexts allowing a reaction, and the *ILTS*, where labels are the minimal contexts allowing a reaction. On those LTSs we can define various kinds of equivalences, such as bisimilarity, trace and failure equivalence. The term *saturated semantics* stands for equivalences defined on the *CTS*, while *standard semantics* stands for equivalences defined on the *ILTS*.

Theorem 1. *Saturated bisimilarity is the coarsest bisimulation on $\rightsquigarrow$ that is also a congruence.*

In our opinion, the standard semantics (using IPOs as labels) is not really observational since the observer has to know exactly the right amount of information that the process needs to react, while saturated semantics are truly observational: the observer plugs the process into some context and observes if a reaction occurs. However, with the current definition it is hard to show that two systems are saturated bisimilar, since *CTS* is often infinite-branching and bisimilarity must consider all possible moves.

3.1 Semi-Saturated Bisimulation

Here we propose an alternative and, (in some cases) finitary characterisation of saturated bisimilarity: in the bisimulation game, one player proposes an IPO transition and the other answers with a contextual transition.

Definition 7 (semi-saturated bisimulation). *A symmetric relation R is a* semi-saturated bisimulation *if whenever $p\,R\,q$, then $p \xrightarrow{C[-]}_I p'$ implies $q \xrightarrow{C[-]}_C q'$ and $p'\,R\,q'$.*

We call the union of all semi-saturated bisimulations semi-saturated bisimilarity *(denoted by $\sim_{SS}$).*

Theorem 2 states that under very weak conditions this kind of bisimilarity coincides with saturated bisimilarity (and thus it is a congruence). In this way we can prove that two processes are saturated bisimilar just starting with IPO moves that are sometimes (see, e.g., Corollary 1) finite in number. Once an IPO move is chosen, the context $C[-]$ is fixed, and thus only the $\rightsquigarrow$ moves from $C[q]$ must be considered. Milner and Leifer have shown that $\sim_{IPO}$ is a congruence if the reactive system has redex RPOs, i.e., if for each redex there exist an RPO. For $\sim_{SS}$ it is sufficient to require that the reactive system has redex IPOs.

Definition 8 (redex IPOs). *A reactive system* has redex IPOs, *if every redex square has at least one IPO as candidate.*

Clearly this constraint is weaker than having redex RPOs, and hence our results can be applied to a larger number of reactive systems. Having RPOs means to have a minimum candidate (i.e., a candidate smaller than all the others), while having IPOs allows to have several minimal candidates (also not comparable among them). The following example (introduced in [21] and inspired by [12]) exemplifies the difference between redex IPOs and redex RPOs.

Example 2 (Abstract Bunch Contexts). *An abstract bunch context is a string of multisets containing elements from some alphabet $\mathcal{K}$ and places (i.e., holes). Abstract bunch contexts form a category having natural numbers as objects and abstract bunch contexts of length n having m holes as arrows $m \to n$. Composition of $a : m \to n$ and $b : n \to o$ is defined by plugging the n multiset of a into the n holes of b. Finally, the identity id_n is $\{-_1\}\{-_2\}\ldots\{-_n\}$.*
This category does not have RPOs: consider the exterior squares in diagrams (i) and (ii) below (note that they are equal). This square has no RPOs since it has as candidates the arrows inside which are not comparable (in the sense that neither is smaller than the other). But note that both are IPOs, since they have as candidates only isomorphic diagrams.

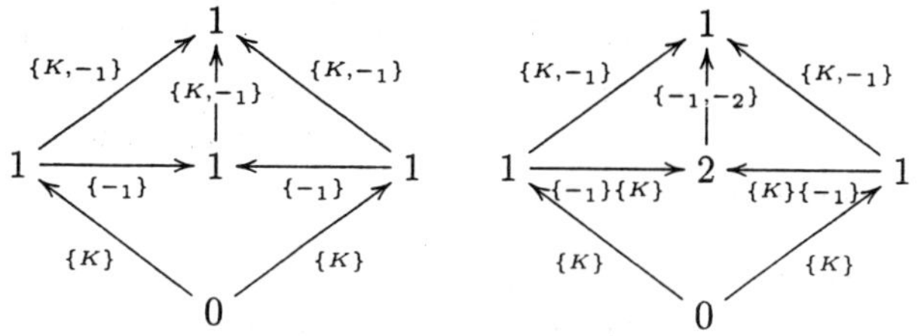

(i) (ii)

Theorem 2. *In a reactive system having redex-IPOs, semi-saturated bisimilarity coincides with saturated bisimilarity (i.e., $p \sim_{SS} q \iff p \sim_{SAT} q$).*

Theorem 3. *In a reactive system having redex-IPOs, a symmetric relation R is a semi-saturated bisimulation iff whenever $p\,R\,q$, then $p \xrightarrow{c}_I p'$ implies the existence of d, e such that $d; e = c$, $q \xrightarrow{d}_I q'$ and $p'\,R\,q'; e$.*

Theorem 3 offers another characterisation of semi-saturated bisimilarity (and thus of saturated bisimilarity) that resembles open [17], asynchronous [1] and large [2] bisimilarity.

3.2 Saturated Trace Equivalences

Besides bisimulation, many other equivalences have been defined on LTSs. Here we introduce ϕ-trace equivalence, a quite general equivalence, parametric with respect to a property ϕ, that generalises trace and S-equivalence of logic programming. This equivalence can be instantiated both on the IPO and on the contextual LTS and, as we did for bisimulation, we define a semi-saturated version of it and we show that it corresponds to saturated equivalence.

Definition 9 (ϕ-trace equivalence). *Let X be a set of states, L a set of labels and $\to \subseteq X \times L \times X$ a transition relation. Let $-;- : L \times L \to L$ be an associative operator on labels and let ϕ be a property on X. We say that $p, q \in X$ are ϕ-trace equivalent ($p \simeq^{\phi} q$) if the following conditions hold:*

- *$\phi(p)$ if and only if $\phi(q)$,*
- *if $p \overset{l}{\twoheadrightarrow} p' \wedge \phi(p')$ then $q \overset{l}{\twoheadrightarrow} q' \wedge \phi(q')$,*
- *if $q \overset{l}{\twoheadrightarrow} q' \wedge \phi(q')$ then $p \overset{l}{\twoheadrightarrow} p' \wedge \phi(p')$,*

where $p \xrightarrow{l}\!\!\!\!\rightarrow p'$ *iff* $p \xrightarrow{l_1} p_2 \ldots p_n \xrightarrow{l_n} p'$ *and* $l = l_1; l_2; \ldots ; l_n$ *with* $n \geq 1$.

Note that if ϕ holds in every state of X and ; is string concatenation, then we obtain the classical trace semantics for $\rightarrow$, while if ϕ holds just for the empty goal $\Box$, $\rightarrow$ is the SLD transition relation and if ; is composition of substitutions, then we obtain S-equivalence of logic programming.

In the rest of this section we will study this equivalence in the setting of reactive systems, and we will fix the ; operator to be context composition. As we did for bisimilarity, we can define this equivalence on the *ILTS* (*standard ϕ-trace equivalence* denoted by $\simeq_I^\phi$) or on the *CTS* (*saturated ϕ-trace equivalence* denoted by $\simeq_{SAT}^\phi$).

In order to obtain a congruence we have to require the following conditions:

1. ϕ is defined on all arrows, and the arrows satisfying ϕ form a composition-reflecting subcategory;
2. all contexts are reactive.

The first requirement is not very strong, and we will show that in our encoding of logic programming, setting $\phi(a) \Leftrightarrow a = \Box$ defines a composition-reflecting sub-category. The second constraint is rather restrictive, but there are many formalisms for which it holds, as for example DPO graph rewriting or logic programming.

Theorem 4. *In a reactive system where all contexts are reactive* $\simeq_{SAT}^\phi$ *is a congruence.*

Standard bisimilarity is a congruence under the constraint of having all redex RPOs, while here standard ϕ-trace equivalence is a congruence under the assumption that RPOs exist not only for redex squares but also for squares where the four arrows are contexts (in reactive systems RPOs are only required for squares where one of the lower arrows is a redex). We say that a reactive system has *redex and context RPOs* if it satisfies this constraint. We have to require this condition since we are working with the transitive closure of $\rightarrow_I$. A similar condition is needed in [4] where the authors require to have all RPOs, in order to show that weak bisimulation is a congruence.

Theorem 5. *In a reactive system with redex and context RPOs, where all contexts are reactive and ϕ defines a composition-reflecting subcategory,* $\simeq_I^\phi$ *is a congruence.*

As for bisimulation we can define a semi-saturated version of ϕ-trace equivalence.

Definition 10. *Let* $\mathbb{C}$ *be a reactive system, and ϕ a property on the arrows of* $\mathbf{C}$. *We say that p and q are* semi-saturated ϕ-trace *equivalent* ($p \simeq_{SS}^\phi q$) *if the following holds:*

- $\phi(p)$ *if and only if* $\phi(q)$,
- *if* $p \xrightarrow{l}\!\!\!\!\rightarrow_I p' \wedge \phi(p')$ *then* $q \xrightarrow{l}\!\!\!\!\rightarrow_C q'$ *and* $\phi(q')$,
- *if* $q \xrightarrow{l}\!\!\!\!\rightarrow_I q' \wedge \phi(q')$ *then* $p \xrightarrow{l}\!\!\!\!\rightarrow_C p'$ *and* $\phi(p')$,

where $\twoheadrightarrow_I$ *and* $\twoheadrightarrow_C$ *are the transitive closures of* $\rightarrow_I$ *and* $\rightarrow_C$.

As semi-saturated bisimilarity corresponds to saturated bisimilarity, semi-saturated ϕ-trace equivalence is saturated ϕ-trace equivalence, under the weak constraint of the existence of redex IPOs.

Theorem 6. *In a reactive system with redex IPOs, where all contexts are reactive, and such that ϕ defines a composition-reflecting subcategory, then* $\simeq_{SS}^\phi = \simeq_{SAT}^\phi$.

4 Logic Programs as Reactive Systems

In this section we will show how logic programs can be seen as reactive systems and how the theory developed above can be applied in this framework. Consider two basic sorts t for terms and p for formulas (predicates are atomic formulas). We use ϵ to denote the empty string and t^n to denote the string composed of n occurrences of t. Given a logic signature $\Gamma = (\Sigma, \Pi)$, we define Γ' as the signature Γ enriched with the symbols $\wedge$ that takes two formulas and returns one formula and $\Box$ a constant formula. Let E be the set of axioms describing that $\wedge$ is associative (not commutative) and has identity $\Box$. Let X_p and X_t be sets of predicate and term variables. We use $T_{\Gamma'/E}(X_p, X_t)$ to denote the Γ'-algebra freely generated by (X_p, X_t) quotiented by E. A term of this algebra in sort p is a logic formula having term and predicate variables from X_t and X_p.

Definition 11. *The category* $\mathrm{Th}[\Gamma'/E]$ *is the free* algebraic theory *[11] associated to the specification* Γ', E.

This category has been used in [5] as base category for a tile system for logic programming. Usually *algebraic theories* are applied to a one sorted signature and the resulting category has natural numbers as objects, while here it is applied to a two sorted signature and it has strings of sorts (i.e., elements of $\{t, p\}^*$) as objects. For example, an object $p^n t^m$ can be thought of as representing n ordered *canonical predicate variables* (i.e., variables indexed from 1 to n) $p_1, \ldots, p_n$ and m ordered *canonical term variables* $x_1, \ldots, x_m$. To avoid confusion, it must be clear that the canonical variables are just placeholders, i.e., their scope is only local. The arrows from s_1 to s_2 are s_1-tuples of elements of $T_{\Gamma'/E}$ with s_2 canonical variables and the composition of arrows is term substitution.

The subcategory of the arrows of the form $t^n \rightarrow t^m$ is isomorphic to the category of finite substitutions on Σ (with canonical sets of variables) and the arrows $t \rightarrow \epsilon$ are closed term over Σ, while arrows $p \rightarrow \epsilon$ are closed formulas over Γ'. Arrows $\mathsf{p} \rightarrow \mathsf{t}^n$ are formulas over n canonical term variables, while arrows $\mathsf{p} \rightarrow \mathsf{pt}^n\mathsf{p}$ are formulas over n canonical term variables and two canonical predicate variables. Consider for example $\langle P(x_1, x_2) \wedge p_1, f(x_1), Q(f(x_2)), p_5\rangle$ where x_1, x_2 are terms variables and p_1, p_5 are predicate variables. This tuple corresponds to an arrow from ptp^2 to $\mathsf{t}^2\mathsf{p}^5$. Note also that the above tuple can represent also an arrow from ptp^2 to tptp^4.

Furthermore the above tuple can be seen as an arrow having as codomain objects $\mathsf{t}^n\mathsf{p}^m$ for $n \geq 2$ and $m \geq 5$, i.e. the codomain does not define the exact index of (term or predicate) variables, but the maximum index that the variables can have. In the following for a goal g and a natural number n larger than the maximal index of variables appearing in g, we will write g^n to denote the arrow $\mathsf{p} \rightarrow \mathsf{t}^n$.

In the classical interpretation by Leifer and Milner, the arrows having domain objects different from 0 (the distinguished object) are seen as contexts which can be precomposed with terms. In our reactive system these arrows are substitutions which instantiate the variables of formulas. Horn clauses, not only must be instantiated by substitutions, but they must be also contextualised with the $\wedge$ operator.

In the rest of this section we will use the formula $f_1 = P(s(x_1), x_2) \wedge P(x_1, t(x_3))$ and the clause $c_1 = P(y_1, t(y_2)) :- Q(y_1)$ as running example. The head of the c_1 must be instantiated (e.g., substituting y_1 with x_1 and y_2 with x_3) and contextualised (plugging it into $P(s(x_1), x_2) \wedge [-]$) in order to match f_1.

Similar problems arise with process calculi where the rules usually are not ground, and have to be instantiated and contextualised. For example, the redex of the CCS rule $a.P \mid \bar{a}.Q \rightsquigarrow P \mid Q$ matches $\nu a.(a.0 \mid \bar{a}.0)$ instantiating P, Q to 0 and plugging the left-hand side into the context $\nu a.[-]$. Usually this problem is avoided by creating infinitely many rules corresponding to all possible instantiations of the rule, and then considering only contextualisation, as it is done for bigraphs [14]. This approach causes the problem of having infinitely many rules and consequently infinitely many transitions. In [10] the notion of open reactive systems is developed in order to overcome this problem, but the resulting theory is quite restrictive. Here we propose a different approach: we simulate contextualisation by substitutions by supplying appropriate variables in the rules. The redex of a rule is not simply an arrow of the form $h : \mathsf{p} \rightarrow \mathsf{t}^n$ that can only be instantiated, but it is an arrow $p_1 \wedge h \wedge p_2 : \mathsf{p} \rightarrow \mathsf{pt}^n\mathsf{p}$ that can be instantiated and contextualised (by instantiating the variables p_1 and p_2). In this way, we also get a finite branching *ILTS*.

Thus, in our reactive system, the head of the clause c_1 above becomes $p_1 \wedge P(y_1, t(y_2)) \wedge p_2$ and, in this way, the head can match the goal instantiating p_1 to $P(s(x_1), x_2)$, p_2 to $\square$ and y_1 to x_1 and y_2 to x_3.

Summarizing, we can say that we allow only substitutions and simulate contextualisations by substitutions by supplying appropriate variables in the rules (see below). In order to integrate this idea with the theory of reactive systems we have "reversed" the arrows, i.e., a formula over n term variables becomes $\mathsf{p} \rightarrow \mathsf{t}^n$ (instead of the maybe more intuitive $\mathsf{t}^n \rightarrow \mathsf{p}$).

Definition 12. *Given a logic program P on a signature Γ, we define a reactive system $R(P)$ as follows:*

- $\mathrm{Th}[\Gamma'/E]$ *is the underlying category*
- p *is the distinguished object*
- *all contexts are reactive*
- *for each clause $h :- b$, let n be the largest index of variables contained in h and b; then we add the rule*

$$(p_1 \wedge h \wedge p_2\ ,\ p_1 \wedge b \wedge p_2)$$

where left and right-hand sides are arrows $\mathsf{p} \rightarrow \mathsf{pt}^n\mathsf{p}$ and p_1, p_2 are predicate variables.

Note that h and b do not necessarily have the same number of variables, while our theory requires that left-hand and right-hand side of a rule have the same interface (i.e., they must be arrows with the same target). In this case we extend the smaller interface.

A generic redex square of this reactive system is depicted in diagram (i) of Figure 2. Arrow c is a substitution that instantiates the variables of g, while arrow d instantiates the variables of h and contextualises h, instantiating the predicate variables p_1 and p_2. Thus for any reaction step an atom of the goal is unified with the head of a clause and p_1 is instantiated with the formula on the left of the chosen atom, and p_2 is instantiated with the formula on the right.

Lemma 1. *The exterior square of diagram (i) in Figure 2 commutes if and only if there exist formulas g_1, g_2 and an atomic formula a such that $g = g_1 \wedge a \wedge g_2$, $p_1; d = g_1; c$, $p_2; d = g_2; c$ and $h; d = a; c$.*

In general, in $R(P)$, given a rule and a goal, there exist several ways of unifying them: one for each atom of the goal that can match the head h. Consider for example the redex of c_1 and the goal f_1. The head of c_1 unifies both with the left predicate of f_1 and with the right one. This means that, given a redex and a goal—seen as arrows—there usually exists no a minimal way of matching them (i.e., no pushout exists). The following lemma assures that each commuting square fixes a "way" of matching, i.e., chooses the atom of the goal that unifies h.

Lemma 2. *Let the exterior square in diagram (i) of Figure 2 be commuting. Let g_1, a, g_2 be formulas as described in Lemma 1. Then for each candidate $\langle e, f, i\rangle$, the following hold: $p_1; f = g_1; e$, $p_2; f = g_2; e$ and $h; f = a; e$.*

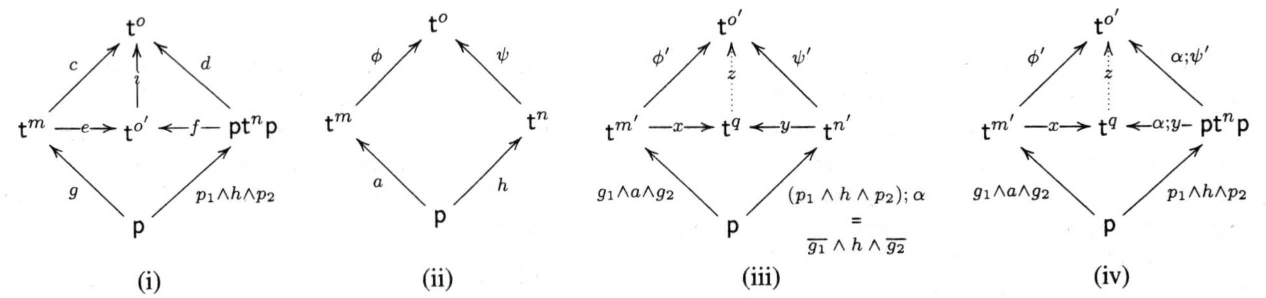

Figure 2. Redex squares, pushouts and RPOs in a reactive system $R(P)$

As a next step we are going to show that in our reactive system a redex RPO is the *mgu* of a and h, together with the instantiation of p_1 and p_2 to appropriate formulas. We start by recalling a theorem from [5].

Theorem 7. *Given two substitutions of terms a and b with disjoint sets of variables, their mgu is the pushout of the arrows a^m and b^n, for m, n larger than the maximal index of variables of a and b.*

Remember that if two substitutions can unify, then there exists an *mgu*. This, together with Theorem 7, assures that for each commuting square of substitutions there exists a pushout. Moreover this result holds not only for substitutions but also for atomic goals since two atomic goals unify iff they consist of the same predicate and the terms within the predicate unify. In the rest of the paper we use $\overline{g}$ to denote a formula having the same predicate symbols as g, but without function symbols and where all variables are different. For example $\overline{f_1} = P(u_1, u_2) \wedge P(u_3, u_4)$. Note that the arrow d of a generic redex square (see Figure 2(i)) can always be decomposed into $\alpha; \psi'$ where α instantiates p_1 and p_2 to $\overline{g_1}$ and $\overline{g_2}$ and ψ' is a substitution. It is exactly this arrow α that chooses which atom of the goal matches h.

The following lemma generalises the theorem above to non-atomic formulas of the form $g_1 \wedge a \wedge g_2$ and $\overline{g_1} \wedge b \wedge \overline{g_2}$.

Lemma 3. *Let a and h be atomic formulas. In Figure 2 $\langle \phi, \psi \rangle$ is the pushout of a and h (depicted in diagram (ii)) if and only if $\langle \phi', \psi' \rangle$ is the pushout of $g_1 \wedge a \wedge g_2$ and $\overline{g_1} \wedge h \wedge \overline{g_2}$ (see diagram (iii)), where ϕ' is equal to ϕ on $Var(a)$ and the identity on the others variables, and ψ' is equal to ψ on $Var(h)$ and such that $g_1; \phi = \overline{g_1}; \psi$ and $g_2; \phi = \overline{g_2}; \psi$.*

The meaning of this lemma is more intuitive if one considers formulas. Suppose that a and h unify, and let $\langle \phi, \psi \rangle$ be their *mgu*. Then also $g_1 \wedge a \wedge g_2$ and $\overline{g_1} \wedge h \wedge \overline{g_2}$ unify and the *mgu* is the *mgu* of a and h (since all the variables of $\overline{g_1}$ and $\overline{g_2}$ are different and can be instantiated to $g_1; \phi$ and $g_2; \psi$).

The following lemma is central since it shows the relationship between RPOs and pushouts: if we fix a way of matching (the arrow α), then we have only one minimal unifier (i.e, pushout) while if we do not fix it, we have several minimal unifiers (i.e., RPOs) one for each way of matching (i.e., for each α).

Lemma 4. *Let a and h be atomic formulas, and α as described above i.e., such that $(p_1 \wedge h \wedge p_2); \alpha = \overline{g_1} \wedge h \wedge \overline{g_2}$. In Figure 2 $\langle x, y \rangle$ is the pushout of $g_1 \wedge a \wedge g_2$ and $\overline{g_1} \wedge h \wedge \overline{g_2}$, and z the mediating morphism (as depicted in diagram (iii)) iff $\langle x, \alpha; y, z \rangle$ is the RPO of the diagram (iv).*

Then, given a commuting square, this fixes a way of matching (i.e., one α) and so there exists a minimal unifier, that is the *mgu* between the head of a clause h and chosen atom a of the formula g.

Theorem 8. *$R(P)$ has redex and context RPOs.*

In the rest of this section we will show that S-equivalence corresponds to standard ϕ-trace equivalence, while correct answer equivalence corresponds to saturated ϕ-trace equivalence. We start by showing that $\rightarrow_C$ corresponds to $\rightarrow$ (as defined in Section 2) while $\rightarrow_I$ corresponds to $\Rightarrow$ (i.e., SLD transitions).

Theorem 9. *Let P be a logic program. Let f, g be two formulas and m, n larger than the maximal index of variables appearing in f and g. Furthermore let σ be a substitution, and let $\theta : \mathsf{t}^m \rightarrow \mathsf{t}^n$ be equal to σ on $Var(f)$ and id otherwise. Then:*

- *$P \Vdash f \xrightarrow{\sigma} g$ iff in $R(P)$ it holds that $f^m \xrightarrow{\theta}_C g^n$,*
- *$P \Vdash f \Rightarrow_\sigma g$ iff in $R(P)$ it holds that $f^m \xrightarrow{\theta}_I g^n$.*

Corollary 1. *In $R(P)$, the ILTS is finite-branching.*

Note that S-equivalence and correct answer equivalence are ϕ-trace equivalence where the predicate ϕ holds only for the empty goal. Formally we define the predicate $\Box()$ over all the arrows of the category $\mathrm{Th}[\Gamma'/E]$: $\Box(a)$ holds iff a is an arrow obtained by decomposing $\Box^n : \mathsf{p} \rightarrow \mathsf{t}^n$, where $\Box^n$ is $\Box : \mathsf{p} \rightarrow \epsilon$ with the interface extended with n extra term variables. Essentially $\Box()$ holds for all term substitutions and for empty formulas. The predicate $\Box()$ defines a composition reflecting subcategory and, since all contexts are reactive, we can apply our theoretical results to $\simeq_I^\Box$, $\simeq_{SAT}^\Box$ and $\simeq_{SS}^\Box$: these three equivalences are congruences (w.r.t. substitutions) and $\simeq_{SAT}^\Box = \simeq_{SS}^\Box$.

Now we show that the first corresponds to $\simeq_S$, while the second (and then also the third) correspond to $\simeq_C$ (that, in the case of infinitely many function symbols, is $\simeq_L$).

Theorem 10. $\simeq_S = \simeq_I^\Box$, $\quad \simeq_C = \simeq_{SAT}^\Box$.

5 Saturated Bisimilarity is Open Bisimilarity

In [8], a reactive system for a subset of the π-calculus is defined in order to study how to model symbolic semantics via reactive systems. The reactive system constructed there is rather complicated, and for this reason we do not fully report it here. Instead we focus on those aspects that relate saturated bisimilarity to *open bisimilarity*. The subset of the π-calculus considered there is the standard π-calculus without matching, τ-prefixes and restriction. The operational semantic is the symbolic LTS whose labels are either actions or fusions. An output $\bar{a}x$, and an input $b(y)$ can synchronise leading to a transition $\xrightarrow{a=b}$. If a and b are equal $a = b$ is the identity fusion denoted by ϵ. Note that also in the original paper introducing open bisimilarity [17], the theory is first developed for the calculus without restriction and distinctions to simplify the presentation. A totally ordered set of names $\{a_1, a_2, \dots\}$ is assumed. Briefly, the underlying category of the defined reactive system has the natural numbers (representing the free names of a process) plus $\star$ as objects. A π-process p is represented as an arrow $p_m : \star \to m$ where $m \geq max\{k \mid a_k \in fn(p)\}$. The contexts in the category represent silent actions ($\tau^m : m \to m$), output actions ($\overline{a_i}^m a_j : m \to m$) and input actions ($a_i{}^m : m \to m+1$) and reaction rules are essentially transitions of the ordinary open π-calculus. When a rule is applied to a process, the IPO construction recreates a transition labeled exactly by the corresponding action, thus essentially embedding the LTS of the ordinary open π-calculus in the *ILTS*. However also fusions ($[a_i = a_j]_m : m \to m-1$) are possible contexts, and when a synchronization rule is selected for a process which has the input and the output actions on different channels, the IPO construction generates a fusion for them. As a consequence, the resulting *ILTS* is essentially the symbolic LTS of the open π calculus.

Lemma 5 (from [8]). *Let p be a process of our subset of π and $m \geq max\{k \mid a_k \in fn(p)\}$. Furthermore let $\to$ and $\to_I$ be the symbolic and the IPO transition relations. Then*

$$p \xrightarrow{\overline{a_h} a_k} p' \Leftrightarrow p_m \xrightarrow{\overline{a_h}^m a_k}_I p'_m,$$

$$p \xrightarrow{a_i(a_j)} p' \Leftrightarrow p_m \xrightarrow{a_i{}^m}_I p'_{m+1}, \quad p \xrightarrow{\epsilon} p' \Leftrightarrow p_m \xrightarrow{\tau^m}_I p'_m,$$

$$p \xrightarrow{a_i=a_j} p' \Leftrightarrow p_m \xrightarrow{\tau^m;[a_i=a_j]_m}_I p'_m; [a_i = a_j]_m.$$

In [8] it is shown that the reactive system has redex RPOs and hence the resulting equivalence $\sim_{IPO}$ is a congruence. However, this does not coincide with open bisimilarity but with *syntactical bisimilarity*, formally defined below.

Definition 13 (Open/Syntactical Bisimilarity). *A symmetric relation R is an* open bisimulation *if whenever $p\,R\,q$ it holds:*

- *if $p \xrightarrow{\alpha} p'$ then $q \xrightarrow{\alpha} q'$ and $p'\,R\,q'$,*
- *if $p \xrightarrow{a=b} p'$ then ($q \xrightarrow{a=b} q' \vee q \xrightarrow{\epsilon} q'$) and $\sigma(p')\,R\,\sigma(q')$.*

where α is an input, an output or ϵ and σ is a fusion that fuses a to b. The union of all open bisimulation is open bisimilarity *(denoted by $\sim_O$).*

Syntactical bisimilarity *(denoted by $\sim_{SYN}$) is obtained by replacing the last condition of open bisimulation with:*

- *if $p \xrightarrow{a=b} p'$ then $q \xrightarrow{a=b} q'$ and $\sigma(p')\,R\,\sigma(q')$.*

It is immediate to see that $\sim_{SYN} \subsetneq \sim_O$ since the conditions for matching transitions for $\sim_O$ are weaker than that the ones for $\sim_{SYN}$. The following example shows that $\sim_{SYN}$ is strictly finer.

Example 3. *Consider the following processes:*

- $p = (\bar{a}b \mid a'(c)) + (\bar{d}e \mid d(f))$
- $q = \bar{a}b.a'(c) + a'(c).\bar{a}b + (\bar{d}e \mid d(f))$

It holds that $p \sim_O q$ since the move $p \xrightarrow{a=a'}$ is matched by the (unique) synchronisation of q. However, $p \not\sim_{SYN} q$ since the transition $p \xrightarrow{a=a'}$ cannot be matched by q.

With Lemma 5 one can show that $\sim_{IPO}$ coincides with $\sim_{SYN}$ (see [8]), in fact in $\sim_{IPO}$ if Alice proposes a fusion moves, then Bob must answer with the same fusion, while in open bisimilarity Bob can answer with a less restrictive fusion. But this is exactly what happens with saturated bisimilarity. In fact look at the characterisation of semi-saturated bisimulation given by Theorem 3. If $p_m \xrightarrow{\tau^m;[a_i=a_j]_m}_I p'_m; [a_i = a_j]_m$, then q_m can answer with $q_m \xrightarrow{\tau^m;[a_i=a_j]_m}_I q'_m; [a_i = a_j]_m$ where $p'_m; [a_i = a_j]_m\,R\,q'_m; [a_i = a_j]_m$ (in this case arrow d of Theorem 3 is $\tau^m; [a_i = a_j]_m$ and $e = id$), or $q_m \xrightarrow{\tau^m}_I q'_m$ where $p'_m; [a_i = a_j]_m\,R\,q'_m; [a_i = a_j]_m$ ($d = \tau^m$, $e = [a_i = a_j]_m$).

Theorem 11. $\sim_O = \sim_{SAT}$.

6 Conclusions and Future Work

In this paper we have proposed a semi-saturated technique for efficiently characterising certain congruences that are usually coarser than those presented by Leifer and Milner in [12]. Our approach applies to different kinds of semantics (here we have handled bisimilarity and trace semantics, but we are confident that it applies to others). In this paper we have integrated semi-saturation within the IPO framework, but it could be applied also to G-reactive systems [18] and open reactive systems [10] where, in our opinion, it might help to relax the constraints of the theory. Another advantage of semi-saturation is that it can be applied to a larger class of reactive systems, because we require only the existence of redex IPOs and not necessarily of redex RPOs.

Besides our examples, there are other cases where saturated bisimilarity seems to be appropriate. In $\sim_{IPO}$, if Alice proposes a fusion move, then Bob must answer with the same syntactic fusion, while in open bisimilarity Bob can answer with a "smaller label" (as it happens in saturated bisimilarity). We conjecture that the same can be said for *asynchronous bisimilarity* [1], since similarly to open bisimilarity, an input move of Alice can be matched with a τ move of Bob. Here we want to emphasize that the "shape" of asynchronous and open bisimulations is really similar to that of semi-saturated bisimulation as expressed by Theorem 3.

The question is still open of where saturated equivalences are appropriate. We have shown that for logic programming and symbolic open π-calculus they capture exactly the right congruences. However, when trying to derive a reasonable LTS semantics from a reduction semantics of process calculi, saturated bisimilarity seems to be too coarse. In fact let us consider two processes that always diverge i.e., such that for every reactive context into which they can be put, they can always react: they will always be saturated bisimilar, since they react in the same contexts. Consider for example the following CCS processes: $P = \tau.P$ and $Q = \tau.Q + a.P$. Putting them into any possible context, we will always get two processes that always diverge. In the standard CCS semantics these processes are definitely considered different. We are confident that a mixed approach, where some labeled transitions are present also in the initial reduction system, might be successful also for contextualizing process calculi. In fact this was already the case for dynamic bisimilarity [16] and for our symbolic π-calculus example. More interesting results could probably be obtained by minimizing the transition labels in the initial system, or by observing actions also in the states as for barbed bisimulation.

Another original contribution of this paper is the encoding of logic programs as reactive systems, where the IPO semantics correspond to S-equivalence while the saturated semantics corresponds to logical equivalence. The encoding of logic programs proposes a new way of handling non-ground rules in reactive systems: even within the theoretical framework proposed by Leifer and Milner we can use arrows that can both instantiate and contextualise the rules. In this way we can work with a finite number of rules and not with infinitely many as it happens, for example, with bigraphs. We conjecture that this approach can be extended to all contexts of the form $[-] \mid p$.

Acknowledgements We would like to thank Roberto Bruni, Andrea Corradini, Fabio Gadducci, Emilio Tuosto and the anonymous referees for their helpful comments.

References

[1] R. M. Amadio, I. Castellani, and D. Sangiorgi. On bisimulations for the asynchronous pi-calculus. In *Proc. of CONCUR'96*, volume 1119 of *LNCS*, 147–162. Springer, 1996.

[2] P. Baldan, A. Bracciali, and R. Bruni. Bisimulation by unification. In *AMAST*, volume 2422 of *LNCS*, 254–270. Springer, 2002.

[3] G. Berry and G. Boudol. The chemical abstract machine. *Theor. Comput. Sci.*, 96:217–248, 1992.

[4] R. Bruni, F. Gadducci, U. Montanari, and P. Sobocinski. Deriving weak bisimulation congruences from reduction systems. In *Proc. of CONCUR'05*, volume 3653 of *LNCS*, 293–307. Springer, 2005.

[5] R. Bruni, U. Montanari, and F. Rossi. An interactive semantics of logic programming. *TPLP*, 1(6):647–690, 2001.

[6] H. Ehrig and B. König. Deriving bisimulation congruences in the DPO approach to graph rewriting. In *Proc. of FoSSaCS'05*, volume 2987 of *LNCS*, 151–166. Springer, 2004.

[7] M. Falaschi, G. Levi, M. Martelli, and C. Palamidessi. Declarative modeling of the operational behavior of logic languages. 69(3):289–318, 1989.

[8] G. Ferrari, U. Montanari, and E. Tuosto. Model checking for nominal calculi. In *Proc. of FoSSaCS'05*, volume 3441 of *LNCS*, 1–24. Springer, 2005.

[9] J. Goguen. What is unification? A categorical view of substitution, equation and solution. In M. Nivat and H. Aït-Kaci, editors, *Resolution of Equations in Algebraic Structures*, 217–261. 1989.

[10] B. Klin, V. Sassone, and P. Sobocinski. Labels from reductions: Towards a general theory. In *Proc. of CALCO'05*, volume 3629 of *LNCS*, 30–50. Springer, 2005.

[11] F. Lawvere. Some algebraic problems in the context of functorial semantics of algebraic theories. In *Proceedings of the Midwest Category Seminar II*, volume 61, 41–61, 1968.

[12] J. J. Leifer and R. Milner. Deriving bisimulation congruences for reactive systems. In *Proc. of CONCUR'00*, volume 1877 of *LNCS*, 243–258. Springer, 2000.

[13] R. Milner. *Communicating and Mobile Systems: the π-Calculus*. Cambridge University Press, 1999.

[14] R. Milner. Bigraphical reactive systems. In *Proc. of CONCUR'01*, volume 2154 of *LNCS*, 16–35. Springer, 2001.

[15] R. Milner and D. Sangiorgi. Barbed bisimulation. In *Proc. of ICALP'92*, volume 623 of *LNCS*, 685–695. Springer, 1992.

[16] U. Montanari and V. Sassone. Dynamic congruence vs. progressing bisimulation for ccs. *Fundam. Inform.*, 16(1):171–199, 1992.

[17] D. Sangiorgi. A theory of bisimulation for the pi-calculus. *Acta Inf.*, 33(1):69–97, 1996.

[18] V. Sassone and P. Sobocinski. Locating reaction with 2-categories. *Theor. Comput. Sci.*, 333(1-2):297–327, 2005.

[19] V. Sassone and P. Sobociński. Reactive systems over cospans. In *Proc. of LICS'05*, 311–320. IEEE, 2005.

[20] P. Sewell. From rewrite to bisimulation congruences. In *Proc. of CONCUR'98*, volume 1466 of *LNCS*, 269–284. Springer, 1998.

[21] P. Sobociński. *Deriving process congruences from reaction rules*. PhD thesis, 2004.

Session 3:
Pushdown Systems

On model-checking trees generated by higher-order recursion schemes

C.-H. L. Ong*
Oxford University Computing Laboratory

Abstract

We prove that the modal mu-calculus model-checking problem for (ranked and ordered) node-labelled trees that are generated by order-n recursion schemes (whether safe or not, and whether homogeneously typed or not) is n-EXPTIME complete, for every $n \geq 0$. It follows that the monadic second-order theories of these trees are decidable.

There are three major ingredients. The first is a certain transference principle *from the tree generated by the scheme – the* value tree *– to an auxiliary* computation tree, *which is itself a tree generated by a related order-0 recursion scheme (equivalently, a regular tree). Using innocent game semantics in the sense of Hyland and Ong, we establish a strong correspondence between* paths *in the value tree and* traversals *in the computation tree. This allows us to prove that a given alternating parity tree automaton (APT) has an (accepting) run-tree over the value tree iff it has an (accepting)* traversal-tree *over the computation tree. The second ingredient is the simulation of an (accepting) traversal-tree by a certain set of annotated paths over the computation tree; we introduce* traversal-simulating *APT as a recognising device for the latter. Finally, for the complexity result, we prove that traversal-simulating APT enjoy a* succinctness property*: for deciding acceptance, it is enough to consider run-trees that have a reduced branching factor. The desired bound is then obtained by analysing the complexity of solving an associated (finite) acceptance parity game.*

1. Introduction

What classes of finitely-presentable infinite-state systems have decidable monadic second-order (MSO) theories? This is a basic problem in Computer-Aided Verification that is important to practice because standard temporal logics such as LTL, CTL and CTL* are embeddable in MSO logic. One of the best known examples of such a class are the *regular trees* as studied by Rabin in 1969. A notable advance occurred some fifteen years later, when Muller and Shupp [13] proved that the *configuration graphs of pushdown systems* have decidable MSO theories. In the 90's, as finite-state technologies matured, researchers embraced the challenges of software verification. A highlight from this period was Caucal's result [5] that *prefix-recognizable graphs* have decidable MSO theories. In 2002 a flurry of discoveries significantly extended and unified earlier developments. In a FOSSACS'02 paper [11], Knapik, Niwiński and Urzyczyn studied the infinite hierarchy of term-trees generated by higher-order recursion schemes that are *homogeneously typed* and satisfy a syntactic constraint called *safety*. They showed that for every $n \geq 0$, trees generated by order-n safe schemes are exactly those that are accepted by *order-n pushdown automata*; further they have decidable MSO theories. Later in the year at MFCS'02 [6], Caucal introduced a tree hierarchy and a graph hierarchy that are defined by mutual recursion, using a pair of powerful transformations that preserve decidability of MSO theories. Caucal's tree hierarchy coincides with the hierarchy of trees generated by higher-order pushdown automata.

Knapik *et al.* [11] have asked if the safety assumption is really necessary for their MSO decidability result. A partial answer has recently been obtained by Aehlig, de Miranda and Ong; they showed at TLCA'05 [2] that all trees up to order 2, whether safe or not, have decidable MSO theories. Independently, Knapik, Niwiński, Urzyczyn and Walukiewicz obtained a sharper result: they proved at ICALP'05 [12] that the modal mu-calculus model-checking problem for trees generated by order-2 recursion schemes (whether safe or not) is 2-EXPTIME complete. In this paper we give a complete answer to the question:

Theorem 1. *The modal mu-calculus model-checking problem for trees generated by order-n recursion schemes (whether safe or not, and whether homogeneously typed or not) is n-*EXPTIME *complete, for every $n \geq 0$. Thus these trees have decidable MSO theories.*

Our approach is to transfer the algorithmic analysis from the tree generated by a recursion scheme, which we call *value tree*, to an auxiliary *computation tree*, which is itself a tree generated by a related order-0 recursion scheme (equivalently, a regular tree). The computation tree recovers useful intensional information about the computational

*users.comlab.ox.ac.uk/luke.ong/index.html

process behind the construction of the value tree. Using innocent game semantics [9], we then establish a strong correspondence (Theorem 3) between *paths* in the value tree and (what we call) *traversals* over the computation tree. In the language of game semantics, paths in the value tree correspond exactly to plays in the strategy-denotation of the recursion scheme; a traversal is then (a representation of) the *uncovering* of such a play. The path-traversal correspondence allows us to prove that a given alternating parity tree automaton (APT) has an accepting run-tree over the value tree if and only if it has an accepting *traversal-tree* over the computation tree (Corollary 4).

Our problem is then reduced to finding an effective way of recognising a set of infinite traversals (over a given computation tree) that satisfy the parity condition. This requires a new idea as a traversal is most unlike a path; it can jump all over the tree and may even visit certain nodes infinitely often. Our solution exploits the game-semantic connection. It is a property of traversals that their *P-views* are paths (in the computation tree). This allows us to simulate a traversal over a computation tree by (the P-views of its prefixes, which are) annotated paths of a certain kind in the same tree. The simulation is made precise in the notion of *traversal-simulating* APT. We establish the correctness of the simulation by proving that a given *property*[1] APT has an accepting traversal-tree over the computation tree if and only if the associated *traversal-simulating* APT has an accepting run-tree over the computation tree (Theorem 5). Note that decidability of the modal mu-calculus model-checking problem for trees generated by recursion schemes follows at once since computation trees are regular, and the APT acceptance problem for regular trees is decidable.

To prove n-EXPTIME completeness of the decision problem, we first establish a certain *succinctness property* (Proposition 6) for traversal-simulating APT: if a traversal-simulating APT C has an accepting run-tree, then it has one with a reduced branching factor. The desired time bound is then obtained by analysing the complexity of solving an associated (finite) acceptance parity game, which is an appropriate product of the traversal-simulating APT and a finite deterministic graph that unfolds to the computation tree in question.

Using a novel finitary semantics of the lambda calculus, Aehlig [3] has shown that model-checking trees generated by recursion schemes (whether safe or not) against all properties expressible by non-deterministic tree automata with the trivial acceptance condition is decidable (i.e. acceptance simply means that the automaton has a run-tree).

This paper is an extended abstract. The reader is directed to the preprint [14] for further details, including proofs.

[1] *Property* APT because the APT corresponds to the property described by a given modal mu-calculus formula.

2. Preliminaries

Types are generated from the base type o using the arrow constructor $\to$. Every type A can be written uniquely as $A_1 \to \cdots \to A_n \to o$ (arrows associate to the right), for some $n \geq 0$ which is called its *arity*; we shall often write A simply as $(A_1, \cdots, A_n, o)$. We define the *order* of a type by: $ord(o) = o$ and $ord(A \to B) = \max(ord(A) + 1, ord(B))$. Let Σ be a *ranked alphabet* i.e. each Σ-symbol f has an arity $ar(f) \geq 0$ which determines its type $(\underbrace{o, \cdots, o}_{ar(f)}, o)$. Further we shall assume that each symbol $f \in \Sigma$ is assigned a finite set $\mathsf{Dir}(f)$ of exactly $ar(f)$ *directions*, and we define $\mathsf{Dir}(\Sigma) = \bigcup_{f \in \Sigma} \mathsf{Dir}(f)$. Let D be a set of directions; a *D-tree* is just a prefix-closed subset of D^*, the free monoid of D. A ***Σ-labelled tree*** is a function $t : \mathsf{Dom}(t) \longrightarrow \Sigma$ such that $\mathsf{Dom}(t)$ is a $\mathsf{Dir}(\Sigma)$-tree, and for every node $\alpha \in \mathsf{Dom}(t)$, the Σ-symbol $t(\alpha)$ has arity k if and only if α has exactly k children and the set of its children is $\{ \alpha i : i \in \mathsf{Dir}(t(\alpha)) \}$ i.e. t is a *ranked*[2] tree. Henceforth we shall assume that the ranked alphabet Σ contains a distinguished nullary symbol $\perp$ which will be used exclusively to label "undefined" nodes.

Note. We write $[m]$ as a shorthand for $\{ 1, \cdots, m \}$. *Henceforth we fix a ranked alphabet* Σ *for the rest of the paper*, and set $\mathsf{Dir}(f) = [ar(f)]$ for each $f \in \Sigma$; hence we have $\mathsf{Dir}(\Sigma) = [ar(\Sigma)]$, writing $ar(\Sigma)$ to mean $\max\{ ar(f) : f \in \Sigma \}$.

For each type A, we assume an infinite collection Var^A of variables of type A, and write Var to be the union of Var^A as A ranges over types. A (deterministic) ***recursion scheme*** is a tuple $G = \langle \Sigma, \mathcal{N}, \mathcal{R}, S \rangle$ where Σ is a ranked alphabet of *terminals*; $\mathcal{N}$ is a set of typed *non-terminals*; $S \in \mathcal{N}$ is a distinguished *start symbol* of type o; $\mathcal{R}$ is a finite set of rewrite rules – one for each non-terminal $F : (A_1, \cdots, A_n, o)$ – of the form

$$F\,\xi_1 \cdots \xi_n \to e$$

where each ξ_i is in Var^{A_i}, and e is an *applicative term*[3] of type o constructed from elements of $\Sigma \cup \mathcal{N} \cup \{ \xi_1, \cdots, \xi_n \}$. The *order* of a recursion scheme is the highest order of its non-terminals.

We use recursion schemes as generators of Σ-labelled trees. The ***value tree*** of (or the tree *generated* by) a recursion scheme G is a possibly infinite applicative term, but viewed as a Σ-labelled tree, *constructed from the terminals*

[2] In the sequel, we shall have occasions to consider unordered trees whose nodes are labelled by symbols of an *unranked* alphabet Γ. To avoid confusion, we shall call these trees ***Γ-labelled unranked trees***.

[3] ***Applicative terms*** are terms constructed from the generators using the application rule: if $d : A \to B$ and $e : A$ then $(de) : B$. Standardly we identify finite Σ-labelled trees with applicative terms of type o generated from Σ-symbols endowed with 1st-order types *as given by their arities*.

in Σ, that is obtained by unfolding the rewrite rules of G *ad infinitum*, replacing formal by actual parameters each time, starting from the start symbol S.

Example 2.1 (***Running***). [*The simple recursion scheme defined here will be used to illustrate various concepts throughout the paper.*] Let G be the order-2 (unsafe) recursion scheme with rewrite rules:

$$\begin{array}{rcl} S & \to & H\,a \\ H\,z^{o} & \to & F\,(g\,z) \\ F\,\varphi^{(o,o)} & \to & \varphi\,(\varphi\,(F\,h)) \end{array}$$

where the arities of the terminals g, h, a are $2, 1, 0$ respectively. The value tree $[\![\,G\,]\!]$ is the Σ-labelled tree defined by the infinite term $g\,a\,(g\,a\,(h\,(h\,(h\,\cdots))))$:

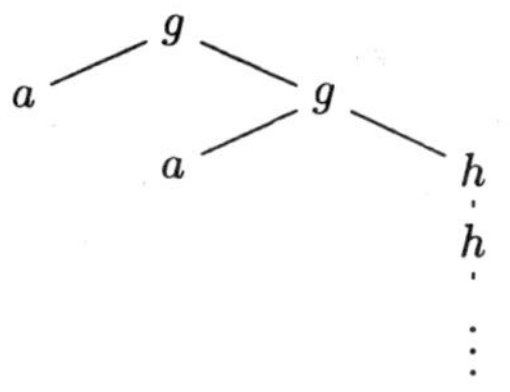

The only infinite ***path*** in the tree is the node-sequence $\epsilon \cdot 2 \cdot 22 \cdot 221 \cdot 2211 \cdots$ (with the corresponding ***trace*** $g\,g\,h\,h\,h \cdots \in \Sigma^{\omega}$).

This paper is concerned with the decision problem: *Given a modal mu-calculus formula φ and an order-n recursion scheme G, does $[\![\,G\,]\!]$ satisfy φ (at ϵ)?* The problem is equivalent [7] to deciding whether a given alternating parity tree automaton $\mathcal{B}$ has an accepting run-tree over $[\![\,G\,]\!]$. To fix notation, an ***alternating parity tree automaton*** (or APT for short) over Σ-labelled trees is a tuple $\langle\, \Sigma,\ Q,\ \delta,\ q_0,\ \Omega\,\rangle$ where Σ is the input ranked alphabet, Q is a finite state-set, $q_0 \in Q$ is the initial state, $\delta : Q \times \Sigma \longrightarrow \mathsf{B}^{+}(\mathsf{Dir}(\Sigma) \times Q)$ is the transition function whereby for each $f \in \Sigma$ and $q \in Q$, we have $\delta(q, f) \in \mathsf{B}^{+}(\mathsf{Dir}(f) \times Q)$ where $\mathsf{B}^{+}(X)$ is the set of positive boolean formulas over elements of X, and $\Omega : Q \longrightarrow \mathbb{N}$ is the priority function.

3. Computation trees and traversals

The ***long transform***, $\overline{G}$, of a recursion scheme G is an order-0 recursion scheme. Its rules are obtained from those of G by applying the following four-stage transformation in turn. For each G-rule:

1. *Expand the RHS to its η-long form*: We hereditarily η-expand every subterm – even if it is of ground type so that $e : o$ expands to $\boldsymbol{\lambda}.e$ – provided it is the *operand* of an occurrence of the application operator.

2. *Insert long-apply symbols $@_A$*: Replace each *ground-type* subterm $D\,e_1 \cdots e_n$ by $@_A\,D\,e_1 \cdots e_n$ where $A = ((A_1, \cdots, A_n, o), A_1, \cdots, A_n, o)$.

3. *Curry the rewrite rule.* I.e. transform the rule $F\,\varphi_1 \,\cdots\, \varphi_n \to e$ to $F \to \boldsymbol{\lambda}\varphi_1 \,\cdots\, \varphi_n.e$.

4. *Rename bound variables afresh.*

$\overline{G}$ is an order-0 recursion scheme with respect to an enlarged ranked alphabet Λ_G, which is Σ augmented by certain variables and lambdas (of the form $\boldsymbol{\lambda}\overline{\xi}$ which is a short hand for $\boldsymbol{\lambda}\xi_1 \cdots \xi_n$ where $n \geq 0$) *but regarded as terminals*. The alphabet Λ_G is a finite subset of the set

$$\underbrace{\Sigma \ \cup\ \mathit{Var} \ \cup\ \{\, @_A : A \in \mathit{ATypes}\,\}}_{\textit{Non-lambdas}} \ \cup\ \underbrace{\{\,\boldsymbol{\lambda}\overline{\xi} : \overline{\xi} \subseteq \mathit{Var}\,\}}_{\textit{Lambdas}}$$

where *ATypes* is the set of types of the shape $((A_1, \cdots, A_n, o), A_1, \cdots, A_n, o)$ with $n \geq 1$. Symbols in Λ_G are ranked as follows. A symbol $\varphi : (A_1, \cdots, A_n, o)$ from Var has arity n. The *long-apply* $@_A$ where $A = ((A_1, \cdots, A_n, o), A_1, \cdots, A_n, o)$ has arity $n + 1$. Lambdas $\boldsymbol{\lambda}\overline{\xi}$ have arity 1. Further, for $f \in \Lambda_G$, we define

$$\mathsf{Dir}(f) \;=\; \begin{cases} [ar(@_A) - 1] \cup \{\,0\,\} & \text{if } f = @_A \\ [ar(f)] & \text{otherwise} \end{cases}$$

For technical convenience, the leftmost child of an @-node is its 0-child, but for all other nodes, the leftmost child is the 1-child. The *non-terminals* of $\overline{G}$ are exactly those of G, except that they are all of type o. We can now define the ***computation tree***[4] $\lambda(G)$ to be $[\![\,\overline{G}\,]\!]$. Thus $\lambda(G)$ is the Λ_G-labelled (ranked and ordered) tree that is obtained by unfolding the $\overline{G}$-rules *ad infinitum* (note that no "β-redex" is contracted in the process).

Example 3.1. Let G be as defined in Example 2.1. We present its long transform $\overline{G}$ as follows and the computation tree $\lambda(G)$ in Figure 1.

$$\overline{G} \;:\; \left\{ \begin{array}{rcl} S & \to & \boldsymbol{\lambda}.@\,H\,(\boldsymbol{\lambda}.a) \\ H & \to & \boldsymbol{\lambda}z.@\,F\,(\boldsymbol{\lambda}y.g\,(\boldsymbol{\lambda}.z)\,(\boldsymbol{\lambda}.y)) \\ F & \to & \boldsymbol{\lambda}\varphi.\varphi\,(\boldsymbol{\lambda}.\varphi\,(\boldsymbol{\lambda}.@\,F\,(\boldsymbol{\lambda}x.h\,(\boldsymbol{\lambda}.x)))) \end{array} \right.$$

In Figure 1, for ease of reference, we give nodes of $\lambda(G)$ numeric names (in square-brackets).

We define a family of binary relations $\vdash_i$, where $i \in \mathsf{Dir}(\Lambda_G)$, between nodes of a computation tree $\lambda(G)$, called ***enabling***, as follows:

- Every lambda-labelled node β, that is the i-child of its parent node α, is *i-enabled* by α.

- A variable node β (labelled ξ_i, say) is *i-enabled* by its ***binder***, which is defined to be the largest prefix of β that is labelled by a lambda $\boldsymbol{\lambda}\overline{\xi}$, for some list $\overline{\xi} = \xi_1 \cdots \xi_n$ in which ξ_i occurs as the i-element.

[4] In recent work on deciding higher-order matching [15], Colin Stirling has introduced *property checking game* over a kind of trees determined by lambda terms. His trees are exactly the same as our computation trees.

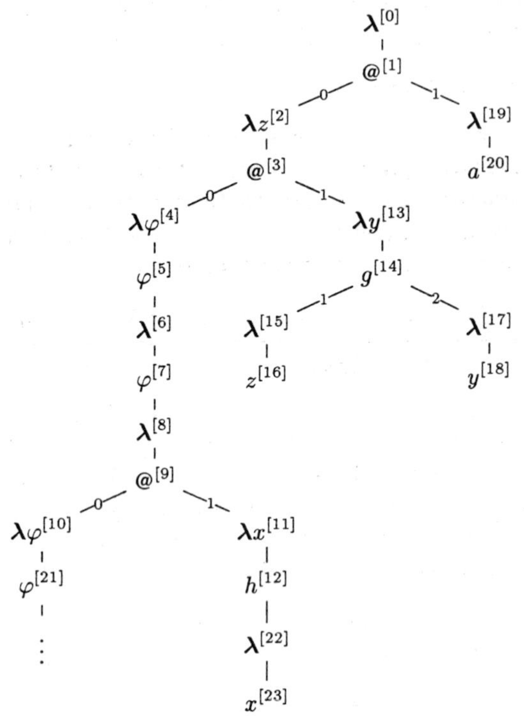

Figure 1. An order-2 computation tree.

We say that β is ***enabled*** by α just if β is i-enabled by α, for some (necessarily unique) i. A node of $\lambda(G)$ is ***initial*** if it is not enabled by any node. The initial nodes of a computation tree are the root node and all nodes labelled by a long-apply or Σ-symbol. A ***justified sequence*** over $\lambda(G)$ is a possibly infinite, lambda / non-lambda alternating sequence of nodes that satisfies the *pointer condition*: Each non-initial node that occurs in it has a pointer to some earlier occurrence of the node that enables it.

Notation $\cdots \overbrace{n_0 \ \cdots \ n}^{j} \cdots$ means that n points to n_0 and n is j-enabled by n_0. We say that n is *j-justified* by n_0 in the justified sequence.

The notion of *view* (of a justified sequence) and the condition of *Visibility* were first introduced in game semantics [9]. Intuitively the *P-view* of a justified sequence is a certain subsequence consisting of moves which player P considers relevant for determining his next move in the play. In the setting here, the lambda nodes are the O-moves, and the non-lambda moves are the P-moves.

The ***P-view***, $\ulcorner t \urcorner$, of a justified sequence t is a subsequence defined by recursion as follows: we let n range over non-lambda nodes

$$\begin{aligned} \ulcorner \lambda \urcorner &= \lambda \\ \ulcorner t\, \overbrace{n \ \cdots \ \lambda\overline{\xi}}^{i} \urcorner &= \ulcorner t \urcorner\, \overbrace{n \ \lambda\overline{\xi}}^{i} \\ \ulcorner t\, \lambda\overline{\xi}\, n \urcorner &= \ulcorner t\, \lambda\overline{\xi} \urcorner\, n \end{aligned}$$

In the second clause above, suppose the non-lambda node n points to some node-occurrence l (say) in t; if l appears in $\ulcorner t \urcorner$, then n in $\ulcorner t \urcorner\, \overbrace{n \ \lambda\overline{\xi}}^{i}$ is defined to point to l; otherwise n has no pointer; similarly for the third clause. We say that a justified sequence t satisfies ***P-visibility*** just in case every non-initial non-lambda node that occurs in the sequence points to some (necessarily lambda) node that appears in the P-view at that point.

Definition 3.2. ***Traversals*** over a computation tree $\lambda(G)$ are justified sequences defined by induction over the following rules. In the following, we refer to nodes of $\lambda(G)$ by their labels, and we let n range over non-lambda nodes.

(Root) The singleton sequence, comprising the root node of $\lambda(G)$, is a traversal.

(App) If $t\,@$ is a traversal, so is $t\, \overbrace{@ \ \lambda\overline{\xi}}^{0}$.

(Sig) If $t\,f$ is a traversal, so is $t\, \overbrace{f \ \lambda}^{i}$ for each $1 \leq i \leq ar(f)$ with $f \in \Sigma$

(Var) If $t\, n\, \overbrace{\lambda\overline{\xi} \ \cdots \ \xi}^{i}$ is a traversal, so is $t\, \overbrace{n \ \lambda\overline{\xi} \ \cdots \ \xi \ \lambda\overline{\eta}}^{i}$.

(Lam) If $t\, \lambda\overline{\xi}$ is a traversal and $\ulcorner t\, \lambda\overline{\xi}\, n \urcorner$ is a path in $\lambda(G)$, then $t\, \lambda\overline{\xi}\, n$ is a traversal.

Thus the way that a traversal can grow is deterministic (and determined by $\lambda(G)$), except when the last node in the justified sequence is a Σ-symbol f of arity $k > 1$, in which case, the traversal can grow in one of k possible directions in the next step.

Lemma 2. *Traversals are well-defined justified sequences that satisfy P-visibility (and O-visibility). Further, the P-view of a traversal is a path in the computation tree.*

Example 3.3. The following are maximal traversals (pointers omitted) over the computation tree shown in Figure 1:

$0 \cdot 1 \cdot 2 \cdot 3 \cdot 4 \cdot 5 \cdot 13 \cdot 14 \cdot 15 \cdot 16 \cdot 19 \cdot 20$

$0 \cdot 1 \cdot 2 \cdot 3 \cdot 4 \cdot 5 \cdot 13 \cdot 14 \cdot 17 \cdot 18 \cdot 6 \cdot 7 \cdot 13 \cdot 14 \cdot 15 \cdot 16 \cdot 19 \cdot 20$

The preceding traversals have the same P-view, namely, $0 \cdot 1 \cdot 19 \cdot 20$. The P-view of $0 \cdots 16$ (i.e. the prefix of the 2nd traversal above that ends in 16) is $0 \cdot 1 \cdot 2 \cdot 3 \cdot 13 \cdot 14 \cdot 15 \cdot 16$.

We state an important result that underpins our approach.

Theorem 3. *Let G be a recursion scheme. There is a one-one correspondence, $p \mapsto t_p$, between maximal paths p in the value tree $[\![G]\!]$ and maximal traversals t_p over the computation tree $\lambda(G)$. Further for every maximal path p in $[\![G]\!]$, we have $t_p \upharpoonright \Sigma^- = p \upharpoonright \Sigma^-$, where $s \upharpoonright \Sigma^-$ denotes the subsequence of s consisting of only Σ^--symbols with $\Sigma^- = \Sigma \setminus \{ \perp \}$.*

Using the language of game semantics, we are claiming (in the Theorem) that the traversal t_p is (a representation of) the *uncovering* of the path p viewed as a play. The proof is by innocent game semantics [9].

Example 3.4. To illustrate Theorem 3, consider the computation tree in Figure 1. The two (maximal) traversals over $\lambda(G)$ given in Example 3.3 correspond respectively to the (maximal) paths $g \cdot a$ and $g \cdot g \cdot a$ in $[\![G]\!]$. The traversal 0·1·2·3·4·5·13·14·17·18·6·7·13·14·17·18·8·9·10·21·11·12 corresponds to the path $g \cdot g \cdot h$.

Relative to a *property* APT $\mathcal{B} = \langle \Sigma, Q, \delta, q_0, \Omega \rangle$ over Σ-labelled trees, an (accepting) traversal-tree of $\mathcal{B}$ over $\lambda(G)$ plays the same rôle as an (accepting) run-tree of $\mathcal{B}$ over $[\![G]\!]$. A path in a traversal-tree is a traversal in which each node is annotated by an element of Q. Formally, we have:

Definition 3.5. A ***traversal-tree*** of a property APT $\mathcal{B}$ over a Λ_G-labelled tree $\lambda(G)$ is a $(\mathsf{Dom}(\lambda(G)) \times Q)$-labelled unranked tree $t : \mathsf{Dom}(t) \longrightarrow \mathsf{Dom}(\lambda(G)) \times Q$, satisfying $t(\varepsilon) = (\varepsilon, q_0)$, and for every $\beta \in \mathsf{Dom}(t)$ with $t(\beta) = (\alpha, q)$:

- If $\lambda(G)(\alpha)$ is an @, then $t(\beta\, 1) = (\alpha\, 0, q)$.
- If $\lambda(G)(\alpha)$ is a Σ-symbol f, then there is some $S \subseteq [ar(f)] \times Q$ such that S satisfies $\delta(q, f)$ – and we pick the smallest such S; and for each $(i, q') \in S$, there is some $1 \leq j \leq ar(\Sigma) \times |Q|$, such that $t(\beta\, j) = (\alpha\, i, q')$.
- If $\lambda(G)(\alpha)$ is a variable, and α is i-justified by α_1 with $t(\beta_1\, 1) = (\alpha_1, q_1)$ for some β_1 and q_1, then $t(\beta\, 1) = (\gamma\, i, q)$ where $t(\beta_1) = (\gamma, q_1)$.

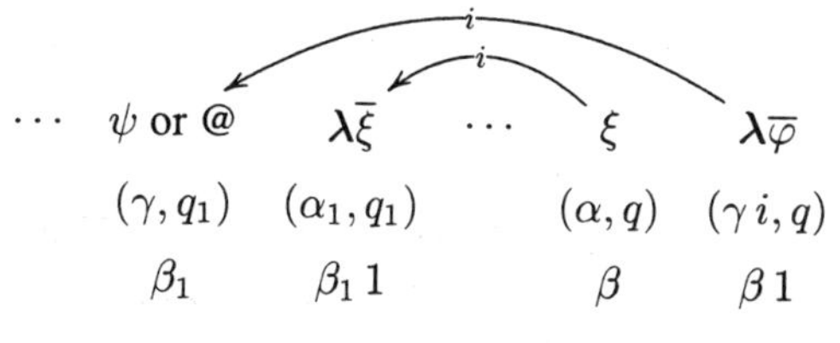

Note that $\gamma\, i$ is a lambda node that is i-justified by γ which is labelled by either an @-symbol or a variable.

- If $\lambda(G)(\alpha)$ is a lambda, then $t(\beta\, 1) = (\alpha\, 1, q)$.

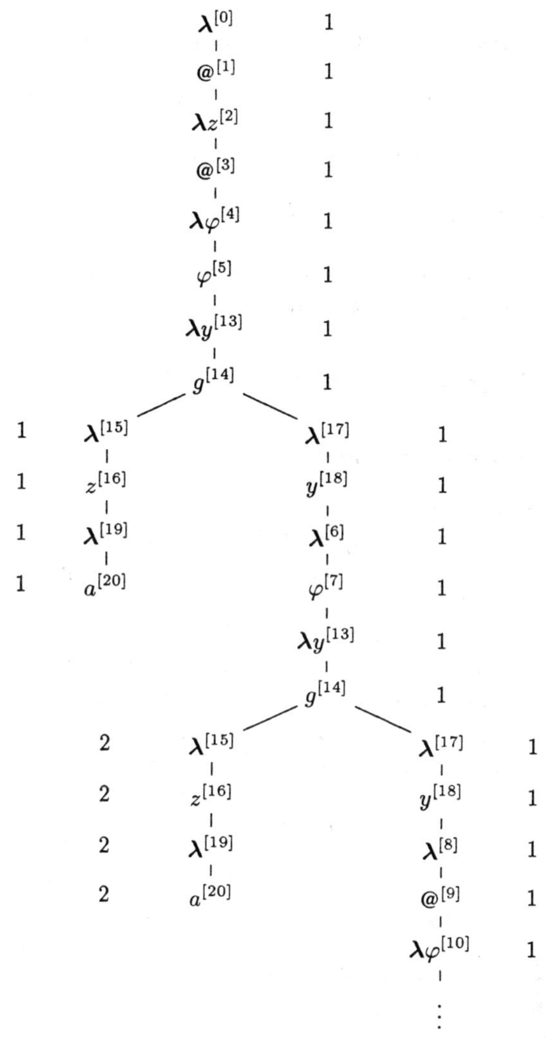

Figure 2. A traversal-tree of an APT over $\lambda(G)$.

A traversal-tree t is ***accepting*** if all infinite traces $(\alpha_0, q_0)\,(\alpha_1, q_{i_1})\,(\alpha_2, q_{i_2}) \cdots$ through it satisfy the parity condition, namely, lim sup $\langle\, \Omega(q_{i_j}) : j \geq 0 \,\rangle$ is even.

It follows from the definition that (the element-wise first-projection of) every trace of a traversal-tree is a traversal over the computation tree.

Example 3.6. Take G as defined in Example 2.1. Consider an APT $\mathcal{B}$ over Σ-labelled trees with state-set $Q = \{ 1, 2 \}$ where 1 is the initial state, and states 1 and 2 have priorities 1 and 2 respectively. The transition map $\delta : Q \times \Sigma \longrightarrow \mathsf{B}^+([ar(\Sigma)] \times Q)$ is defined as follows:

$$\delta : \begin{cases} (1, g) & \mapsto & ((1,1) \wedge (2,1)) \vee ((1,2) \wedge (2,1)) \\ (1, a) & \mapsto & \mathsf{true} \\ (2, a) & \mapsto & \mathsf{true} \end{cases}$$

In Figure 2, we present a traversal-tree of $\mathcal{B}$ over $\lambda(G)$.

We state a straightforward consequence of Theorem 3:

Corollary 4. *There is a one-one correspondence between*

(i) accepting run-trees of $\mathcal{B}$ over $[\![G]\!]$

(ii) accepting traversal-trees of $\mathcal{B}$ over $\lambda(G)$.

Our task is therefore reduced to that of effectively recognising accepting traversal-trees.

4. The traversal-simulating APT

An informal explanation

We want to find a device that can recognise accepting traversal-trees of a property APT $\mathcal{B}$ over a computation tree. This is far from trivial since a traversal can jump all over the tree and may even visit some nodes infinitely often. Our idea is to exploit Lemma 2: The P-view of a traversal is a path. Thus a maximal traversal can be simulated by the set of P-views of all its finite prefixes. The challenge is then to define an alternating parity automaton (which we will call *traversal-simulating* in order to distinguish it from the *property* APT) that recognises precisely the set of paths of the computation tree that simulate an *accepting* traversal-tree of $\mathcal{B}$.

Fix a property APT $\mathcal{B} = \langle \Sigma, Q, \delta, q_0, \Omega \rangle$ with p priorities. Suppose a traversal jumps from a node labelled φ with simulating state $q_1 \in Q$ to a subtree (denoting the actual parameter of that formal parameter φ) rooted at a node labelled $\boldsymbol{\lambda} y_1 y_2$; suppose it subsequently exits the subtree through y_1 with simulating state q_2, and rejoins the original subtree through the first $\boldsymbol{\lambda}$-child of the φ-labelled node, as follows:

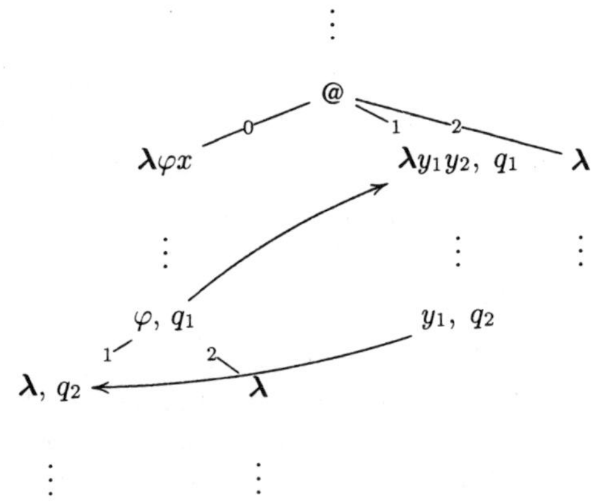

We simulate the traversal by *paths* in the computation tree, making appropriate *guesses*, which will need to be verified subsequently:

- When reading the node φ with simulating state q_1, the automaton, having *guessed* that the jump to $\boldsymbol{\lambda} y_1 y_2$ will eventually return to the 1-child of the node φ with simulating state q_2, descends in direction 1.
- In order to verify the guess, an automaton is *spawn* to read the root of the subtree that denotes the actual parameter of φ (i.e. the node labelled by $\boldsymbol{\lambda} y_1 y_2$).

At a node α that is labelled by @, in addition to the main simulating automaton that descends in the direction of the leftmost child labelled by $\boldsymbol{\lambda}\xi_1 \cdots \xi_n$ (say), we *guess*, for each variable $\xi_i : A_i$ in the list of formal parameters $\xi_1 \cdots \xi_n$, a number of quadruples of the shape (ξ_i, q, m, c), which we call *profiles* for ξ_i, where

- $q \in Q$ is the state that is simulated when a ξ_i-labelled node (a descendent of α) is encountered by the descending automaton, simulating the traversal
- $m \in [p]$ is the maximal priority that will have been seen at that point, since reading the node labelled by $\boldsymbol{\lambda}\xi_1 \cdots \xi_n$
- The *interface* c, which is a subset of $\bigcup_{i=1}^n \mathbf{VP}_G^{\mathcal{B}}(A_i)$, where $\mathbf{VP}_G^{\mathcal{B}}(A)$ is the set of profiles of variables of type A occurring in $\lambda(G)$ with respect to the property APT $\mathcal{B}$, captures the manner in which the traversal, which now jumps to a neighbouring subtree denoting the actual parameter of ξ_i, will eventually return to the children of the ξ_i-labelled node (i.e. with what simulating state, and through which child of ξ_i).

Formal definition

Henceforth we fix a recursion scheme G and its associated computation tree $\lambda(G)$, and fix a *property* APT

$$\mathcal{B} = \langle Q,\ \Sigma,\ \delta : Q \times \Sigma \longrightarrow \mathsf{B}^+([ar(\Sigma)] \times Q),\ q_0,\ \Omega \rangle$$

with p priorities, over Σ-labelled trees. Let Var_G^A be the (finite) set of variables of type A that occur as labels in $\lambda(G)$.

Definition 4.1. (i) The set $\mathbf{VP}_G^{\mathcal{B}}(A)$ of ***profiles*** for variables of type A in $\lambda(G)$ relative to $\mathcal{B}$ are defined as follows:

$$\mathbf{VP}_G^{\mathcal{B}}(A_1, \cdots, A_n, o) \;=\; Var_G^A \times Q \times [p] \times \mathcal{P}(\bigcup_{i=1}^{n} \mathbf{VP}_G^{\mathcal{B}}(A_i))$$

If $n = 0$, we have $\mathbf{VP}_G^{\mathcal{B}}(o) = Var_G^o \times Q \times [p] \times \mathcal{P}(\varnothing)$. For every variable $\xi : A$ that occurs as a label in $\lambda(G)$, we write $\mathbf{VP}_G^{\mathcal{B}}(\xi : A)$ for the set of profiles for ξ. Take any $(\xi, q, m, c) \in \mathbf{VP}_G^{\mathcal{B}}(\xi : A)$; we shall refer to m as the ***priority*** and c the ***interface*** of the profile respectively.

(ii) An ***active profile*** is a pair θ^b where θ is a profile and $b \in \{\mathsf{t}, \mathsf{f}\}$. The boolean value b is the answer to the question:

"Is the highest priority seen thus far (since the creation of the active profile) equal to m?" An ***environment*** is a set of active profiles for variables that occur as labels in $\lambda(G)$.

Notations. Take an active profile $(\xi, q, m, c)^b$. For any priority $l \leq p$, we define an *update* function of b:

$$(\xi, q, m, c)^b \uparrow l = \begin{cases} (\xi, q, m, c)^{b \vee [l=m]} & \text{if } l \leq m \\ \text{undefined} & \text{otherwise} \end{cases}$$

where $[l{=}m]$ denotes the Boolean value of the equality test "$l = m$". For any profile θ, we define $\theta \uparrow m$ (by abuse of notation) to be $\theta^{\mathsf{f}} \uparrow l$. Let ρ be an environment. We define $\rho \uparrow l$ by point-wise extension i.e. we say that $\rho \uparrow l$ is defined just if $\theta^b \uparrow l$ is defined for all active profiles $\theta^b \in \rho$, and is equal to $\{ \theta^b \uparrow l : \theta^b \in \rho \}$.

Definition 4.2. The auxiliary ***traversal-simulating alternating parity automaton*** (w.r.t. $\mathcal{B}$) over Λ_G-labelled trees is given by $\mathcal{C} = \langle \Lambda_G, Q_\mathcal{C}, \delta_\mathcal{C}, q_0 \varnothing, \Omega_\mathcal{C} \rangle$ where $Q_\mathcal{C}$ consists of pairs $q\,\rho$ and triples $q\,\rho\,\theta$ such that $q \in Q$ is the $\mathcal{B}$-state being simulated – called the *simulating state*, ρ is an environment, and θ is a variable profile; the pair $q_0\,\varnothing$ is the initial state. The priority of a $\mathcal{C}$-state, or ***$\mathcal{C}$-priority***, is defined by cases:

$$\Omega_\mathcal{C} : \begin{cases} q\,\rho & \mapsto \quad \Omega(q) \\ q\,\rho\,\theta & \mapsto \quad m, \quad \text{where } m \text{ is the priority of } \theta. \end{cases}$$

Given a $\mathcal{C}$-state $d = q\,\rho$ or $q\,\rho\,\theta$, we say that its ***$\mathcal{B}$-priority*** is $\Omega(q)$.

Definition of the transition function $\delta_\mathcal{C}$

The automaton starts by reading the root node ε of $\lambda(G)$ with the initial state $q_0\,\varnothing$. Rather than giving the positive Boolean formula $\delta_\mathcal{C}(d, l)$ for each $d \in Q_\mathcal{C}$ and $l \in \Lambda_G$, we describe the action of the automaton with state $d = q\,\rho$ or $q\,\rho\,\theta$ reading a node α of the computation tree, by a case analysis of $l = \lambda(G)(\alpha)$.

Cases of the label l:

Case 1: l is a Σ-symbol f of arity $r \geq 0$, and $d = q\,\rho$.

If $\delta(q, f) \in \mathsf{B}^+([ar(f)] \times Q)$ is not satisfiable, the automaton aborts; otherwise, guess a satisfying set, say

$$S = \{ (i_1, q_{j_1}), \cdots, (i_k, q_{j_k}) \}$$

where $k \geq 0$ (with $k = 0$ iff $S = \varnothing$), and guess environments $\rho_1, \cdots, \rho_k$, such that

$$\bigcup_{i=1}^{k} \rho_i = \rho. \tag{1}$$

Spawn k automata with states

$$q_{j_1}\;\rho_1 \uparrow \Omega(q_{j_1}), \quad \cdots, \quad q_{j_k}\;\rho_k \uparrow \Omega(q_{j_k})$$

in directions $i_1, \cdots, i_k$ respectively provided $\rho_i \uparrow \Omega(q_{j_i})$ is defined for all i, otherwise the automaton aborts.

Note. In case the arity $r = 0$, since $\delta(q, f) \in \mathsf{B}^+([0] \times Q)$ and $[0] = \varnothing$, we have $\delta(q, f)$ is either true or false. If the former, note that true is satisfied by the every set in $\mathcal{P}([0] \times Q)$, namely $\varnothing$; it follows that equation (1) can only be satisfied provided $\rho = \varnothing$.

Case 2: l is a variable $\varphi : (A_1, \cdots, A_n, o)$ where $n \geq 0$, and $d = q\,\rho\,\theta$.

We check that θ has the shape (φ, q, m, c) for some interface c and $m \leq p$ such that $(\varphi, q, m, c)^{\mathsf{t}} \in \rho$; otherwise the automaton aborts. Suppose

$$c = \{ \underbrace{(\xi_{i_j}, q_{l_j}, m_j, c_j)}_{\theta_j} \mid 1 \leq j \leq r \}$$

for some $r \geq 0$ (with $c = \varnothing$ iff $r = 0$). (In case φ is order 2 or higher, we may assume that $\xi_j : A_j$ so that we have $1 \leq i_j \leq n$.)

Guess ρ' to be one of ρ or $\rho \setminus \{ (\varphi, q, m, c)^{\mathsf{t}} \}$. For each $1 \leq j \leq r$, guess distinct environments $\rho_{j1}, \cdots, \rho_{jr_j}$ with $r_j \geq 1$, such that

$$\bigcup_{j=1}^{r} \bigcup_{k=1}^{r_j} \rho_{jk} = \rho'. \tag{2}$$

For each $1 \leq j \leq r$ and each $1 \leq k \leq r_j$, spawn an automaton with $\mathcal{C}$-state

$$q_{l_j} \quad (\rho_{jk} \uparrow m_j) \cup (c_j \uparrow \Omega(q_{l_j})) \quad \theta_j$$

in direction i_j, provided $(\rho_{jk} \uparrow m_j) \cup (c_j \uparrow \Omega(q_{l_j}))$ is defined for all j and k, otherwise the automaton aborts.

Note. If φ is order 0, the interface c in θ is necessarily empty (i.e. $r = 0$). Thus, for equation (2) to hold, we must have $\rho' = \varnothing$; it follows that we must have $\rho = \{ (\varphi, q, m, \varnothing) \}$.

Case 3: l is @ of type $((A_1, \cdots, A_n, o), A_1, \cdots, A_n, o)$ where $n \geq 1$, and $d = q\,\rho$.

Guess a set of profiles $c \subseteq \bigcup_{i=1}^{n} \mathbf{VP}_G^{\mathcal{B}}(\xi_i : A_i)$ and spawn an automaton with state $q\; c \uparrow \Omega(q)$ in direction 0, with

$$c = \{ \underbrace{(\xi_{i_j}, q_{l_j}, m_j, c_j)}_{\theta_j} : 1 \leq j \leq r \}$$

(say) where $r \geq 0$ (with $r = 0$ iff $c = \varnothing$). Note that $1 \leq i_j \leq n$. For each $1 \leq j \leq r$, guess distinct environments $\rho_{j1}, \cdots, \rho_{jr_j}$ with $r_k \geq 1$ such that

$$\bigcup_{j=1}^{r} \bigcup_{k=1}^{r_j} \rho_{jk} = \rho. \tag{3}$$

For each $1 \leq j \leq r$ and $1 \leq k \leq r_j$, spawn an automaton with $\mathcal{C}$-state

$$q_{l_j} \quad (\rho_{jk} \uparrow m_j) \cup (c_j \uparrow \Omega(q_{l_j})) \quad \theta_j$$

in direction i_j, provided $(\rho_{jk} \uparrow m_j) \cup (c_j \uparrow \Omega(q_{l_j}))$ is defined for all j and k, otherwise the automaton aborts.

Case 4: l is a lambda, with state $d = q\,\rho$ or $q\,\rho\,\theta$.

Spawn an automaton in direction 1 with $\mathcal{C}$-state e where $e = q\,\rho\,\tau$ for some $\tau^b \in \rho$ if the guess is that the label of the child node is a variable, otherwise $e = q\,\rho$.

Example 4.3. Take the computation tree $\lambda(G)$ and the property APT $\mathcal{B}$ as defined in Example 3.6. In Table 1 we give an initial part of an (accepting) run-tree of the corresponding traversal-simulating APT $\mathcal{C}$. We shall see in the sequel that the run-tree is a simulation (in the sense of Theorem 5) of the traversal-tree in Figure 2.

5. Correctness of the simulation

For the rest of the paper, we shall fix a recursion scheme G and an associated computation tree $\lambda(G)$. We shall also fix a property APT $\mathcal{B} = \langle \Sigma, Q, \delta, q_0, \Omega \rangle$ over Σ-labelled trees, and write $\mathcal{C}$ as the associated traversal-simulating APT over Λ_G-labelled trees. Our notion of simulation is correct, in the following sense:

Theorem 5. *The following are equivalent:*

(i) There is an accepting traversal-tree of $\mathcal{B}$ over $\lambda(G)$.

(ii) There is an accepting run-tree of $\mathcal{C}$ over $\lambda(G)$.

Since $\lambda(G)$ is a regular tree, an immediate corollary of the Theorem is that the modal mu-calculus model-checking problem for trees generated by arbitrary recursion schemes is decidable. In this Section we briefly sketch a proof of the Theorem.

From traversal-trees of $\mathcal{B}$ to run-trees of $\mathcal{C}$

Suppose there is an accepting traversal-tree $\mathbf{t}$ of the property APT $\mathcal{B}$ over $\lambda(G)$. Recall that $\mathbf{t}$ is a $(\mathsf{Dom}(\lambda(G)) \times Q)$-labelled unranked tree. We first perform a succession of annotation operations on $\mathbf{t}$, transforming it eventually to a $(\mathsf{Dom}(\lambda(G)) \times Q_{\mathcal{C}})$-labelled unranked tree $\widehat{\mathbf{t}}$, which has the same underlying tree as $\mathbf{t}$ i.e. $\mathsf{Dom}(\widehat{\mathbf{t}}) = \mathsf{Dom}(\mathbf{t})$. We then show that the set of P-views of traces of $\widehat{\mathbf{t}}$ gives an accepting run-tree of the traversal-simulating APT $\mathcal{C}$.

Run-trees of a traversal-simulating APT can have a rather large (though necessarily bounded) branching factor. Fortunately we can prove a kind of *succinctness result*: We show that if a traversal-simulating APT has an accepting run-tree, then it has a "narrow" accepting run-tree in the sense that it has a reduced branching factor.

Definition 5.1. A ***narrow run-tree*** of a traversal-simulating APT $\mathcal{C}$ is a run-tree satisfying the rules of Definition 4.2 except that in (2) of Case 2, for each $1 \leq j \leq r$, we guess exactly one environment $\rho_j = \rho_{j1}$ (so that $r_j = 1$) such that $\bigcup_{j=1}^{r} \rho_j = \rho$; similarly in (3) of Case 3. (Note that a narrow run-tree of $\mathcal{C}$ is *a fortiori* a run-tree of $\mathcal{C}$ in the sense of Definition 4.2.)

Proposition 6. *If the traversal-simulating APT $\mathcal{C}$ has an accepting run-tree then it has one that is narrow. The branching factor of a narrow run-tree is bounded above by the number of distinct variable profiles.*

From run-trees of $\mathcal{C}$ to traversal-trees of $\mathcal{B}$

Take an accepting run-tree $\mathbf{r}$ of $\mathcal{C}$ over $\lambda(G)$. We first construct an annotated traversal-tree $\mathbf{t}$, which is a $(\mathsf{Dom}(\lambda(G)) \times Q_{\mathcal{C}})$-labelled unranked tree. Let $\mathbf{t}^-$ be the $(\mathsf{Dom}(\lambda(G)) \times Q)$-labelled unranked tree that is obtained from $\mathbf{t}$ by replacing the $\mathcal{C}$-state that annotates each node by the $\mathcal{B}$-state that is simulated. It is straightforward to show that $\mathbf{t}^-$ is a traversal-tree of $\mathcal{B}$ over $\lambda(G)$; the tricky part is to prove that $\mathbf{t}^-$ is accepting, which follows from:

Proposition 7. *Every infinite path w in the traversal-tree $\mathbf{t}^-$ determines an infinite path p_w in the accepting run-tree $\mathbf{r}$ such that the highest $\mathcal{B}$-priority that occurs infinitely often in the former coincides with the highest $\mathcal{C}$-priority that occurs infinitely often in the latter.*

To prove the Proposition, we first need to construct p_w from a given w. Note that an infinite path w in $\mathbf{t}$ is just an infinite ($\mathcal{C}$-state annotated) traversal in $\lambda(G)$. We define a binary relation $\preccurlyeq$ over prefixes of a traversal w, called ***view order***, as follows. Let $u, v \leq w$. We say that $u \preccurlyeq v$ just in case u is a prefix of v, and $\mathbf{l}(u)$ – the last node of u – and hence every node in the P-view of u, appear in the P-view of v. (Note that the last clause implies, but is not implied by, $\ulcorner u \urcorner \leq \ulcorner v \urcorner$.)

An infinite strictly-increasing (w.r.t. prefix ordering) sequence of prefixes of w, namely $u_1 < u_2 < u_3 < \cdots$, is called a ***spinal decomposition*** of w just if

(i) $u_1 \preccurlyeq u_2 \preccurlyeq u_3 \preccurlyeq \cdots$, and

(ii) $|\ulcorner u_1 \urcorner| < |\ulcorner u_2 \urcorner| < |\ulcorner u_3 \urcorner| < \cdots$ ($|...|$ means length)

We set p_w in the above Proposition to be the infinite path in $\lambda(G)$ defined by the infinite strictly-increasing sequence $\ulcorner u_1 \urcorner < \ulcorner u_2 \urcorner < \ulcorner u_3 \urcorner < \cdots$, which we call the (associated) ***spine*** of the spinal decomposition. (Note that neither (i) nor (ii) above is a consequence of the other.)

Lemma 8. *(i) The highest $\mathcal{B}$-priority that occurs infinitely often in w coincides with the highest $\mathcal{C}$-priority that occurs infinitely often in p_w.*

(ii) Every infinite traversal w has a spinal decomposition.

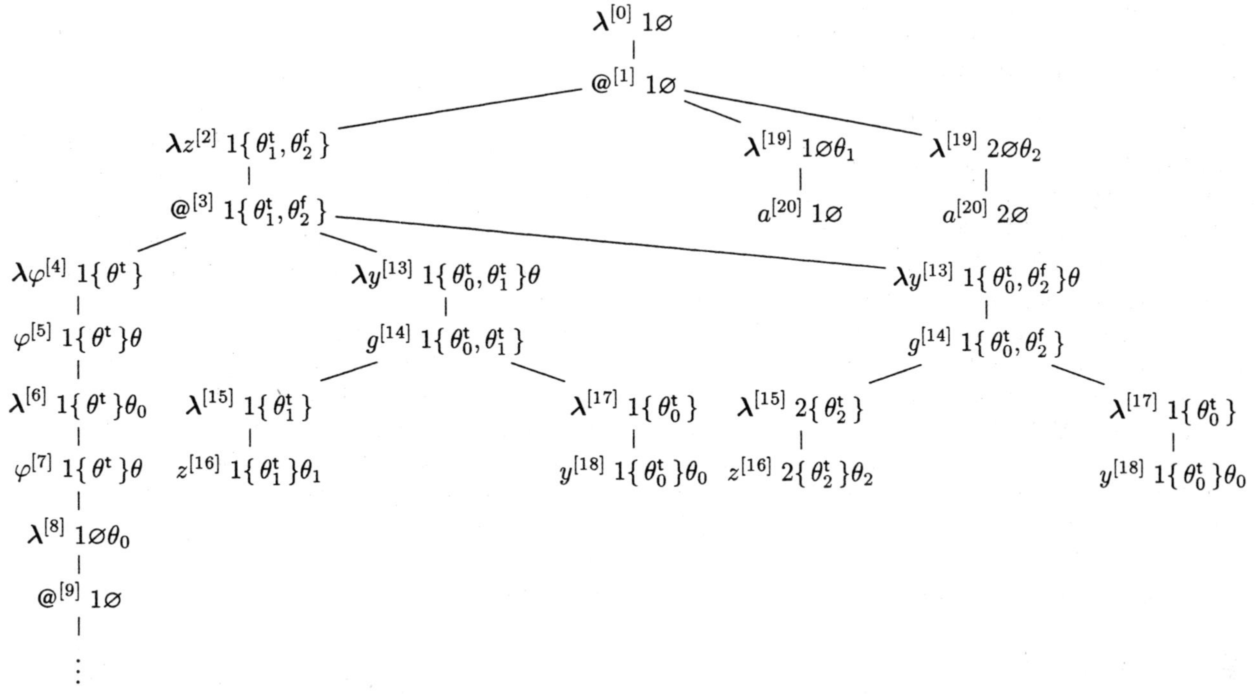

Shorthand notation: $\theta = (\varphi, 1, 1, \{\theta_0\})$ $\theta_0 = (y, 1, 1, \varnothing)$ $\theta_1 = (z, 1, 1, \varnothing)$ $\theta_2 = (z, 2, 2, \varnothing)$.

Table 1. A run-tree of the traversal-simulating APT associated with the property APT in Example 3.6.

6. Complexity analysis

We briefly sketch a proof that the modal mu-calculus model-checking problem for trees generated by order-n recursion scheme is n-EXPTIME complete. The n-EXPTIME hardness of the problem follows from Cachat's result [4] that the (sub)problem of model-checking trees generated by *safe* order-n recursion schemes is n-EXPTIME hard. We prove n-EXPTIME decidability by analysing the complexity of solving an associated acceptance parity game $\mathbf{G}(Gr(G), \mathcal{C})$, which is an appropriate product of the traversal-simulating APT $\mathcal{C} = \langle \Lambda_G, Q_\mathcal{C}, \delta_\mathcal{C}, q_0, \Omega_\mathcal{C} \rangle$ and a (finite) Λ_G-labelled deterministic directed graph

$$Gr(G) = \langle V, \rightarrow \subseteq V \times V, \lambda_G : V \longrightarrow \Lambda_G, v_0 \in V \rangle$$

which unfolds to the Λ_G-labelled computation tree $\lambda(G)$. The graph $Gr(G)$ has root v_0, and λ_G is the vertex-labelling function; it is *ranked* in the sense that the edge-set $\rightarrow = \bigcup_{i \in \mathsf{Dir}(\Lambda_G)} \rightarrow_i$, where each $\rightarrow_i \subseteq V \times V$ is a partial function such that $\rightarrow_i(v)$ is well-defined for each $v \in V$ and $i \in \mathsf{Dir}(\lambda_G(v))$.

For each $v \in V$ and $P \subseteq \mathsf{Dir}(\lambda_G(v)) \times Q_\mathcal{C}$, we write $[P]_v = \{ (u, q) : (i, q) \in P \wedge \rightarrow_i(v) = u \}$.

Definition 6.1. The underlying digraph of the ***acceptance parity game*** $\mathbf{G}(Gr(G), \mathcal{C})$ has two kinds of vertices. *A-Vertices* (A for Abelard) are sets of the form $[P]_v$, with $v \in V$ and $P \subseteq \mathsf{Dir}(\lambda_G(v)) \times Q_\mathcal{C}$; and *E-Vertices* (E for Eloise) are pairs of the form (v, q) with $v \in V$ and $q \in Q_\mathcal{C}$. The *source vertex* is the E-vertex (v_0, q_0). The edges are defined as follows.

- For each A-vertex $[P]_v$, and for each $(u, q) \in [P]_v$, there is an edge from $[P]_v$ to (u, q).
- For each E-vertex (v, q), and for each $P \subseteq \mathsf{Dir}(\lambda_G(v)) \times Q_\mathcal{C}$ such that P satisfies $\delta_\mathcal{C}(q, \lambda_G(v))$, there is an edge from (v, q) to $[P]_v$.

The priority map $\Omega_\mathbf{G}$ is defined by cases as follows:

$$\Omega_\mathbf{G} = \begin{cases} (v, q) & \mapsto \quad \Omega_\mathcal{C}(q) \\ [P]_v & \mapsto \quad \min\{ \Omega_\mathcal{C}(q) : (u, q) \in [P]_v \}. \end{cases}$$

A *play* is a (possibly infinite) path in $\mathbf{G}(Gr(G), \mathcal{C})$ of the form $(v_0, q_0) \cdot [P_0]_{v_0} \cdot (v_1, q_1) \cdot [P_1]_{v_1} \cdots$. (For ease of reading, we use $\cdot$ as item separator in the sequence.)

Eloise resolves the E-vertices, and Abelard the A-vertices. If the play is finite and the last vertex is an A-vertex (respectively E-vertex) which is terminal, Eloise (respectively Abelard) is said to win the play. If the play is infinite, Eloise wins just if the maximum that occurs infinitely often in the following numeric sequence is even.

$$\Omega_{\mathbf{G}}(v_0, q_0) \cdot \Omega_{\mathbf{G}}([P_0]_{v_0}) \cdot \Omega_{\mathbf{G}}(v_1, q_1) \cdot \Omega_{\mathbf{G}}([P_1]_{v_1}) \cdots$$

Proposition 9. *Eloise has a (history-free) winning strategy in the acceptance parity game* $\mathbf{G}(Gr(G), \mathcal{C})$ *iff the traversal-simulating APT* $\mathcal{C}$ *accepts the* Λ_G*-labelled computation tree* $\lambda(G)$*, which is the unfolding of* $Gr(G)$.

Let G be an order-n recursion scheme and take a property APT $\mathcal{B}$ as before. For $i < n$ we define $\mathbf{VP}^{\mathcal{B}}_G(i)$ to be the union of sets of the form $\mathbf{VP}^{\mathcal{B}}_G(A)$, as A ranges over order-i types that occur in $\overline{G}$. It follows from the definition of variable profiles that $|\mathbf{VP}^{\mathcal{B}}_G(i)| = \mathsf{exp}_i O(|G| \cdot |Q| \cdot p)$ where $|G|$ is a measure of the recursion scheme G, $|Q|$ is the number of elements of Q, and exp_i is the tower-of-exponentials function of height i. Next we set $\mathbf{VP}^{\mathcal{B}}_G = \bigcup_{i=0}^{n-1} \mathbf{VP}^{\mathcal{B}}_G(i)$ and $Env^{\mathcal{B}}_G = \mathcal{P}(\mathbf{VP}^{\mathcal{B}}_G)$. It follows that $|\mathbf{VP}^{\mathcal{B}}_G| = \mathsf{exp}_{n-1} O(|G| \cdot |Q| \cdot p)$ and $|Env^{\mathcal{B}}_G| = \mathsf{exp}_n O(|G| \cdot |Q| \cdot p)$. Finally, as $Q_{\mathcal{C}} = (Q \times Env^{\mathcal{B}}_G) \cup (Q \times Env^{\mathcal{B}}_G \times \mathbf{VP}^{\mathcal{B}}_G)$, we have $|Q_{\mathcal{C}}| = \mathsf{exp}_n O(|G| \cdot |Q| \cdot p)$.

We appeal to a result due to Jurdziński [10]:

Theorem 10 (Jurdziński). *The winning region of Eloise and her winning strategy in a parity game with* $|V|$ *vertices and* $|E|$ *edges and* $p \geq 2$ *priorities can be computed in time*

$$O\left(p \cdot |E| \cdot \left(\frac{|V|}{\lfloor p/2 \rfloor}\right)^{\lfloor p/2 \rfloor}\right)$$

Suppose the parity acceptance game $\mathbf{G}(Gr(G), \mathcal{C})$ has vertex-set V and edge-set E. The A-vertices of the game are sets of the form $[P]_v$, where $P \subseteq \mathsf{Dir}(l(v)) \times Q_{\mathcal{C}}$ and v ranges over nodes of $Gr(G)$. Thanks to the narrowing transform (see Proposition 6), it is enough to restrict P to subsets of $\mathsf{Dir}(l(v)) \times Q_{\mathcal{C}}$ that have size at most $|\mathbf{VP}^{\mathcal{B}}_G|$. This gives a tighter upper bound on the number of A-vertices of the game, namely, $(|\mathsf{Dir}(\Lambda_G)| \times |Q_{\mathcal{C}}|)^{|\mathbf{VP}^{\mathcal{B}}_G|} = \mathsf{exp}_n O(|G| \cdot |Q| \cdot p)$. It follows that $|V| = \mathsf{exp}_n O(|G| \cdot |Q| \cdot p)$. Since $|E|$ is at most $|V|^2$, time complexity for solving $\mathbf{G}(Gr(G), \mathcal{C})$ is $O\left(p \cdot (|V|)^{\lfloor p/2 \rfloor + 2}\right) = \mathsf{exp}_n O(|G| \cdot |Q| \cdot p)$. Thus[5] we have:

Theorem 11. *The acceptance parity game* $\mathbf{G}(Gr(G), \mathcal{C})$ *can be solved in time* $\mathsf{exp}_n O(|G| \cdot |Q| \cdot p)$.

7 Further directions

Does safety constrain expressiveness? This is the most pressing open problem. Despite [1], we conjecture that there are *inherently* unsafe trees. I.e.

[5] Though (as far as we know) Jurdziński's bound is the sharpest to date, a relatively coarse time complexity of $|V|^{O(p)}$ (based on an early result of Emerson and Lei [8]) is all that we need to prove Theorem 11.

Conjecture 12. *There is an unsafe recursion scheme whose value tree is not the value tree of any safe recursion scheme.*

Higher-order pushdown automata (PDA) characterize *safe* term-trees. A variant class of higher-order PDA *with links* (in the sense of [1]), which we call *collapsible PDA*, characterize trees generated by arbitrary higher-order recursion schemes. This work will be reported elsewhere.

What is the corresponding hierarchy of *graphs* generated by high-order recursion schemes? Are their MSO theories decidable?

We would like to develop further the pleasing mix of Semantics (games) and Verification (games) in the paper. A specific project, *pace* [3], is to give a denotational semantics of the lambda calculus "relative to an APT". More generally, construct a cartesian closed category, parameterized by APTs, whose maps are witnessed by the *variable profiles* (or "guesses" in Definition 4.1).

References

[1] K. Aehlig, J. G. de Miranda, and C.-H. L. Ong. Safety is not a restriction at level 2 for string languages. In *Proc. FOSSACS'05*, pp. 490–501, 2005. LNCS 3411

[2] K. Aehlig, J. G. de Miranda, and C.-H. L. Ong. The monadic second order theory of trees given by arbitrary level two recursion schemes is decidable. In *Proc. TLCA'05*, pp. 39–54, 2005. LNCS 3461

[3] K. Aehlig. A finite semantics of simply-typed lambda terms for infinite runs of automata. Submitted. 2006

[4] T. Cachat. Higher order pushdown automata, the Caucal hierarchy of graphs and parity games. In *Proc. ICALP'03*, pp. 556–569, 2003. LNCS 2719

[5] D. Caucal. On infinite transition graphs having a decidable monadic theory. In *Proc. ICALP'96*, pp. 194–205. 1996.

[6] D. Caucal. On infinite terms having a decidable monadic theory. In *Proc. MFCS'02*, pp. 165–176, 2002. LNCS 2420

[7] E. A. Emerson and C. S. Jutla. Tree automata, mu-calculus and determinacy. In *Proc. FOCS'91*, pp. 368–377, 1991.

[8] E. A. Emerson and C. Lei. Efficient model checking in fragments of propositional mu-calculus. In *Proc. LICS'86*, pp. 267–278, 1986.

[9] J. M. E. Hyland and C.-H. L. Ong. On Full Abstraction for PCF: I, II & III. *Info. & Comp.*, 163:285–408, 2000.

[10] M. Jurdziński. Small progress measures for solving parity games. In *Proc. STACS*, pp. 290–301, 2000. LNCS 1770

[11] T. Knapik, D. Niwiński, and P. Urzyczyn. Higher-order pushdown trees are easy. In *Proc. FOSSACS'02*, pp. 205–222, 2002. LNCS Vol. 2303

[12] T. Knapik, D. Niwiński, P. Urzyczyn, and I. Walukiewicz. Unsafe grammars and panic automata. In *Proc. ICALP'05*, pp. 1450–1461. 2005. LNCS 3580

[13] D. E. Muller and P. E. Schupp. The theory of ends, pushdown automata, and second-order logic. *TCS*, 37:51–75, 1985.

[14] C.-H. L. Ong. On model-checking trees generated by higher-order recursion schemes. Preprint, 42 pp. 2006. `http://users.comlab.ox.ac.uk/luke.ong/publications/ntrees.ps`

[15] C. Stirling. A game-theoretic approach to deciding higher-order matching. In *Proc. ICALP06*, LNCS, 2006. To appear.

Monadic chain logic over iterations and applications to pushdown systems

Dietrich Kuske
Institut für Informatik, Universität Leipzig, Germany
kuske@informatik.uni-leipzig.de

Markus Lohrey
Universität Stuttgart, FMI, Germany
lohrey@informatik.uni-stuttgart.de

Abstract

Logical properties of iterations of relational structures are studied and these decidability results are applied to the model checking of a powerful extension of pushdown systems. It is shown that the monadic chain theory of the iteration of a structure $\mathcal{A}$ (in the sense of Shelah and Stupp) is decidable in case the first-order theory of the structure $\mathcal{A}$ is decidable. This result fails if Muchnik's clone-predicate is added. A model of pushdown automata, where the stack alphabet is given by an arbitrary (possibly infinite) relational structure, is introduced. If the stack structure has a decidable first-order theory with regular reachability predicates, then the same holds for the configuration graph of this pushdown automaton. This result follows from our decidability result for the monadic chain theory of the iteration.

1. Introduction

In this paper, we study iterations of relational structures, their logical properties, and apply our results to the model checking of a powerful extension of pushdown systems.

The *local full iteration* $\mathcal{A}^*_{\text{loc}}$ of a relational base structure $\mathcal{A}$ with universe A consists of the set A^* of finite words over A. One of its relations is the immediate successor relation son. The sons of a word w carry the relations of the base structure $\mathcal{A}$. Furthermore, Muchnik's unary clone predicate collects all words whose final two letters are identical. Semenov [20] sketched a proof of what is now known as Muchnik's preservation theorem: The monadic second order (MSO for short) theory of the local full iteration $\mathcal{A}^*_{\text{loc}}$ can be reduced to the MSO-theory of the base structure $\mathcal{A}$, and, if two base structures have the same MSO-theory, then the same holds for their iterations. Hence, if the MSO-theory of a structure $\mathcal{A}$ is decidable, then also the MSO-theory of the local full iteration $\mathcal{A}^*_{\text{loc}}$ is decidable. A full proof of this result was given by Walukiewicz in [25]. A first-order variant of Muchnik's theorem for first-order logic follows from [14]. For modulo counting extensions of MSO and for guarded second order logic, a preservation theorem was shown by Blumensath and Kreutzer [3].

The *full iteration* $\mathcal{A}^*_{\text{fu}}$ differs from the local full iteration only in as far as it contains the prefix relation on A^* instead of the immediate successor relation son. Since this prefix relation is the transitive closure of son, there is an MSO-interpretation of the full iteration in the local full iteration. As an immediate consequence from [25, 3], one obtains a preservation theorem for MSO and its modulo counting extensions for this full iteration in place of the local full iteration. Since one can express in first-order logic that an element of the full iteration (i.e., a word over the base structure) represents a path in the base structure, both parts of the preservation theorem fail for the full iteration and first-order logic (Propositions 3.4 and 3.5).

To overcome this problem, Section 4 is devoted to the study of the *basic iteration* $\mathcal{A}^*_{\text{ba}}$ where one omits Muchnik's clone predicate but keeps the prefix order. For basic iterations, the preservation theorem for MSO was proved by Stupp [22] (cf. [21]). Rabin's seminal result on the decidability of the MSO-theory of the complete infinite binary tree [18] is an immediate corollary of this preservation theorem. For this basic iteration we are able to prove the preservation theorem for first-order logic. In fact, we can show even more: If a structure has a decidable first-order theory, then its basic iteration has a decidable MSO^{ch}-theory (Thm. 4.10). MSO^{ch} is the fragment of MSO where second-order quantification is restricted to chains (i.e., ordered subsets) with respect to the tree structure of the iteration. MSO^{ch} on trees was investigated in [23]. To reduce the MSO^{ch}-theory of the basic iteration to the first-order theory of the base structure, we proceed as follows: First, we show that quantification over chains can be restricted to ultimately periodic chains of bounded offset and period length (Thm. 4.7). Truth of MSO^{ch}-formulas with bounded quantification can be determined in a bounded prefix of the basic iteration. Finally, this bounded prefix can be interpreted in the base structure. Since all these bounds can be computed effectively, our preservation theorem follows.

Roughly speaking, the results from Section 3 and Section 4 show that, in order to have a first-order preservation theorem for the iteration, we are not allowed to copy an in-

1043-6871/06 $20.00 © 2006 IEEE

finite amount of information between the levels of the tree structure — this is in some sense the essence of the clone-predicate. Thus, the clone-predicate has an immense effect on the expressive power of the basic iteration although it looks quite innocent at first glance. It should be also noted that the clone-predicate allows to define the unraveling of a graph G within the full iteration of G (cf. [6]).

In Section 5 we present an application of our decidability result for $\mathrm{MSO}^{\mathrm{ch}}$ over basic iterations to pushdown systems. Pushdown systems were used to model the state space of sequential programs with nested procedure calls, see e.g. [9]. Model-checking problems for pushdown systems were studied for various temporal logics (LTL, CTL, modal μ-calculus) [1, 9, 13, 24]. When modeling recursive sequential programs via pushdown systems, it is necessary to abstract local variables (which have to be stored on the stack) with an infinite range (like for instance integers) to some finite range, in order to obtain a finite pushdown alphabet. This abstraction may lead to so called spurious counterexamples [8]. Here, we introduce pushdown systems where the stack alphabet is the (possibly infinite) universe of an arbitrary stack structure $\mathcal{A}$. With any change of the control state, our pushdown model associates one of three basic operations: (i) replacing the topmost symbol of the stack by another one according to some binary predicate of the stack structure, (ii) pushing or (iii) popping a symbol from some unary predicate of the stack structure. Such a pushdown system can model programs with nested procedure calls, where procedures use variables with an infinite domain. The configuration graph of such a pushdown system is defined as for finite stack alphabets. We study the logic FOREG for these configuration graphs. FOREG is the extension of first-order logic which allows to define new binary predicates by regular expressions over the binary predicates of the base structure $\mathcal{A}$. Variants of FOREG were studied in [15, 19, 26]. FOREG is a suitable language for the specification of reachability properties of reactive systems; its expressive power is between first-order logic and MSO. Based on our decidability result Thm. 4.10 we show that if FOREG is decidable for the base structure $\mathcal{A}$ of a pushdown system, then FOREG remains decidable for the configuration graph of the pushdown system (Thm. 5.1). For this result, it is important that in our pushdown model procedure calls and returns cannot transfer an infinite amount of information to another call level. This reflects our undecidability result Proposition 3.4 for the clone predicate.

2. Preliminaries

Let Σ be a (not necessarily finite) alphabet. With Σ^+ we denote the set of all finite non-empty words over Σ. Then $\Sigma^* = \Sigma^+ \cup \{\varepsilon\}$ with ε the empty word. With $\preceq$ we denote the prefix relation on finite words and $\prec$ is its non-reflexive part. For a subalphabet $\Gamma \subseteq \Sigma$ and a word $u \in \Sigma^*$ we denote with $|u|_\Gamma$ the number of occurrences of symbols from Γ in u. In case Σ is finite, $\mathrm{REG}(\Sigma)$ denotes the set of all regular languages over the alphabet Σ.

2.1. Iterations

Let $\mathcal{A} = (A, (R^{\mathcal{A}})_{R\in\sigma})$ be a relational structure over the finite relational signature σ. The *basic iteration* $\mathcal{A}^*_{\mathrm{ba}}$ *of* $\mathcal{A}$ is the structure

$$\mathcal{A}^*_{\mathrm{ba}} = (A^*, \preceq, (\widehat{R})_{R\in\sigma}, \varepsilon) \text{ where}$$
$$\widehat{R} = \{(ua_1, \dots, ua_n) \mid u \in A^*, (a_1, \dots, a_n) \in R^{\mathcal{A}}\}.$$

Example 2.1 *Suppose the structure $\mathcal{A}$ has two elements a and b and two unary relations $R_1 = \{a\}$ and $R_2 = \{b\}$. Then $\widehat{R}_1 = \{a,b\}^*a$ and $\widehat{R}_2 = \{a,b\}^*b$. Hence the basic iteration $\mathcal{A}^*_{\mathrm{ba}}$ can be visualized as a complete binary tree with unary predicates telling whether the current node is the first or the second son of its father. In addition, the root ε is a constant of the structure $\mathcal{A}^*_{\mathrm{ba}}$.*

In the *full iteration* $\mathcal{A}^*_{\mathrm{fu}}$ of $\mathcal{A}$, we have the additional unary *clone predicate* $\mathrm{cl} = \{uaa \mid u \in A^*, a \in A\}$, i.e.,

$$\mathcal{A}^*_{\mathrm{fu}} = (A^*, \preceq, \mathrm{cl}, (\widehat{R})_{R\in\sigma}, \varepsilon)\ .$$

We will also consider a relaxation of the full iteration where the prefix relation is replaced by the direct successor relation $\mathrm{son} = \{(u, ua) \mid a \in A^*, a \in A\}$, i.e.,

$$\mathcal{A}^*_{\mathrm{loc}} = (A^*, \mathrm{son}, \mathrm{cl}, (\widehat{R})_{R\in\sigma}, \varepsilon)\ .$$

We refer to this iteration as *local iteration.* Note that $\mathcal{A}^*_{\mathrm{fu}}$ is MSO-definable (but not first-order definable) in $\mathcal{A}^*_{\mathrm{loc}}$.

2.2. Logics

Let σ be some signature. *Atomic formulas* are $R(x_1, \dots, x_n)$, $x_1 = x_2$, and $x_1 \in X$ where $x_1, \dots, x_n$ are *individual variables,* $R \in \sigma$ is an n-are relational symbol, and X is a *set variable. Monadic second-order formulas* are obtained from atomic formulas by conjunction, negation, and quantification $\exists x$ and $\exists X$ for x an individual and X a set variable. The satisfaction relation $(\mathcal{A}, \bar{a}, \bar{C}) \models \varphi(\bar{x}, \bar{X})$ is defined as usual with the understanding that set variables range over subsets of A. A *first-order formula* is a monadic second-order formula without set variables.

Now let $\preceq$ be a designated binary relation symbol in σ. A *monadic second-order chain formula* or $\mathrm{MSO}^{\mathrm{ch}}$-formula is just a monadic second-order formula. For these $\mathrm{MSO}^{\mathrm{ch}}$-formulas, we define a new satisfaction relation $\models^{\mathrm{ch}}$: it is defined as $\models$ with the only difference that set variables range over chains (i.e., sets whose elements are mutually comparable) in $(A, \preceq)$. Note that if φ is a first-order formula, then $\mathcal{A} \models \varphi$ if and only if $\mathcal{A} \models^{\text{ch}} \varphi$.

Let $\mathcal{A}$ and $\mathcal{B}$ be two σ-structures. Then we write $\mathcal{A} \equiv_m^{\text{MSO}} \mathcal{B}$ if, for any MSO-formula φ of quantifier depth at most m, we have $\mathcal{A} \models \varphi \iff \mathcal{B} \models \varphi$. This relation is an equivalence relation. If we only consider first-order formulas (MSO^{ch}-formulas, resp.) φ of quantifier depth at most m, then we write $\mathcal{A} \equiv_m^{\text{FO}} \mathcal{B}$ ($\mathcal{A} \equiv_m^{\text{ch}} \mathcal{B}$, resp.).

3. The theory of the full iteration

We first deal with MSO-theories. Muchnik's theorem sharpens an earlier result of Stupp. Its full proof can be found in [25] (cf. also [2]).[1]

Theorem 3.1 *Let σ be some finite relational signature. There exists a computable function* red : $\text{MSO}(\sigma, \text{cl}, \text{son}) \to \text{MSO}(\sigma)$ *such that, for any σ-structure $\mathcal{A}$, we have $\mathcal{A} \models \text{red}(\varphi)$ if and only if $\mathcal{A}^*_{\text{loc}} \models \varphi$.*

One infers immediately:

Corollary 3.2 *If the MSO-theory of a structure $\mathcal{A}$ is decidable, then the MSO-theory of its local iteration $\mathcal{A}^*_{\text{loc}}$ is decidable as well.*

To derive another corollary, let $m \in \mathbb{N}$ be arbitrary. Then, there is a finite set Φ of MSO-formulas such that any MSO-sentence of quantifier depth at most m is logically equivalent to some sentence from Φ. Let n be an upper bound for the quantifier depth of $\text{red}(\varphi)$ for $\varphi \in \Phi$. This observation yields:

Corollary 3.3 *For any $m \in \mathbb{N}$, there exists $n \in \mathbb{N}$ such that, for any two σ-structures $\mathcal{A}$ and $\mathcal{B}$ with $\mathcal{A} \equiv_n^{\text{MSO}} \mathcal{B}$, we have $\mathcal{A}^*_{\text{loc}} \equiv_m^{\text{MSO}} \mathcal{B}^*_{\text{loc}}$.*

Note that the MSO-theories of the local and the full iteration can be reduced onto each other. Hence Muchnik's Thm. 3.1 and Corollaries 3.2 and 3.3 hold for the full iteration $\mathcal{A}^*_{\text{fu}}$ in place of the local iteration $\mathcal{A}^*_{\text{loc}}$ equally well. Surprisingly, this is not the case for first-order logic as we show next.

Proposition 3.4 *There exists a structure $\mathcal{A}$ with a decidable first-order theory such that the full iteration $\mathcal{A}^*_{\text{fu}}$ has an undecidable first-order theory.*

[1] Thm. 3.1 and its two corollaries also hold for counting extensions of MSO and for guarded second-order logic [3].

Proof. Let $\mathcal{M}$ be a Turing machine that accepts a non-recursive set L (we assume that $\mathcal{M}$ accepts with empty tape). Let Σ be the set of tape symbols and states of $\mathcal{M}$. Then consider the following structure $\mathcal{A} = (A, E, (E_a)_{a\in\Sigma})$ where A is the set of configurations of $\mathcal{M}$ and, for any configurations c_1, c_2 and any $a \in \Sigma$, we have

- $(c_1, c_2) \in E$ if and only if c_2 can be obtained from c_1 by one step of the Turing machine.
- $(c_1, c_2) \in E_a$ if and only if $c_2 = c_1 a$.

The first-order theory of $\mathcal{A}$ is decidable since $\mathcal{A}$ is automatic [12]. There is a formula α with one free variable x such that $(\mathcal{A}, c) \models \alpha$ if and only if c is a configuration with empty tape. Furthermore, from a state q and an input word w, we can write a first-order formula φ_{qw} with one free variable x such that, for any configuration c, $(\mathcal{A}, c) \models \varphi_{qw}$ if and only if $c = qw$.

Now consider the full iteration of $\mathcal{A}$. The formulas $\widehat{\alpha}$ and $\widehat{\varphi_{qw}}$ are obtained by restricting the quantification to siblings of the free variable x. Furthermore, let w be some input word and let q_0 be the initial state of $\mathcal{M}$. Then w is accepted if and only if there exists a sequence of configurations $u = c_0 c_1 \dots c_n \in A^*$ such that the following hold in the full iteration of $\mathcal{A}$: (i) the minimal nonempty prefix c_0 of u satisfies $\widehat{\varphi_{q_0 w}}$, (ii) u satisfies $\widehat{\alpha}$, and (iii) for all proper and non-empty prefixes v of u, we have

$$\exists v', v'' : v \lessdot v' \preceq u \wedge v \lessdot v'' \wedge \text{cl}(v'') \wedge \widehat{E}(v'', v'),$$

where $x \lessdot y$ is shorthand for $x \prec y \wedge \forall z(x \preceq z \prec y \to x = z)$. Since the language of the Turing machine $\mathcal{M}$ is non-recursive, this proves that the first-order theory of the full iteration of $\mathcal{A}$ is undecidable. □

Hence, Corollary 3.2 and therefore Thm. 3.1 with the full iteration taking the place of the local iteration and first-order logic replacing MSO do not hold. A similar problem arises with respect to Corollary 3.3.

Proposition 3.5 *For every $n \in \mathbb{N}$ there exist structures $\mathcal{A}_n$ and $\mathcal{B}_n$ such that $\mathcal{A}_n \equiv_n^{\text{FO}} \mathcal{B}_n$ but $(\mathcal{A}_n)^*_{\text{fu}} \not\equiv_6^{\text{FO}} (\mathcal{B}_n)^*_{\text{fu}}$.*

Proof. For $n \in \mathbb{N}$, let $\mathcal{A}_n$ denote the structure $\mathcal{A}_n = (\mathbb{Z}, \text{succ}, 0, 2^{n+1})$ that consists of a copy of the integers with successor relation and two constants a and b. Note that in $\mathcal{A}_n$ there is a path of length 2^{n+1} from a to b. We will also consider the structure $\mathcal{B}_n = (\mathbb{Z}, \text{succ}, 2^{n+1}, 0)$ that differs from $\mathcal{A}_n$ only in the values of the constants (that are exchanged). Then the structures $\mathcal{A}_n$ and $\mathcal{B}_n$ cannot be distinguished by any first-order sentence of quantifier rank at most n, i.e., $\mathcal{A}_n \equiv_n^{\text{FO}} \mathcal{B}_n$.

Now consider the following sentence φ in the language of the full iteration of $\mathcal{A}_n$ and $\mathcal{B}_n$:

$$\exists x \in \widehat{a}\, \exists z \in \widehat{b} : x \preceq z \wedge$$
$$\forall y : x \preceq y \prec z \rightarrow \exists y' \exists y'' \left\{ \begin{array}{l} y \lessdot y' \preceq z \wedge y \lessdot y'' \wedge \\ \mathrm{cl}(y'') \wedge \widehat{E}(y'', y') \end{array} \right\}$$

To show that $\mathcal{A}_n$ satisfies φ, take $x = 0$ and $z = 0\,1\,2 \ldots 2^{n+1}$. Since the last letters of these words are a and b, resp., they belong to $\widehat{a}$ and $\widehat{b}$, resp. Any word y with $x \preceq y \prec z$ has the form $0\,1 \ldots i$ for some $0 \leq i < 2^{n+1}$. Then $y' = y\,(i+1)$ and $y'' = y\,i$ ensure that φ indeed holds.

On the other hand, $\mathcal{B}_n^*$ does not satisfy φ: Suppose it would, i.e., there are $x = x'a$ and $z = xa_1a_2 \ldots a_kb$ satisfying the second line of the formula φ. Then $a\,a_1\,a_2 \ldots a_k\,b$ is a path in $\mathcal{B}$ from a to b - but such a path does not exist. Since φ has quantifier rank 6, we obtain $(\mathcal{A}_n)^*_{\mathrm{fu}} \not\equiv^{\mathrm{FO}}_6 (\mathcal{B}_n)^*_{\mathrm{fu}}$. □

In Proposition 3.4 and 3.5, the interplay between the prefix relation and the clone-predicate is crucial. If just one of these two relations is present, a first-order version of Muchnik's theorem and its corollaries holds. For the clone-predicate, this follows from a more general result on so called factorized unfoldings from our earlier paper [14] (see Theorem 3.6 below). For the prefix relation, we prove the result in this paper (Theorem 4.10 and Corollary 4.11).

Theorem 3.6 ([14]) *Let σ be a finite relational signature.*

- *Let σ be some finite relational signature. There exists a computable function* $\mathrm{red} : \mathrm{FO}(\sigma, \mathrm{cl}, \mathrm{son}) \rightarrow \mathrm{FO}(\sigma)$ *such that, for any σ-structure $\mathcal{A}$, we have $\mathcal{A} \models \mathrm{red}(\varphi)$ if and only if $\mathcal{A}^*_{\mathrm{loc}} \models \varphi$.*
- *If the first-order theory of a structure $\mathcal{A}$ is decidable, then the first-order theory of its local iteration $\mathcal{A}^*_{\mathrm{loc}}$ is decidable as well.*
- *For any $m \in \mathbb{N}$, there exists $n \in \mathbb{N}$ such that, for any two σ-structures $\mathcal{A}$ and $\mathcal{B}$ with $\mathcal{A} \equiv^{\mathrm{FO}}_n \mathcal{B}$, we have $\mathcal{A}^*_{\mathrm{loc}} \equiv^{\mathrm{FO}}_m \mathcal{B}^*_{\mathrm{loc}}$.*

4. The $\mathrm{MSO}^{\mathrm{ch}}$-theory of the basic iteration

In this section, we will show that statements analogous to Muchnik's Thm. 3.1 and Corollaries 3.2 and 3.3 hold for basic iterations and first-order logic. In doing so, it turns out that we can even consider the $\mathrm{MSO}^{\mathrm{ch}}$-theory of the basic iteration. Let us fix a base structure $\mathcal{A} = (A, (R)_{R \in \sigma})$ over a signature σ. In the rest of Section 4, we write

$$t = \mathcal{A}^*_{\mathrm{ba}}. \tag{1}$$

4.1. Preliminaries

For $i, \ell \in \mathbb{N}$, let $\tau_{i,\ell}$ be the extension of the signature $(\sigma, \preceq)$ by i individual and ℓ chain constants. We write τ_i for $\tau_{i,0}$. From ℓ and m, one can effectively compute a finite upper bound $N_i(\ell, m)$ for the number of equivalence classes of $\equiv^{\mathrm{ch}}_m$ on the class of all $\tau_{i,\ell}$-structures, see [10].

For $u \in A^*$, let t_u be the structure $(uA^*, \sqsubseteq, (\bar{R})_{R \in \sigma}, u)$ over the signature τ_1, where (i) the relation $\sqsubseteq$ is the restriction of $\preceq$ to uA^* and (ii) $\bar{R}$ is the restriction of $\widehat{R}$ to uA^+ (the restriction to uA^* could contain tuples of the form $(u, u, \ldots, u)$ which are excluded from $\bar{R}$). For any $u, v \in A^*$, the mapping $f : t_u \rightarrow t_v$ with $f(ux) = vx$ is an isomorphism – this is the reason to consider $\bar{R}$ and not the restriction of $\widehat{R}$ to uA^*. Similarly, the τ_2-structure $t_{u,v} = (uA^* \setminus vA^+, \sqsubseteq, (\bar{R})_{R \in \sigma}, u, v)$ is defined for $u, v \in A^*$ with $u \preceq v$. Here, again, $\bar{R}$ is the restriction of $\widehat{R}$ to $uA^+ \setminus vA^+$.

Example 2.1 (continued). In the case of Example 2.1, t_u is just the subtree rooted at the node u. On the other hand, $t_{u,v}$ is obtained from t_u by deleting all descendents of v and marking the node v as a constant. Thus, we can think of $t_{u,v}$ as a tree with a marked leaf. These *special trees* are fundamental in the work of Gurevich and Shelah [11] and in Thomas' study of the monadic second-order chain theory of the complete binary tree [23]. The following constructions generalize those from [11, 23] to the more general context of basic iterations as considered here.

In the following, fix some $\ell \in \mathbb{N}$. We then define the operations of product and infinite product of $\tau_{i,\ell}$-structures: If $\mathcal{A}$ is a $\tau_{2,\ell}$-structure with second individual constant v and $\mathcal{B}$ a disjoint $\tau_{i,\ell}$-structure with first individual constant u, then their *product* $\mathcal{A} \cdot \mathcal{B}$ is a $\tau_{i,\ell}$-structure. It is obtained from the union of $\mathcal{A}$ and $\mathcal{B}$ by identifying v and u and erasing it from the list of constants. In other words, the individual constants in $\mathcal{A} \cdot \mathcal{B}$ are the first constant from $\mathcal{A}$ and all but the first constant from $\mathcal{B}$. Furthermore, the chains from $\mathcal{A}$ and $\mathcal{B}$ are united. Now let $\mathcal{A}_n$ be disjoint $\tau_{2,\ell}$-structures with individual constants u_n and v_n for $n \in \mathbb{N}$. Then the *infinite product* $\prod_{n \in \mathbb{N}} \mathcal{A}_n$ is a $\tau_{1,\ell}$-structure. It is obtained from the union of the structures $\mathcal{A}_n$ by identifying v_n and u_{n+1} for any $n \in \mathbb{N}$. The only individual constant of this infinite product is u_0. If $\mathcal{A}_n \cong \mathcal{A}_{n+1}$ for all $n \in \mathbb{N}$, then we write simply $\mathcal{A}_0^\omega$ for the infinite product of the structures $\mathcal{A}_n$. Standard applications of Ehrenfeucht-Fraïssé-games (cf. [7]) yield:

Proposition 4.1 *Let $m, \ell \in \mathbb{N}$, $\mathcal{A}_n, \mathcal{A}'_n$ be $\tau_{2,\ell}$-structures for $n \in \mathbb{N}$ and let $\mathcal{B}, \mathcal{B}'$ be some $\tau_{i,\ell}$-structures such that $\mathcal{A}_n \equiv^{\mathrm{ch}}_m \mathcal{A}'_n$ for $n \in \mathbb{N}$ and $\mathcal{B} \equiv^{\mathrm{ch}}_m \mathcal{B}'$. Then*

$$\mathcal{A}_0 \cdot \mathcal{B} \equiv^{\mathrm{ch}}_m \mathcal{A}'_0 \cdot \mathcal{B}' \quad \text{and} \quad \prod_{n \in \mathbb{N}} \mathcal{A}_n \equiv^{\mathrm{ch}}_m \prod_{n \in \mathbb{N}} \mathcal{A}'_n.$$

4.2. Ultimately periodic chains and their combinatorics

For a word $u \in A^\infty = A^* \cup A^\omega$, let $\downarrow u \subseteq A^*$ denote the set of finite prefixes of u, and $\Downarrow u = \downarrow u \setminus \{u\}$. Similarly, $\downarrow C = \bigcup\{\downarrow u \mid u \in C\}$ for $C \subseteq A^*$. Finally, $u^{-1}C = \{v \in A^* \mid uv \in C\}$ for $u \in A^*$ and $C \subseteq A^*$.

A chain $C \subseteq A^*$ is *ultimately periodic* if it can be written as $E \cup uv^*F$ with $E, F \subseteq A^*$ finite and $u, v \in A^*$. If $E \subseteq \Downarrow u$ and $F \subseteq \Downarrow v$, it is *ultimately* $|v|$*-periodic with offset* $|u|$. Since $v = \varepsilon$ is possible, finite chains are ultimately 0-periodic. Furthermore, if C is ultimately p-periodic with offset q, then it is also ultimately xp-periodic with offset $q+y$ for any $x, y \in \mathbb{N}$ with $x \geq 1$.

In the following, we will consider the structure t from (1) together with $\ell + 1$ chains $C_1, \ldots, C_\ell, C$. To make the presentation more concise, write $\bar{C}$ for the ℓ-tuple $(C_1, \ldots, C_\ell)$. We will also meet structures t_u and $t_{u,v}$ together with the restriction of $\bar{C}, C$ to their domain. Again for simplicity, we write, e.g., (t_u, C) for $(t_u, C \cap uA^*)$.

4.3. Shortening ultimately periodic chains

Suppose we are in the realm of Example 2.1 and let $C_i \subseteq A^*$ be regular and let $u_i \in A^*$. Then, as a corollary from Rabin's tree theorem, for any $C \subseteq A^*$, there exists a *regular* set $D \subseteq A^*$ that satisfies the same MSO-formulas of quantifier depth m in the structure $(t, C_1, \ldots, C_\ell, u_1, \ldots, u_n)$ as C does. In this section, we want to prove a similar result for basic iterations. For this, "regular set" is replaced by "ultimately periodic chain". In addition, we want to bound the offset and the period of the chain D.

We start showing that some ultimately periodic chain D exists that can take the role of C (Proposition 4.2). Proposition 4.6 will allow to bound the period of D (thereby possibly enlarging the offset). Finally, Lemma 4.3 bounds the size of the offset (without changing the period). Finally, Thm. 4.7 shows that we succeeded in our attempt to find an equivalent ultimately periodic chain D of small period and offset.

4.3.1. Existence of ultimately periodic chains

Proposition 4.2 *Let $m \in \mathbb{N}$, $C_1, \ldots, C_\ell \subseteq A^*$ be ultimately periodic chains and let $C \subseteq A^*$ be any chain. Then there exists an ultimately periodic chain D such that $(t, \bar{C}, C) \equiv_m^{\mathrm{ch}} (t, \bar{C}, D)$.*

Proof. Assume C not to be ultimately periodic (and therefore infinite) and let $\alpha \in A^\omega$ with $C \subseteq \downarrow\alpha$. By Ramsey's theorem (see [16] for this application), there is a strictly increasing sequence $u_1 \prec u_2 \prec u_3 \cdots$ of non-empty prefixes of α such that,

(a) $|u_1|$ exceeds the offset of all the chains $C_1, C_2, \ldots, C_\ell$,

(b) for any $1 \leq i \leq \ell$ and for any $n \geq 1$, the period length of C_i divides $|u_{n+1}| - |u_n|$, and

(c) for any $1 \leq i < j$, we have $(t_{u_1,u_2}, \bar{C}, C) \equiv_m^{\mathrm{ch}} (t_{u_i,u_j}, \bar{C}, C)$.

This implies

$$\begin{aligned}(t, \bar{C}, C) &= (t_{\varepsilon,u_1}, \bar{C}, C) \cdot \prod_{n>0} (t_{u_n,u_{n+1}}, \bar{C}, C)\\ &\equiv_m^{\mathrm{ch}} (t_{\varepsilon,u_1}, \bar{C}, C) \cdot (t_{u_1,u_2}, \bar{C}, C)^\omega\end{aligned}$$

Now let $v \in A^+$ with $u_1 v = u_2$ and consider $E = C \cap \downarrow u_1$, $F = u_1^{-1}(C \cap \downarrow u_2) = u_1^{-1}C \cap \downarrow v$, and $D = E \cup u_1 v^* F$. Because of (a) and (b) we can continue as follows:

$$\begin{aligned}&= (t_{\varepsilon,u_1}, \bar{C}, E) \cdot (t_{u_1,u_2}, \bar{C}, F)^\omega\\ &\cong (t_{\varepsilon,u_1}, \bar{C}, D) \cdot \prod_{n\geq 0} (t_{u_1v^n,u_1v^{n+1}}, \bar{C}, D)\\ &= (t, \bar{C}, D).\end{aligned}$$

Since $E \subseteq \downarrow u_1 v^\omega$ and $F \subseteq \downarrow v^\omega$, the set D is linearly ordered and therefore ultimately periodic. □

4.3.2. Ultimately periodic chains with small offset

Lemma 4.3 *Let $m > 0$, $C_i \subseteq A^*$ be an ultimately p_i-periodic chain with offset q_i for $1 \leq i \leq \ell$ and let $C \subseteq A^*$ be an ultimately p-periodic chain with offset $q > \max(q_1, \ldots, q_\ell) + \mathrm{lcm}(p_1, \ldots, p_\ell) \cdot (N_1(\ell+1, m) + 2)$. Then there exists an ultimately p-periodic chain D with offset $q - \mathrm{lcm}(p_1, \ldots, p_\ell)$ such that $(t, \bar{C}, C) \equiv_m^{\mathrm{ch}} (t, \bar{C}, D)$.*

Proof. Let $C = E \cup uv^*F$ with $E \subseteq \Downarrow u$, $F \subseteq \Downarrow v$, $|u| = q$ and $|v| = p$. Then we can write $u = u'xyz$ such that $|u'| = \max(q_1, \ldots, q_\ell)$, $|x|, |y| > 0$ are multiples of $\mathrm{lcm}(p_1, \ldots, p_\ell)$, $z \neq \varepsilon$, and $(t_{u'x}, \bar{C}, C) \equiv_m^{\mathrm{ch}} (t_{u'xy}, \bar{C}, C)$.

When deleting in the structure $(t, \bar{C}, C)$ all nodes from $u'xA^+ \setminus u'xyA^*$, we end up with $(t_{\varepsilon,u'x}, \bar{C}, C) \cdot (t_{u'xy}, \bar{C}, C)$. Since u' is long enough and the lengths of x and y are multiples of $\mathrm{lcm}(p_1, \ldots, p_\ell)$, the structures $(t, \bar{C})$ and $(t_{\varepsilon,u'x}, \bar{C}) \cdot (t_{u'xy}, \bar{C})$ are isomorphic. Hence there is a chain $D \subseteq A^*$ such that

$$\begin{aligned}(t, \bar{C}, C) &= (t_{\varepsilon,u'x}, \bar{C}, C) \cdot (t_{u'x}, \bar{C}, C)\\ &\equiv_m^{\mathrm{ch}} (t_{\varepsilon,u'x}, \bar{C}, C) \cdot (t_{u'xy}, \bar{C}, C)\\ &\cong (t, \bar{C}, D).\end{aligned}$$

This chain has the same period as C, but the offset is reduced by $|y| \geq \mathrm{lcm}(p_1, \ldots, p_\ell)$. □

A similar proof yields the following lemma.

Lemma 4.4 *Let $m > 0$, $C_i \subseteq A^*$ be an ultimately p_i-periodic chain with offset q_i for $1 \leq i \leq k$ and let $u_i \in A^*$ be words with $|u_i| = q_i$ for $k < i \leq \ell$ and let $u \in A^*$ with $|u| \geq \max(q_1, \ldots, q_\ell) + \text{lcm}(p_1, \ldots, p_k) \cdot (N_1(\ell + 1, m) + 2)$. Then there exists a word $v \in A^*$ with $|v| \leq |u| - \text{lcm}(p_1, \ldots, p_k)$ and $(t, \bar{C}, \bar{u}, u) \equiv_m^{\text{ch}} (t, \bar{C}, \bar{u}, v)$.*

4.3.3. Ultimately periodic chains with small period

Lemma 4.5 *Let $m \in \mathbb{N}$, $C_i \subseteq A^*$ be an ultimately p_i-periodic chain with offset q_i for $1 \leq i \leq \ell$ and let $C \subseteq A^*$ be an ultimately p-periodic chain with offset q. Suppose furthermore $p > 2\,\text{lcm}(p_1, \ldots, p_\ell)(N_2(\ell + 1, m) + 2)$ is a multiple of $\text{lcm}(p_1, \ldots, p_\ell)$. Then there exists an ultimately p'-periodic chain $D \subseteq A^*$ such that $p' < p$ is a multiple of $\text{lcm}(p_1, \ldots, p_\ell)$ and $(t, \bar{C}, C) \equiv_m^{\text{ch}} (t, \bar{C}, D)$.*

Proof. It is sufficient to consider an infinite chain C. In this case, one first shows the existence of $u, w \in A^*$, $v \in w^+$ and $F, F_1, \ldots, F_\ell \subseteq A^*$ such that the following hold:

- $|w| = \text{lcm}(p_1, \ldots, p_\ell)$ and $p = |v|$
- $\emptyset \neq F \subseteq \Downarrow v$ and $v^* F = u^{-1}C =: C'$
- $\emptyset \neq F_i \subseteq \Downarrow w$ and $w^* F_i = u^{-1}C_i =: C_i'$ for $1 \leq i \leq \ell$

The word v can be factorized as $x_1x_2x_3$ such that $x_1, x_2 \in w^+, x_3 \in w^*$, and

$$(t_{x_1,vx_1}, \bar{C}', C') \equiv_m^{\text{ch}} (t_{x_1x_2,vx_1}, \bar{C}', C').$$

For $n > 0$, we have $v^n x_1 = x_1(x_2x_3x_1)^n$. One can show that

$$(t_{x_1,vx_1}, \bar{C}', C') \cong (t_{v^n x_1, v^{n+1}x_1}, \bar{C}', C') \text{ and}$$
$$(t_{x_1x_2,vx_1}, \bar{C}', C') \cong (t_{v^n x_1 x_2, v^{n+1}x_1}, \bar{C}', C').$$

Hence we have

$$\begin{aligned}
(t, \bar{C}', C') &= (t_{\varepsilon,vx_1}, \bar{C}', C') \cdot \prod_{n>0} (t_{v^n x_1, v^{n+1}x_1}, \bar{C}', C') \\
&\cong (t_{\varepsilon,vx_1}, \bar{C}', C') \cdot (t_{x_1,vx_1}, \bar{C}', C')^\omega \\
&\equiv_m^{\text{ch}} (t_{\varepsilon,vx_1}, \bar{C}', C') \cdot (t_{x_1x_2,vx_1}, \bar{C}', C')^\omega \\
&\cong (t_{\varepsilon,vx_1}, \bar{C}', C') \cdot \prod_{n>0} (t_{v^n x_1 x_2, v^{n+1}x_1}, \bar{C}', C') \\
&\cong (t, \bar{C}', D')
\end{aligned}$$

for some $|x_3x_1|$-periodic chain D'.

Then $p' := |x_3x_1|$ is a multiple of $\text{lcm}(p_1, \ldots, p_\ell)$. Furthermore

$$\begin{aligned}
(t, \bar{C}, C) &= (t_{\varepsilon,u}, \bar{C}, C) \cdot (t_u, \bar{C}, C) \\
&\cong (t_{\varepsilon,u}, \bar{C}, C) \cdot (t, \bar{C}', C') \\
&\equiv_m^{\text{ch}} (t_{\varepsilon,u}, \bar{C}, C) \cdot (t, \bar{C}', D') \\
&\cong (t, \bar{C}, D)
\end{aligned}$$

with $D = (C \cap \Downarrow u) \cup uD'$. Since the period length of D' equals p', the chain D is ultimately p'-periodic. □

Proposition 4.6 *Let $m \in \mathbb{N}$, $C_i \subseteq A^*$ be an ultimately p_i-periodic chain with offset q_i for $1 \leq i \leq \ell$ and let $C \subseteq A^*$ be an ultimately p-periodic chain. Then there exists an ultimately p'-periodic chain D such that $(t, \bar{C}, C) \equiv_m^{\text{ch}} (t, \bar{C}, D)$ and $p' \leq 2\,\text{lcm}(p_1, \ldots, p_\ell) \cdot (N_2(\ell + 1, m) + 2)$.*

Proof. Set $p_0' = p \cdot 2\,\text{lcm}(p_1, \ldots, p_\ell) \cdot (N_2(\ell + 1, m) + 2)$. This allows to apply Lemma 4.5 iteratively. The result is a sequence of ultimately p_i'-periodic chains with $p_0' > p_1' > \cdots p_n'$. This process terminates once $p_n' \leq 2\,\text{lcm}(p_1, \ldots, p_\ell) \cdot (N_2(\ell + 1, m) + 2)$. □

Now we can finally prove that any chain C can be replaced by an ultimately periodic chain D of small period and offset without changing the MSO^{ch}-properties:

Theorem 4.7 *Let $m \in \mathbb{N}$, $C_i \subseteq A^*$ be ultimately p_i-periodic chains with offset q_i for $1 \leq i \leq \ell$ and let $C \subseteq A^*$ be a chain. Then there exists an ultimately p'-periodic chain D with offset $q' \leq \max(q_1, \ldots, q_\ell) + \text{lcm}(p_1, \ldots, p_\ell) \cdot (N_1(\ell + 1, m) + 2)$ and $p' \leq 2\,\text{lcm}(p_1, \ldots, p_\ell) \cdot (N_2(\ell + 1, m) + 2)$ such that $(t, \bar{C}, C) \equiv_m^{\text{ch}} (t, \bar{C}, D)$.*

Proof. By Prop. 4.2, we can assume C to be ultimately periodic. Prop. 4.6 allows to bound its period by $2\,\text{lcm}(p_1, \ldots, p_\ell) \cdot (N_2(\ell + 1, m) + 2)$. Although this increases the offset, an iterative application of Lemma 4.3 shortens the offset again to a value of at most $\max(q_1, \ldots, q_\ell) + \text{lcm}(p_1, \ldots, p_\ell) \cdot (N_1(\ell + 1, m) + 2)$ without increasing the period. □

4.4. Bounded MSO^{ch}-theory

For an MSO^{ch}-formula ψ and $q, p \in \mathbb{N}$ let $\exists C \leq (q, p) : \psi$ stand for "there exists an ultimately p'-periodic chain C with offset at most q and $p' \leq p$ such that ψ holds". Similarly, $\exists x \leq q : \psi$ means "there exists a word x of length at most q such that ψ holds". The formulas $\forall C \leq (q, p) : \psi$ and $\forall x \leq q : \psi$ should be understood similarly. A *bounded* MSO^{ch}*-sentence* is an expression of the form

$$Q_1 C_1 \leq (q_1, p_1) \cdots Q_\ell C_\ell \leq (q_\ell, p_\ell)$$
$$Q_1' x_1 \leq r_1 \cdots Q_k' x_k \leq r_k : \psi$$

where ψ is a Boolean combination of atomic formulas and $Q_i, Q_j' \in \{\exists, \forall\}$. Standard techniques allow to shift set quantifiers to the front in a prenex normalform formula (at the expense of additional quantifiers). Hence Thm. 4.7 and Lemma 4.4 imply:

Proposition 4.8 *From an* $\mathrm{MSO}^{\mathrm{ch}}$*-sentence* φ*, one can effectively compute a bounded* $\mathrm{MSO}^{\mathrm{ch}}$*-sentence* ψ *such that, for any structure* $\mathcal{A}$*, we have* $\mathcal{A}^*_{\mathrm{ba}} \models^{\mathrm{ch}} \varphi$ *if and only if* $\mathcal{A}^*_{\mathrm{ba}} \models^{\mathrm{ch}} \psi$*.*

Remark 4.9 *If we restrict set quantification in* $\mathrm{MSO}^{\mathrm{ch}}$*-sentences further to ultimately periodic chains, we obtain a new satisfaction relation* $\models^{\mathrm{period}}$ *(that only makes sense for iterations). The above proposition implies in particular that this seemingly new satisfaction relation equals* $\models^{\mathrm{ch}}$*. This consequence parallels Rabin's result [17] where he restricts set quantifications to run over regular sets.*

4.5. Reduction of the $\mathrm{MSO}^{\mathrm{ch}}$-theory to the first-order theory

Theorem 4.10 *From an* $\mathrm{MSO}^{\mathrm{ch}}$*-sentence* φ*, one can effectively compute a first-order sentence* φ' *such that, for any structure* $\mathcal{A}$*, we have* $\mathcal{A}^*_{\mathrm{ba}} \models^{\mathrm{ch}} \varphi$ *if and only if* $\mathcal{A} \models \varphi'$*.*

Proof. Let $\mathcal{A}$ be some structure. For $n \in \mathbb{N}$ let $\mathcal{A}^{\leq n} = (A^{\leq n}, \preceq, (\widehat{R})_{R\in\sigma}, \mathrm{eq})$ where (i) $A^{\leq n}$ is the set of words in A^* of length at most n and (ii) $(u, v) \in \mathrm{eq}$ if and only if there exist $a \in A$ and $u', v' \in A^*$ with $u = u'a$ and $v = v'a$. Now let φ be a bounded $\mathrm{MSO}^{\mathrm{ch}}$-sentence with first-order kernel ψ and let $n \in \mathbb{N}$ be the maximal number appearing in the bounds in φ. Note that ψ does not relate the chains C_i directly, but only indirectly via the individual variables x_j. This allows to write a first-order formula α in the language of $\mathcal{A}^{\leq n}$ such that $\mathcal{A}^*_{\mathrm{ba}} \models^{\mathrm{ch}} \varphi$ if and only if $\mathcal{A}^{\leq n} \models \alpha$. Here, the predicate eq is necessary in order to express the periodicity of a chain.

Note that the first-order theory of $\mathcal{A}^{\leq n}$ can be reduced to that of $\mathcal{A}$. There is even such a reduction that works uniformly in n and $\mathcal{A}$. Hence the proof is complete. □

Since Thm. 4.10 parallels Muchnik's Theorem 3.1, we can derive similar corollaries:

Corollary 4.11 *Let* σ *be some finite relational signature.*

- *If the first-order theory of a* σ*-structure* $\mathcal{A}$ *is decidable, then the* $\mathrm{MSO}^{\mathrm{ch}}$*-theory of its basic iteration* $\mathcal{A}^*_{\mathrm{ba}}$ *is decidable as well.*
- *For any* $m \in \mathbb{N}$*, there exists* $n \in \mathbb{N}$ *such that, for any two* σ*-structures* $\mathcal{A}$ *and* $\mathcal{B}$ *with* $\mathcal{A} \equiv^{\mathrm{FO}}_n \mathcal{B}$*, we have* $\mathcal{A}^*_{\mathrm{ba}} \equiv^{\mathrm{ch}}_m \mathcal{B}^*_{\mathrm{ba}}$*.*

5. FOREG over pushdown systems

In this section we apply our decidability result for $\mathrm{MSO}^{\mathrm{ch}}$ over basic iterations to pushdown systems. We introduce pushdown systems where the stack alphabet is the (possibly infinite) universe of an arbitrary base structure G. Push- and pop operations are triggered via the relations of the base structure G and a finite set of control states, but are independent from the topmost stack symbol. The configuration graph of such a pushdown system is defined as for finite stack alphabets. We study the logic FOREG for these configuration graphs. FOREG is the extension of first-order logic which allows to define new binary predicates by regular expressions over the binary predicates of the base structure $\mathcal{A}$. Based on our decidability result Corollary 4.11 we show that if FOREG is decidable for the base structure G of a pushdown system, then FOREG remains decidable for the configuration graph of the pushdown system (Thm. 5.1).

5.1. The logic FOREG

Let Σ be a finite alphabet of labels and let $G = (A, (E_\sigma)_{\sigma\in\Sigma}, R_1, \ldots, R_m)$ be a relational structure, where $E_\sigma \subseteq A \times A$ is a binary relation and $R_1, \ldots, R_m$ are additional non-binary relations. For a word $w = \sigma_1 \cdots \sigma_n$ with $\sigma_i \in \Sigma$ we define the binary relation $\xrightarrow{w}_G = E_{\sigma_1} \circ \cdots \circ E_{\sigma_n}$. We have $\xrightarrow{\varepsilon}_G = \mathrm{id}_A$ and $\xrightarrow{\sigma}_G = E_\sigma$ for $\sigma \in \Sigma$. For a regular language $L \subseteq \Sigma^*$ we define $\mathrm{reach}_L = \bigcup_{w\in L} \xrightarrow{w}_G$. An *FOREG-formula* over the structure G is simply a first-order formula over the extended structure $(A, (\mathrm{reach}_L)_{L\in\mathrm{REG}(\Sigma)}, R_1, \ldots, R_m)$.

5.2. Pushdown systems over infinite stack alphabets

A *pushdown system* $S = (Q, G, \tau)$ over a *stack structure* G is given by the following data:

- G is a relational structure of the form $G = (A, (\mathrm{eq}_\alpha)_{\alpha\in\Sigma_1}, (\mathrm{push}_\beta)_{\beta\in\Sigma_2}, (\mathrm{pop}_\gamma)_{\gamma\in\Sigma_3}, \bot)$, where Σ_1, Σ_2, Σ_3 are finite and mutually disjoint alphabets (let $\Sigma = \Sigma_1 \cup \Sigma_2 \cup \Sigma_3$ in the following), $\mathrm{eq}_\alpha \subseteq A \times A$, $\mathrm{push}_\beta, \mathrm{pop}_\gamma \subseteq A$, and $\bot \in A$.
- Q is a finite set of states such that $Q \cap A = \emptyset$.
- $\tau : \Sigma \to Q \times Q$

With S we associate the configuration graph $\mathcal{C}(S) = (A^+Q, (E_\sigma)_{\sigma\in\Sigma})$, where:

- $E_\alpha = \{(wap, wbq) \mid w \in A^*, (a, b) \in \mathrm{eq}_\alpha, \tau(\alpha) = (p, q)\}$ for $\alpha \in \Sigma_1$
- $E_\beta = \{(wp, waq) \mid w \in A^+, a \in \mathrm{push}_\beta, \tau(\beta) = (p, q)\}$ for $\beta \in \Sigma_2$
- $E_\gamma = \{(wap, wq) \mid w \in A^+, a \in \mathrm{pop}_\gamma, \tau(\gamma) = (p, q)\}$ for $\gamma \in \Sigma_3$

The following theorem is the main result of this section:

Theorem 5.1 *Let G be a stack structure with decidable FOREG-theory. Then the configuration graph $\mathcal{C}(S)$ has a decidable FOREG-theory.*

The rest of this section is devoted to the proof of this theorem. The idea is to define, using the logic FOREG, a suitable structure $\mathcal{A}$ in the stack structure G. Since we assume that the FOREG-theory of G is decidable, it follows that the first-order theory of $\mathcal{A}$ is decidable. Thus, by Corollary 4.11 the MSO^{ch}-theory of the basic iteration $\mathcal{A}^*_{\text{ba}}$ is decidable. To obtain Thm. 5.1, we give an MSO^{ch}-interpretation of the configuration graph $\mathcal{C}(S)$ in $\mathcal{A}^*_{\text{ba}}$.

For a finite automaton T and states μ and ν of T, let $L(T, \mu, \nu)$ be the set of words that label some path from μ to ν in T.

Fix regular languages $L_1, \ldots, L_k \subseteq \Sigma^*$. Then there exists a finite automaton $T = (\Theta, \Sigma, \delta)$ with state set Θ such that every language L_i is a union of languages of the form $L(T, \mu, \nu)$ for certain states $\mu, \nu \in \Theta$. For $\mu, \nu \in \Theta$ let

$$\text{reach}_{\mu,\nu} = \{(up, vq) \in A^+Q \times A^+Q \mid \exists w \in L(T, \mu, \nu) : up \xrightarrow{w}_{\mathcal{C}(S)} vq\}.$$

Thus, $\text{reach}_{\mu,\nu} = \text{reach}_L$ for $L = L(T, \mu, \nu)$. We will show that the first-order theory of the structure

$$\mathcal{B} = (A^+Q, (\text{reach}_{\mu,\nu})_{\mu,\nu\in\Theta}) \tag{2}$$

is decidable. Since the decision procedure for the first-order theory of $\mathcal{B}$ will be uniform in the automaton T, this proves Thm. 5.1.

Let $\mu, \nu \in \Theta$, $p, q \in Q$, $u \in A^+$, and $a \in A$. We write $(up, uaq) \in \text{reach}^{(+)}_{\mu,\nu}$ if and only if there exist $\beta \in \Sigma_2$ and $x \in \Sigma^*$ such that $\beta x \in L(T, \mu, \nu)$, $up \xrightarrow{\beta x}_{\mathcal{C}(S)} uaq$, $|y|_{\Sigma_2} \geq |y|_{\Sigma_3}$ for every prefix y of x, and $|x|_{\Sigma_2} = |x|_{\Sigma_3}$. Thus, (up, uaq) belongs to the relation $\text{reach}^{(+)}_{\mu,\nu}$ if there exists a path from up to uaq in the configuration graph $\mathcal{C}(S)$ whose label belongs to $L(T, \mu, \nu)$ such that all the configurations along this path except the very first one up are of the form uvr for some $v \in A^+$, and $r \in Q$. Note that $(up, uaq) \in \text{reach}^{(+)}_{\mu,\nu}$ implies $(vp, vaq) \in \text{reach}^{(+)}_{\mu,\nu}$ for all $v \in A^+$. Symmetrically, we write $(uap, uq) \in \text{reach}^{(-)}_{\mu,\nu}$ if and only if there exist $\gamma \in \Sigma_3$ and $x \in \Sigma^*$ such that $x\gamma \in L(T, \mu, \nu)$, $uap \xrightarrow{x\gamma}_{\mathcal{C}(S)} uq$, $|y|_{\Sigma_2} \geq |y|_{\Sigma_3}$ for every prefix y of x, and $|x|_{\Sigma_2} = |x|_{\Sigma_3}$. Finally, for $\mu, \nu \in \Theta$, $p, q \in Q$, $u, v \in A^+$ we write $(up, vq) \in \text{reach}^{(=)}_{\mu,\nu}$ if and only if there exists $w \in L(T, \mu, \nu)$ such that $up \xrightarrow{w}_{\mathcal{C}(S)} vq$, $|y|_{\Sigma_2} \geq |y|_{\Sigma_3}$ for every prefix y of w, and $|w|_{\Sigma_2} = |w|_{\Sigma_3}$. Thus, (up, vq) belongs to the relation $\text{reach}^{(+)}_{\mu,\nu}$ if there exists a path from up to vq in the configuration graph $\mathcal{C}(S)$ whose label belongs to $L(T, \mu, \nu)$ such that all the configurations along this path are of the form wr for some $r \in Q$ and $w \in A^+$ with $|w| = |u| = |v|$. Thus, $(uap, ubq) \in \text{reach}^{(=)}_{\mu,\nu}$ for some (and hence all) $u \in A^*$ if and only if $(ap, bq) \in \text{reach}_{\mu,\nu}$.

Lemma 5.2 *For $c, d \in A^+Q$ and $\mu, \nu \in \Theta$ we have $(c, d) \in \text{reach}_{\mu,\nu}$ if and only if there exist $m, n \geq 0$, $\mu_m, \ldots, \mu_0, \nu_0, \ldots, \nu_n \in \Theta$, and configurations $c_m, \ldots, c_0, d_0, \ldots, d_n \in A^+Q$ such that:*

- $c_m = c$, $d_n = d$, $\mu_m = \mu$, $\nu_n = \nu$
- $(c_i, c_{i-1}) \in \text{reach}^{(-)}_{\mu_i,\mu_{i-1}}$ *for* $1 \leq i \leq m$
- $(c_0, d_0) \in \text{reach}^{(=)}_{\mu_0,\nu_0}$
- $(d_{j-1}, d_j) \in \text{reach}^{(+)}_{\nu_{j-1},\nu_j}$ *for* $1 \leq j \leq n$

Proof. The if-direction is obvious. For the other direction take for c_0 (resp. d_0) the leftmost (resp. rightmost) occurrence of a configuration of minimal height along a path in $\mathcal{C}(S)$ from the configuration c to the configuration d. □

For all $p, q \in Q$ and $\mu, \nu \in \Theta$ define a binary predicate

$$H(p, \mu, q, \nu) = \{(a, b) \in A \times A \mid (ap, bq) \in \text{reach}_{\mu,\nu}\}.$$

Lemma 5.3 *The relation $H(p, \mu, q, \nu)$ is effectively FOREG-definable over the stack structure G.*

Proof. We will construct effectively a finite automaton B with state set $Q \times \Theta$ and alphabet Σ_1 such that $(ap, bq) \in \text{reach}_{\mu,\nu}$ if and only if $a \xrightarrow{u}_G b$ for some $u \in L(B, (p, \mu), (q, \nu))$, which proves the lemma. For this, we will construct a finite sequence of automata B_i ($i \geq 0$) with state set $Q \times \Theta$ and alphabet Σ_1, which converges to the automaton B. The finite state automaton B_0 contains the transition $(p, \mu) \xrightarrow{\alpha} (q, \nu)$ if and only if $\tau(\alpha) = (p, q)$ and $\mu \xrightarrow{\alpha}_T \nu$ for some $\alpha \in \Sigma_1$. Now assume that B_i is already constructed and assume that

- in T there are transitions $\mu \xrightarrow{\beta}_T \mu'$, ($\beta \in \Sigma_2$) and $\nu' \xrightarrow{\gamma}_T \nu$ ($\gamma \in \Sigma_3$),
- $\tau(\beta) = (p, p')$, $\tau(\gamma) = (q', q)$, and
- there exist $a \in \text{push}_\beta, b \in \text{pop}_\gamma$, and $u \in L(B_i, (p', \mu'), (q', \nu'))$ such that $a \xrightarrow{u}_G b$.

Note that the last point is decidable, since the FOREG-theory of G is decidable. In this situation we add the ε-transition $(p, \mu) \xrightarrow{\varepsilon} (q, \nu)$ to B_i and call the resulting automaton B_{i+1}. We repeat this process as long as we will add new ε-transitions. Note that in each step the state set is not changed. Let B be the resulting automaton. It is not difficult to prove $(ap, bq) \in \text{reach}_{\mu,\nu}$ if and only if $a \xrightarrow{u}_G b$, for some $u \in L(B, (p, \mu), (q, \nu))$, which proves the lemma. □

Define for all $p, q \in Q$ and $\mu, \nu \in \Theta$ unary predicates $D(p, \mu, q, \nu), U(p, \mu, q, \nu) \subseteq A$ as follows:

$$a \in D(p, \mu, q, \nu) \Leftrightarrow$$
$$\bigvee_{\substack{p' \in Q, \mu' \in \Theta, \\ \gamma \in \Sigma_3}} \exists b \in \text{pop}_\gamma : \left\{ \begin{array}{l} (a, b) \in H(p, \mu, p', \mu') \land \\ \tau(\gamma) = (p', q) \land \mu' \xrightarrow{\gamma}_T \nu \end{array} \right\}$$

$$a \in U(p, \mu, q, \nu) \Leftrightarrow$$
$$\bigvee_{\substack{p' \in Q, \mu' \in \Theta, \\ \beta \in \Sigma_2}} \exists b \in \text{push}_\beta : \left\{ \begin{array}{l} (b, a) \in H(p', \mu', q, \nu) \land \\ \tau(\beta) = (p, p') \land \mu \xrightarrow{\beta}_T \mu' \end{array} \right\}$$

By Lemma 5.3, the unary predicates $D(p, \mu, q, \nu)$ and $U(p, \mu, q, \nu)$ are FOREG-definable in the stack structure G. The next lemma follows directly from the definition of the predicates $D(p, \mu, q, \nu)$, $H(p, \mu, q, \nu)$, and $U(p, \mu, q, \nu)$.

Lemma 5.4 *We have:*

$$D(p, \mu, q, \nu) = \{a \in A \mid \exists u \in A^+ : (uap, uq) \in \text{reach}^{(-)}_{\mu,\nu}\}$$
$$U(p, \mu, q, \nu) = \{a \in A \mid \exists u \in A^+ : (up, uaq) \in \text{reach}^{(+)}_{\mu,\nu}\}$$

Note that in Lemma 5.4, one might replace the quantifier $\exists u \in A^+$ by $\forall u \in A^+$. Lemma 5.2 and Lemma 5.4 imply:

Lemma 5.5 *We have $(up, vq) \in \text{reach}_{\mu,\nu}$ if and only if there exist $m, n \geq 0$, $w \in A^*$, $a_i \in A, p_i \in Q, \mu_i \in \Theta$ $(0 \leq i \leq m)$, and $b_j \in A, q_j \in Q, \nu_j \in \Theta$ $(0 \leq j \leq m)$ such that:*

- $\mu = \mu_m$, $\nu = \nu_n$, $p = p_m$, $q = q_n$,
- $u = wa_0 \cdots a_m$, $v = wb_0 \cdots b_n$,
- $a_i \in D(p_i, \mu_i, p_{i-1}, \mu_{i-1})$ *for all* $1 \leq i \leq m$,
- $(a_0, b_0) \in H(p_0, \mu_0, q_0, \nu_0)$,
- $b_j \in U(q_{j-1}, \nu_{j-1}, q_j, \nu_j)$ *for all* $1 \leq j \leq n$

Define the binary relations $D(p, \mu, q, \nu)^*, U(p, \mu, q, \nu)^* \subseteq A^+ \times A^+$ as follows:

$(u, v) \in D(p, \mu, q, \nu)^*$ if and only if there exist $m \geq 0$, $a_1, \ldots, a_m \in A$, $p_0, \ldots, p_m \in Q$, $\mu_0, \ldots, \mu_m \in \Theta$ with

- $u = va_1 \cdots a_m$,
- $p = p_m$, $q = p_0$, $\mu = \mu_m$, $\nu = \mu_0$, and
- $a_i \in D(p_i, \mu_i, p_{i-1}, \mu_{i-1})$ for $1 \leq i \leq m$.

$(u, v) \in U(p, \mu, q, \nu)^*$ if and only if there exist $n \geq 0$, $b_1, \ldots, b_n \in A$, $q_0, \ldots, q_n \in Q$, $\nu_0, \ldots, \nu_n \in \Theta$ with

- $v = ub_1 \cdots b_n$,
- $p = q_0$, $q = q_n$, $\mu = \nu_0$, $\nu = \nu_n$, and
- $b_j \in U(q_{j-1}, \nu_{j-1}, q_j, \nu_j)$ for $1 \leq j \leq n$.

These definitions and Lemma 5.5 imply:

Lemma 5.6 *We have $(up, vq) \in \text{reach}_{\mu,\nu}$ if and only if there exist $u', v' \in A^+$, $p', q' \in Q$, $\mu', \nu' \in \Theta$ such that:*

$$(u, u') \in D(p, \mu, p', \mu')^*$$
$$(u', v') \in \{(xa, xb) \mid x \in A^*, (a, b) \in H(p', \mu', q', \nu')\}$$
$$(v', v) \in U(q', \nu', q, \nu)^*$$

Now, let us consider the structure

$$\mathcal{A} = (A \cup Q, (q)_{q \in Q}, (D(p, \mu, q, \nu))_{p,q \in Q, \mu,\nu \in \Theta}, (H(p, \mu, q, \nu))_{p,q \in Q, \mu,\nu \in \Theta}, (U(p, \mu, q, \nu))_{p,q \in Q, \mu,\nu \in \Theta}).$$

Since each of its relations is FOREG-definable in the stack structure G, and G has a decidable FOREG-theory, $\mathcal{A}$ has a decidable first-order theory. Thus, by Thm. 4.10,

$$\mathcal{A}^*_{\text{ba}} = ((A \cup Q)^*, \preceq, (\widehat{q})_{q \in Q}, (\widehat{D(p, \mu, q, \nu)})_{p,q \in Q, \mu,\nu \in \Theta}, (\widehat{H(p, \mu, q, \nu)})_{p,q \in Q, \mu,\nu \in \Theta}, (\widehat{U(p, \mu, q, \nu)})_{p,q \in Q, \mu,\nu \in \Theta})$$

has a decidable MSO^{ch}-theory. We finally show that the structure $\mathcal{B}$ from (2), for which we have to show decidability of the first-order theory, is MSO^{ch}-interpretable in $\mathcal{A}^*_{\text{ba}}$, which proves Thm. 5.1. Clearly, the universe A^+Q of $\mathcal{B}$ is first-order definable in $\mathcal{A}^*_{\text{ba}}$ using the prefix relation $\preceq$ and the unary relations $\widehat{q} = (A \cup Q)^* q$ for $q \in Q$. In order to define the relations $\text{reach}_{\mu,\nu}$ of $\mathcal{B}$ it suffices by Lemma 5.6 to define the binary relations $D(p, \mu, q, \nu)^*, U(p, \mu, q, \nu)^*, \{(xa, xb) \mid x \in A^*, (a, b) \in H(p, \mu, q, \nu)\} \subseteq A^+ \times A^+$ in $\mathcal{A}$ using MSO^{ch}. The relation $\{(xa, xb) \mid x \in A^*, (a, b) \in H(p, \mu, q, \nu)\}$ can be defined as $\widehat{H(p, \mu, q, \nu)} \cap A^+ \times A^+$; note that A^+ is first-order definable in $\mathcal{A}$ using the prefix relation $\preceq$ and the relations $\widehat{q}$ for $q \in Q$. Finally, the MSO^{ch}-definitions of $D(p, \mu, q, \nu)^*$ and $U(p, \mu, q, \nu)^*$ follow Büchi's technique for expressing the existence of a successful run of an automaton on a finite word in MSO. This completes the proof of Thm. 5.1.

6. Open problems

We have shown that the MSO^{ch}-theory (i.e., the fragment of the full MSO-theory where set quantification is restricted to chains) of the basic iteration $\mathcal{A}^*_{\text{ba}}$ of a structure $\mathcal{A}$ can be reduced to the first-order theory of $\mathcal{A}$. Using this result, we have shown that the FOREG-theory of the configuration graph $\mathcal{C}(S)$ of a pushdown system S over an infinite stack structure $\mathcal{A}$ can be reduced to the FOREG-theory of $\mathcal{A}$. We plan to investigate whether similar preservation theorems can be shown also for temporal logics like CTL, CTL*, or the modal μ-calculus. Another interesting candidate for investigations of this kind is TC^2 [26], i.e., first-order logic extended by the transitive closure operator for binary relations.

References

[1] R. Alur, M. Benedikt, K. Etessami, P. Godefroid, T. W. Reps, and M. Yannakakis. Analysis of recursive state machines. *ACM Trans. Program. Lang. Syst*, 27(4):786–818, 2005.

[2] D. Berwanger and A. Blumensath. The monadic theory of tree-like structures. In *Automata, logics, and infinite games*, LNCS 2500, pages 285–301. Springer, 2002.

[3] A. Blumensath and S. Kreutzer. An extension of muchnik's theorem. *J. Log. Comput.*, 15:59–64, 2005.

[4] A. Carayol and S. Wöhrle. The Caucal hierarchy of infinite graphs in terms of logic and higher-order pushdown automata. In *FSTTCS 2003*, LNCS 2914, pages 112–123. Springer, 2003.

[5] D. Caucal. On the transition graphs of Turing machines. *Theor. Comput. Sci.*, 296(2):195–223, 2003.

[6] B. Courcelle and I. Walukiewicz. Monadic second-order logic, graph coverings and unfoldings of transition systems. *Ann. Pure Appl. Logic*, 92(1):35–62, 1998.

[7] H.-D. Ebbinghaus and J. Flum. *Finite Model Theory*. Springer, 1991.

[8] J. Esparza, S. Kiefer, and S. Schwoon. Abstraction refinement with Craig interpolation and symbolic pushdown systems. In *TACAS 06*, LNCS 3920, pages 489–503. Springer, 2006.

[9] J. Esparza, A. Kucera, and S. Schwoon. Model checking LTL with regular valuations for pushdown systems. *Inf. Comput.*, 186(2):355–376, 2003.

[10] Y. Gurevich. Monadic second-order theories. In J. Barwise and S. Feferman, editors, *Model-Theoretic Logics*, pages 479–506. Springer, 1985.

[11] Y. Gurevich and S. Shelah. Rabin's uniformization problem. *J. of Symb. Logic*, 48:1105–1119, 1983.

[12] B. Khoussainov and A. Nerode. Automatic presentations of structures. In *Logic and Computational Complexity*, LNCS 960, pages 367–392. Springer, 1995.

[13] O. Kupferman and M. Y. Vardi. An automata-theoretic approach to reasoning about infinite-state systems. In *CAV 2000*, LNCS 1855, pages 36–52. Springer, 2000.

[14] D. Kuske and M. Lohrey. Logical aspects of Cayley-graphs: The monoid case. *Int. J. Algebra Comput.*, 16(2):307–340, 2006.

[15] F. Neven and T. Schwentick. Expressive and efficient pattern languages for tree-structured data. In *PODS'00*, pages 145–156. ACM Press, 2000.

[16] D. Perrin and J.-E. Pin. *Infinite Words. Automata, semigroups, logic and games*. Pure and Applied Mathematics vol. 141. Elsevier, 2004.

[17] M. Rabin. *Automata on infinite objects and Church's problem*. American Mathematical Society, Providence, R.I., 1972. Conference Board of the Mathematical Sciences Regional Conference Series in Mathematics, No. 13.

[18] M. O. Rabin. Decidability of second-order theories and automata on infinite trees. *Trans. Am. Math. Soc.*, 141:1–35, 1969.

[19] T. Schwentick. On diving in trees. In *MFCS'00*, LNCS 1893, pages 660–669. Springer, 2000.

[20] A. L. Semenov. Decidability of monadic theories. In *MFCS'84*, LNCS 176, pages 162–175. Springer, 1984.

[21] S. Shelah. The monadic theory of order. *Ann. Math. (2)*, 102:379–419, 1975.

[22] J. Stupp. The lattice-model is recursive in the original model. The Hebrew University, Jerusalem, 1975.

[23] W. Thomas. On chain logic, path logic, and first-order logic over infinite trees. In *LICS'87*, pages 245–256. IEEE Computer Society Press, 1987.

[24] I. Walukiewicz. Pushdown processes: Games and model-checking. *Inf. Comput.*, 164(2):234–263, 2001.

[25] I. Walukiewicz. Monadic second-order logic on tree-like structures. *Theor. Comput. Sci.*, 275(1–2):311–346, 2002.

[26] S. Wöhrle and W. Thomas. Model checking synchronized products of infinite transition systems. In *LICS'04*, pages 2–11. IEEE Computer Society Press, 2004.

An Automata-Theoretic Approach for Model Checking Threads for LTL Properties

Vineet Kahlon and Aarti Gupta
NEC Labs America,
Princeton, NJ 08540, USA.

Abstract

In this paper, we propose a new technique for the verification of concurrent multi-threaded programs. In general, the problem is known to be undecidable even for programs with just two threads [1]. However, we exploit the observation that, in practice, a large fraction of concurrent programs can either be modeled as Pushdown Systems communicating solely using locks or can be reduced to such systems by applying standard abstract interpretation techniques or by exploiting separation of data from control. Moreover, standard programming practice guidelines typically recommend that programs use locks in a nested fashion. In fact, in languages like Java and C#, locks are guaranteed to be nested. For such a framework, we show, by using the new concept of Lock Constrained Multi-Automata Pair (LMAP), that pre^**-closures of regular sets of states can be computed efficiently. This is accomplished by reducing the* pre^**-closure computation for a regular set of states of a concurrent program with nested locks to those for its individual threads. Leveraging this new technique then allows us to formulate a fully automatic, efficient and exact (sound and complete) decision procedure for model checking threads communicating via nested locks for indexed linear-time temporal logic formulae.*

1 Introduction

The widespread use of concurrent multi-threaded programs in operating systems, embedded systems and databases coupled with their behavioral complexity necessitates the use of formal methods to debug such systems. Unfortunately most existing methods for verifying concurrent programs suffer from at least one of the following drawbacks: the technique does not scale to large programs due to state explosion; it is sound but not guaranteed complete thus resulting in bogus error traces; or it relies on manual and hence time-consuming abstractions to compress the state space enough to make verification amenable. Moreover, a lot of existing techniques cater only to the verification of reachability properties whereas the debugging of reactive concurrent programs like operating systems requires the verification of a much richer class of properties. In this paper, we give a new technique for model checking threads communicating via nested locks that is fully automatic, efficient, sound and complete, and works for a broad range of linear-time properties.

We consider concurrent multi-threaded programs where each thread is modeled as a Pushdown System (PDS). A PDS has a finite control part corresponding to the valuation of the variables of the thread it represents and a stack which provides a means to model recursion. It is thus a natural and therefore a widely used formalism for modeling sequential programs[1] (cf. [2]). While for a single PDS the model checking problem is efficiently decidable for very expressive logics – both linear and branching time ([2, 3]), it was shown in [1] that even simple properties like reachability become undecidable for systems with only two PDSs communicating using CCS-style pairwise rendezvous.

However, in a large fraction of real-world concurrent software used, for example, in file systems, databases or device drivers, the key issue is to resolve conflicts between different threads competing for access to shared resources. Conflicts are typically resolved using locks which allow mutually exclusive access to a shared resource. Before a thread can gain access to a shared resource it has to acquire the lock associated with that resource which is released after executing all the intended operations. For such software, the interaction between concurrently executing threads is very limited making them loosely coupled. For instance, in a standard file system the control flow in the implementation of the various file operations is usually independent of the data being written to or read from a file. Consequently such programs can either be directly modeled as systems comprised of PDSs communicating via locks or can be reduced to such systems either by applying standard abstract interpretation techniques or by exploiting separation of control and data. A case in point is the Daisy file system [4]. There-

[1]Henceforth we shall use the terms thread and PDS interchangeably

fore, in this paper, we consider the model checking problem for PDSs interacting using locks.

Correctness properties are expressed using Indexed Linear Temporal Logic (LTL) which is a rich formalism that can encode most properties of interest including safety, e.g., presence of conflicts like data races, as well as liveness. In addition, we also consider deadlockability. In general, the model checking problem for even *reachability*, and hence more broadly LTL, is undecidable for systems with just *two* PDSs communicating via locks [5]. However, most real-world concurrent programs use locks in a nested fashion, viz., each thread can only release the lock that it acquired last and that has not yet been released. Indeed, practical programming guidelines used by software developers often require that locks be used in a nested fashion. In fact, in Java and C# locking is syntactically guaranteed to be nested. For the case of nested locks, it was shown in [5] that the model checking problems for pairwise reachability, viz., $\mathsf{EF}(a_i \wedge b_j)$; single-index properties interpreted solely over finite paths; and deadlockability are decidable.

In this paper, we propose a new efficient technique for computing *pre**-closures of regular sets of states of systems comprised of multiple PDSs interacting via nested locks. Towards that end, we introduce the new concept of *Lock-Constrained Multi-Automata Pair (LMAP)* which allows us to decompose the computation of *pre**-closures of regular sets of configurations of a multi-PDS system communicating via nested locks to that of its constituent PDSs for which existing efficient techniques (see [2]) can be leveraged. This decomposition enables us to avoid the state explosion problem thereby resulting in an efficient procedure for computing *pre**-closures. An LMAP $\mathcal{A}$ accepting a regular set of configurations C of a system $\mathcal{CP}$ comprised of PDSs T_1 and T_2 is a pair of multi-automata $\mathcal{A} = (\mathcal{A}_1, \mathcal{A}_2)$, where $\mathcal{A}_i$ is a multi-automaton accepting the set of local configurations of T_i occurring in the global configurations of $\mathcal{CP}$ in C. The lock interaction among the PDSs is encoded in the acceptance criterion for an LMAP which filters out those pairs of local configurations of T_1 and T_2 which are not simultaneously reachable due to lock enforced mutual exclusion and are therefore not in C. Specifically, to capture lock interaction, we track patterns of lock acquisitions and releases using the new concepts of *backward acquisition history (BAH)* and *forward acquisition history (FAH)*.

Next, we show how to apply our *pre**-closure computation technique to formulate an efficient model checking procedure for threads interacting via nested locks for linear time properties. Towards that end, we invoke the automata-theoretic paradigm to first construct a Büchi system $\mathcal{BP}$ from the given multi-threaded program $\mathcal{CP}$ and linear time formula f. The model checking problem then reduces to deciding whether $\mathcal{BP}$ has an accepting path, viz., a path along which final states occurs infinitely often. For finite state systems, along any infinite path some state must occur infinitely often and so along any accepting path p of $\mathcal{BP}$ there must be an occurrence of a final state along a subsequence p_s of p that starts and ends at the same state s. This observation reduces the problem of deciding the non-emptiness of $\mathcal{BP}$ to showing the existence of a finite *lollipop*, viz., a finite path of $\mathcal{BP}$ leading to a cycle with an accepting state which can be pumped indefinitely to yield an accepting computation. For infinite-state systems, however, the above observation is no longer valid. Indeed, in our case each thread has a stack which could potentially grow to be of unbounded depth and so the existence of a cycle of global states as discussed above is not guaranteed.

To overcome this problem, we first formulate the *Dual Pumping Lemma*[2], which allows us to reduce the problem of deciding whether there exists an accepting computation of $\mathcal{BP}$, to showing the existence of a finite (pseudo-)lollipop like witness with a special structure. The witness is essentially comprised of a stem u which is a finite path of $\mathcal{BP}$, and a (pseudo-)cycle which is a sequence v of transitions with an accepting state of $\mathcal{BP}$ having the following two properties (i) executing v returns each thread of the concurrent program to the same control location with the same symbol at the top of its stack as it started with, and (ii) executing v does not drain the stack of any thread, viz., any symbol that is not at the top of the stack of a thread to start with, is not popped during v's execution. These two properties ensure that we can pump the local computations of the individual threads along v by executing them back-to-back, even though each pumping may increase the stack depth of the thread. This allows us to then construct a valid accepting sequence of $\mathcal{BP}$ by interleaving the local pumping sequences of the individual threads via an intricate scheduling of the transitions of the threads occurring along v to effectively pump the pseudo-lollipop, i.e., execute the sequence u followed by the sequence v back-to-back indefinitely. The intricate scheduling is required in order to accommodate lock interaction among threads. The special structure of the witness guarantees the existence of such a scheduling.

Next, by exploiting the special structure of the witness (pseudo-)lollipop, we reduce the problem of deciding its existence to the computation of *pre**-closures of regular sets of configurations of $\mathcal{CP}$. It follows from the Dual Pumping Lemma, that for model checking indexed LTL formulae, it suffices to either (1) compute *pre**-closures for a set C of configurations in which all locks are free, or (2) compute lock-free configurations of the *pre**-closure of a set (that possibly contains configurations in which some locks are held). The notion of BAH is used in the first case while FAH in the second one. Decomposition is then achieved by showing that given an LMAP $\mathcal{A} = (\mathcal{A}_1, \mathcal{A}_2)$, if $\mathcal{B}_i$ is an

[2]For simplicity we consider programs with two threads only. In general, we can analogously formulate a *Multi-Pumping Lemma*

MA accepting the pre^*-closure of the configurations of the *individual thread* T_i accepted by $\mathcal{A}_i$, then, in the two cases of interest mentioned above, the LMAP $\mathcal{B} = (\mathcal{B}_1, \mathcal{B}_2)$ accepts the pre^*-closure of the regular set of the *concurrent program* $\mathcal{CP}$ accepted by $\mathcal{A}$. Thus the decomposition results from maintaining the local configurations of the constituent threads separately as multi-automata and computing the pre^*-closures on these multi-automata individually for each thread.

The rest of the paper is organized as follows. Section 2 introduces the system model. LMAPs are introduced in Section 3 while the Dual Pumping Lemma is formulated in section 4. We conclude with some remarks and comparison to related work in section 5.

2 System Model

We consider multi-threaded programs wherein threads communicate using locks. We model each thread as a *pushdown system (PDS)* [2]. A PDS has a finite control part corresponding to the valuation of the variables of the thread it represents and a stack which models recursion. Formally, a PDS is a five-tuple $\mathcal{P} = (P, Act, \Gamma, c_0, \Delta)$, where P is a finite set of *control locations*, *Act* is a finite set of *actions*, Γ is a finite *stack alphabet*, and $\Delta \subseteq (P \times \Gamma) \times Act \times (P \times \Gamma^*)$ is a finite set of *transition rules*. If $((p, \gamma), a, (p', w)) \in \Delta$ then we write $\langle p, \gamma \rangle \overset{a}{\hookrightarrow} \langle p', w \rangle$. A *configuration* of $\mathcal{P}$ is a pair $\langle p, w \rangle$, where $p \in P$ denotes the control location and $w \in \Gamma^*$ the *stack content*. We call c_0 the *initial configuration* of $\mathcal{P}$. The set of all configurations of $\mathcal{P}$ is denoted by $\mathcal{C}$. For each action a, we define a relation $\overset{a}{\rightarrow} \subseteq \mathcal{C} \times \mathcal{C}$ as follows: if $\langle q, \gamma \rangle \overset{a}{\hookrightarrow} \langle q', w \rangle$, then $\langle q, \gamma v \rangle \overset{a}{\rightarrow} \langle q', wv \rangle$ for every $v \in \Gamma^*$.

A concurrent program with n threads and m locks $l_1, ..., l_m$ is formally defined as a tuple of the form $\mathcal{CP} = (T_1, ..., T_n, L_1, ..., L_m)$, where for each i, $T_i = (P_i, Act_i, \Gamma_i, c_i, \Delta_i)$ is a pushdown system (thread), and for each j, $L_j \subseteq \{\perp, T_1, ..., T_n\}$ is the possible set of values that lock l_j can be assigned. A global configuration of $\mathcal{CP}$ is a tuple $c = (t_1, ..., t_n, l_1, ..., l_m)$ where $t_1, ..., t_n$ are, respectively, the configurations of threads $T_1, ..., T_n$ and $l_1, ..., l_m$ the values of the locks. If no thread holds lock l_i in configuration c, then $l_i = \perp$, else l_i is the thread currently holding it. The initial global configuration of $\mathcal{CP}$ is $(c_1, ..., c_n, \perp, ..., \perp)$, where c_i is the initial configuration of thread T_i. Thus all locks are *free* to start with. We extend the relation $\overset{a}{\longrightarrow}$ to global global configurations of $\mathcal{CP}$ in the usual way. The reachability relation $\Rightarrow$ is the reflexive and transitive closure of the successor relation $\rightarrow$ defined above. A sequence $x = x_0, x_1, ...$ of global configurations of $\mathcal{CP}$ is a *computation* if x_0 is the initial global configuration of $\mathcal{CP}$ and for each i, $x_i \overset{a}{\rightarrow} x_{i+1}$, where either for some j, $a \in Act_j$ or for some k, $a = release(l_k)$ or $a = acquire(l_k)$. Given a thread T_i and a reachable global configuration $\mathbf{c} = (c_1, ..., c_n, l_1, ..., l_m)$ of $\mathcal{CP}$, we use *Lock-Set*$(T_i, \mathbf{c})$ to denote the set of locks held by T_i in $\mathbf{c}$, viz., the set $\{l_j \mid l_j = T_i\}$. Also, given a thread T_i and a reachable global configuration $\mathbf{c} = (c_1, ..., c_n, l_1, ..., l_m)$ of $\mathcal{CP}$, the *projection* of $\mathbf{c}$ onto T_i, denoted by $c \downarrow T_i$, is defined to be the configuration $(c_i, l'_1, ..., l'_m)$ of the concurrent program comprised solely of the thread T_i, where $l'_i = T_i$ if $l_i = T_i$ and $\perp$, otherwise (locks not held by T_i are freed).

Multi-Automata (see [2]) Multi-Automata are used to capture regular (potentially infinite) sets of configurations of a PDS in a finite form. Let $\mathcal{P} = (P, Act, \Gamma, c_0, \Delta)$ be a pushdown system, where $P = \{p_1, ..., p_m\}$. A *$\mathcal{P}$-multi-automaton* ($\mathcal{P}$-MA for short) is a tuple $\mathcal{A} = (\Gamma, Q, \delta, I, F)$ where Q is a finite set of states, $\delta \subseteq Q \times \Gamma \times Q$ is a set of transitions, $I = \{s_1, ..., s_m\} \subseteq Q$ is a set of initial states and $F \subseteq Q$ is a set of final states. Each initial state s_i corresponds to a control state p_i of $\mathcal{P}$, and vice versa. We define the transition relation $\longrightarrow \subseteq Q \times \Gamma^* \times Q$ as the smallest relation satisfying the following: (i) if $(q, \gamma, q') \in \delta$ then $q \overset{\gamma}{\longrightarrow} q'$, (ii) $q \overset{\epsilon}{\longrightarrow} q$ for every $q \in Q$, and (iii) if $q \overset{w}{\longrightarrow} q''$ and $q'' \overset{\gamma}{\longrightarrow} q'$ then $q \overset{w\gamma}{\longrightarrow} q'$. We say that $\mathcal{A}$ accepts a configuration $\langle p_i, w \rangle$ iff $s_i \overset{w}{\longrightarrow} q$ for some $q \in F$. The set of configurations recognized by $\mathcal{A}$ is denoted by *Conf*$(\mathcal{A})$.

Nested Lock Access. We say that a concurrent program accesses locks in a *nested* fashion iff along each computation of the program a thread can only release the last lock that it acquired along that computation and that has not yet been released. In this paper, we only consider multi-threaded programs with nested access to locks. This is because even reachability, and hence LTL model checking, is known to be undecidable, in general, for programs with even two threads which allow non-nested access to locks (cf. [5]).

3 Lock-Constrained Multi-Automata Pair

In this section, we introduce the new concept of *Lock-Constrained Multi-Automata Pair (LMAP)* which we use to represent regular sets of configurations of concurrent programs with threads communicating via nested locks. We show that LMAPs are closed under (i) boolean operations, and also, (ii) in certain cases of interest, under computation of pre^* closures. Then we formulate a Dual Pumping Lemma which allows us to reduce the LTL model checking problem for threads interacting via nested locks to computation of pre^*-closures of regular sets of configurations accepted by LMAPs. Thus LMAPs plays the same role as Multi-Automata (MAs) do in the model checking of a single PDS for LTL properties, by allowing us to succinctly (and finitely) represent potentially infinite sets of configurations of the given concurrent program in a way that enables us to compute their pre^*-closure efficiently. This helps us to efficiently decide the LTL model checking problem at hand.

3.1 Lock Constrained Multi-Automata Pair

To motivate the concept of *Lock-Constrained Multi-Automata Pair (LMAP)* we revisit the key idea behind multi-automata (see section 2) that are used in the LTL model checking of a single PDS. An MA $\mathcal{A}$ accepting a (regular) set of configurations C of a PDS $T = (P, Act, \Gamma, \mathbf{c_0}, \Delta)$ has an *initial* state s_i of $\mathcal{A}$ corresponding to each control state $p_i \in P$ and transitions labeled with stack symbols from the set Γ such that $\langle p_i, w\rangle \in C$ iff there is a path in $\mathcal{A}$ starting at s_i labeled with w and leading to a final state of $\mathcal{A}$. Thus the stack content in each configuration of C is stored as a sequence of labels along an accepting path of $\mathcal{A}$.

In a concurrent program $\mathcal{CP}$ comprised of the two threads $T_1 = (P_1, Act_1, \Gamma_1, \mathbf{c}_1, \Delta_1)$ and $T_2 = (P_2, Act_2, \Gamma_2, \mathbf{c}_2, \Delta_2)$, for each configuration we need to keep track of the contents of the stacks of both T_1 and T_2. This is accomplished by using a pair of multi-automata $\mathcal{A} = (\mathcal{A}_1, \mathcal{A}_2)$, where $\mathcal{A}_i$ is a multi-automaton accepting a set of regular configurations of T_i. The broad idea is that a global configuration $\mathbf{c}$ is accepted by $\mathcal{A}$ iff the local configurations of T_1 and T_2 in $\mathbf{c}$ are accepted by $\mathcal{A}_1$ and $\mathcal{A}_2$, respectively.

However, we also need to factor in lock interaction among the threads that prevents them from simultaneously reaching certain pairs of local configurations. To capture lock interaction, we introduce the new concept of *backward acquisition history (BAH)* and generalize the existing concept of *acquisition history* [5] to that of *forward acquisition history (FAH)*. It turns out (using the Dual Pumping Lemma) that for model checking LTL formulae, we need to either (1) compute *pre**-closures for a set C of configurations in which all locks are free, or (2) compute those configurations of the *pre**-closure of a set (that possibly contains configurations in which some locks are held), in which all locks are free. The notion of BAH is used in the first case while FAH in the second one.

Key Insight. By tracking patterns of lock acquisition and releases, we will show that an LMAP accepting the *pre**-closure of the set of configurations accepted by the LMAP $\mathcal{A} = (\mathcal{A}_1, \mathcal{A}_2)$ is the pair $\mathcal{B} = (\mathcal{B}_1, \mathcal{B}_2)$, where $\mathcal{B}_i$ is a multi-automaton accepting the *pre**-closure of the set of configurations of thread T_i accepted by $\mathcal{A}_i$ (which can be computed efficiently using the techniques given in [2]). This reduces the *pre**-closure computation of a set of configurations of a concurrent program with threads interacting via nested locks to its individual threads and thereby not only avoids the state explosion problem but, as we shall show, makes our procedure efficient.

3.1.1 Backward Acquisition History

We motivate the notion of BAH using the example concurrent program $\mathcal{CP}$ comprised of the two PDSs shown in figure 1 with locks l_1 and l_2. Suppose that we are in-

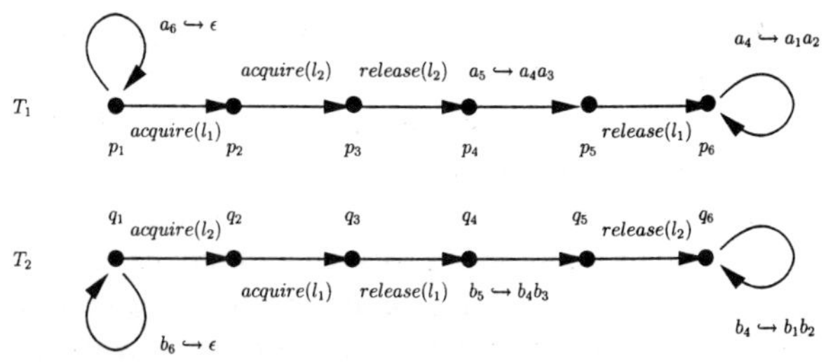

Figure 1. Example Concurrent Program

terested in computing the *pre**-closure of the set $LC = \{(\langle p_6, a_1a_2a_3\rangle, \langle q_6, b_1b_2b_3\rangle, \bot, \bot)\}$, i.e., the set of configurations $\mathbf{c}$ of $\mathcal{CP}$ such there is a path from $\mathbf{c}$ to a configuration $\mathbf{d}$ in LC. Note that in each configuration of LC all locks are free. The key insight is that by tracking patterns of backward lock releases we can reduce this to evaluating the *pre**-closures of regular sets of configurations $LC_1 = \{\langle p_6, a_1a_2a_3\rangle, \bot, \bot)\}$ of thread T_1 and $LC_2 = \{\langle q_6, b_1b_2b_3\rangle, \bot, \bot)\}$ of T_2 for the concurrent programs comprised *solely of the individual threads* T_1 and T_2, respectively, instead of the original multi-threaded program.

Consider, for example, the configuration $(\langle p_2, a_5\rangle, T_1, \bot)$, which belongs to $pre^*_{T_1}(LC_1)$[3] the path $(\langle p_2, a_5\rangle, T_1, \bot) \xrightarrow{acquire(l_2)} (\langle p_3, a_5\rangle, T_1, T_1) \xrightarrow{release(l_2)} (\langle p_4, a_5\rangle, T_1, \bot) \longrightarrow (\langle p_5, a_4a_3\rangle, T_1, \bot) \xrightarrow{release(l_1)} (\langle p_6, a_4a_3\rangle, \bot, \bot) \longrightarrow (\langle p_6, a_1a_2a_3\rangle, \bot, \bot)$ of T_1; and the configuration $(\langle q_2, b_5\rangle, \bot, T_2)$ which belongs to $pre^*_{T_2}(LC_2)$ via the path $(\langle q_2, b_5\rangle, \bot, T_2) \xrightarrow{acquire(l_1)} (\langle q_3, b_5\rangle, T_2, T_2) \xrightarrow{release(l_1)} (\langle q_4, b_5\rangle, \bot, T_2) \longrightarrow (\langle q_5, b_4b_3\rangle, \bot, T_2) \xrightarrow{release(l_2)} (\langle q_6, b_4b_3\rangle, \bot, \bot) \longrightarrow (\langle q_6, b_1b_2b_3\rangle, \bot, \bot)$ of T_2. Note that even though T_1 and T_2 hold different sets of locks, i.e., $\{l_1\}$ and $\{l_2\}$, respectively, at control locations p_2 and q_2, there does not exist a global configuration of $\mathcal{CP}$ with T_1 and T_2 in the local configurations $(\langle p_2, a_5\rangle, T_1, \bot)$ and $(\langle q_2, b_5\rangle, \bot, T_2)$, respectively, that is backward reachable in $\mathcal{CP}$ from $(\langle p_6, a_1a_2a_3\rangle, \langle q_6, b_1b_2b_3\rangle, \bot, \bot)$. The reason is that in order for T_1 to reach p_6 from p_2 it first has to acquire (and release) lock l_2. However, in order to do that T_2, which currently holds lock l_2, must release it. But for T_2 to release l_2, it first has to acquire (and release) l_1 which is currently held by T_1. This creates an unresolvable cyclic dependency.

In general, when testing for backward reachability of $\mathbf{c}$ from $\mathbf{d}$ in $\mathcal{CP}$, it suffices to test whether there exist local paths x and y in the individual threads from states $\mathbf{c}_1 = \mathbf{c} \downarrow T_1$ to $\mathbf{d}_1 = \mathbf{d} \downarrow T_1$ and from $\mathbf{c}_2 = \mathbf{c} \downarrow T_2$ to $\mathbf{d}_2 = \mathbf{d} \downarrow T_2$, respectively, such that along x and y locks can be acquired in a compatible fashion. Compatibility ensures that we do not end up with an unresolvable cyclic dependency as above. This allows us to reconcile x and y to get

[3]Unless clear from the context, we use $pre^*_{T_i}(C)$ to denote the pre^*-closures for a set C of configurations of thread T_i.

a valid path of $\mathcal{CP}$ from $\mathbf{c}$ to $\mathbf{d}$. Next we define the notion of backward acquisition history, which captures patterns of lock releases from $\mathbf{d}$ to $\mathbf{c}$ that are used to test compatibility. Our discussion above is then formalized in theorem 2.

Definition 1 (Backward Acquisition History). *Let x be a computation of a concurrent program $\mathcal{CP}$ leading from configurations $\mathbf{c}$ to $\mathbf{d}$. Then for thread T_i and lock l_j of $\mathcal{CP}$, if $l_j \notin$ Lock-Set$(T_i, \mathbf{c})$ then $BAH(T_i, \mathbf{c}, l_j, x)$ is defined to be the empty set $\emptyset$. If $l_j \in$ Lock-Set$(T_i, \mathbf{c})$, then $BAH(T_i, \mathbf{c}, l_j, x)$ is the set of locks that were released (and possibly acquired) by T_i after the last release of l_j by T_i in traversing backward along x from $\mathbf{d}$ to $\mathbf{c}$. If $l_j \in$ Lock-Set$(T_i, \mathbf{c})$ and l_j wasn't released along x, then $BAH(T_i, \mathbf{c}, l_j, x)$ is the set of locks that were released (and possibly acquired) by T_i in traversing backwards along x.*

Theorem 2 (Backward Decomposition Result) *Let $\mathcal{CP}$ be a concurrent program comprised of the two threads T_1 and T_2 with nested locks. Then configuration $\mathbf{c}$ of $\mathcal{CP}$ is backward reachable from configuration $\mathbf{d}$ in which all locks are free iff configurations $\mathbf{c}_1 = \mathbf{c} \downarrow T_1$ of T_1 and $\mathbf{c}_2 = \mathbf{c} \downarrow T_2$ of T_2 are backward reachable from configurations $\mathbf{d}_1 = \mathbf{d} \downarrow T_1$ and $\mathbf{d}_2 = \mathbf{d} \downarrow T_2$, respectively, via computation paths x and y of programs comprised solely of threads T_1 and T_2, respectively, such that*

1. Lock-Set$(T_1, \mathbf{c}_1) \cap$ Lock-Set$(T_2, \mathbf{c}_2) = \emptyset$

2. there do not exist locks $l \in$ Lock-Set$(T_1, \mathbf{c}_1)$ and $l' \in$ Lock-Set$(T_2, \mathbf{c}_2)$ such that $l \in BAH(T_2, \mathbf{c}_2, l', y)$ and $l' \in BAH(T_1, \mathbf{c}_1, l, x)$.

BAH enhanced pre^*-computation To make use of the above result while computing $pre^*(C)$ for a set C such that all locks are free in each configuration of $\mathcal{CP}$ in C, we augment the configurations of each individual thread with a BAH entry for each lock. Thus a configuration of a program comprised solely of thread T_i is now of the form $(\langle c, w\rangle, l_1, ..., l_m, BAH_1, ..., BAH_m)$ where BAH_i tracks the BAH of lock l_i.

Reworking our example (fig 1) with BAH-augmented configurations, we see that augmented configuration $(\langle p_2, a_5\rangle, T_1, \perp, \{l_2\}, \emptyset)$ of thread T_1 belongs to $pre^*_{T_1}(\{\mathbf{d}_1\})$ via the path (of augmented configurations) x : $(\langle p_2, a_5\rangle, T_1, \perp, \{l_2\}, \emptyset) \overset{acquire(l_2)}{\longrightarrow} (\langle p_3, a_5\rangle, T_1, T_1, \{l_2\}, \emptyset) \overset{release(l_2)}{\longrightarrow} (\langle p_4, a_5\rangle, T_1, \perp, \emptyset, \emptyset) \longrightarrow (\langle p_5, a_4a_3\rangle, T_1, \perp, \emptyset, \emptyset) \overset{release(l_1)}{\longrightarrow} (\langle p_6, a_4a_3\rangle, \perp, \perp, \emptyset, \emptyset) \longrightarrow (\langle p_6, a_1a_2a_3\rangle, \perp, \perp, \emptyset, \emptyset)$. Note that in traversing backwards from the configuration $(\langle p_6, a_4a_3\rangle, \perp, \perp, \emptyset, \emptyset)$ via the transition $release(l_1)$, we set $l_1 = T_1$ indicating that l_1 is now held by T_1. Next, in traversing backwards from the configuration $(\langle p_4, a_5\rangle, T_1, \perp, \emptyset, \emptyset)$ via the transition $release(l_2)$ and set $l_2 = T_1$ and add lock l_2 to the backward acquisition history of lock l_1 as it is currently held by T_1. Similarly we can see that configuration $(\langle q_2, b_5\rangle, \perp, T_2, \emptyset, \{l_1\})$ of the augmented thread T_2 belongs to $pre^*_{T_2}(\{\mathbf{d}_2\})$ via the path y : $(\langle q_2, b_5\rangle, \perp, T_2, \emptyset, \{l_1\}) \overset{acquire(l_1)}{\longrightarrow} (\langle q_3, b_5\rangle, T_2, T_2, \emptyset, \{l_1\}) \overset{release(l_1)}{\longrightarrow} (\langle q_4, b_5\rangle, \perp, T_2, \emptyset, \emptyset) \longrightarrow (\langle q_5, b_4b_3\rangle, \perp, T_2, \emptyset, \emptyset) \overset{release(l_2)}{\longrightarrow} (\langle q_6, b_4b_3\rangle, \perp, \perp, \emptyset, \emptyset) \longrightarrow (\langle q_6, b_1b_2b_3\rangle, \perp, \perp, \emptyset, \emptyset)$. Since the states $\mathbf{c}_1 = (\langle p_2, a_5\rangle, T_1, \perp, \{l_2\}, \emptyset)$ and $\mathbf{c}_2 = (\langle q_2, b_5\rangle, \perp, T_2, \emptyset, \{l_1\})$ are not BAH-compatible as $l_2 \in BAH(T_1, \mathbf{c}_1, l_1, x) = \{l_2\}$ and $l_1 \in BAH(T_2, \mathbf{c}_2, l_2, y) = \{l_1\}$, by theorem 2, global configuration $\mathbf{c}$ is not backward reachable from $\mathbf{d}$ in $\mathcal{CP}$.

However, it can be seen that $\mathbf{c}'_1 = (\langle p_1, a_5\rangle, \perp, \perp, \emptyset, \emptyset)$ is backward reachable from $\mathbf{d}_1$ in T_1 and $\mathbf{c}'_2 = (\langle q_1, b_5\rangle, \perp, \perp, \emptyset, \emptyset)$ from $\mathbf{d}_2$ in T_2. Note that since all locks of $\mathcal{CP}$ are free in $\mathbf{c}'_1$ and $\mathbf{c}'_2$, the BAH of each lock is the empty set in these configurations. In this case, however, since $\mathbf{c}'_1$ and $\mathbf{c}'_2$ are trivially BAH-compatible, $\mathbf{c}' = (\langle p_1, a_5\rangle, \langle q_1, b_5\rangle, \perp, \perp)$ is backward reachable from $\mathbf{d}$ in $\mathcal{CP}$.

BAH-enhanced pre^*-computation To construct an MA accepting the pre^*-closure of a regular set of BAH-enhanced configurations accepted by a given MA (used later in the pre^*-closure computation of LMAPs), we slightly modify the procedure given in [2] for constructing an MA accepting the pre^*-closure of a regular set of (non-enhanced) configurations accepted by a given MA. The only difference is that since now we are also tracking BAHs, whenever we encounter a lock operation, we modify the BAHs accordingly. Thus using results from [2], we have,

Lemma 3 *Given a PDS $\mathcal{P}$, and a regular set of BAH-augmented configurations accepted by a $\mathcal{P}$-MA $\mathcal{A}$, we can construct a $\mathcal{P}$-MA $\mathcal{A}_{pre^*}$ recognizing $pre^*(Conf(\mathcal{A}))$ in time polynomial in the sizes of $\mathcal{A}$ and the control states of $\mathcal{P}$ and exponential in the number of locks of $\mathcal{P}$.*

3.1.2 Forward Acquisition History

The notion of *Forward Acquisition History (FAH)* is motivated by our goal of using backward reachability to compute those configurations in the pre^*-closure of a set C of global configurations of $\mathcal{CP}$ in which all locks are free. It is an extension of the concept of acquisition histories, defined in [5]. The basic difference is that while acquisition histories were defined for computation paths starting at the initial state, FAHs are defined for paths starting at arbitrary states. The only property of the initial state that was used in developing the theory of [5] was that all locks are free in the initial state. Since we are only interested in those configurations of $pre^*(C)$ is which all locks are free, we need to consider only those computation paths that start at configurations of $\mathcal{CP}$ in which all locks are free and so the decomposition result in [5] also extends to this case with minor modifications. This is formulated below as the Forward Decomposition Result.

Definition 4 (Forward Acquisition History). *Let x be a computation of a concurrent program $\mathcal{CP}$ leading from configurations* $\mathbf{c}$ *to* $\mathbf{d}$. *For thread T_i and lock l_j of $\mathcal{CP}$, if $l_j \notin$ Lock-Set$(T_i, \mathbf{d})$ then $FAH(T_i, \mathbf{c}, l_j, x)$ is defined to be the empty set $\emptyset$. If $l_j \in$ Lock-Set$(T_i, \mathbf{d})$, then we define $FAH(T_i, \mathbf{c}, l_j, x)$ to be the set of locks that were acquired (and possibly released) by T_i after the last acquisition of l_j by T_i in traversing forward along x from* $\mathbf{c}$ *to* $\mathbf{d}$. *If $l_j \in$ Lock-Set$(T_i, \mathbf{d})$ but l_j was not acquired along x, then $FAH(T_i, \mathbf{c}, l_j, x)$ is the set of locks that were acquired (and possibly released) by T_i along x.*

Theorem 5 (Forward Decomposition Result) *Let $\mathcal{CP}$ be a concurrent program comprised of the two threads T_1 and T_2 with nested locks. Then configuration* $\mathbf{c}$ *of $\mathcal{CP}$ in which all locks are free is backward reachable from* $\mathbf{d}$ *iff configurations $\mathbf{c}_1 = \mathbf{c} \downarrow T_1$ of T_1 and $\mathbf{c}_2 = \mathbf{c} \downarrow T_2$ of T_2 are backward reachable from configurations $\mathbf{d}_1 = \mathbf{d} \downarrow T_1$ and $\mathbf{d}_2 = \mathbf{d} \downarrow T_2$, respectively, via computation paths x and y of programs comprised solely of threads T_1 and T_2, respectively, such that*

1. *Lock-Set$(T_1, \mathbf{d}_1) \cap$ Lock-Set$(T_2, \mathbf{d}_2) = \emptyset$, and*
2. *there do not exist locks $l \in$ Lock-Set$(T_1, \mathbf{d}_1)$ and $l' \in$ Lock-Set$(T_2, \mathbf{d}_2)$ such that $l \in FAH(T_2, \mathbf{c}_2, l', y)$ and $l' \in FAH(T_1, \mathbf{c}_1, l, x)$.*

Unlike pre^*-closure for BAH-augmented configurations, an important issue that arises when computing pre^*-closure for FAH-augmented configurations, is that we need to compute FAHs while performing a backward reachability analysis. For that we need to augment the configurations of each thread with two extra fields as we now illustrate.

FAH-enhanced pre^***-computation** Suppose that we want to compute the lock free configurations of $pre^*(\{\mathbf{d}\})$, where $\mathbf{d}$ is the configuration $(\langle p_5, a_4a_3\rangle, \langle q_5, b_4b_3\rangle, T_1, T_2)$ of the concurrent program shown in figure 1. Let $\mathbf{d}_1 = \mathbf{d} \downarrow T_1 = (p_5, a_4a_3, T_1, \bot)$ and $\mathbf{d}_2 = \mathbf{d} \downarrow T_2 = (q_5, b_4b_3, \bot, T_2)$. By theorem 5, it suffices to compute the set of all pairs of lock-free configurations $\mathbf{c}_1$ and $\mathbf{c}_2$ of T_1 and T_2, respectively, such that the FAHs of $\mathbf{c}_1$ and $\mathbf{c}_2$ along some paths of T_1 and T_2 starting at $\mathbf{c}_1$ and $\mathbf{c}_2$ and ending at $\mathbf{d}_1$ and $\mathbf{d}_2$, respectively, are compatible. Note that, by definition, the FAH of l along a path x from $\mathbf{c}_1$ to $\mathbf{d}_1$ is the set of locks that were acquired and released since the last acquisition of l in traversing forward along x. Thus while traversing x backwards, we stop updating the FAH of l after encountering the first acquisition of l along x as all lock operations on l encountered after that are immaterial. To ensure that, we maintain two extra entries in the FAH-augmented configurations. The first entry LHI is the set of locks held initially in $\mathbf{d}_1$ when starting the backward reachability. The second entry LR is the set of locks from LHI that have been acquired so far in the backward search. For a lock $l \in LHI$, once a transition acquiring l is encountered for the first time while performing backward reachability, we add it to LR and stop modifying it's FAH even if it is acquired or released again during the backward search. Thus an FAH-augmented configuration is of the form $(\langle p, w\rangle, l_1, ..., l_m, FAH_1, ..., FAH_m, LHI, LR)$.

Going back to our example, we see that the FAH-augmented configuration $(\langle p_1, a_5\rangle, \bot, \bot, \{l_2\}, \emptyset, \{l_1\}, \{l_1\})$ of the augmented thread T_1 belongs to $pre^*_{T_1}(\{\mathbf{d}_1\})$ via the backwardly traversed path x : $(\langle p_5, a_4a_3\rangle, T_1, \bot, \emptyset, \emptyset, \{l_1\}, \emptyset) \leftarrow (\langle p_4, a_5\rangle, T_1, \bot, \emptyset, \emptyset, \{l_1\}, \emptyset) \overset{release(l_2)}{\longleftarrow} (\langle p_3, a_5\rangle, T_1, T_1, \{l_2\}, \emptyset, \{l_1\}, \emptyset) \overset{acquire(l_2)}{\longleftarrow} (\langle p_2, a_5\rangle, T_1, \bot, \{l_2\}, \emptyset, \{l_1\}, \emptyset) \overset{acquire(l_1)}{\longleftarrow} (\langle p_1, a_5\rangle, \bot, \bot, \{l_2\}, \emptyset, \{l_1\}, \{l_1\})$. Similarly, the FAH-augmented configuration $(\langle q_1, b_5\rangle, \bot, \bot, \emptyset, \{l_1\}, \{l_2\}, \{l_2\})$ of the thread T_2 belongs to $pre^*_{T_2}(\{\mathbf{d}_2\})$ via the backwardly traversed path y : $(\langle q_5, b_4b_3\rangle, \bot, T_2, \emptyset, \emptyset, \{l_2\}, \emptyset) \leftarrow (\langle q_4, b_5\rangle, \bot, T_2, \emptyset, \emptyset, \{l_2\}, \emptyset) \overset{release(l_1)}{\longleftarrow} (\langle q_3, b_5\rangle, T_2, T_2, \emptyset, \{l_1\}, \{l_2\}, \emptyset) \overset{acquire(l_1)}{\longleftarrow} (\langle q_2, b_5\rangle, \bot, T_2, \emptyset, \{l_1\}, \{l_2\}, \emptyset) \overset{acquire(l_2)}{\longleftarrow} (\langle q_1, b_5\rangle, \bot, \bot, \emptyset, \{l_1\}, \{l_2\}, \{l_2\})$. Since augmented states $\mathbf{c}_1 = (\langle p_1, a_5\rangle, \bot, \bot, \{l_2\}, \emptyset, \{l_1\}, \{l_1\})$ and $\mathbf{c}_2 = (\langle q_1, b_5\rangle, \bot, \bot, \emptyset, \{l_1\}, \{l_2\}, \{l_2\})$ are not FAH-compatible as $l_2 \in \{l_2\} = FAH(T_1, \mathbf{c}_1, l_1, x)$ and $l_1 \in \{l_1\} = FAH(T_2, \mathbf{c}_2, l_2, y)$, by theorem 5 global configuration $\mathbf{c}$ is not backward reachable from $\mathbf{d}$ in $\mathcal{CP}$.

Given an MA $\mathcal{A}$ accepting a regular set of FAH-augmented configurations of a PDA $\mathcal{P}$, we can, as for BAH-augmented configurations, efficiently construct an MA accepting $pre^*(Conf(\mathcal{A}))$. As for the BAH case, using results from [2], we have the following.

Lemma 6 *Given a PDS $\mathcal{P}$, and a regular set of FAH-augmented configurations accepted by a $\mathcal{P}$-MA $\mathcal{A}$, we can construct a $\mathcal{P}$-MA $\mathcal{A}_{pre^*}$ recognizing $pre^*(Conf(\mathcal{A}))$ in time polynomial in the sizes of $\mathcal{A}$ and the control states of $\mathcal{P}$ and exponential in the number of locks of $\mathcal{P}$.*

3.1.3 Lock Constrained Multi-Automata Pair

Given a concurrent program $\mathcal{CP}$ comprised of the two threads $T_1 = (P_1, Act_1, \Gamma_1, \mathbf{c}_1, \Delta_1)$ and $T_2 = (P_2, Act_2, \Gamma_2, \mathbf{c}_2, \Delta_2)$, we define a *Lock-Constrained Multi-Automata Pair (LMAP)* for $\mathcal{CP}$, denoted by $\mathcal{CP}$-LMAP, as a pair $(\mathcal{A}_1, \mathcal{A}_2)$, where $\mathcal{A}_i = (\Gamma_i, Q_i, \delta_i, I_i, F_i)$ is a multi-automaton accepting a (regular) set of configurations of thread T_i. To track lock interactions, we augment the configurations of each thread with their respective backward and forward acquisition histories and the LHI and LR fields as discussed in the last two subsections. Thus an augmented configuration of thread T_i is of the form $(\langle c, w\rangle, l_1, ..., l_m, BAH_1, ..., BAH_m, FAH_1, ..., FAH_m, LHI, LR)$, where BAH_i and FAH_i are used to track the backward and forward acquisition histories, respectively, of lock l_i. As in the case of a multi-automaton, we have an initial state of $\mathcal{A}_i$ corresponding to each configuration of T_i, and vice versa. Since in this case the configurations are augmented with FAHs and BAHs, each initial state of $\mathcal{A}_i$ is of the form $(\langle s_i, w\rangle, l_1, ..., l_m, BAH_1, ..., BAH_m, FAH_1, ..., FAH_m, LHI, LR)$, where $(\langle p_i, w\rangle, l_1, ..., l_m, BAH_1, ..., BAH_m, FAH_1, ..., FAH_m, LHI, LR)$ is an augmented configuration of T_i.

Motivated by theorems 2 and 5, we say that augmented configurations $s = (\langle c, w\rangle, l_1, ..., l_m, BAH_1, ..., BAH_m, FAH_1, ..., FAH_m, LHI, LR)$ and $t = (\langle c', w'\rangle, l'_1, ..., l'_m, BAH'_1, ..., BAH'_m, FAH'_1, ..., FAH'_m, LHI', LR')$ of T_1 and T_2, respectively, are *FAH-compatible* iff there do not exist locks l_i and l_j such that $l_i = T_1$, $l'_j = T_2$, $l_i \in FAH'_j$ and $l_j \in FAH_i$. Analogously, we say that s and t are *BAH-compatible* iff there do not exist locks l_i and l_j such that $l_i = T_1$, $l'_j = T_2$, $l_i \in BAH'_j$ and $l_j \in BAH_i$.

Definition 7 *Let $\mathcal{A} = (\mathcal{A}_1, \mathcal{A}_2)$ be a $\mathcal{CP}$-LMAP. We say that $\mathcal{A}$ accepts global configuration $(\langle p_i, w\rangle, \langle q_j, v\rangle, l_1, ..., l_m)$ of $\mathcal{CP}$ iff there exist sets $FAH_1, ..., FAH_m, BAH_1, ..., BAH_m, LHI, LR, FAH'_1, ..., FAH'_m, BAH'_1, ..., BAH'_m, LHI', LR'$ such that if $s_1 = (\langle p_i, w\rangle, l'_1, ..., l'_m, BAH_1, ..., BAH_m, FAH_1, ..., FAH_m, LHI, LR)$ and $s_2 = (\langle q_j, v\rangle, l''_1, ..., l''_m, BAH'_1, ..., BAH'_m, FAH'_1, ..., FAH'_m, LHI', LR')$, where $l'_i = T_1$ if $l_i = T_1$ and $\perp$ otherwise and $l''_i = T_2$ if $l_i = T_2$ and $\perp$ otherwise, then*

1. *$\mathcal{A}_i$ accepts s_i, and*
2. Lock-Set$(T_1, s_1) \cap$ Lock-Set$(T_2, s_2) = \emptyset$ *and* $LHI \cap LHI' = \emptyset$.
3. *s_1 and s_2 are BAH-compatible and FAH-compatible.*

Given a *$\mathcal{CP}$-LMAP $\mathcal{A}$*, we use $Conf(\mathcal{A})$ to denote the set of configurations of $\mathcal{CP}$ accepted by $\mathcal{A}$. A set of configurations C of $\mathcal{CP}$ is called *lock-constrained regular* if there exists a *$\mathcal{CP}$-LMAP $\mathcal{A}$* such that $C = Conf(\mathcal{A})$. For model checking LTL properties of concurrent programs interacting via nested locks we need two key properties of LMAPs
(i) closure under boolean operations, and
(ii) closure under *pre**-computation.

Closure of LMAPs under Boolean Operations. Let $\mathcal{A} = (\mathcal{A}_1, \mathcal{A}_2)$ and $\mathcal{B} = (\mathcal{B}_1, \mathcal{B}_2)$, be given $\mathcal{CP}$-LMAPs and *op* a boolean operation. Then, broadly speaking, the closure of LMAPs under *op* follows from the facts that (1) $\mathcal{A}$ *op* $\mathcal{B} = (\mathcal{A}_1$ *op* $\mathcal{B}_1, \mathcal{A}_2$ *op* $\mathcal{B}_2)$, and (2) MAs are closed under boolean operations (see [2]). In this section, we focus only on the intersection operation which is what we require for the LTL model checking of threads, the rest of the operations being handled similarly.

Proposition 8 (Closure under Intersection). *Given $\mathcal{CP}$-*LMAP*s $\mathcal{A} = (\mathcal{A}_1, \mathcal{A}_2)$ and $\mathcal{B} = (\mathcal{B}_1, \mathcal{B}_2)$, we can construct a $\mathcal{CP}$-*LMAP *accepting $Conf(\mathcal{A}) \cap Conf(\mathcal{B})$.*

Computing the pre*-closure of an LMAP. Let LC be a lock-constrained regular set accepted by a $\mathcal{CP}$-LMAP $\mathcal{A} = (\mathcal{A}_1, \mathcal{A}_2)$. In this section, we show that we can efficiently, in polynomial time, construct a $\mathcal{CP}$-LMAP $\mathcal{B} = (\mathcal{B}_1, \mathcal{B}_2)$ accepting (1) $pre^*(LC)$ in case all locks are free in each configuration of LC, or (2) those configurations of $pre^*(LC)$ in which all locks are free.

The Procedure. Since $\mathcal{A}_1$ and $\mathcal{A}_2$ are MAs accepting regular sets of configurations of the individual PDSs T_1 and T_2, respectively, we can construct, using the efficient techniques given in sections 3.1.1 and 3.1.2, multi-automata $\mathcal{B}_1$ and $\mathcal{B}_2$, accepting, respectively, the *pre**-closures, $pre^*_{T_1}(Conf(\mathcal{A}_1))$ and $pre^*_{T_2}(Conf(\mathcal{A}_2))$.

In the first case, since all locks are free in each configuration of LC, the forward acquisition history of each lock as well as the LHI and LR fields are $\emptyset$. Thus these fields do not come into play and so $\mathcal{B}_1$ and $\mathcal{B}_2$ can be computed using the procedure given in section 3.1.1, thereby giving us the following.

Proposition 9 *Let LC be a lock-constrained regular set of configurations of $\mathcal{CP}$ such that all locks are free in every configuration $c \in LC$. If $\mathcal{A}$ is a $\mathcal{CP}$-LMAP accepting LC and if $\mathcal{B}$ is the $\mathcal{CP}$-LMAP constructed from $\mathcal{A}$ as above, then $Conf(\mathcal{B}) = pre^*(LC)$.*

In the second case, we are interested only in those configurations c of $pre^*(LC)$ in which all locks are free and due to which each BAH field of c is the empty set. Thus, in this case, the BAH fields are immaterial, and so $\mathcal{B}_1$ and $\mathcal{B}_2$ can be computed using the procedure in section 3.1.2.

Proposition 10 *If $\mathcal{A}$ is a $\mathcal{CP}$-LMAP accepting a lock-constrained regular set LC and if $\mathcal{B}$ is the $\mathcal{CP}$-LMAP constructed from $\mathcal{A}$ as above, then $Conf(\mathcal{B}) \cap LF = pre^*(LC) \cap LF$, where LF is the set of all configurations of $\mathcal{CP}$ in which all locks are free.*

Requirement of Nestedness of Locks. It is important to note that, in general, we can carry out the above *pre**-closure construction for LMAPs only for threads communicating via *nested* locks. If the locks are not nested then the problems of deciding reachability of a global configuration of $\mathcal{CP}$ to or from a configuration in which all locks are free are both undecidable as was shown in [5]. If, on the other hand, a concurrent program has nested locks, then from theorems 2 and 5 we can see that both these problems are not only decidable but efficiently so.

Complexity Analysis. Note that the computation of an LMAP accepting the *pre**-closure of given LMAP $\mathcal{A} =$

$(\mathcal{A}_1, \mathcal{A}_2)$ reduces to the computation of MAs $\mathcal{B}_i$ accepting the pre^*-closure of $Conf(\mathcal{A}_i)$ for each individual thread T_i, instead of the entire program $\mathcal{CP}$. From lemmas 3 and 6, $\mathcal{B}_i$ can be computed in time polynomial in the sizes of $\mathcal{A}_i$ and the control states of T_i and exponential in the number of locks of T_i. Thus we have the following

Theorem 11 (Efficient pre^*-closure computation) *Given a concurrent program $\mathcal{CP}$ comprised of threads T_1 and T_2 interacting via nested locks, and a $\mathcal{CP}$-LMAP $\mathcal{A} = (\mathcal{A}_1, \mathcal{A}_2)$, then in the two cases considered above, we can construct a $\mathcal{CP}$-LMAP $\mathcal{A}_{pre^*}$ recognizing $pre^*(Conf(\mathcal{A}))$ in time polynomial in the sizes of $\mathcal{A}_i$ and the control states of T_i and exponential in the number of locks of $\mathcal{CP}$.*

4 Dual Pumping

In this section, we formulate the *Dual Pumping Lemma* which allows to us leverage the efficient pre^*-closure computation procedure for LMAPs given above towards model checking threads for indexed LTL\X formulae. Note that the use of stuttering-insensitive indexed logics is natural when reasoning about multi-threaded programs with interleaving semantics. This is because every global transition results from the firing of a local transition of a single thread thereby forcing other threads to stutter. Furthermore, we observe that the model checking problem for doubly-indexed LTL properties wherein atomic propositions are interpreted over the control states of two or more threads is undecidable for system comprised of multiple PDSs even when the PDSs do not interact with each other. Broadly speaking, this is due to the fact that such a formula can be used to restrict the model checking for control state reachability to those sets of computations of $\mathcal{CP}$ that simulate CCS-style pairwise rendezvous thereby yielding undecidability by reduction from the undecidability result of [1]. We now consider the model checking problem for single-index LTL\X properties.

Let $\mathcal{CP}$ be a concurrent program comprised of the threads $T_1 = (P_1, Act, \Gamma_1, c_1, \Delta_1)$ and $T_2 = (P_2, Act, \Gamma_2, c_2, \Delta_2)$, and let $f = \bigwedge_i \mathsf{E} f_i$, where f_i is an LTL\X formula interpreted over the control states of T_i (Formulae of the form $f = \bigwedge_i \mathsf{A} f_i$ can be handled by taking their negation and then model checking for each i, the simpler formula $\mathsf{E}\neg f_i$). We use $\mathcal{BP}$ to denote the system resulting from the interleaved parallel composition of the *Büchi-augmented* threads $\mathcal{BP}_i$ formed by taking the product of T_i and $\mathcal{B}_{\neg f_i}$, the Büchi automaton corresponding to $\neg f_i$. We then say that a global configuration $\mathbf{c}$ of $\mathcal{BP}$ is an accepting global configuration of $\mathcal{BP}_i$ iff $\mathbf{c} \downarrow T_i$ is an accepting local configuration of the Büchi-augmented thread $\mathcal{BP}_i$. Then the model checking problem for f reduces to deciding whether there exists an *accepting path* of $\mathcal{BP}$, viz., a path along which for each i, an accepting state of $\mathcal{BP}_i$ occurs infinitely often.

Checking that $\mathcal{BP}$ has an accepting path is complicated by the fact that systems comprised of PDSs have infinitely many states in general. To overcome this problem, we now formulate the *Dual Pumping Lemma*, that allows us to reduce the problem of deciding whether there exists an accepting computation of $\mathcal{BP}$, to showing the existence of a finite lollipop-like witness with a special structure comprised of a stem ρ which is a finite path of $\mathcal{BP}$, and a (pseudo-)cycle which is a sequence v of transitions with an accepting state of $\mathcal{BP}$ having the following two properties (i) executing v returns each thread of the concurrent program to the same control location with the same symbol at the top of its stack as it started with, and (ii) executing it does not drain the stack of any thread, viz., any symbol that is not at the top of the stack of a thread to start with is not popped during the execution of the sequence. These properties enable us to construct a valid accepting sequence of $\mathcal{BP}$ by executing the sequence v repeatedly resulting in the pumping of each of the threads. However the lock interaction among the threads complicates the interleaved execution of the pumping sequences of the individual threads which therefore requires an intricate scheduling of their local transitions. To begin with, for ease of exposition we make the assumption that along all infinite runs of $\mathcal{BP}$ any lock that is acquired is eventually released. Later on we drop this restriction.

Theorem 12 (Dual Pumping Lemma) *$\mathcal{BP}$ has an accepting run starting from an initial configuration c if and only if there exist $\alpha \in \Gamma_1, \beta \in \Gamma_2$; $u \in \Gamma_1^*, v \in \Gamma_2^*$; accepting configurations g_i of $\mathcal{BP}_i$; configurations lf_0, lf_1, lf_2 and lf_3 in which all locks are free; lock values $l_1, ..., l_m, l'_1, ..., l'_m$; control states $p', p''' \in P_1$, $q', q'' \in P_2$; $u', u'', u''' \in \Gamma_1^*$; and $v', v'', v''' \in \Gamma_2^*$ satisfying the following conditions*

1. $c \Rightarrow (\langle p, \alpha u\rangle, \langle q', v'\rangle, l_1, ..., l_m)$
2. $(\langle p, \alpha\rangle, \langle q', v'\rangle, l_1, ..., l_m) \Rightarrow lf_0 \Rightarrow (\langle p', u'\rangle, \langle q, \beta v\rangle, l'_1, ..., l'_m)$
3. $(\langle p', u'\rangle, \langle q, \beta\rangle, l'_1, ..., l'_m)$
$\Rightarrow lf_1 \Rightarrow g_1 \Rightarrow lf_2 \Rightarrow g_2 \Rightarrow lf_3$
$\Rightarrow (\langle p, \alpha u''\rangle, \langle q'', v''\rangle, l_1, ..., l_m) \Rightarrow lf_4$
$\Rightarrow (\langle p''', u'''\rangle, \langle q, \beta v'''\rangle, l'_1, ..., l'_m)$

The above result gives us the required witness with the special structure shown in fig 2. Here ρ, σ, ν are the sequences of global configurations realizing conditions 1, 2 and 3, respectively, in the statement of the theorem. We now show how to interleave the execution of the local pumping sequences of the two threads to construct a valid accepting path of $\mathcal{BP}$. Towards that end, we first define sequences of transitions spliced from ρ, σ and ν that we will concatenate appropriately to construct the accepting path.

- l_{11}: the local sequence of T_1 fired along σ.

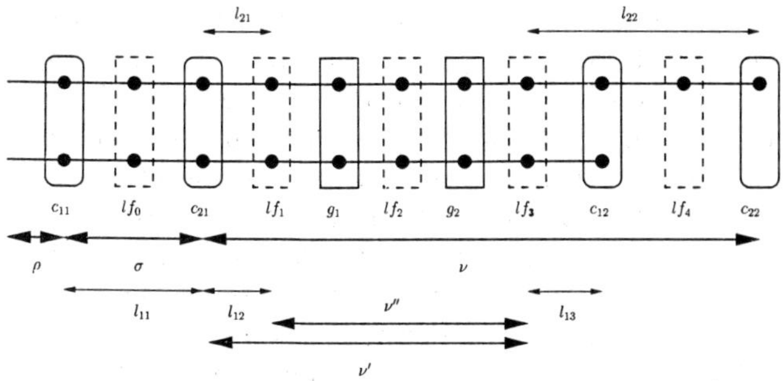

Figure 2. Pumpable Witness

- l_{12}: the local sequence of T_1 fired along ν between $c_{21} = (\langle p', u'\rangle, \langle q, \beta\rangle, l'_1, ..., l'_m)$ and lf_1.
- l_{13}: the local sequence of T_1 fired along ν between lf_3 and $c_{12} = (\langle p, \alpha u''\rangle, \langle q'', v''\rangle, l_1, ..., l_m)$.
- l_{21}: the local sequence of T_2 fired along ν between $c_{21} = (\langle p', u'\rangle, \langle q, \beta\rangle, l'_1, ..., l'_m)$ and lf_1.
- l_{22}: the local sequence of T_2 fired along ν between lf_3 and $c_{22} = (\langle p''', u'''\rangle, \langle q, \beta v'''\rangle, l_1, ..., l_m)$.
- ν': the sequence of global transitions fired along ν till lf_3.
- ν'': the sequence of global transitions fired along ν between lf_1 and lf_3.

Then $\pi : \rho\, \sigma\, \nu'\, (\, l_{13}\, l_{11}\, l_{12}\, l_{22}\, l_{21}\, \nu''\,)^\omega$ is a scheduling realizing an accepting valid run of $\mathcal{BP}$. Intuitively, thread T_1 is pumped by firing the local transitions occurring along the sequences $l_{13}l_{11}l_{12}$ followed by the local computation of T_1 along ν''. Similarly, T_2 is pumped by firing the local transitions occurring along the sequences $l_{22}l_{21}$ followed by the local computation of T_2 along ν''. Note that the pumping sequences of the two threads are staggered with respect to each other. The lock free configurations $lf_0, ..., lf_4$ are *breakpoints* that help in scheduling to ensure that π is a valid path. Indeed, starting at lf_3, we first let T_1 fire the local sequences l_{13}, l_{11} and l_{12}. This is valid as T_2, which currently does not hold any locks, does not execute any transition and hence does not compete for locks with T_1. Executing these sequences causes T_1 to reach the local configuration $lf_1 \downarrow T_1$ which is lock free. Thus T_2 can now fire the local sequences l_{22} and l_{21} to reach $lf_1 \downarrow T_2$ after which we let $\mathcal{CP}$ fire ν'' and then repeat the procedure.

To drop the lock restriction, we note that if there is a set of locks L' that are acquired along a run π of $\mathcal{BP}$ but never released then all operations on such locks are executed only along some finite prefix π_p of π which, wlog, we can assume to be a prefix of the stem ρ of the witness lollipop. Then the Dual Pumping Lemma is simply modified to add the extra proviso that there exists a set of locks L', all of which are held in c_{11} such that no operation on these locks is executed along σ and ν. Thus in the *pre**-closure computation to check for existence of σ and ν (see below), we do not execute transitions that operate on these locks.

Formulating Dual Pumping as Reachability Next we show how conditions 1, 2 and 3 in the statement of the Dual Pumping Lemma can be re-formulated as a set of reachability problems for regular sets of configurations. Let

$R_0 = pre^*(\{p\} \times \alpha\Gamma_1^* \times P_2 \times \Gamma_2^* \times \{(l_1, ..., l_m)\})$

Then condition 1 can be re-written as $c \in R_0$. Similarly, if

$R_1 = P_1 \times \Gamma_1^* \times \{q\} \times \beta\Gamma_2^* \times \{(l'_1, ..., l'_m)\}$

$R_2 = pre^*(R_1) \cap P_1 \times \Gamma_1^* \times P_2 \times \Gamma_2^* \times \{(\bot, ..., \bot)\}$.

$R_3 = pre^*(R_2) \cap \{p\} \times \{\alpha\} \times P_2 \times \Gamma_2^* \times \{(l_1, ..., l_m)\}$

then condition 2 can be captured as $R_3 \neq \emptyset$. Finally, let

$R_4 = P_1 \times \Gamma_1^* \times \{q\} \times \beta\Gamma_2^* \times \{(l'_1, ..., l'_m)\}$

$R_5 = pre^*(R_4) \cap P_1 \times \Gamma_1^* \times P_2 \times \Gamma_2^* \times \{(\bot, ..., \bot)\}$.

$R_6 = pre^*(R_5) \cap \{p\} \times \alpha\Gamma_1^* \times P_2 \times \Gamma_2^* \times \{(l_1, ..., l_m)\}$.

$R_7 = pre^*(R_6) \cap P_1 \times \Gamma_1^* \times P_2 \times \Gamma_2^* \times \{(\bot, ..., \bot)\}$.

$R_8 = pre^*(R_7) \cap G_2 \times L_1 \times ... \times L_m$, *where* $G_2 = \bigcup_{g_2}(P_1 \times \Gamma_1^* \times \{g_2\} \times \Gamma_2^*)$ *with* g_2 *being an accepting local state of* $\mathcal{BP}_2$.

$R_9 = pre^*(R_8) \cap P_1 \times \Gamma_1^* \times P_2 \times \Gamma_2^* \times \{(\bot, ..., \bot)\}$.

$R_{10} = pre^*(R_9) \cap G_1 \times L_1 \times ... \times L_m$, *where* $G_1 = \bigcup_{g_1}(\{g_1\} \times \Gamma_1^* \times P_2 \times \Gamma_2^*)$ *with* g_1 *being an accepting local state of* $\mathcal{BP}_1$.

$R_{11} = pre^+(R_{10}) \cap P_1 \times \Gamma_1^* \times P_2 \times \Gamma_2^* \times (\bot, ..., \bot)$.

$R_{12} = pre^*(R_{11}) \cap P_1 \times \Gamma_1^* \times \{q\} \times \{\beta\} \times \{(l'_1, ..., l'_m)\}$.

Then condition 3 can be captured as $R_{12} \neq \emptyset$.

Complexity Analysis. To compute R_0, we start by constructing an LMAP $\mathcal{A} = (\mathcal{A}_1, \mathcal{A}_2)$ accepting the set $\{p\} \times \alpha\Gamma_1^* \times P_2 \times \Gamma_2^* \times \{(l_1, ..., l_m)\}$. Towards that end, we construct an MA $\mathcal{A}_1$ accepting $\{p\} \times \alpha\Gamma_1^* \times \{(l'_1, ..., l'_m, \emptyset, ..., \emptyset, LHI, \emptyset)\}$ and an MA $\mathcal{A}_2$ accepting $P_2 \times \Gamma_2^* \times \{(l''_1, ..., l''_m, \emptyset, ..., \emptyset, LHI'', \emptyset)\}$, where (i) $l'_i = T_1$ if $l_i = T_1$ and $\bot$ otherwise, and $l''_i = T_2$ if $l_i = T_2$ and $\bot$, otherwise, (ii) $LHI' = \{l_i | l_i = T_1\}$ and $LHI'' = \{l_i | l_i = T_2\}$, and (iii) the BAH and FAH entries are set to $\emptyset$. Note that $\mathcal{A}_i$ is polynomial in the size of thread T_i. Similarly, one can construct LMAPs $\mathcal{B}$ and $\mathcal{C}$ accepting R_1 and R_4, acting as starting points for computing the other sets listed above, in (i) polytime in the size control states of the individual threads, viz., $O(poly(|T_1|) + poly(|T_2|))$, with $|T_i|$ being the number of control states of T_i, and (ii) exponential time in the number of locks of $\mathcal{CP}$. Note that because of the witness structure, sets R_2, R_5, R_7, R_9 and R_{11} are comprised of configurations in which all locks are free. The first consequence is that by theorem 11, the *pre**-closure of these sets can be computed in time polynomial in the sizes of control states of the individual threads and exponential in the number of locks of $\mathcal{CP}$. The second consequence is that we need only compute the subset of those configurations of the *pre**-closures of R_1, R_4, R_6, R_8, and R_{10}, in which all locks are free. Again by theorem 11, these computations can be carried out in polytime in the sizes of the control states of the individual threads and exponential time in the number of locks of $\mathcal{CP}$. Note that we have to carry out the above pre^*-closure computations for every possible 4-tuple (α, β, p, q). Thus we have the following

Theorem 13 *The accepting run problem for a Büchi system for a concurrent system $\mathcal{CP}$ with PDSs interacting via nested locks can be solved in polynomial time in the sizes of control states of $\mathcal{CP}$ and exponential time in the number of locks of $\mathcal{CP}$.*

Note that even though the complexity of the model checking problem is exponential time in the number of locks it does not have a significant impact as the number of locks is usually small in practice. Thus we have:

Theorem 14 *The model checking problem for a fixed single-index LTL formula for a system $\mathcal{CP}$ comprised of multiple PDSs interacting via nested locks is decidable in time polynomial in the size of the control states of $\mathcal{CP}$ and exponential in the number of locks.*

Checking Nestedness of Locks. Let $T = (P, Act, \Gamma, c_0, \Delta)$ be a thread of a concurrent program $\mathcal{CP}$ using locks $l_1, ..., l_m$. For testing whether T accesses locks in a nested fashion, all we need to do is to keep information regarding the order in which locks are accessed by T. Thus each state of the augmented thread T_a is now of the form $(c, \mathsf{l}_{i_1} ... \mathsf{l}_{i_k})$ where $\mathsf{l}_{i_1} ... \mathsf{l}_{i_k}$ is a sequence indicating the order in which locks were acquired by T with i_{i_k} being the most recent lock to be acquired. It is easy to see that for $j \neq l$, $\mathsf{l}_{i_j} \neq \mathsf{l}_{i_l}$. For each transition acquiring lock l and augmented state (c, λ) of T_a we concatenate l to λ. For any transition releasing lock l and augmented state (c, λ), we check to see whether l is the lock at the end of the sequence λ. If it is, then we remove l from λ, else we let T_a transit to a newly introduced control state Non-Nested. Then locks are nested in T iff the control state Non-Nested is not reachable in T_a which can be done efficiently using the model checking algorithm given in [2].

5 Conclusions and Related Work

Among prior work on the verification for concurrent programs, [6] attempts to generalize the techniques given in [2] to handle pushdown systems communicating via CCS-style pairwise rendezvous. However since even reachability is undecidable for such a framework, the procedures are not guaranteed to terminate in general but only for certain special cases, some of which the authors identify. The key idea here is to restrict interaction among the threads so as to bypass the undecidability barrier. Another natural way to obtain decidability is to explore the state space of the given concurrent multi-threaded program for a bounded number of context switches among the threads [7].

Other related interesting work includes the use of tree automata [8] and logic programs [9] for model checking the processes algebra PA which allows modeling of non-determinism, sequential and parallel composition and recursion. The reachability analysis of Constrained Dynamic Pushdown Networks which extend the PA framework by allowing PDSs that can spawn new PDSs to model fork operations, was considered in [10]. However, neither model allows communication among processes.

We, on the other hand, have identified a practically important case of threads communicating using locks and shown how to reason efficiently about a rich class of properties. Our methods are sound and complete, and cater to automatic error trace recovery. A key advantage of our method is that by reducing verification of a multi-threaded program to its individual threads, we bypass the state explosion problem, thereby guaranteeing scalability of our approach. Thus unlike existing methods our technique has *all* the desirable features of (i) being sound and complete, (ii) fully automatic, (iii) efficient, and (iv) catering to the verification of a rich class of linear temporal properties, not just reachability. Finally, our technique can easily be incorporated into current tools by exploiting existing efficient implementations for computing pre^*-closures.

References

[1] G. Ramalingam, "Context-Sensitive Synchronization-Sensitive Analysis is Undecidable," in *ACM Trans. Program. Lang. Syst.*, vol. 22(2), pp. 416–430, 2000.

[2] A. Bouajjani, J. Esparza, and O. Maler, "Reachability Analysis of Pushdown Automata: Application to Model-Checking," in *CONCUR*, LNCS 1243, pp. 135–150, 1997.

[3] I. Walukiewicz, "Model Checking CTL Properties of Pushdown Systems," in *FSTTCS*, LNCS 1974, 2000.

[4] "Joint CAV/ISSTA Special Event on Specification, Verification, and Testing of Concurrent Software," in *http://research.microsoft.com/ qadeer/cav-issta.htm.*

[5] V. Kahlon, F. Ivančić, and A. Gupta, "Reasoning about Threads Communicating via Locks," in *CAV*, 2005.

[6] A. Bouajjani, J. Esparza, and T. Touili, "A Generic Approach to the Static Analysis of Concurrent Programs with Procedures," in *IJFCS*, vol. 14(4), pp. 551–, 2003.

[7] S. Qadeer and J. Rehof, "Context-Bounded Model Checking of Concurrent Software," in *TACAS*, 2005.

[8] D. Lugiez and P. Schnoebelen, "The Regular Viewpoint on PA-Processes," in *Theor. Comput. Sci.*, vol. 274(1-2), 2002.

[9] J. Esparza and A. Podelski, "Efficient Algorithms for pre^* and $post^*$ on Interprocedural Parallel Flow Graphs," in *POPL*, 2000.

[10] A. Bouajjani, M. Olm, and T. Touili, "Regular Symbolic Analysis of Dynamic Networks of Pushdown Systems," in *CONCUR*, 2005.

On Typability for Rank-2 Intersection Types with Polymorphic Recursion *

Tachio Terauchi
EECS Department
University of California, Berkeley

Alex Aiken
Computer Science Department
Stanford University

Abstract

We show that typability for a natural form of polymorphic recursive typing for rank-2 intersection types is undecidable. Our proof involves characterizing typability as a context free language (CFL) graph problem, which may be of independent interest, and reduction from the boundedness problem for Turing machines. We also show a property of the type system which, in conjunction with the undecidability result, disproves a misconception about the Milner-Mycroft type system. We also show undecidability of a related program analysis problem.

1 Introduction

Among the interesting aspects of intersection types is the decidability of type inference for any finite rank for the pure λ-calculus (i.e., without recursive definitions) [8, 6], principal typing [5, 17, 8], the rank-2 fragment [9, 4], which is closely related to ML-types, and connections with polyvariant flow analysis [12]. Recursive definitions such as `fix` $x.e$ are important in practice. Indeed, it is difficult to find a real-world programming language without some form of recursive definitions. If x appears more than once in the body of e of the recursive definition, it may be desirable to give an polymorphic type to x, which leads to polymorphic recursive typing. Jim [4] proposed a natural way to use intersection types for this purpose in the rank-2 fragment. He named the type system $\mathbf{I}_2+$**REC-INT**, where $\mathbf{I}_2$ refers to rank-2 intersection types and **REC-INT** is the name of the rule used to type recursive definitions. While it is known that type inference without polymorphic recursion is decidable for any finite rank intersection types [8, 6], the decidability question has been open for $\mathbf{I}_2$ + **REC-INT**.

$\mathbf{I}_2+$**REC-INT** is not the most powerful polymorphic recursive type system, but it appears to be capable of typing many programming situations requiring polymorphic recursion (for example, see [2] which studies a similar system). To the best of our knowledge, there is no known polymorphic recursive type system with decidable typability that is both sound and more powerful than $\mathbf{I}_2$ + **REC-INT**. This paper shows that typability for even $\mathbf{I}_2$ + **REC-INT** is undecidable.

The rest of the paper is organized as follows. Section 2 discusses related work. Section 3 gives an overview of $\mathbf{I}_2$ + **REC-INT**. Section 4 gives a novel reduction of a context free language (CFL) graph problem to typability for $\mathbf{I}_2+$**REC-INT**. Section 5 reduces the boundedness problem to the CFL graph problem to complete the proof of undecidability of typability of $\mathbf{I}_2+$**REC-INT**. The last two sections show related results that follow from the proof of undecidability. Section 6 shows a property of $\mathbf{I}_2$ + **REC-INT** that disproves a misconception about the Milner-Mycroft type system. Section 7 proves undecidability of a related program analysis problem. The companion technical report contains the proofs omitted from the conference version [16].

2 Related Work

While being careful to leave the question open, Jim in his original paper [4] considered the possibility of undecidability of $\mathbf{I}_2+$**REC-INT** typability citing the resemblance to the Milner-Mycroft type system [10] whose typability was already known to be undecidable [7, 3]. More recently, Damiani [1] noted that there seems to be no "obvious way" to find a bound on the size of $|I|$ (see the type rule **REC-INT** in Section 3). Our result confirms these suspicions.

Our proof reduces typability to the boundedness problem of Turing machines. The boundedness problem was also used in the undecidability proof of semi-unification [7].

A step in our proof shows an equivalence between unification type constraints and a CFL graph problem that may be of independent interest to researchers interested in relating type-based program analysis to CFL-based program analysis. While it is suspected that many CFL-based program analyses correspond closely to type-based ones, there

*This research was supported in part by NSF Grant No. CCR-0326577. The information presented here does not necessarily reflect the position or the policy of the Government and no official endorsement should be inferred.

1043-6871/06 $20.00 © 2006 IEEE

$$\begin{array}{rcl} e & ::= & x \mid e\, e' \mid \lambda x.e \mid \texttt{fix}\ x.e \\ \tau & ::= & \alpha \mid \tau \rightarrow \tau \\ \sigma & ::= & \tau \mid (\bigwedge_{i \in I} \tau_i) \rightarrow \sigma \end{array}$$

Figure 1. Terms and types language.

$$\frac{\Gamma(x) = \bigwedge_{i \in I} \tau_i \quad j \in I}{\Gamma \vdash x : \tau_j}\ \textbf{VAR}$$

$$\frac{\Gamma, x{:}\bigwedge_{i \in I} \tau_i \vdash e : \sigma}{\Gamma \vdash \lambda x.e : (\bigwedge_{i \in I} \tau_i) \rightarrow \sigma}\ \textbf{FUN}$$

$$\frac{\Gamma \vdash e : (\bigwedge_{i \in I} \tau_i) \rightarrow \sigma \quad \forall i \in I.(\Gamma \vdash e' : \tau_i)}{\Gamma \vdash e\, e' : \sigma}\ \textbf{APP}$$

$$\frac{\forall i \in I.(\Gamma, x{:}\bigwedge_{j \in I} \tau_j \vdash e : \tau_i) \quad k \in I}{\Gamma \vdash \texttt{fix}\ x.e : \tau_k}\ \textbf{REC-INT}$$

Figure 2. $\mathbf{I}_2$ + REC-INT.

have been few formal results [14, 13]. One benefit of such correspondences is for proving the soundness of a CFL-based program analysis, which is almost never done, by proving the soundness of an equivalent type-based one, which is, in contrast, a common practice.

Our work seems to be the second time CFL graphs have been used to prove an undecidability result in program analysis. Reps proved undecidability of context-sensitive data-dependence analysis via undecidability of a CFL graph reachability problem [15]. However, the proof strategy used in this paper is different from his.

3 $\mathbf{I}_2$ + REC-INT

Terms and types are defined in Figure 1. Function application $e\, e'$ is left associative, i.e., $e_1\, e_2\, e_3 = (e_1\, e_2)\, e_3$. Binding of variables extends as far to the right as possible. Types consist of rank-0 types τ and rank-2 types σ. (Rank-1 types are of the form $\bigwedge_{i \in I} \tau_i$.) I is a finite non-empty set of indices. Function types are right associative, i.e., $\tau_1 \rightarrow \tau_2 \rightarrow \tau_3 = \tau_1 \rightarrow (\tau_2 \rightarrow \tau_3)$.

The rank-2 intersection type system with recursive definitions, $\mathbf{I}_2$ + **REC-INT**, is defined in Figure 2. $\mathbf{I}_2$ + **REC-INT** is similar to the Milner-Mycroft type system, though not exactly equivalent. For example $\texttt{fix}\ x.x\, x$ is typable in the Milner-Mycroft type system but not in $\mathbf{I}_2$ + **REC-INT**.

$\mathbf{I}_2$ + **REC-INT** with a monomorphism restriction for **REC-INT**, i.e.,

$$\frac{\Gamma, x{:}\tau \vdash e : \tau}{\Gamma \vdash \texttt{fix}\ x.e : \tau}\ \textbf{REC-INT'}$$

$$\begin{array}{rcl} id & \equiv & \lambda x.x \\ e; e' & \equiv & (id\, (\lambda x.e'))\, e \\ & & \text{where } x \notin fvars(e') \\ \texttt{same}(e, e') & \equiv & id\, (\lambda x.x\, e; x\, e') \\ & & \text{where } x \notin fvars(e) \cup fvars(e') \\ e \times e' & \equiv & id\, (\lambda x.\texttt{same}(x, e); e') \\ & & \text{where } x \notin fvars(e) \cup fvars(e') \end{array}$$

Figure 3. Encoding of $e; e'$, $e \times e'$, and $\texttt{same}(e, e')$.

is closely related to ML-types and the type inference is decidable, in fact, it is DEXP-time complete [4].

The main result of this paper is the undecidability of $\mathbf{I}_2$ + **REC-INT** typability. Formally, the typability problem of $\mathbf{I}_2$ + **REC-INT** is defined as follows: Given a closed term e, is e typable, i.e., is there a type derivation $\Gamma \vdash e : \tau$ for some τ and Γ? Note that it is safe to restrict $dom(\Gamma) = fvars(e)$. (Here, $fvars(e)$ denotes the set of free variables of e.) Our proof shows that even when e is restricted to closed terms (i.e., $fvars(e) = \emptyset$), the typability problem is undecidable.

3.1 Example

One might naively think that, at each **REC-INT**, $|I|$ should at most be the number of occurrences of x in e (see Figure 2). Such a bound on $|I|$ would make type inference easy. However, because any computable bound on $|I|$ would imply decidability, the result in this paper shows that there is no computable way to obtain a bound in general.

We define some syntactic shortcuts to show an example where $|I|$ is greater than the number of variable occurrences. Let $e; e'$ be a sequential composition, $e \times e'$ be a pair, and let $\texttt{same}(e, e')$ force the types of e and e' to be equal. Sequential composition associates to the left and has the weakest precedence, e.g., $e_1\, e_2; e_3; e_4 = ((e_1\, e_2); e_3); e_4$. These expressions are encoded as shown in Figure 3. The reason for the use of id in the encodings is to force types to be of rank 0. For example, if we want to ensure that e can be typed rank-0, we apply id to e to force existence of a sub-derivation where e has a rank-0 type. (See the **APP** rule in Figure 2.) Note that in this encoding, a pair $\tau \times \tau'$ has a function type $\tau \rightarrow \tau'$. While the encoded pair does not have the expected semantics, it has the expected types. Both pair terms and pair types are right associative.

Let e be the following term:

$$\begin{array}{ll} \lambda x.\lambda y.\lambda z. & (\lambda u.\lambda v.\lambda w.\texttt{same}(f\ u\ v\ w, x \times y)); \\ & (\lambda u.\lambda v.\lambda w.\texttt{same}(f\ u\ v\ w, (x \times x) \times y)); \\ & y \times z \end{array}$$

$$\frac{\Gamma(x) = \bigwedge_{i\in I} \tau_i \qquad j \in I}{\Gamma \vdash_0 x : \tau_j} \textbf{ VAR}$$

$$\frac{\Gamma, x{:}\tau \vdash_0 e : \tau'}{\Gamma \vdash_0 \lambda x.e : \tau \to \tau'} \textbf{ FUN}$$

$$\frac{\Gamma \vdash_0 e : \tau \to \tau' \qquad \Gamma \vdash_0 e' : \tau}{\Gamma \vdash_0 e\, e' : \tau'} \textbf{ APP}$$

$$\frac{\forall i \in I.(\Gamma, x{:}\bigwedge_{j\in I} \tau_j \vdash_0 e : \tau_i) \qquad k \in I}{\Gamma \vdash_0 \mathtt{fix}\ x.e : \tau_k} \textbf{ REC-INT}$$

Figure 4. I + REC-INT.

We show that $\mathtt{fix}\ f.e$ is typable. Let

$$\begin{aligned}
\tau_1 &= \alpha \to \alpha \to \alpha \to (\alpha \times \alpha)\\
\tau_2 &= \alpha \to \alpha \to (\alpha \times \alpha) \to (\alpha \times (\alpha \times \alpha))\\
\tau_3 &= \alpha \to (\alpha \times \alpha) \to \alpha \to ((\alpha \times \alpha) \times \alpha)\\
\tau_4 &= \alpha \to (\alpha \times \alpha) \to (\alpha \times \alpha) \to ((\alpha \times \alpha) \times (\alpha \times \alpha))
\end{aligned}$$

Note that $f : \tau_1 \wedge \tau_3 \vdash e : \tau_1$ by assigning τ_1 to the first occurrence of f and τ_3 to the second occurrence of f. Similarly,

$$\begin{aligned}
f{:}\tau_1 \wedge \tau_3 &\vdash e : \tau_2\\
f{:}\tau_2 \wedge \tau_4 &\vdash e : \tau_3\\
f{:}\tau_2 \wedge \tau_4 &\vdash e : \tau_4
\end{aligned}$$

Therefore,

$$\frac{\forall i \in I.(f{:}\bigwedge_{j\in I} \tau_j \vdash e : \tau_i) \qquad k \in I}{\emptyset \vdash \mathtt{fix}\ f.e : \tau_k}$$

where $I = \{1, 2, 3, 4\}$.

On the other hand, there is no derivation that can type this term with $|I| < 4$. It is immediately obvious from $x \times y$ and $(x \times x) \times y$ that $f\ u\ v\ w$ must be given the types $\tau_x \times \tau_y$ and $(\tau_x \times \tau_x) \times \tau_y$ for some τ_x, τ_y. But due to $y \times z$, this implies that y must have the types τ_x and $\tau_x \times \tau_x$. Therefore, we actually need two kinds of τ_y's, i.e., τ_x and $\tau_x \times \tau_x$, which implies that there must be at least four types for $f\ u\ v\ w$.

4 Typability as a CFL Graph Problem

For this proof, we introduce the simpler type system **I + REC-INT** shown in Figure 4. In general, typability in **I + REC-INT** does not coincide with typability in **I**$_2$ **+ REC-INT** (e.g., $\lambda x.x\ x$). However, we prove that even when restricted to the set of terms that are typable in **I**$_2$ **+ REC-INT** iff typable in **I + REC-INT**, the typability problem is undecidable. More generally, let us define the subset of terms B as follows:

$$B \ ::= \ x \mid id\,(\lambda x.B) \mid B\,B \mid \mathtt{fix}\ x.B$$

$$\begin{aligned}
&[\![\lambda x.e]\!]_\Gamma = (\beta, C \cup \{\beta = \alpha \to \tau\}, X \cup \{\alpha, \beta\})\\
&\text{where } \alpha \in \mathit{Base} \setminus (X \cup \mathit{ran}(\Gamma))\\
&\qquad \beta \in \mathit{Base} \setminus (X \cup \mathit{ran}(\Gamma) \cup \{\alpha\})\\
&\qquad (\tau, C, X) = [\![e]\!]_{\Gamma, x:\alpha}
\end{aligned}$$

$$\begin{aligned}
&[\![e_1\ e_2]\!]_\Gamma = (\beta, C, X_1 \cup X_2 \cup \{\alpha, \beta\})\\
&\text{where } \alpha \in \mathit{Base} \setminus (X_1 \cup X_2 \cup \mathit{ran}(\Gamma))\\
&\qquad \beta \in \mathit{Base} \setminus (X_1 \cup X_2 \cup \mathit{ran}(\Gamma) \cup \{\alpha\})\\
&\qquad X_1 \cap X_2 = \emptyset\\
&\qquad (\tau_1, C_1, X_1) = [\![e_1]\!]_\Gamma\\
&\qquad (\tau_2, C_2, X_2) = [\![e_2]\!]_\Gamma\\
&\qquad C = C_1 \cup C_2 \cup \{\tau_1 = \alpha \to \beta, \tau_2 = \alpha\}
\end{aligned}$$

$$\begin{aligned}
&[\![x]\!]_\Gamma = (\Gamma(x), \emptyset, \emptyset)\\
&\text{where } x \in \mathit{dom}(\Gamma)
\end{aligned}$$

$$\begin{aligned}
&[\![\mathtt{fix}\ x.e]\!]_\Gamma = (\tau, C, X')\\
&\text{where } \Sigma = \{a \mid x^a \in \mathit{fvars}(e)\}\\
&\qquad X' = X \cup \{\alpha_a \mid a \in \Sigma\}\\
&\qquad \forall a \in \Sigma.\alpha_a \in \mathit{Base} \setminus (\mathit{ran}(\Gamma) \cup X' \setminus \{\alpha_a\})\\
&\qquad (\tau, C', X) = [\![e]\!]_{\Gamma \cup \bigcup_{a\in\Sigma}\{x^a:\alpha_a\}}\\
&\qquad C'' = \textstyle\bigcup_{a\in\Sigma}\{\tau'^a = \tau' \mid \tau' \in \mathit{ran}(\Gamma)\} \cup \{\tau^a = \alpha_a\}\\
&\qquad C = \textstyle\bigcup_{s\in\Sigma^*}(C' \cup C'')^s
\end{aligned}$$

Figure 5. Constraint generation.

Lemma 4.1 *For all closed B, $\emptyset \vdash_0 B : \sigma$ iff $\emptyset \vdash B : \sigma$.*

Closed B terms do not include all of the terms whose typability in **I**$_2$ **+ REC-INT** coincides with typability in **I + REC-INT** but are sufficient for our purpose. In the rest of the paper, typable means typable in $\vdash_0$ and type means rank-0 type unless stated otherwise.

4.1 Type Constraints

As in conventional type inference algorithms, we formulate the typability problem as a constraint satisfaction problem. However, the purpose here is not to solve the constraints but to show its undecidability.

We warn that the phrase "constraint generation" is somewhat misleading because there is no terminating algorithm to generate the constraints. (The set of constraints may be infinite.) When we say that the set of constraints is generated, we mean that the set exists (in standard set theory). Existence is sufficient for our purpose of proving undecidability.

The generated constraint set may contain infinitely many type variables. To this end, we annotate type variables with superscripts. Let *Base* be the set of type variables without superscripts, or equivalently, with an empty string as the superscript. Let meta variables α, β, etc. range over type variables with a (possibly empty) superscript. For a type variable α and a string s, α^s is a type variable whose superscript is a concatenation of the superscript of α followed by s. For example, $(\beta^{s_1})^{s_2} = \beta^{s_1 s_2}$. For a type τ and a string s, τ^s is a type obtained by replacing each type variable α in τ by α^s. For example, $(\alpha^{s_1} \rightarrow \beta^{s_1})^{s_2} = \alpha^{s_1 s_2} \rightarrow \beta^{s_1 s_2}$. For a set of type equality constraints C, $C^s = \{(\tau_1^s = \tau_2^s) \mid (\tau_1 = \tau_2) \in C\}$.

We annotate term variables with superscripts so that each occurrence of a fix-bound variable is annotated with a distinct number, e.g., $\texttt{fix}\ x.\texttt{fix}\ y.x^0\ \lambda z.x^1\ y^2\ z$. These numbers form the alphabet of the strings annotating the type variables. We use meta variables x, y, etc. to range over variables with a (possibly empty) superscript.

Constraint generation is shown in Figure 5. A mapping Γ from variables to types is a *type environment*. Intuitively, $[\![e]\!]_\Gamma$ returns a triple (τ, C, X) such that τ is the type of e, X is the set of base type variables introduced while analyzing e, and C is the set of constraints generated while analyzing e. The use of set X is a standard technique for avoiding unnecessary introduction of the same type variable in two different contexts. The first three rules are self-explanatory, and coincide with a typical constraint-based type inference algorithm for simply typed λ-calculus.

The fourth rule handles $\texttt{fix}\ x.e$. The goal is to build a constraint set representing the infinite unrolling of the recursive body e. Recall that occurrences of fix-bound variables are annotated with distinct numbers. In the rule, Σ is the set of numbers annotating x. Each $a \in \Sigma$ has the associated base type variable α_a. The line $\forall a \in \Sigma.\alpha_a \in \mathit{Base} \setminus (\mathit{ran}(\Gamma) \cup X' \setminus \{\alpha_a\})$ ensures that these variables are distinct. Thus (τ, C', X) is the result of analyzing the body of the recursive definition e by assigning a distinct type variable to each x^a. Intuitively, C' is the template constraint that should be repeated indefinitely, and C contains infinitely many copies of C' distinguished by superscripts. Therefore, C'^{as} represents the constraint of the body e unrolled at x^a appearing in the body e that itself was unrolled from the root according to s. C also contains copies of C'', which is used to connect the copies of C' (note that C'^{s_1} and C'^{s_2} share no type variables when $s_1 \neq s_2$). C'' consists of two parts. The first part, $\bigcup_{a\in\Sigma}\{\tau'^a = \tau' \mid \tau' \in \mathit{ran}(\Gamma)\}$, ensures that free variables in e get the same types in the unrolling.[1] The second part, $\bigcup_{a\in\Sigma}\{\tau^a = \alpha_a\}$, equates the type of x^a (i.e., α_a) with the type of the body e unrolled at x^a (i.e., τ^a).

We connect typability to constraint satisfaction as follows. An assignment S is a mapping from type variables to types. For τ, $S(\tau)$ is the type obtained by replacing each type variable α in τ by $S(\alpha)$. An assignment S is a solution of C, written $S \models C$, if for each $\tau = \tau' \in C$, $S(\tau) = S(\tau')$. We say that S is a *finite-range solution* if the range of S, $\mathit{ran}(S)$, is a finite set. We write $S \models_{\mathit{fin}} C$ if S is finite-range and $S \models C$. We write $\models C$ if C is satisfiable, i.e., if there exists S such that $S \models C$. We write $\models_{\mathit{fin}} C$ if C is finitary-satisfiable, i.e., if there exists S such that $S \models_{\mathit{fin}} C$. A term e is typable iff the constraints generated for e are finitary-satisfiable, i.e.,

Lemma 4.2 *Let e be a closed term. Let e′ be e such that each occurrence of a* fix*-bound variable is annotated with a distinct number. Then e is typable in* **I + REC-INT** *iff* $\models_{\mathit{fin}} C$ *where* $(\tau, C, X) = [\![e']\!]_\emptyset$ *for some* τ *and* X.

Example Consider the term $\texttt{fix}\ x.x^0\ x^1$. Then,

$$\begin{array}{l}
[\![x^0]\!]_{x^0:\gamma,x^1:\kappa} = (\gamma, \emptyset, \emptyset)\\
[\![x^1]\!]_{x^0:\gamma,x^1:\kappa} = (\kappa, \emptyset, \emptyset)\\
[\![x^0\ x^1]\!]_{x^0:\gamma,x^1:\kappa} = (\beta, \{\gamma = \alpha\rightarrow\beta, \kappa = \alpha\}, \{\alpha, \beta\})\\
[\![\texttt{fix}\ x.x^0\ x^1]\!]_\emptyset = (\beta, C, \{\alpha, \beta, \gamma, \kappa\})
\end{array}$$

where

$$C = \bigcup_{s\in\{0,1\}^*} \{\gamma = \alpha\rightarrow\beta, \kappa = \alpha, \beta^0 = \gamma, \beta^1 = \kappa\}^s$$

For any S such that $S \models C$, it must be the case that $S \models C'$ where $C' = \{\beta^{0s} = \beta^{1s}\rightarrow\beta^s \mid s \in \{0,1\}^*\}$. But C' clearly has no finite range solution. Therefore, C has no finite range solution, and $\texttt{fix}\ x.x\ x$ is not typable. (Note that there is an infinite-range solution for C'. However, it is not always the case that an untypable term has an infinite-range solution.)

4.2 Constraints as a CFL Graph

The next step of the proof is to represent constraints as a context free language (CFL) graph. We treat constraints symmetrically, i.e, $\tau = \tau'$ is equivalent to $\tau' = \tau$. Let C be a constraint generated from a closed term e, i.e., $(\tau, C, X) = [\![e]\!]_\emptyset$ for some τ and X. Note that all of the constraints in C are of the form $\alpha = \beta$ or $\alpha = \beta\rightarrow\gamma$. We use the notation $\mathit{ftvars}(\tau)$ to denote the set of types variables in τ. Let $\mathit{ftvars}(C) = \bigcup_{(\tau=\tau')\in C}(\mathit{ftvars}(\tau) \cup \mathit{ftvars}(\tau'))$. The CFL graph of C, written $\mathit{graph}(C)$, is the graph (V, E) where

$$\begin{array}{rcl}
V & = & \mathit{ftvars}(C)\\
E & = & \{\alpha \xrightarrow{\epsilon} \beta \mid (\alpha = \beta) \in C\}\\
 & & \cup\{\alpha \xrightarrow{(} \gamma, \beta \xrightarrow{[} \gamma \mid (\alpha\rightarrow\beta = \gamma) \in C\}\\
 & & \cup\{\gamma \xrightarrow{)} \alpha, \gamma \xrightarrow{]} \beta \mid (\alpha\rightarrow\beta = \gamma) \in C\}
\end{array}$$

For example, let $C = \{\beta_0 = \alpha_1\rightarrow\beta_1, \beta_1 = \alpha_2\rightarrow\beta_2, \beta_0 =$

[1] Technically, this part is inessential as all $\texttt{fix}\ x.e$ used in the rest of the paper are closed. However, it is included here for completeness and to make the proof of Lemma 4.2 succinct.

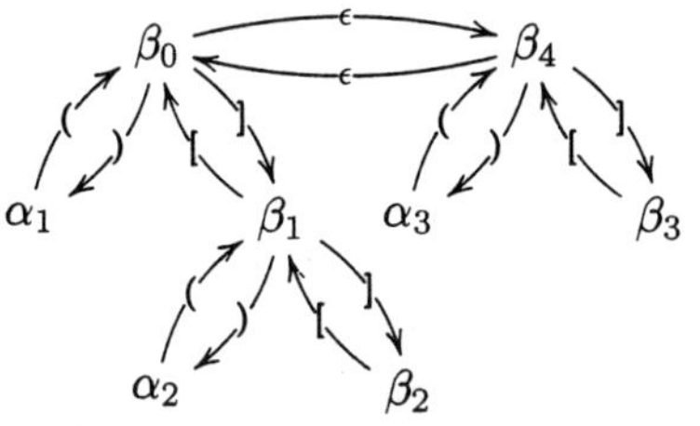

Figure 6. Example.

$$
\begin{aligned}
proj(\tau, \epsilon) &= \tau \\
proj(\tau \to \tau',)s) &= proj(\tau, s) \\
proj(\tau \to \tau',]s) &= proj(\tau', s)
\end{aligned}
$$

Figure 7. Path projection.

$\beta_4, \beta_4 = \alpha_3 \to \beta_3\}$. Then $graph(C)$ is as shown in Figure 6.

Given a path p in the graph, let $s(p)$ be the string obtained by concatenating in order the labels of edges in p. Let ϵ denote an empty string. Let $L(A)$ be the set of strings generated by the following grammar:

$$A ::= \epsilon \mid A\ A \mid (\ A\ ) \mid [\ A\ ]$$

A *match elimination* $\to_m$ is defined as follows:

$$
\begin{aligned}
t_1\ (\,)\ t_2 &\to_m t_1 t_2 \\
t_1\ [\,]\ t_2 &\to_m t_1 t_2
\end{aligned}
$$

For a path p, the *match-eliminated string* of p, written $sm(p)$, is a $\to_m$-normalized $s(p)$, i.e., a string t such that $s(p) \to_m^* t$ where no substring of t is in $L(A)$. We write $\alpha \overset{t}{\leadsto} \beta$ to denote a path p from α to β such that $sm(p) = t$. For example, there is a path $\beta_2 \overset{]}{\leadsto} \beta_3$ in Figure 6.

We call p a *matched path* if $sm(p)$ is an empty string. For convenience, we say that every variable has a (self) matched path to itself, i.e., $\alpha \overset{\epsilon}{\leadsto} \alpha$. We say that a string t is *positive* if t consists only of ')' and ']'. We call p a *positive path* if it is a matched path or if $sm(p)$ is a positive string. The *depth* of a positive path p, $depth(p)$, is the length of $sm(p)$.

We want to show that $\models_{fin} C$ iff the depth of positive paths in $graph(C)$ is bounded. To this end, we relate types to paths as follows. For a positive string t and a type τ, the t-projection of τ, $proj(\tau, t)$ is defined as shown in Figure 7. Note that $proj(\tau, t)$ may be undefined. For example, $proj(\alpha \to \alpha \to \beta,)))$ is undefined. The following lemma says that positive paths imply type-structural constraints.

Lemma 4.3 *Let p be a path from α to β in $graph(C)$ such that $sm(p)$ is a positive string. Suppose $S \models C$. Then there exists τ such that $proj(\tau, sm(p)) = \beta$ and $S(\alpha) = S(\tau)$.*

We say τ is smaller than τ' if $size(\tau) < size(\tau')$ where *size* is defined

$$
\begin{aligned}
size(\alpha) &= 1 \\
size(\tau \to \tau') &= size(\tau) + size(\tau')
\end{aligned}
$$

For a set X of positive strings and a type variable α, we define $pathsType(X, \alpha)$ to be the smallest type τ containing only α such that for each $t \in X$, $proj(\tau, t)$ is defined (so $proj(\tau, t) = \alpha$). For example,

$$pathsType(\{\ )]),\ ]]\ \}, \alpha) = (\alpha \to (\alpha \to \alpha)) \to \alpha \to \alpha$$

Note that for X finite, $pathsType(X, \alpha)$ is always defined. Given a type variable α in a CFL graph G, let $posPaths(\alpha, G)$ be the set of all positive paths from α. We are now ready to prove the main result of this section.

Lemma 4.4 *$\models_{fin} C$ iff there exists a positive integer n such that for any positive path p in $graph(C)$, $depth(p) \leq n$.*

Proof:

If

Let n be a positive integer such that for any positive path p in $graph(C) = G = (V, E)$, $depth(p) \leq n$. Fix a type variable δ. Let F be a mapping from type variables to sets of positive strings such that for each $\alpha \in V$, $F(\alpha) = \{sm(p) \mid p \in posPaths(\alpha, G)\}$. Define S as follows

$$S = \{\alpha \mapsto pathsType(F(\alpha), \delta) \mid \alpha \in V\}$$

Because depths of positive paths are bounded, $F(\alpha)$ must be finite for every α. Hence each $pathsType(F(\alpha), \delta)$ is defined, and so S is defined. Furthermore, $ran(S)$ is finite, in particular, $|ran(S)| < 2^{n+1}$. Hence it suffices to show that $S \models C$.

Pick $(\alpha = \beta) \in C$. By construction, $\alpha \overset{\epsilon}{\to} \beta$ and $\beta \overset{\epsilon}{\to} \alpha$. Hence $F(\alpha) = F(\beta)$. Therefore $S(\alpha) = S(\beta)$ as required.

Pick $(\alpha = \beta \to \gamma) \in C$. Suppose $t \in F(\beta)$. then there exists a path $\beta \overset{t}{\leadsto} \kappa$ for some κ. By construction, there is an edge $\alpha \overset{)}{\to} \beta$. Hence there is a path $\alpha \overset{)}{\to} \beta \overset{t}{\leadsto} \kappa$, and so there is a path p' from α such that $sm(p') =)t$. Thus, $)t \in F(\alpha)$. Conversely, suppose $)t \in F(\alpha)$. Let p be a path from α such that $sm(p) =)t$. Let β' be a node such that p is $\alpha \overset{)}{\leadsto} \beta' \overset{t}{\leadsto} \kappa$ where κ is the end vertex of p. By construction, there is an edge $\beta \overset{(}{\to} \alpha$. Therefore, there is a path $\beta \overset{(}{\to} \alpha \overset{)}{\leadsto} \beta' \overset{t}{\leadsto} \gamma$, and so there is a path p' from β such that $sm(p') = t$. Thus, $t \in F(\beta)$.

Hence $t \in F(\beta)$ iff $)t \in F(\alpha)$. By a similar argument, $t \in F(\gamma)$ iff $]t \in F(\alpha)$. Therefore $S(\alpha) = S(\beta) \to S(\gamma)$ as required, and $S \models C$.

Only If

Suppose there exists no n such that for any positive path p in $graph(C)$, $depth(p) \leq n$. For the sake of obtaining a contradiction, suppose there exists S such that $S \models_{fin} C$. Let

m be a number such that for any $\tau \in \mathit{ran}(S)$, $\mathit{size}(\tau) < m$. Pick a path p in $\mathit{graph}(C)$ such that $\mathit{depth}(p) > m$. Let α be the starting vertex and β be the ending vertex of p. Then by Lemma 4.3, there exists τ such that $\mathit{proj}(\tau, \mathit{sm}(p)) = \beta$ and $S(\alpha) = S(\tau)$. But $|\mathit{sm}(p)| > m$ implies $\mathit{size}(S(\alpha)) = \mathit{size}(S(\tau)) > m$, a contradiction.
□

5 Reduction from the Boundedness Problem

We reduce the *boundedness problem* to the problem of finding a bound on the depth of positive paths in $\mathit{graph}(C)$. The boundedness problem is known to be undecidable [7], and hence this reduction shall show that the problem of finding a bound on the depth of positive paths in $\mathit{graph}(C)$ is undecidable, which in turn implies the undecidability of typability. Here, we present the boundedness problem as it is defined in [7].

An Intercell Turing Machine (symmetric ITM) is a triple of the form $Y = \langle Q, A, T \rangle$, where

- Q is a finite set of states,
- A is a finite tape alphabet, and
- $T \subseteq Q \times \{-1, +1\} \times A \times A \times Q$ is a transition relation.

An instantaneous description (ID) of Y takes the form $\langle w_1, \alpha, m, w_2 \rangle$ where $w_1 w_2$ is the tape content with all but finitely many blank symbols and the head is positioned between the $(m-1)$-th and the m-th cells, which is between w_1 and w_2. [2] The next move relation $\vdash_Y$ on ID's of Y is defined as follows:

$$\begin{array}{l} \text{for } \langle \alpha, -1, a, b, \beta \rangle \in T \\ \quad \langle w_1 a, \alpha, m, w_2 \rangle \vdash_Y \langle w_1, \beta, m-1, b w_2 \rangle \\ \text{for } \langle \alpha, +1, a, b, \beta \rangle \in T \\ \quad \langle w_1, \alpha, m, a w_2 \rangle \vdash_Y \langle w_1 b, \beta, m+1, w_2 \rangle \end{array}$$

An ITM Y is *bounded* if there exists a positive integer n such that if M is an arbitrary ID of Y, then the number of different ID's reachable by Y from M is at most n.

Let $Y = \langle Q, A, T \rangle$ be an ITM. The *symmetric closure* of Y is $Y_S = \langle Q, A, T_S \rangle$ where

$$T_S = T \cup \{\langle \alpha, -x, a, b, \beta \rangle \mid \langle \beta, x, b, a, \alpha \rangle \in T\}$$

The *boundedness problem for symmetrically-closed* ITMs is the problem of deciding for a given deterministic ITM $Y = \langle Q, \{0, 1\}, T \rangle$ with 0 as the blank symbol, whether Y_S is bounded.

Theorem 5.1 ([7]) *The boundedness problem for symmetrically-closed* ITMs *is undecidable.*

[2] Strictly speaking, m is redundant since w_1 and w_2 precisely determine the location of the head. But m makes the proof more readable.

We now reduce the boundedness problem of symmetrically-closed ITMs to the problem of finding a bound on the depth of positive paths. Our goal is to construct a closed term e_Y for an ITM Y such that Y_S is bounded iff the depth of positive paths in $\mathit{graph}(C)$ is bounded where $(\tau, C, X) = [\![e_Y]\!]_\emptyset$ for some X and τ. The idea is that C would look like an infinite binary tree in which each left move of Y_S is represented by a down move in the tree (from a parent to a child), and each right move of Y_S is represented by an up move in the tree (from a child to the parent). The tape content to the right of the head records which branch was taken at each down move. This ensures that up moves use the edges actually belonging to the tree. The tape content to the left of the head records whether a (edge or a [edge is followed at each up move so that a down move must use a) edge to match a (up move and a] edge to match a [up move. Symmetry of ITM is needed in part because our CFL graphs are bi-directional, i.e., $(\alpha \xrightarrow{)} \beta) \in E$ iff $(\beta \xrightarrow{(} \alpha) \in E$, and similarly for], [, and ϵ edges. However, it turns out that the CFL graphs must be bi-directional anyway to simulate a symmetric-or-asymmetric ITM with our proof technique.

Instead of introducing e_Y at this point, it is more helpful to describe the constraint C_Y such that $\mathit{graph}(C_Y)$ simulates Y_S in the way described above. We then construct the term e_Y that generates C_Y. Let $Y = \langle Q, \{0, 1\}, T \rangle$ be a deterministic ITM. Let $\{M_1, \ldots, M_n\} \subseteq T_S$ be the set of all left transitions of Y_S. For each $M_\ell \in T_S$, let γ_ℓ be a distinct type variable. For each $M_\ell = \langle \alpha, -1, b, a, \beta \rangle$, define types $\tau_{a,\ell}$ and $\kappa_{a,\ell}$ as follows:

$$\begin{aligned} \tau_{a,\ell} &\equiv \begin{cases} \beta \times \gamma_\ell & \text{if } b = 0 \\ \gamma_\ell \times \beta & \text{if } b = 1 \end{cases} \\ \kappa_{a,\ell} &\equiv \alpha \end{aligned}$$

Note that we have intentionally picked type variable names that correspond to the state names in Y. C_Y is defined as follows:

$$C_Y = \bigcup_{s \in \{0,1\}^*} \{\kappa_{a,\ell} = \tau^a_{a,\ell} \mid a \in \{0,1\}, \ell \in \{1, \ldots, p\}\}^s$$

As an example, consider $Y = \{\{\alpha_1, \alpha_2, \alpha_3\}, \{0, 1\}, T\}$ where

$$T = \{\langle \alpha_1, -1, 1, 0, \alpha_3 \rangle, \langle \alpha_3, -1, 0, 1, \alpha_2 \rangle\}$$

Figure 8 shows the subgraph of $\mathit{graph}(C_Y)$ for the variables with superscripts s, $0s$, and $1s$. The entire $\mathit{graph}(C_Y)$ is infinite. In particular, $\mathit{graph}(C_Y)$ can be obtained by repeating the structure in the diagram. That is, there are edges between α_1^{0s} and α_3^{00s}, edges between α_1^{0s} and γ_1^{00s}, edges between α_3^{0s} and α_2^{10s}, and so on. Pictorially, $\mathit{graph}(C_Y)$ is an infinite binary tree such that for any s, variables with

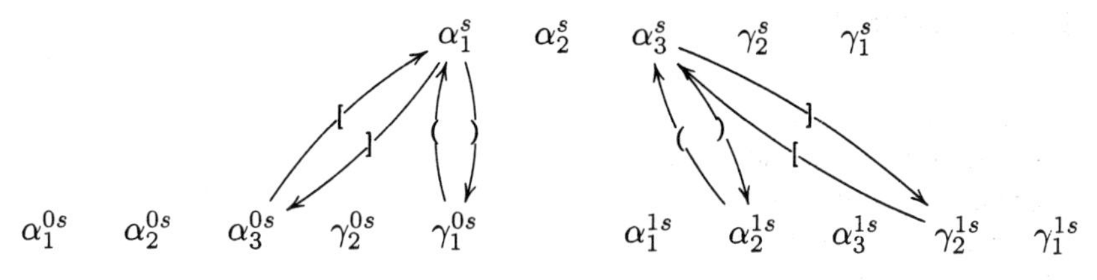

Figure 8. Example.

the superscript s collectively form a node (s-node) with the $0s$-node being the left child and the $1s$-node being the right child. Note that any edge may only connect a variable in a parent node with a variable in its child node.

We now construct the term e_Y. We use the vector notation $\overrightarrow{x}$ to denote a sequence of variables. We write $\lambda\overrightarrow{x}.e$ to mean $id(\lambda x_1.id(\lambda x_2.\ldots id(\lambda x_n.e)))$ where $\overrightarrow{x} = x_1, \ldots, x_n$. We write $e'\overrightarrow{x}$ to mean the sequence of function applications $e'\, x_1\, x_2 \ldots x_n$ where $\overrightarrow{x} = x_1, \ldots, x_n$.

For each $\alpha \in Q$, let x_α be a distinct variable. For each γ_ℓ, let y_ℓ be a distinct program variable. For each $M_\ell = \langle \alpha, -1, b, a, \beta \rangle$, define terms $e_{a,\ell}$ and $v_{a,\ell}$ as follows:

$$e_{a,\ell} \equiv \begin{cases} x_\beta \times y_\ell & \text{if } b = 0 \\ y_\ell \times x_\beta & \text{if } b = 1 \end{cases}$$
$$v_{a,\ell} \equiv x_\alpha$$

For each $a \in \{0,1\}$, let $e_a = e_{a,1} \times e_{a,2} \times \ldots \times e_{a,n}$ and $v_a = v_{a,1} \times v_{a,2} \times \ldots \times v_{a,n}$. Recall that $e \times e'$ is defined in Figure 3. Let $X = \mathit{fvars}(e_0) \cup \mathit{fvars}(e_1) \cup \mathit{fvars}(v_0) \cup \mathit{fvars}(v_1)$. Let d_0 and d_1 be distinct variables not in X. Let $\overrightarrow{x}$ be a sequence of variables from $X \cup \{d_0, d_1\}$. Let $\overrightarrow{z}$ be distinct variables not in $\overrightarrow{x}$ such that $|\overrightarrow{z}| = |\overrightarrow{x}|$. Let

$$\begin{aligned} e_Y = {} & \mathtt{fix}\ f.\lambda\overrightarrow{x}. \\ & (\lambda\overrightarrow{z}.\mathtt{same}(f^0\ \overrightarrow{z}, v_0 \times d_0)); \\ & (\lambda\overrightarrow{z}.\mathtt{same}(f^1\ \overrightarrow{z}, d_1 \times v_1)); \\ & (e_0 \times e_1) \end{aligned}$$

Recall that $e; e'$ and $\mathtt{same}(e, e')$ are defined in Figure 3. Let $(\tau, C, X) = [\![e_Y]\!]_\emptyset$. C is not exactly C_Y, but simple algebraic manipulation shows that $\models_{fin} C$ iff $\models_{fin} C_Y$.

We now show that Y_S is bounded iff positive paths in $graph(C_Y)$ have a bounded depth. For a positive string t, let $r(t)$ be reverse of t with) replaced by 0 and] replaced by 1. For an infinitely long sequence w, let $w|_n$ be the string consisting of the first n symbols of w. For a string $s \in \{0,1\}^*$, let $s0^\infty$ be an infinitely long sequence w such that $w|_{|s|} = s$ and the ith symbol of w is 0 for all $i > |s|$. For clarity, we sometimes write $s_1@s_2$ to mean the concatenation $s_1 s_2$. We show that if Y_S is bounded then positive paths in $graph(C_Y)$ have a bounded depth.

Lemma 5.2 *Let p be a path from α^{s_1} to β^{s_2} in $graph(C_Y)$ such that $sm(p)$ is a positive string. Then $\langle w@r(sm(p)), \alpha, m, s_1 0^\infty \rangle$ and $\langle w, \beta, m - |sm(p)|, s_2 0^\infty \rangle$ are reachable from each other in Y_S.*

We now prove the other direction, i.e., if positive paths in $graph(C_Y)$ have a bounded depth then Y_S is bounded.

Lemma 5.3 *Suppose $\langle w@r(t_1), \alpha, m, s_1 0^\infty \rangle$ and $\langle w@r(t_2), \beta, m - |t_1| + |t_2|, s_2 0^\infty \rangle$ are reachable from each other in Y_S without moving the head below the position $m - |t_1|$ and without moving the head above the position $m + |s_1|$. Further suppose $|t_1| + |s_1| = |t_2| + |s_2|$. Suppose $\alpha^{s_1} \overset{t_1}{\rightsquigarrow} \gamma^{s_3}$ in $graph(C_Y)$. Then $\beta^{s_2} \overset{t_2}{\rightsquigarrow} \gamma^{s_3}$ in $graph(C_Y)$.*

Lemma 5.4 *Suppose there is an ID of Y_S from which the head can be moved n positions left or right. Then there exists a positive path of depth n in $graph(Y_S)$.*

Proof: Suppose $\langle w_1, \alpha, m, w_1' \rangle$ and $\langle w_2, \beta, m + n, w_2' \rangle$ are reachable from each other. Consider a series of transitions from $\langle w_1, \alpha, m, w_1' \rangle$ to $\langle w_2, \beta, m + n, w_2' \rangle$. Let $\langle w_3, \gamma, m, w_3' \rangle$ be an intermediate ID in this series such that following transitions in the series do not move the head below the position m. Note that such an ID must always exist. Let m' be the highest position reached during the series of transitions. Let $s_3 = w_3'|_{m'-m}$ and $s_2 = w_2'|_{m'-(m+n)}$. Let t be the string such that $w_3 t = w_2$. Note that $|t| = n$. We thus have $\langle w_3, \gamma, m, s_3 0^\infty \rangle$ and $\langle w_3 t, \beta, m - |t|, s_2 0^\infty \rangle$ reachable from each other without moving the head below the position m and without moving the head above the position $m' = m + |s_3|$. Also, $|s_3| = m' - m = |t| + |s_2|$. Trivially, $\gamma^{s_3} \overset{\epsilon}{\rightsquigarrow} \gamma^{s_3}$. Therefore, by Lemma 5.3, $\beta^{s_2} \overset{t}{\rightsquigarrow} \gamma^{s_3}$. □

From Lemma 5.2 and Lemma 5.4, it follows that,

Lemma 5.5 *Y_S is bounded iff there exists a positive integer n such that for any positive path p in $graph(C_Y)$, $depth(p) \leq n$.*

Finally, by Lemma 4.1, Lemma 4.2, Lemma 4.4, Lemma 5.5 and Theorem 5.1,

Theorem 5.6 *Typability of* $\mathbf{I}_2$ + **REC-INT** *is undecidable.*

6 Insufficiency of Unification Tests

One way to cope with the undecidability result is to reject some typable terms for the sake of an incomplete but terminating typability algorithm. Mycroft [10] proposed the following test as a rejection method for the Milner-Mycroft type system. For each `fix` $x.e$ and each occurrence of x in e, unify the type of the body e with the type of the occurrence of x and check that the constraints are satisfiable. The test rejects the term if any of the constraints are unsatisfiable, and otherwise runs the actual type inference algorithm hoping to have rejected any "bad" term that would make the algorithm diverge. For example, this method rejects the term `fix` $x.x\,x$ (which is typable in the Milner-Mycroft type system) because unifying the type of the first occurrence of x with the type of the body $x\,x$ results in a constraint of the form $\alpha \rightarrow \beta = \beta$, which is unsatisfiable. Here, we show that not only is this test insufficient for designing a terminating typability algorithm for $\mathbf{I}_2 +$ **REC-INT**, but it is actually not sufficient even for the Milner-Mycroft type system.

We claim the following.

Lemma 6.1 *Suppose* $[\![\texttt{fix}\,x.e]\!]_\emptyset = (\tau, C, X)$ *and* C *is finitary satisfiable. Then for any* $s \in \{a \mid x^a \in \mathit{fvars}(e)\}^*$, $C \cup \{\tau^s = \tau\}$ *is still finitary satisfiable.*

Let $[\![\texttt{fix}\,x.e]\!]_\emptyset = (\tau, C, X)$. Suppose e contains no occurrence of `fix`. Then, applying the unification test in Lemma 6.1 for each string of length 1 (i.e., single characters) is more conservative than Mycroft's unification test. That is, if $C \cup \{\tau = \tau^a\}$ is satisfiable for each a in the alphabet $\{a \mid x^a \in \mathit{fvars}(e)\}$, then `fix` $x.e$ passes Mycroft's unification test. However, Lemma 4.2 and Lemma 6.1 imply that these tests do not reject any typable term of the form `fix` $x.e$. Recall e_Y from Section 5 is of the form `fix` $x.e$ such that e contains no occurrence of `fix`. Because the proof of Theorem 5.6 shows that even typability of e_Y terms is undecidable for $\mathbf{I}_2 +$ **REC-INT**, it follows that Mycroft's unification test is insufficient for designing an incomplete but terminating typability algorithm for $\mathbf{I}_2 +$ **REC-INT**.

Furthermore, it can be shown from the proof of undecidability of the Milner-Mycroft type system [7, 3] that a term of the form e_Y is typable in the Milner-Mycroft type system iff Y_S is bounded. Therefore, somewhat surprisingly, e_Y is typable in the Milner-Mycroft type system iff it is typable in $\mathbf{I}_2 +$ **REC-INT**. Thus, Mycroft's unification test is insufficient for an incomplete but terminating typability algorithm even for the Milner-Mycroft type system.

In fact, Lemma 6.1 implies an even stronger result. An algorithm that tests $\tau = \tau^s$ for all strings s (not just single characters), regardless of whether such an algorithm exists or not, would be insufficient. More precisely,

$$\begin{array}{rcl} \alpha \sqcup \beta & = & \begin{cases} \alpha & \text{if } \beta < \alpha \\ \beta & \text{otherwise} \end{cases} \\ \alpha \sqcup (\tau \rightarrow \tau') & = & \tau \rightarrow \tau' \\ (\tau \rightarrow \tau') \sqcup \alpha & = & \tau \rightarrow \tau' \\ (\tau_1 \rightarrow \tau_2) \sqcup (\tau_1' \rightarrow \tau_2') & = & (\tau_1 \sqcup \tau_1') \rightarrow (\tau_2 \sqcup \tau_2) \end{array}$$

Figure 9. $S_1 \sqcup S_2$.

Corollary 6.2 *Let*

$$\begin{array}{rcl} A & = & \{\texttt{fix}\,x.e \mid [\![\texttt{fix}\,x.e]\!]_\emptyset = (\tau, C, X) \\ & & \wedge \forall s \in \{a \mid x^a \in \mathit{fvars}(e)\}^*. \\ & & \models_{\mathit{fin}} C \cup \{\tau^s = \tau\}\} \end{array}$$

The following problem is undecidable. Let e be a closed term such that there exists e′ ∈ A such that e′ is e with each occurrence of a `fix`*-bound variable annotated with a distinct number. Decide whether e is typable in* $\mathbf{I}_2 +$ **REC-INT**.

Corollary 6.2 follows from the fact that untypability of $\mathbf{I}_2 +$ **REC-INT** is not recursively enumerable (since typability is recursively enumerable). An analogous result holds for the Milner-Mycroft type system.

We now prove Lemma 6.1. Let $<$ be some total ordering over the type variables. Figure 9 defines the operation $\sqcup$ over the types. Note that $\sqcup$ is associative and commutative. We extend $\sqcup$ to constraint assignments as follows:

$$S_1 \sqcup S_2 = \{\alpha \mapsto S_1(\alpha) \sqcup S_2(\alpha) \mid \alpha \in \mathit{dom}(S_1) \cap \mathit{dom}(S_2)\}$$

Clearly, if S_1 and S_2 are both finite range then so is $S_1 \sqcup S_2$. Furthermore, if S_1 and S_2 both satisfy C, then so does $S_1 \sqcup S_2$, i.e.,

Lemma 6.3 *Suppose* $S_1 \models C$ *and* $S_2 \models C$. *Then* $S_1 \sqcup S_2 \models C$.

The following lemma says that we may "shift up" solutions for a constraint set of the form $\bigcup_{s \in \Sigma^*} C^s$.

Lemma 6.4 *Let* C *be a set of constraints and* Σ *be an alphabet. Let* $C' = \bigcup_{s \in \Sigma^*} C^s$. *Suppose* $S \models C'$. *Then for any* $s \in \Sigma^*$, $\{\alpha \mapsto S(\alpha^s)\} \models C'$.

We are now ready to prove Lemma 6.1, restated here.

Lemma 6.1 *Suppose* $[\![\texttt{fix}\,x.e]\!]_\emptyset = (\tau, C, X)$ *and* C *is finitary satisfiable. Then for any* $s \in \{a \mid x^a \in \mathit{fvars}(e)\}^*$, $C \cup \{\tau^s = \tau\}$ *is still finitary satisfiable.*

Proof: By inspection of the constraint generation rules (Figure 5), it must be the case that τ is a base type variable, say $\tau = \alpha$. Let $S \models_{\mathit{fin}} C$. We use the notation t^i to mean a string t concatenated i times. Since $\mathit{ran}(S)$ is finite, there must be m and n such that $m < n$ and $S(\alpha^{s^m}) = S(\alpha^{s^n})$.

For each $i \geq 0$, let $S_i = \{\beta \mapsto S(\beta^{s^i}) \mid \beta \in \mathit{dom}(S)\}$. By Lemma 6.4, it must be the case that $S_i \models C$ for each S_i. Furthermore, since $\mathit{ran}(S_i) \subseteq \mathit{ran}(S)$, each S_i is a finite range solution. Note that for each $i > 0$ and a type variable β, $S_i(\beta) = S_{i-1}(\beta^s)$. Also, $S(\alpha^{s^m}) = S(\alpha^{s^n})$ implies that $S_m(\alpha) = S_n(\alpha) = S_{n-1}(\alpha^s)$. Therefore,

$$\begin{aligned}
&(\textstyle\bigsqcup_{m \leq i \leq (n-1)} S_i)(\alpha) \\
&\quad = S_m(\alpha) \sqcup S_{m+1}(\alpha) \sqcup \ldots \sqcup S_{n-1}(\alpha) \\
&\quad = S_{n-1}(\alpha^s) \sqcup S_m(\alpha^s) \sqcup \ldots \sqcup S_{n-2}(\alpha^s) \\
&\quad = (\textstyle\bigsqcup_{m \leq i \leq (n-1)} S_i)(\alpha^s)
\end{aligned}$$

But by Lemma 6.3, $(\bigsqcup_{m \leq i \leq (n-1)} S_i) \models C$. Since each S_i is finite range, so is $\bigsqcup_{m \leq i \leq (n-1)} S_i$. Therefore, $(\bigsqcup_{m \leq i \leq (n-1)} S_i) \models_{\mathit{fin}} C \cup \{\alpha = \alpha^s\}$. □

7 Undecidability of REC-REACH

The constraint generation in Section 4 motivates the following program analysis problem. We extend the language with two constants, `red` and `blue`, and extend the constraint generation as follows:

$$\begin{aligned}
[\![\texttt{red}]\!]_\Gamma &= (\mathit{red}, \emptyset, \emptyset) \\
[\![\texttt{blue}]\!]_\Gamma &= (\mathit{blue}, \emptyset, \emptyset)
\end{aligned}$$

Here, *red* and *blue* are base type variables distinct from all other type variables. The problem is to check that there exists no path of the form $\mathit{red}^{s_1} \overset{\epsilon}{\leadsto} \mathit{blue}^{s_2}$. Let us call this program analysis **REC-REACH**. This kind of *reachability* query is commonly seen in CFL-based program analyses [14] with applications in control flow analysis, points-to analysis, and other safety analyses. **REC-REACH** is a straightforward polymorphic recursive extension of a simple monomorphic unification-based flow analysis.

We use the framework developed in this paper to prove that **REC-REACH** is undecidable. In fact, it is not even recursively enumerable, which implies that there exists no type system equivalent to **REC-REACH** (in the sense of [11, 12]). While **REC-REACH** looks similar to the problem studied by Reps [15], our CFL graphs are more constrained, and we do not know whether his proof approach can be adopted.

Let $Y = \langle Q, A, T\rangle$ be an ITM such that $\mathit{red}, \mathit{blue} \in Q$. We build e_Y and obtain C_Y as in Section 5. Obviously, both Lemma 5.2 and Lemma 5.3 still hold. Furthermore, it is apparent from its proof that Lemma 5.2 can be strengthened to the following:

Lemma 7.1 *Let p be a path from α^{s_1} to β^{s_2} in graph(C_Y) such that sm(p) is a positive string. Then $\langle w@r(\mathit{sm}(p)), \alpha, m, s_1 0^\infty\rangle$ and $\langle w, \beta, m - |\mathit{sm}(p)|, s_2 0^\infty\rangle$ are reachable from each other in Y_S without moving the head below the position $m - |\mathit{sm}(p)|$.*

Combining Lemma 7.1 and Lemma 5.3, we have the following:

Lemma 7.2 *The following are equivalent:*

(1) There exists s_1 and s_2 such that there exists a path $\mathit{red}^{s_1} \overset{\epsilon}{\leadsto} \mathit{blue}^{s_2}$ in graph(C_Y).

(2) There exists w_1 and w_2 such that $\langle w, \mathit{red}, m, w_1\rangle$ and $\langle w, \mathit{blue}, m, w_2\rangle$ are reachable from each other in Y_S without moving the head below the position m.

(3) There exists w_1, w_2, and an ID W such that $\langle w, \mathit{red}, m, w_1\rangle$ reaches W in Y without moving the head below the position m and $\langle w, \mathit{blue}, m, w_2\rangle$ reaches W in Y without moving the head below the position m.

Problem (3) can be proved to be undecidable via the reduction from the halting problem. Therefore, problem (1) is undecidable. It is easy to see that problem (1) is recursively enumerable. Since **REC-REACH** is the dual of problem (1), it follows that

Theorem 7.3 **REC-REACH** *is not recursively enumerable.*

8 Conclusions

This paper shows that typability of $\mathbf{I}_2 + $**REC-INT** is undecidable by means of characterizing typability as a CFL graph problem and reducing from the boundedness problem of Turing machines. We found reducing to an infinite graph problem leads to a more understandable proof than reasoning directly on infinite type constraints. We suspect that a similar proof can be used to show that the problem remains undecidable for extensions to any higher rank (e.g., the system investigated in [2]).

As a corollary of the undecidability result, we showed that the unification test is insufficient to build an incomplete but terminating typability algorithm for $\mathbf{I}_2 + $**REC-INT** or the Milner-Mycroft type system. We also proved undecidability of the related program analysis **REC-REACH** by using the same CFL graph framework.

One open question is whether the following problem is decidable. Given a closed e, is there S such that $S \models C$ where $[\![e]\!]_\emptyset = (\tau, C, X)$ for some τ and X? Note that if we strengthened the requirement to $S \models_{\mathit{fin}} C$ then the problem becomes the typability problem for $\mathbf{I}_2 + $**REC-INT** and therefore becomes undecidable. There is a larger open question: where the boundary between decidability and undecidability is when it comes to polymorphic recursion (and how to state this question in a formal way).

References

[1] F. Damiani. Rank-2 intersection and polymorphic recursion. In *Typed Lambda Calculi and Applications: 7th International Conference (TLCA 2005)*, volume 3461 of *LNCS*, pages 146–161. Springer, Apr. 2005.

[2] J. J. Hallett and A. J. Kfoury. Programming examples needing polymorphic recursion. In *In Proceedings 3rd International Workshop Intersection Types and Related Systems (ITRS 2004)*, pages 57–102, 2004.

[3] F. Henglein. Type inference with polymorphic recursion. *ACM Transactions on Programming Languages and Systems*, 15(2):253–289, Apr. 1993.

[4] T. Jim. Rank 2 type systems and recursive definitions. Technical Report MIT/LCS/TM-531, Cambridge, MA, USA, 1995.

[5] T. Jim. What are principal typings and what are they good for? In *Proceedings of the 23rd Annual ACM SIGPLAN-SIGACT Symposium on Principles of Programming Languages*, pages 42–53, St. Petersburg Beach, Florida, Jan. 1996.

[6] A. J. Kfoury, H. G. Mairson, F. A. Turbak, and J. B. Wells. Relating typability and expressiveness in finite-rank intersection type systems (extended abstract). In *Proceedings of the fourth ACM SIGPLAN International Conference on Functional Programming*, pages 90–101, Paris, France, Sept. 1999.

[7] A. J. Kfoury, J. Tiuryn, and P. Urzyczyn. The undecidability of the semi-unification problem. *Information and Computation*, 102(1):83–101, 1993.

[8] A. J. Kfoury and J. B. Wells. Principality and type inference for intersection types using expansion variables. *Theoretical Computer Science*, 311:1–70, 2004.

[9] D. Leivant. Polymorphic type inference. In *Proceedings of the 10th Annual ACM SIGPLAN-SIGACT Symposium on Principles of Programming Languages*, pages 88–98, Austin, Texas, 1983.

[10] A. Mycroft. Polymorphic type schemes and recursive definitions. In *Proceedings of the 6th International Conference on Programming*, number 167 in LNCS, 1984.

[11] J. Palsberg and P. O'Keefe. A type system equivalent to flow analysis. In *Proceedings of the 22nd Annual ACM SIGPLAN-SIGACT Symposium on Principles of Programming Languages*, pages 367–378, San Francisco, California, Jan. 1995.

[12] J. Palsberg and C. Pavlopoulou. From polyvariant flow information to intersection and union types. In *Proceedings of the 25th Annual ACM SIGPLAN-SIGACT Symposium on Principles of Programming Languages*, pages 197–208, San Diego, California, Jan. 1998.

[13] J. Rehof and M. Fähndrich. Type-based flow analysis: From polymorphic subtyping to cfl-reachability. In *Proceedings of the 28th Annual ACM SIGPLAN-SIGACT Symposium on Principles of Programming Languages*, pages 54–66, London, United Kingdom, Jan. 2001.

[14] T. Reps. Program analysis via graph reachability. *Information and Software Technology*, 40(11/12):701–726, November/December 1998.

[15] T. Reps. Undecidability of context-sensitive data-dependence analysis. *ACM Transactions on Programming Languages and Systems*, 22(1):162–186, 2000.

[16] T. Terauchi and A. Aiken. On typability for rank-2 intersection types with polymorphic recursion. Technical Report UCB/EECS-2006-66, University of California, Berkeley, May 2006.

[17] J. B. Wells. The essence of principal typings. In *Proc. 29th Int'l Coll. Automata, Languages, and Programming*, volume 2380 of *LNCS*, pages 913–925. Springer-Verlag, 2002.

Invited Talk

Adapting Logics

Andreas Blass
Mathematics Department, University of Michigan, Ann Arbor, MI 48109, U.S.A., and
Microsoft Research, One Microsoft Way, Redmond, WA 98052, U.S.A.
ablass@umich.edu

1. Introduction

I plan to survey some of the adaptations and variations of logic that have been introduced for various purposes. For obvious reasons, I shall concentrate mainly on purposes related to computer science and on adaptations that have played a role in my own research. Along the way, I shall touch on some open problems.

2. Prehistory

Long ago, there was only logic, not logics in the current sense. Logic was intended to capture all the laws of precise thought. First-order logic (FO) was singled out, for foundational purposes, by Skolem's proposal that the notion of "definite property" in Zermelo's axioms of set theory be taken to mean "first-order definable property." FO remained a special fragment of logic, as indicated by names like "der engere Funktionenkalkül" and even by "first order," but it grew in importance as its model theory was developed in ways that were impossible for more powerful logics.

An essential prerequisite for Skolem's foundational use of first-order logic was the discovery by Dedekind, amplified by Zermelo, that inductive definitions can be made explicit by first-order formulations, in the context of set theory.

3. Inductive Definitions

Once logic began to be used systematically in computer science, the extensions of FO by inductive definitions — especially the least fixed-point construct (LFP) but also the inflationary fixed point (IFP) and partial fixed point (PFP) — became important in several ways: to remedy the obvious weakness of FO as a database query language, in the characterization of complexity classes like PTime on ordered finite structures, and in the description of pre- and post-conditions for certain sorts of programs. For some of these purposes, a natural logic is obtained by, on the one hand, adding LFP to FO but, on the other hand, removing universal quantification (and therefore some uses of negation). The resulting existential least-fixed-point logic (∃LFP) was given a reasonable, though necessarily infinitary, axiomatization by Compton. There are apparently open questions about what can be proved in a natural, finitary axiomatization of FO+LFP.

In formalizing ∃LFP, it was convenient to distinguish *negatable* and *positive* predicate symbols. For similar reasons, it is natural to soften the prohibition of universal quantification by working with a multi-sorted logic and allowing ∀ over some sorts. The places where negation and ∀ are allowed are intuitively those governed by a "closed world" assumption.

I plan to comment on the curious situation of LFP and IFP, which have the same expressive power (Gurevich, Shelah, Kreutzer) yet support very different computational intuitions. If time permits, I'll also touch on the connection of ∃LFP with topos theory, the possible computational significance of this connection, and a related open problem.

4. Games

The idea of a logic of games grew slowly, from Lorenzen's attempt to characterize intuitionistic logic by dialogs, through my observation that natural operations on games obey Girard's linear logic (and more), to exact matches between formal systems and game semantics. The exact matches are obtained in two ways: Modify game semantics to obtain completeness, indeed full completeness, for linear logic (Abramsky, Jagadeesan, Hyland, Ong), or insist on a natural game semantics and seek a complete axiomatization for it (Japaridze). In the latter direction, Japaridze has a sound and complete axiomatization for a large part of the logic (with additive and multiplicative connectives), but it has an unorthodox flavor for a logical system. It would be interesting to obtain a more traditional-looking axiomatization, or to understand why such a thing is impossible.

1043-6871/06 $20.00 © 2006 IEEE

Session 4:
Logics of Programs

Managing Digital Rights using Linear Logic

Adam Barth
Stanford University
abarth@cs.stanford.edu

John C. Mitchell
Stanford University
mitchell@cs.stanford.edu

Abstract

Digital music players protect songs by enforcing licenses that convey specific rights for individual songs or groups of songs. For licenses specified in industry, we show that deciding whether a license authorizes a sequence of actions is NP-complete, with a restricted version of the problem solvable efficiently using a reduction to maximum network flow. The authorization algorithm used in industry is online, deciding which rights to exercise as actions occur, but we show that all online algorithms are necessarily non-monotonic*: each allows actions under one license that it does not allow under a more flexible license. In one approach to achieving monotonicity, we exhibit the unique maximal set of licenses on which there exists a monotonic online algorithm. This set of well-behaved licenses induces an approximation algorithm by replacing each license with a well-behaved license. In a second approach, we consider allowing the player to revise its past decisions about which rights to exercise while still ensuring compliance with the license. We propose an efficient algorithm based on Linear Logic, with linear negation used to revise past decisions. We prove our algorithm monotonic, live, and sound with respect to the semantics of licenses.*

1 Introduction

Media players, such as iTunes and Windows Media Player, can impose restrictions on the use of media though Digital Rights Management (DRM). DRM systems typically separate content from licenses, employing a trusted DRM agent in media players to ensure that consumers do not exceed the digital rights granted by licenses. In this model, consumers can download encrypted songs from unsecured servers but are unable to play the songs without a license. A music provider can distribute promotional "play once" licenses to allow potential customers to hear songs and decide whether to purchase licenses for additional plays or for additional devices. Music providers can also sell time-limited licenses that allow unlimited plays during a fixed time period or sell subscription licenses that allow a fixed total number of plays the consumer can allocate among music from a large library.

In this paper, we explore some logical and algorithmic problems related to the use and management of licenses both concretely, in an language from industry, and abstractly, in a language based on Propositional Linear Logic. A license is a collection of individual rights, each of which is defined by one or more constraints. To authorize an action, a DRM agent exercises a right, perhaps consuming it completely or leaving behind a residual right. A DRM agent might hold several rights that authorize the same action. The choice of which of these rights to exercise when the consumer performs the action impacts what future actions are allowed under the license because rights maintain state. For example, if an agent holds a right to play either song a or b once, and the agent exercises that right to play song a, then the agent has foreclosed the ability to exercise that right to play song b. The agent can either prompt the consumer to make this choice, or it make the choice automatically.

Previous work on rights expression languages [4, 7, 1] treats the choice of which right to exercise exogenously, requiring the assignment of actions to rights as input to the authorization algorithm. We believe this provides a poor user experience, however, and that the choice should be made by the agent automatically. This choice is complicated because many languages, including XrML [2] (based on [9]) and ODRL [5] (a descendant of DigiBox [8]), support rights allowing the consumer to allocate a fixed total number of plays among several songs, for example allowing a consumer a fixed number of plays from a particular album. Although many of our results are general, we focus our discussion on version 2.0 of the Rights Expression Language [6] specified by the Open Mobile Alliance (OMA), a large industry consortium whose members include Cingular, Intel, Microsoft, and Nokia. In addition to providing for manual allocation, the OMA explicitly specify an algorithm for allocating actions to rights, but this algorithm is unsatisfactory because it leads to certain anomalies, as illustrated in the following example.

Example. Consider an online music scenario in which Alice receives some promotional rights to play several digital songs on a mobile music player. Alice visits the music web site and enters her promotional code. The site encrypts several songs (a, b, and c) and transfers them to her mobile music player, along with the right to play the songs a total of ten times. Alice plays song a twice, b four times, and c three times, for a total of nine plays. The DRM agent in her music player decrypts the songs, allows Alice to play the songs, and notes that she has one play remaining.

The following day, Alice receives another promotion. Pleased with her previous experience, she returns to the music web site and is offered the choice of two rights. The first is the right to play song d once before the end of the month. The second is the right to play either song a or song d once before the end of the month. She opts for the second right because she reasons that it is more flexible. The rights Alice now possesses are summarized below:

1. Play either song a, b, or c (acquired the first day).
2. Play either song a or d before the end of the month.

Alice decides to first play song a and then play song d. She reason this should be permitted by her rights because the first play should be authorized by her first right and the second play should be authorized by her second right. The DRM agent in her mobile music player, however, forbids her from playing song d because it exercised the second right to play song a, leaving Alice without the right to play song d. In fact, had Alice opted for the less flexible first option, the DRM agent would have allowed Alice to play those songs (as it would have been forced to assign the play of a to the first right). Alice is infuriated.

Monotonicity. The particular algorithm the OMA specifies for assigning actions to rights is non-monotonic in the sense that a sequence of actions allowed under one license might not be allowed under a more flexible license. In fact, we show that all algorithms that assign actions to rights *as the actions occur* are non-monotonic with respect to license flexibility. Each such online algorithm allows a sequence of actions under one right that it does not allow under a more flexible right because it must commit to exercising certain rights without knowledge of future actions.

We suggest that a trusted DRM agent need not assign actions to rights as the actions occur. The agent need only ensure that the complete sequence of actions performed does not exceed the license. After being requested to perform further actions, the agent is free to reassign actions to different rights because no one observes which rights are exercised for which actions. If the consumer wishes to perform an otherwise foreclosed action, the agent can revise its past commitments and authorize the action. With this added flexibility, the agent is able to perform monotonically.

Results. In this paper, we consider the static case, where consumers first acquire rights and then perform actions. We show that offline authorization for the OMA Rights Expression Language is NP-complete, but we exhibit a polynomial-time algorithm for a substantial fragment of the language by reducing the restricted problem to maximum network flow. We then show (under some technical conditions) that all online algorithms, including the algorithm specified by the OMA, fail to be monotonic.

To investigate monotonic algorithms, we interpret a conjunctive fragment of Propositional Linear Logic [3] as a rights expression language (extending the tractable OMA licenses). The logical formalism of syntax, semantics, and deduction facilitate a precise exposition of two approaches to achieving monotonicity. The first approach syntactically characterizes the unique maximal set of licenses on which there exists a monotonic online algorithm. These well-behaved licenses induce a monotonic "over-approximation" by approximating arbitrary licenses with "nearby" well-behaved licenses. The second approach relaxes the requirement that a DRM agent commit to exercising rights as actions occur. An agent using a rights expression language enriched with linear negation can use the negated terms to revise its past assignment of actions to rights. These more expressive rights admit an efficient authorization algorithm that is both sound and monotonic.

Without the contraction rule, Linear Logic easily expresses that a right can be exercised only a fixed number of times. The lack of the weakening rule seems less essential, but does ensure that agents do not drop rights indiscriminately. Although a more thorough study might conclude that another substructural logic is more appropriate, Linear Logic provides a convenient logical basis for investigating digital rights. In this treatment, licenses transform via linear implication to authorize actions. The operator & captures flexibility within a right and $\otimes$ captures the combination of rights into licenses.

The remainder of the paper is organized as follows. Section 2 describes the OMA Rights Expression Language and contains our complexity results. Section 3 demonstrates the non-monotonicity of online schemes for OMA licenses. Section 4 introduces Linear Logic semantics for digital rights. Section 5 concludes.

2 Offline Authorization for DRM Licenses

In this section, we consider the offline evaluation of Digital Rights Management licenses, specifically determining whether a sequence of actions complies with a license. We show that answering this question for the OMA Rights Expression Language is NP-complete and then exhibit a fragment of the OMA language in which authorization can be decided in polynomial time.

The computational complexity arises because a given action might be authorized by several rights within a license. As these rights have state, further authorizations depend on which right is exercised for the given action. Once actions are assigned to rights, evaluating a license is simple, but determining the assignment is computationally complex. We begin by describing the OMA Rights Expression Language.

2.1 OMA Rights Expression Language

In the OMA Rights Expression Language, a license is a forest of trees whose nodes are rights. Each right is defined by a list of constraints. A right authorizes an action if all of its constraints (and all the constraints of its ancestor rights) are satisfied. After allowing an action, an agent updates its state by transforming the constraints of the exercised right.

Actions. An action is defined by a number of parameters, including the principal performing the action, the kind of action (e.g., "play"), and the digital content on which the action is performed. Formally, an action is defined as a tuple (p, s, k, d, t, m) where

- p is the principal performing the action,
- s is the system performing the action,
- k is the kind of action,
- d is the date on which the action occurs,
- t is the duration of the action, and
- m is the digital content the action is performed on.

Rights. A right is defined by a list of constraints. These constraints can be stateful (e.g., "use this right at most five times") or temporal (e.g., "use this right only after January 1, 2006"). We consider nine kinds of constraints, listed below, that are satisfied by action (p, s, k, d, t, m) as follows:

- $\mathrm{Individual}(\hat{p})$ is satisfied if $p = \hat{p}$.
- $\mathrm{System}(\hat{s})$ is satisfied if $s = \hat{s}$.
- $\mathrm{Kind}(K)$ is satisfied if $k \in K$.
- $\mathrm{Date}(d_1, d_2)$ is satisfied if $d_1 \leq d \leq d + t \leq d_2$.
- $\mathrm{Content}(\hat{m})$ is satisfied if $m = \hat{m}$.
- $\mathrm{Count}(n)$ is satisfied if $n > 0$.
- $\mathrm{Interval}(\hat{t})$ is always satisfied.
- $\mathrm{Accumulated}(\hat{t})$ is satisfied if $t \leq \hat{t}$.
- $\mathrm{TimedCount}(n, \hat{t})$ is satisfied if $n > 0$.

Constraints are "subtractive:" including additional constraints reduces the circumstances in which a right can be exercised. For example, a right with the constraints $\mathrm{Count}(5)$ and $\mathrm{Count}(3)$ can be exercised only three times.[1]

Exercising a right can modify its state, for example reducing the number of plays remaining from five to four. This is modeled by transforming the $\mathrm{Count}(5)$ constraint into a $\mathrm{Count}(4)$ constraint. The stateful constraints of a right exercised to authorize action (p, s, k, d, t, m) are transformed as follows:

$$\begin{aligned}
\mathrm{Count}(n) &\leadsto \mathrm{Count}(n-1) \\
\mathrm{Interval}(\hat{t}) &\leadsto \mathrm{Date}(d, d+\hat{t}) \\
\mathrm{Accumulated}(\hat{t}) &\leadsto \mathrm{Accumulated}(\hat{t}-t) \\
\mathrm{TimedCount}(n, \hat{t}) &\leadsto \mathrm{TimedCount}(n-1, \hat{t})
\end{aligned}$$

The timed count transformation occurs only if $t > \hat{t}$. These transformations ensure, for example, that a right with constraint $\mathrm{Count}(n)$ is exercised at most n times and that a right with constraint $\mathrm{Interval}(\hat{t})$ is only exercised within t time units of when it is first exercised. The computational complexity of deciding whether a license authorizes a sequence of actions arises from selecting which rights to exercise for which actions.

Licenses. A license organizes rights as nodes in a forest of trees. The edges impose an "inheritance" relation on rights. A right can be exercised only if (1) it has no descendants, (2) all of its constraints are satisfied, and (3) the constraints of all of its ancestors are satisfied. When a right is exercised, its constraints, as well as the constraints of all of its ancestor rights in the tree, are transformed. Thus, state maintained by a right is effectively shared by its descendants. For example, consider the license with rights r_1 and r_2, descendants of right r, constrained as follows:

$$\begin{aligned}
r &: \mathrm{Count}(5) \\
r_1 &: \mathrm{Kind}(\mathrm{Play}), \mathrm{Content}(a) \\
r_2 &: \mathrm{Kind}(\mathrm{Play}), \mathrm{Content}(b)
\end{aligned}$$

This license authorizes a consumer to play both songs a and b, but only five times in total. The consumer can play song a three times and song b twice, or a twice and b three times, but not a three times and b three times. The OMA Rights Expression Language restricts inheritance to one level, requiring that child rights not in turn be parent rights.

[1] The OMA specification is ambiguous regarding whether an action that exhausts an accumulated constraint can be continued using another right. We assume an action (p, s, k, d, t, m) that exhausts a right with constraint $\mathrm{Accumulated}(\hat{t})$ can be decomposed into two actions $(p, s, k, d, \hat{t}, m)$ and $(p, s, k, d + \hat{t}, t - \hat{t}, m)$, provided $\hat{t} \leq t$.

2.2 Complexity of Authorization

In the OMA Rights Expression Language, deciding whether a license authorizes a sequence of actions is NP-complete. The difficulty stems from interval constraints (with inheritance) because it is hard to determine when to first exercise a right with an interval constraint. Exercising a right with an interval constraint transforms that constraint into a date constraint, authorizing some additional actions, but also preventing the right from authorizing other actions. This can be related to satisfiability of Boolean formulas, where assigning "true" or "false" to a variable satisfies some clauses but also precludes using that variable to satisfy some other clauses.

Theorem 1. *Deciding whether a license authorizes a sequence of actions is NP-complete. This is the case even for licenses containing only interval and content constraints.*

Proof idea. Given a SAT instance, we construct a license and a sequence of actions such that the license authorizes the actions if, and only if, the SAT instance is satisfiable. Each clause is represented by two actions, one occurring at time t_1 and another occurring at time t_2, say at times 10 and 20. Each variable is represented by a parent right with an Interval(1) constraint. Each occurrence of a variable in a clause is represented by a child right inheriting from the variable's interval right. If the variable occurs positively (negatively), the right is constrained, using a content constraint, to authorizing the clause's action at time 10 (time 20). Additionally, each clause is also represented by an Interval(1)-constrained parent right with two children: one authorizing the clause's action at time 10 and the other authorizing the clause's action at time 20.

First, we show that if the constructed license authorizes the sequence of actions, the SAT instance is satisfiable. If a variable's interval right is first exercised before time 10, the variable is assigned "true." Otherwise, the variable is assigned "false." Of the actions representing a given clause, one must be authorized by a variable's interval right, and that variable satisfies the clause under this truth assignment.

Second, we show that if the SAT instance is satisfiable, the license authorizes the actions. If a variable is assigned "true" ("false"), exercise its interval right at time 10 (time 20). Of the actions representing a given clause, at least one must be authorized. Authorize the other one with the interval right representing the clause. Thus, the license authorizes the sequence of actions if, and only if, the SAT instance is satisfiable. □

While deciding whether an OMA license authorizes a sequence of actions is NP-complete in general, there exists a fragment of the OMA language for which authorization is decidable efficiently. A license is called *manageable* if it does not contain interval constraints and does not contain more than one kind of constraint among count, timed count, and accumulated (but can freely contain individual, system, kind, date, and content constraints). Authorization for manageable licenses can be decided in polynomial time. The class of manageable licenses contains many useful licenses, for example licenses allowing a limited number of promotional plays from various music collections and allowing unlimited plays of purchased music. For this class, authorization can be computed via a reduction to maximum network flow through the license graph, where each unit of flow represents an action.

Theorem 2. *It can be decided in polynomial time whether a manageable license authorizes a sequence of actions.*

Proof sketch. We sketch the proof for licenses containing count constraints. The argument is similar for licenses containing timed count or accumulated constraints. The reduction to MAX-FLOW proceeds by building a network flow graph. The actions in the sequence are represented by nodes in the graph, as are the rights in the license. The source is connected with a unit capacity edge to each of the action nodes. Each action node is connected with a unit capacity edge to a rights node if the action can be authorized by the right (ignoring count constraints). The nodes for each rights constrained with Count(n) are connected to their parents with a capacity n edge (those without parents are connected to the sink). If a rights node does not have a count constraint, it is connected with an infinite capacity edge.

If the maximum flow saturates the edges leaving the source, then the license authorizes the sequence of actions. Tracing the flow from an action node to the sink reveals which right authorizes that action. The edge capacities ensure the count constraints are satisfied. Conversely, if there is some satisfactory assignment of actions to rights, there is a flow that saturates the edges leaving the source. □

There is a gap between these two theorems. The complexity of deciding authorization for arbitrary licenses without interval constraints is left open.

3 Online Authorization of Actions

In the preceding section, we considered the offline problem of determining whether a license authorizes a sequence of actions. In practice, however, DRM agents are usually asked to compute such authorizations online, as consumers attempt to perform actions. The Open Mobile Alliance specifies a particular online algorithm for determining which rights to exercise, but that algorithm is problematic, as in fact are all online algorithms.

Consider a consumer Alice who possesses a certain license. She might reasonably believe that if she instead possessed a more flexible license, she would still be authorized to perform every sequence of actions she can perform with the less flexible license. We call schemes that enjoy this property *monotonic* (defined precisely in Sect. 3.2). However, no online authorization scheme for OMA licenses is monotonic. Thus, Alice might "upgrade" to a more flexible license and lose the ability to perform a sequence of actions.

3.1 Automata Semantics for Licenses

In order to authorize an action, a DRM agent must exercise a right. Exercising a right might consume it, for example when it contains the constraint Count(1), or more generally simply modify its state. Exercising a stateful right can foreclose the authorization to perform some future action. In order to study how licenses evolve as actions are performed, we represent licenses as states in an (infinite) automata. When a consumer performs an action, the agent follows a transition labeled by the action in the automata, arriving at a new state. This new state represents the rights remaining after performing the action. In general there might be multiple transitions labeled with the same action, corresponding to exercising different rights.

The *authorization transition relation* for an action a (written $\xrightarrow{a}$) is a binary relation on $\mathcal{L}$, the set of licenses. If $\varphi \xrightarrow{a} \varphi'$, then license φ can transform into license φ' by authorizing a. For example, if φ is a license to play a certain song three times and a is the act of playing that song on a particular date, then φ' is a license to play that song twice. We call $\mathcal{L}$ together with the transition relations $\xrightarrow{a}$ the *license automata* $\mathfrak{A}$. The non-deterministic automata $\mathfrak{A}$ provides semantics for licenses:

Def. License φ *authorizes* a sequence of actions $a_1 \cdots a_n$ (written $a_1 \cdots a_n \in \mathfrak{A}[\![\varphi]\!]$) if there is a path starting at φ labeled by $a_1 \cdots a_n$ in the license automata $\mathfrak{A}$.

These semantics induce a natural "flexibility" partial ordering on licenses:

$$\varphi_1 \leq \varphi_2 \qquad \text{if } \mathfrak{A}[\![\varphi_1]\!] \subseteq \mathfrak{A}[\![\varphi_2]\!]$$

For example, a license that allows four plays of a song is less flexible than a license that allows five plays of that song.

OMA Licenses. For licenses φ and φ' in the OMA Rights Expression Language, $\varphi \xrightarrow{a} \varphi'$ if (1) action a is authorized by φ and (2) φ' is a license resulting from exercising some right of φ to authorize action a, as defined in Sect. 2.1. For the OMA licenses, only a finite portion of the automata is reachable from a given license. This finite subautomata can be used to model-check properties of that license.

The automata semantics of OMA licenses are *commutative*: if a sequence of actions is authorized, then every permutation of that sequence is also authorized. In the license automata, whenever $\varphi \xrightarrow{a} \varphi'$ it is the case that $\varphi' \leq \varphi$. We could have represented the semantics of licenses using multisets, but we chose sequences in anticipation of online authorization schemes that are not commutative.

3.2 Authorization Schemes

DRM agents employ authorization schemes to interpret licenses. Each scheme induces its own semantics on licenses, based on the sequences of actions allowed by an agent employing the scheme. In principle, authorization schemes could transform licenses arbitrarily, bearing no relation to the usual license automata.

Def. An *authorization scheme* A is an automata whose states are licenses and whose edges are labeled by actions.

As with the license automata, an authorization scheme allows a sequence of actions under a license if there is a path starting at the license labeled by the actions. We focus on four properties of authorization schemes:

Def. An authorization scheme A is

- *sound* if A is a subautomata of $\mathfrak{A}$,
- *online* if A is deterministic,
- *live* if $a \in \mathfrak{A}[\![\varphi]\!]$ implies $a \in \mathsf{A}[\![\varphi]\!]$,
- *monotonic* if $\varphi_1 \leq \varphi_2$ implies $\mathsf{A}[\![\varphi_1]\!] \subseteq \mathsf{A}[\![\varphi_2]\!]$,

for all licenses φ, φ_1, and φ_2 and all actions a.

A sound authorization scheme never allows a sequence of actions that is not authorized by the license automata.

A DRM agent employing an online authorization scheme decides which rights to exercise as actions occur, without knowledge of what future actions the consumer wishes to perform. A sound, online authorization scheme includes at most one transition from the full license automata for each license and each action. The included transitions indicate which right to exercise.

Some sound, online authorization schemes are degenerate, such as the empty automata, which does not allow any actions. Requiring schemes to be live removes this degeneracy. A live authorization scheme always allows an individual action if that action is authorized by the license automata. The sound, live, online authorization schemes can be characterized as subautomata:

Lemma 3. *An authorization scheme* A *is sound, live, and online if, and only if,* A *is a maximal deterministic subautomata of* $\mathfrak{A}$

In a monotonic authorization scheme, if a sequence of actions is allowed under a license, it is allowed under every more flexible license as well. The notion of flexibility here is semantic, but a weaker notion of monotonicity could be defined syntactically (for example, monotonic with respect to adding rights to a license). The authorization scheme defined in the OMA specification is sound, live, and online, but not monotonic. In fact, all sound, live, online schemes for OMA licenses fail to be monotonic even in a weak sense.

Theorem 4. *No sound, live, online authorization scheme for OMA licenses is monotonic.*

Proof. Given a sound, live, online authorization scheme A, consider three actions, a, b, and c, and the license φ:

$$\begin{aligned} r &: \text{Count}(1) \\ r_1 &: \text{A descendant of } r \text{ that authorizes } a. \\ r_2 &: \text{A descendant of } r \text{ that authorizes } b. \\ s &: \text{Count}(1) \\ s_1 &: \text{A descendant of } s \text{ that authorizes } a. \\ s_2 &: \text{A descendant of } s \text{ that authorizes } c. \end{aligned}$$

Because A is live and deterministic, there must be a unique license φ' such that $\varphi \xrightarrow{a}_{\mathsf{A}} \varphi'$. The scheme must have exercised either r_1 or s_1 (say r_1). Then, the count constraint of r in φ' is zero and $b \notin \mathfrak{A}[\![\varphi']\!]$. Thus, the sequence $a \cdot b \notin \mathsf{A}[\![\varphi]\!]$ (by soundness). Now consider the license θ consisting of r, r_2, s, and s_1. We have $\theta \leq \varphi$, but $a \cdot b \in \mathsf{A}[\![\theta]\!]$ (by liveness of A). Therefore, A is not monotonic. □

Notice every sound, live, online authorization scheme on OMA licenses fails to be monotonic even with respect to adding rights to a license. A DRM agent employing scheme A allows a sequence of actions under the license consisting of rights r, r_2, s, and s_1 that it would not allow if the rights r_1 and s_2 were added to the license.

4 Linear Semantics for Digital Rights

The semantics of digital rights can be understood using Linear Logic. Linear Logic eschews the usual weakening and contraction rules in favor of maintaining control over the multiplicity of syntactic terms, mirroring the control over the multiplicity of actions in DRM licenses. We interpret a conjunctive fragment of Propositional Linear Logic as a DRM Rights Expression Language, taking the regulated actions as propositions and building more complex licenses using the familiar Linear Logic operators. Authorization is captured through linear implication. If φ is the formula representing a license and $\varphi \multimap a \otimes \varphi'$, then φ authorizes action a with remaining rights φ'. The right to perform action a has been "separated" from the remaining rights φ'.

In this section, we use Linear Logic to investigate monotonic approximations and to describe a monotonic authorization scheme on licenses enriched with linear negation. Negated terms are used to specify the rights remaining after performing an action both exactly and compactly. These negated terms enable agents to revise their decisions about which rights to exercise for which actions, giving rise to a efficient authorization algorithm that is both sound and monotonic for these licenses.

4.1 Syntax, Semantics, and Deduction

Syntax. Licenses are built from a countable set of possible actions, denoted $\mathcal{A}$, which serve as the linear propositions. From these actions, licenses are built using the usual Linear Logic operators. We use formulas from the following grammar:

$$\psi ::= a \mid \psi \,\&\, \psi \qquad \varphi ::= \mathbf{1} \mid !a \mid \psi \mid \varphi \otimes \varphi,$$

where $a \in \mathcal{A}$. The symbol & represents an internal choice between authorizing one of two actions, ! represents unbounded replication, and $\otimes$ represents parallel combination of rights. Formulas from this grammar are the parallel combination of *atomic rights*, each of which is a choice between authorizing several individual actions.

In this grammar, the ! modality can be applied only to individual actions (and not their &-combination). This might appear overly restrictive as the license $!(a \,\&\, b)$ seems reasonable, but formulas $!\psi$ are equivalent to formulas in the grammar as $!(\psi_1 \,\&\, \psi_2) \multimap\!\!\circ\, !\psi_1 \otimes !\psi_2$. We also assume, without loss of expressiveness, that actions occurring in the scope of a ! do not occur elsewhere in the formula. Such formulas are in *normal form*. Formulas without & or ! are called *basic* licenses.

OMA licenses containing individual, system, kind, data, content, and count constraints are expressible as Linear Logic formulas from the above grammar. Accumulated and timed count constraints are excluded for simplicity, but interval constraints are excluded in order to maintain tractability. Individual, system, kind, date, and content constraints are simple to capture because they are stateless. Count constraints are expressible because atomic rights occurring outside the scope of a ! can be exercised only a limited number of times. Inheritance between rights is handled by the & operator, and the combination of rights into licenses is handled by the $\otimes$ operator. For example, the license used in the proof of Theorem 4 can be expressed as $(a \,\&\, b) \otimes (a \,\&\, c)$.

Semantics. With each formula φ, we associate a set of multisets of actions $\mathcal{S}[\![\varphi]\!]$, defined in Fig. 1. Performing all the actions in one of these multisets exhausts the license. Formally, a multiset is a function from $\mathcal{A}$ to $\mathbb{N}$. The multiset operator $\uplus$ is the usual disjoint union that adds the contents

$$
\begin{array}{ll}
s \in \mathcal{S}[\![\mathbf{1}]\!] & \text{if } s = \varnothing \\
s \in \mathcal{S}[\![a]\!] & \text{if } s = \{a\} \\
s \in \mathcal{S}[\![\varphi_1 \,\&\, \varphi_2]\!] & \text{if } s \in \mathcal{S}[\![\varphi_1]\!] \text{ or } s \in \mathcal{S}[\![\varphi_2]\!] \\
s_1 \uplus s_2 \in \mathcal{S}[\![\varphi_1 \otimes \varphi_2]\!] & \text{if } s_1 \in \mathcal{S}[\![\varphi_1]\!] \text{ and } s_2 \in \mathcal{S}[\![\varphi_2]\!] \\
s \in \mathcal{S}[\![!\varphi]\!] & \text{if } s = s_1 \uplus \cdots \uplus s_n, \text{ where} \\
& s_i \in \mathcal{S}[\![\varphi]\!] \text{ for all } i \text{ from 1 to } n
\end{array}
$$

Figure 1. Multiset semantics for licenses

of its two operands. For each formula φ, the set $\mathcal{S}[\![\varphi]\!]$ contains exactly those multisets "promised" by the formula. If we take sets of multisets as models, we can provide a connection between semantic entailment and linear implication by defining every superset of $\mathcal{S}[\![\varphi]\!]$ to be a model of φ:

$$S \models \varphi \text{ if, and only if, } S \supseteq \mathcal{S}[\![\varphi]\!]$$

Each model of a formula contains every choice of multiset "promised" by the formula. Semantic entailment is as usual: $\varphi_1 \models \varphi_2$ if every model of φ_1 is a model of φ_2.

Deduction. Before defining the transition relation for the license automata, we define a leftist deductive system over formulas with the inference rules in Fig. 2 and a single axiom, $\varphi \vdash \varphi$. These rules are the usual left deduction rules of two-sided Classical Linear Logic for these connectives, with the exception of the $\mathbf{1}$-elimination rule. This rule is usually captured through right deduction rules. Note that none of these inference rules modify Δ. The deductive system is sound with respect to semantic implication.

Lemma 5 (Soundness). *For all formulas φ and φ',*

$$\varphi \vdash \varphi' \textit{ implies } \varphi \models \varphi'.$$

This deductive system is not complete for our semantics, for example semantically $(a \& b) \otimes (a \& c) \models a \otimes (a \& b \& c)$ but not syntactically. If a complete deductive system were used, licenses could reach exponential length. The relation $\vdash$ is the "exercise" relation on licenses. As a formula moves across $\vdash$, non-determinism is resolved, corresponding to the DRM agent deciding which rights to exercise. Specifically, a right is *exercised* whenever a &-rule is applied to it. The sequent $\varphi \vdash a \otimes \varphi'$ indicates that action a can be authorized under license φ with remaining rights φ'. The authorization for a has been "separated" from the remaining rights φ'. This motivates our definition of the transition relation for the license automata $\mathfrak{A}$:

$$\varphi \xrightarrow{a} \varphi' \qquad \text{if, and only if,} \qquad \varphi \vdash a \otimes \varphi'$$

$$
\frac{\Gamma, \psi_1 \vdash \Delta}{\Gamma, \psi_1 \,\&\, \psi_2 \vdash \Delta} \qquad \frac{\Gamma, \psi_2 \vdash \Delta}{\Gamma, \psi_1 \,\&\, \psi_2 \vdash \Delta}
$$

$$
\frac{\Gamma, !\psi, !\psi \vdash \Delta}{\Gamma, !\psi \vdash \Delta} \qquad \frac{\Gamma, \psi \vdash \Delta}{\Gamma, !\psi \vdash \Delta} \qquad \frac{\Gamma \vdash \Delta}{\Gamma, \mathbf{1} \vdash \Delta} \qquad \frac{\Gamma, \mathbf{1} \vdash \Delta}{\Gamma \vdash \Delta}
$$

$$
\frac{\Gamma, \varphi_1, \varphi_2 \vdash \Delta}{\Gamma, \varphi_1 \otimes \varphi_2 \vdash \Delta} \qquad \frac{\Gamma, \varphi_1 \otimes \varphi_2 \vdash \Delta}{\Gamma, \varphi_1, \varphi_2 \vdash \Delta} \qquad \frac{\Gamma, \varphi_2, \varphi_1 \vdash \Delta}{\Gamma, \varphi_1, \varphi_2 \vdash \Delta}
$$

Figure 2. Rules for negation-free licenses

This transition relation yields a close connection between the automata semantics of a license formula, $\mathfrak{A}[\![\varphi]\!]$, and the multiset semantics of the formula, $\mathcal{S}[\![\varphi]\!]$.

Lemma 6. *A sequence $\sigma \in \mathfrak{A}[\![\varphi]\!]$ if, and only if, the multiset of actions occurring in σ is a subset of a multiset in $\mathcal{S}[\![\varphi]\!]$.*

4.2 Monotonic Approximations

Although sound, live, online authorization schemes for these linear licenses are not monotonic, there is a unique maximal set of licenses on which there exists a monotonic, sound, live, online scheme. In each of these well-behaved licenses, the rights authorizing a given action are linearly ordered by flexibility. The monotonic scheme on these licenses can be "lifted" to arbitrary licenses by approximating a given license with the closest well-behaved license. The resulting scheme is monotonic on all licenses but it is not sound: the approximation allows some sequences of actions that are not actually authorized by the license. The total number of actions allowed is the same, but the consumer is given more flexibility as to which actions to perform.

Before describing the set of well-behaved licenses, we define the *support* of a license: the support of a license φ, written $\mathrm{support}(\varphi)$, is the set of actions that occur as propositions in φ.

Def. Let $C_{\max}$ be the set of licenses φ such that, for all atomic rights ψ_1 and ψ_2 occurring in φ, if $\mathrm{support}(\psi_1) \cap \mathrm{support}(\psi_2)$ is non-empty, then

$$
\begin{array}{l}
\mathrm{support}(\psi_1) \subseteq \mathrm{support}(\psi_2) \text{ or} \\
\mathrm{support}(\psi_2) \subseteq \mathrm{support}(\psi_1).
\end{array}
$$

In a $C_{\max}$ license, if an action is authorized by several rights, then those rights are linearly ordered by flexibility. Exercising the least flexible right forecloses the fewest future authorizations. This leads to a natural online authorization scheme on $C_{\max}$, which we call the greedy scheme. Given a license in $C_{\max}$ and an action a, the greedy scheme exercises the atomic right containing a whose support is inclusion-minimal (this is unique by the definition of $C_{\max}$). This scheme is monotonic, sound, live, and online on $C_{\max}$.

Theorem 7. *The set of licenses C_{max} is the unique inclusion-maximal set of licenses (containing the basic licenses) on which there exists a monotonic, sound, live, online authorization scheme.*

Proof. The greedy scheme is monotonic, sound, live, and online on $C_{\max}$. Suppose, by way of contradiction, there exists a set of licenses C such that (1) C contains the basic licenses, (2) C contains $\varphi \notin C_{\max}$, and (3) there exists a monotonic, sound, live, online authorization scheme A on C. Then, φ must contain two atomic rights ψ_1 and ψ_2 such that $\text{support}(\psi_1) \cap \text{support}(\psi_2)$ is non-empty and neither is a subset of the other. In particular, fix

$$\begin{aligned} &a \in \text{support}(\psi_1) \cap \text{support}(\psi_2), \\ &b \in \text{support}(\psi_1) - \text{support}(\psi_2), \text{ and} \\ &c \in \text{support}(\psi_2) - \text{support}(\psi_1). \end{aligned}$$

Starting with φ, repeatedly authorize a until A exercises either ψ_1 or ψ_2 (say ψ_1). Next, repeatedly authorize b until the remaining rights no longer authorize b. Let σ be the sequence of actions authorized thus far. Sequence $\sigma \cdot b \notin \mathsf{A}[\![\varphi]\!]$ because the rights remaining after σ do not authorize b. Now, let θ be the $\otimes$-combination (with repetition) of the actions in $\sigma \cdot b$. License $\theta \in C$ (because θ is a basic license) and $\theta \leq \varphi$ (because ψ_1 need not be exercised to authorize σ). However, $\sigma \cdot b \in \mathsf{A}[\![\theta]\!]$, and therefore A is not monotonic on C, a contradiction. □

The greedy scheme on $C_{\max}$ induces an approximation scheme on all licenses by way of an approximation structure. An approximation structure projects arbitrary licenses onto an identified set of licenses.

Def. An *approximation structure* is a pair (C, π), where

- C is a set of licenses (the set of *approximates*),
- π is a $\leq$-monotonic function from licenses to C, and
- $\pi(\varphi)$ is minimal such that $\varphi \leq \pi(\varphi)$, for all $\varphi \in \mathcal{L}$.

In an approximation structure (C, π), every license φ is approximated by the license $\pi(\varphi)$. The function π chooses one of the closest licenses in C to approximate each license. The approximation structure lifts an authorization scheme A on C to an authorization scheme A_C on all licenses: $\varphi \xrightarrow{a}_{\mathsf{A}_C} \varphi'$ if, and only if, $\pi(\varphi) \xrightarrow{a}_{\mathsf{A}} \varphi'$. Thus,

$$\mathsf{A}_C[\![\varphi]\!] = \mathsf{A}[\![\pi(\varphi)]\!].$$

The lifted scheme uses the approximate license to determine the sequences of actions allowed by a license. Two key properties lift with the authorization scheme.

Lemma 8. *For all approximation structures (C, π) and all authorizations schemes A,*

- *If A is monotonic on C, then A_C is monotonic.*
- *If A is live on C, then A_C is live.*

The more approximates, the *tighter* the approximation, the fewer "extra" sequences of actions allowed by the approximation. In the extreme, if $C = \mathcal{L}$, no extra action sequences are allowed. This all-inclusive C does not admit a monotonic, sound, live, online authorization scheme, but $C_{\max}$ does. In fact, approximation scheme induced by the greedy scheme is the tightest of its class because of the unique maximality of $C_{\max}$.

Corollary 9. *The greedy scheme is the tightest monotonic approximation scheme arising from sound, live, online authorization schemes on approximation structures.*

Even though this scheme is the tightest approximation of its class, it still allows many extra actions. Particularly problematic are licenses containing many atomic rights that overlap each other slightly. The approximation scheme does not allow a greater *total* number of actions, but it does allow each individual action to be performed a greater number of times. This suggests a "price for monotonicity" with these licenses. Expanding the expressiveness of licenses, however, enables monotonic online authorization schemes that do not allow any extra actions.

4.3 Linear Characterization of Remaining Rights

Online authorization schemes on OMA licenses fail to be monotonic because they are forced to commit to exercising rights as actions occur. Without the flexibility to later revise their past commitments, agents are unable to behave monotonically. A monotonic, sound, live, online scheme does exists, however, if the license automata $\mathfrak{A}$ is expanded to enable agents to revise commitments. The states in this enlarged automata $\mathfrak{B}$ record previously exercised rights and the transitions enable agents to "unexercise" these rights (while maintaining soundness). Both automata, $\mathfrak{A}$ and $\mathfrak{B}$, authorize exactly the same sequences of actions for the licenses they share in common.

The states of $\mathfrak{B}$ record exactly the future action sequences that can be performed. The description of these sequences must be compact in order to maintain efficiency. Simply listing the available continuations would require exponential space. To achieve an efficient representation, we expand the grammar of license formulas to include linearly negated actions, such as $a^{\perp}$. These negated terms represent "undoing" an action, or an authorization debt to be paid. New transitions are included in the automata that make use of these extra terms.

Linear Negation. Consider the license $(a \,\&\, b) \otimes (a \,\&\, c)$. In the $\mathfrak{A}$ automata, $(a \,\&\, b) \otimes (a \,\&\, c) \xrightarrow{a} a \,\&\, c$, foreclosing the possibility of authorizing b, but, in the $\mathfrak{B}$ automata,

$$(a \,\&\, b) \otimes (a \,\&\, c) \xrightarrow{a} (\mathbf{1} \,\&\, (a^{\perp} \otimes b)) \otimes (a \,\&\, c),$$

and the action b is still authorized:

$$(\mathbf{1} \,\&\, (a^{\perp} \otimes b)) \otimes (a \,\&\, c) \multimap b$$

Authorizing action b causes the $a^{\perp}$ term to eliminate the $a \,\&\, c$ term. This is because $a \,\&\, c$ is exercised to a, which is used in combination with $\mathbf{1} \,\&\, (a^{\perp} \otimes b)$ to reconstruct $a \,\&\, b$. In turn, $a \,\&\, b$ used to authorize b. In order to authorize b, the authorization debt $a^{\perp}$ must be paid. The generality of this approach is elucidated by the following valid formula:

$$a_1 \,\&\, \cdots \,\&\, a_n \multimapboth a_1 \otimes (\mathbf{1} \,\&\, (a_1^{\perp} \otimes (a_2 \,\&\, \cdots \,\&\, a_n)))$$

Syntax. To express these states, we enrich our grammar for rights with linear negation:

$$\varphi ::= \cdots \mid \mathbf{1} \,\&\, (a^{\perp} \otimes \psi) \mid \cdots$$

Notice the negated terms can appear only in specific syntactic surroundings. When exercised, an atomic right produces two terms: the authorized action and a term containing that action negated. The negated term can later be used to reassign that action to a different atomic right. This reassignment reconstructs the initial right, at the cost of the newly assigned right.

Semantics. To interpret these new pieces of syntax, we expand our notion of a multiset to include multisets with negatively occurring objects. That is, a multiset is a function from actions $\mathcal{A}$ to the integers $\mathbb{Z}$.

$$s \in \mathcal{S}[\![a^{\perp}]\!] \qquad \text{if } s = \{a : -1\}$$

The set $\mathcal{S}[\![a^{\perp}]\!]$ contains a single multiset that contains one negative occurrence of a. Every license denotes at least one multiset free of negatively occurring objects.

Deduction. We expand our deductive system to be the full two-sided Classical Linear Logic deductive system. This gives us the following deductive theorems:

$$(a \,\&\, \psi) \otimes \varphi \vdash a \otimes (\mathbf{1} \,\&\, (a^{\perp} \otimes \psi)) \otimes \varphi \quad (1)$$

$$a \otimes (\mathbf{1} \,\&\, (a^{\perp} \otimes \psi)) \otimes \varphi \vdash (a \,\&\, \psi) \otimes \varphi \quad (2)$$

Notice Deduction 1 commits a right to authorizing an action a and Deduction 2 reverses that commitment. The transitions of license automata $\mathfrak{B}$ are defined analogously to those for $\mathfrak{A}$: $\varphi \xrightarrow{a} \varphi'$ if, and only if, $\varphi \vdash a \otimes \varphi'$.

Automata $\mathfrak{B}$ contains only formulas described by the enriched grammar. Even though the deductive system derives $\mathbf{1} \vdash a \otimes a^{\perp}$, the transition $\mathbf{1} \xrightarrow{a} a^{\perp}$ is not available because $a^{\perp}$ is not a valid state of the automata, preventing actions from being inappropriately authorized.

Lemma 10 (Soundness). *$\varphi \vdash \varphi'$ implies $\varphi \models \varphi'$*

The sequences of actions authorized by automata $\mathfrak{B}$ are exactly the same as those authorized by automata $\mathfrak{A}$, for licenses present in both automata.

Lemma 11. *$\mathfrak{A}[\![\varphi]\!] = \mathfrak{B}[\![\varphi]\!]$, for all licenses φ of $\mathfrak{A}$.*

An Online Scheme. Authorization scheme A_{opt} is defined by an algorithm for constructing a proof. Given a license φ and an action a, A_{opt} finds a license φ' such that $\varphi \vdash a \otimes \varphi'$ by running MAX-FLOW on the following graph:

- A distinguished source s and a distinguished sink t.
- A nodes for each $a_i \in \text{support}(\varphi)$
- A node for each $!\psi$, with an infinite capacity edge to t.
- A node for each ψ with a unit capacity edge to t.
- A node for each $\mathbf{1} \,\&\, (b^{\perp} \otimes \psi)$.
- A unit capacity edge from s to a.
- An edge from a_i to $!\psi$ if $a_i \in \text{support}(!\psi)$.
- An edge from a_i to ψ if $a_i \in \text{support}(\psi)$.
- An edge from a_i to $\mathbf{1} \,\&\, (b^{\perp} \otimes \psi)$ if $a_i \in \text{support}(\psi)$.
- An edge from each $\mathbf{1} \,\&\, (b^{\perp} \otimes \psi)$ to b.

If there is a non-zero flow, then a is authorized and A_{opt} constructs φ' as follows. Tracing the flow backwards from the sink, A_{opt} determines the inference rules to apply. The final edge of the flow travels to the sink from a node x.

1. The flow travels to x from some action b and x is either an atomic right $b \,\&\, \psi$ or a right $!b$. In the first case, apply Deduction 1. In the second case, apply $!b \otimes \varphi \vdash b \otimes !b \otimes \varphi$. In either case, a b $\otimes$-conjunct is produced.
2. If $b = a$, then A_{opt} halts and has produced the required φ'. Otherwise, tracing the flow backwards leads to a $\mathbf{1} \,\&\, (b^{\perp} \otimes \psi)$ node, for some ψ. Apply Deduction 2 to eliminate the b $\otimes$-conjunct and relabel the node $b \,\&\, \psi$. Return to Step 1 with this node as x.

Eventually the termination condition must obtain and the desired license formula φ' is produced. The residual flow graph is essentially the flow graph for φ' (possibly differing on edges leading to the source and from the sink). A practical implementation would not reconstruct the flow graph for each action, but reuse the residual flow graph. The algorithm can be understood as computing MAX-FLOW over the initial rights (as in Theorem 2) by using an augmenting path for each action. Reversed edges in the residual flow graph are represented in the formula by linear negation.

Theorem 12. *Online authorization scheme* $\mathsf{A}_{\mathrm{opt}}$ *is sound, live, and monotonic.*

Proof sketch. Scheme $\mathsf{A}_{\mathrm{opt}}$ is sound because the φ' is constructed using the inference rules. Because $\mathsf{A}_{\mathrm{opt}}$ is essentially computing MAX-FLOW over the initial rights, $\mathsf{A}_{\mathrm{opt}}[\![\varphi]\!] = \mathfrak{B}[\![\varphi]\!]$ for all licenses. Thus, $\mathsf{A}_{\mathrm{opt}}$ is live and monotonic. □

Moreover, because $\mathfrak{B}[\![\varphi]\!] = \mathfrak{A}[\![\varphi]\!]$ for licenses φ in $\mathfrak{A}$, $\mathsf{A}_{\mathrm{opt}}$ is a monotonic, live, online scheme that is semantically equivalent to $\mathfrak{A}$ in the sense that $\mathsf{A}_{\mathrm{opt}}$ allows a sequence of actions if, and only if, $\mathfrak{A}$ authorizes that sequence. DRM agents employing $\mathsf{A}_{\mathrm{opt}}$ for OMA licenses achieve monotonicity without allowing extra actions by revising their internal commitment as needed to authorize more actions.

4.4 Dynamically Acquired Rights

Thus far, we have considered the static case, where consumers who first acquire rights and then perform actions. In practice, however, consumers often interleave acquiring rights and performing actions. Acquiring the right ψ can be represented by additional transitions in the automata:

$$\varphi \overset{\psi}{\dashrightarrow} \psi \otimes \varphi$$

These acquisition transitions can be interleaved with action transitions. Something curious occurs if a term negated in φ appears in ψ. Suppose Alice initially possessed the right $a \mathbin{\&} b$, performed action a, and then acquired right a:

$$a \mathbin{\&} b \xrightarrow{a} \mathbf{1} \mathbin{\&} (a^{\perp} \otimes b) \overset{a}{\dashrightarrow} a \otimes \mathbf{1} \mathbin{\&} (a^{\perp} \otimes b) \xrightarrow{b} \mathbf{1}$$

We hope to investigate the dynamic case in future work.

5 Conclusions

In specifying a DRM Rights Expression Language, the Open Mobile Alliance failed to consider the consequences of their authorization algorithm. On the surface, their algorithm seems plausible, but it leads to anomalous semantics, which we characterize by introducing the notion of monotonicity. We investigate the question of how to assign actions to rights in Digital Rights Management licenses. We discover that finding the optimum assignment of actions to rights in OMA licenses is NP-complete. The difficulty stems from determining when to first exercise rights with "interval" constraints. We argue this complexity is not endemic to DRM licenses as optimum assignments for a substantial fragment of the OMA language are computable efficiently.

Every online authorization scheme for OMA licenses is non-monotonic. We investigate monotonicity on two fronts. First, we characterized the maximal set of licenses on which there exists a monotonic online authorization scheme, giving rise to a monotonic approximation for arbitrary licenses. Second, monotonicity can be achieved on licenses enriched with linear negation because agents can revise their past allocation of actions to rights after learning which other actions consumers wish to perform. The authorization algorithm, which essentially computes maximum network flow, is efficiently computable, sound, live, and monotonic.

Acknowledgments. We thank Darryn McDade, Jefferson Owen, and Paul Bromley from ST Microelectronics Inc. for suggesting an investigation of the OMA DRM design. This work was partially supported by the National Science Foundation though CyberTrust grants including the PORTIA project and the TRUST Science and Technology Center

References

[1] C. N. Chong, R. Corin, S. Etalle, P. Hartel, W. Jonker, and Y. W. Law. LicenseScript: A novel digital rights language and its semantics. In *WEDELMUSIC: Proceedings of the 3rd International Conference on Web Delivering of Music*, pages 122–129, Washington, DC, 2003. IEEE Computer Society.

[2] ContentGuard. eXtensible rights Markup Language, 2006. http://www.xrml.org/.

[3] J.-Y. Girard. Linear logic. *Theoretical Computer Science*, 50:1–102, 1987.

[4] C. Gunter, S. Weeks, and A. Wright. Models and languages for digital rights. In *HICSS '01: Proceedings of the 34th Annual Hawaii International Conference on System Sciences*, volume 9, page 9076, Washington, DC, 2001. IEEE Computer Society.

[5] ODRL Initiative. The Open Digital Rights Language Initiative, 2006. http://www.odrl.net/.

[6] Open Mobile Alliance. DRM Rights Expression Language: Candidate Version 2.0 — 25 Aug 2005, 2005. http://www.openmobilealliance.org/.

[7] R. Pucella and V. Weissman. A logic for reasoning about digital rights. In *CSFW '02: Proceedings of the 15th IEEE Computer Security Foundations Workshop (CSFW'02)*, page 282, Washington, DC, 2002. IEEE Computer Society.

[8] O. Sibert, D. Bernstein, and D. V. Wie. The DigiBox: A self-protecting container for information commerce. In *Proceedings of the 1st USENIX Workshop on Electronic Commerce*.

[9] M. J. Stefik. Letting loose the light: Igniting commerce in electronic publication. *Forum on Technology-Based Intellectual Property*, pages 78–81, March 1997.

Variables as Resource in Hoare Logics

Matthew Parkinson and Richard Bornat
School of Computing
Middlesex University
LONDON, UK
mjp41@cam.ac.uk, R.Bornat@mdx.ac.uk

Cristiano Calcagno
Department of Computing
Imperial College
University of London, LONDON, UK
ccris@doc.ic.ac.uk

Abstract

Hoare logic is bedevilled by complex but coarse side conditions on the use of variables. We define a logic, free of side conditions, which permits more precise statements of a program's use of variables. We show that it admits translations of proofs in Hoare logic, thereby showing that nothing is lost, and also that it admits proofs of some programs outside the scope of Hoare logic. We include a treatment of reference parameters and global variables in procedure call (though not of parameter aliasing). Our work draws on ideas from separation logic: program variables are treated as resource rather than as logical variables in disguise. For clarity we exclude a treatment of the heap.

1. Introduction

The glory of Hoare logic [10] is the variable-assignment axiom, which converts difficult semantic arguments about program state into simple syntactic substitutions. That success depends on punning program variables in commands with identically-named logical variables in assertions, but program variables are not logical variables: they have location (lvalue or lv in Strachey's classification [19], otherwise 'address') as well as value (Strachey's rvalue or rv, otherwise 'content').

The price of the pun is a proliferation of well-chosen but complex side conditions on the invariance rule, on procedure-call [11, 9, 7] and on concurrency [16]. The invariance rule, for example, is

$$\frac{\{Q\}\,C\,\{R\}}{\{Q \wedge P\}\,C\,\{R \wedge P\}}\ \text{mods}(C) \cap \text{FV}(P) = \varnothing$$

The side condition lets the programmer know that variables not in $\text{mods}(C)$ are preserved. We can suppose that this imposes a useful discipline, that the writing footprint of commands should be considered when setting them in a wider context. But the side condition is too coarse. Consider, for example the procedure definition

$$\text{let } f(b) = \text{if } b \text{ then } x := 1 \text{ else } y := 0 \text{ fi}$$

It is obvious that $f(true)$ does not modify y and $f(false)$ does not modify x, but a simple modifies clause would have it that $\text{mods}(f(\_))$ is $\{x, y\}$, and the invariance rule will not help us to establish

$$\{y = 3\}\, f(\text{true})\, \{x = 1 \wedge y = 3\} \qquad (1)$$

Side conditions on the use of global variables in procedures, on reference parameters and on concurrency are equally coarse but far more complicated, and can call for global oversight to establish the validity of a small part of a program; the effect can be that local changes in variable use can invalidate already-established proofs of distant parts of a program.

In the logic we present in this paper we can make more precise statements about the variable-resource footprints of program parts. We can specify, for example

$$\begin{array}{l}\{(x_\top \Vdash B) \vee (y_\top \Vdash \neg B)\}\\ \quad f(B)\\ \{(x_\top \Vdash x = 1 \wedge B) \vee (y_\top \Vdash y = 0 \wedge \neg B)\}\end{array}$$

– $f(\text{true})$ has total permission to read and write x, but cannot touch y, and vice-versa $f(\text{false})$ can read and write y but cannot access x. We can then use separation logic's frame rule (see table 2), a version of the invariance rule, to establish

$$\{x_\top, y_\_ \Vdash y = 3\}\, f(\text{true})\, \{x_\top, y_\_ \Vdash x = 1 \wedge y = 3\}$$

This is a more precise statement of (1), stating that a program which has permission to write x ($x_\top$) and read y ($y_\_$) can call $f(\text{true})$ and rely on the fact that the value of y will not be changed.

By requiring variable-resource descriptions in assertions, we have pushed the side conditions into the logic, eliminating them from the rules. This does not eliminate the need for the programmer to follow rules of program hygiene, but it does allow the possibility that accurate statements of resource footprint could be included in a program text to be checked by a compiler entirely locally, with the combination of separately-checked program parts requiring only that their resource claims are compatible. It also permits a simple treatment of shared-variable concurrency (dealt with in this paper) and, we anticipate, parameter aliasing (the subject of a future paper). Examples of the use of a similar logic to reason about shared-variable concurrency are given in Bornat et al. [4]; in particular there is a treatment of two versions of the readers and writers problem [8, 1], neither of which obeys the restrictions imposed by the side conditions of, for example, [16].

Despite the absence of side conditions, our logic can prove all the programs that conventional Hoare logic can prove. We have not abandoned the variable-assignment axiom and made assignment alter locations rather than program/logical variables, in the same way as separation logic [17, 13, 18] treats the heap. This has enabled our assertions to include the same sort of statements about the values of variables as are made in conventional Hoare logic, which would not be possible if 'stack' variables were forced into the heap.

Our work, however, draws on ideas from separation logic: program variables are treated as resource and resource claims are separated with $\star$. For clarity we exclude a treatment of the heap, though our logic can be extended to to deal with it: that is, we deal only with separation logic's 'stack'.

2. Variables as resource

Before setting out the formal details, we describe some intuitive notions behind variables as resource. Hoare logic does not allow us to describe the ownership of variables, as illustrated by the triple

$$\{y = 0\}\, x := 7\, \{y = 0\}$$

which alters x but disingenuously avoids mentioning the fact. But x should be mentioned, because to execute $x := 7$ there must be a variable x in the stack. Furthermore, the assignment must *own* that variable, in the sense that no concurrent program can safely be permitted to read it. We must also know that variable y cannot be altered by some other program, else the assertion $y = 0$ cannot be assumed to be invariant. And then there is the matter of variable aliasing: x and y, distinct as names and as logical variables, must name distinct program variables – that is, distinct locations in the stack.

3. A logic of variables as resource

The syntax of assertions Φ is

$$\begin{array}{rcl}\Phi & ::= & E = E \mid \mathbf{emp_s} \mid \mathrm{Own}_p(x) \mid \pi = \pi \mid \\ & & \Phi \Rightarrow \Phi \mid \mathrm{false} \mid \forall X \cdot \Phi \mid \Phi \star \Phi \mid \Phi \mathrel{-\!\!\star} \Phi\end{array}$$

We distinguish integer logical variables $X, Y, \ldots$, permission logical variables $p, \ldots$ and integer program variables $x, y, \ldots$. We do not quantify over the values of program variables. E and π range over integer and permission expressions respectively.

3.1. Model

Permissions [3] are fundamental to our logic. They allow us to describe the division of variables between the threads of a concurrent program, including read/write private ownership of variables (with total permission), read-only sharing of variables (with partial permissions in all the accessing threads) and correct access to critical variables (for example with ownership ascribed to the resource accessed in a conditional critical region). We can use them in a version of separation logic's frame rule to constrain access to global variables. They enable us to describe the variable usage of procedures. The side-conditions of Hoare logic are replaced by a careful description of the variable permissions required by each part of a program. Those descriptions allow more precise control than the old side conditions.

Following [3], a total permission $\top$ may be split into two read permissions, which may themselves be split further, and split permissions may be recombined ($p \circledast p'$). Any permission at all gives read access.

There is a set of permissions Perms, equipped with a partial function $\circledast : \mathsf{Perms} \times \mathsf{Perms} \rightharpoonup \mathsf{Perms}$ and a distinguished element $\top \in \mathsf{Perms}$, such that $(\mathsf{Perms}, \circledast)$ forms a partial cancellative[1] commutative semigroup with the properties divisibility, total permission, and no unit:

$$\begin{array}{r}\forall c \in \mathsf{Perms} \cdot \exists c', c'' \in \mathsf{Perms} \cdot (c' \circledast c'' = c) \\ \forall c \in \mathsf{Perms} \cdot (\top \circledast c \text{ is undefined}) \\ \forall c, c' \in \mathsf{Perms} \cdot (c \circledast c' \neq c)\end{array}$$

Example models are: (1) $\mathsf{Perms} = \{z \mid 0 < z \leq 1\}$, $\top = 1$, $\circledast$ is $+$ (only defined if the result does not exceed 1); (2) $\mathsf{Perms} = \{S \mid S \subseteq \mathbb{N}, S \text{ infinite}\}$, $\top = \mathbb{N}$, $\circledast$ is $\uplus$.

ι ranges over elements of Perms. Permission expressions π have the following syntax:

$$\pi ::= \iota \mid p \mid \pi \circledast \pi$$

Separation logic divides the store into stack – the variables used by a program – and heap – dynamically allocated records – but does not give any formal treatment of

[1] Cancellative: $\iota \circledast \iota' = \iota \circledast \iota'' \Rightarrow \iota' = \iota''$.

the stack. In this paper we concentrate on program variables in the stack and logical and permission variables in the 'interpretation'.

Stacks s are finite partial maps from program variable names to pairs of an integer and a permission. Interpretations i are finite partial maps from logical variable names to integers and permissions. We only consider interpretations that define all the logical variables we use.

$$\begin{array}{rcl} s : \mathcal{S} & \stackrel{\text{def}}{=} & \mathsf{PVarNames} \rightharpoonup_{\text{fin}} \mathsf{Int} \times \mathsf{Perms} \\ i : \mathcal{R} & \stackrel{\text{def}}{=} & \mathsf{LVarNames} \rightharpoonup_{\text{fin}} \mathsf{Int} \cup \mathsf{Perms} \end{array}$$

We use $[\![E]\!]_{(s,i)}$ for the (partial) evaluation of expressions, and $[\![E]\!]_s$ will do when E does not contain logical variables:

$$\begin{array}{rcl} [\![E1 + E2]\!]_{(s,i)} & = & [\![E1]\!]_{(s,i)} + [\![E2]\!]_{(s,i)} \\ [\![0]\!]_{(s,i)} & = & 0 \\ [\![x]\!]_{(s,i)} & = & \begin{cases} s(x) & x \in dom(s) \\ \text{undefined} & \text{otherwise} \end{cases} \\ [\![X]\!]_{(s,i)} & = & i(X) \end{array}$$

We define a (partial) evaluation operation on permissions expressions:

$$\begin{array}{rcl} [\![\pi 1 \circledast \pi 2]\!]_{(s,i)} & = & [\![\pi 1]\!]_{(s,i)} \circledast [\![\pi 2]\!]_{(s,i)} \\ [\![\iota]\!]_{(s,i)} & = & \iota \\ [\![p]\!]_{(s,i)} & = & i(p) \end{array}$$

A forcing semantics is given in table 1. $s\#s'$ asserts that two stacks are compatible, agreeing about values where their domains intersect and not claiming too much permission; $s \star s'$ expresses separation of stacks; $\langle a, b\rangle$ is an element of a function; $\oplus$ is function update; $\uplus$ is disjoint function extension.

$\mathrm{Own}_\pi(x)$ asserts ownership of a stack containing a variable called x and permission π to access it. Crucially it also asserts that this is *all* that the stack contains. It says nothing about the content of the variable; it is purely about the lvalue of x (contrast $E \mapsto F$ in separation logic, which asserts a single-cell heap and describes its content). $\mathrm{Own}_\top(x)$ asserts total permission, i.e. ownership, and $\mathrm{Own}\_(x)$ means $\exists p \cdot (\mathrm{Own}_p(x))$. $\mathbf{emp_s}$ asserts the empty stack, and true holds of any stack at all. Following separation logic, $(\star)$ combines stack assertions: $\mathrm{Own}\_(x) \star \mathrm{Own}\_(y)$ is a two-variable stack; $\mathrm{Own}_\pi(x) \star \mathrm{Own}_{\pi'}(x)$ is equivalent to $\mathrm{Own}_{\pi \circledast \pi'}(x)$ and therefore $\mathrm{Own}_\top(x) \star \mathrm{Own}_\pi(x)$ is false; $\mathrm{Own}\_(x) \star \mathrm{true}$ is a stack which contains at least the variable x.

Arithmetic equality and inequality imply a level of ownership but are *loose* about the stack in which they operate: $x = 1$, for example, implicitly asserts $\mathrm{Own}\_(x) \star \mathrm{true}$. Our logic does not admit as a tautology $E \neq F \iff \neg(E = F)$. $x \neq 1$, for example, is satisfied by any stack in which there is a cell called x which does not contain 1; $\neg(x = 1)$, on the other hand, is satisfied by the same stacks and by those (for example $\mathbf{emp_s}$) in which x does not occur at all.

Definition 1.

$$x1_{\pi 1}, \ldots, xn_{\pi n} \Vdash P \stackrel{\mathit{def}}{=} (\mathrm{Own}_{\pi 1}(x1) \star \ldots \star \mathrm{Own}_{\pi n}(xn)) \wedge P$$

3.2. Rules

Our programming language is the language of Hoare logic plus variable declarations 'local-in-end' and procedure declarations 'let-=-in-end'. For simplicity we consider procedures each of which have a single call-by-reference parameter x and a single call-by-value parameter y. It would be straightforward to extend this treatment to deal with other cases.

The rules of our program logic are given in table 2.[2] Γ is the function context, a set of specifications $\{\Phi\} f(x; Y) \{\Phi'\}$, and O ranges over ownership assertions $x1_{\pi 1}, \ldots, xn_{\pi n}$. The first assignment axiom can be used in forward reasoning. The second is a weakest pre-condition version which can be derived from the first. The if and while rules have an antecedent $\Phi \Rightarrow B = B$, which ensures that variables mentioned in B are in the stack. In the let rule we give the function body C total permission to access the value parameter y. The first function-call rule deals with reference arguments by straightforward α-conversion. The second, an axiom, deals with value arguments, and is subtle. You might have expected to see

$$\Gamma, \{\Phi\}\, f(x; Y)\, \{\Phi'\} \vdash_{vr} \{\Phi[E/Y]\} \;\; f(x; E) \;\; \{\Phi'[E/Y]\}$$

But suppose that Φ is $Y = 3 \wedge \mathbf{emp_s}$: then Φ claims no stack, but $\Phi[E/Y]$ is $E = 3 \wedge \mathbf{emp_s}$, which is false if E mentions any program variables. Or you you might have expected

$$\Gamma, \{\Phi\}\, f(x; Y)\, \{\Phi'\} \vdash_{vr} \{\Phi \wedge Y = E\} \;\; f(x; E) \;\; \{\Phi'\}$$

But if Φ is $Y = 3 \wedge \mathrm{Own}_\top(x)$, then the precondition $Y = 3 \wedge \mathrm{Own}_\top(x) \wedge Y = E$ is false if E mentions any program variables other than x. In the axiom of table 2 Ψ claims the stack that E claims but Φ does not, and $(\Phi \star \Psi) \wedge Y = E$ allows the procedure call to read and/or write variables that are mentioned both in E and Φ as well as to be provided with a value to use in place of Y.

[2] We subscript turnstiles to distinguish logics: $\vdash_{vr}$ for proof in the variables-as-resource logic in table 2; $\vdash_H$ for proof in Hoare logic in table 5.

$$(s,i) \models \Phi$$

$$\begin{array}{lll}
(s,i) \models E1 = E2 & \iff & [\![E1]\!]_{(s,i)} = [\![E2]\!]_{(s,i)} \wedge [\![E1]\!]_{(s,i)} \text{ and } [\![E2]\!]_{(s,i)} \text{ are defined} \\
(s,i) \models \Phi \Rightarrow \Phi' & \iff & ((s,i) \models \Phi) \Rightarrow ((s,i) \models \Phi') \\
(s,i) \models \Phi \star \Phi' & \iff & \exists s1, s2 \cdot (s = s1 \star s2 \wedge ((s1,i) \models \Phi) \wedge ((s2,i) \models \Phi')) \\
(s,i) \models \Phi \mathrel{-\!\!\star} \Phi' & \iff & \forall s1 \cdot (s \# s1 \wedge ((s1,i) \models \Phi) \Rightarrow ((s \star s1, i) \models \Phi')) \\
(s,i) \models \mathrm{Own}_\pi(x) & \iff & [\![\pi]\!]_{(s,i)} \text{is defined} \wedge s = \{\langle x, (_, [\![\pi]\!]_{(s,i)})\rangle\} \\
(s,i) \models \mathbf{emp_s} & \iff & s = \{\} \\
(s,i) \models \text{false} & \iff & \text{false} \\
(s,i) \models \forall X \cdot \Phi & \iff & \forall v \cdot ((s, i \oplus \langle X, v \rangle) \models \Phi)
\end{array}$$

We encode true, $\wedge$, $\vee$, $\exists$ and $\neg$: e.g. $A \vee B$ is $(A \Rightarrow \text{false}) \Rightarrow B$.

$$s \# s' \iff \forall x, v, v', \iota, \iota' \cdot (s(x) = (v, \iota) \wedge s'(x) = (v', \iota') \Rightarrow v = v' \wedge \exists \iota'' \cdot (\iota'' = \iota \circledast \iota'))$$

$$s \star s' = \begin{cases} \left\{ \langle x, (v, \iota) \rangle \;\middle|\; \begin{array}{l} (s(x) = (v, \iota) \wedge x \notin dom(s')) \\ \vee (s'(x) = (v, \iota) \wedge x \notin dom(s)) \\ \vee (s(x) = (v, \iota') \wedge s'(x) = (v, \iota'') \wedge \iota = \iota' \circledast \iota'') \end{array} \right\}, & \text{where } s \# s'; \\ \text{undefined}, & \text{otherwise.} \end{cases}$$

3.3. Soundness

An operational semantics is given in table 3. In $s \xrightarrow[\rho]{C\ n} s'$

- s and s' are stacks;
- C is a command;
- ρ maps procedure names to a triple (x, y, C') of reference-parameter name x, value-parameter name y and command C'; and
- n is a recursion-depth counter.

A *safe computation* – the top part of the table and definition 2 – does not access stack locations that are undefined. The lower part of the table deals with unsafe computations, which access variables for which they have no permission.

Definition 2. $s \xrightarrow[\rho]{C\ n}$ safe *iff* $\forall n. \neg (s \xrightarrow[\rho]{C\ n}$ unsafe$)$

Lemma 3. *If* $s \xrightarrow[\rho]{C\ n}$ safe *and* $s' \# s$ *then* $s \star s' \xrightarrow[\rho]{C\ n}$ safe

Proof. By induction on the evaluation rules. □

Lemma 4 (Locality). *If* $s \xrightarrow[\rho]{C\ n}$ safe *and* $s' \# s$ *and* $s \star s' \xrightarrow[\rho]{C\ n}$ $s1$ *then* $\exists s2 \cdot s \xrightarrow[\rho]{C\ n} s2$ *and* $s2 \star s' = s1$.

Proof. By induction on the evaluation rules. □

Choice of fresh variable does not affect the reduction, and hence the semantics are deterministic with respect to the stack.

Definition 5 (Variable interchange: $\leftrightarrow$).

$$((y \leftrightarrow x)s)\ x \stackrel{def}{=} ((x \leftrightarrow y)s)\ x \stackrel{def}{=} s\ y;$$
$$((x \leftrightarrow y)s)\ z \stackrel{def}{=} s\ z.$$

Lemma 6.

$$\begin{array}{lll} (z \leftrightarrow x)s \xrightarrow[\rho]{C[z/x]\ n} (z \leftrightarrow x)s' & \Rightarrow & s \xrightarrow[\rho]{C\ n} s' \\ (z \leftrightarrow x)s \xrightarrow[\rho]{C[z/x]\ n} \text{unsafe} & \iff & s \xrightarrow[\rho]{C\ n} \text{unsafe} \end{array},$$

(z fresh for C and ρ, $x \notin \mathrm{dom}(s)$).

Proof. By induction on the evaluation rules. □

Lemma 7 (Determinacy).
If $s \xrightarrow[\rho]{C\ n} s1$ *and* $s \xrightarrow[\rho]{C\ n} s2$ *then* $s1 = s2$.

Proof. By induction on the evaluation rules. The rules for local require lemma 6. Other rules hold trivially. □

In the semantics of triples, the precondition implies a safe computation, in contrast to the semantics of standard Hoare logic.

Definition 8.

$$\rho \models_n \{\Phi\} C \{\Phi'\} \stackrel{def}{=} \forall s, s', i \cdot \left((s,i) \models \Phi \Rightarrow \left(\begin{array}{l} s \xrightarrow[\rho]{C\ n} \text{safe} \wedge \\ (s \xrightarrow[\rho]{C\ n} s' \Rightarrow (s', i) \models \Phi') \end{array} \right) \right)$$

$$\Gamma \vdash_{vr} \{\Phi\}\ C\ \{\Phi\}$$

$$\Gamma \vdash_{vr} \{x_\top, O \Vdash X = E\}\ x := E\ \{x_\top, O \Vdash x = X\}$$

$$\Gamma \vdash_{vr} \{\exists X \cdot X = E \wedge (\mathrm{Own}_\top(x) \star ((x = X \wedge \mathrm{Own}_\top(x)) \mathrel{-\!\!\star} \Phi))\}\ x := E\ \{\Phi\} \quad (X \text{ fresh for } \Phi)$$

$$\frac{\Phi \Rightarrow B = B \quad \Gamma \vdash_{vr} \{\Phi \wedge B\}\ C1\ \{\Phi'\} \quad \Gamma \vdash_{vr} \{\Phi \wedge \neg B\}\ C2\ \{\Phi'\}}{\Gamma \vdash_{vr} \{\Phi\}\ \text{if } B \text{ then } C1 \text{ else } C2 \text{ fi}\ \{\Phi'\}} \qquad \frac{\Phi \Rightarrow B = B \quad \Gamma \vdash_{vr} \{\Phi \wedge B\}\ C\ \{\Phi\}}{\Gamma \vdash_{vr} \{\Phi\}\ \text{while } B \text{ do } C \text{ od}\ \{\Phi \wedge \neg B\}}$$

$$\frac{\Gamma \vdash_{vr} \{\mathrm{Own}_\top(z) \star \Phi\}\ C[z/x]\ \{\mathrm{Own}_\top(z) \star \Phi'\}}{\Gamma \vdash_{vr} \{\Phi\}\ \text{local } x \text{ in } C \text{ end}\ \{\Phi'\}} \quad (\text{fresh } z)$$

$$\frac{\Phi \Rightarrow \Phi' \quad \Gamma \vdash_{vr} \{\Phi'\}\ C\ \{\Psi'\} \quad \Psi' \Rightarrow \Psi}{\Gamma \vdash_{vr} \{\Phi\}\ C\ \{\Psi\}} \qquad \frac{\Gamma \vdash_{vr} \{\Phi\}\ C\ \{\Psi\}}{\Gamma \vdash_{vr} \{\exists X \cdot \Phi\}\ C\ \{\exists X \cdot \Psi\}} \qquad \frac{\Gamma \vdash_{vr} \{\Phi\}\ C\ \{\Phi'\}}{\Gamma \vdash_{vr} \{\Phi \star \Psi\}\ C\ \{\Phi' \star \Psi\}}$$

$$\frac{\Gamma' \vdash_{vr} \{\Phi\}\ C1\ \{\Phi'\} \quad \Gamma' \vdash_{vr} (\{\Psi \star \mathrm{Own}_\top(y) \wedge y = Y\}\ C\ \{\Psi' \star \mathrm{Own}_\top(y)\})[w, z/x, y]}{\Gamma \vdash_{vr} \{\Phi\}\ \text{let } f(x; y) = C \text{ in } C1 \text{ end}\ \{\Phi'\}} \quad (\text{fresh } w, z;\ \Gamma' = \Gamma, \{\Psi\}\ f(x;Y)\ \{\Psi'\})$$

$$\frac{\Gamma, (\{\Psi 1\}\ f(x;Y)\ \{\Psi 2\})[z/x] \vdash_{vr} \{\Phi\}\ C\ \{\Phi'\}}{\Gamma, \{\Psi 1\}\ f(x;Y)\ \{\Psi 2\} \vdash_{vr} \{\Phi\}\ C\ \{\Phi'\}} \quad (z \text{ fresh for } \{\Psi 1\}\ f(x;Y)\ \{\Psi 2\})$$

$$\Gamma \vdash_{vr} \{(\Phi \star \Psi) \wedge Y = E\}\ f(x;E)\ \{\Phi' \star \Psi\} \quad (\{\Phi\}\ f(x;Y)\ \{\Phi'\} \in \Gamma)$$

Definition 9.
$\rho \models_n \Gamma \stackrel{def}{=}$ *for every* $\{\Phi\}\ f(x;Y)\ \{\Phi'\}$ *in* Γ, $\langle f, (x', y, C)\rangle$ *is in* ρ *such that, for fresh* z *and* w,

$$\rho \models_n \left(\begin{array}{c} \{\Phi \star (y_\top \Vdash y = X)\} \\ C[x/x'] \\ \{\Phi' \star \mathrm{Own}_\top(y)\} \end{array} \right) [z, w/x, y]$$

Definition 10 (Semantics of judgements).

$$\Gamma \models_n \{\Phi\} C \{\Phi'\} \stackrel{def}{=} \forall \rho \cdot (\ (\rho \models_n \Gamma) \Rightarrow (\rho \models_{n+1} \{\Phi\} C \{\Phi'\})\ )$$

Theorem 11. *If* $\Gamma \vdash_{vr} \{\Phi\}\ C\ \{\Phi'\}$ *is derivable then* $\forall n \cdot (\Gamma \models_n \{\Phi\} C \{\Phi'\})$

Proof. By induction on the derivation. □

4. Substitution

In Hoare logic substitution is used to model assignment and parameter passing, but simple properties of substitution do not hold in our logic. In particular, substitution of formulae can affect ownership. $X = E \wedge \Phi \Rightarrow \Phi[E/X]$, for example, is not a tautology. (Here is a counter-example:

$$\begin{array}{l} X = E \wedge ((X = X \wedge \mathbf{emp_s}) \star E = E) \\ \quad \not\Rightarrow (E = E \wedge \mathbf{emp_s}) \star E = E) \end{array}$$

– the left side of the implication is satisfiable, while the right is false if E contains program variables.) In the rest of this section we consider a subset of the logic in which substitution is well-behaved. As a result, we derive the following assignment axiom.

$$\Gamma \vdash_{vr} \{x_\top, O \Vdash \phi[E/x] \wedge E = E\}\ x := E\ \{x_\top, O \Vdash \phi\} \quad (2)$$

A stack-imprecise formula does not notice extension of the stack and does not care about the quantity of permission it has for any variable.

Definition 12. Φ *is* stack imprecise $\stackrel{def}{=}$
$\forall s, s', i \cdot$
$(\ ((s,i) \models \Phi) \wedge \lfloor s \rfloor \subseteq \lfloor s' \rfloor \Rightarrow ((s', i) \models \Phi)\ )$
where $\lfloor s \rfloor = \{\langle x, v\rangle \mid \langle x, (v, p)\rangle \in s\}$

Lemma 13. *If* Φ *and* Ψ *are stack imprecise, then* $\models \Phi \star \Psi \Leftrightarrow \Phi \wedge \Psi$

Corollary 14. *If* Φ *is stack imprecise, then* $\models \Phi \star E = E' \Leftrightarrow \Phi \wedge E = E'$

We define implication in the same way as when intuitionistic implication is encoded into classical separation logic [12].

Definition 15 (Stack-imprecise $\Rightarrow$ and $\neg$).
$\Phi \stackrel{s}{\Rightarrow} \Phi' \stackrel{def}{=} \text{true} \mathrel{-\!\!\star} (\Phi \Rightarrow \Phi')$ *and* $\stackrel{s}{\neg} \Phi \stackrel{def}{=} \Phi \stackrel{s}{\Rightarrow} \text{false}$.

Note: $E \neq E' \iff \stackrel{s}{\neg}(E = E')$ is a tautology.

If we restrict the syntax of formulae our logic can use substitution of equals for equals.

$$s \xrightarrow{C}{}^{n}_{\rho}\, s' \qquad s \xrightarrow{C}{}^{n}_{\rho}\, \mathsf{unsafe}$$

$$s \xrightarrow{\text{skip}}{}^{n}_{\rho}\, s \qquad \frac{s(x) = (\_, \top)}{s \xrightarrow{x:=E}{}^{n}_{\rho}\, s \oplus \langle x, (\llbracket E \rrbracket_s, \top)\rangle}$$

$$\frac{\llbracket B \rrbracket_s = \text{true} \quad s \xrightarrow{C_{\text{true}}}{}^{n}_{\rho}\, s'}{s \xrightarrow{\text{if } B \text{ then } C_{\text{true}} \text{ else } C_{\text{false fi}} \text{ fi}}{}^{n}_{\rho}\, s'} \qquad \frac{\llbracket B \rrbracket_s = \text{false} \quad s \xrightarrow{C_{\text{false}}}{}^{n}_{\rho}\, s'}{s \xrightarrow{\text{if } B \text{ then } C_{\text{true}} \text{ else } C_{\text{false fi}} \text{ fi}}{}^{n}_{\rho}\, s'}$$

$$\frac{s \xrightarrow{\text{if } B \text{ then } (C;\text{while } B \text{ do } C \text{ od}) \text{ else skip fi}}{}^{n}_{\rho}\, s'}{s \xrightarrow{\text{while } B \text{ do } C \text{ od}}{}^{n}_{\rho}\, s'} \qquad \frac{s \xrightarrow{C1}{}^{n}_{\rho}\, s' \quad s' \xrightarrow{C2}{}^{n}_{\rho}\, s''}{s \xrightarrow{C1;C2}{}^{n}_{\rho}\, s''}$$

$$\frac{s \uplus \langle z, (\_, \top)\rangle \xrightarrow{C[z/x]}{}^{n}_{\rho}\, s' \uplus \langle z, (\_, \top)\rangle}{s \xrightarrow{\text{local } x \text{ in } C \text{ end}}{}^{n}_{\rho}\, s'}\ \text{(fresh } z\text{)} \qquad \frac{s \xrightarrow{C'}{}^{n}_{\rho \oplus \langle f, (y,z,C)\rangle}\, s'}{s \xrightarrow{\text{let } f(y;z)=C \text{ in } C' \text{ end}}{}^{n}_{\rho}\, s'}$$

$$\frac{\rho(f) = (y, z, C) \quad s \xrightarrow{\text{local } z \text{ in } z:=E;\, C[x/y] \text{ end}}{}^{n}_{\rho}\, s'}{s \xrightarrow{f(x;E)}{}^{n+1}_{\rho}\, s'}\ \text{(fresh } z'\text{)}$$

$$\frac{\langle x, (\_, \top)\rangle \notin s}{s \xrightarrow{x:=E}{}^{n}_{\rho}\, \mathsf{unsafe}} \quad \frac{\llbracket E \rrbracket_s \text{ is undefined}}{s \xrightarrow{x:=E}{}^{n}_{\rho}\, \mathsf{unsafe}} \quad \frac{\llbracket B \rrbracket_s \text{ is undefined}}{s \xrightarrow{\text{if } B \text{ then } C1 \text{ else } C2 \text{ fi}}{}^{n}_{\rho}\, \mathsf{unsafe}}$$

Definition 16 (restricted formulae).
$\phi ::= E{=}E \mid \phi \wedge \phi \mid \phi \vee \phi \mid \phi \overset{s}{\Rightarrow} \phi \mid \phi \mathrel{-\!\!\star} \phi \mid \pi = \pi \mid \phi \star \phi \mid \forall X.\phi \mid \exists X.\phi \mid \text{false} \mid \text{true} \mid \overset{s}{\neg} \phi$

Lemma 17. *Restricted formulae are stack imprecise.*

Proof. Structural induction on ϕ. □

Lemma 18.
$(s, i) \vDash X = E \quad \Rightarrow \quad \llbracket E' \rrbracket_{(s,i)} = \llbracket E'[E/X] \rrbracket_{(s,i)}$

Proof. By induction on structure of E' □

Lemma 19. $\vDash X = E \;\Rightarrow\; (\phi \Leftrightarrow \phi[E/X])$

Proof. By structural induction on ϕ. The ($\star$) and ($\mathrel{-\!\!\star}$) cases require lemma 14, and the ($=$) case requires lemma 18. □

Definition 20. $\text{vars}(O) \overset{\textit{def}}{=} \{x \mid (x)_p \in O\}$

Lemma 21. $(O1 \Vdash \phi 1) \star (O2 \Vdash \phi 2) \Rightarrow (O1, O2 \Vdash \phi 1 \star \phi 1)$

Lemma 22. *If* $\text{FV}(\phi 1) \subseteq \text{vars}(O1)$ *and* $\text{FV}(\phi 2) \subseteq \text{vars}(O2)$ *and* $\vDash O \Vdash \text{true} \iff O1 \Vdash \text{true} \star O2 \Vdash \text{true}$ *then* $\vDash (O \Vdash \phi 1 \star \phi 2) \Rightarrow (O1 \Vdash \phi 1) \star (O2 \Vdash \phi 2)$.

Lemma 23. $\vDash (\overline{y}_{\overline{\pi}} \Vdash \phi \star \psi) \iff \exists \overline{p1}, \overline{p2} \cdot ((\overline{y}_{\overline{p1}} \Vdash \phi) \star (\overline{y}_{\overline{p1}} \Vdash \psi)) \wedge (\overline{\pi} = \overline{p1} \circledast \overline{p2})$

Theorem 24 (Assignment by substitution). *The assignment axiom in (2) is derivable.*

Proof.

$$\cfrac{\cfrac{\cfrac{\cfrac{\cfrac{}{\left\{x_\top, \overline{y}_{\overline{p1}} \Vdash E{=}X\right\} x := E \left\{x_\top, \overline{y}_{\overline{p1}} \Vdash x{=}X\right\}}}{\left\{(x_\top, \overline{y}_{\overline{p1}} \Vdash E{=}X) \star \begin{pmatrix}(\overline{y}_{\overline{p2}} \Vdash \phi[X/x]) \\ \wedge(\overline{p1} \circledast \overline{p1} = \overline{\pi})\end{pmatrix}\right\} x := E \left\{(x_\top, \overline{y}_{\overline{p1}} \Vdash x{=}X) \star \begin{pmatrix}(\overline{y}_{\overline{p2}} \Vdash \phi[X/x]) \\ \wedge(\overline{p1} \circledast \overline{p1} = \overline{\pi})\end{pmatrix}\right\}}}{\left\{\exists \overline{p1}, \overline{p2}.\ (x_\top, \overline{y}_{\overline{p1}} \Vdash E{=}X) \star \begin{pmatrix}(\overline{y}_{\overline{p2}} \Vdash \phi[X/x]) \\ \wedge(\overline{p1} \circledast \overline{p1} = \overline{\pi})\end{pmatrix}\right\} x := E \left\{\exists \overline{p1}, \overline{p2}.\ (x_\top, \overline{y}_{\overline{p1}} \Vdash x{=}X) \star \begin{pmatrix}(\overline{y}_{\overline{p2}} \Vdash \phi[X/x]) \\ \wedge(\overline{p1} \circledast \overline{p1} = \overline{\pi})\end{pmatrix}\right\}}}{\{x_\top, \overline{y}_{\overline{\pi}} \Vdash E{=}X \wedge \phi[E/x]\}\, x := E\, \{x_\top, \overline{y}_{\overline{\pi}} \Vdash \phi\}}}{\{\exists X \cdot x_\top, \overline{y}_{\overline{\pi}} \Vdash E{=}X \wedge \phi[E/x]\}\, x := E\, \{\exists X \cdot x_\top, \overline{y}_{\overline{\pi}} \Vdash \phi\}}}{\{x_\top, \overline{y}_{\overline{\pi}} \Vdash E{=}E \wedge \phi[E/x]\}\, x := E\, \{x_\top, \overline{y}_{\overline{\pi}} \Vdash \phi\}}$$

The first use of the rule of consequence requires

$$\begin{aligned}
& x_{\top}, \overline{y}_{\overline{\pi}} \Vdash E{=}X \wedge \phi[E/x] \\
& \Rightarrow x_{\top}, \overline{y}_{\overline{\pi}} \Vdash E{=}X \wedge \phi[X/x][E/X] \qquad (X \notin \phi) \\
& \Rightarrow x_{\top}, \overline{y}_{\overline{\pi}} \Vdash (E{=}X) \star \phi[X/x] \qquad \text{(Lemmas 19,14)} \\
& \Rightarrow \exists p, p', \overline{p1}, \overline{p2}. \\
& \qquad ((x_p, \overline{y}_{\overline{p1}} \Vdash E{=}X) \star (x_{p'}, \overline{y}_{\overline{p2}} \Vdash \phi[X/x])) \\
& \qquad \wedge (p \circledast p' = \top) \wedge (\overline{p1} \circledast \overline{p2} = \overline{\pi}) \qquad \text{(Lemma 23)} \\
& \Rightarrow \exists \overline{p1}, \overline{p2}. ((x_{\top}, \overline{y}_{\overline{p1}} \Vdash E{=}X) \star (\overline{y}_{\overline{p2}} \Vdash \phi[X/x])) \\
& \qquad \wedge (\overline{p1} \circledast \overline{p2} = \overline{\pi}) \qquad \text{(Lemma 21)} \\
& \Rightarrow \exists \overline{p1}, \overline{p2}. (x_{\top}, \overline{y}_{\overline{p1}} \Vdash E{=}X) \\
& \qquad \star ((\overline{y}_{\overline{p2}} \Vdash \phi[X/x]) \wedge (\overline{p1} \circledast \overline{p2} = \overline{\pi}))
\end{aligned}$$

and

$$\begin{aligned}
& \exists \overline{p1}, \overline{p2}. (x_{\top}, \overline{y}_{\overline{p1}} \Vdash x{=}X) \\
& \qquad \star ((\overline{y}_{\overline{p2}} \Vdash \phi[X/x]) \wedge (\overline{p1} \circledast \overline{p2} = \overline{\pi})) \\
& \Rightarrow x_{\top}, \overline{y}_{\overline{\pi}} \Vdash (x{=}X) \star \phi[X/x] \text{ (Lemma 21)} \\
& \Rightarrow x_{\top}, \overline{y}_{\overline{\pi}} \Vdash x{=}X \wedge \phi[X/x] \quad \text{(Lemma 14)} \\
& \Rightarrow x_{\top}, \overline{y}_{\overline{\pi}} \Vdash \phi \qquad \text{(Lemma 19)}
\end{aligned}$$

The second use of the rule of consequence requires

$$E = E \Rightarrow \exists X \cdot E = X$$

□

5. Encoding Hoare logics

We must at least be able to prove all assertions provable in Hoare logic. We demonstrate this by showing that Hoare logic proofs can be translated into our logic. We present a translation of a Hoare logic with reference and value parameters in procedure definitions. We use ϕ and ψ to range over Hoare logic assertions since there is an implicit translation to restricted formulae: $\overset{s}{\Rightarrow}$ for $\Rightarrow$, $\overset{s}{\neg}$ for $\neg$.

A Hoare-logic function context $\mathbb{F}$ (cf. Γ) is a set of specifications $\{\phi\}\, f(x; y)[\overline{u}; \overline{v}]\, \{\psi\}$ where

- f is a function name, x a reference-parameter name and y a value-parameter name;
- ϕ is the precondition and ψ the postcondition of $f(x; y)$;
- $\overline{u}$ is a set of the names of the global variables modifed by $f(x; y)$ and $\overline{v}$ a set of the names of global variables it reads;
- $\overline{u} \subseteq \overline{v}$.

Table 4 defines $\text{mods}(\mathbb{F}, C)$, the variables written by C, and $\text{free}(\mathbb{F}, C)$, its free variables: because of the complexities of the let definition we require two definitions for function call but, because let declares functions one at a time, we do not need a fixed-point iteration. Table 5 gives the rules of the Hoare logic which we encode.

Lemma 25 (The logics are equivalent on defined assertions).

$$\begin{aligned}
& \text{FV}(\phi) \subseteq \text{dom}(s) \Rightarrow \\
& \quad (\ (\lfloor s \rfloor, i) \vDash_H \phi \iff (s, i) \vDash \phi\ )
\end{aligned}$$

where $\vDash$ is the forcing semantics given in table 1, and $\vDash_H$ is the forcing semantics of Hoare logic.

Proof. Structural induction on ϕ. The interesting case is $\star$, which requires that ϕ is stack imprecise. □

Definition 26 (Supporting write and read variables).

$$\begin{aligned}
& \text{supports}_{\overline{p}}(\overline{u}; \overline{v}) \overset{\text{def}}{=} \\
& \quad (\overline{u}_1)_{\top}, \ldots, (\overline{u}_m)_{\top}, (\overline{w}_1)_{\overline{p}_1}, \ldots, (\overline{w}_n)_{\overline{p}_n} \\
& \quad \text{where } \overline{w} = \overline{v} \setminus \overline{u}
\end{aligned}$$

Definition 27 (Supporting a command).

$$\text{supports}_{\overline{p}}(\mathbb{F}, C) \overset{\text{def}}{=} \text{supports}_{\overline{p}}(\text{mods}(\mathbb{F}, C); \text{free}(\mathbb{F}, C))$$

In Hoare logic program variables and logical variables are conflated. In our translation of $\{\phi\}\, C\, \{\psi\}$ we turn all the free variables of ϕ and ψ that are not used in C into logical variables.

Definition 28 (Triple translation).

$$\begin{aligned}
& [\![\{\phi\}\, C\, \{\psi\}]\!]_{\mathbb{F}} \overset{\text{def}}{=} \{O \Vdash \phi[\overline{U}/\overline{u}]\}\ C\ \{O \Vdash \psi[\overline{U}/\overline{u}]\} \\
& \quad \text{where } O = \text{supports}_{\overline{p}}(\mathbb{F}, C); \\
& \qquad \overline{u} = \text{FV}(\phi, \psi) \setminus \text{vars}(O); \\
& \qquad \text{fresh } \overline{p}, \overline{U}
\end{aligned}$$

(Here $\overline{p}$ and $\overline{U}$ are sets of fresh logical variables, implicitly quantified at the level of the triple: that is, because of the semantics of triples, the fresh $\overline{p}, \overline{U}$ can be thought of as universally quantified.

$$\forall \overline{p}, \overline{U} \cdot \{O \Vdash \phi[\overline{U}/\overline{u}]\}\ C\ \{O \Vdash \psi[\overline{U}/\overline{u}]\}$$

Clearly, the translation is deterministic.)

Although our translation replaces some integer program variables with new logical variables, we can always retrieve the original specification by extending O and using the frame rule to enforce an invariant which equates the values of new and old variables.

Lemma 29 (From proof with logical variables infer proof with program variables.).

$\mathrm{mods}(\mathbb{F}, C)$ $\mathrm{free}(\mathbb{F}, C)$

C	$\mathrm{mods}(\mathbb{F}, C)$	$\mathrm{free}(\mathbb{F}, C)$
$x := E$	$\{x\}$	$\mathrm{FV}(E) \cup \{x\}$
$C_1; C_2$	$\mathrm{mods}(\mathbb{F}, C_1) \cup \mathrm{mods}(\mathbb{F}, C_2)$	$\mathrm{free}(\mathbb{F}, C_1) \cup \mathrm{free}(\mathbb{F}, C_2)$
skip	$\varnothing$	$\varnothing$
while B do C od	$\mathrm{mods}(\mathbb{F}, C)$	$\mathrm{FV}(B) \cup \mathrm{free}(\mathbb{F}, C)$
local x in C end	$\mathrm{mods}(\mathbb{F}, C) \setminus \{x\}$	$\mathrm{free}(\mathbb{F}, C) \setminus \{x\}$
if B then C_1 else C_2 fi	$\mathrm{mods}(\mathbb{F}, C_1) \cup \mathrm{mods}(\mathbb{F}, C_2)$	$\mathrm{FV}(B) \cup \mathrm{free}(\mathbb{F}, C_1) \cup \mathrm{free}(\mathbb{F}, C_2)$
let $f(x; y) = C$ in C' end where $\mathbb{F}' = \mathbb{F}, \{\_\} f(x; y)[\overline{u}; \overline{v}]\{\_\}$; $\overline{u} = \mathrm{mods}(\mathbb{F}, C) \setminus \{x, y\}$; $\overline{v} = \mathrm{free}(\mathbb{F}, C) \setminus \{x, y\}$	$\mathrm{mods}(\mathbb{F}', C')$	$\mathrm{free}(\mathbb{F}', C')$
$f(x; E)$ (normal case, $\{\_\} f(x; y)[\overline{u}; \overline{v}]\{\_\} \in \mathbb{F}$)	$\{x\} \cup \overline{u}$	$\{x\} \cup \mathrm{FV}(E) \cup \overline{v}$
$f(x; E)$ (bootstrap case, $\{\_\} f(\_; \_)[\_; \_]\{\_\} \notin \mathbb{F}$)	$\{x\}$	$\{x\} \cup \mathrm{FV}(E)$

$\mathbb{F} \vdash_H \{\phi\}\ C\ \{\phi\}$

$$\frac{}{\mathbb{F} \vdash_H \{\phi[E/x]\}\ x := E\ \{\phi\}} \qquad \frac{}{\mathbb{F} \vdash_H \{\phi\}\ \mathrm{skip}\ \{\phi\}}$$

$$\frac{\mathbb{F} \vdash_H \{\phi \wedge B\}\ C_1\ \{\psi\} \quad \mathbb{F} \vdash_H \{\phi \wedge \neg B\}\ C_2\ \{\psi\}}{\mathbb{F} \vdash_H \{\phi\}\ \text{if } B \text{ then } C_1 \text{ else } C_2 \text{ fi}\ \{\psi\}} \qquad \frac{\mathbb{F} \vdash_H \{\phi \wedge B\}\ C\ \{\phi\}}{\mathbb{F} \vdash_H \{\phi\}\ \text{while } B \text{ do } C \text{ od}\ \{\phi \wedge \neg B\}}$$

$$\frac{\phi' \Rightarrow \phi \quad \mathbb{F} \vdash_H \{\phi\}\ C\ \{\psi\} \quad \psi \Rightarrow \psi'}{\mathbb{F} \vdash_H \{\phi'\}\ C\ \{\psi'\}} \qquad \frac{\mathbb{F} \vdash_H \{\phi\}\ C\ \{\phi'\}}{\mathbb{F} \vdash_H \{\phi \wedge \psi\}\ C\ \{\phi' \wedge \psi\}}\ \mathrm{mods}(\mathbb{F}, C) \cap \mathrm{FV}(\psi) = \varnothing$$

$$\frac{\mathbb{F} \vdash_H \{\phi\}\ C\ \{\psi\}}{\mathbb{F} \vdash_H \{\exists x.\phi\}\ C\ \{\exists x.\psi\}}\ x \notin \mathrm{free}(\mathbb{F}, C) \qquad \frac{\mathbb{F} \vdash_H \{\phi\}\ C[y/x]\ \{\psi\}}{\mathbb{F} \vdash_H \{\phi\}\ \text{local } x \text{ in } C \text{ end}\ \{\psi\}}\ y \text{ fresh}$$

$$\frac{}{\mathbb{F} \vdash_H \{\phi[w, Y/x, y] \wedge E = Y\}\ f(w; E)\ \{\psi[w, Y/x, y]\}}\ w \notin \overline{u}, \overline{v};\ \{\phi\}\, f(x; y)[\overline{u}; \overline{v}]\, \{\psi\} \in \mathbb{F}$$

$$\frac{\mathbb{F}' \vdash_H \{\phi\}\ C\ \{\psi\} \quad \mathbb{F}' \vdash_H (\{\phi'\}\ \text{local } z \text{ in } z := y; C'[z/y] \text{ end}\ \{\psi'\})[w/x]}{\mathbb{F} \vdash_H \{\phi\}\ \text{let } f(x; y) = C' \text{ in } C \text{ end}\ \{\psi\}}\ \begin{array}{l}\mathbb{F}' = \mathbb{F}, \{\phi'\}\, f(x; y)[\overline{u}; \overline{v}]\, \{\psi'\};\\ \overline{u} = \mathrm{free}(\mathbb{F}, C') \setminus \{x, y\};\ \overline{v} = \mathrm{mods}(\mathbb{F}, C') \setminus \{x, y\}\\ \text{fresh } w\end{array}$$

Proof.

$$\dfrac{\dfrac{\dfrac{\{O \Vdash \phi[Z/z]\}\ C\ \{O \Vdash \psi[Z/z]\}}{\left\{\begin{array}{l}(z_\pi \Vdash Z = z)\\ \star (O \Vdash \phi[Z/z])\end{array}\right\}\ C\ \left\{\begin{array}{l}(z_\pi \Vdash Z = z)\\ \star (O \Vdash \psi[Z/z])\end{array}\right\}}}{\left\{\exists Z \cdot \left(\begin{array}{l}(z_\pi \Vdash Z = z)\\ \star (O \Vdash \phi[Z/z])\end{array}\right)\right\}\ C\ \left\{\exists Z \cdot \left(\begin{array}{l}(z_\pi \Vdash Z = z)\\ \star (O \Vdash \psi[Z/z])\end{array}\right)\right\}}}{\{O, z_\pi \Vdash \phi\}\ C\ \{O, z_\pi \Vdash \psi\}}$$

□

Definition 30 (Translation of procedure environment).

$$[\![\mathbb{F}]\!] \stackrel{def}{=} \left\{ \left[\!\!\left[\begin{array}{c}\{\phi[Y/y]\}\\ f(x; Y)\\ \{\psi[Y/y]\}\end{array} \right]\!\!\right]_{\mathbb{F}} \;\middle|\; \{\phi\} f(x; y)[\overline{u}; \overline{v}]\{\phi\} \in \mathbb{F} \right\}$$

Note: For convenience, we assume that triple translation treats Y in $f(x; Y)$ as a constant.

Theorem 31 (Completeness of encoding).

$$(\mathbb{F} \vdash_H \{\phi\}\, C\, \{\psi\}) \Rightarrow ([\![\mathbb{F}]\!] \models_{vr} [\![\{\phi\}\, C\, \{\psi\}]\!]_{\mathbb{F}})$$

Proof. By induction on the Hoare-logic derivation. □

Theorem 32 (Soundness of encoding).

$$([\![\mathbb{F}]\!] \models_{vr} [\![\{\phi\}\, C\, \{\psi\}]\!]_{\mathbb{F}}) \Rightarrow (\mathbb{F} \models_H \{\phi\}\ C\ \{\psi\})$$

Proof.

$$\begin{array}{l}(\mathbb{F} \models_{vr} [\![\{\phi\}\, C\, \{\psi\}]\!]_{\mathbb{F}})\\ \qquad \Rightarrow (\mathbb{F} \models_{vr} \{O, O' \Vdash \phi\}\ C\ \{O, O' \Vdash \psi\})\end{array}$$

where $O = \text{supports}_{\overline{p}}(\mathbb{F}, C)$, and $\text{vars}(O, O') \supseteq \text{FV}(\phi, \psi)$ follows directly from repeated application of lemma 29. Then

$$(\mathbb{F} \models_{vr} \{O, O' \Vdash \phi\}\ C\ \{O, O' \Vdash \psi\}) \Rightarrow (\mathbb{F} \models_{H} \{\phi\}\ C\ \{\psi\})$$

follows directly from lemma 25. □

6. Concurrency

Hoare-logic concurrency rules have complex side conditions and restrictions constraining the use of variables. In our logic we do not need any of that. The rules are given with respect to a resource context, Δ, which maps a resource identifier b to its corresponding invariant. The invariants must be precise [6]. Table 6 gives the rules.

6.1. Soundness

Brookes has shown this logic to be sound [5].

6.2. Translation

We can translate Brookes's rules for concurrent separation logic [6] into our own (we omit his treatment of the heap). The key to his soundness proof is the notion of critical variable. A variable is critical if it is modified in one thread and free in another: in $x := y \| y := z$, for example, y is critical.

Each critical variable is associated with a *resource* and each access must be within a critical region for that resource. A resource context $\mathbb{R}$ maps a resource name b to a critical-variable list $\overline{u}$ and an invariant ψ. There are two operations on these contexts: (1) $\text{crit}(\mathbb{R})$ delivers the critical variables in $\mathbb{R}$; and (2) $\text{FV}(\mathbb{R})$ the variables free in the invariants as well as all critical variables. Brookes's parallel rule has a side condition:

$$\begin{array}{l} \text{FV}(\Phi 1, \Phi 1') \cap \text{mods}(C2) = \varnothing \\ \text{FV}(\Phi 2, \Phi 2') \cap \text{mods}(C1) = \varnothing \\ \text{FV}(C1) \cap \text{mods}(C2) \subseteq \text{crit}(\mathbb{R}) \\ \text{FV}(C2) \cap \text{mods}(C1) \subseteq \text{crit}(\mathbb{R}) \end{array}$$

The $x := E$ rule has the side condition $x \notin \text{FV}(\mathbb{R})$. There is also an additional constraint on the well-formedness of judgements $\mathbb{R} \vdash_{H} \{\Phi\}\ C\ \{\Phi'\}$: the critical variables may not be mentioned in the pre- or post-condition, i.e. $crit(\mathbb{R}) \cap \text{FV}(\Phi, \Phi') = \varnothing$.

Definition 33.

$$\text{supports}_{\overline{p}}(\mathbb{R}, C) \stackrel{def}{=} \text{supports}_{\overline{p}}((\text{mods}(C) \setminus \text{FV}(\mathbb{R})); (\text{free}(C) \setminus \text{crit}(\mathbb{R})))$$

Definition 34 (Triple translation).

$[\![\{\phi\}\, C\, \{\psi\}]\!]_{\mathbb{R}} \stackrel{def}{=} \{O \Vdash \phi[\overline{U}/\overline{u}]\}\ C\ \{O \Vdash \psi[\overline{U}/\overline{u}]\}$ *where* $O = \text{supports}_{\overline{p}}(\mathbb{R}, C)$, $\overline{u} = \text{FV}(\phi, \psi) \setminus \text{vars}(O)$, *and* $\overline{p}$, $\overline{U}$ *are sets of fresh logical variables.*

Definition 35 (Context translation, $[\![\mathbb{R}]\!]$). *We translate each element of the context to*

$$[\![r[\overline{u}] : \psi]\!] \quad = \quad r : \text{supports}_{\overline{p}}(\overline{u}, \text{FV}(\psi)) \Vdash \psi$$

Lemma 36.

$$\text{supports}_{\overline{p}}(\mathbb{R}, C) = \text{supports}_{\overline{p}}(\overline{u}, \text{FV}(\psi)) \star \text{supports}_{\overline{p}}(\mathbb{R} \uplus \langle b, (\overline{u}, \psi)\rangle, C)$$

Theorem 37 (Completeness of encoding).

$$\mathbb{R} \vdash_{H} \{\phi\}\, C\, \{\psi\} \quad \Rightarrow \quad [\![\mathbb{R}]\!] \vdash_{vr} [\![\{\phi\}\, C\, \{\psi\}]\!]_{\mathbb{R}}$$

Proof. By induction on the derivation for Brookes's rules. □

Theorem 38 (Soundness of encoding).

Proof. Same as theorem 32 □

7. Conclusions

We have a logic which admits translations of all Hoare logic proofs and in which there are no side conditions on the use of variables or restrictions on the action of concurrent programs. In addition we are able (though not within the space constraints of this presentation) to deal with the heap in the same way. By working through several examples, Bornat et al. have previously shown that this kind of logic deals conveniently with the verification of shared-variable concurrency programs [4]. Their logic can be translated into our own, and its soundness is a consequence of the soundness of our own.

In all other previous Hoare logics a simultaneous treatment of concurrency, procedure call and the heap requires complex side conditions on the use of variables, as well as restrictions on the action of programs which are extremely difficult to check in a mechanical proof tool. Smallfoot [2], for example, uses a treatment of concurrency based on Brookes' and O'Hearn's treatment in separation logic, and must make a completely global static analysis when dealing with the restrictions on concurrent programs. The analysis takes several pages to describe, and is extremely intricate to implement. No such analysis would be required in a tool based on our new logic.

$$\frac{\Delta \vdash_{vr} \{\Phi 1\}\ C1\ \{\Phi 1'\} \quad \Delta \vdash_{vr} \{\Phi 2\}\ C2\ \{\Phi 2'\}}{\Delta \vdash_{vr} \{\Phi 1 \star \Phi 2\}\ C1 \| C2\ \{\Phi 1' \star \Phi 2'\}} \qquad \frac{\Delta, b : \Psi \vdash_{vr} \{\Phi\}\ C\ \{\Phi'\}}{\Delta \vdash_{vr} \{\Phi \star \Psi\}\ \text{resource}\ b\ \text{in}\ C\ \text{end}\ \{\Phi' \star \Psi\}}$$

$$\frac{\Delta \vdash_{vr} \{(\Phi \star \Psi) \wedge B\}\ C\ \{\Phi' \star \Psi\} \quad \Phi \star \Psi \Rightarrow B = B}{\Delta, b : \Psi \vdash_{vr} \{\Phi\}\ \text{with}\ b\ \text{when}\ B\ \text{do}\ C\ \text{od}\ \{\Phi'\}}$$

Acknowledgements

Like much of our previous work in program logic, this paper emerges from repeated rumbustious discussions within the East London Massive, a frequent but irregular gathering at Queen Mary, University of London. We acknowledge in particular the seminal contribution of Peter O'Hearn in proposing that we undertake this work and then attempting to trip us up at ever turn, right up to the very last. Hongseok Yang, from outside the Massive, provided a model for Bornat's proposed formalism and inspired us to begin this work.

This work was supported by EPSRC grants EP/C523997/1 (Parkinson and Bornat) and EP/C544757/1 (Calcagno). Parkinson and Bornat also thank Intel Research Cambridge for their support.

References

[1] G. Andrews. *Concurrent Programming: Principles and Practice*. Benjamin Cummings, 1991.

[2] J. Berdine, C. Calcagno, and P. W. O'Hearn. Modular automatic assertion checking with separation logic. Draft, Nov. 2005.

[3] R. Bornat, C. Calcagno, P. O'Hearn, and M. Parkinson. Permission accounting in separation logic. In *POPL '05: Proceedings of the 32nd ACM SIGPLAN-SIGACT sysposium on Principles of programming languages*, pages 259–270, New York, NY, USA, Jan. 2005. ACM Press.

[4] R. Bornat, C. Calcagno, and H. Yang. Variables as resource in separation logic. Presented at MFPS XXI, Birmingham, May 2005. To appear in Electronic Notes in Computer Science, 2005.

[5] S. Brookes. Variables as resource for shared-memory programs: Semantics and soundness. In *Proceedings of MFPS XXII*. Elsevier ENTCS., May 2006.

[6] S. D. Brookes. A semantics for concurrent separation logic. In *CONCUR'04: 15th International Conference on Concurrency Theory*, volume 3170 of *Lecture Notes in Computer Science*, pages 16–34, London, Aug. 2004. Springer. Extended version to appear in *Theoretical Computer Science*.

[7] R. Cartwright and D. Oppen. Unrestricted procedure calls in hoare's logic. In *POPL '78: Proceedings of the 5th ACM SIGACT-SIGPLAN symposium on Principles of programming languages*, pages 131–140, New York, 1978. ACM Press.

[8] P. J. Courtois, F. Heymans, and D. L. Parnas. Concurrent control with "readers" and "writers". *Commun. ACM*, 14(10):667–668, 1971.

[9] D. Gries and G. Levin. Assignment and procedure call proof rules. *ACM Transactions on Programming Languages and Systems*, 2(4), Oct. 1980.

[10] C. A. R. Hoare. An axiomatic basis for computer programming. *Commun. ACM*, 12(10):576–580, 1969.

[11] C. A. R. Hoare. Towards a theory of parallel programming. *Operating Systems Techniques*, 1971.

[12] S. S. Ishtiaq and P. W. O'Hearn. BI as an assertion language for mutable data structures. In *Symposium on Principles of Programming Languages*, pages 14–26, 2001.

[13] P. O'Hearn, J. Reynolds, and H. Yang. Local reasoning about programs that alter data structures. In L. Fribourg, editor, *CSL 2001*, pages 1–19. Springer-Verlag, 2001. LNCS 2142.

[14] P. W. O'Hearn. Resources, concurrency and local reasoning. To appear in *Theoretical Computer Science*; preliminary version published as [15].

[15] P. W. O'Hearn. Resources, concurrency and local reasoning. In *CONCUR'04: 15th International Conference on Concurrency Theory*, volume 3170 of *Lecture Notes in Computer Science*, pages 49–67, London, Aug. 2004. Springer. Extended version is [14].

[16] S. Owicki and D. Gries. An axiomatic proof technique for parallel programs. *Acta Informatica*, 19:319–340, 1976.

[17] J. C. Reynolds. Intuitionistic reasoning about shared mutable data structure. In J. Davies, B. Roscoe, and J. Woodcock, editors, *Millennial Perspectives in Computer Science*, pages 303–321. Palgrave, 2000.

[18] J. C. Reynolds. Separation logic: A logic for shared mutable data structures. In *LICS '02: Proceedings of the 17th Annual IEEE Symposium on Logic in Computer Science*, pages 55–74, Washington, DC, USA, 2002. IEEE Computer Society.

[19] C. Strachey. Fundamental concepts in programming languages. *Higher Order Symbolic Computation*, 13(1-2):11–49, 2000.

Independence and Concurrent Separation Logic

Jonathan Hayman and Glynn Winskel
Computer Laboratory, University of Cambridge

Abstract

A compositional Petri net based semantics is given to a simple pointer-manipulating language. The model is then applied to give a notion of validity to the judgements made by concurrent separation logic that emphasizes the process-environment duality inherent in such rely-guarantee reasoning. Soundness of the rules of concurrent separation logic with respect to this definition of validity is shown. The independence information retained by the Petri net model is then exploited to characterize the independence of parallel processes enforced by the logic. This is shown to permit a refinement operation capable of changing the granularity of atomic actions.

1. Introduction

The foundational work of Hoare on parallel programming [9] identified the fact that attaching an interleaved semantics to parallel languages is problematic. Three areas of difficulty were isolated, quoted directly:

- *That of defining a "unit of action".*
- *That of implementing the interleaving on genuinely parallel hardware.*
- *That of designing programs to control the fantastic number of combinations involved in arbitrary interleaving.*

The significance of these problems increases with developments in hardware, such as multiple-core processors, that allow primitive machine actions to occur at the same time.

As Hoare went on to explain, a feature of concurrent systems in the real world is that they are often *spatially separated*, operating on completely different resources and not interacting. When this is so, the parallel processes are *independent* of each other. For instance, computer processes are spatially separated if they operate on different memory locations. The problems above are intuitively resolved if the occurrence of non-independent parallel actions is prohibited except in rare cases where we can assume atomicity, as might be enforced using the constructs proposed in [8, 3].

Independence models for concurrency allow the problems associated with an interleaved semantics to be resolved by recording when actions are independent. Independent actions can be run in either order or even concurrently with no consequence on their effect. This mitigates the increase in the state space since unnecessary interleavings of independent actions need not be considered (see *e.g.* [6] for applications to model checking). Independence models also permit easier notions of refinement which allow us to change the assumed atomicity of actions.

It is surprising that, to our knowledge, there has been no comprehensive study of the semantics of programming languages inside an independence model. The first component of this work gives such a semantics in terms of a well-known independence model, namely Petri nets. Our model isolates the specification of the control flow of programs from their effect on the shared environment.

The language that we consider is motivated by the emergence of *concurrent separation logic* [14], the rules of which form a partial correctness judgement about the execution of pointer-manipulating concurrent programs. Reasoning about such programs has traditionally proven difficult due to the problem of *variable aliasing*. For instance, Owicki and Gries' system for proving properties of parallel programs [16] essentially requires that they operate on disjoint collections of variables, thereby allowing judgements to be composed. In the presence of pointers, the same condition cannot be imposed just from the syntax of terms since distinct variables may point to the same memory location, thereby allowing arbitrary interaction between the processes.

At the core of separation logic [18, 10], initially presented for non-concurrent programs, is the *separating conjunction*, $\varphi * \psi$, which asserts that the memory may be split into two parts, one part satisfying φ and the other ψ. The separating conjunction was used by O'Hearn to adapt Owicki and Gries' system to provide a rule for parallel composition suitable for pointer-manipulating programs [14].

As we shall see, the rule for parallel composition is informally understood by splitting the initial state into two parts, one *owned* by the first process and the other by the second. Ownership can be seen as a dynamic constraint on the interference to be assumed: parallel processes always own disjoint sets of locations and only ever act on locations

1043-6871/06 $20.00 © 2006 IEEE

that they own. As processes evolve, ownership of locations may be transferred using a system of *invariants* (an example is presented in Section 4). A consequence of this notion of ownership is that the rules discriminate between the parallel composition of processes and their interleaved expansion. For example, the logic does *not* allow the judgement

$$\vdash \{\ell \mapsto 0\}\ [\ell] := 1 \parallel [\ell] := 1\ \{\ell \mapsto 1\},$$

which informally means that the effect of two processes acting in parallel which both assign the value 1 to the memory location ℓ from a state in which ℓ holds 0 is to yield a state in which ℓ holds 1. However, if we adopt the usual rule for the nondeterministic sum of processes, the corresponding judgement *is* derivable for their interleaved expansion,

$$([\ell] := 1; [\ell] := 1) + ([\ell] := 1; [\ell] := 1).$$

The rules of concurrent separation logic contain a good deal of subtlety, and so lacked a completely formal account until the pioneering proof of their soundness due to Brookes [4]. The proof that Brookes gives is based on a form of interleaved trace semantics. The presence of pointers within the model alongside the possibility that ownership of locations is transferred means, however, that the way in which processes are separated is absolutely non-trivial, which motivates strongly the study of the language within an independence model. We therefore give a proof of soundness using our net model and then characterize entirely semantically the independence of concurrent processes in Theorem 12.

The proof technique that we employ defines validity of assertions in a way that captures the rely-guarantee reasoning [11] emanating from *ownership* in separation logic directly, and in a way that might be applied in other situations.

In [19], Reynolds argues that separation allows store actions that were assumed to be atomic, in fact, to be implemented as composite actions (seen as a change in their *granularity*) with no effect on the validity of the judgement. Independence models are suited to modeling situations where actions are not atomic, as advocated by Lamport and Pratt [17, 13]. We introduce a novel form of refinement, inspired by that of [20], and apply this to address the issue of granularity using our characterization of independence.

2. Terms and states

We begin by defining the *terms* of our language.

$$\begin{aligned} t ::=\ & \alpha \mid t;t \mid t \parallel t \mid \alpha.t + \alpha.t \mid \texttt{while}\ b\ \texttt{do}\ t\ \texttt{od} \\ & \mid \texttt{resource}\ x\ \texttt{do}\ t\ \texttt{od} \\ & \mid \texttt{with}\ r\ \texttt{do}\ t\ \texttt{od} \mid \texttt{with}\ x\ \texttt{do}\ t\ \texttt{od} \\ & \mid \texttt{alloc}(\ell) \mid \texttt{dealloc}(\ell) \end{aligned}$$

We use α to represent primitive *heap actions* and use b to distinguish *boolean guards* that proceed only if b holds, having no effect on the heap, but otherwise blocking. The *guarded sum* $\alpha.t + \alpha'.t'$ is a process that executes as t if α takes place or as t' if α' takes place.

A heap is an assignment of values to *allocated*, or *current*, heap locations. We denote the set of heap locations Loc and use ℓ to range over its elements, and we denote the set of values Val and use v to range over its elements. The heap model allows locations to hold pointers to other locations, so we require that Loc $\subseteq$ Val. There is no implicit restriction that only current locations may be pointed at, thereby allowing the model to cope with 'dangling' pointers. Locations become current through $\texttt{alloc}(\ell)$, which makes a location current and sets ℓ to point at this location. For symmetry, $\texttt{dealloc}(\ell)$ makes the location pointed to by ℓ non-current if ℓ points to a current location. A heap action α does not change which locations are current.

In addition to acting on the heap, we allow the language to declare new binary semaphores, drawn from a set of *resource names* Res, and use these to protect critical regions. A critical region protected by a resource r is represented by $\texttt{with}\ r\ \texttt{do}\ t\ \texttt{od}$, which executes t if no other process is inside a critical region protected by r. The $\texttt{resource}\ x\ \texttt{do}\ t\ \texttt{od}$ construct represents that a globally unused resource is to be chosen and then used in place of x in t. It is therefore necessary to record, in addition to which resources are *available*, which resources are *current*; we shall write $\mathsf{curr}(r)$ if r is current. We say that the declaration $\texttt{resource}\ x\ \texttt{do}\ t\ \texttt{od}$ *binds* the variable x within t, and that the variable x is *free* within $\texttt{with}\ x\ \texttt{do}\ t\ \texttt{od}$. We write $\mathrm{fv}(t)$ for the set of variables free within term t and $[r/x]t$ for the term obtained by substituting the name r for the variable x within t avoiding capture. As standard, we identify terms up to α-conversion. In addition, we say that the resource name r is free within $\texttt{with}\ r\ \texttt{do}\ t\ \texttt{od}$.

These two components form the shared state in which processes execute. Motivated by the net semantics that we shall give, we define the following sets:

$$\begin{aligned} \mathbf{D} &\stackrel{\text{def}}{=} \mathrm{Loc} \times \mathrm{Val} & \mathbf{L} &\stackrel{\text{def}}{=} \{\mathsf{curr}(\ell) \mid \ell \in \mathrm{Loc}\} \\ \mathbf{R} &\stackrel{\text{def}}{=} \mathrm{Res} & \mathbf{N} &\stackrel{\text{def}}{=} \{\mathsf{curr}(r) \mid r \in \mathrm{Res}\}. \end{aligned}$$

A state σ is defined to be a tuple

$$(D, L, R, N)$$

where the set $D \subseteq \mathbf{D}$, the set $L \subseteq \mathbf{L}$, the set $R \subseteq \mathbf{R}$ and the set $N \subseteq \mathbf{N}$. The sets $\mathbf{D}$, $\mathbf{L}$, $\mathbf{R}$ and $\mathbf{N}$ are disjoint, so no ambiguity arises from writing, for example, $(\ell, v) \in \sigma$.

The interpretation of a state for the heap is that $(\ell, v) \in D$ if ℓ holds value v and that $\mathsf{curr}(\ell) \in L$ if L is current. For resources, $r \in R$ if the resource r is available and $\mathsf{curr}(r) \in N$ if r is current. It is clear that only certain such tuples of subsets are sensible.

Definition 1 (Consistent state) *The state* (D, L, R, N) *is* consistent *if we have*

$$R \subseteq \{r \mid \mathsf{curr}(r) \in N\}, \quad L = \{\mathsf{curr}(\ell) \mid \exists v.(\ell, v) \in D\}$$

and for any ℓ, v *and* v', *if* $(\ell, v) \in D$ *and* $(\ell, v') \in D$ *then* $v = v'$.

3. Process models

We give both an operational and a net semantics to *closed* terms. The operational semantics is presented to aid understanding of the net model, and is given by means of labelled transition relations of the forms $\langle t, \sigma\rangle \xrightarrow{\lambda} \langle t', \sigma'\rangle$ and $\langle t, \sigma\rangle \xrightarrow{\lambda} \sigma'$. As usual, the first form of transition indicates that t performs an action labelled λ in state σ to yield a resumption t' and a state σ'. The second indicates that t in state σ performs an action labelled λ to terminate and yield a state σ'. Labels follow the grammar:

$$\begin{array}{lll}\lambda & ::= & \mathsf{act}(D_1, D_2) \mid \mathsf{decl}(r) \mid \mathsf{end}(r) \mid \mathsf{get}(r) \mid \\ & & \mathsf{rel}(r) \mid \mathsf{alloc}(\ell, v, \ell', v') \mid \mathsf{dealloc}(\ell, \ell', v).\end{array}$$

We assume that we are given the semantics of primitive actions in the following form:

$$\mathcal{A}[\![\alpha]\!] \in \mathcal{P}ow(\mathcal{P}ow(\mathbf{D}) \times \mathcal{P}ow(\mathbf{D}))$$

The interpretation is that α can proceed in heap D if there are $(D_1, D_2) \in \mathcal{A}[\![\alpha]\!]$ such that, whenever D_1 is defined, D has the same value. The resulting heap is formed by updating D to have the same value as D_2 wherever it is defined. It is significant that this definition allows us to infer precisely the set of locations upon which an action depends. In order to preserve consistent markings, we shall require that D_1 and D_2 are (the graphs of) partial functions with the same domain if $(D_1, D_2) \in \mathcal{A}[\![\alpha]\!]$.

An example action is copying the value held at one location to another:

$$\mathcal{A}[\![[\ell] := [\ell']]\!] \stackrel{\text{def}}{=} \begin{array}{l}\{(\{(\ell, v), (\ell', v')\}, \\ \quad \{(\ell, v'), (\ell', v')\}) \mid v, v' \in \mathrm{Val}\}\end{array}$$

Boolean guards b are actions that wait until the boolean expression holds and may then take place. For example,

$$\mathcal{A}[\![[\ell] = v]\!] \stackrel{\text{def}}{=} \{(\{(\ell, v)\}, \{(\ell, v)\})\}$$

gives the semantics of an action that proceeds only if ℓ holds value v. We omit the specification of boolean constructs such as conjunction ($\wedge$), disjunction ($\vee$), negation ($\neg$) and further forms of equality, though these are easily definable.

The operational semantics is presented in Figure 1 (we omit the symmetric rules). Notice that special items `rel` r and `end` r are attached to the ends of terms for critical regions and to the end of scope of a resource. We write $\sigma \oplus \sigma'$ for the union of the components of two states where they are disjoint, and impose the implicit side-condition that this is defined wherever it is used. For conciseness, we do not give an error semantics to situations in which non-current locations or resources are used (*e.g.* action on a non-current location); they shall be excluded by the logic.

3.1. Net structure

The particular variant of Petri net upon which we base our model is that where conditions are marked without multiplicity (*c.f.* the 'basic' nets of [7, 22]).

Within the nets that we give for processes, we distinguish two forms of condition, namely *control conditions* and *state conditions*. The marking of these sets of conditions determines the control point of the process and the state in which it is executing, respectively. When we give the net semantics, we will make use of the closure of the set of control conditions under various operations.

Definition 2 (Conditions) *Define the set of control conditions* $\mathbf{C}$*, ranged over by* c*, to be the least set such that:*

- $\mathbf{C}$ *contains distinguished elements* $*$ *and* $\diamond$,
- *if* $c \in \mathbf{C}$ *then* $r{:}c \in \mathbf{C}$ *for all* $r \in \mathrm{Res}$ *and* $i{:}c \in \mathbf{C}$ *for all* $i \in \{1, 2\}$, *and*
- *if* $c, c' \in \mathbf{C}$ *then* $(c, c') \in \mathbf{C}$.

Define the set of state conditions $\mathbf{S}$ *to be* $\mathbf{D} \cup \mathbf{L} \cup \mathbf{R} \cup \mathbf{N}$.

A state $\sigma = (D, L, R, N)$ corresponds to the marking $D \cup L \cup R \cup N$ of state conditions in the obvious way, and we continue to restrict to markings corresponding to consistent states. Similarly, if C is a marking of control conditions, the pair (C, σ) corresponds to the marking $C \cup \sigma$. We therefore use the notations interchangeably.

The nets that we form are *extensional* in the sense that two events are identified if they have the same preconditions and the same postconditions. An event is therefore regarded as a tuple,

$$e = (C, \sigma, C', \sigma'),$$

and we write ${}^\bullet e$ for $C \cup \sigma$ and $e^\bullet$ for $C' \cup \sigma'$. The control conditions in C occur as preconditions of e, as do the state conditions in σ. Similarly, the set $C' \cup \sigma'$ forms the postconditions of e. To obtain a concise notation for working with events, we write ${}^{\mathrm{C}}e$ for ${}^\bullet e \cap \mathbf{C}$, which is the set of control conditions that occur as preconditions to e. We likewise define notations e^{C}, ${}^{\mathrm{D}}e$, ${}^{\mathrm{L}}e$ *etc.*, and call these the *components* of e by virtue of the fact that it is sufficient to define an event through defining its components.

Two (disjoint) markings of control conditions are of particular importance: those marked when the process starts executing and those marked when the process has terminated. We call these the *initial* control conditions I and *terminal* control conditions T, respectively. We shall call a net with a partition of its conditions into control and state with the subsets of control conditions I and T an *embedded net*. For an embedded net N, we write $\mathrm{Ic}(N)$ for I and $\mathrm{Tc}(N)$ for T, and we write $\mathrm{Ev}(N)$ for its set of events. Observe that no initial marking of state conditions is specified. Write $N : (C, \sigma) \xrightarrow{e} (C', \sigma')$ if the token game for nets allows the marking $C \cup \sigma$ to proceed to $C' \cup \sigma'$ by event e.

The semantics of terms shall be an embedded net, written $\mathcal{N}[\![t]\!]$. No confusion arises, so we shall write $\mathrm{Ic}(t)$ for $\mathrm{Ic}(\mathcal{N}[\![t]\!])$, and $\mathrm{Tc}(t)$ and $\mathrm{Ev}(t)$ for $\mathrm{Tc}(\mathcal{N}[\![t]\!])$ and $\mathrm{Ev}(\mathcal{N}[\![t]\!])$, respectively. The nets that we form shall always have the same sets of control and state conditions, though it

$$\frac{(D_1,D_2)\in\mathcal{A}[\![\alpha]\!] \quad D_1\subseteq D \quad D'=(D\setminus D_1)\cup D_2}{\langle\alpha,(D,L,R,N)\rangle \xrightarrow{\mathsf{act}(D_1,D_2)} (D',L,R,N)} \qquad \frac{\langle b,\sigma\rangle \xrightarrow{\lambda} \sigma}{\langle \texttt{while}\ b\ \texttt{do}\ p\ \texttt{od},\sigma\rangle \xrightarrow{\lambda} \langle p;\texttt{while}\ b\ \texttt{do}\ p\ \texttt{od},\sigma\rangle} \qquad \frac{\langle \neg b,\sigma\rangle \xrightarrow{\lambda} \sigma}{\langle \texttt{while}\ b\ \texttt{do}\ p\ \texttt{od},\sigma\rangle \xrightarrow{\lambda} \sigma}$$

$$\frac{\langle t_1,\sigma\rangle \xrightarrow{\lambda} \langle t_1',\sigma'\rangle}{\langle t_1 \parallel t_2,\sigma\rangle \xrightarrow{\lambda} \langle t_1' \parallel t_2,\sigma'\rangle} \qquad \frac{\langle t_1,\sigma\rangle \xrightarrow{\lambda} \sigma'}{\langle t_1 \parallel t_2,\sigma\rangle \xrightarrow{\lambda} \langle t_2,\sigma'\rangle} \qquad \begin{array}{l}\langle \texttt{with}\ r\ \texttt{do}\ t\ \texttt{od},\sigma\oplus\{r\}\rangle \xrightarrow{\mathsf{get}(r)} \langle t;\texttt{rel}\ r,\sigma\rangle \\ \langle \texttt{rel}\ r,\sigma\rangle \xrightarrow{\mathsf{rel}(r)} \sigma\oplus\{r\}\end{array}$$

$$\frac{\langle t_1,\sigma\rangle \xrightarrow{\lambda} \langle t_1',\sigma'\rangle}{\langle t_1;t_2,\sigma\rangle \xrightarrow{\lambda} \langle t_1';t_2,\sigma'\rangle} \qquad \frac{\langle t_1,\sigma\rangle \xrightarrow{\lambda} \sigma'}{\langle t_1;t_2,\sigma\rangle \xrightarrow{\lambda} \langle t_2,\sigma'\rangle} \qquad \begin{array}{l}\langle \texttt{resource}\ x\ \texttt{do}\ t\ \texttt{od},\sigma\rangle \xrightarrow{\mathsf{decl}(r)} \langle [r/x]t;\texttt{end}\ r,\sigma\oplus\{r,\mathsf{curr}(r)\}\rangle \\ \langle \texttt{end}\ r,\sigma\oplus\{r,\mathsf{curr}(r)\}\rangle \xrightarrow{\mathsf{end}(r)} \sigma\end{array}$$

$$\frac{\langle \alpha_1,\sigma\rangle \xrightarrow{\lambda} \sigma'}{\langle \alpha_1.t_1+\alpha_2.t_2,\sigma\rangle \xrightarrow{\lambda} \langle t_1,\sigma'\rangle} \qquad \begin{array}{l}\langle \texttt{alloc}(\ell),\sigma\oplus\{(\ell,v)\}\rangle \xrightarrow{\mathsf{alloc}(\ell,v,\ell',v')} \sigma\oplus\{(\ell,\ell'),(\ell',v'),\mathsf{curr}(\ell')\} \\ \langle \texttt{dealloc}(\ell),\sigma\oplus\{(\ell,\ell'),(\ell',v'),\mathsf{curr}(\ell')\}\rangle \xrightarrow{\mathsf{dealloc}(\ell,\ell',v')} \sigma\oplus\{(\ell,\ell')\}\end{array}$$

Figure 1. Operational semantics

is a trivial matter to restrict to those that are actually used.

As we give the semantics of terms, we make use of some constructions on nets. For example, we wish the events of parallel processes to operate on disjoint sets of control conditions. This is conducted using a *tagging* operation on events. We define $1{:}e$ to be the event e changed so that

$$^{\mathrm{C}}(1{:}e) \stackrel{\text{def}}{=} \{1{:}c \mid c \in {}^{\mathrm{C}}e\} \qquad (1{:}e)^{\mathrm{C}} \stackrel{\text{def}}{=} \{1{:}c \mid c \in e^{\mathrm{C}}\}$$

but otherwise unchanged in its action on state conditions. We define the notations $2{:}e$ and $r{:}e$ where $r \in \mathrm{Res}$ similarly, and extend the notations pointwise to sets of events.

Another useful operation is what we call *gluing* two embedded nets together. For example, when forming the sequential composition of processes $t_1;t_2$, we want to enable the events of t_2 when t_1 has terminated. This is done by 'gluing' the two nets together, having made them disjoint on control conditions, at the terminal conditions of t_1 and the initial conditions of t_2. Therefore, rather than using a terminal condition c of $\mathrm{Tc}(t_1)$, the events of t_1 use the set of conditions $\{1{:}c\} \times (2{:}\mathrm{Ic}(t_2))$. Similarly, the events of t_2 use the set of conditions $(1{:}\mathrm{Tc}(t_1)) \times \{2{:}c'\}$ instead of an initial condition c' of $\mathrm{Ic}(t_2)$.

An example of gluing follows, indicating how gluing is used to sequentially compose events.

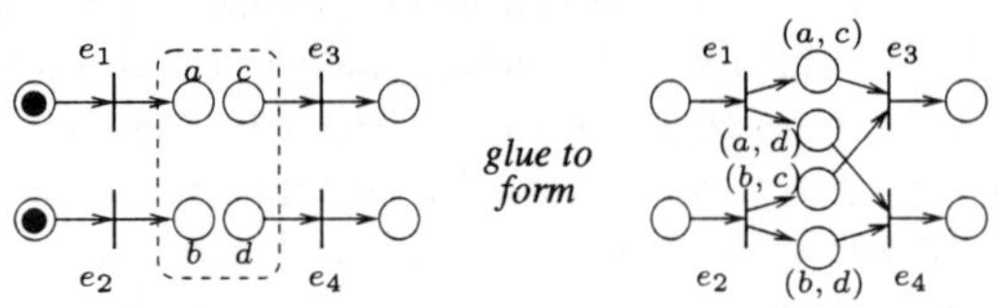

A variety of control properties that the nets we form possess, such as that all events have at least one pre-control condition, allow us to infer that it is impossible for an event of t_2 to occur before t_1 has terminated, and thereon it is impossible for t_1 to resume.

Assume a set $P \subseteq \mathbf{C}\times\mathbf{C}$. Useful definitions to represent gluing are:

$$\begin{aligned} P \lhd C &\stackrel{\text{def}}{=} \{(c_1,c_2) \mid c_1 \in C \text{ and } (c_1,c_2)\in P\} \\ &\quad \cup \{c_1 \mid c_1 \in C \text{ and } \nexists c_2.(c_1,c_2)\in P\} \\ P \rhd C &\stackrel{\text{def}}{=} \{(c_1,c_2) \mid c_2 \in C \text{ and } (c_1,c_2)\in P\} \\ &\quad \cup \{c_2 \mid c_2 \in C \text{ and } \nexists c_1.(c_1,c_2)\in P\} \end{aligned}$$

Extend the notation to events so that $^{\mathrm{C}}(P \lhd e) \stackrel{\text{def}}{=} P \lhd ({}^{\mathrm{C}}e)$ and $(P \lhd e)^{\mathrm{C}} \stackrel{\text{def}}{=} P \lhd (e^{\mathrm{C}})$, and similarly for $P \rhd e$, and extend this to sets of events in the obvious manner. Observe that the operations of gluing and tagging affect only the control flow of events, not their effect on the marking of state conditions.

3.2. Net semantics

The net semantics that we now give for closed terms is defined by induction on their size, given in the obvious way.

Action Let $\mathsf{act}_{(C,C')}(D_1,D_2)$ denote an event e with

$$^{\mathrm{C}}e = C \quad e^{\mathrm{C}} = C' \quad {}^{\mathrm{D}}e = D_1 \quad e^{\mathrm{D}} = D_2$$

and all other components empty. For an action α, we define $\mathrm{Ic}(\alpha) = \{\diamond\}$ and $\mathrm{Tc}(\alpha) = \{*\}$. The set of events $\mathrm{Ev}(\alpha)$ is the least set such that if $(D_1,D_2) \in \mathcal{A}[\![\alpha]\!]$ then it contains $\mathsf{act}_{(\{\diamond\},\{*\})}(D_1,D_2)$. The following diagram shows a net for assigning value 5 to ℓ.

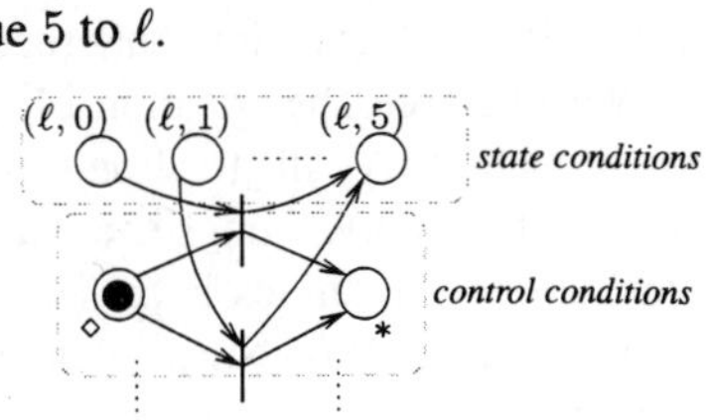

Sequential composition The sequential composition of terms involves gluing the terminal marking of the net for t_1 to the initial marking of the net for t_2. The operation is therefore performed on the set

$$P = 1{:}\mathrm{Tc}(t_1) \times 2{:}\mathrm{Ic}(t_2).$$

Following the intuition above, we take

$$\begin{aligned} \mathrm{Ic}(t_1;t_2) &\stackrel{\text{def}}{=} 1{:}\mathrm{Ic}(t_1) \qquad \mathrm{Tc}(t_1;t_2) \stackrel{\text{def}}{=} 2{:}\mathrm{Tc}(t_2) \\ \mathrm{Ev}(t_1;t_2) &\stackrel{\text{def}}{=} (P \lhd 1{:}\mathrm{Ev}(t_1)) \cup (P \rhd 2{:}\mathrm{Ev}(t_2)). \end{aligned}$$

Parallel composition The control flow of the parallel composition of processes is autonomous; interaction occurs only through the state. We therefore force the events of the two processes to work on disjoint sets of control conditions:

$$\mathrm{Ev}(t_1 \parallel t_2) \stackrel{\text{def}}{=} 1{:}\mathrm{Ev}(t_1) \cup 2{:}\mathrm{Ev}(t_2)$$
$$\mathrm{Ic}(t_1 \parallel t_2) \stackrel{\text{def}}{=} 1{:}\mathrm{Ic}(t_1) \cup 2{:}\mathrm{Ic}(t_2)$$
$$\mathrm{Tc}(t_1 \parallel t_2) \stackrel{\text{def}}{=} 1{:}\mathrm{Tc}(t_1) \cup 2{:}\mathrm{Tc}(t_2)$$

Guarded sum Let t be the term $\alpha_1.t_1 + \alpha_2.t_2$. The sum is formed by prefixing the actions and then gluing the sets of terminal conditions. Let $P = (1{:}\mathrm{Tc}(t_1)) \times (2{:}\mathrm{Tc}(t_2))$. Define the initial and terminal conditions

$$\mathrm{Ic}(t) \stackrel{\text{def}}{=} \{*\} \qquad \mathrm{Tc}(t) \stackrel{\text{def}}{=} P$$

and the events $\mathrm{Ev}(t)$ to be

$$\begin{aligned} &\{\mathsf{act}_{(\{\diamond\},1:\mathrm{Ic}(t_1))}(D_1, D_2) \mid (D_1, D_2) \in \mathcal{A}[\![\alpha_1]\!]\} \\ \cup\ &\{\mathsf{act}_{(\{\diamond\},2:\mathrm{Ic}(t_2))}(D_1, D_2) \mid (D_1, D_2) \in \mathcal{A}[\![\alpha_2]\!]\} \\ \cup\ &P \lhd (1{:}\mathrm{Ev}(t_1)) \cup P \rhd (2{:}\mathrm{Ev}(t_2)). \end{aligned}$$

Iteration Intuitively, we glue the initial and terminal conditions of $b.t$ together and then add events to exit the loop when $\neg b$ holds. Let $P = \{\diamond\} \times 1{:}\mathrm{Tc}(t)$. Define:

$$\mathrm{Ic}(\texttt{while}\ b\ \texttt{do}\ t\ \texttt{od}) \stackrel{\text{def}}{=} P \quad \mathrm{Tc}(\texttt{while}\ b\ \texttt{do}\ t\ \texttt{od}) \stackrel{\text{def}}{=} \{*\}.$$

The set of events $\mathrm{Ev}(\texttt{while}\ b\ \texttt{do}\ t\ \texttt{od})$ is defined to be

$$\begin{aligned} &\{\mathsf{act}_{(P,1:\mathrm{Ic}(t))}(D_{\mathrm{t}}, D_{\mathrm{t}}) \mid (D_{\mathrm{t}}, D_{\mathrm{t}}) \in \mathcal{A}[\![b]\!]\} \\ \cup\ &\{\mathsf{act}_{(P,\{*\})}(D_{\mathrm{f}}, D_{\mathrm{f}}) \mid (D_{\mathrm{f}}, D_{\mathrm{f}}) \in \mathcal{A}[\![\neg b]\!]\} \\ \cup\ &P \rhd (1{:}\mathrm{Ev}(t)). \end{aligned}$$

Semaphores and critical regions We introduce the following notations for resource events. These all have ${}^{\mathrm{C}}e = C$ and $e^{\mathrm{C}} = C'$, and the components other than those listed are empty. Observe that the event $\mathsf{decl}_{(C,C')}(r)$ will avoid contact, and thus be able to occur, only if the resource r is non-current.

$$\begin{aligned} \mathsf{decl}_{(C,C')}(r){:}\quad & e^{\mathrm{R}} = \{r\} \text{ and } e^{\mathrm{N}} = \{\mathsf{curr}(r)\} \\ \mathsf{end}_{(C,C')}(r){:}\quad & {}^{\mathrm{R}}e = \{r\} \text{ and } {}^{\mathrm{N}}e = \{\mathsf{curr}(r)\} \\ \mathsf{get}_{(C,C')}(r){:}\quad & {}^{\mathrm{R}}e = \{r\} \\ \mathsf{rel}_{(C,C')}(r){:}\quad & e^{\mathrm{R}} = \{r\} \end{aligned}$$

The initial conditions of the nets representing both constructs are $\{\diamond\}$, and their terminal conditions are $\{*\}$.

First consider $\texttt{resource}\ x\ \texttt{do}\ t\ \texttt{od}$. Its events form the least set containing, for each $r \in \mathrm{Res}$, where $t' = [r/x]t$:

$$\mathsf{decl}_{(\{\diamond\},\{r\,:\,\mathrm{Ic}(t')\})}(r) \cup r{:}\mathrm{Ev}(t') \cup \mathsf{end}_{(r\,:\,\mathrm{Tc}(t'),\{*\})}(r).$$

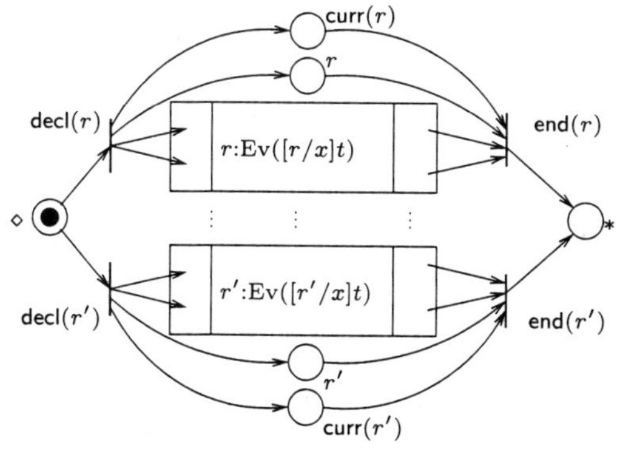

Now consider the closed term $\texttt{with}\ r\ \texttt{do}\ t\ \texttt{od}$. Its events are precisely

$$\{\mathsf{get}_{(\{\diamond\},1:\mathrm{Ic}(t))}(r)\} \cup 1{:}\mathrm{Ev}(t) \cup \{\mathsf{get}_{(1:\mathrm{Tc}(t),\{*\})}(r)\}.$$

Allocation and deallocation The command $\texttt{alloc}(\ell)$ activates, by making current and assigning an arbitrary value, a non-current location and makes ℓ point at it. For symmetry, $\texttt{dealloc}(\ell)$ deactivates the current location pointed to by ℓ.

We begin by defining two further event notations, which both have ${}^{\mathrm{C}}e = C$ and $e^{\mathrm{C}} = C'$ and empty components except those stated. First, $\mathsf{alloc}_{(C,C')}(\ell, v, \ell', v')$ is the event e such that

$${}^{\mathrm{D}}e = \{(\ell, v)\} \quad e^{\mathrm{D}} = \{(\ell, \ell'), (\ell', v')\} \quad e^{\mathrm{L}} = \{\mathsf{curr}(\ell')\},$$

which changes ℓ' from being non-current to current, gives it value v' and changes the value of ℓ from v to ℓ'. The event has concession only if the location ℓ' is not current. Second, $\mathsf{dealloc}_{(C,C')}(\ell, \ell', v')$ is the event e such that

$${}^{\mathrm{D}}e = \{(\ell, \ell'), (\ell', v')\} \quad e^{\mathrm{D}} = \{(\ell, \ell')\} \quad {}^{\mathrm{L}}e = \{\mathsf{curr}(\ell')\},$$

which does the converse of allocation.

The initial conditions of both $\texttt{alloc}(\ell)$ and $\texttt{dealloc}(\ell)$ are $\{\diamond\}$ and their terminal conditions are $\{*\}$. The events for $\texttt{alloc}(\ell)$ form the least set containing, for all $\ell' \in \mathrm{Loc}$ and $v, v' \in \mathrm{Val}$, $\mathsf{alloc}_{(\{\diamond\},\{*\})}(\ell, v, \ell', v')$. Similarly, the events for $\texttt{dealloc}(\ell)$ form the least set containing, for all $\ell' \in \mathrm{Loc}$ and $v, v' \in \mathrm{Val}$, $\mathsf{dealloc}_{(\{\diamond\},\{*\})}(\ell, \ell', v')$.

A well-known property of independence models is that they support a form of *run* in which independent actions are not interleaved: Given any sequential run of events of the net between two markings, we can swap the consecutive occurrences of any two independent events to yield a run between the same two markings. As seen in for example [22], this allows us to form an equivalence class of runs between the same markings, generating a Mazurkiewicz trace. This yields a partially ordered multiset, or *pomset*, run [17], in which the independence of event occurrences is captured through them being incomparable.

As we have progressed, the event notations introduced have corresponded to labels of the operational semantics. Write $|e|$ for the label corresponding to event e. The following theorem shows how the net and operational semantics correspond. It assumes a definition of open map bisimulation [12] based on paths as pomsets, $(N, M) \sim (N', M')$, relating paths of net N from marking M to paths of N' from M'. The bisimulations that we form respect terminal markings and markings of state conditions.

Theorem 3 *Let t be a closed term and σ be a consistent state.*

- *If $\langle t, \sigma\rangle \xrightarrow{\lambda} \sigma'$ then there exists e such that $|e| = \lambda$ and $\mathcal{N}[\![t]\!] : (\mathrm{Ic}(t), \sigma) \overset{e}{\twoheadrightarrow} (\mathrm{Tc}(t), \sigma')$.*
- *If $\langle t, \sigma\rangle \xrightarrow{\lambda} \langle t', \sigma'\rangle$ then there exists e such that $|e| = \lambda$*

and $\mathcal{N}[\![t]\!] : (\mathrm{Ic}(t), \sigma) \overset{e}{\twoheadrightarrow} (C', \sigma')$ *and* $(\mathcal{N}[\![t]\!], C', \sigma') \sim (\mathcal{N}[\![t']\!], \mathrm{Ic}(t'), \sigma')$.

- *If* $\mathcal{N}[\![t]\!] : (\mathrm{Ic}(t), \sigma) \overset{e}{\twoheadrightarrow} (C', \sigma')$ *then* $\langle t, \sigma \rangle \xrightarrow{|e|} \langle t', \sigma' \rangle$ *and* $(\mathcal{N}[\![t]\!], C', \sigma') \sim (\mathcal{N}[\![t']\!], \mathrm{Ic}(t'), \sigma')$, *or* $\langle t, \sigma \rangle \xrightarrow{|e|} \sigma'$ *and* $C' = \mathrm{Tc}(t)$.

4. Separation logic

We begin by presenting the intuition for the key judgement of concurrent separation logic, $\Gamma \vdash \{\varphi\}\ t\ \{\psi\}$:

If initially φ *holds of the heap defined at the locations* owned *by the process, then, after t runs to completion,* ψ *holds of the heap defined at the locations owned by the process; during any such run, the process only accesses locations that it owns and preserves* invariants *in* Γ.

The fundamental rules of concurrent separation logic are presented in Figure 2; the remainder are as presented in [4]. We refer the reader to [14] for a full introduction.

Notice just from the syntax of terms that the rule for `resource` x `do` t `od` forces us to work on terms with free variables and that it inserts the variable x into the domain of Γ. We assume that the domain of Γ covers all the free variables of t, and therefore work with respect to an assignment ρ taking variables in the domain of Γ injectively to resources. We denote the net so-formed $\mathcal{N}[\![t]\!]_\rho$. To ensure that no non-current resources are accessed, we require that t has no free resource names.

The rules of separation logic are founded on the *heap logic*, the semantics of which arises as an instance of the classical 'Kripke resource monoid' semantics of Logic of Bunched Implications [15]. At the core of the heap logic are the associated notions of heap composition and the separating conjunction. Two heaps, D_1 and D_2, may be composed if they are defined over disjoint sets of locations:

$$D_1 \cdot D_2 \overset{\text{def}}{=} D_1 \cup D_2 \text{ if } \mathrm{dom}(D_1) \cap \mathrm{dom}(D_2) = \emptyset.$$

A heap satisfies the separating conjunction $\varphi_1 * \varphi_2$ if it can be split into two parts, one satisfying φ_1 and the other φ_2:

$$D \models \varphi_1 * \varphi_2 \quad \text{iff} \quad \exists D_1, D_2.\ D = D_1 \cdot D_2 \text{ and } D_1 \models \varphi_1 \text{ and } D_2 \models \varphi_2.$$

An instance of the separating conjunction is seen in the rule for parallel composition. Intuitively (ignoring for the moment the invariants referred to above), the rule is sound because the heap restricted to the owned locations can be split into two disjoint parts, one satisfying φ_1 and the other satisfying φ_2. The first process only accesses locations used to satisfy φ_1 and the second process only accesses locations used to satisfy φ_2. Consequently, interaction between the processes is limited.

The collection of locations that a process owns may change as the process evolves. As seen in the rule, after an allocation event has taken place, the process owns the newly current location. Similarly, deallocation of a location leads to loss of ownership.

To enable more interesting interaction between processes, the judgement environment Γ records, for each free variable of t, an *invariant*, which is a *precise* heap logic formula. A formula χ is precise if, for any D, there is at most one $D_0 \subseteq D$ such that $D_0 \models \chi$. Recall that the assignment ρ takes the variables in the domain of Γ to resources. If r is in the image of ρ, then there is an invariant in Γ associated with it; we call r *open*. We call non-open resources *closed*.

Whenever a process gains control of an open resource, it gains ownership of the locations satisfying the invariant in Γ associated with it. Reasoning relies on the fact that the invariant is satisfied if the resource is available. Whenever a process releases an open resource, ownership of a collection of locations satisfying the invariant is relinquished, and it is our obligation to guarantee that such a collection exists. Precision is used here so that at any stage we may determine which locations are owned by the process.

Notice that the rules allow ownership of locations to be transferred. Assume, for example, that the process owns location ℓ which has value 2 and there is an invariant for x that is $\ell' \mapsto 0 \vee (\ell' \mapsto 1 * \ell \mapsto 2)$. The only way in which the invariant could be satisfied disjointly from the locations that the process owns is for ℓ' to hold value 0. Consequently, as the process enters the critical region, it gains ownership of location ℓ'. If the process sets the value of ℓ' to 1, when the process leaves the critical region it would then be necessary to use ℓ to restore the invariant, so ownership of ℓ is lost.

4.1. Ownership model

We now formalize the meaning of judgements presented at the start of the previous section. We begin with the observation that the judgement will remain valid if other 'external' processes operate on the state providing they maintain invariants and do not access the locations owned by the process. In particular, external processes might soundly change the values held at unowned locations, allocate new locations and deallocate locations that they own, declare new resources and may enter critical regions thereby gaining ownership of any associated heap locations. This is all that we *rely* on when reasoning about the effect of other processes.

To model this, we construct an *interference net* for the process in Γ with ρ. This involves adding *ownership conditions* $\omega_{\mathsf{proc}}(\ell)$, $\omega_{\mathsf{inv}}(\ell)$ and $\omega_{\mathsf{oth}}(\ell)$ for each location ℓ. We restrict to markings W where precisely one of these is marked for each current location. The intuition is that $\omega_{\mathsf{proc}}(\ell)$ is marked if ℓ is owned by the process, $\omega_{\mathsf{inv}}(\ell)$ if ℓ is used to satisfy the invariant for an available open resource, and $\omega_{\mathsf{oth}}(\ell)$ if ℓ is current but owned by another process.

It is convenient to record similar information for re-

$$\frac{\text{for all } D \models \varphi \text{ and } (D_1, D_2) \in \mathcal{A}[\![\alpha]\!] : \begin{pmatrix} \mathrm{dom}(D_1) \subseteq \mathrm{dom}(D) \\ D_1 \subseteq D \text{ implies } (D \setminus D_1) \cup D_2 \models \psi \end{pmatrix}}{\Gamma \vdash \{\varphi\}\ \alpha\ \{\psi\}} \qquad \frac{\Gamma \vdash \{\varphi_1\}\ t_1\ \{\psi_1\} \quad \Gamma \vdash \{\varphi_2\}\ t_2\ \{\psi_2\}}{\Gamma \vdash \{\varphi_1 * \varphi_2\}\ t_1 \parallel t_2\ \{\psi_1 * \psi_2\}} \qquad \frac{\Gamma \vdash \{\varphi\}\ \alpha_1; t_1\ \{\psi\} \quad \Gamma \vdash \{\varphi\}\ \alpha_2; t_2\ \{\psi\}}{\Gamma \vdash \{\varphi\}\ \alpha_1.t_1 + \alpha_2.t_2\ \{\psi\}}$$

$$\frac{\Gamma, x : \chi \vdash \{\varphi\}\ t\ \{\psi\} \quad (\chi \text{ precise})}{\Gamma \vdash \{\varphi * \chi\}\ \texttt{resource}\ x\ \texttt{do}\ t\ \texttt{od}\ \{\psi * \chi\}} \qquad \frac{\Gamma \vdash \{\varphi * \chi\}\ t\ \{\psi * \chi\}}{\Gamma, x : \chi \vdash \{\varphi\}\ \texttt{with}\ x\ \texttt{do}\ t\ \texttt{od}\ \{\psi\}}$$

$$\frac{}{\Gamma \vdash \{\ell \mapsto -\}\ \texttt{alloc}(\ell)\ \{\exists i(\ell \mapsto i * i \mapsto -)\}} \qquad \frac{}{\Gamma \vdash \{\exists i(\ell \mapsto i * i \mapsto -)\}\ \texttt{dealloc}(\ell)\ \{\exists i(\ell \mapsto i)\}}$$

Figure 2. Selected rules of concurrent separation logic

source names, so we introduce conditions $\omega_{\mathsf{proc}}(r)$, $\omega_{\mathsf{inv}}(r)$ and $\omega_{\mathsf{oth}}(r)$ for each resource r.

Table 1 defines a number of notations for events corresponding to the permitted interference described; they act according to the current ownership. The interference net is defined to comprise the following events:

- $\overline{\mathsf{act}}(D_1, D_2)$ for all D_1 and D_2 with the same domain
- $\overline{\mathsf{alloc}}(\ell, v, \ell', v')$ and $\overline{\mathsf{dealloc}}(\ell, \ell', v')$ for all locations ℓ and ℓ' and values v and v'
- $\overline{\mathsf{decl}}(r)$ and $\overline{\mathsf{end}}(r)$ for all resource names r
- $\overline{\mathsf{get}}(r)$ and $\overline{\mathsf{rel}}(r)$ for all closed resource names r
- $\overline{\mathsf{get}}(r, D_0)$ and $\overline{\mathsf{rel}}(r, D_0)$ for all open r associated with an invariant χ where $D_0 \models \chi$

The events described above describe how the locations owned by other processes is *dynamic* and how this *constrains* their action. The rule for parallel composition requires that the behaviour of the process being reasoned about conforms to these constraints, allowing its action to be seen as interference when reasoning about the other process. This requirement may be captured by *synchronizing* the events of the process with those from the interference net in the following way:

- The process event $\mathsf{act}_{(C,C')}(D, D')$ synchronizes with $\overline{\mathsf{act}}(D, D')$, and similarly for allocation, deallocation, declaration and events for critical region entry and exit where the critical region is protected by a closed resource.
- If r is an open resource associated with the invariant χ, the process event $\mathsf{get}_{(C,C')}(r)$ synchronizes with every $\overline{\mathsf{get}}(r, D_0)$ such that $D_0 \models \chi$. Similarly, $\mathsf{rel}_{(C,C')}(r)$ synchronizes with every $\overline{\mathsf{rel}}(r, D_0)$ such that $D_0 \models \chi$.

Suppose that two events synchronize, e from the process and e' from the interference net. The event e' is the event that would fire in the net for the other parallel process to simulate the event e; it is its dual. Let $e \cdot e'$ be the event formed by taking the union of the preconditions of e and e', other than using $\omega_{\mathsf{proc}}(\ell)$ in place of $\omega_{\mathsf{oth}}(\ell)$, and similarly $\omega_{\mathsf{proc}}(r)$ in place of $\omega_{\mathsf{oth}}(r)$.

Definition 4 *$\mathcal{W}[\![t, \Gamma]\!]_\rho$ is the net formed with the previous definitions of control, state and ownership conditions, and events:*

- *Every event from the interference net.*
- *Every event $e \cdot e'$ where e is an event of $\mathcal{N}[\![t]\!]_\rho$ and e' from the interference net such that e and e' synchronize.*

Let M be a marking of $\mathcal{W}[\![t, \Gamma]\!]_\rho$. We say that the process has violated its guarantees, or M is *violating*, if there exists an event e of $\mathcal{N}[\![t]\!]_\rho$ that has concession in marking M but there is no event e' from the interference net that synchronizes with e such that $e \cdot e'$ has concession. If no violation is ever encountered, the behaviour of $\mathcal{W}[\![t, \Gamma]\!]_\rho$ encapsulates all that of $\mathcal{N}[\![t]\!]_\rho$.

The following example shows how release of an open resource will cause a violation if the invariant is not restored.

Example 5 *Let r be an open resource associated with the invariant $\ell \mapsto 0$ and $D_0 = \{(\ell, 0)\}$. As only $D_0 \models \ell \mapsto 0$, the only associated interference event for release in the environment is $\overline{\mathsf{rel}}(r, D_0)$. This synchronizes with an event $\mathsf{rel}_{(C,C')}(r)$ in $\mathcal{N}[\![t]\!]_\rho$ to form the event e in $\mathcal{W}[\![t, \Gamma]\!]_\rho$ with*

$$\begin{aligned} {}^\bullet e &= \{\omega_{\mathsf{proc}}(r), \omega_{\mathsf{proc}}(\ell), (\ell, 0)\} \cup C \\ e^\bullet &= \{\omega_{\mathsf{inv}}(r), r, \omega_{\mathsf{inv}}(\ell), (\ell, 0)\} \cup C'. \end{aligned}$$

This will not have concession if the invariant is not re-established, whereas the event $\mathsf{rel}_{(C,C')}(r)$ may have.

4.2. Soundness and validity

The rule for parallel composition tells us that the ownership of the heap is initially split between the two processes, so that what one process owns is seen as owned by an external process by the other.

Definition 6 (Ownership split) *Let W be a marking of ownership conditions. W_1 and W_2 form an* ownership split *of W if (with the same constraints for each r):*

- *$\omega_{\mathsf{oth}}(\ell) \in W$ iff $\omega_{\mathsf{oth}}(\ell) \in W_1$ and $\omega_{\mathsf{oth}}(\ell) \in W_2$.*
- *$\omega_{\mathsf{inv}}(\ell) \in W$ iff $\omega_{\mathsf{inv}}(\ell) \in W_1$ and $\omega_{\mathsf{inv}}(\ell) \in W_2$.*
- *$\omega_{\mathsf{proc}}(\ell) \in W$ iff $\omega_{\mathsf{proc}}(\ell) \in W_1$ and $\omega_{\mathsf{oth}}(\ell) \in W_2$, or $\omega_{\mathsf{proc}}(\ell) \in W_2$ and $\omega_{\mathsf{oth}}(\ell) \in W_1$.*

Following Brookes' lead, we are now able to prove the lemma upon which the proof of soundness lies. The effect of this lemma is that we can determine the terminal states of

Abbreviation	Preconditions	Postconditions
$\overline{\mathsf{act}}(D_1, D_2)$	$D_1 \cup \{\omega_{\mathsf{oth}}(\ell) \mid \exists v.(\ell, v) \in D_1\}$	$D_2 \cup \{\omega_{\mathsf{oth}}(\ell) \mid \exists v.(\ell, v) \in D_2\}$
$\overline{\mathsf{alloc}}(\ell, v, \ell', v')$	$\{\omega_{\mathsf{oth}}(\ell), (\ell, v)\}$	$\{\omega_{\mathsf{oth}}(\ell), \omega_{\mathsf{oth}}(\ell'), \mathsf{curr}(\ell'), (\ell, \ell'), (\ell', v')\}$
$\overline{\mathsf{dealloc}}(\ell, \ell', v')$	$\{\omega_{\mathsf{oth}}(\ell), \omega_{\mathsf{oth}}(\ell'), \mathsf{curr}(\ell'), (\ell, \ell'), (\ell', v')\}$	$\{\omega_{\mathsf{oth}}(\ell), (\ell, \ell')\}$
$\overline{\mathsf{decl}}(r)$	$\{\}$	$\{\omega_{\mathsf{oth}}(r), \mathsf{curr}(r), r\}$
$\overline{\mathsf{end}}(r)$	$\{\omega_{\mathsf{oth}}(r), \mathsf{curr}(r), r\}$	$\{\}$
$\overline{\mathsf{get}}(r)$	$\{\omega_{\mathsf{oth}}(r), r\}$	$\{\omega_{\mathsf{oth}}(r)\}$
$\overline{\mathsf{rel}}(r)$	$\{\omega_{\mathsf{oth}}(r)\}$	$\{\omega_{\mathsf{oth}}(r), r\}$
$\overline{\mathsf{get}}(r, D_0)$	$\{\omega_{\mathsf{inv}}(r), r\} \cup D_0 \cup \{\omega_{\mathsf{inv}}(\ell) \mid \exists v.(\ell, v) \in D_0\}$	$\{\omega_{\mathsf{oth}}(r)\} \cup D_0 \cup \{\omega_{\mathsf{oth}}(\ell) \mid \exists v.(\ell, v) \in D_0\}$
$\overline{\mathsf{rel}}(r, D_0)$	$\{\omega_{\mathsf{oth}}(r)\} \cup D_0 \cup \{\omega_{\mathsf{oth}}(\ell) \mid \exists v.(\ell, v) \in D_0\}$	$\{\omega_{\mathsf{inv}}(r), r\} \cup D_0 \cup \{\omega_{\mathsf{inv}}(\ell) \mid \exists v.(\ell, v) \in D_0\}$

Table 1. Interference events

parallel processes simply by observing the terminal states of its components if we split the ownership of the initial state correctly. For convenience, the lemma is stated without intimating the particular event that takes place on the net transition relation.

Lemma 7 (Parallel decomposition) *Let* $M = (1{:}C_1 \cup 2{:}C_2, \sigma, W)$ *be a marking of the net* $\mathcal{W}[\![t_1 \parallel t_2, \Gamma]\!]_\rho$*, and let* W_1 *and* W_2 *form an ownership split of* W*.*

If, for both $i \in \{1, 2\}$*,* $M_i = (C_i, \sigma, W_i)$ *is not violating in* $\mathcal{W}[\![t_i, \Gamma]\!]$*, then* M *is not violating in* $\mathcal{W}[\![t_1 \parallel t_2, \Gamma]\!]$*.*

Furthermore, if $(1{:}C_1 \cup 2{:}C_2, \sigma, W) \twoheadrightarrow (1{:}C_1' \cup 2{:}C_2', \sigma', W')$ *in* $\mathcal{W}[\![t_1 \parallel t_2, \Gamma]\!]_\rho$ *then there exist* W_1' *and* W_2' *forming an ownership split of* W' *such that* $(C_1, \sigma, W_1) \twoheadrightarrow (C_1', \sigma', W_1')$ *in* $\mathcal{W}[\![t_1, \Gamma]\!]_\rho$ *and* $(C_2, \sigma, W_2) \twoheadrightarrow (C_2', \sigma', W_2')$ *in* $\mathcal{W}[\![t_2, \Gamma]\!]_\rho$*.*

Say that a state σ with an ownership marking W satisfies the formula φ and the invariants in Γ if the heap restricted to the owned locations satisfies φ and the invariants are met for all the available resources. In the formalization of this, we write $\mathrm{inv}(\Gamma, \rho, R)$ for the formula $\chi_1 * \ldots * \chi_n$ where $x_i : \chi_i \in \Gamma$ and x_i is available in R, *i.e.* $\rho(x_i) \in R$. We also use the notation

$$D \restriction_W \mathsf{proc} \stackrel{\text{def}}{=} \{(\ell, v) \mid \omega_{\mathsf{proc}}(\ell) \in W\}$$

for the heap at owned locations, and define similar notations $D \restriction_W \mathsf{inv}$ and $D \restriction_W \mathsf{oth}$.

Definition 8 *A marking* $(C, (D, L, R, N), W)$*, where* (D, L, R, N) *is consistent,* satisfies φ in Γ *if:*

- $D \restriction_W \mathsf{proc} \models \varphi$ *and* $D \restriction_W \mathsf{inv} \models \mathrm{inv}(\Gamma, \rho, R)$
- *all the open resource constants are current in* N
- *the resource* r *is owned as an invariant if* r *is open and available in* R

There is no restriction on how the ownership of the non-open and held resource names is split.

Definition 9 (Validity) *Let* t *be a term containing no free names with free variables contained in the domain of* Γ*.*

$\Gamma \models \{\varphi\}\ t\ \{\psi\}$ *if for any marking* $(\mathrm{Ic}(t), \sigma, W)$ *that satisfies* φ *in* Γ *and any assignment* ρ*, in the net* $\mathcal{W}[\![t, \Gamma]\!]_\rho$ *no violating marking is reachable and any reachable marking* $(\mathrm{Tc}(t), \sigma', W')$ *satisfies* ψ *in* Γ*.*

An analysis essentially following that in Brookes' proof allows us to arrive at:

Theorem 10 (Soundness)

$$\Gamma \vdash \{\varphi\}\ t\ \{\psi\}\ \textit{implies}\ \Gamma \models \{\varphi\}\ t\ \{\psi\}.$$

Corollary 11 *Let* t *be a closed term with no free resource names. If* $\emptyset \vdash \{\varphi\}\ t\ \{\psi\}$ *then, from any state in which the heap satisfies* φ*, the process* t *never accesses a non-current heap location or resource, and, whenever the process terminates, the resulting heap satisfies* ψ*.*

We conclude this section by characterizing the independence of parallel processes, which implies Brookes' race freedom result. Say that two events are *control independent* if they share no common pre- or post-control condition, and observe that two such events may be enabled only if they arise from different components of a parallel composition.

Theorem 12 (Separation) *Suppose that* $\emptyset \vdash \{\varphi\}\ t\ \{\psi\}$ *and that* σ *is a state in which the heap satisfies* φ*. If* M *is a marking reachable from* $(\mathrm{Ic}(t), \sigma)$ *in* $\mathcal{N}[\![t]\!]$ *and* e_1 *and* e_2 *are control independent events then:*

- *If* $M \xrightarrow{e_1} M_1 \xrightarrow{e_2} M'$ *then either* e_1 *and* e_2 *are independent or* e_1 *releases a resource name, resource or a location that* e_2 *correspondingly binds, takes or allocates.*
- *If* $M \xrightarrow{e_1} M_1$ *and* $M \xrightarrow{e_2} M_2$ *then either* e_1 *and* e_2 *are independent or* e_1 *and* e_2 *compete either to declare the same resource name, take the same resource or to allocate the same location.*

The first part of the preceding theorem tells us how the event occurrences of parallel processes *causally depend* on each other: the way in which the ability of one process to affect the global state in a particular way is dependent on events of the other process. The second part tells us how the enabled events of parallel processes *conflict* with each other in a state: the way in which one parallel process can prevent the other acting in a particular way on the global state.

Observe that, although there is neither conflict nor causal dependence arising from heap events (and hence the processes are race-free in the sense of Brookes), there may be interaction through allocation and deallocation events. One may therefore give judgements for parallel processes that interact *without* using critical regions. Suppose, for example, that we have a heap $\{(\ell_0,\ell_1),(\ell_1,v),(\ell_2,v')\}$. If we place the process $t_1;\texttt{dealloc}(\ell_0)$ in parallel with

$$\texttt{alloc}(\ell_2);\quad \texttt{while}\ [\ell_2]\neq\ell_1\ \texttt{do alloc}(\ell_2)\ \texttt{od};\quad t_2,$$

the process t_2 only takes place once t_1 has terminated.

5. Refinement

As we remarked in the introduction, the atomicity assumed of primitive actions, also called their *granularity*, is of significance when considering parallel programs. For example, suppose that an assignment $[\ell] := [\ell'] + 1$ is in fact executed as $[\ell] := [\ell']$ followed by $[\ell] := [\ell] + 1$. Now suppose that there is process running concurrently that performs some action if ℓ and ℓ' hold the same value. Running from a state in which they do not, the first interpretation falsely suggests that this may never happen. In [19], Reynolds proposes that the absence of races allows our semantics to be insensitive to the atomicity assumed of actions. We now provide a form of *refinement*, similar to but more general than that of [20], that captures these ideas. We relate the nets representing processes by regarding them as alternative substitutions into a *context*.

We begin with the observation that our embedded nets have certain properties: the sets of initial and terminal control conditions are disjoint and nonempty; all events have at least one precondition and one postcondition; and if any reachable marking of control conditions C contains the terminal conditions T of the net, then $C = T$ and no event has concession on its control conditions.

Definition 13 *Define a* context K *to be an embedded net with a distinguished event* $[-]$. *The event* $[-]$ *is such that* ${}^\bullet[-]^\bullet \subseteq \mathbf{C}$ *and its pre- and postconditions form disjoint, nonempty sets.*

Let K *and* N *have disjoint sets of control conditions and the same sets of state conditions. Define the sets*

$$P_\mathrm{i} \stackrel{\mathit{def}}{=} {}^\bullet[-] \times \mathrm{Ic}(N) \qquad P_\mathrm{t} \stackrel{\mathit{def}}{=} [-]^\bullet \times \mathrm{Tc}(N)$$

and let $K[N]$ *be the net formed with events*

$$\begin{aligned}\mathrm{Ev}(K[N]) \;&\stackrel{\mathit{def}}{=}\; (P_\mathrm{i}\cup P_\mathrm{t}) \lhd (\mathrm{Ev}(K)\setminus\{[-]\})\\ &\cup\; (P_\mathrm{i}\cup P_\mathrm{t}) \rhd \mathrm{Ev}(N).\end{aligned}$$

To investigate the properties of substitutions, we write $N:\sigma\Downarrow\sigma'$ if there exists a run from the marking $\mathrm{Ic}(N)\cup\sigma$ to $\mathrm{Tc}(N)\cup\sigma'$ within N. We also define a notion of equivalence $\simeq$ as:

$$N_1 \simeq N_2 \quad \text{iff} \quad (\forall\sigma,\sigma')N_1:\sigma\Downarrow\sigma' \iff N_2:\sigma\Downarrow\sigma'.$$

Intuitively, if the substituend N were an atomic event, it would start running only if the conditions P_i were marked and P_t were not. There are two distinct ways in which the context K can affect the execution of N. Firstly, it might affect the marking of conditions in P_i or P_t whilst N is running. Secondly, it might change the marking of state conditions in a way that affects the execution of N. An instance of the latter form of interference can be inferred from the example at the start of this section. We now define a form of constrained substitution, guided by Theorem 12, so that N is not subject to these forms of interference.

Say that a control condition c is *internal* to N within $K[N]$ if c is a condition of N not in $\mathrm{Ic}(N)$ or $\mathrm{Tc}(N)$. Given a marking M of $K[N]$, say that N is *active* if $P_\mathrm{i}\subseteq M$ or there exists an internal condition of N in M.

Definition 14 *For a given marking of state conditions* σ, *we say that* $K[N]$ *is a* non-interfering substitution *if, for all markings* M *reachable from* $(\mathrm{Ic}(K[N]),\sigma)$:

- *if* $P_\mathrm{i}\subseteq M$ *then* $P_\mathrm{t}\cap M=\emptyset$, *and*
- *if* N *is active in* M *then no enabled event of* K *has a pre- or postcondition in* P_i *or* P_t, *and*
- *if* $M \xrightarrow{e_1} M_1 \xrightarrow{e_2} M'$, *one of* e_1 *and* e_2 *is from* N *and the other from* K *and* N *is active in* M *and* M_1, *then* e_1 *and* e_2 *are independent.*

Theorem 15 *If* $N_1\simeq N_2$ *and* $K[N_1]$ *and* $K[N_2]$ *are non-interfering substitutions from state* σ, *then, for any* σ':

$$K[N_1]:\sigma\Downarrow\sigma' \quad \mathit{iff} \quad K[N_2]:\sigma\Downarrow\sigma'.$$

The proof of the preceding theorem relies on the fact that, since consecutive actions of K and N are independent, their occurrence in any run may be swapped (in fact, this is all we require; independence is not strictly necessary). Consequently, we only need to reason about runs in which there is no interleaving of events of K with events of N.

Suppose that we have $\emptyset\models\{\varphi\}\ t\ \{\psi\}$ and that there is an occurrence of α inside $\mathcal{N}[\![t]\!]$ not at the head of a sum or as the boolean of a while loop. It follows from Theorem 12 that this forms a non-interfering substitution with the rest of the net for t. If N is an embedded net such that $\mathcal{N}[\![\alpha]\!]\simeq N$ that accesses the same locations as α along any run between two states, it follows that this also forms a non-interfering substitution. Thus Corollary 11 also holds for the net where the occurrence of α is replaced by N.

6. Related work and conclusions

The first component of this work provides an inductive definition of the semantics of command terms as a net. This is a relatively novel technique, but has in the past been applied to give the semantics of a language for investigating security protocols, SPL [7], though our language involves a richer collection of constructs. Other independence models for terms include the Box calculus [1] and the event structure and net semantics of CCS [21, 22], though these model interaction as synchronized communication rather than occurring through shared state.

The proof of soundness of separation logic here is led by Brookes' earlier work [4]. There are a few minor differences in the syntax of processes, including that we allow the dynamic binding of resource variables. More notably, our store model does not include the *stack variable*, which may be seen as a particular form of memory location to which other locations may not point. In Brookes' model, interference of parallel processes through stack variables is constrained by the use of a side condition on the rule rather than using the concept of ownership; an area of current research on 'permissions' [2] promises a uniform approach. We have chosen not to include stack variables in our model in order to highlight the concept of ownership. To obtain a more useable programming language without weakening this concept, the language could be extended with a $\mathtt{let}\ x = e\ \mathtt{in}\ t$ construct, where e may evaluate to a location. This would come at the cost of a detailed, though straightforward, technical analysis of open terms (which proves convenient for providing Hoare's law of existential elimination).

At the core of Brookes' work is a 'local enabling relation', which gives the semantics of programs over a restricted set of 'owned' locations. Our notion of validity involves maintaining a record of ownership and using this to constrain the occurrence of events in the interference net augmented to the process. This allows the intuition of ownership in O'Hearn's introduction of concurrent separation logic [14] to be seen directly as constraining interference. Though the relationship between our model and Brookes' is fairly obvious, we believe that our approach leads to a clearer parallel decomposition lemma, upon which the proof of soundness critically stands.

The most significant difference between our work and Brookes' is that the net model captures, as a primitive property, the independence of parallel processes enforced by the logic. We have used this property to apply a straightforward, yet general, form of refinement suited to proving that race freedom obviates the problem of granularity. This is in contrast to [5], which provides a different form of trace semantics to tackle the issue of granularity, tailored very specifically to reasoning about processes that are race-free. Furthermore, our separation result is much stronger than the existing proof of race freedom, for example showing that interaction between parallel processes may occur through allocation and deallocation. This is significant, as such interaction leads to examples of the incompleteness of concurrent separation logic.

There are a number of areas for further research. At present, we are investigating semantic models that deal more elegantly with name binding and how local reasoning may be used to establish liveness properties.

Acknowledgements We would like to thank Peter O'Hearn and Matthew Parkinson for helpful discussions and the anonymous referees for constructive suggestions.

References

[1] E. Best, R. Devillers, and J. G. Hall. The box calculus: A new causal algebra with multi-label communication. In *Advances in Petri Nets*, volume 609 of *LNCS*. Springer Verlag, 1992.

[2] R. Bornat, C. Calcagno, P. O'Hearn, and M. Parkinson. Permission accounting in separation logic. In *Proc. POPL '05*. ACM Press, 2005.

[3] P. Brinch Hansen. Structured multiprogramming. *Comm. ACM*, 15(7):574–578, 1972.

[4] S. Brookes. A semantics for concurrent separation logic. In *Proc. CONCUR '04*, volume 3170 of *LNCS*. Springer Verlag, 2004.

[5] S. Brookes. A grainless semantics for parallel programs with shared mutable data. In *Proc. MFPS XXI*, ENTCS, 2005.

[6] E. M. Clarke, O. Grumberg, M. Minea, and D. Peled. State space reduction using partial order techniques. *Int. Journal on Software Tools for Technology Transfer*, 2(3), 1999.

[7] F. Crazzolara and G. Winskel. Events in security protocols. In *Proc. CCS '01*, New York, 2001. ACM Press.

[8] E. Dijkstra. Cooperating sequential processes. In F. Genuys, editor, *Programming Languages*. Academic Press, 1968.

[9] C. A. R. Hoare. Towards a theory of parallel programming. In C. A. R. Hoare and R. H. Perrot, editors, *Operating Systems Techniques*. Academic Press, 1972.

[10] S. S. Ishtiaq and P. W. O'Hearn. BI as an assertion language for mutable data structures. In *Proc. POPL '01*. ACM Press.

[11] C. B. Jones. Specification and design of (parallel) programs. In R. E. A. Mason, editor, *Information Processing 83: Proc. IFIP Congress*, pages 321–332, 1983.

[12] A. Joyal, M. Nielsen, and G. Winskel. Bisimulation from open maps. In *Proc. LICS '93*, volume 127(2) of *Information and Computation*. Elsevier, 1993.

[13] L. Lamport. On interprocess communication. *Distributed Computing*, 1(2):77–101, June 1986.

[14] P. W. O'Hearn. Resources, concurrency and local reasoning. *Theoretical Computer Science*, 2004. To appear.

[15] P. W. O'Hearn and D. J. Pym. The logic of bunched implications. *Bulletin of Symbolic Logic*, 5(2), 1999.

[16] S. Owicki and D. Gries. Verifying properties of parallel programs: An axiomatic approach. *Comm. ACM*, 19(5):279–285, 1976.

[17] V. Pratt. Modeling concurrency with partial orders. *Int. Journal of Parallel Programming*, 15(1), 1986.

[18] J. C. Reynolds. Intuitionistic reasoning about shared mutable data structure. In *Millennial Perspectives in Computer Science*, 2000.

[19] J. C. Reynolds. Towards a grainless semantics for shared variable concurrency. In *Proc. FSTTCS '04*, volume 3328 of *LNCS*. Springer Verlag, 2004.

[20] R. J. van Glabbeek and U. Goltz. Equivalence notions for concurrent systems and refinement of actions. In *Proc. MFCS '89*, volume 379 of *LNCS*. Springer Verlag, 1989.

[21] G. Winskel. Event structure semantics for CCS and related languages. In *Proc. ICALP '82*, volume 140 of *LNCS*. Springer Verlag, 1982.

[22] G. Winskel and M. Nielsen. Models for concurrency. In *Handbook of Logic and the Foundations of Computer Science*, volume 4, pages 1–148. OUP, 1995.

Matching explicit and modal reasoning about programs: a proof theoretic delineation of dynamic logic

Daniel Leivant*
Indiana University
leivant@cs.indiana.edu

Abstract

We establish a match between two broad approaches to reasoning about programs: modal (dynamic logic) proofs on the one hand, and explicit higher-order reference to program semantics, on the other. We show that Pratt-Segerberg's first-order dynamic logic **DL** proves precisely program properties that are provable in second-order logic with set-existence restricted to a natural class of formulas, well-known to be related to computation theory.

The set-existence principle is for *computational formulas,* i.e. of the form $\forall R \exists \vec{x} F$ where R is relational, F quantifier-free. Depending on the exact nature of the programs considered, some fine tuning is needed. We establish a descriptive match, of independent interest, between programming languages L and particular classes D_L of computational formulas, in the following sense: the semantics of programs $\alpha \in L$ is explicitly definable, in all relational structures, by a formula φ_α of D_L; and for every formula φ of D_L there is a program in L whose termination is equivalent to φ. In particular, we match the class of regular programs with random assignments to computational formulas that are "sequential", and the regular programs (without random assignments) to formulas we dub "definite", and that obey a natural variable scoping condition.

I Introduction

I.1 Calibrating reasoning about programs

There are two approaches to reasoning about programs. The *Explicit* approach treats program-semantics as data, incorporating it into a formal deductive theory along with other data. An early historical example is Kleene's treatment of equational programs: he coded program semantics, i.e. computation traces, by natural numbers (since he insisted on using $\mathbb{N}$ as the only data type); the termination of a program α is then expressible as a Π^0_2 formula $\forall x \, \exists y \, T(e_\alpha, x, y)$ (where e_α is the code of P and T is a particular primitive-recursive relation). A slightly more generic treatment was used in the 1970's by the Hungarian school of Andreka, Nemeti & als.[1] In [11] second-order logic was proposed as a framework for explicit rendition of program semantics. In fact, due in great part to Michael Gordon (e.g. [3, 4]), higher-order logic is now broadly recognized as the deductive framework of choice for formal methods, including program verification and hardware specification. The second-order definability of program semantics was noted along the years by many others, including [2] and [10].

Dual to the explicit approach is the *modal approach,* which articulates and demonstrates properties of programs while avoiding explicit reference to their semantic. Hoare's logics for imperative languages, as well as various dynamic, temporal and process logics, all exemplify this approach.

Within each approach one deductive calculus might be more *expressive* than another; for instance, dynamic logic formulas express a broader range of program properties than Hoare's logic. More subtle is the question of whether one calculus is *deductively* stronger than another; for instance, does dynamic logic prove more *partial-correctness assertions* (PCAs) than Hoare's Logic? The answer here is yes [12]. Similarly, second-order logic with second-order set-existence proves more than second-order logic with first-order set-existence.

Calibrating and separating the deductive power of formalisms is of considerable interest, for both theoretical and practical reasons. It elucidates the nature of each formalism, in particular as to the role of various axioms and rules, and suggests what is and is not possible in automating these calculi. Indeed, deductive calibration

*Research partially supported by NSF grant CCR-CCR-0105651.

[1] That school dubbed itself by the misleading phrase "non-standard dynamic logic"; their explicit approach is "non-standard" merely in that it has non-standard models.

of formalisms has been a central theme of Proof Theory, where the main tools have been transfinite ordinals (i.e., for which ordinals does a given formalism prove transfinite induction), and set-existence principles (i.e. what formulas are taken as defining a legitimate set). Notably, the Reverse Mathematics project of Friedman and Simpson [19] has established that much of Classical Analysis can be classified into a small number of such principles. These proof theoretic methods are directly applicable to explicit forms of reasoning about programs. In contrast, it seems that no such methods have been developed to date for modal logics of programs.

We claim that in fact no such separate methods are needed. Instead, one can match the deductive power of modal logics of programs with that of explicit methods, and the calibration methods for the latter transfer automatically to the former. Indeed, such a match is of independent interest, as it suggests which explicit methods of reasoning about programs can be captured by modal logics of programs. In [11] we established such a correspondence for Hoare's Logic, showing that a PCA is provable in Hoare's Logic (for **while** programs) iff its explicit second-order rendition is provable in second-order logic with first-order set-existence. Thus, Hoare's Logic can be viewed as a syntactic sugaring of first-order logic, specifically adapted to PCAs.

Since, as we have noted, Dynamic Logic is deductively stronger than Hoare's Logic, it must be more than a syntactic sugaring of first-order logic. The purpose of this paper is to delineate the set-existence principle underlying the Pratt-Segerberg formalism for (first-order) Dynamic Logic. That is, we prove that DL is sound and complete for those dynamic logic formulas whose explicit rendition is proved in second-order logic with set-existence restricted to a natural collection of formulas. In doing so we give a purely logical delineation of Dynamic Logic, thereby also providing the tool for calibrating first-order Dynamic Logic among logics of programs.

A comparison of our completeness result with Harel's Completeness Theorem for Dynamic Logic is in order. In [6, 8] Harel defines a deductive system for Dynamic Logic, that includes a rule of convergence. That rule is sound only for structures that are "arithmetical", that is with a definable substructure isomorphic to $\mathbb{N}$. This class of structures is itself not axiomatizable.[2] Since Harel's calculus is not sound, no comparison with a sound formalism such as Second-Order Logic is possible.

In fact, Harel's Completeness Theorem does not delineate even his variant of Dynamic Logic, just as Cook's Relative Completeness Theorem is not a delineation of Hoare's Logic **H**. Recall that relative completeness is a "local" notion: **H** is complete *at a structure* $\mathcal{S}$ if every partial-correctness assertion (PCA) valid in $\mathcal{S}$ is proved in **H** from the first-order theory $Th(\mathcal{S})$ of $\mathcal{S}$. Cook's Theorem states that **H** is complete at every structure in which the PCA *true* $[\alpha]\,\varphi$ is first-order expressible. Similarly, Harel's Theorem states that first-order Pratt-Segerberg's DL augmented with the Convergence Rule is complete at every structure in which the natural numbers are definable.

Because of their local nature, Cook's and Harel's Theorems do not delineate logics of programs in the same sense that, for example, Gödel's Completeness Theorem delineates classical first-order logic, or Kripke's Completeness Theorem delineates constructive logic. If $\mathbf{H}^+$ is Hoare's Logic **H** extended with PCAs that are valid but not provable in **H**, then $\mathbf{H}^+$ is both sound and relatively complete. Consequently, Cook's Completeness does not explicate the naturalness of **H** as a logic of programs. Moreover, while it is often said that relative completeness of **H** factorizes reasoning about imperative programs (over a given structure $\mathcal{S}$) into a dynamic aspect (program behavior) and a static one (first-order properties of $\mathcal{S}$), the proof of relative completeness is in fact based on the exact opposite: the operational behavior of programs is captured by the logic only when these two aspects are inextricably intertwined. Finally, a relative completeness result does not solidify our conviction in the usefulness of a logic, since it states that the logic is complete whenever it is dispensable, i.e. when we have at our disposal the entire first order theory of the structure in hand, and when moreover that theory already expresses, in coded form, all we need to know about program semantics. Indeed, if $\mathcal{S}$ is an expressive structure in the sense of Cook, and we posit as given its first-order theory $Th(\mathcal{S})$, then we need not fuss at all over proving a PCA $\varphi[\alpha]\psi$: if it is true, then so is the first-order formula expressing it in

[2]In [13] it is observed that Harel's Convergence Rule is derived in DL modulo a conversion of numeric quantifiers to suitable boxed and diamonded programs.

the structure, which is therefore given to us as an axiom! For the same reasons, Harel's Completeness Theorem does not delineate his dynamic logic system, nor does it explain the naturalness of the Pratt-Segerberg axioms. Moreover, the Convergence Rule is not sound in general, and the class of structures to which the theorem applies is not axiomatizable.

II Dynamic Logic for regular programs

II.1 Regular programs

Arguably, the hard core of imperative programming is **while** programs, and regular programs offer a particularly elegant and streamlined framework for reasoning about **while** programs. Given a vocabulary V (i.e. "similarity type", "signature"), the *atomic programs* over V are *assignments* $x := \mathbf{t}$ of V-terms to variables, and *tests* $?\varphi$, where φ is a quantifier-free V-formula.[3] We shall also consider an extended language with random assignments as a third type of basic program, writing $!x$ for the nondeterministic assignment of a structure element to variable x.[4] Compound programs are generated from basic programs by composition, union, and Kleene's $*$ (nondeterministic iteration). We can then define **while** programs: $(\texttt{if}\ \varphi\ \texttt{then}\ \alpha\ \texttt{else}\ \beta)$ is an abbreviation for $(?\varphi);\ \alpha \cup (?\neg\varphi);\ \beta$, and $(\texttt{while}\ \varphi\ \texttt{do}\ \alpha)$ for $(?\varphi;\ \alpha)^*;\ ?(\neg\varphi)$. We refer to [8] for background and detail.

Given a V-structure $\mathcal{S}$, the *states* are the $\mathcal{S}$-environments, i.e. partial functions from the set of variables to elements of $\mathcal{S}$. Each V-program α is interpreted semantically as a binary relation over states, denoted $\xrightarrow{\alpha}$, or $\xrightarrow[\mathcal{S}]{\alpha}$ when $\mathcal{S}$ is not obvious from the context. These relations are defined by recurrence on α:

- $\eta \xrightarrow{x:=\mathbf{t}} \eta'$ iff $\eta' = \eta[x \leftarrow \mathbf{t}_{\mathcal{S},\eta}]$ (where $\mathbf{t}_{\mathcal{S},\eta}$ is the value of the term $\mathbf{t}$ in the interpretation $(\mathcal{S}, \eta)$)
- $\eta \xrightarrow{!x} \eta'$ iff η' agrees with η on all variables other than x;
- $\eta \xrightarrow{?\varphi} \eta'$ iff $\eta' = \eta$ and $\mathcal{S}, \eta \models \varphi$;
- $\xrightarrow{\alpha;\beta}$ is the composition of $\xrightarrow{\alpha}$ and $\xrightarrow{\beta}$;
- $\xrightarrow{\alpha\cup\beta}$ is the union of $\xrightarrow{\alpha}$ and $\xrightarrow{\beta}$;
- $\xrightarrow{\alpha^*}$ is $(\xrightarrow{\alpha})^*$.

II.2 Dynamic logic formulas

Given a vocabulary V, the DL V-formulas are generated inductively, just like first-order V-formulas, but with the added clause: If φ is a formula, and α a program, then $[\alpha]\varphi$ is a formula. The operator $\langle\alpha\rangle$, dual to $[\alpha]$, can be defined by $\langle\alpha\rangle\,\varphi \equiv_{\text{df}} \neg[\alpha]\neg\varphi$.

The definition of the satisfaction relation $\mathcal{S}, \eta \models \varphi$ is as usual by recurrence on φ. In particular, $\mathcal{S}, \eta \models [\alpha]\varphi$ iff $\mathcal{S}, \eta' \models \varphi$ whenever $\eta \xrightarrow{\alpha} \eta'$. Consequently, $\mathcal{S}, \eta \models \langle\alpha\rangle\,\varphi$ iff $\mathcal{S}, \eta' \models \varphi$ for some environment η' where $\eta \xrightarrow{\alpha} \eta'$.

II.3 Complexity of Dynamic Logic

The set of valid DL formulas is highly complex. In fact, even DL formulas of a seemingly modest appearance have a decision problem more complex than that of first-order arithmetic:

Proposition 1 *1. The validity problem for DL formulas is Π^1_1. 2. Even the validity problem for formulas of the form $\exists\vec{x}.[\alpha]\,\varphi$, where α is a deterministic program and φ is quantifier-free, is Π^1_1 hard.*

Proof. (1) is easy, and proved in [8, Theorem 13.1], where (2) is also stated and proved, but for φ first-order and α non-deterministic. On closer inspection, the proof there, which uses a Π^1_1-hard tiling problem, yields the result with φ quantifier-free.

However, already basic properties of Π^1_1 easily imply the refinement stated here (with α deterministic). Recall that every Π^1_1 formula φ is equivalent over $\mathbb{N}$ to a formula of the form

$$\forall f\, \exists x.\ g_f(x) = 0 \tag{1}$$

[3] $?\varphi$ is intended to convey "if φ then skip else abort."

[4] Alternative notations include $x :=?$ and $x \leftarrow \exists$. Random assignments represent unbounded nondeterminism, and are a computational analogue of the existential quantifier, see [7]. As noted there, an assignment $x := \mathbf{t}$ can be simulated by the program $!y;\ ?(y = \mathbf{t});\ !x;\ ?(x = y)$. Here y is a fresh variable, needed in case x occurs in $\mathbf{t}$.

where f ranges over unary functions, and g_f is defined uniformly from f by primitive-recursion. More precisely, if D_g is the conjunction of the recurrence equations defining g_f from f, and $\vec{u}$ the variables free in D_g, then (1) is expressed by

$$\forall f, g, \vec{h} \, (\forall \vec{u} \, D_g \rightarrow \exists x. \, g(x) = 0 \,) \qquad (2)$$

(where $\vec{h}$ are the auxiliary functions used in D_g).

The truth of (2) in $\mathbb{N}$ is equivalent to the validity in all structures (over the vocabulary in hand) of the informal statement

$$\forall \vec{u}.D_g \;\wedge\; \forall v.\text{"}f(v) \text{ is the denotation of a numeral"} \rightarrow \exists x.g(x) = 0 \quad (3)$$

where the numerals are the terms 0, $s(0)$, $s(s(0))$ (with s intended to denote the successor function).[5]

Now, with p intended to denote the predecessor function, let ψ be the conjunction of the three formulas

$$p(0) = 0$$
$$\forall y \; p(s(y)) = y$$
and $$\forall y, w \; (\, p(y) = p(w) \;\wedge\; y \neq 0 \;\wedge w \neq 0 \rightarrow \; y = w \,)$$

Thus, if ψ holds in a structure, and N is the program

$$z := f(v); \; \texttt{while} \; z \neq 0 \; \texttt{do} \; z := p(z) \; \texttt{end}$$

then N terminates iff $f(v)$ is the denotation of some numeral. Therefore, (3) can be expressed in DL as

$$\forall \vec{u}.D_g \;\wedge\; \forall v.\langle N \rangle \texttt{true} \;\rightarrow\; \exists x \, g(x) = 0 \qquad (4)$$

Since v and z are the only variables in N, quantifiers over other variables commute with $[N]$, and so (4) can be converted into an equivalent formula of the form stated in the Proposition. ⊣

II.4 Axiomatization of Dynamic logic

One way of addressing the challenge presented by Proposition 1 is to consider an infinitary deductive system. So-called omega-rules go back to the 1930's and their adaptation to logics of programs is due to Mirkowska [14]. In [8, Theorem 14.7] Mirkowska's completeness proof is adapted to Dynamic Logic.

Since no effective axiomatization of DL can be complete for validity, the dual question is all the more interesting: articulate a *natural* axiomatization of DL, and delineate it in terms of a familiar deductive system. This is analogous to the situation with Hoare's Logic: the validity problem for PCAs is complete Π^0_2 [8, Theorem 13.5], implying that Hoare's Logic is not complete for validity, and that alternative completeness properties are essential for determining its significance.

The formalization **DL** is due primarily to Pratt [15, 5]. The assignment rule is Hoare's, and the others are related to Segerberg's Propositional Dynamic Logic for regular programs [18]. (This is closely related to the formalism 14.12 of [8], with the Convergence Rule omitted.) For first-order quantifier rules, the definition of 'free occurrence of variable x in formula φ" is amended to exclude the scope of $[\alpha]$ and $\langle\alpha\rangle$ in case x is assigned-to in α. A natural deductive calculus **DL** for Dynamic Logic is obtained by augmenting the natural deduction rules of first-order logic (see e.g. [16]) with natural-deduction rendition of the rules of Table 1.

Generalization:	$\dfrac{\vdash \varphi}{\vdash [\alpha]\varphi}$
Box:	$[\alpha](\varphi \rightarrow \psi) \rightarrow ([\alpha]\varphi \rightarrow [\alpha]\psi)$
Assignment:	$[x := \mathbf{t}]\, \varphi \leftrightarrow \{\mathbf{t}/x\}\varphi$ $\mathbf{t}$ free for x in φ
Random-assnt:	$[!x]\, \varphi \leftrightarrow \forall x.\varphi$
Test:	$[?\chi]\varphi \leftrightarrow (\chi \rightarrow \varphi)$
Composition:	$[\alpha; \beta]\varphi \leftrightarrow [\alpha][\beta]\varphi$
Union:	$[\alpha \cup \beta]\varphi \leftrightarrow [\alpha]\varphi \wedge [\beta]\varphi$
Iteration:	$[\alpha^*]\varphi \leftrightarrow \varphi \wedge [\alpha][\alpha^*]\varphi$
Invariance:	$\dfrac{\vdash \varphi \rightarrow [\alpha]\,\varphi}{\vdash \varphi \rightarrow [\alpha^*]\,\varphi}$

Table 1: Pratt-Segerberg's Dynamic Logic

From the Invariance Rule we obtain the Schema of

[5]The denotations of the numerals form a copy of $\mathbb{N}$ in a structure satisfying Peano's Third and Fourth Axioms, which we could include here trivially. However, (3) remains true in structures that identify the values of some distinct numerals!

Induction:

$$\psi \wedge [\alpha^*](\psi \rightarrow [\alpha]\psi) \rightarrow [\alpha^*]\psi$$

Indeed, taking $\varphi \equiv \psi \wedge [\alpha^*](\psi \rightarrow [\alpha]\psi)$, we have $\vdash \varphi \rightarrow [\alpha]\varphi$ using the remaining axioms and rules, and so $\varphi \rightarrow [\alpha^*]\varphi$ by Iteration. The Induction template above readily follows.

A *V-theory* is a set of closed first-order *V*-formulas. Given a *V*-theory **T** we write **DL**(**T**) for the deductive formalism **DL** augmented with the formulas in **T** as axioms. We refer to **T** as the *background theory*.

By a straightforward induction on derivations, we conclude that **DL** is sound:

THEOREM 2 (Soundness of DL) *Let* **T** *be a V-theory,* φ *a DL V-formula. Suppose* **DL**(**T**) $\vdash \varphi$. *Then* **T** $\models \varphi$*; that is* φ *is true in every model of* **T**.

$$
\begin{aligned}
M^k_{x_i:=t}[\vec{x},\vec{v}] &\equiv v_i = t[\vec{x}] \wedge \textstyle\bigwedge_{j\neq i} v_j = x_j\\
M^k_{!x_i}[\vec{x},\vec{v}] &\equiv \textstyle\bigwedge_{j\neq i} v_j = x_j\\
M^k_{?\psi}[\vec{x},\vec{v}] &\equiv \psi[\vec{x}] \wedge \vec{v} = \vec{x}\\
M^k_{\beta;\gamma}[\vec{x},\vec{v}] &\equiv \exists\vec{u}.\, M^k_\beta[\vec{x},\vec{u}] \wedge M^k_\gamma[\vec{u},\vec{v}]\\
M^k_{\beta\cup\gamma}[\vec{x},\vec{v}] &\equiv M^k_\beta[\vec{x},\vec{v}] \vee M^k_\gamma[\vec{x},\vec{v}]\\
M^k_{\beta^*}[\vec{x},\vec{v}] &\equiv \forall Q.\, Q(\vec{x}) \wedge \mathrm{Cl}^k_\beta[Q] \rightarrow Q(\vec{v})\\
&\quad \text{where}\\
\mathrm{Cl}^k_\beta[Q] &\equiv \forall \vec{z},\vec{w}.\\
&\quad Q(\vec{z}) \wedge M^k_\beta[\vec{z},\vec{w}] \rightarrow Q(\vec{w})
\end{aligned}
$$

Table 2: Explicit definition of program semantics

III A DESCRIPTIVE CLASSIFICATION OF PROGRAM CONSTRUCTS

III.1 Rendition of program semantics

It is well-known that the semantics of programming languages is definable (uniformly over relational structures) in higher-order logic. To define the semantics of *regular* programs (with random assignments) it suffices to use an extension of first-order logic with relational variables and quantification over them. For each program α whose variables are among $\vec{x} = x_1 \ldots x_k$, we define a formula $M^k_\alpha \equiv M^k_\alpha[\vec{x},\vec{v}]$ with free variables among the $2k$ distinct variables $\vec{x} = x_1 \ldots x_k$, and $\vec{v} = v_1 \ldots v_k$, with the following property. For every V-structure S, and every environment η therein, $S,\eta \models M^k_\alpha[\vec{x},\vec{v}]$ iff there is an execution of α starting in environment η and terminating in environment $\eta[\vec{x} := \eta\vec{v}]$. The definition of the formulas M^k_α is by recurrence on α, and given in Table 2, where R and Q are relational variables of the appropriate arity. We omit the superscript k when in no danger of confusion.

III.2 Computational formulas

The formulas M_α have the following syntactic properties: (1) Object-quantifiers are all positively-occurring $\exists$. (2) The relational-quantifiers are all positively-occurring $\forall$. (3) No relational-variable occurs free in the scope of another. We dub such formulas *computational*, since they can be construed as a general description of computational processes, as we explain momentarily.

Note that computational formulas, when converted to prenex form, take the form $\forall\vec{R}_1\exists\vec{x}_1 \cdots \forall\vec{R}_n\exists\vec{x}_n.\,\varphi$ with φ quantifier-free with.[6] This form can be further simplified by invoking the choice schema

$$\forall x_1 \ldots x_n \,\exists R\, \varphi[R] \rightarrow \exists Q\, \forall x_1 \ldots x_n\, \varphi[Q_{\vec{x}}] \qquad (5)$$

where R is an m-ary relational variable for some m, Q is $(m+n)$-ary, and $Q_{\vec{x}}(\vec{y})$ stands for $Q(\vec{x},\vec{y})$. Using this choice principle in contrapositive form,[7] we can eliminate the quantifier alternation above and obtain a formula of the form $\forall\vec{Q}\exists\vec{y}.\psi$, with ψ quantifier-free. Note, however, that (5) is highly non-constructive.[8]

An analogy with classical Recursive Functions Theory is of interest. An important level of Kleene's analytical hierarchy is Π^1_1, consisting of the relations over $\mathbb{N}$ definable by formulas of the form $\forall\vec{f}.\varphi$, $\vec{f}$ function

[6] The scoping condition (3) is usually lost; that is, the syntactic condition that defines computational formulas is not preserved under semantic equivalence.

[7] Note that the converse of the choice schema holds trivially

[8] For example, in second-order arithmetic with arithmetical-set-existence we can prove that for all n there exists a set S_n which is Σ^0_n-complete, but we cannot prove the existence of the combined set $\{(n,x) \mid x \in S_n\}$, since the latter is not arithmetical.

variables and φ first-order. In fact, each such relation can already be defined by a formula of the simpler form $\forall f \exists x.\psi$ where ψ is a bounded first-order formula. In many ways, Π^1_1 is analogous over $\mathbb{N}$ to Σ^0_1 (see e.g. [17]). Π^1_1 formulas can also be expressed using relational quantifiers, and simplified to normal forms $\forall R \exists x \forall y.\psi$, ψ quantifier-free. However, the alternation of existential and universal object-quantifiers is essential: Kreisel observed that formulas $\forall R \exists x\, \psi$ not only fail to capture Π^1_1 definability, but in fact define over $\mathbb{N}$ no more that the effectively enumerable (RE) relations. This observation underlies the generalization of Computability Theory to the broad class of countable admissible structures [1]. V-formulas of the form $\forall R \exists \vec{x}.\psi$ where ψ is quantifier free, are dubbed *strict* $\forall^1_1$ in [2].

III.3 Computational normal forms

The computational nature of a strict $\forall^1_1$ formula $\forall R\, \exists \vec{x}\, \psi$ comes across when it is arranged in a *computational normal form,* as follows. Write ψ in disjunctive normal form, and distribute $\exists \vec{x}$ over the disjuncts, yielding

$$(\exists \vec{x}.\psi_0) \vee \cdots \vee (\exists \vec{x}.\psi_n) \tag{6}$$

where each ψ_i is a conjunctive clause. Classify these clauses into those where the relational variables $\vec{R}$ appear negatively (and possibly also positively), and those where none does. The multiple disjunction is then equivalent to the implication whose premise is the conjunction of the former clauses negated, and whose conclusion is the disjunction of the latter clauses. Each one of the former formulas can be rewritten as $\forall \vec{x}.A \wedge \kappa \rightarrow \delta$, where A is a quantifier-free V-formula, κ is a conjunction (possibly empty) of atomic formulas of the form $R(\vec{\mathbf{t}})$, and δ is a disjunction of (one or more) such atomic formulas. Moreover, we may assume that in the atomic formulas $R(\vec{\mathbf{t}})$ the terms $\vec{\mathbf{t}}$ are all variables; for instance, $\forall \vec{x}\, A \wedge R(\vec{\mathbf{t}}) \rightarrow R(\vec{\mathbf{s}})$ is equivalent to $\forall \vec{x}, \vec{u}, \vec{v}\, A \wedge R(\vec{u}) \wedge \vec{u} = \vec{\mathbf{t}} \wedge \vec{v} = \vec{\mathbf{s}} \;\rightarrow\; R(\vec{v})$. We thus obtain

$$\wedge_i\, \forall \vec{x}\, (A_i \wedge \kappa_i \rightarrow \delta_i) \;\rightarrow\; \vee_j\, \exists \vec{x}\, (A'_j \wedge \kappa'_j) \tag{7}$$

where the A_i and A'_j are quantifier-free V-formulas, and $\kappa_i, \kappa_j{}'$ and δ_i are as above. The premise of (7) states closure conditions for the relations $\vec{R}$ (including initialization conditions where κ_i is empty), and the conclusion expresses testable termination conditions.

More generally, every computational formula φ can be converted to a computational normal form that displays its computational nature, by iterating the process above, yielding a formula of the form

$$\begin{aligned} \forall \vec{R}.\ (\wedge_i\ (\ \forall \vec{x}\ (A_i \wedge \psi_i \wedge \kappa_i \rightarrow \delta_i)\ ) \\ \rightarrow\ \vee_j\ (\ \exists \vec{x}\ (A'_j \wedge \psi'_j \wedge \kappa'_j)\ )) \end{aligned} \tag{8}$$

where each ψ_i, ψ'_j is a conjunction of computational formulas in which R does not occur.

III.4 Variants of computational formulas as a classification of programming constructs

It is well-known that certain programming constructs, such as higher-order procedures and strong forms of polymorphism, have a semantics whose description exceeds second-order logic. By carefully identifying natural classes of computational formulas, we can similarly demarcate between more elementary programming constructs. What we propose is a descriptive match between programming languages L and syntactic classes F of second-order formulas, of the form: the semantics of every program α in L is explicitly definable (uniformly over all relational structures) by a formula in F; and for every formula φ in F there is a program in L whose termination is equivalent (uniformly in all structures) to φ.

In particular, we consider a simple and natural syntactic property of computational formulas that we dub "sequentiality", and establish their match with Pratt's regular programs with random assignments. We then show that regular programs (without random assignments) match with sequential formulas that are also "definite".

We shall show elsewhere that definite computational formulas (not necessarily sequential) match with recursive programs with local variables, and that permitting, in addition, random assignments yields a match with unrestricted computational formulas.

III.5 Sequential computational formulas and regular programs with random assignments

Consider the normal form (8) above for a computational formula. We say that that formula is *sequential* if all closure conditions have at most one atomic premise $R(\mathbf{t})$ and at most one atomic conclusion. This corresponds to a *sequential* iterative process. In fact, from the defining clauses of M_α in Table 2 we clearly have

PROPOSITION 3 *If α is a regular program with random assignment, then the formula M_α, that explicitly renders the semantics of α, is a sequential computational formula.* ⊣

Proposition 3 establishes an interpretation of regular programs with random assignments by restricted second-order formulas. We now prove a converse interpretation, of such sequential computational formulas φ by regular programs with assignments:

THEOREM 4 *For every sequential computational formula φ there is a regular program with random assignment, α_φ, such that for each relational structure S and environment therein φ holds iff the program α_φ terminates.*

Proof. We give detail here for the case where φ is a strict-$\forall^1_1$ formula, as in (7). The generalization to arbitrary computational formulas (8) is straightforward.

By the sequentiality condition, each closure condition ψ in φ is equivalent to a formula of the form

$$\forall \vec{x}, \vec{u}, \vec{y}.\, A \wedge R(\vec{x}) \to R(\vec{y})$$

where A is quantifier-free and without relational variables. For each such ψ, let β_ψ be the program

$$!\vec{u};\ !\vec{y};\ ?A;\ \vec{x} := \vec{y}$$

Thus, each invocation of the closure condition ψ, leading from the premise $R(\vec{x})$ to the conclusion $R(\vec{y})$, corresponds to an execution of the program β_ψ, with input $\vec{x}$.

Now, φ is of the form

$$\forall R.(\wedge_i\, \psi_i) \;\to\; (\vee_j\, \chi_j)$$

where each ψ_i is as above, and each χ_j is of the form

$$\exists \vec{u}_j\ B_j \wedge R(\vec{\mathbf{t}}_{j1}) \ldots \wedge R(\vec{\mathbf{t}}_{jk_j})$$

Define α_φ to be the program

$$\begin{array}{l} \cup_j\ \ (!\vec{u}_j; \\ \quad (\cup_i \beta_{\psi_i})^*\ ;\ ?\,\vec{x} = \vec{\mathbf{t}}_{j1}; \\ \quad \cdots\ \ ; \\ \quad (\cup_i \beta_{\psi_i})^*\ ;\ ?\,\vec{x} = \vec{\mathbf{t}}_{jk}; \\ \quad ?B_j) \end{array}$$

That is, the program chooses nondeterministically a target condition, and guesses the values of the corresponding existentially-quantified variables. It then checks that each of the corresponding term-vectors $\vec{\mathbf{t}}_{j\ell}$, evaluated for the given guess for $\vec{u}$, is indeed generated by the closure conditions of φ. (Any k-tuple of generated values is obtainable, since the star construct is nondeterministic.) Note that the order between the k cycles is immaterial, because $\cup_i \beta_{\psi_i}$ guarantees that the output is repeatedly randomized. Finally, the program checks that the quantifier-free formula B_j in the target condition selected is satisfied. Clearly, α_φ terminates iff φ is true. ⊣

III.6 Sequential-definite computational formulas and regular programs

We say that a closure condition $(\cdots \wedge \kappa_i) \to \delta_i$ is *definite* if every variable free in δ_i is a direct argument of R in κ_i. For example $R(f(x,y),x) \wedge R(y, f(x,y)) \;\to\; R(x,y)$ is definite, whereas $R(f(x,y),x) \to R(y,f(x,y))$ and $R(x,y) \to R(y,z)$ are not. We call (8) *definite* if all closure conditions are definite, and the existential quantifiers in the conclusion $\bigvee_j \cdots$ are vacuous.

A definite computational formula corresponds to an iterative process without guesses of structure values. From the definition of the formulas M_α, we have

PROPOSITION 5 *If α is a regular program, then the formula M_α is a computational formula which is both sequential and definite.* ⊣

From the proof of Theorem 4 we clearly have:

THEOREM 6 *For every sequential and definite computational formula φ there is a regular program, α_φ, such that for each relational structure S and environment therein, φ holds iff the program α_φ terminates.*

IV A DEDUCTIVE DELINEATION OF DYNAMIC LOGICS

IV.1 Explicit rendition of DL

An explicit rendition $\varphi^\#$ for each DL formula φ is defined by recurrence on φ, with the main clause being: if all variables in α are among $\vec{x} = x_1 \ldots x_k$, then

$$([\alpha]\varphi)^\# \quad \equiv_{\text{df}} \quad \forall \vec{v}.\ M_\alpha[\vec{x}, \vec{v}] \to \varphi[\vec{v}]^\#$$

Here $\vec{v} = v_1 \ldots v_k$ are fresh variables, mutually distinct and different from $\vec{x}$, and $\varphi[\vec{v}]$ stands for the result $\{\vec{v}/\vec{x}\}\varphi$ of simultaneously substituting $\vec{v}$ in φ for all free occurrences of $\vec{x}$.

Thus, each formula $\varphi^{\#}$ is the result of substituting, in a first-order formula (relational variables allowed) computational formulas for relational variables. We call such a formula *quasi-computational*, and further qualify it as *sequential* or *definite* if all computational components therein are sequential or definite, respectively. In other words, the quasi-computational formulas are generated inductively from computational formulas and atomic formulas using connectives and first-order quantifiers. In particular, if φ is a DL formula, then $\varphi^{\#}$ is quasi-computational.

PROPOSITION 7 *If $\varphi[R]$ is a [sequential] {definite} quasi-computational formula, with free relation-variable R, and ψ is a [sequential] {definite} quasi-computational formula, then so is the formula $\varphi[\lambda\vec{x}.\psi]$, i.e. the result of substituting for R in φ a predicate defined by ψ.*

Proof. In a computational formula no relation-variable occurs free in the cope of another, from which it follows that the same holds of a quasi-computational formula. Thus the substitution of $\lambda\vec{x}.\psi$ for R acts on occurrences of R that are not in the scope of relational variables, and the result is a computational formula. The sequentiality and definiteness properties are trivially inherited in such substitutions. ⊣

COROLLARY 8 *The following properties are equivalent.*

1. *Provability with set-existence for first-order formulas and for [sequential] {definite} computational formulas.*

2. *Provability by a normal natural-deduction proof with set-existence as in (1).*

3. *Provability with set-existence for [sequential] {definite} quasi-computational formulas.*

4. *Provability by a normal natural-deduction proof with set-existence as in (3).*

IV.2 Second-order provability and set-existence principles

Since the valid second-order formulas are not effectively enumerable, there is no deductive system which is sound and complete for second-order logic. Nonetheless, second-order logic does have a natural deductive system, which is sound and complete for Henkin-structures [9]. Moreover, it lends itself to natural restrictions and proof-theoretic calibration.[9]

A natural formalism for second-order logic is obtained by extending first-order logic with variables and quantifiers over relations, and with the "set existence" schema

$$\forall\vec{x}.\exists R \forall\vec{u}.\ R(\vec{u}) \leftrightarrow \psi[\vec{u},\vec{x}] \qquad R \text{ not free in } \psi \quad (9)$$

This schema may be conveyed by inference rules for relational quantifiers. For natural deduction the rules for universal quantification over relations are

$$\frac{\Gamma \vdash \varphi[Q]}{\Gamma \vdash \forall R\, \varphi[R]} \qquad \frac{\Gamma \vdash \forall R\, \varphi[R]}{\Gamma \vdash \varphi[\lambda\vec{x}\psi]}$$

Q not free in Γ $\qquad$ $(Var(\psi) \subseteq \vec{x})$, ψ free for R in φ

Here $\varphi[\lambda\vec{x}\psi]$ stands for the result of replacing every subformula $R(\mathbf{t}_1 \ldots \mathbf{t}_k)$ by $\{\mathbf{t}_1 \ldots \mathbf{t}_k/x_1 \ldots x_k\}\psi$ (that is, ψ with $x_1 \ldots x_k$ replaced simultaneously by $\mathbf{t}_1 \ldots \mathbf{t}_k$, respectively).

Let $\mathbf{L}_2$ be the resulting deductive calculus. $\mathbf{L}_2$ is trivially sound for the standard semantics of the relational variables, and is a powerful formalism in which we can interpret full second-order arithmetic [16].

Of considerable interest are sub-formalisms of $\mathbf{L}_2$ in which set-existence is restricted to a class $\mathcal{C}$ of formulas, with no variables other than the ones referred to in

[9]There are other logics adequate for capturing program semantics, but we believe that second-order logic is the optimal choice. Fixpoint logic is one alternative, but its proof theory is less friendly. Constructive versions of infinitary logic have also been referred to extensively, but the infinitary formulas used are in fact merely the unwinding of second-order formulas, and thus the infinitary framework is a moot complication. Omega-logic, which refer to structures containing a standard copy of the natural numbers, seem to be a red herring as well: the standard semantics of iteration can be captured by second-order formulas, as illustrated below, and the explicit presence of the natural numbers is both unnecessary and an impediment to a streamlined proof theory.

the Comprehension Schema. Referring to the rule of relational ∀-elimination above, this means that the eigenformula ψ is required to be in $\mathcal{C}$. We write $\mathbf{L}_2[\mathcal{C}]$ for the resulting formalism.

IV.3 Main results: the delineation of dynamic logics

THEOREM **9** *Let φ be a DL formula over a vocabulary V. If φ refers to regular programs with random assignments, then φ is provable in* **DL** *iff the second-order formula $\varphi^{\#}$ is provable in $\mathbf{L}_2$ using set-existence for first order formulas and for sequential computational formulas (alternatively: set existence for sequential quasi-computational formulas). Moreover, the latter can be further restricted to definite formulas if φ does not refer to random assignments.*

The first half of Theorem 9 is easy:

PROPOSITION **10** *If a DL formula φ is provable in* **DL** *then the second-order formula $\varphi^{\#}$ is provable in $\mathbf{L}_2$ with set-existence for first-order formulas and for sequential computational formulas. Moreover, the latter can be further restricted to definite computational formulas if φ refers only to regular programs.*

Proof Outline.
The first statement is proved by induction on proofs in **DL**. The translations of the axioms are all trivially provable in $\mathbf{L}_2$. The main step of interest is the iteration rule, where the use of set-existence is central.

For the restricted cases we need first to observe that if φ does not use random assignments, and is provable in **DL**, then it has a proof that does not use random assignments; and similarly for φ referring only to **while** programs. Then the translation of Iteration is provable in $\mathbf{L}_2$ using merely the corresponding restricted forms of set-existence. ⊣

We wish to show that for each DL formula φ, if $\mathbf{L}_2$ proves $\varphi^{\#}$ then **DL** proves φ. A normal (i.e. cut-free) proof of first-order logic uses only formulas that are structurally at most as complex as the derived formula. Not so for second-order logic: a second-order proof, even if normal (in the sense of [16]) can involve formulas far more complex than the derived one. However, invoking the restriction of set-existence to computational formulas, and using our ability to represent computational formulas by DL formulas, we can interpret the relevant proofs of $\mathbf{L}_2$ in **DL**.

The following is straightforward by induction on derivations. Crucial to the proof is the fact that in computational formulas no relational-variable occurs free in the scope of another. For instance, this condition is violated in $\forall R(\varphi \rightarrow \forall Q\psi)$ if R occurs free in ψ.

LEMMA **11** *If a derivation of $\mathbf{L}_2$, with set existence for sequential (and definite) quasi-computational formulas, is normal (in the sense of [16], i.e. cut-free), and derives a sequential (and definite) quasi-computational formula from such formulas as assumptions, then every formula in the derivation is such a formula.*

We can now safely focus on sequential quasi-computational formulas φ, for which we define an interpretation $\varphi^{\flat}$ in DL, by recurrence on the definition of φ from computational formulas. For a computational formula φ define $\varphi^{\flat}$ to be $\langle\alpha_\varphi\rangle\,\mathtt{true}$, where α_φ is as above. For the recurrence step the definition commutes with connectives and (first-order) quantifiers.

LEMMA **12** *For every program α and DL-formula φ, the DL formula*

$$(\forall\vec{v}.\,[\alpha_{M_\alpha[\vec{x},\vec{v}]}]\,\varphi) \quad\leftrightarrow\quad [\alpha]\varphi$$

is provable in ***DL***.

Proof. By induction on α. ⊣

LEMMA **13** *Every DL formula φ is provably equivalent in* ***DL*** *to $(\varphi^{\#})^{\flat}$.*

Proof. By induction on φ. The crucial step is for the box operator, for which we invoke Lemma 12 ⊣

We now prove the backward direction of Theorem 9, by providing an interpretation of computational set-existence in **DL**.

LEMMA **14** *Suppose $\varphi \equiv \forall R.\varphi_0[R]$ is a computational formula, as in the previous section. Then for every DL formula ψ, the formula $\langle\alpha_\varphi\rangle\mathtt{true} \rightarrow \varphi_0[\lambda\vec{x}.\psi]$ is provable in* **DL**.

The proof idea is straightforward: the premise of $\varphi_0[\lambda\vec{x}.\psi]$ permits the introduction of iterations, via the Iteration Rule of **DL**, and $\langle\alpha_\varphi\rangle\mathtt{true}$ is then used to assert the conclusion of $\varphi_0[\lambda\vec{x}.\psi]$.

LEMMA **15** *For every sequential (and definite) quasi-computational formula φ, if φ is provable in $\mathbf{L}_2$ with set-existence for such formulas, then $\varphi^\flat$ is provable in* **DL**.

Proof Sketch.
By induction on natural-deduction derivations, which by Lemmas 11 and 8 we may assume are normal and use only sequential and definite quasi-computational formulas. The crucial step is set-existence, for which we invoke Lemma 14. ⊣

We can now put the pieces together, and complete the proof of Theorem 9, given here for the case of computational formulas and programs with random assignments.

For the forward (soundness) direction of the Theorem, if a DL formulas φ is provable in **DL**, then $\varphi^\#$ is provable in $\mathbf{L}_2$ with the corresponding set-existence condition, by Proposition 10.

For the converse (completeness) direction, assume that $\varphi^\#$ is provable in $\mathbf{L}_2$ with set-existence appropriately restricted. By Lemma 11 we can assume that the proof uses only sequential (and definite) quasi-computational formulas. By Lemma 15, this implies that $(\varphi^\#)^\flat$ is provable in **DL**. By Lemma 13 it follows that φ is provable in **DL** as well. ⊣

References

[1] Jon Barwise. *Admissible sets and structures*. Springer-Verlag, Berlin, 1975.

[2] Andreas Blass and Yuri Gurevich. Existential fixed-point logic. In E. Boerger, editor, *Logic and complexity*, pages 20–36. Springer Verlag, LNCS 270, 1987.

[3] M. Gordon and L. Claesen. Higher order logic theorem proving and its applications. In *Proceedings of workshop, Leuven, September 1992*, Amsterdam, 1993. North-Holland.

[4] M. Gordon and T. F. Melham. *Introduction to HOL: a theorem-proving environment for higher-order logic*. Cambridge University Press, Cambridge, 1993.

[5] D. Harel, A. Meyer, and V. Pratt. Computability and completeness in logics of programs. In *Proceedings of the ninth symposium on the Theorey of Computing*, pages 261–268, Providence, 1977. ACM.

[6] David Harel. *First-order Dynamic Logic*. LNCS 68. Springer-Verlag, Berlin, 1979.

[7] David Harel and Dexter Kozen. A programming language for the inductive sets, and applications. *Information and Control*, 63:118–139, 1984.

[8] David Harel, Dexter Kozen, and Jerzy Tiuryn. *Dynamic Logic*. MIT Press, Cambridge, MA, 2000.

[9] Leon Henkin. Completeness in the theory of types. *Journal of Symbolic Logic*, 15:81–91, 1950.

[10] K. Honda, N. Yoshida, and M. Berger. An observationally complete program logic for imperative higher-order functions. In *LiCS'05*, 2005.

[11] Daniel Leivant. Logical and mathematical reasoning about imperative programs. In *Conference Record of the Twelfth Annual Symposium on Principles of Programming Languages*, pages 132–140, New York, 1985. ACM. An expanded and revised journal version is forthcoming.

[12] Daniel Leivant. Partial corretness assertions provable in dynamic logics. In Igor Walukiewicz, editor, *Proceedings of the Conference on Foundations of Software Science and Computation Structures (FOSSACS'04)*. Springer Verlag, LNCS, 2004.

[13] Daniel Leivant. Proving termination assertions in dynamic logics. In *Proceedings of the Nineteenth IEEE Conference on Logic in Computer Science*, pages 89–99, Washington, 2004. IEEE Computer Society Press.

[14] G. Mirkowska. On formalized systems of algorithmic logic. *Bull. Acad. Polon. Sci.*, 19:421–428, 1971.

[15] V. Pratt. Semantical considerations on Floyd-Hoare logic. In *Proceedings of the seventeenth symposium on Foundations of Computer Science*, pages 109–121, Washington, 1976. IEEE Computer Society.

[16] D. Prawitz. *Natural Deduction*. Almqvist and Wiksell, Uppsala, 1965.

[17] H. Rogers. *Theory of Recursive Functions and Effective Computability*. McGraw-Hill, New York, 1967.

[18] Krister Segerberg. A completeness theorem in the modal logic of programs (preliminary report). *Notics of the American Mathematical Society*, 24(6):A–552, 1977.

[19] Stephen Simpson. *Subsystems of Second Order Arithmetic*. Springer-Verlag, Berlin, 1999.

Session 5:
Proof Theory

Context Semantics, Linear Logic and Computational Complexity*

Ugo Dal Lago†
Laboratoire d'Informatique de Paris-Nord
Université Paris 13, France
dallago@lipn.univ-paris13.fr

Abstract

We show that context semantics can be fruitfully applied to the quantitative analysis of proof normalization in linear logic. In particular, context semantics lets us define the weight *of a proof-net as a measure of its inherent complexity: it is both an upper bound to normalization time (modulo a polynomial overhead, independently on the reduction strategy) and a lower bound to the number of steps to normal form (for certain reduction strategies). Weights are then exploited in proving strong soundness theorems for various subsystems of linear logic, namely elementary linear logic, soft linear logic and light linear logic.*

1 Introduction

Linear logic has always been claimed to be resource-conscious: structural rules are applicable only when the involved formulas are modal, i.e. in the form $!A$. Indeed, while (multiplicative) linear logic embeds intuitionistic logic, restricting the rules governing the exponential operator ! leads to characterizations of interesting complexity classes [2, 12, 16]. On the other hand, completely forbidding duplication highlights strong relations between proofs and boolean circuits [20]. These results demonstrate the relevance of linear logic in implicit computational complexity, where the aim is obtaining machine-independent, logic-based characterization of complexity classes. Nevertheless, relations between copying and complexity are not fully understood yet. Bounds on normalization time for different fragments of linear logic are indeed obtained by ad-hoc techniques which cannot be easily generalized.

Context semantics [14] is a powerful framework for the analysis of proof and program dynamics. It can be considered as a model of Girard's geometry of interaction [10, 9] where the underlying algebra consists of *contexts*. Context semantics and the geometry of interaction have been used to prove the correctness of optimal reduction algorithms [14] and in the design of sequential and parallel interpreters for the lambda calculus [17, 18]. There are evidences that these semantic frameworks are useful in capturing quantitative as well as qualitative properties of programs. The inherent computational difficulty of normalizing a proof has indeed direct counterpart in its interpretation. It is well known that strongly normalizing proofs are exactly the ones having finitely many so-called regular paths in the geometry of interaction [7]. A class of proof-nets which are not just strongly normalizing but normalizable in elementary time can still be captured in the geometry of interaction framework, as suggested by Baillot and Pedicini [3]. Until recently, it was not known whether this correspondence scales down to smaller complexity classes, such as polynomial time computable functions. The usual measure based on the length of regular paths cannot be used, since there are proof-nets which can be normalized in polynomial time but whose regular paths have exponential length (as we are going to show in the following). Context semantics has been recently exploited by the author in the quantitative analysis of linear lambda calculi with higher-order recursion [5]. Noticeably, context semantics is powerful enough to induce bounds on the algebraic potential size of terms, a parameter which itself bounds normalization time (up to a polynomial overhead). From existing literature, it is not clear whether similar results can be achieved for linear logic, where exponentials take the place of recursion in providing the essential expressive power.

In this paper, we show that context semantics reveals precise quantitative information on the dynamics of second order multiplicative and exponential linear logic. More specifically, a weight W_G is assigned to every proof-net G in such a way that:

- Both the number of steps to normal form *and* the size of any reduct of G are bounded by $p(W_G, |G|)$, where $p : \mathbb{N}^2 \to \mathbb{N}$ is a fixed polynomial and $|G|$ is the size of G.

*The author is partially supported by PRIN project FOLLIA (2004) and ANR project NOCOST (2005).

†This paper has been written while the author was a doctoral student at Dipartimento di Scienze dell'Informazione, Università di Bologna, Italy.

- There is a reduction strategy which *realizes* W_G, i.e. there is a proof-net H such that $G \longrightarrow^{W_G} H$.

Moreover, studying W_G is easier than dealing directly with the underlying syntax. In particular, we here prove strong soundness theorems (any proof can be reduced in a bounded amount of time, independently on the underlying reduction strategy) for various subsystems of multiplicative linear logic by studying how restricting exponential rules reflect to W_G. These proofs are simpler than similar ones from the literature [12, 2, 19, 16], which in many cases refer to weak rather than strong soundness.

The weight W_G of a proof-net G will be defined from the context semantics of G following two ideas:

- The cost of a given box inside G is the number of times it can be copied during normalization;
- The weight of G is the sum of costs of boxes inside G.

As a consequence, W_G only takes into account the exponential portion of G and is null whenever G does not contain any instance of the exponential rules.

The rest of this paper is organized as follows. In Section 2, we will define linear logic as a sequent calculus and as a system of proof-nets. In Section 3, context semantics is defined and some examples of proof-nets are presented, together with their interpretation. Section 4 is devoted to relationships between context semantics and computational complexity and presents the two main results. Section 5 describe how context semantics can be useful in studying subsystems of linear logic, namely elementary linear logic, soft linear logic and light linear logic.

An extended version of this paper including all proofs is available [4].

2 Syntax

We here introduce multiplicative linear logic as a sequent calculus. Then, we will show how a proof-net can be associated to any sequent-calculus proof. The results described in the rest of this paper are formulated in terms of proof-nets.

The language of *formulae* is defined by the following productions:

$$A ::= \alpha \mid A \multimap A \mid A \otimes A \mid !A \mid \forall\alpha.A$$

where α ranges over a countable set of *atoms*. The rules in Figure 1 define a sequent calculus for (intuitionistic) multiplicative and exponential linear logic (with second order). We shall use MELL as a shorthand for this system.

Proof-nets [11] are graph-like representations for proofs. We here adopt a system of intuitionistic proof-nets; in other words, we do not map derivations in MELL to usual, classical, proof-nets.

Let $\mathscr{L}$ be the set

$$\{R_{\multimap}, L_{\multimap}, R_{\otimes}, L_{\otimes}, R_{\forall}, L_{\forall}, R_!, L_!, W, X, D, N, P, C\}$$

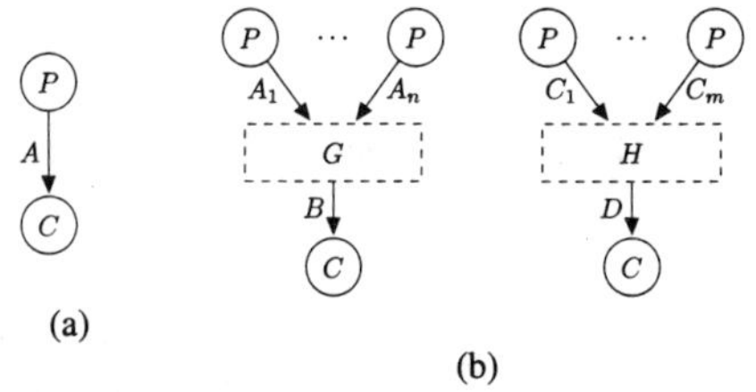

Figure 2. Base cases.

A *proof-net* is a graph-like structure G. It can be defined inductively as follows: a proof-net is either the graph in Figure 2(a) or one of those in Figure 3 where G, H are themselves proof-nets as in Figure 2(b). If G is a proof-net, then V_G denotes the set of vertices of G, E_G denotes the set of direct edges of G, α_G is a labelling functions mapping every vertex in V_G to an element of $\mathscr{L}$ and β_G maps every edge in E_G to a formula. We do not need to explicitly denote axioms and cuts by vertices in V_G.

Note that each of the rules in figures 2(a) and 3 closely corresponds to a rule in the sequent calculus. Given a sequent calculus proof π, a proof-net G_π corresponding to π can be built. Nodes labelled with C (respectively, P) mark the conclusion (respectively, the premises) of the proof-net. Notice that the rule corresponding to $P_!$ (see Figure 3) allows seeing interaction graphs as nested structures, where nodes labelled with $R_!$ and $L_!$ delimit a *box*. If $e \in E_G$, $\theta_G(e)$ denotes the vertex labelled with $R_!$ delimiting the box containing e (if such a box exists, otherwise $\theta_G(e)$ is undefined). If $v \in V_G$, $\theta_G(v)$ has the same meaning. If v is a vertex with $\alpha_G(v) = R_!$, then $\rho_G(v)$ denotes the edge departing from v and going outside the box. Expressions $\sigma_G(e)$ and $\sigma_G(v)$ are shorthand for $\rho_G(\theta_G(e))$ and $\rho_G(\theta_G(v))$, respectively.

If $e = (u, v) \in E_G$, and $\alpha_G(u) = R_!$, then e is said to be a *box-edge*. B_G is the set of all box-edges of G. Given a box-edge e, $P_G(e)$ is the number of premises of the box. I_G is the set of all vertices $v \in V_G$ with $\alpha_G(v) \notin \{R_!, L_!\}$. If $v \in V_G$, then $\partial(v)$ is the so-called box-depth of v, i.e. the number of boxes where v is included; similarly, $\partial(e)$ is the box-depth of $e \in E_G$, while $\partial(G)$ is the box-depth of the whole proof-net G. The size $|G|$ of a proof-net G is simply the number of vertices in V_G.

Cut elimination is performed by graph rewriting in proof-nets. There are eight different rewriting rules $\longrightarrow_S$, where $S \in \mathscr{C} = \{\multimap, \otimes, \forall, !, X, D, N, W\}$. Lack of space prevents us from reporting rules here (see [4]). If $\mathscr{Q} \subseteq \mathscr{C}$, then $\longrightarrow_{\mathscr{Q}}$ is the union of $\longrightarrow_S$ over $S \in \mathscr{Q}$. The relation $\longrightarrow$ is simply $\longrightarrow_{\mathscr{C}}$. The notion of a normal form proof-net is the usual one. If $S \in \mathscr{C}$, an edge linking two nodes that interact in $\longrightarrow_S$ is called an S-cut.

$$\frac{}{A \vdash A}\ A \qquad \frac{\Gamma \vdash A \quad \Delta, A \vdash B}{\Gamma, \Delta \vdash B}\ U \qquad \frac{\Gamma \vdash B}{\Gamma, !A \vdash B}\ W \qquad \frac{\Gamma, !A, !A \vdash B}{\Gamma, !A \vdash B}\ X$$

$$\frac{\Gamma, A \vdash B}{\Gamma \vdash A \multimap B}\ R_{\multimap} \qquad \frac{\Gamma \vdash A \quad \Delta, B \vdash C}{\Gamma, \Delta, A \multimap B \vdash C}\ L_{\multimap} \qquad \frac{\Gamma \vdash A \quad \Delta \vdash B}{\Gamma, \Delta \vdash A \otimes B}\ R_{\otimes} \qquad \frac{\Gamma, A, B \vdash C}{\Gamma, A \otimes B \vdash C}\ L_{\otimes}$$

$$\frac{A_1, \ldots, A_n \vdash B}{!A_1, \ldots, !A_n \vdash !B}\ P_! \qquad \frac{A, \Gamma \vdash B}{!A, \Gamma \vdash B}\ D_! \qquad \frac{!!A, \Gamma \vdash B}{!A, \Gamma \vdash B}\ N_! \qquad \frac{\Gamma \vdash A \quad \alpha \notin FV(\Gamma)}{\Gamma \vdash \forall \alpha.A}\ R_{\forall} \qquad \frac{\Gamma, A\{B/\alpha\} \vdash C}{\Gamma, \forall \alpha.A \vdash C}\ L_{\forall}$$

Figure 1. A sequent calculus for MELL

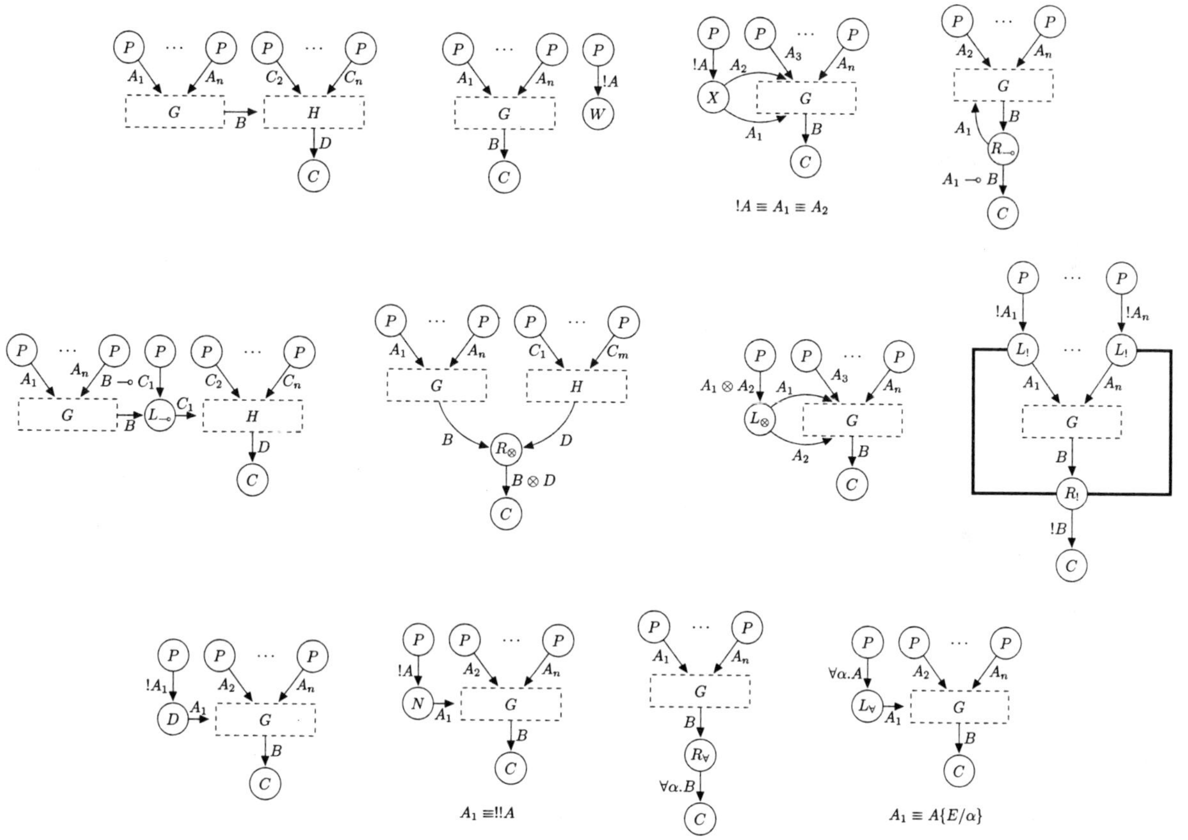

Figure 3. Inductive cases

Given a proof-net G, the expression $||G||_{\rightarrow}$ denotes the natural number

$$\max_{G \longrightarrow^* H} |H|.$$

The expression $[G]_{\rightarrow}$ denotes the natural number

$$\max_{G \longrightarrow^n H} n.$$

These are well-defined concepts, since the calculus is strongly normalizing.

The relation $\Longrightarrow$ is a restriction on $\longrightarrow$ defined as follows: $G \Longrightarrow H$ iff $G \longrightarrow_S H$ where $S = W$ only in case any cut in G is a W-cut. This is a reduction strategy, i.e. $G \Longrightarrow^* H$ whenever H is the normal form of G. The expressions $||G||_{\Rightarrow}$ and $[G]_{\Rightarrow}$ are defined in the obvious way, similarly to $||G||_{\rightarrow}$ and $[G]_{\rightarrow}$. Studying $\Longrightarrow$ is easier than studying $\longrightarrow$. From a complexity point of view, this is not problematic, since results about $\Longrightarrow$ can be easily transferred to $\longrightarrow$:

Lemma 1 (Standardization) *For every proof-net G, both $[G]_{\Rightarrow} = [G]_{\rightarrow}$ and $||G||_{\Rightarrow} = ||G||_{\rightarrow}$.*

In the following, we will prove properties of $\Longrightarrow$ that, by lemma 1, can be easily transferred to $\longrightarrow$. Consider the following further conditions on $\Longrightarrow$:

1. For every $n \in \mathbb{N}$, a cut at level $n+1$ is fired only when any cut at levels from 1 to n is a W-cut.
2. For every $n \in \mathbb{N}$, a !-cut at level n is fired only when any cut at level n is either a W-cut or a !-cut

These two conditions induce another relation $\longrightarrow\!\!\!\!\triangleright$, which is itself a reduction strategy. Note that firing a cut at level n does not introduce cuts at levels strictly smaller than n, while firing a !-cut at level n only introduces cuts at level $n+1$. As a consequence, $\longrightarrow\!\!\!\!\triangleright$ can be considered as a "level-by-level" strategy [2, 19].

3 Context Semantics

In this section, the context semantics of proof-nets is studied. The context semantics of a proof-net is essentially a set of paths; studying the length and numerosity of paths for a proof-net G helps inferring useful quantitative properties of G.

The first needed preliminary concept is that of an exponential signature. Exponential signatures are trees whose nodes are labelled with symbols $\mathsf{e}, \mathsf{r}, \mathsf{l}, \mathsf{n}, \mathsf{p}$. They serve as contexts while constructing a path in a proof-net, similarly to what *context marks* do in Gonthier, Abadi and Lévy's framework [15]. Label p has a special role and helps capturing the tricky combinatorial behavior of rule $N_!$ (see Figure 1). For similar reasons, a binary relation $\sqsubseteq$ on exponential signatures is needed.

Definition 1 • *The language $\mathscr{E}$ of* exponential signatures *is defined by induction from the following sets of productions:*

$$t, u, v, w ::= \mathsf{e} \mid \mathsf{r}(t) \mid \mathsf{l}(t) \mid \mathsf{p}(t) \mid \mathsf{n}(t, t).$$

- *A* standard *exponential signature is one that does not contain the constructor* p.
- *The binary relation $\sqsubseteq$ on $\mathscr{E}$ is defined as follows:*

$$\begin{array}{rcl}
\mathsf{e} & \sqsubseteq & \mathsf{e};\\
\mathsf{r}(t) & \sqsubseteq & \mathsf{r}(u) \Leftrightarrow t \sqsubseteq u;\\
\mathsf{l}(t) & \sqsubseteq & \mathsf{l}(u) \Leftrightarrow t \sqsubseteq u;\\
\mathsf{p}(t) & \sqsubseteq & \mathsf{p}(u) \Leftrightarrow t \sqsubseteq u;\\
\mathsf{p}(t) & \sqsubseteq & \mathsf{n}(u, v) \Leftrightarrow t \sqsubseteq v;\\
\mathsf{n}(t, u) & \sqsubseteq & \mathsf{n}(v, w) \Leftrightarrow t \sqsubseteq v \text{ and } u = w.
\end{array}$$

If $u \sqsubseteq t$ then u is a simplification *of t.*

- *A* stack element *is either an exponential signature or one of the following characters:* $\mathsf{a}, \mathsf{o}, \mathsf{s}, \mathsf{f}, \mathsf{x}$. *$\mathscr{S}$ is the set of stack elements. $\mathscr{S}$ is ranged over by s, r.*
- *A* polarity *is either $+$ or $-$. $\mathscr{B}$ is the set of polarities. The following notation is useful: $+\downarrow$ is $-$, while $-\downarrow$ is $+$.*
- *If $U \in \mathscr{S}^*$, then $||U||$ denotes the number of exponential signatures in U.*

Please observe that if t is standard and $t \sqsubseteq u$, then $t = u$. The structure $(\mathscr{E}, \sqsubseteq)$ is a partial order:

Lemma 2 *The relation $\sqsubseteq$ is reflexive, transitive and antisymmetric.*

We are finally ready to define the context semantics for a proof-net G. Given a proof-net G, the set of *contexts* for G is

$$C_G = E_G \times \mathscr{E}^* \times \mathscr{S}^+ \times \mathscr{B}.$$

Vertices of G with labels $R_{\multimap}, L_{\multimap}, R_{\otimes}, L_{\otimes}, R_{\forall}, L_{\forall}, R_!, L_!, X, D, N$ induce rewriting rules on C_G. These rules are detailed in Table 1 and Table 2. For any such rule

$$(e, U, V, b) \longmapsto_G (g, W, Z, c)$$

the *dual* rule

$$(g, W, Z, c\downarrow) \longmapsto_G (e, U, V, b\downarrow).$$

holds as well. In other words, relation $\longmapsto_G$ is the smallest binary relation on C_G including every instance of rules in Table 1 and Table 2, together with every instance of their duals.

The role of the four components of a context can be intuitively explained as follows:

- The first component is an edge in the proof-net G. As a consequence, from every sequence $C_1 \longmapsto_G C_2 \longmapsto_G \ldots \longmapsto_G C_n$ we can extract a sequence $e_1, e_2, \ldots, e_n$ of edges. Rewriting rules in tables 1 and 2 enforce this sequence to be a path in G, i.e. e_i has a vertex in common with e_{i+1}. The only exception is caused by the last rule induced by boxes (see Table 2): in that case e and h do not share any vertex, but the two vertices v and w (which are adjacent to e and h, respectively) are part of the same box.
- The second component is a (possibly empty) sequence of exponential signatures which keeps track of which copies of boxes we are currently traveling into. More specifically, if e and U are the first and second components of a context, then the $\partial(e)$ rightmost exponential signatures in U correspond to copies of the $\partial(e)$ boxes where e is contained. Although the definition of a context does not prescribe this correspondence (U can be empty even if $\partial(e)$ is strictly positive), it is preserved by rewriting.

Table 1. Rewrite Rules for Vertices $R_{\multimap}$, $L_{\multimap}$, $R_{\otimes}$, $L_{\otimes}$, $R_{\forall}$, $L_{\forall}$

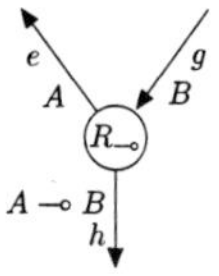	$(e, U, V, -) \longmapsto_G (h, U, V \cdot \mathsf{a}, +)$ $(g, U, V, +) \longmapsto_G (h, U, V \cdot \mathsf{o}, +)$
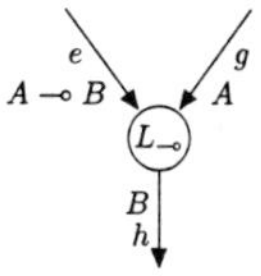	$(e, U, V \cdot \mathsf{a}, +) \longmapsto_G (g, U, V, -)$ $(e, U, V \cdot \mathsf{o}, +) \longmapsto_G (h, U, V, +)$
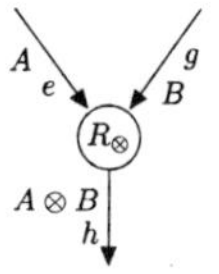	$(e, U, V, +) \longmapsto_G (h, U, V \cdot \mathsf{f}, +)$ $(g, U, V, +) \longmapsto_G (h, U, V \cdot \mathsf{x}, +)$
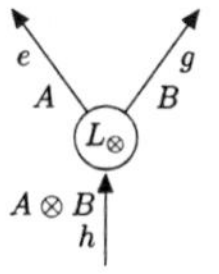	$(h, U, V \cdot \mathsf{f}, +) \longmapsto_G (e, U, V, +)$ $(h, U, V \cdot \mathsf{x}, +) \longmapsto_G (g, U, V, +)$
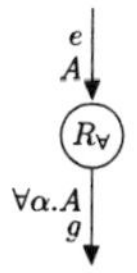	$(e, U, V, +) \longmapsto_G (g, U, V \cdot \mathsf{s}, +)$
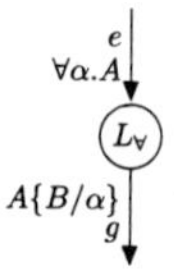	$(e, U, V \cdot \mathsf{s}, +) \longmapsto_G (g, U, V, +)$

- The third component is a nonempty sequence of stack elements. It keeps track of the history of previously visited edges. In this way, the fundamental property called *path-persistence* is enforced: any path induced by the context semantics is preserved by normalization [15]. This property is fundamental for proving the correctness of optimal reduction algorithms [14], but it is not directly exploited in this paper. Notice that exponential signatures can float from the second component to the third component and vice versa (see the rules induced by vertices $R_!$ and $L_!$).
- The only purpose of the last component is forcing rewriting to be (almost) deterministic: for every C there is at most one context D such that $C \longmapsto_G D$, except when $C = (e, U, t, -)$ and $e \in B_G$. In fact, $C \longmapsto_G (g_i, U, t, -)$ for every i, where $g_1, \ldots, g_n$ are the premises of the box whose conclusion is e.

The way we have defined context semantics, namely by a set of contexts endowed with a rewrite relation, is fairly standard [14, 15]. In particular, our definition owes much to Danos and Regnier's Interaction Abstract Machine (IAM, see [8]). Both our machinery and the IAM are reversible, but while IAM can be considered as a bideterministic automaton, our context semantics cannot, due to the last rule induced by boxes. Noticeably, a fragment of MELL called light linear logic does enforce strong determinacy, as we will detail in Section 5

Although context semantics can be defined on sharing

Table 2. Rewrite Rules for Vertices X, D, N, $L_!$ and $R_!$.

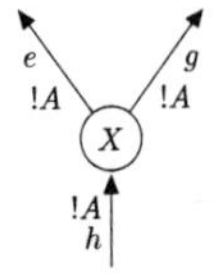	$(h, U, V \cdot \mathsf{l}(t), +) \longmapsto_G (e, U, V \cdot t, +)$ $(h, U, V \cdot \mathsf{r}(t), +) \longmapsto_G (g, U, V \cdot t, +)$
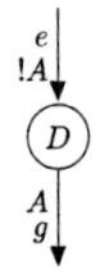	$(e, U, V \cdot \mathsf{e}, +) \longmapsto_G (g, U, V, +)$
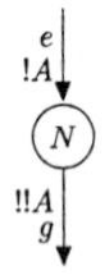	$(e, U, V \cdot \mathsf{n}(t, u), +) \longmapsto_G (g, U, V \cdot t \cdot u, +)$ $(e, U, \mathsf{p}(t), +) \longmapsto_G (g, U, t, +)$
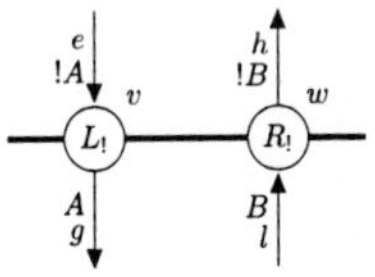	$(e, U, V \cdot t, +) \longmapsto_G (g, U \cdot t, V, +)$ $(l, U \cdot t, V, +) \longmapsto_G (h, U, V \cdot t, +)$ $(e, U, t, +) \longmapsto_G (h, U, t, +)$

graphs as well, proof-nets have been considered here. Indeed, sharing graphs are more problematic from a complexity viewpoint, since a computationally expensive read-back procedure is necessary in order to retrieve the proof (or term) corresponding to a sharing graph in normal form (see [1]).

Observe that the semantic framework we have just introduced is *not* a model of geometry of interaction as described by Girard [10]. In particular, jumps between distinct conclusions of a box are not permitted in geometry of interaction, which is completely local in this sense. Moreover, algebraic equations induced by rule N are here slightly different. As we are going to see, this mismatch is somehow necessary in order to capture the combinatorial behavior of proofs independently on the underlying reduction strategy.

3.1 Motivating Examples

We now define some proof-nets together with observations about how context-semantics reflects the complexity of normalization.

The first example (due to Danos and Regnier) is somehow discouraging: a family of proof-nets which normalize in polynomial time having paths of exponential lengths. For every positive natural number n and for every formula A, a proof-net $G_n(A)$ can be defined. We go by induction on n:

- The proof-net $G_1(A)$ is the following:

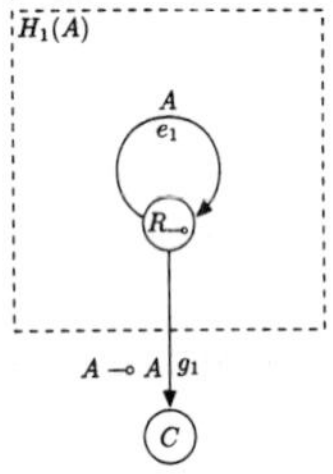

  Notice we have implicitly defined a sub-graph $H_1(A)$ of $G_1(A)$.

- If $n > 1$, then $G_n(A)$ is the following proof-net:

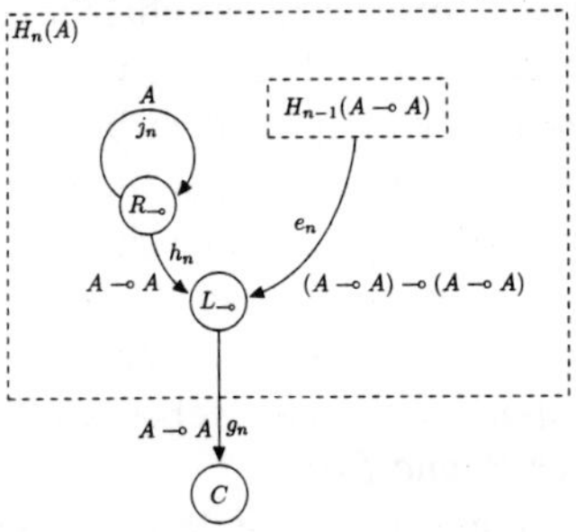

  Notice we have implicitly defined a sub-graph $H_n(A)$ of $G_n(A)$.

Although the size of $G_n(A)$ is $2n$ and, most important, $G_n(A)$ normalizes in $n-1$ steps to $G_1(A)$, we can easily prove the following, surprising, fact: for every n, for every A and for every $V \in \mathscr{S}^*$,

$$(g_n, \varepsilon, V \cdot \mathsf{a}, -) \longmapsto^{f(n)}_{G_n(A)} (g_n, \varepsilon, V \cdot \mathsf{o}, +)$$
$$(g_n, \varepsilon, V \cdot \mathsf{o}, -) \longmapsto^{f(n)}_{G_n(A)} (g_n, \varepsilon, V \cdot \mathsf{a}, +)$$

where $f(n) = O(2^n)$. In other words, proof-nets in the family $\{G_n(A)\}_{n\in\mathbb{N}}$ normalize in polynomial time but have exponentially long paths. The weights $W_{G_n(A)}$, as we are going to see, will be null. This is accomplished by focusing on paths starting from boxes, this in contrast to the execution formula [10], which takes into account conclusion-to-conclusion paths only.

The second example is a proof-net G:

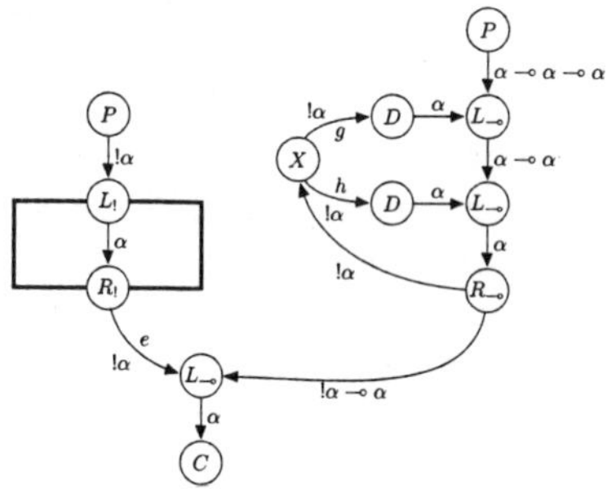

Observe $G \longrightarrow^* H$ where H is the following cut-free proof:

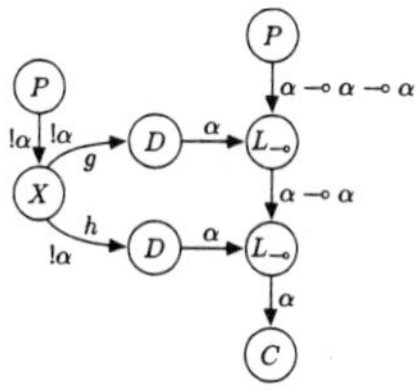

There are finitely many paths in C_G, all of them having finite length. But the context semantics of G reflects the fact that G is strongly normalizing in another way, too: there are finitely many exponential signatures t such that $(e, \varepsilon, t, +) \longmapsto^*_G (k, U, \mathsf{e}, +)$, where $k \in E_G$ and $U \in \mathscr{E}^+$. We can concentrate on e since it is the only box-edge on G. In particular:

$$(e, \varepsilon, \mathsf{e}, +) \longmapsto^*_G (e, \varepsilon, \mathsf{e}, +)$$
$$(e, \varepsilon, \mathsf{r}(\mathsf{e}), +) \longmapsto^*_G (h, \varepsilon, \mathsf{e}, +)$$
$$(e, \varepsilon, \mathsf{l}(\mathsf{e}), +) \longmapsto^*_G (g, \varepsilon, \mathsf{e}, +)$$

Intuitively, the exponential signature e corresponds to the initial status of the single box in G, while $\mathsf{l}(\mathsf{e})$ and $\mathsf{r}(\mathsf{e})$ correspond to the two copies of the same box appearing after some normalization steps. In the following section, we will formally investigate this new way of exploiting the context semantics as a method of studying the quantitative behavior of proofs.

Let us now present one last example. Consider the proof-net J:

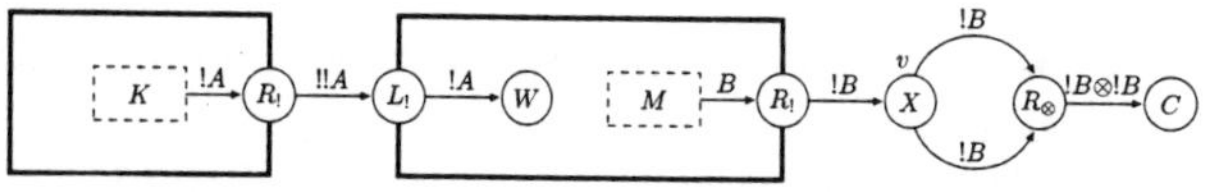

The leftmost box (i.e. the box containing K) can interact with the vertex v and, as a consequence, can be copied:

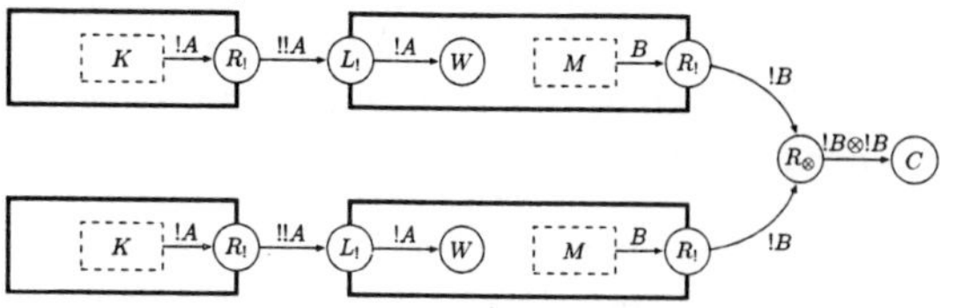

However, there is not any persistent path (in the sense of [15]) between the box and v. The reason is simple: there is not any *path* between them. This mismatch shows why an extended notion of path encompassing jumps between box premises and conclusions is necessary in order to capture the quantitative behavior of proofs (at least if *every* reduction strategy is taken into account).

4 Context Semantics and Time Complexity

We are now in a position to define the weight W_G of a proof-net G. As already mentioned, W_G takes into account the number of times each box in G is copied during normalization. Suppose G contains a sub-net matching the left-hand side of the rule $\longrightarrow_X$. There is a box-edge e in G such that the corresponding box will be duplicated at least once. In the context semantics, for every $t \in \{\mathsf{e}, \mathsf{l}(\mathsf{e}), \mathsf{r}(\mathsf{e})\}$ there are $g \in E_G$ and $V \in \mathscr{E}^*$ such that

$$(e, U, t, +) \longmapsto^*_G (g, V, \mathsf{e}, b). \tag{1}$$

As a consequence, we would be tempted to define the "weight" of *any* box-edge e as the number of "maximal" exponential signatures satisfying (1). What we need, in order to capture "maximality" is a notion of final contexts.

Definition 2 (Final Stacks, Final Contexts) *Let G be a proof-net. Then:*

- *First of all, we need to define what a* final stack $U \in \mathscr{S}^+$ *is. We distinguish* positive *and* negative *final stacks and define them mutually recursively:*
  - *A positive final stack is either* e *or* $V \cdot \mathsf{a}$ *(where V is a negative final stack) or $V \cdot s$ (where $s \in \{\mathsf{o}, \mathsf{f}, \mathsf{x}, \mathsf{s}\}$ and V is a positive final stack) or* $V \cdot \mathsf{e}$ *(where V is a positive final stack).*

- *A negative final stack is either $V \cdot \mathsf{a}$ (where V is a positive final stack) or $V \cdot s$ (where $s \in \{\mathsf{o}, \mathsf{f}, \mathsf{x}, \mathsf{s}\}$ and V is a negative final stack) or $V \cdot t$ (where V is a negative final stack and t is an exponential signature).*
- *A context $C \in C_G$ is* final *iff one of the following four cases hold:*
  - *If $C = ((u, v), U, V, +)$, $\alpha_G(v) = W$ and V is a positive final stack;*
  - *If $C = ((u, v), U, V, +)$, $\alpha_G(v) = C$ and V is a positive final stack;*
  - *If $C = ((u, v), U, \mathsf{e}, +)$ and $\alpha_G(v) = D$;*
  - *If $C = ((u, v), U, V, -)$, $\alpha_G(v) = P$ and V is a negative final stack;*

Although the definition of a final stack is not trivial, the underlying idea is very simple: if we reach a final context C from $(e, U, t, +)$, then the exponential signature t must have been completely "consumed" along the path. Moreover, if C is final, then there are not any context D such that $C \longmapsto_G D$. For example, the stack $\mathsf{e} \cdot \mathsf{a} \cdot \mathsf{n}(\mathsf{e}, \mathsf{e})$ is negative final, while $\mathsf{e} \cdot \mathsf{a} \cdot \mathsf{f} \cdot \mathsf{a}$ is positive final.

Now, consider exponential signatures t such that

$$(e, U, t, +) \longmapsto_G^* C \qquad (2)$$

where C is final. Apparently, (2) could take the place of (1) in defining what the weight of any box-edge should be. However, this does not work due to rewriting rule $\longrightarrow_N$ which, differently from $\longrightarrow_X$, duplicates a *box* without duplicating its *content*. The binary relation $\sqsubseteq$ will help us to manage this mismatch.

Definition 3 (Copies, Canonicity, Cardinalities) *Let G be a proof-net. Then:*

- *A* copy for $e \in B_G$ on $U \in \mathscr{E}^*$ *is a standard exponential signature t such that for every $u \sqsubseteq t$ there is a final context C such that $(e, U, u, +) \longmapsto_G^* C$.*
- *A sequence $U \in \mathscr{E}^*$ is said to be* canonical *for $e \in E_G$ iff one of the following conditions holds:*
  - *$\theta_G(e)$ is undefined and U is the empty sequence;*
  - *$\theta_G(e) = v$, V is canonical for $\rho_G(v)$, t is a copy for $\rho_G(v)$ under V, and $U = V \cdot t$.*

  $L_G(e)$ is the class of canonical sequences for e. If $v \in V_G$, then $L_G(v)$ is defined similarly.
- *The* cardinality $R_G(e, U)$ of $e \in B_G$ under $U \in \mathscr{E}^*$ *is the number of different simplifications of copies of e under U.*

Observe that $|U| = \partial(e)$ whenever U is a canonical sequence for e.

Consider a proof-net G, an edge $e \in B_G$ such that $\partial(e) = 0$ and let H be the box whose conclusion is e. Observe that the only canonical sequence for e is ε. Each copy of e under ε corresponds to a potential copy of the *content* of H. Indeed, if $g \in B_G$, $\partial(g) = 1$, and $\rho_G(g) = e$, canonical sequences for g are precisely the copies of e under ε. The cardinality $R_G(e, \varepsilon)$ will be the number of exponential cut-elimination steps potentially involving H, which is not necessarily equal to the number of copies of e under ε.

For every proof-net G, W_G is defined as follows:

$$W_G = \sum_{e \in B_G} \sum_{U \in L_G(e)} (R_G(e, U) - 1).$$

The quantity W_G is the *weight* of the proof-net G. As we will show later, W_G cannot increase during cut-elimination. However, it is not guaranteed to decrease at any cut-elimination step and, moreover, it is not necessarily a bound to the size $|G|$ of G. As a consequence, we need to define another quantity, called T_G:

$$T_G = \sum_{v \in I_G} |L_G(v)| + \sum_{e \in B_G} P_G(e) \sum_{U \in L_G(e)} (2R_G(e, U) - 1).$$

Since any box-edge $e \in B_G$ is charged for $P_G(e)$ in T_G, T_G is clearly greater or equal to $|G|$. Please notice that W_G and T_G can in principle be infinite.

By carefully studying how cut-elimination reflects to W_G and T_G, the following crucial result can be obtained

Proposition 1 (Monotonicity) *Let G be a proof-net. Then*

1. *$W_G \geq W_H$ and $T_G > T_H$ whenever $G \Longrightarrow H$;*
2. *$W_G \leq W_H + 1$ whenever $G \longrightarrow H$,*

As a consequence of Proposition 1, T_G bounds the number of cut-elimination steps necessary to rewrite G to its normal form. As it can be easily shown, T_G is also an upper bound on $|G|$. The following result can then be obtained by proving appropriate inequalities between W_G, $|G|$ and T_G:

Theorem 1 *There is a polynomial $p : \mathbb{N}^2 \rightarrow \mathbb{N}$ such that for every proof-net G, $[G]_{\longrightarrow}, ||G||_{\longrightarrow} \leq p(W_G, |G|)$.*

The weight W_G can only decrease during cut-elimination. Moreover, it decreases by at most one at any normalization step when performing the level-by-level strategy. As a consequence, the following theorem is obtained:

Theorem 2 *Let G be a proof-net. There is H with $G \longrightarrow^{W_G} H$.*

Theorems 1 and 2 highlights the existence of strong relations between context semantics and computational complexity. The two results can together be seen as a strengthening of the well-known correspondence between strongly normalizing nets and finiteness of regular paths (see [7]). This has very interesting consequences: for example, a family $\mathscr{G}$ of proof-nets can be normalized in polynomial (respectively, elementary) time iff there is a polynomial (respectively, an elementary function) p such that $W_G \leq p(|G|)$ for every $G \in \mathscr{G}$. This will greatly help in the following section, where we sketch new proofs of soundness for various subsystems of linear logic.

Now, suppose t is a copy of $e \in B_G$ under $U \in \mathscr{E}^*$. By definition, there is a finite (possibly empty) sequence $C_1, \ldots, C_n$ such that

$$(e, U, t, +) \longmapsto_G C_1 \longmapsto_G C_2 \longmapsto_G \ldots \longmapsto_G C_n$$

and C_n is final. But what else can be said about this sequence? Let $C_i = (g_i, V_i, W_i, b_i)$ for every i. By induction on i, the leftmost component of W_i must be an exponential signature, i.e. $W_i = u_i \cdot Z_i$ for every i. Moreover, every u_i must be a subtree of t (another easy induction on i). This observation can in fact be slightly generalized into the following result:

Proposition 2 (Subtree Property) *Suppose t is a standard exponential signature. For every subtree u of t, there is $v \sqsubseteq t$ such that, whenever G is a proof-net, $U \in \mathscr{E}^*$ is canonical for $e \in B_G$ and t is a copy of e on U, there are $g \in E_G$ and $V \in \mathscr{E}^*$ with $(e, U, v, +) \longmapsto_G^* (g, V, u, +)$.*

The subtree property is extremely useful when proving bounds on $R_G(e, U)$ and W_G in subsystems of MELL.

5 Subsystems

In this section, we will give some arguments about the usefulness of context semantics by analyzing three subsystems of MELL from a complexity viewpoint.

Elementary linear logic (ELL, [12]) is just MELL with a weaker modality: rules $D_!$ and $N_!$ are not part of the underlying sequent calculus. This restriction enforces the following property at the semantic level:

Lemma 3 (Stratification) *Let G be a ELL proof-net. If $(e, U, V, b) \longmapsto_G^* (g, W, Z, c)$, then $||U|| + ||V|| = ||W|| + ||Z||$.*

By exploiting stratification together with the subtree property, we can easily prove the following result:

Proposition 3 (ELL Soundness) *For every $n \in \mathbb{N}$ there is an elementary function $p_n : \mathbb{N} \to \mathbb{N}$ such that $W_G \leq p_{\partial(G)}(|G|)$ for every ELL proof-net G.*

By Proposition 3 and Theorem 1, normalization of ELL proof-nets can be done in elementary time, provided $\partial(G)$ is fixed. To this respect, observe that ordinary encodings of data structures such as natural numbers, binary lists or trees have bounded box-depth.

Soft linear logic (SLL, [16]) can be defined from ELL by replacing rule X with M as follows:

$$\frac{\Gamma, A, \ldots, A \vdash B}{\Gamma, !A \vdash B}\ M$$

In proof-nets for SLL, there are vertices labelled with M and equipped with an arbitrary number of outgoing edges:

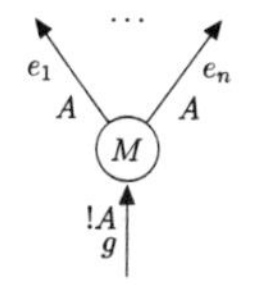

Exponential signatures becomes simpler:

$$t ::= \mathsf{e} \mid \mathsf{m}(i)$$

where i ranges over natural numbers. The new vertex induce the following rewriting rules:

$$\begin{array}{rcl} (h, U, V \cdot \mathsf{m}(i), +) & \longmapsto_G & (e_i, U, V, +) \\ (e_i, U, V, -) & \longmapsto_G & (h, U, V \cdot \mathsf{m}(i), -) \end{array}$$

It can be easily verified that for every $e \in B_G$ and for every $U \in \mathscr{E}^*$, it holds that $R_G(e, U) \leq |G|$. Indeed, if $(e, U, t \cdot V, b) \longmapsto_G^* (g, W, Z, c)$, then $Z = t \cdot Y$. As a consequence:

Proposition 4 (SLL Soundness) *For every $n \in \mathbb{N}$ there is a polynomial $p_n : \mathbb{N} \to \mathbb{N}$ such that $W_G \leq p_{\partial(G)}(|G|)$ for every SLL proof-net G.*

Light linear logic (LLL, [12]) can be obtained from ELL by enriching the language of formulae with a new modal operator § and splitting rule $P_!$ into two rules:

$$\frac{\Gamma \vdash B \quad |\Gamma| \leq 1}{!\Gamma \vdash !B}\ S_! \qquad \frac{\Gamma, \Delta \vdash A}{!\Gamma, \S\Delta \vdash \S A}\ S_\S$$

At the proof-nets level, two box constructions, !-boxes and §-boxes, correspond to $S_!$ and $S_\S$. As for the underlying context semantics, !-boxes induce the usual rewriting rules on C_G (see Table 2), while the last rule and its dual are not valid for §-boxes. This enforces *strong determinacy*, which does not hold for MELL or ELL: for every $C \in C_G$, there is at most one context $D \in C_G$ such that $C \longmapsto_G D$. As a consequence, weights can be bounded by appropriate polynomials:

Proposition 5 (LLL soundness) *For every $n \in \mathbb{N}$ there is an polynomial $p_n : \mathbb{N} \to \mathbb{N}$ such that $W_G \leq p_{\partial(G)}(|G|)$ for every LLL proof-net G.*

6 Conclusions

In this paper, we define a context semantics for linear logic proof-nets, showing it gives precise quantitative information on the dynamics of normalization. Theorems 1 and 2 are the main achievements of this work: they show that the weight W_G of a proof-net G is a *tight* estimate of the time needed to normalize G. Interestingly, proving bounds on

W_G is in general easier than bounding normalization time by purely syntactic arguments. Section 5 presents some evidence supporting this claim.

Results described in this paper can be transferred to affine logical systems, which offer some advantages over their linear counterparts (for example, additive connectives can be expressed in the logic).

An interesting problem (which we leave for future work) is characterizing the expressive power of other fragments of MELL, such as 4LL or TLL (see [6]), about which very few results are actually known. We believe that the semantic techniques described here could help dealing with them. Any sharp result would definitely help completing the picture.

Interestingly, the way bounded linear logic [13] is defined is very reminiscent to the way context semantics is used here. We are currently investigating relations between the two frameworks.

Acknowledgments

The author wishes to thank Patrick Baillot for many interesting discussions about the topics of this paper and the anonymous referees for useful comments.

References

[1] A. Asperti and S. Guerrini. *The optimal implementation of functional programming languages*. Cambridge University Press, 1998.

[2] A. Asperti and L. Roversi. Intuitionistic light affine logic. *ACM Transactions on Computational Logic*, 3(1):137–175, 2002.

[3] P. Baillot and M. Pedicini. Elementary complexity and geometry of interaction. *Fundamenta Informaticae*, 45(1-2):1–31, 2001.

[4] U. Dal Lago. Context semantics, linear logic and computational complexity. Extended Version. Available at `http://arxiv.org/cs.LO/0510092`, 2005.

[5] U. Dal Lago. The geometry of linear higher-order recursion. In *Proc. 20th Annual Symposium on Logic in Computer Science*, pages 366–375. IEEE Computer Society, 2005.

[6] V. Danos and J.-B. Joinet. Linear logic and elementary time. *Information and Computation*, 183(1):123–137, 2003.

[7] V. Danos and L. Regnier. Proof-nets and Hilbert space. In J.-Y. Girard, Y. Lafont, and L. Regnier, editors, *Advances in Linear Logic*, pages 307–328. Cambridge University Press, 1995.

[8] V. Danos and L. Regnier. Reversible, irreversible and optimal lambda-machines. *Theoretical Computer Science*, 227(1-2):79–97, 1999.

[9] J.-Y. Girard. Geometry of interaction 2: deadlock-free algorithms. In *Proc. Conference on Computer Logic*, volume 417 of *LNCS*, pages 76–93, 1988.

[10] J.-Y. Girard. Geometry of interaction 1: interpretation of system F. In *Proc. Logic Colloquium '88*, pages 221–260, 1989.

[11] J.-Y. Girard. Proof-nets: the parallel syntax for proof-theory. In A. Ursini and P. Agliano, editors, *Logic and Algebra*, volume 180 of *Lecture Notes in Pure and Applied Mathematics*, pages 97–124. Marcel Dekker, New York, 1995.

[12] J.-Y. Girard. Light linear logic. *Information and Computation*, 143(2):175–204, 1998.

[13] J.-Y. Girard, A. Scedrov, and P. J. Scott. Bounded linear logic: A modular approach to polynomial-time computability. *Theoretical Computer Science*, 97(1):1–66, 1992.

[14] G. Gonthier, M. Abadi, and J.-J. Lévy. The geometry of optimal lambda reduction. In *Proc. 12th ACM Symposium on Principles of Programming Languages*, pages 15–26, 1992.

[15] G. Gonthier, M. Abadi, and J.-J. Lévy. Linear logic without boxes. In *Proc. 7th Annual Symposium on Logic in Computer Science*, pages 223–234, 1992.

[16] Y. Lafont. Soft linear logic and polynomial time. *Theoretical Computer Science*, 318:163–180, 2004.

[17] I. Mackie. The geometry of interaction machine. In *Proc. 22nd ACM Symposium on Principles of Programming Languages*, pages 198–208, 1995.

[18] J. S. Pinto. Parallel implementation models for the lambda-calculus using the geometry of interaction. In *Proc. 5th International Conference on Typed Lambda Calculi and Applications*, pages 385–399, 2001.

[19] K. Terui. Light affine lambda calculus and polytime strong normalization. In *Proc. of 16th Annual IEEE Symposium on Logic in Computer Science*, pages 209–220, 2001.

[20] K. Terui. Proof nets and boolean circuits. In *Proc. 7th Annual Symposium on Logic in Computer Science*, pages 182–191, 2004.

Obsessional cliques: a semantic characterization of bounded time complexity

Olivier Laurent*†
Preuves Programmes Systèmes
CNRS - Paris 7
E-mail: Olivier.Laurent@pps.jussieu.fr

Lorenzo Tortora de Falco*‡
Dipartimento di filosofia
Roma III
E-mail: tortora@uniroma3.it

Abstract

We give a semantic characterization of bounded complexity proofs. We introduce the notion of obsessional clique *in the relational model of linear logic and show that restricting the morphisms of the category $\mathcal{REL}$ to obsessional cliques yields models of* ELL *and* SLL*. Conversely, we prove that these models are* relatively complete*: an* LL *proof whose interpretation is an obsessional clique is always an* ELL/SLL *proof. These results are achieved by introducing a system of* ELL/SLL *untyped proof-nets, which is both correct and complete with respect to elementary/polynomial time complexity.*

1. Introduction

It is widely acknowledged that computational complexity is a central topic in modern science: the famous P versus NP question appears in several (apparently) unrelated areas of pure and applied mathematics and theoretical computer science. Behind it, lies our capability of handling resources and of keeping control on their use: a crucial point for the contemporary computer scientist. The difficulty of the problem seems related to our yet incomplete understanding of the very nature of polynomial time.

Many of the scientists who tried to fathom the secrets of polytime produced alternative definitions of computability within a given bound, without any explicit reference to the bound itself. Usually, these characterizations are driven by the cultural background of their authors, who expect some help from the techniques developed in their own fields of research. This approach (having among his forerunners Kalmar and his inductive definition of the class of elementary recursive functions dating back to 1943) involves various branches of mathematical logic: (finite) model theory, recursion theory, proof-theory. Let us quote some of the main contributions: Fagin's characterization of NPTIME [12] on the model-theoretical side, limitations of the recursion schemata [6, 4] on the recursion-theoretical side, propositional proof complexity [7] and Buss' Bounded Arithmetic [5] on the proof-theoretical side. These results contributed to the birth of a new research area, now called *Implicit Computational Complexity*.

Taking the "Curry-Howard looking glass" (a proof is a program whose execution corresponds to applying the cut-elimination procedure to the proof), the approach to complexity is based on the idea that the expressive power of a logical system is the complexity of its cut-elimination/normalization procedure. Much work has been done in the framework of typed λ-calculus (for example [18]): roughly speaking, some limitations on the way λ-terms "communicate" allow to keep normalization polynomial. From the (strictly) logical point of view, the introduction of Linear Logic (LL [13]) was an important step: LL is a refinement of intuitionistic and classical logics characterized by the introduction of new connectives (the exponentials) which give a *logical* status to the operations of erasing and copying (corresponding to the *structural rules* of intuitionistic and classical logics). This shed a new light on the duplication process responsible of the "explosion" of the size (and time) during the cut-elimination procedure, and led to a first result in [16]. But, in this Bounded Linear Logic, polynomials appear explicitly. A notable breakthrough is Girard's Light Linear Logic (LLL [15]): a very careful handling of LL's exponentials allows the author to keep enough control on the duplication process. He proves that a function f is representable in LLL if and only if f is polytime. More recently, other "light systems" have been introduced by Asperti and Roversi [1, 2], Danos and Joinet [10], Lafont [17] and others: several simplifications are proposed and suggest that LLL is only one among the possible solutions (rather a research theme than a logical system).

Since the beginning [15], light systems are presented as subsystems of LL obtained by restricting the use of the exponentials: some principles (formulas) provable in LL do

* Supported by the project "Coop. Italia/France CNR–CNRS n° 19188".
† Supported by the French project "ANR JC05_43380 No-Cost".
‡ Supported by the Italian project "FOLLIA".

1043-6871/06 $20.00 © 2006 IEEE

not hold in light systems. However, a more geometric perspective on light logic is possible. It comes from the introduction of proof-nets, a geometric way of representing computations; actually one of the most important consequences of the logical status given by LL to the structural rules. Light proofs have been presented in [15] as proof-nets and the geometric view was corroborated by a crucial property of light proof(-net)s: *stratification*. Computations are performed layer by layer: the so-called *depth* of the proof-net (a geometric parameter) is invariant during computation. This viewpoint was stressed in [10], where the authors give a geometric characterization of those proof-nets with an elementary cut-elimination: the system is not modified and a global condition on the graph representation of proofs allows to isolate the "elementary" ones. A similar work for LLL has been done in [20]. We feel these results are little steps towards a more abstract vision of bounded complexity.

Among the questions and problems arisen from [15], the quest of a denotational semantics (a semantics of proofs in logical terms, or more generally a model) suitable for light systems is maybe the main one: hopefully, such a semantics will inspire a new mathematical point of view on the nature of polytime. Indeed, the general goal of denotational semantics is to give a "mathematical" counterpart to syntactical devices such as proofs and programs, thus bringing to the fore their essential properties. It maps the concrete syntactical objects to an algebraic, geometric, categorical, ... description, which stresses basic invariants and, sometimes, eventually results in improvements of the syntax: LL itself comes from a denotational model of second order intuitionistic logic. The basic pattern is to associate with every formula/type some structure and with every proof/program of the formula/type an element of the structure (called its *interpretation*). Clearly, interpreting LL proofs allows to interpret proofs of a given light system but gives no information on the "lightness" of proofs; the point is to find a denotational semantics of a light system which *is not* a denotational semantics of LL. To our knowledge only two proposals [21, 3] have been made up to now. While technically rather different ([21] is based on game semantics and [3] on coherent semantics), the two works are similar in spirit: the structures (games, coherent spaces) associated with logical formulas are modified, so that the principles valid in LL but not in the chosen light system do not hold in the semantics. One can also mention the works by M. Hofmann *et al.* introducing realisability models where resource-boundedness is explicitly required on realisers (see [8] for example).

We propose a new approach to the semantics of proofs of light systems. Following the same spirit of the previously mentioned geometric perspective on light logic, instead of modifying the structures associated with logical formulas, we look for a property of the elements of the structures (the interpretations of proofs) characterizing those elements which *can* interpret polytime proofs. For this purpose, nothing like full completeness/surjectivity ("every element of the structure interpreting a provable formula is the interpretation of a proof") is required (by the way, in the models we consider, this property fails). The idea we develop here is to choose a light system and a denotational model of LL, and to prove that an LL proof π is a proof of the chosen light system if and only if the interpretation $[\![\pi]\!]$ of π satisfies some given (semantic) property. In order to obtain a model of the light system, we then need to check that the property has a "good behaviour" (mainly, it must be stable with respect to composition). Notice that in case we succeed, we get (much) more than a model: a *relatively complete* model, whose morphisms are *exactly* the ones of the LL model satisfying the semantic property. Of course, the "quality" of the model will depend on the "quality" of the semantic property. The property we propose is obsessionality: it is very simple and rather natural; however (as explained in the conclusion) it does not say much on the elements which are not interpretations of proofs.

In this work, we choose as light logical systems ELL for elementary time and SLL for polynomial time, as model the relational one (but coherent semantics would also do). These choices are discussed in the conclusion. We introduce the notion of *obsessional clique*: a clique is obsessional when it is closed with respect to the (appropriate) action of the monoid $\mathbb{N}^*$ (definition 3). We prove that an LL proof π is a proof of ELL/SLL if and only if $[\![\pi]\!]$ is obsessional (with the appropriate variant for ELL/SLL) and that obsessionality is a property with a "good behaviour" (as mentioned above).

One of the (striking) features of obsessional cliques is the absence of any explicit reference to stratification: this seems to be an interesting achievement, and a small step towards a truly semantic view of bounded complexity. What can be certainly affirmed is that our analysis is not syntax-driven, but a natural refinement of tools introduced for other purposes. Technically speaking, the starting point of this work is the notion of obsessional experiment introduced in [25]: it was used to "rebuild" an LL proof from its interpretation in (relational or coherent) semantics. In general this is not possible: there are different LL proofs with the same semantics as it is shown in [25]. However, the relational (resp. coherent) interpretation of a proof (and more precisely the result of an obsessional experiment of the proof) is enough to rebuild that part of the proof allowing to distinguish ELL (resp. SLL) proofs from the others.

Roughly speaking, obsessional cliques have been introduced following the idea that, in case the clique is the interpretation of a proof-net, obsessional experiments "have all to be available". It turned out (and this was not *a priori* obvious) that obsessional cliques compose and yield a model of propositional ELL (resp. SLL): the category

$\mathcal{OREL}$ (resp. $\mathcal{SREL}$), as proved in section 2. One could prove a relative completeness theorem in the style of theorem 4 in a propositional framework, but one would not obtain a "semantic characterization of bounded time complexity": the considered fragments are not expressive enough to represent all elementary (resp. polynomial) computations. In ELL/SLL, the second order quantifiers are necessary to encode polytime computations [19]. Instead of dealing with the semantics of second order quantifiers (which is delicate), we moved from the typed to the untyped framework, thus avoiding the difficulty, in the spirit of [11]. The complexity of the cut-elimination procedures of [15, 17] does not depend on the complexity of cut-formulas, but only on the graph representation of the proofs as proof-nets. The elementary/polynomial complexity bound can thus be straightforwardly extended from the typed to the untyped case. Conversely, whatever can be represented in a typed framework can also be represented in an untyped one: simply forget types!

In the spirit of the semantics of λ-calculus (a model of the untyped λ-calculus is a model of the typed λ-calculus with a reflexive object), we decided to first present the typed framework (section 2) and move later to the untyped one. Section 3 is devoted to introduce (untyped) nets, an extension of Danos-Regnier's untyped proof-nets. In section 4, following [10], we define untyped ELL and SLL nets in geometric terms. Finally, we prove the main result of the paper in section 5: we introduce a space for "untyped obsessionality" in the spirit of the relational model and of the other models of the untyped λ-calculus. We adapt the notion of experiment of a proof-net (introduced in [13]) to define a model of our untyped nets and we prove the relative completeness theorem (theorem 4).

2. Typed case

After a short presentation of the two systems ELL and SLL, we are going to extend the relational model of linear logic with an action of $\mathbb{N}^*$ (the set of positive integers) on sets in order to define denotational models of these two systems.

2.1. Second order ELL and SLL

We consider the two subsystems ELL [15] and SLL [17] of LL which respectively correspond to elementary time and polynomial time complexities. See figures 1 and 2 for ELL, and figures 1 and 3 for SLL.

In ELL, integers are represented by proofs of $\mathbb{U} = \forall X ?(X \otimes X^\perp) \parr\, !(X^\perp \parr X)$, and functions are represented by proofs of $\vdash \mathbb{U}^\perp, !^p\mathbb{U}$. As shown in [15, 10], representable functions in ELL are exactly elementary time functions.

In SLL, binary integers are represented by proofs of $\mathbb{W} = \forall X ?(\mathbb{B} \otimes X \otimes X^\perp) \parr X^\perp \parr X$ where $\mathbb{B} = \forall X X^\perp \parr X^\perp \parr (X \otimes X)$, and predicates over integers are represented by proofs of $\vdash \mathbb{W}^\perp, \dots, \mathbb{W}^\perp, \mathbb{B}$ which do not contain any $?m$-rule (for the application of a predicate to an argument in $\mathbb{W}$, we first have to duplicate it the appropriate number of times). As shown in [19], representable predicates in SLL are exactly polynomial time predicates.

2.2. Obsessional relational model

Notations. If E is a set, we denote by $\mathcal{M}_f(E)$ the set of finite multisets of elements of E (*i.e.* the free commutative monoid generated by E). $[]$ is the empty multiset and $+$ is the commutative monoid law. If $x_1, \dots, x_n$ are elements of E and $k_1, \dots, k_n$ are natural numbers, $[k_1x_1, \dots, k_nx_n]$ is the multiset containing k_1 copies of x_1, ..., k_n copies of x_n.

The category $\mathcal{REL}$ of sets and relations is one of the simplest models of LL. The interpretation of connectives is given by: $1 = \perp = \{\star\}$, $\otimes = \parr = \times$ and $! = ? = \mathcal{M}_f$.

In the spirit of coherent spaces, we call *cliques* of A (denoted $c \sqsubset A$) the subsets of A.

Definition 1 ($\mathbb{N}$-set)
A $\mathbb{N}$-*set* is given by a set A and a function $(k, a) \mapsto a^{(k)}$ from $\mathbb{N}^* \times A$ to A, called the *action*, which is an action of the monoid $(\mathbb{N}^*, \cdot, 1)$ on A (that is $a^{(1)} = a$ and $a^{(kk')} = (a^{(k)})^{(k')}$).

The constructions of $\mathbb{N}$-sets are obtained from the corresponding constructions of sets and the actions are built in the following way:

- on $1 = \{\star\}$, we use the only possible action
- the action on $A \times B$ is given by $(a, b)^{(k)} = (a^{(k)}, b^{(k)})$
- if $t \in \mathbb{N}$, we define $!_tA$ (resp. $?_tA$) as the $\mathbb{N}$-set with underlying set $\mathcal{M}_f(A)$ and the action on $!_tA$ (resp. $?_tA$) is given by:

$$[a_1, \dots, a_n]^{(k)} = \begin{cases} [a_1^{(k)}, \dots, a_n^{(k)}] & \text{if } n \leq t \\ [ka_1^{(k)}, \dots, ka_n^{(k)}] & \text{if } n > t \end{cases}$$

Definition 2 (Category $\mathbb{N}\mathcal{REL}$)
The category $\mathbb{N}\mathcal{REL}$ is given by:

- objects: $\mathbb{N}$-sets
- morphisms: $\mathbb{N}\mathcal{REL}(A, B)$ is the set of cliques of $A \times B$

The categories $\mathcal{REL}$ and $\mathbb{N}\mathcal{REL}$ are equivalent categories, thus $\mathbb{N}\mathcal{REL}$ is a model of LL.

We are now able to define the key notion of this paper.

Definition 3 (Obsessional clique)
Let A be a $\mathbb{N}$-set, a clique c is *obsessional* if $\forall a \in c, \forall k \in \mathbb{N}^*, a^{(k)} \in c$.

Proposition 1 (Category $\mathcal{OREL}$)
The category $\mathcal{OREL}$ is the subcategory of $\mathbb{N}\mathcal{REL}$ with all objects and only obsessional cliques as morphisms.

The $\star$-autonomous structure of $\mathbb{N}\mathcal{REL}$ respects obsessionality: the cliques $(A \times B) \times C \simeq A \times (B \times C)$, $A \times B \simeq B \times A$ and $A \times 1 \simeq A$ are all obsessional, and if $x \sqsubset A \times C$ and $y \sqsubset B \times D$ are obsessional then $x \times y = \{((a,b),(c,d)) \mid (a,c) \in x \wedge (b,d) \in y\} \sqsubset (A \times B) \times (C \times D)$ is obsessional.

Concerning the exponential structure:

- If $x \sqsubset A \times B$ is obsessional, $!x = \{([a_1,\dots,a_n],[b_1,\dots,b_n]) \mid \forall 1 \leq i \leq n, (a_i,b_i) \in x\} \sqsubset !_tA \times !_tB$ is obsessional for any t.
- $\{(([a_1,\dots,a_n],[b_1,\dots,b_n]),[(a_1,b_1),\dots,(a_n,b_n)])\} \sqsubset (!_tA \times !_tB) \times !_t(A \times B)$ is obsessional for any t.
- $\{(\star,[n\star]) \mid n \in \mathbb{N}\} \sqsubset 1 \times !_t1$ is obsessional for any t.
- $\{([a_1,\dots,a_n],(a_1,\dots,a_n))\} \sqsubset !_tA \times \prod_n A$ is obsessional for $t \geq n$. In particular if $n = 0$, $\{([],\star)\} \sqsubset !_tA \times 1$ is obsessional for any t.
- $\{(\mu+\nu,(\mu,\nu))\} \sqsubset !_0A \times (!_0A \times !_0A)$ is obsessional.

Conversely, obsessionality allows to "refute" the usual representation of various principles:

- contraction is not obsessional in $!_tA \times (!_tA \times !_tA)$ as soon as $t > 0$
- digging is not obsessional in $!_tA \times !_t!_tA$ for any t
- dereliction is not obsessional in $!_0A \times A$

Theorem 1
$\mathcal{OREL}$ is a model of propositional (additive-free) ELL, *interpreting every formula of type $!A$ by $!_0A$.*

Proof. We have shown that the required constructions preserve obsessionality, and using the faithful functor U into $\mathcal{REL}$ given by $U(A,\_^{(\cdot)}) = A$ and $U(x) = x$ if $x \sqsubset A \times B$, we can show that all the required diagrams commute. □

Definition 4 (Category $\mathcal{SREL}$[1])
The category $\mathcal{SREL}$ is given by:

- objects: an object is a set with a family of actions indexed by $\mathbb{N}$ giving it $\mathbb{N}$-set structures $(A_n)_{n\in}$
- morphisms: elements of $\mathcal{SREL}((A_n)_{n\in}, (B_n)_{n\in})$ are cliques x of $A \times B$ such that there exists some $t \in \mathbb{N}$ with for any $n \geq t$, x is an obsessional clique of $A_n \times B_n$

Any $\mathbb{N}$-set A can be turned into an object in $\mathcal{SREL}$ by choosing all the actions of the family to be the action of A. In the same spirit, constructions on objects of $\mathbb{N}\mathcal{REL}$ can be turned into constructions on objects of $\mathcal{SREL}$ by applying them for each n. As specific constructions, we define: $!(A_n)_{n\in} = (!_nA_n)_{n\in}$ and $?(A_n)_{n\in} = (?_nA_n)_{n\in}$.

Theorem 2
$\mathcal{SREL}$ is a model of propositional (additive-free) SLL.

Proof. As for ELL, using a forgetful functor into $\mathcal{REL}$. □

[1] In a parallel work, B. Redmond [22] is developing a categorical interpretation of SLL. It seems that $\mathcal{SREL}$ can be obtained by applying one of his constructions. The relationships has to be investigated further.

3. Nets

We extend Danos-Regnier's notion of untyped proof-nets [9, 23] to a more liberal notion which contains the direct translation of second order multiplicative exponential LL.

Definition 5 (Proof-structure)
A *proof-structure* is a finite directed acyclic graph[2] whose nodes are defined together with an arity and a coarity, *i.e.* a given number of incident edges called the *premisses* of the node and a given number of emergent edges called the *conclusions* of the node. The valid nodes are the following:

nodes	*ax*	*cut*	$\otimes, \parr, ?c$	$1, \bot, ?w$	$!, ?d, ?p$
arity	0	2	2	0	1
coarity	2	0	1	1	1

We allow edges with a source but no target, they are called *conclusions* of the proof-structure.

Some edges are labelled with the ? symbol according to the following rules:

- conclusions of *ax*, 1, $\bot$, $\otimes$, $\parr$ and !-nodes are not labelled,
- conclusions of $?d$, $?c$, $?w$ and $?p$-nodes are ?-labelled,
- premisses of $?c$ and $?p$-nodes are ?-labelled.

Moreover, a proof-structure $\mathcal{R}$ has to satisfy the following two properties:

- *!-box condition:*
  - with every !-node n is associated a subgraph B^n of $\mathcal{R}$, such that one of the conclusions of B^n is the conclusion of n and every other conclusion of B^n (there might be no other conclusion) is the conclusion of a $?p$-node. B^n is called a *box* and it is represented by a rectangular frame. n is called the *main door* of B^n
  - with every $?p$-node p is associated the box B^n of some !-node n, such that the conclusion of p is conclusion of B^n. The node p is called an *auxiliary door* of B^n.
- *nesting condition:* two boxes are either disjoint or included one in the other.

We will often speak of a box, a node or an edge of a proof-structure $\mathcal{R}$ contained in a box B of $\mathcal{R}$. In case of nodes, we will not consider the doors of B as nodes contained in B. The *depth* of an edge is the number of boxes containing it. The *depth* of $\mathcal{R}$ is the maximal depth of its edges.

The ? labels are the only kind of typing we consider. It is somehow the heart of linear logic: the distinction between duplicable/erasable formulas and the others. The reader should notice that these labels introduce constraints

[2] When drawing a proof-structure we represent edges oriented up-down so that we may speak of moving upwardly or downwardly in the graph, and of nodes or edges "above" or "under" a given node/edge.

$$A ::= X \mid X^{\perp} \mid 1 \mid \perp \mid A \otimes A \mid A \parr A \mid !A \mid ?A \mid \forall X A \mid \exists X A$$

Figure 1. Second order LL formulas.

$$\frac{}{\vdash A, A^{\perp}}\,ax \qquad \frac{\vdash \Gamma, A \qquad \vdash \Delta, A^{\perp}}{\vdash \Gamma, \Delta}\,cut$$

$$\frac{\vdash \Gamma, A \qquad \vdash \Delta, B}{\vdash \Gamma, \Delta, A \otimes B}\,\otimes \qquad \frac{\vdash \Gamma, A, B}{\vdash \Gamma, A \parr B}\,\parr \qquad \frac{}{\vdash 1}\,1 \qquad \frac{\vdash \Gamma}{\vdash \Gamma, \perp}\,\perp$$

$$\frac{\vdash \Gamma, A}{\vdash ?\Gamma, !A}\,!f \qquad \frac{\vdash \Gamma, ?A, ?A}{\vdash \Gamma, ?A}\,?c \qquad \frac{\vdash \Gamma}{\vdash \Gamma, ?A}\,?w$$

$$\frac{\vdash \Gamma, A}{\vdash \Gamma, \forall X A}\,\forall \quad (X \notin \Gamma) \qquad \frac{\vdash \Gamma, A[^{B}/_{X}]}{\vdash \Gamma, \exists X A}\,\exists$$

Figure 2. ELL **rules.**

$$\frac{}{\vdash A, A^{\perp}}\,ax \qquad \frac{\vdash \Gamma, A \qquad \vdash \Delta, A^{\perp}}{\vdash \Gamma, \Delta}\,cut$$

$$\frac{\vdash \Gamma, A \qquad \vdash \Delta, B}{\vdash \Gamma, \Delta, A \otimes B}\,\otimes \qquad \frac{\vdash \Gamma, A, B}{\vdash \Gamma, A \parr B}\,\parr \qquad \frac{}{\vdash 1}\,1 \qquad \frac{\vdash \Gamma}{\vdash \Gamma, \perp}\,\perp$$

$$\frac{\vdash \Gamma, A}{\vdash ?\Gamma, !A}\,!f \qquad \frac{\vdash \Gamma, A, \ldots, A}{\vdash \Gamma, ?A}\,?m$$

$$\frac{\vdash \Gamma, A}{\vdash \Gamma, \forall X A}\,\forall \quad (X \notin \Gamma) \qquad \frac{\vdash \Gamma, A[^{B}/_{X}]}{\vdash \Gamma, \exists X A}\,\exists$$

Figure 3. SLL **rules.**

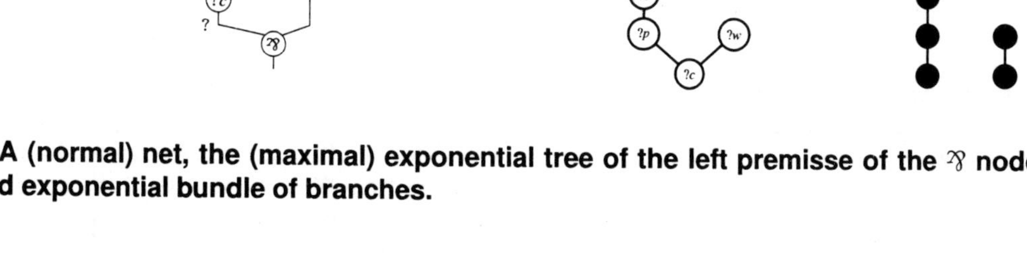

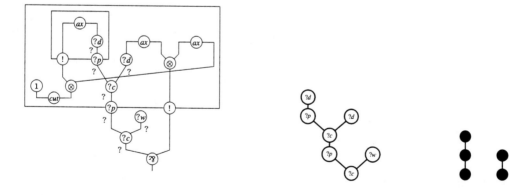

Figure 4. A (normal) net, the (maximal) exponential tree of the left premisse of the ⅋ node and the associated exponential bundle of branches.

on proof-structures: for example the conclusion of an *ax*-node cannot be the premise of a $?c$-node.

Definition 6 (Net)
Let $\mathcal{R}$ be a proof-structure and let $B_1, \ldots, B_k$ be the boxes of $\mathcal{R}$ with depth zero. With $\mathcal{R}$ is naturally associated an undirected graph $G_{\mathcal{R}}$ with a given set of pairs of edges:

- substitute for each box B_i ($1 \leq i \leq k$), a node with the conclusions of the doors of the box as conclusions,
- keep the other 0-depth nodes and forget the orientation,
- associate with every $⅋$-node (resp. $?c$-node) of $\mathcal{R}$ with depth zero the (unordered) pair of its premisses.

A switching S of $\mathcal{R}$ is the choice of an edge for every pair of $G_{\mathcal{R}}$. With each switching S is associated a subgraph $S(\mathcal{R})$ of $G_{\mathcal{R}}$: for every pair of $G_{\mathcal{R}}$, erase the edges of $G_{\mathcal{R}}$ which are selected by S.

We say that $\mathcal{R}$ is a *net* when:

- for every switching S of $\mathcal{R}$, $S(\mathcal{R})$ is acyclic,
- for every box B_i ($1 \leq i \leq k$), the proof-structure $\mathcal{R}_i$ contained in B_i is a net.

Due to the weak conditions we put on the way nodes can be used, we cannot guarantee that we have a way to reduce all cuts. This is strongly different from what happens with Danos-Regnier's untyped proof-nets where a weak notion of typing is enough to ensure reducibility of any *cut*-node.

The two edges premisses of a *cut*-node are *dual* when:

- they are conclusions of a $\otimes$-node and of a $⅋$-node,
- they are conclusions of a 1-node and of a $\perp$-node,
- one is conclusion of a !-node and the other one is ?-labelled.

Definition 7 (Deadlock)
A *cut*-node of a net is a *deadlock* when the premisses of the *cut*-node are not dual edges and none of the two is the conclusion of an *ax*-node.

Definition 8 (Cut-elimination)
The reduction steps are defined as usual [13]:

- *ax*-step: this step applies when one of the premisses of the *cut*-node is the conclusion of an *ax*-node. In this case one erases as usual both the *cut*-node and the *ax*-node[3].
- $⅋/\otimes$-step: for a cut between a $⅋$-node and a $\otimes$-node.
- $\perp/1$-step: for a cut between a $\perp$-node and a 1-node.
- $?d$-step: for a cut between a $?d$-node and a !-node.
- $?w$-step: for a cut between a $?w$-node and a !-node.
- $?c$-step: for a cut between a $?c$-node and a !-node.
- $?p$-step: for a cut between a $?p$-node and a !-node.

Proposition 2
If the procedure of cut-elimination cannot be applied to the net $\mathcal{R}$, then every cut-node of $\mathcal{R}$ is a deadlock (in particular, $\mathcal{R}$ might be cut-free). We call normal *such a net $\mathcal{R}$.*

[3]Notice that there is a choice when performing this step, in case both the premisses of the *cut*-node are premisses of an *ax*-node: clearly, the two possibilities yield the same graph after reduction.

Proposition 3 (Preservation of correction)
If $\mathcal{R}$ is a net and $\mathcal{R}$ reduces to $\mathcal{R}'$, then $\mathcal{R}'$ is a net.

Proof. $\mathcal{R}'$ is clearly a proof-structure. The fact that, moreover, $\mathcal{R}'$ is a net is standard (see [9]). □

We said that we are extending the Danos-Regnier's notion of untyped proof-nets. Indeed, a Danos-Regnier's untyped proof-net (see [9] for the precise definition) is a net: the edges labelled by $?I$ become ?-labelled and the other labels are erased.

Notice that cut-elimination *does not* hold for nets, for two different reasons:

- *Deadlocks*: normal nets might contain cuts. Take two cut-free nets and connect them by means of a *cut*-node whose premisses are not dual. Such a graph is a normal net which is not cut-free: the *cut*-node cannot be eliminated according to definition 8.
- *The calculus is untyped*: some nets have no normal form. Danos-Regnier's untyped proof-nets were able to encode the untyped λ-calculus. This is still the case for our nets, which means that the cut-elimination procedure applied to the nets corresponding to the fixpoints of the untyped λ-calculus never leads to a normal net.

Proposition 4 (Confluence)
If a net $\mathcal{R}$ reduces to $\mathcal{R}_1$ and $\mathcal{R}_2$ by some sequences of reductions, then there exists a net $\mathcal{R}'$ such that both $\mathcal{R}_1$ and $\mathcal{R}_2$ can be reduced to $\mathcal{R}'$.

Remark 1
Proof-nets were introduced in [13]. For additive-free second order LL, the notion currently used (and that we consider here) is obtained by combining [13, 9, 14], like in [24].

With every proof-net is naturally associated a net: simply forget formulas and erase the quantifier nodes. Notice that such a net is always deadlock-free. Conversely, it is sometimes possible to label a (deadlock-free) net by means of LL formulas (in such a way that the type of a ?-labelled edge is of the shape $?A$) thus obtaining a proof-net: when this is the case we say that the net is *typable*.

With every sequent calculus proof (of additive-free second order LL) is associated a proof-net, and thus a net.

Proposition 5 (Simulation)
If $\mathcal{R}$ is a proof-net, let us denote by $\mathcal{R}^-$ the net associated with $\mathcal{R}$. If $\mathcal{R}^-$ reduces to $\mathcal{S}^-$ in one reduction step then $\mathcal{R}$ reduces to $\mathcal{S}$ in at least *one reduction step.*

Proof. This is because cut-elimination for proof-nets does not depend on the formulas labelling the edges of the proof-nets (only the nodes matter). One might have more than one step from $\mathcal{R}$ to $\mathcal{S}$ because of the presence of second order nodes in proof-nets (which are not present in the corresponding nets). □

Proposition 6

- *The reduct of any typable net is typable (thus deadlock-free).*
- *Every typable net is strongly normalizing.*
- *The normal form of a typable net is unique and cut-free.*

4. Untyped ELL and SLL

We are going to define restrictions of nets corresponding to (untyped versions of) the systems ELL [15] and SLL [17].

Definition 9 (Exponential tree)
An *exponential tree* is a tree whose nodes are: binary $?c$-nodes, unary $?p$-nodes, 0-ary $?w$-nodes and 0-ary $?d$-nodes.

Let a be a ?-labelled edge of the net $\mathcal{R}$, its *exponential tree* is given according to the node it is conclusion of:

- for a $?d$-node, the exponential tree of a is (?d)
- for a $?w$-node, the exponential tree of a is (?w)
- for a $?p$-node whose premisse is a', the exponential tree of a is obtained by adding a $?p$-node under the root of the exponential tree of a':

- for a $?c$-node whose premisses are a' and a'', the exponential tree of a is obtained by adding a $?c$-node under the roots of the exponential trees of a' and a'':

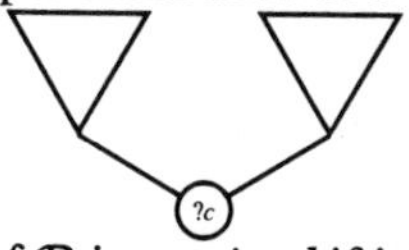

An exponential tree of $\mathcal{R}$ is *maximal* if it is the exponential tree of a ?-labelled edge which is not a premisse of a $?p$ or $?c$-node in $\mathcal{R}$.

Definition 10 (Exponential bundle of branches)
An *exponential bundle of branches* is a multiset of non-empty total orders (*i.e.* "filiform" trees or *branches*).

The exponential bundle of branches associated with an exponential tree is obtained in the following way:

- if the root of the tree is a $?d$-node, then (the tree is reduced to this $?d$-node and) the bundle is reduced to one branch which is itself reduced to one node
- if the root of the tree is a $?p$-node under a tree $\mathcal{T}$, we consider the bundle $\mathcal{F}$ associated with $\mathcal{T}$ and we add a node under each branch
- if the root of the tree is a $?w$-node, then (the tree is reduced to this $?w$-node and) the associated bundle is empty
- if the root of the tree is a $?c$-node under the trees $\mathcal{T}_1$ and $\mathcal{T}_2$, and if the associated bundles are $\mathcal{F}_1$ and $\mathcal{F}_2$, we obtain the (multiset) union of $\mathcal{F}_1$ and $\mathcal{F}_2$.

This mainly corresponds to extracting the multiset of branches ending with $?d$-nodes in the tree.

The exponential bundle of branches of an edge of a net is the exponential bundle of branches associated with its exponential tree. The exponential bundles of branches of a net are the exponential bundles associated with its maximal exponential trees (see figure 4 for an example).

Definition 11 (Untyped ELL and SLL)
The systems uELL and uSLL are defined as restrictions on nets:

- a net is in uELL if its exponential bundles of branches are all of the shape:

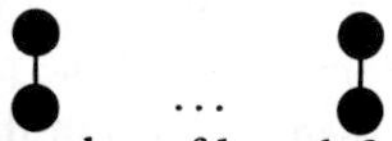

that is with only branches of length 2.
- a net is in uSLL if its exponential bundles of branches are all of one of the following two shapes:

that is either with only branches of length 1 or the bundle containing exactly one branch of length 2.

These constraints on nets are not preserved by arbitrary reduction, but it is possible to define a strategy which preserves them: each time we reduce a cut with a ?-labelled premisse, we reduce the newly created cuts until the exponential tree of the original ?-labelled edge has been completely destroyed. In particular, if $\mathcal{R} \in u$ELL (resp. $\mathcal{R} \in u$SLL) then its normal form is in uELL (resp. uSLL).

Proposition 7 (Complexity of representable functions)

- *f is an elementary time function from integers to integers iff it is representable in uELL.*
- *P is a polynomial time predicate over binary integers iff it is representable in uSLL.*

5. Semantics

By adapting the notion of obsessional clique of section 2.2 to the untyped syntactical setting we have developed in the previous section, it is now possible to define models of uELL and uSLL.

5.1. A space for untyped obsessionality

We define *points* by the following grammar:

$$x ::= 1 \mid \bot \mid x \otimes x \mid x \parr x \mid !\mu \mid ?\mu \qquad \mu ::= [x_1, \ldots, x_n]$$

where $[x_1, \ldots, x_n]$ denotes a finite multiset of points. D is the set of all points[4], and $?D$ is the subset of D containing only elements of the shape $?\mu$. A *clique* is a subset of D.

We define the dual $\overline{x}$ of the point x by $\overline{1} = \bot$, $\overline{\bot} = 1$, $\overline{x \otimes y} = \overline{x} \parr \overline{y}$, $\overline{x \parr y} = \overline{x} \otimes \overline{y}$, $\overline{![x_1, \ldots, x_n]} = ?[\overline{x_1}, \ldots, \overline{x_n}]$ and $\overline{?[x_1, \ldots, x_n]} = ![\overline{x_1}, \ldots, \overline{x_n}]$.

[4]We can also define $D_0 = \{1, \bot\}$, $D_{n+1} = D_n \cup \{(\otimes, x, y) \mid (x, y) \in D_n^2\} \cup \{(\parr, x, y) \mid (x, y) \in D_n^2\} \cup \{(!, \mu) \mid \mu \in \mathcal{M}_f(D_n)\} \cup \{(?, \mu) \mid \mu \in \mathcal{M}_f(D_n)\}$, and $D = \cup_{n=0}^{\infty} D_n$.

Definition 12 (Experiment)
An *experiment* of a net $\mathcal{R}$ is defined by induction on the depth of $\mathcal{R}$. It is a labelling of the 0-depth edges with elements of D such that:

- if the edge is ?-labelled, the label is an element of $?D$
- if x is the label of a conclusion of an *ax*-node, the label of the other one is $\overline{x}$
- if x is the label of a premisse of a *cut*-node, the label of the other one is $\overline{x}$
- if x is the label of the conclusion of a 1-node (resp. $\perp$-node) then $x = 1$ (resp. $x = \perp$)
- if x and y are the labels of the premisses of a $\otimes$-node (resp. $⅋$-node) then the label of the conclusion is $x \otimes y$ (resp. $x ⅋ y$)
- if x is the label of the premisse of a $?d$-node then the label of the conclusion is $?[x]$
- if x is the label of the conclusion of a $?w$-node then $x = ?[]$
- if x and y are the labels of the premisses of a $?c$-node, they have the shape $x = ?\mu$ and $y = ?\nu$, and the label of the conclusion must be $?(\mu + \nu)$
- if x is the label of the conclusion of a !-node and $x_1, \ldots, x_n$ are the labels of the conclusions of the auxiliary doors of the corresponding box then we must have $x = ![y_1, \ldots, y_k]$ and there must exist k experiments of the content of the box associating the labels $y_i, ?\mu_1^i, \ldots, ?\mu_n^i$ with the conclusions of the content of the box with the property $x_j = ?(\mu_j^1 + \cdots + \mu_j^k)$ for $1 \leq j \leq n$.

The *result* of an experiment is the point $(\cdots((x_1 ⅋ x_2) ⅋ x_3)\ldots) ⅋ x_n$ where $x_1, \ldots, x_n$ are the labels of the conclusions of the net. The semantics $[\![\mathcal{R}]\!]$ of a net $\mathcal{R}$ is the set of the results of its experiments, thus a clique.

An *h-experiment* is an experiment which takes exactly h experiments in the content of each box.

Theorem 3 (Correctness)
If $\mathcal{R}$ reduces to $\mathcal{R}'$ then $[\![\mathcal{R}]\!] = [\![\mathcal{R}']\!]$.

Proof. See [13] for coherent semantics, the relational case we consider here is almost the same. □

Remark 2
A 1-experiment is obtained by putting exactly one label on each conclusion of each *ax*-node of a net (in fact a pair of dual labels for the pairs of conclusions of the *ax*-nodes), and by propagating labels in a top-down way (in particular when crossing a box, we just propagate labels with $x \mapsto ![x]$ for the main door). This is always possible for a cut-free net and thus experiments of cut-free nets always exist. This entails that the semantics of a net having a cut-free normal form is never empty.

Definition 13 (Action)
Let $t \geq 0$ be a natural number, the *t-action* on D is the function $(k, x) \mapsto (x)_t^{(k)}$ from $\mathbb{N}^* \times D$ to D given by:

$$(1)_t^{(k)} = 1 \qquad (\perp)_t^{(k)} = \perp$$

$$(x \otimes y)_t^{(k)} = (x)_t^{(k)} \otimes (y)_t^{(k)}$$

$$(x ⅋ y)_t^{(k)} = (x)_t^{(k)} ⅋ (y)_t^{(k)}$$

$$(![x_1, \ldots, x_n])_t^{(k)} = \begin{cases} ![(x_1)_t^{(k)}, \ldots, (x_n)_t^{(k)}] & \text{if } n \leq t \\ ![k(x_1)_t^{(k)}, \ldots, k(x_n)_t^{(k)}] & \text{if } n > t \end{cases}$$

$$(?[x_1, \ldots, x_n])_t^{(k)} = \begin{cases} ?[(x_1)_t^{(k)}, \ldots, (x_n)_t^{(k)}] & \text{if } n \leq t \\ ?[k(x_1)_t^{(k)}, \ldots, k(x_n)_t^{(k)}] & \text{if } n > t \end{cases}$$

A clique c is *t-obsessional* if $\forall x \in c$, $\forall k \in \mathbb{N}^*$, $(x)_t^{(k)} \in c$. A clique c is *obsessional from* t if for any $t' \geq t$, c is t'-obsessional.

5.2. Models of uELL and uSLL

If we define D_i as D equipped with the i-action, then D_0 and $(D_i)_{i\in}$ are *reflexive objects* respectively in $\mathcal{OREL}$ and $\mathcal{SREL}$. Meaning that 1, $\perp$, $D_0 \otimes D_0$, $D_0 ⅋ D_0$, $!D_0$ and $?D_0$ are retracts of D_0 in $\mathcal{OREL}$ (and the same for $(D_i)_{i\in}$ in $\mathcal{SREL}$).

Proposition 8 (Models)

- *0-obsessional cliques in D are a model of uELL.*
- *Cliques which are obsessional from some t are a model of uSLL.*

5.3. Relative completeness

We are going to prove a converse of this last proposition. While every proof in uELL/uSLL is interpreted by an obsessional clique (0-obsessional for uELL and obsessional from some t for uSLL), it is clear that there exist obsessional cliques which are not the interpretation of a proof of the corresponding system (uELL or uSLL) mainly because the relational model is not complete for LL (and even not for MLL which is included in both uELL and uSLL and for which any clique is obsessional). Nevertheless, we can ask this question for a clique for which we already know that it is the interpretation of an LL-proof: if this clique is obsessional, is it the interpretation of a uELL/uSLL-proof? A positive answer is what we call *relative completeness* and it will be the main result of the paper: theorem 4.

Definition 14 (h-point)
For a given $h \in \mathbb{N}$, *h-points* are the elements of D inductively given by:

- 1 and $\perp$ are h-points
- $x \otimes y$ and $x ⅋ y$ are h-points if x and y are h-points
- $?[x_1, \ldots, x_n]$ is an h-point if x_1, ..., x_n are h-points
- $![x_1, \ldots, x_n]$ is an h-point if $n = h$ and x_1, ..., x_n are h-points

Lemma 1 (h**-points and** h**-experiments)**
Let $\mathcal{R}$ be a cut-free net and x be the result of an experiment e of $\mathcal{R}$, x is an h-point iff e is an h-experiment.

Definition 15 ($?$**-trees)**
Let x be an element of D, $\mathcal{T}(x)$ is the subset of $\mathbb{N}$ defined inductively by:

- $\mathcal{T}(1) = \mathcal{T}(\bot) = \emptyset$
- $\mathcal{T}(x \otimes y) = \mathcal{T}(x \parr y) = \mathcal{T}(x) \cup \mathcal{T}(y)$
- $\mathcal{T}(![x_1, \ldots, x_n]) = \mathcal{T}(x_1) \cup \cdots \cup \mathcal{T}(x_n)$
- $\mathcal{T}(?[x_1, \ldots, x_n]) = \{n\} \cup \mathcal{T}(x_1) \cup \cdots \cup \mathcal{T}(x_n)$

Lemma 2 (Action on $?$**-trees)**
Let x be an element of D, $h > 0$ and $t \geq 0$ be two natural numbers, we have:

$$\mathcal{T}((x)_t^{(h)}) =$$
$$\{hn \mid n \in \mathcal{T}(x) \wedge n > t\} \cup \{n \mid n \in \mathcal{T}(x) \wedge n \leq t\}$$

With the base h representation of a number n (denoted by $\overline{n}^h$), it is possible to associate an exponential bundle of branches. If $\overline{n}^h = n_k \ldots n_0$, we consider the bundle containing $n_0 + \cdots + n_k$ branches and: for each $0 \leq i \leq k$, we have n_i branches of length $i + 1$. For example, $\overline{11}^3 = 102$ and the corresponding exponential bundle is:

The contraction size $cosize(\mathcal{R})$ of a net $\mathcal{R}$ is the maximum number of branches of its exponential bundles of branches. In particular, if $\mathcal{R}$ is a net associated with a sequent calculus proof π in SLL, its contraction size is the maximal width of the $?m$-rules of π.

Lemma 3 (Computation of bundles of branches)
Let $\mathcal{R}$ be a cut-free net, if $h > cosize(\mathcal{R})$ and if x is an h-point of $[\![\mathcal{R}]\!]$ then $\mathcal{T}(x)$ is the set of all n such that $\overline{n}^h$ is an exponential bundle of branches of $\mathcal{R}$.

Proof. Using $h > cosize(\mathcal{R})$, we first show that, in any h-experiment, the size of the multiset associated with a $?$-labelled edge is n where $\overline{n}^h$ corresponds to the exponential bundle of branches of this edge.

We can now verify, by induction on $\mathcal{R}$, that if x is the result of an experiment e of $\mathcal{R}$ then $\mathcal{T}(x)$ contains exactly the sizes of the labels associated (by some experiment used to build e, either at depth 0 or inside a box) with the $?$-labelled edges of $\mathcal{R}$ which are not premisse of a $?p$ or $?c$-node. We conclude with lemma 1. $\square$

We have already seen (remark 2) how 1-experiments are built. It is immediate that the result x of such an experiment is a 1-point with $\forall n \in \mathcal{T}(x),\ n \leq cosize(\mathcal{R})$.

More generally, starting from a 1-experiment, we can repeat it h times in each box. This is always possible for a cut-free net and gives an h-experiment thus an h-point.

Theorem 4 (Relative completeness)
Let $\mathcal{R}$ be a cut-free net,

- *$\mathcal{R} \in u$ELL iff $[\![\mathcal{R}]\!]$ is 0-obsessional*
- *$\mathcal{R} \in u$SLL iff $[\![\mathcal{R}]\!]$ is obsessional from some t*

Proof. We have already seen (see proposition 8) that if $\mathcal{R} \in u$ELL then $[\![\mathcal{R}]\!]$ is 0-obsessional.

Let x be the result of a 1-experiment of $\mathcal{R}$ and let h be a natural number such that $h > cosize(\mathcal{R})$. If $[\![\mathcal{R}]\!]$ is 0-obsessional, one has $(x)_0^{(h)} \in [\![\mathcal{R}]\!]$ which is an h-point. If $\mathcal{R}$ is not in uELL, then it contains an exponential bundle of branches such that:

- a branch contains at least three nodes: by lemma 3 there exists $n \in \mathcal{T}((x)_0^{(h)})$ such that $\overline{n}^h = n_k \ldots n_0$ with $n_j \geq 1$ ($j \geq 2$) thus $n \geq h^2$. This is impossible since, by lemma 2, the elements of $\mathcal{T}((x)_0^{(h)})$ are bounded by $h \cdot cosize(\mathcal{R}) < h^2$.
- a branch has length 1: by lemma 3 there exists $n \in \mathcal{T}((x)_0^{(h)})$ such that $\overline{n}^h = n_k \ldots n_0$ with $n_0 \geq 1$. This is impossible, by lemma 2, since the sizes of the multisets of $(x)_0^{(h)}$ are all multiples of h.

We have already seen (see proposition 8) that if $\mathcal{R} \in u$SLL then $[\![\mathcal{R}]\!]$ is obsessional from some t.

Conversely, there exists some $t > cosize(\mathcal{R})$ such that $[\![\mathcal{R}]\!]$ is t-obsessional. Let x be the t-point obtained by repeating t times in each box a 1-experiment of $\mathcal{R}$. By lemma 3, the elements of $\bigcup_{x\ t\text{-point} \in [\![\mathcal{R}]\!]} \mathcal{T}(x)$ are bounded. Since x is a t-point, we can easily check that $(x)_t^{(h)}$ is also a t-point (for any $h \in \mathbb{N}^*$). If we consider the family of t-points $((x)_t^{(h)})_{h \in\ ^*}$ of $[\![\mathcal{R}]\!]$, boundedness entails by lemma 2 that $\forall n \in \mathcal{T}(x),\ n \leq t$. By lemma 3, any exponential bundle of branches in $\mathcal{R}$ corresponds to a natural number n (with $\overline{n}^t = n_k \ldots n_0$) belonging to $\mathcal{T}(x)$. Since $n \leq t$, we have either $k = 1$, $n_1 = 1$ and $n_0 = 0$, or $k = 0$. So that $\mathcal{R}$ is in uSLL. $\square$

The restriction to cut-free nets is perfectly reasonable since the encoding of elementary/polynomial time algorithms is done with typable nets. As shown in proposition 6, the reduction of such nets leads to cut-free normal forms (and by correctness of the model, the interpretation of a net and of its normal form are the same).

6. Conclusion

Let us first comment on different choices we made:

- The multiplicative-exponential setting is powerful enough to express elementary/polynomial time in our untyped context. However it would be possible to add the *additive connectives* in order to simplify the encoding of certain computations. In the case of ELL, this can be done without any problem (in the spirit of [10]) and leads to an extension of the relative completeness result. In the case of SLL, things are much more complicated and the interaction between additive and exponential connectives is not clear enough (up to now) to get relative completeness.

- The model we consider is based on the relational model of LL. The use of "multiset based" *coherent semantics* would change nothing except that we would have to define the various constructions applied to the coherence relation. Our choice of the relational setting is only justified by the induced simplicity of the presentation.
- Concerning subsystems of LL for *polynomial time*, instead of SLL, a very natural choice would be LLL [15]. However we would face two different problems. First, relative completeness (as stated here) for LLL (as given in [15]) would fail for coherent semantics. The second problem is that our approach by obsessionality gives an analysis of proof-nets according to their exponential trees without any consideration about the different boxes crossed by these trees. In LLL, the "at most one auxiliary door" constraint would require to compare the boxes with which the $?p$-nodes are associated and this is something we are not able to do at the moment.

Concerning the other extensions of our work, the most natural one is to try to find relative completeness results with other models, other subsystems of LL (trying to say something for LLL for example), ... Moreover many systems for bounded time complexity are defined as subsystems of the λ-calculus and it is natural to address the question of relative completeness in the setting of the λ-calculus instead of LL.

Another direction is related to the main defect of relative completeness: it tells us something about the obsessional elements of the model which are interpretations of proofs of LL but *nothing* for the other obsessional elements. What would be very nice, in the context of implicit computational complexity, is to find a property which is both "absolute for complexity" (meaning that any element of the model satisfying the property would be in a given complexity class, this element being the interpretation of a proof or not) and relatively complete.

Acknowledgments. We would like to thank P. Baillot who has been our reference for various informations about ELL, LLL, SLL, ... and who suggested us to use an untyped setting for encoding second order. We also thank P. Boudes, T. Ehrhard, D. Mazza and P.-A. Melliès for discussions related to the topics of this paper.

References

[1] A. Asperti. Light affine logic. In *LICS*. IEEE Computer Society Press, 1998.

[2] A. Asperti and L. Roversi. Intuitionistic light affine logic. *ACM Trans. on Computational Logic*, 1(3):1–39, 2002.

[3] P. Baillot. Stratified coherent spaces: a denotational semantics for light linear logic. *Theoretical Computer Science*, 318(1–2):29–55, 2004.

[4] S. J. Bellantoni and S. A. Cook. A new recursion-theoretic characterization of the polytime functions. *Computational Complexity*, 2:97–110, 1992.

[5] S. R. Buss. *Bounded Arithmetic*. Ph.D. thesis, Princeton University, 1985.

[6] A. Cobham. The intrinsic computational difficulty of functions. In *International Congress for Logic, Methodology, and the Philosophy of Science*. North-Holland, 1964.

[7] S. Cook. The complexity of theorem proving procedures. In *Conference Record of Third Annual ACM Symposium on Theory of Computing*, pages 151–158, 1971.

[8] U. Dal Lago and M. Hofmann. Quantitative models and implicit complexity. In *Proceedings of FSTTCS*, volume 3821 of *LNCS*. Springer, 2005.

[9] V. Danos. *La Logique Linéaire appliquée à l'étude de divers processus de normalisation (principalement du λ-calcul)*. Ph.D. thesis, Université Paris VII, 1990.

[10] V. Danos and J.-B. Joinet. Linear logic and elementary time. *Information and Computation*, 183(1):123–137, 2003.

[11] D. de Carvalho. Ph.D. thesis, Université Aix-Marseille II. In preparation.

[12] R. Fagin. Generalized first-order spectra and polynomial-time recognizable sets. In *Complexity and computation, SIAM-AMS Proceedings*, pages 43–73, 1974.

[13] J.-Y. Girard. Linear logic. *Theoretical Computer Science*, 50:1–102, 1987.

[14] J.-Y. Girard. Quantifiers in linear logic II. In *Nuovi problemi della logica e della filosofia della scienza*. CLUEB, 1991.

[15] J.-Y. Girard. Light linear logic. *Information and Computation*, 143(2):175–204, 1998.

[16] J.-Y. Girard, A. Scedrov, and P. J. Scott. Bounded linear logic: a modular approach to polynomial time computability. *Theoretical Computer Science*, 97:1–66, 1992.

[17] Y. Lafont. Soft linear logic and polynomial time. *Theoretical Computer Science*, 318(1–2):163–180, 2004.

[18] D. Leivant and J.-Y. Marion. Lambda calculus characterizations of poly-time. *Fundamenta Informaticae*, 19(1–2):167–184, 1993.

[19] H. Mairson and K. Terui. On the computational complexity of cut-elimination in linear logic. In *Proceedings of ICTCS*, volume 2841 of *LNCS*, pages 23–36. Springer, 2003.

[20] D. Mazza. *Logica Lineare e Complessità Computazionale*. Tesi di laurea, Università di Roma Tre, 2002.

[21] A. Murawski and C.-H. L. Ong. Discreet games, light affine logic and ptime computation. In *CSL*, volume 1862 of *LNCS*, pages 55–92. Springer, 2000.

[22] B. Redmond. *Multiplexor categories and models of soft linear logic*. Ph.D. thesis, University of Ottawa. In preparation.

[23] L. Regnier. *Lambda-Calcul et Réseaux*. Ph.D. thesis, Université Paris VII, 1992.

[24] L. Tortora de Falco. *Réseaux, cohérence et expériences obsessionnelles*. Ph.D. thesis, Université Paris VII, 2000.

[25] L. Tortora de Falco. Obsessional experiments for linear logic proof-nets. *Mathematical Structures in Computer Science*, 13(6):799–855, 2003.

A Conditional Lower Bound for a System of Constant-Depth Proofs with Modular Connectives

Alexis Maciel
Clarkson University
Department of Computer Science
Potsdam, NY 13699-5815, U.S.A.
alexis@clarkson.edu

Toniann Pitassi
University of Toronto
Department of Computer Science
Toronto, Ontario, Canada
toni@cs.toronto.edu

Abstract

It is known that constant-depth Frege proofs of some tautologies require exponential size. No such lower bound result is known for more general proof systems. We consider Sequent Calculus proofs in which formulas can contain modular connectives and only the cut formulas are restricted to be of constant depth. Under a plausible hardness assumption concerning small-depth Boolean circuits, we prove an exponential lower bound for such proofs. We prove this lower bound directly from the computational hardness assumption. By using the same approach, we obtain the following additional results. We provide a much simpler proof of a known (unconditional) lower bound in the case where only conjunctions and disjunctions are allowed. We establish a conditional exponential separation between the power of constant-depth proofs that use different modular connectives. Finally, under a plausible hardness assumption concerning the polynomial-time hierarchy, we show that the hierarchy G_i^* of quantified propositional proof systems does not collapse.

1. Introduction

Restricted proof systems have attracted a lot of attention, in large part due to their role in automated theorem provers. For example, Haken [4] showed that the Pigeonhole Principle, a simple, natural and ubiquitous tautology, requires exponential-size Resolution proofs. This means that any theorem prover that works by constructing a Resolution proof—and that is virtually all propositional theorem provers—will require exponential time to prove the Pigeonhole Principle, no matter how efficient it is at finding a proof.

Various extensions of Resolution have also been investigated. For example, constant-depth Frege proofs were also shown unable to prove the Pigeonhole Principle in subexponential size [1, 11, 14]. And Cutting Planes were shown to have no subexponential proof of a certain basic principle concerning colorings of undirected graphs [6, 15].

To this day, however, no lower bound result is known for any proof system more general than constant-depth Frege. For example, a natural extension of constant-depth Frege is to permit the use of modulo m connectives in the proofs, for some constant m. We call this proof system $\mathrm{ACC}^0[m]$-Frege, because of its relation to the circuit class $\mathrm{ACC}^0[m]$.

In this article, we consider a variant of $\mathrm{ACC}^0[m]$-Frege and prove a lower bound for this proof system under a plausible hardness assumption concerning $\mathrm{ACC}^0[m]$ circuits.

The proofs that we consider are tree-like Sequent Calculus proofs in which formulas contain conjunctions, disjunctions, negations and modulo m connectives of unbounded arity and the cut formulas are restricted to be of constant depth. We call this system $\mathrm{ACC}^0[m]$-PK*. This is a natural proof system that has at least one advantage over the usual definition of constant-depth Frege systems: it is complete for all tautologies, not just constant-depth formulas.

Note that the power of $\mathrm{ACC}^0[m]$-PK* is closely related to the power of $\mathrm{ACC}^0[m]$-Frege: over constant-depth tautologies, the two systems are polynomially equivalent. This means that for any constant-depth tautology, there is a polynomial relation between the size of the smallest $\mathrm{ACC}^0[m]$-PK* proof and the size of the smallest $\mathrm{ACC}^0[m]$-Frege proof.

The hardness assumption concerns $\mathrm{ACC}^0[m]$ circuits. It is known that $\mathrm{ACC}^0[p]$ circuits require exponential size to compute the modulo q function, if p and q are distinct primes. It is also known that $\mathrm{ACC}^0[p]$ circuits of subexponential size can compute this function correctly on at most a $1/2 + o(1)$ fraction of the inputs [16, 17]. In the case of AC^0 circuits, the hardness result is much stronger: AC^0 circuits of depth d and subexponential size can approximate the modulo q function on at most a $1/2 + 1/2^{n^{1/(d+1)}}$ frac-

1043-6871/06 $20.00 © 2006 IEEE

tion of the inputs [5]. Since modulo p gates are known not to be useful in the (exact) computation of the modulo q function [16], it is natural to conjecture that a stronger hardness results also holds for $\mathrm{ACC}^0[p]$ circuits; that is, that $\mathrm{ACC}^0[p]$ circuits of depth d and subexponential size cannot compute the modulo q function (or some other polynomial-size $\mathrm{ACC}^0[q]$ function) correctly on more than a $1/2 + 1/2^{n^{1/(d+1)}}$ fraction of the inputs. In fact, it also seems likely that if q is a prime that does not divide m, then there is an $\mathrm{ACC}^0[q]$ function that cannot be computed correctly by depth-d $\mathrm{ACC}^0[m]$ circuits of subexponential size on more than a $1/2 + 1/2^{n^{1/(d+1)}}$ fraction of the inputs.

It is under this last assumption that we show that $\mathrm{ACC}^0[m]$-PK* proofs of a variant of the Pigeonhole Principle must be of exponential size. Let q be a prime that does not divide m. The tautology is defined by replacing each of the variables of the Pigeonhole Principle by an AND-OR-NOT formula expressing an $\mathrm{ACC}^0[q]$ function Hard_q that is hard to approximate by $\mathrm{ACC}^0[m]$ circuits. Each of these formulas is over a separate subset of the original propositional variables. We call this tautology $\mathrm{PHP}(\mathrm{Hard}_q)$.

As far as we know, this is the first known lower bound result for an extension of constant-depth Frege proofs under an assumption seemingly weaker than NP not closed under complementation. And note that size-s $\mathrm{ACC}^0[m]$-PK* proofs of $\mathrm{PHP}(\mathrm{Hard}_q)$ imply size-s $\mathrm{ACC}^0[m]$-Frege proofs of the Pigeonhole Principle. Therefore, our new lower bound is a necessary condition for a lower bound on the size of $\mathrm{ACC}^0[m]$-Frege proof of the Pigeonhole Principle.

We now say a word about the approach we use to obtain our lower bound result. The Pigeonhole Principle lower bound for AC^0-Frege was obtained by adapting the technique used to prove that AC^0 circuits require exponential size to compute the parity function [5]. Knowing that when p and q are distinct primes $\mathrm{ACC}^0[p]$ circuits require exponential size to compute the modulo q function [16], it is natural to hope that the technique behind that circuit lower bound might be useful in proving a lower bound for $\mathrm{ACC}^0[p]$-Frege proofs. Unfortunately, attempts at adapting this circuit lower bound technique to prove the corresponding proof complexity lower bound have been unsuccessful, despite considerable effort.

On the other hand, the lower bounds for the Cutting Planes proof system were obtained by using circuit lower bounds directly, not the underlying techniques. This approach relies on the fact that the Cutting Planes proof system has the interpolation property: small Cutting Planes proofs of tautologies of a certain type yield small circuits computing a function related to the tautology. A lower bound on the size of these circuits then implies a lower bound on the size of the proofs. Unfortunately, constant-depth Frege, and all of its extensions, probably do not have the interpolation property, as this would imply that Blum integers can be factored in time 2^{n^ε} for arbitrary small ε [2].

Our lower bound result for $\mathrm{ACC}^0[m]$-PK* is obtained by using the above-mentioned circuit hardness conjecture directly but not through the interpolation method. Instead, we essentially show that the cut formulas, which are $\mathrm{ACC}^0[m]$ formulas, are unable to help the proof figure out the value of the Hard_q formulas contained in the $\mathrm{PHP}(\mathrm{Hard}_q)$ tautology. In some sense, the proof then reduces to a cut-free proof of the Pigeonhole Principle and it is known that such proofs have exponential size.

By using the same approach, we obtain several additional results. First, we apply the lower bound technique AC^0-PK*. This leads to a much simpler proof of the known (unconditional) result that AC^0-PK* proofs of $\mathrm{PHP}(\mathrm{MOD}_2)$ must have exponential size.

Second, we establish a conditional exponential separation between the power of constant-depth proofs that use different modular connectives. In particular, we show that under the assumption that some $\mathrm{ACC}^0[q]$ function cannot be approximated by $\mathrm{ACC}^0[m]$ circuits, there exists a tautology that has quasipolynomial-size $\mathrm{ACC}^0[q]$-PK* proofs, but that requires exponential-size $\mathrm{ACC}^0[m]$-PK* proofs.

Finally, we apply our approach to Sequent Calculus style proofs systems for quantified Boolean formulas. The system G introduced by Krajíček and Pudlák [9] and given in its present form by Cook and Morioka [3], is a proof system for reasoning about quantified Boolean formulas. The system G_i^* is a subsystem of G obtained by restricting the cut rule to formulas with at most i alternations of quantifiers. For each i, the G_i^* proof system is essentially a nonuniform version of Buss's well-studied bounded arithmetic system S_2^i. We show that the G_i^* hierarchy does not collapse, under a hardness assumption about the polynomial-time hierarchy.

The rest of the article is organized as follows. In Section 2, we provide definitions and background, including a precise definition of the proof systems. In Section 3, we state our main result, the conditional lower bound for $\mathrm{ACC}^0[m]$-PK* proofs. In Sections 4 and 5, we prove the lower bound for the simpler but representative case of AC^0-PK*. The lower bound proof proceeds in two parts. First, in Section 4, we reduce the proof complexity lower bound to a lower bound on the search complexity of a certain problem in a decision tree model. Then, in Section 5, we present the proof of the decision tree lower bound. In Section 6, we prove the separation results for $\mathrm{ACC}^0[m]$-PK* proofs. In Section 7, we present our results concerning the hierarchy G_i^* of quantified propositional proof systems. We conclude, in Section 7, with a discussion of further work.

2. Definitions and Background

2.1. The Propositional Sequent Calculus

First we define the Sequent Calculus propositional proof system for AND, OR, NOT and modular connectives.

The formulas of the system are defined as usual but with connectives of unbounded arity. For example, $\vee(A_1, \ldots, A_n)$ denotes the logical OR of the multiset consisting of $A_1, \ldots, A_n$. Similarly for the AND connective. Thus commutativity of the connectives is implicit. The modular connectives $\oplus_{m,b}$, for $0 \leq b < m$, are interpreted to be true if the sum of their arguments is congruent to b modulo m. In what follows, we will omit the m subscript and simply write $\oplus_b$ when there is no confusion possible.

The proof system operates on *sequents*, which are sets of formulas of the form $A_1, \ldots, A_r \rightarrow B_1, \ldots, B_t$. The intended meaning of the sequent $\Gamma \rightarrow \Delta$ is that the conjunction of the formulas in Γ implies the disjunction of the formulas in Δ.

A proof of a sequent S is normally a tree of sequents such that the root of the tree is S, the leaves of the tree are initial sequents and every non-leaf sequent in the tree follows from its children by one of the rules of inference. A sequent calculus proof can also be a directed acyclic graph (dag) with similar properties.

The *initial sequents* are of the following form: $x \rightarrow x$ where x is a propositional variable; $\rightarrow \wedge()$; $\vee() \rightarrow$; $\rightarrow \oplus_0()$; and $\oplus_b() \rightarrow$, for $1 \leq b < m$.

The rules of inference are as follows. First we have simple structural rules such as weakening (formulas can always be added to the left or to the right of a sequent), contraction (two copies of the same formula on the same side of a sequent can be replaced by one), and permutation (formulas on one side of a sequent can be reordered).

The remaining rules are the cut rule and logical rules that allow us to introduce each connective on both the left side and the right side of sequents. With the cut rule, we can derive $\Gamma \rightarrow \Delta$ from $\Gamma, A \rightarrow \Delta$ and $\Gamma \rightarrow A, \Delta$. The formula A is called the *cut formula*. The logical rules are:

- (Negation-left) From $\Gamma \rightarrow A, \Delta$, derive $\neg A, \Gamma \rightarrow \Delta$.
- (Negation-right) From $A, \Gamma \rightarrow \Delta$, derive $\Gamma \rightarrow \neg A, \Delta$.
- (And-left) From $A_1, \wedge(A_2, \ldots, A_n), \Gamma \rightarrow \Delta$, derive $\wedge(A_1, \ldots, A_n), \Gamma \rightarrow \Delta$.
- (And-right) From $\Gamma \rightarrow A_1, \Delta$ and $\Gamma \rightarrow \wedge(A_2, \ldots, A_n), \Delta$, derive $\Gamma \rightarrow \wedge(A_1, \ldots, A_n), \Delta$.
- (Or-left) From $A_1, \Gamma \rightarrow \Delta$ and $\vee(A_2, \ldots, A_n), \Gamma \rightarrow \Delta$, derive $\vee(A_1, \ldots, A_n), \Gamma \rightarrow \Delta$.
- (Or-right) From $\Gamma \rightarrow A_1, \vee(A_2, \ldots, A_n), \Delta$, derive $\Gamma \rightarrow \vee(A_1, \ldots, A_n), \Delta$.
- (Mod-left) From $A_1, \oplus_{b-1}(A_2, \ldots, A_n), \Gamma \rightarrow \Delta$ and $\oplus_b(A_2, \ldots, A_n), \Gamma \rightarrow A_1, \Delta$, derive $\oplus_b(A_1, \ldots, A_n), \Gamma \rightarrow \Delta$.
- (Mod-right) From $A_1, \Gamma \rightarrow \oplus_{b-1}(A_2, \ldots, A_n), \Delta$ and $\Gamma \rightarrow A_1, \oplus_b(A_2, \ldots, A_n), \Delta$, derive $\Gamma \rightarrow \oplus_b(A_1, \ldots, A_n), \Delta$.

The size of a proof is the total size of all the sequents it contains.

Definition 1 *Let $F = \{(\Gamma_n \rightarrow \Delta_n) : n \in \mathbf{N}\}$ be a family of sequents. Then $P = \{P_n : n \in \mathbf{N}\}$ is a family of* $\mathrm{ACC}^0[m]$-PK* *proofs for F if there is a constant d such that, for every n:*

1. *P_n is a valid (tree-like) proof of $(\Gamma_n \rightarrow \Delta_n)$.*
2. *The cut formulas in P_n have depth at most d.*

We say that P is a family of AC^0-PK* *proofs for F if no modular connectives occur in P. We say that P is a family of* $\mathrm{ACC}^0[m]$-PK *or* AC^0-PK *proofs if the proofs are permitted to be dag-like instead of just tree-like.*

Constant-depth Frege systems can also be defined in terms of the sequent calculus. An $\mathrm{ACC}^0[m]$-Frege proof is simply a dag-like $\mathrm{ACC}^0[m]$-PK* proof in which every formula has constant-depth. Similarly for AC^0-Frege.

In this article, we will only consider tautologies consisting of AND, OR and NOT connectives. The connectives will have unbounded arity. Because the sequent calculus is cut-free complete, the $\mathrm{ACC}^0[m]$-PK* proof system is complete for all tautologies while $\mathrm{ACC}^0[m]$-Frege is complete for constant-depth tautologies.

The size of a sequent calculus proof is measured in terms of the size of its conclusion. For example, if F is a family of sequents of size t_n, then a polynomial-size $\mathrm{ACC}^0[m]$-PK* proof of F would have size $t_n^{O(1)}$.

The power of $\mathrm{ACC}^0[m]$-PK* is closely related to the power of $\mathrm{ACC}^0[m]$-Frege when we consider only tautologies of constant depth:

Theorem 2 *The size of the smallest* $\mathrm{ACC}^0[m]$-PK* *proof of a constant-depth tautology is polynomially-related to the size of its smallest* $\mathrm{ACC}^0[m]$*-Frege proof. Similarly for* AC^0-PK* *and* AC^0*-Frege.*

Proof All the formulas in an $\mathrm{ACC}^0[m]$-PK* proof must be either subformulas of the conclusion or formulas that will be the target of a cut. Therefore, in an $\mathrm{ACC}^0[m]$-PK* proof of a constant-depth tautology, all the formulas must have constant depth, which implies that the $\mathrm{ACC}^0[m]$-PK* proof is actually an $\mathrm{ACC}^0[m]$-Frege proof.

On the other hand, any $\mathrm{ACC}^0[m]$-Frege proof of size s and depth d can be transformed into a tree-like $\mathrm{ACC}^0[m]$-Frege proof of size $s^{O(1)}$ and depth $d + 1$ [7]. Such a proof is a special case of an $\mathrm{ACC}^0[m]$-PK* proof. □

In general, the Pigeonhole Principle says that if $m > n$ and m pigeons are placed into n holes, then one hole must receive more than one pigeon. This tautology can be expressed as the following sequent, which we denote by PHP_n^m:

$$\bigvee_{j=1}^{n} p_{1j},\ \ldots,\ \bigvee_{j=1}^{n} p_{mj} \\ \rightarrow\ p_{11} \wedge p_{21},\ p_{11} \wedge p_{31},\ \ldots,\ p_{nn} \wedge p_{mn},$$

When m is much larger than n, typically when $m \geq 2n$, we refer to this tautology as the Weak Pigeonhole Principle. The case $m = n + 1$ is usually what is meant simply by the Pigeonhole Principle. We will use PHP to denote the corresponding tautology PHP_n^{n+1}.

One consequence of the close relationship between the AC^0-PK* and AC^0-Frege proof systems (Theorem 2) is an exponential lower bound on the size of AC^0-PK* proofs of the Pigeonhole Principle. This follows from the corresponding lower bound for AC^0-Frege proofs [1, 11, 14].

In this article, we consider variants of PHP in which the propositional variables are replaced by polynomial-size AND-OR-NOT formulas expressing a particular function f. Each of these formulas is over a separate subset of the original propositional variables. These subsets, which we call blocks, will always be of equal size. We denote such a tautology by $\mathrm{PHP}(f)$.

Typically, the formula expressing the function f will not be of constant depth. However, assuming f is not a constant function, then the $\mathrm{ACC}^0[m]$-PK* complexity of $\mathrm{PHP}(f)$ is related to the $\mathrm{ACC}^0[m]$-Frege complexity of PHP in the following way: if $\mathrm{PHP}(f)$ has an $\mathrm{ACC}^0[m]$-PK* proof of size s, then PHP has an $\mathrm{ACC}^0[m]$-PK* proof of size s and such a proof is also an $\mathrm{ACC}^0[m]$-Frege proof. Therefore, a lower bound on the size of $\mathrm{ACC}^0[m]$-PK* proofs of $\mathrm{PHP}(f)$ is a necessary condition for a lower bound on the size of $\mathrm{ACC}^0[m]$-Frege proofs of the Pigeonhole Principle.

In the following sections, we will use the symbols 0 and 1 in formulas. These symbols will simply stand for the formulas $x \wedge \neg x$ and $x \vee \neg x$, respectively. In particular, the sequents $0 \rightarrow$ and $\rightarrow 1$ have tree-like, cut-free proofs of constant size.

2.2. Constant-Depth Boolean Circuits

In this article, we will consider the standard Boolean circuit classes AC^0 and $\mathrm{ACC}^0[m]$, for constant m. All these circuits are of constant depth and consist of gates of unbounded fan-in. AC^0 circuits allow only AND, OR and NOT gates. $\mathrm{ACC}^0[m]$ also permit MOD_m gates that output 1 when the sum of their inputs is divisible by m.

It is known that AC^0 and $\mathrm{ACC}^0[p]$ circuits of subexponential size cannot compute the MOD_q function if p and q are distinct primes [5, 16]. It is also known that these circuits cannot approximate this function very well:

Theorem 3 ([5]) *Let C be a depth-d AC^0 circuit of size $2^{n^{1/(d+1)}}$. Then C cannot compute MOD_q correctly on more than a $1/2 + 1/2^{n^{1/(d+1)}}$ fraction of the inputs, for sufficiently large n.*

Theorem 4 ([16, 17]) *Let C be a depth-d $\mathrm{ACC}^0[p^k]$ circuit of size $2^{o(n^{1/2d})}$. Suppose that p and q are distinct primes. Then C cannot compute MOD_q correctly on more than a $1/2 + o(1)$ fraction of the inputs, for sufficiently large n.*

As mentioned in the introduction, it is natural to conjecture that a stronger hardness result also holds for $\mathrm{ACC}^0[p^k]$ and even $\mathrm{ACC}^0[m]$ circuits:

Conjecture 5 *There exists a function Hard_q with the following properties. First, Hard_q can be computed by $\mathrm{ACC}^0[q]$ circuits of polynomial size. Second, let C be a depth-d $\mathrm{ACC}^0[m]$ circuit of size $2^{n^{1/(d+1)}}$ and suppose that q is a prime number that does not divide m. Then C cannot compute Hard_q correctly on more than a $1/2 + 1/2^{n^{1/(d+1)}}$ fraction of the inputs, for sufficiently large n.*

3. Main Result and Overview of Proof

Our main result is that the hardness conjecture for $\mathrm{ACC}^0[m]$ circuits implies an exponential lower bound on the size of $\mathrm{ACC}^0[m]$-PK* proofs.

Theorem 6 *Suppose that q is a prime that does not divide m and that Conjecture 5 is true. Consider the tautology $\mathrm{PHP}(\mathrm{Hard}_q)$ with a block size $B = (6n^2)^{d+2}$. Then any depth-d $\mathrm{ACC}^0[m]$-PK* proof of $\mathrm{PHP}(\mathrm{Hard}_q)$ has size at least $2^{\frac{1}{3}N^{1/(2d+6)}}$, for N large enough, where N is the total number of variables in the tautology.*

Note that since the block size B depends on d, we have a different tautology for each depth. We can prove a lower bound with a single tautology for every depth but the lower bound is slightly smaller:

Theorem 7 *Suppose that q is a prime that does not divide m and that Conjecture 5 is true. Let $f(n)$ be unbounded and consider the tautology $\mathrm{PHP}(\mathrm{Hard}_q)$ with a block size $B = n^{f(n)}$. Then any $\mathrm{ACC}^0[m]$-PK* proof of $\mathrm{PHP}(\mathrm{Hard}_q)$ has size at least $2^{N^{1/(f(N)+3)}}$, for N large enough, where N is the total number of variables in the tautology.*

This is no longer an exponential lower bound, but it is still very large and certainly much larger that quasipolynomial. For example, with $f(n) = \log\log n$, we get a lower bound of $2^{N^{1/(\log\log N+3)}}$.

In the next two sections, we will prove an exponential lower bound on the size of AC^0-PK* proofs:

Theorem 8 *Consider the tautology* PHP(parity) *with a block size* $B = (6n^2)^{d+2}$. *Then any depth-d* AC^0-PK* *proof of* PHP(parity) *has size at least* $2^{\frac{1}{3}N^{1/(2d+6)}}$, *for N large enough, where N is the total number of variables in the tautology.*

The proof of this lower bound is slightly simpler but extends in a straightforward way to a proof of Theorem 6.

Note that Theorem 8 is an unconditional lower bound since the required hardness assumption is not a conjecture, as in Theorem 6, but an actual result (Theorem 3).

The lower bound of Theorem 8 is not new. As explained earlier (Theorem 2), the AC^0-PK* lower bound follows directly from the known exponential lower bound on the size of AC^0-Frege proofs of the Pigeonhole Principle [1, 11, 14]. However, the proof we present here for AC^0-PK* is much simpler than the proof of the AC^0-Frege lower bound.

The lower bound will be proved in two steps. First, we convert the proof into a decision tree of the same size that solves an associated search problem. Second, we prove a lower bound on the size of that decision tree.

In general, to any tautologically valid sequent $\Gamma \to \Delta$, we can associate a search problem as follows. Given any assignment to the underlying variables of the sequent, the problem is to output either a formula in Γ that is false, or a formula in Δ that is true. In the case of the PHP, this can be viewed as producing a pigeon i that goes nowhere or a hole j that receives more than one pigeon. While this search problem is trivial in most models of computation, we will show that it is hard for a certain type of decision tree.

4. Converting Proofs to Decision Trees

Let $\Gamma \to \Delta$ be a sequent. A decision tree T solving the search problem for $\Gamma \to \Delta$ will be defined as follows. The tree T is rooted and directed and has fan-out 2 (and fan-in 1). The leaves of T are labeled with formulas $f_i \in \Gamma$ or $g_i \in \Delta$. Each non-leaf vertex v is labeled with a formula f and is said to *query* that formula. The two outgoing edges from v are labeled by $f = 0$ and $f = 1$, respectively. For every total truth assignment α to the underlying variables of the sequent, if α is consistent with a path p in T with leaf label f_p, then either f_p is in Γ and α falsifies f_p, or f_p is in Δ and α satisfies f_p. The *size* of T is sum of the sizes of all formulas labeling vertices in T.

Now let $F = \{(\Gamma_n \to \Delta_n) : n \in \mathbf{N}\}$ be a family of tautologically valid sequents, where n denotes the number of distinct variables in the sequent. Let C be a circuit class. A family of C *decision trees* for F is a sequence $\{T_n : n \in \mathbf{N}\}$ of rooted, directed trees that satisfy the following properties:

1. Each T_n is a decision tree that solves the search problem for $\Gamma_n \to \Delta_n$.
2. The queries of T_n are either expressible as C circuits or are subformulas of formulas occurring in $\Gamma_n \to \Delta_n$.
3. If p is a path in T_n, f is a subformula of a formula in $\Gamma_n \to \Delta_n$ and f' is a subformula of f, then f' can appear on path p only if f appeared earlier on that path.

We now show that any small, depth-d AC^0-PK* proof can be converted into a small AC^0_d decision tree that solves the associated search problem. AC^0_d denotes AC^0 circuits of depth d.

Theorem 9 *Let P be a size-s, depth-d* AC^0-PK* *proof of* $\Gamma \to \Delta$. *There exists an* AC^0_d *decision tree T of size at most s that solves the search problem for* $\Gamma \to \Delta$.

Proof The proof is by induction on the number of lines in P. If P has only one line, then $\Gamma \to \Delta$ is an axiom $x \to x$ and thus the decision tree contains a single vertex labeled x. When $x = 0$ the leaf is labeled by $x \in \Gamma$ and when $x = 1$ the leaf is labeled by $x \in \Delta$. For the inductive step, there are several cases.

The first case is when the final inference in P is the cut inference. That is, the final line, $C = \Gamma \to \Delta$, is derived from $A = \Gamma, f \to \Delta$ and $B = \Gamma \to \Delta, f$ by cutting on $f \in C$. By induction, there is a decision tree T_A of the correct size solving the search problem for A, and similarly a decision tree T_B for B. The tree T for C will first query f. The subtree T_A will hang from the edge labeled $f = 1$, and the subtree T_B will hang from the other edge labeled $f = 0$. Consider an assignment α. If $f(\alpha) = 1$, then T_A on assignment α must output a formula in Γ that is false, or a formula in Δ that is true. Similarly, if $f(\alpha) = 0$, then T_B on assignment α must output a formula in Γ that is false, or a formula in Δ that is true. Thus T solves the search problem for C, and is of the required size.

The second case is when the final inference in P is an OR-left. That is, the final line, $C = \Gamma, (f \vee g) \to \Delta$ is derived from $A = \Gamma, f \to \Delta$ and $B = \Gamma, g \to \Delta$. Again, let T_A and T_B be the subtrees guaranteed by the inductive assumption. Modify T_B to obtain T'_B by replacing any leaf labeled by g to the label $(g \vee f)$. The tree T for C will first query f. The tree T_A will hang from the edge labeled $f = 1$ and the tree T'_B will hang from the edge labeled $f = 0$.

Now consider an assignment α. Suppose that $f(\alpha) = 1$. Then T_A on α must output some formula in Γ that is false, or some formula in Δ that is true, because f is satisfied by α. Now suppose that $f(\alpha) = 0$. Then the tree T_B on α will either output a formula in $\Gamma \cup \{f\}$ that is false, or a formula in Δ that is false. Since T'_B replaces the label g by $(g \vee f)$, the tree T'_B on alpha will either output a formula in $\Gamma \cup \{(f \vee g)\}$ that is false, or a formula in Δ that is false. This completes this case.

The AND-right case is very similar to the above OR-left case. All remaining rules take one sequent to one sequent.

For these rules, the same decision tree used for the upper sequent can be used for the derived sequent as well. □

5. The Decision Tree Lower Bound

In this section, we show that small decision trees cannot solve the search problem associated with PHP(parity).

Theorem 10 *Consider the tautology* PHP(parity) *with a block size* $B = (6n^2)^{d+2}$. *Let* T *be an* AC^0_d *decision tree that solves the associated search problem. Then the size of* T *is at least* $2^{\frac{1}{3}N^{1/(2d+6)}}$*, for* N *large enough, where* N *is the total number of variables in* PHP(parity).

Recall that the size of T is the total size of the queries in T. In addition, in the case of PHP(parity), the fact that T is an AC^0_d decision tree implies that the queries of T are either

1. depth-d, AND-OR formulas,
2. P_{ij}'s, or
3. subformulas of the P_{ij}'s with the restriction that a subformula cannot be queried before the P_{ij} that contains it is queried.

Note that if a subformula of a P_{ij} also happens to be a depth-d, AND-OR formula, then it can be queried without restrictions.

We will also derive a lower bound that applies to a single tautology and decision trees with AC^0 queries of any depth:

Theorem 11 *Let* $f(n)$ *be unbounded and consider the tautology* PHP(parity) *with a block size* $B = n^{f(n)}$. *Let* T *be an* AC^0 *decision tree that solves the associated search problem. Then the size of* T *is at least* $2^{N^{1/(f(N)+3)}}$*, for* N *large enough, where* N *is the total number of variables in* PHP(parity).

The proof of these lower bounds can be seen as an iterative process that starts at the root of the tree and moves down towards the leaves. The formal proof will be by induction. Before carrying out the complete argument, we will first sketch the initial step of this induction. It is simpler than the general case but will be sufficient to illustrate the main ideas of the proof.

Say that T is an AC^0_d decision tree. Suppose that T is small. Start at the root of T and follow all paths down the decision tree until you hit either a leaf or a node that queries some P_{ij}. This generates a subtree of T. If this subtree has at least 2^n leaves, then we are done: we have shown that T is large. Otherwise, some leaf X_1 of this subtree will be reached by more than a $1/2^n$ fraction of all possible assignments. That is, by more than $2^{(n+1)nB-n}$ assignments.

Note that the nodes on the path to X_1 can only query small, depth-d, AND-OR formulas. This means that the set of assignments leading to X_1 is the set of ones of the conjunction g of these formulas. The formula g is a small, depth-$(d+1)$, AND-OR formula.

Now either X_1 is a leaf of T or it queries some P_{ij}. We will first establish that, in fact, X_1 cannot be a leaf. For the sake of contradiction, suppose that it is. Then X_1 is labeled by either a pigeon or by a hole.

Suppose first that X_1 is labeled by pigeon i. Then all the assignments that lead to X_1, i.e., the set of assignments that satisfy g, should send pigeon i to no hole. However, consider P_{i1}. Since P_{i1} is a parity formula and g is a small, depth-$(d+1)$, AND-OR formula, we know that g approximates P_{i1} very badly. In fact, at least 1/4 of the assignments that satisfy g satisfy P_{i1} and at least 1/4 satisfy $\overline{P_{i1}}$. This implies that at least some of the assignments leading to X_1 send pigeon i to hole 1. Therefore, X_1 cannot be labeled by pigeon i.

Now suppose that X_1 is labeled by hole j. Then at least $1/4^{n+1}$ of the assignments that lead to X_1 satisfy $\overline{P_{1j}} \cap \cdots \cap \overline{P_{(n+1)j}}$. Since $2^{(n+1)nB-n}/4^{n+1} = 2^{(n+1)nB-(3n+2)} > 1$, some of the assignments that lead to X_1 send no pigeon to hole j. Therefore, X_1 cannot be labeled by hole j.

Note how we already used twice the fact that small, depth-$(d+1)$, AND-OR formulas cannot approximate the parity function. We will use this hardness result once more in what follows.

We now know that X_1 cannot be a leaf so it is labeled by some P_{ij}, say $P_{i_1 j_1}$. This implies that X_1 has two children, one for the assignments that send pigeon i_1 to hole j_1 and one for the other assignments. Among all the assignments that lead to X_1, at least $1/4^{n+1}$ send pigeon i_1 to hole j_1 and no other pigeon to hole j_1. These assignments will lead to the left child of X_1. On the other hand, at least $1/4^{n+1}$ of the assignments that lead to X_1 send no pigeon to hole j_1. These assignments lead to the right child of X_1.

Essentially, this means that querying g gives virtually no information about whether pigeon i_1 goes to hole j_1. It should also be clear that at either child of X_1, we have essentially no information about which of the remaining $n-1$ holes gets more than one pigeon or about which of the remaining pigeons goes nowhere. In particular, if i is any pigeon and $j_2 \neq j_1$, then at least 1/4 of the assignments that lead to the left child of X_1 will send pigeon i to hole j_2 and at least 1/4 will not.

So at each child of X_1, we have to solve a search problem similar to the original one but involving one less hole and, on the left side, one less pigeon. Inductively, we will show that these search problems require decision trees of size 2^{n-1}, so that the total size of T is at least 2^n.

This concludes our overview of the first step of the induction. The general inductive step is more complicated since it needs to address two main differences. These differences can be illustrated by comparing the first and second steps. First, in the initial step of the induction, the decision tree solves the search problem for the entire set of assignments. In the second step, we are dealing with a restricted set of assignments. For example, at the left child of X_1 we will consider only the assignments that satisfy g, send pigeon i_1 to hole j_1 and send no other pigeon to hole j_1.

The second difference concerns the path leading to X_1. In the first step of the induction, only depth-d, AND-OR formulas could be queried on that path. In the second step, we will identify a node X_2 that will play a role similar to that of X_1. But on the path to X_2, we will find queries to depth-d, AND-OR formulas, a query to $P_{i_1 j_1}$ and, possibly, queries to subformulas of $P_{i_1 j_1}$.

We now give the precise statement of the general induction step. Let A_{ij} denote the set of all assignments that send pigeon i to hole j and no other pigeon to hole j. Let A_{0j} denote the set of all assignments that send no pigeon to hole j.

Theorem 12 *Consider the tautology* PHP(parity) *with a block size* $B \geq (6n^2)^{d+2}$. *Let* T *be an* AC^0_d *decision tree that solves the associated search problem. Suppose that the size of* T *is at most* 2^n. *Let* $0 \leq k \leq n$ *and let* X_0 *be a node in* T. *Suppose that*

$$R = \{\text{all assignments that lead to } X_0\} \cap A_{i_1 j_1} \cap \cdots \cap A_{i_k j_k}$$

where $j_1, \ldots, j_k$ *are the holes queried along the path to* X_0 *and where each* i_r *is either* 0 *or the pigeon that was queried when hole* j_r *was queried for the first time. If* $|R| \geq 2^{(n+1)nB-5kn}$ *and* n *is large enough, then the subtree rooted at* X_0 *has size at least* 2^{n-k}.

It is easy to verify that when X_0 is the root of T, which implies that $k = 0$, this theorem implies both Theorem 10 and Theorem 11.

As indicated earlier, the fact that small, depth-d, AND-OR formulas cannot approximate the parity function will play a central role in the proof of Theorem 12. The key lemma that will be used is as follows:

Lemma 13 *Consider some* P_{ij} *and suppose that* $B \geq (6n^2)^{d+2}$. *Let* R *be the set of assignments that satisfy the conjunction of*

a) a depth-$(d+1)$*,* AND-OR *formula* g *of size at most* $2^{B^{1/(d+2)}}$*, and*

b) subformulas of other P_{ij}*'s.*

If $|R| \geq 2^{(n+1)nB-5n^2}$ *and* n *is large enough, then both* $R \cap P_{ij}$ *and* $R \cap \overline{P_{ij}}$ *have size at least* $|R|/4$.

Proof Any assignment to the underlying variables of PHP(parity) can be written as (α, β) where α is an assignment to the variables *inside* the block of P_{ij} and β is an assignment to the variables *outside* the block of P_{ij}. For any β, let $R_\beta = \{\alpha \mid (\alpha, \beta) \in R\}$. Then $|R_\beta|$ is the number of assignments in R that agree with β, so that $|R| = \sum_\beta |R_\beta|$. Similarly, $|R \cap P_{ij}| = \sum_\beta |R_\beta \cap P_{ij}|$. Therefore, to show that $|R \cap P_{ij}| \leq (3/4)|R|$, which implies that $|R \cap \overline{P_{ij}}| \geq |R|/4$, it is enough to show that each $|R_\beta \cap P_{ij}|$ is sufficiently small.

Suppose that R is the set of ones of $g \wedge S$ where S is the conjunction of the subformulas of other P_{ij}'s referred to in the statement of the lemma. Then

$$R_\beta = \{\alpha \mid (g(\alpha, \beta) = 1) \wedge (S(\alpha, \beta) = 1)\}.$$

Since $S(\alpha, \beta)$ depends only on β, then either R_β is empty or it is the set of ones of the function g_β defined by $g_\beta(\alpha) = g(\alpha, \beta)$, i.e., the restriction of g by β. Note that g_β is also a depth-$(d+1)$, AND-OR formula of size at most $2^{B^{1/(d+2)}}$.

If R_β is nonempty, then g_β agrees with P_{ij} on the set $(R_\beta \cap P_{ij}) \cup (\overline{R_\beta} \cap \overline{P_{ij}})$. By Theorem 3, this means that $|R_\beta \cap P_{ij}| + |\overline{R_\beta} \cap \overline{P_{ij}}| \leq (1/2 + \varepsilon)2^B$, where $\varepsilon = 1/2^{B^{1/(d+2)}}$. Since $|\overline{R_\beta} \cap \overline{P_{ij}}| = (1/2)2^B - |R_\beta \cap \overline{P_{ij}}|$, we have that $|R_\beta \cap P_{ij}| - |R_\beta \cap \overline{P_{ij}}| \leq \varepsilon 2^B$. This implies that $|R_\beta \cap P_{ij}| \leq |R_\beta|/2 + (1/2)\varepsilon 2^B$.

Adding over all β, we get that $|R \cap P_{ij}| \leq |R|/2 + 2^{(n+1)nB-B}(1/2)\varepsilon 2^B$. It is easy to verify that this is no more than $(3/4)|R|$. A similar argument shows that $|R \cap \overline{P_{ij}}| \leq (3/4)|R|$. □

Proof of Theorem 12 Let T_0 be the subtree rooted at X_0. The proof is by induction on k. The base case is when $k = n$ and it is trivial since T_0 contains at least one node.

Now suppose that $0 \leq k \leq n-1$. Start at X_0 and follow all paths down the decision tree until you hit either a leaf or a node that queries some P_{ij} for $j \notin \{j_1, \ldots, j_k\}$. That is, a P_{ij} that corresponds to a hole that is not queried on the path to X_0. This generates a subtree of T_0. If this subtree has at least 2^n leaves, then we are done. Otherwise, some leaf X of this subtree will be reached by more than a $1/2^n$ fraction of all assignments in R. Let R' be the set of assignments that reach X. The size of R' is at least $2^{(n+1)nB-5kn-n}$.

The nodes on the path from the root of T to X can only query depth-d, AND-OR formulas and subformulas of P_{ij}'s with $j \in \{j_1, \ldots, j_k\}$. This implies that R' is the set of assignments in R that satisfy a conjunction of depth-d, AND-OR formulas and subformulas of P_{ij}'s with $j \in \{j_1, \ldots, j_k\}$. But R itself is the set of assignments that satisfy such a conjunction of formulas, since each A_{ij} with $j \in \{j_1, \ldots, j_k\}$ can be defined by P_{ij}'s with $j \in \{j_1, \ldots, j_k\}$. Therefore, R' is the set of assignments that satisfy a conjunction of depth-d, AND-OR formulas and subformulas of P_{ij}'s with $j \in \{j_1, \ldots, j_k\}$. Let

g be the conjunction of all these depth-d, AND-OR formulas. The formula g is a depth-$(d+1)$, AND-OR formula of size at most 2^n.

We now establish that X cannot be a leaf. Suppose first that X is labeled by pigeon i. Since $k < n$, let j be some hole not in $\{j_1, \ldots, j_k\}$. Consider P_{ij}. Since $2^n \leq 2^{B^{1/(d+2)}}$, Lemma 13 implies that $R' \cap P_{ij}$ has size at least $|R'|/4$. Since $2^{(n+1)nB-5kn-n-2} \geq 1$, this implies that at least some of the assignments leading to X send pigeon i to hole j. Therefore, X cannot be labeled by pigeon i.

Now suppose that X is labeled by hole j. Because R' is contained in $A_{i_1 j_1} \cap \cdots \cap A_{i_k j_k}$, j cannot be in $\{j_1, \ldots, j_k\}$. Then, by repeated applications of Lemma 13, at least $1/4^{n+1}$ of the assignments in R' satisfy $\overline{P_{1j}} \cap \cdots \cap \overline{P_{(n+1)j}}$. Since $2^{(n+1)nB-5kn-3n-2} \geq 1$, some of the assignments that lead to X send no pigeon to hole j. Therefore, X cannot be labeled by hole j.

So we now know that X must be labeled by some P_{ij} with $j \notin \{j_1, \ldots, j_k\}$. Among all the assignments that lead to X, at least $1/4^{n+1}$ send pigeon i to hole j and no other pigeon to hole j. This set of assignments is $R' \cap A_{ij}$ and it leads to the left child of X. Since $|R' \cap A_{ij}| \geq 2^{(n+1)nB-5kn-n-2(n+1)} \geq 2^{(n+1)nB-5(k+1)n}$, the inductive hypothesis implies that the subtree rooted at the left child of X has a total query size of at least $2^{n-(k+1)}$.

Similarly, at least $1/4^{n+1}$ of the assignments that lead to X send no pigeon to hole j. This implies that the total query size of the subtree rooted at the right child of X is also at least $2^{n-(k+1)}$. Therefore, T_0 has a total query size of at least 2^{n-k}. □

6. A Separation Result for the $\mathrm{ACC}^0[m]$ and AC^0-PK* systems

The lower bound on the size of $\mathrm{ACC}^0[m]$-PK* proofs of $\mathrm{PHP}(\mathrm{Hard}_q)$, for a prime q not dividing m, is interesting in part because it is a necessary step towards a lower bound on the size of $\mathrm{ACC}^0[m]$-Frege proofs of PHP. But by focusing on a different tautology, we can use our lower bound technique to prove a separation result for the $\mathrm{ACC}^0[m]$ and AC^0-PK* systems.

Consider the Weak Pigeonhole Principle with $m = 2n$ pigeons and n holes. We will simply use WPHP to denote the corresponding tautology PHP^{2n}_n. It is known that WPHP has AC^0-Frege proofs of quasipolynomial size [13, 12]. An immediate consequence is that WPHP also has AC^0-PK* proofs of quasipolynomial size.

Using this fact and the lower bound technique of this paper, we use the tautology $\mathrm{WPHP}(\mathrm{MOD}_q)$ to separate $\mathrm{ACC}^0[q]$-PK* from AC^0-PK*.

Up until now, there has been no need to define the AND-OR-NOT formula MOD_q. But now, for the upper bound part of the separation result, we need a precise definition. Let MOD_q be the formula defined recursively as follows:

$$\sum_{i=1}^{n} x_i \equiv 0 \text{ iff } \bigvee_{b=0}^{q-1} \left(\sum_{i=1}^{n/2} x_i \equiv b \wedge \sum_{i=n/2+1}^{n} x_i \equiv q-b \right)$$

Theorem 14 *Consider the tautology* $\mathrm{WPHP}(\mathrm{MOD}_q)$ *with a block size* $B = (6n^2)^{d+2}$.

1. $\mathrm{WPHP}(\mathrm{MOD}_q)$ *has* $\mathrm{ACC}^0[q]$-PK* *proofs of quasipolynomial size.*
2. *Any* AC^0_d-PK* *proof of* $\mathrm{WPHP}(\mathrm{MOD}_q)$ *has size at least* $2^{\frac{1}{3}N^{1/(2d+6)}}$, *for* N *large enough, where* N *is the total number of variables in the tautology.*

Proof (Sketch) The lower bound follows simply from the fact that the argument used to prove the lower bound for $\mathrm{PHP}(\mathrm{MOD}_q)$ (Theorem 8) depends only on the number of holes not the number of pigeons.

A small $\mathrm{ACC}^0[q]$-PK* proof of $\mathrm{WPHP}(\mathrm{MOD}_q)$ can be constructed in two stages. First, prove that the AND-OR-NOT formula MOD_q is equivalent to a formula consisting of a single $\oplus_{q,0}$ connective. Second, prove $\mathrm{WPHP}(\oplus_{q,0})$ by using essentially the AC^0-PK* proof of WPHP [12]. Finally, prove $\mathrm{WPHP}(\mathrm{MOD}_q)$ from $\mathrm{WPHP}(\oplus_{q,0})$ using the fact that MOD_q is equivalent to $\oplus_{q,0}$. □

We can also prove a conditional separation of $\mathrm{ACC}^0[q]$-PK* from $\mathrm{ACC}^0[m]$-PK* when q is a prime that does not divide m. According to Conjecture 5, let Hard_q be an $\mathrm{ACC}^0[q]$ function that is hard for $\mathrm{ACC}^0[m]$. Then Hard_q can be expressed as an $\mathrm{ACC}^0[q]$ formula F_q. In this formula, replace each of the $\oplus_{q,0}$ connectives by an equivalent AND-OR-NOT MOD_q formula. This produces an AND-OR-NOT formula that expresses the $\mathrm{ACC}^0[q]$ function Hard_q. We will again abuse notation and use Hard_q to denote this formula.

Theorem 15 *Suppose that* q *is a prime that does not divide* m *and that Conjecture 5 is true. Consider the tautology* $\mathrm{WPHP}(\mathrm{Hard}_q)$ *with a block size* $B = (6n^2)^{d+2}$.

1. $\mathrm{WPHP}(\mathrm{Hard}_q)$ *has* $\mathrm{ACC}^0[q]$-PK* *proofs of quasipolynomial size.*
2. *Any* $\mathrm{ACC}^0_d[m]$-PK* *proof of* $\mathrm{WPHP}(\mathrm{Hard}_q)$ *has size at least* $2^{\frac{1}{3}N^{1/(2d+6)}}$, *for* N *large enough, where* N *is the total number of variables in the tautology.*

Proof (Sketch) The lower bound again follows simply from the fact that the argument used to prove the lower bound for $\mathrm{PHP}(\mathrm{Hard}_q)$ (Theorem 6) depends only on the number of holes not the number of pigeons.

A small $\mathrm{ACC}^0[q]$-PK* proof of $\mathrm{WPHP}(\mathrm{Hard}_q)$ can be constructed in two stages. First, prove that the AND-OR-NEG formula Hard_q is equivalent to the $\mathrm{ACC}^0[q]$ formula F_q that expresses the function Hard_q. Second, prove $\mathrm{WPHP}(F_q)$ by using essentially the AC^0-PK* proof of WPHP [12]. Finally, prove $\mathrm{WPHP}(\mathrm{Hard}_q)$ from $\mathrm{WPHP}(F_q)$ by using the fact that Hard_q is equivalent to F_q. □

7. Lower Bounds for QBF Proof Systems

Krajíček and Pudlák [9] extended the propositional Sequent Calculus to obtain a proof system for proving the validity of quantified Boolean formulas. The version we present here is due to Cook and Morioka [3]. The language of QBF formulas is: Boolean connectives $\vee, \wedge, \neg$, quantifier connectives $\exists, \forall$, parentheses (and), and variables p_i, x_i, $i \geq 0$. The p-variables denote free variables, and the x-variables are bound variables. A QBF formula is defined inductively as follows: (1) The atomic formulas are (T), (F), (p_i) and (x_i) for every $i \geq 0$; (2) if ϕ and ψ are formulas, then so are $(\phi \vee \psi)$, $(\phi \wedge \psi)$, $(\neg\phi)$, $(\exists x_i \phi)$, $(\forall x_i \phi)$. Both Σ_0^q and Π_0^q denote the set of propositional formulas. For $i \geq 1$, Σ_i^q is the set of QBF formulas that can be written in prenex form with at most $i-1$ quantifier alternations beginning with $\exists$. Similarly, Π_i^q is the set of QBF formulas with at most $i-1$ quantifier alternations beginning with $\forall$. It is well known that the evaluation problem for Σ_i^q sentences (and Π_i^q sentences) is complete Σ_i^p (Π_i^p), the ith level of the polynomial-time hierarchy. Further it is not hard to see that there exists a proof system in which every valid QBF formula has a polynomial-size proof if and only if NP = PSPACE. Similarly, for every $i \geq 0$, there exists a proof system in which every valid Σ_i^q formula has a polynomial-size proof if and only if $\mathrm{NP} = \Pi_{i+1}^p$.

The system G for QBF formulas is a Sequent Calculus system obtained by augmenting the propositional version with the following four quantifier-introduction rules, with the additional restriction that the target of every $\forall$-left and $\exists$-right step be quantifier-free.

- ($\exists$-left) From $A(p), \Gamma \rightarrow \Delta$, derive $\exists x A(x), \Gamma \rightarrow \Delta$.
- ($\exists$-right) From $\Gamma \rightarrow \Delta, A(B)$, derive $\Gamma \rightarrow \Delta, \exists x A(x)$.
- ($\forall$-left) From $A(B), \Gamma \rightarrow \Delta$, derive $\forall x A(x)\Gamma \rightarrow \Delta$.
- ($\forall$-right) From $\Gamma \rightarrow \Delta, A(p)$, derive $\Gamma \rightarrow \Delta, \forall x A(x)$.

For $i \geq 0$, G_i is G with cuts restricted to $\Sigma_i^q \cup \Pi_i^q$ formulas. G_i^* is the tree-like version of G_i. There is a close connection between the G_i systems and systems of bounded arithmetic; in particular, for each i, G_i^* is the nonuniform analog of S_2^i and G_i is the nonuniform analog of T_2^i, for bounded formulas [8]. It is an important open problem whether the S_i hierarchies or the G_i hierarchies collapse. Krajíček, Pudlák and Takeuti [10] proved that the S_2^i (and T_2^i) hierarchy does not collapse, assuming that the polynomial-time hierarchy does not collapse. However, the analogous result for the G_i hierarchy has not been resolved. As an application of our method, we will prove that under a plausible hardness assumption, the G_i^* hierarchy also does not collapse.

Conjecture 16 *Let $i, j \geq 0$, where $i > j$. Then the (i,j)-QBF hardness conjecture is as follows. There exists a Boolean function $\mathrm{Hard}_{\mathrm{QBF}}^{i,j}$ of n input variables with the following properties. First, for all n, there is a polynomial-size Σ_i^q formula computing $\mathrm{Hard}_{\mathrm{QBF}}^{i,j}$. Secondly, any Σ_j^q formula of size $2^{n^{1/(d+1)}}$ cannot compute $\mathrm{Hard}_{\mathrm{QBF}}^{i,j}$ correctly on more than a $1/2 + 1/2^{polylog(n)}$ fraction of inputs, for sufficiently large n.*

Theorem 17 *If the (i,j)-QBF conjecture is true for $i > j \geq 0$, then G_j^* cannot polynomially simulate G_i^*.*

Proof (sketch) Consider the tautology $\mathrm{WPHP}(\mathrm{Hard}_{\mathrm{QBF}}^{i,j})$ with block size $B = n^5$. First, we will show that $\mathrm{WPHP}(\mathrm{Hard}_{\mathrm{QBF}}^{i,j})$ has G_i^* proofs of quasipolynomial size. As in the proof of the separation results of the previous section, we prove $\mathrm{WPHP}(\mathrm{Hard}_{\mathrm{QBF}}^{i,j})$ by using essentially the AC^0-PK* proof of WPHP [12]. Applying this upper bound to $\mathrm{WPHP}(\mathrm{Hard}_{\mathrm{QBF}}^{i,j})$ gives rise to G_i^* proofs of quasipolynomial size.

Secondly, we need to see that $\mathrm{WPHP}(\mathrm{Hard}_{\mathrm{QBF}}^{i,j})$ requires superpolynomial-size G_j^* proofs. This follows by adapting the lower bound argument from Theorem 6. Namely, given an alleged polynomial-size G_j^* proof of $\mathrm{WPHP}(\mathrm{Hard}_{\mathrm{QBF}}^{i,j})$, we first show how this implies a polynomial-size decision tree for the search problem associated with $\mathrm{WPHP}(\mathrm{Hard}_{\mathrm{QBF}}^{i,j})$. Now the decision tree will be a Σ_j^q decision tree, meaning that the queries will be either Σ_j^q formulas, $P_{i,j}$'s or subformulas of the $P_{i,j}$'s with the restriction that a subformula cannot be queried before the $P_{i,j}$ that contains it is queried. Secondly, we show that no polynomial-size Σ_j^q decision tree can correctly solve the search problem associated with $\mathrm{WPHP}(\mathrm{Hard}_{\mathrm{QBF}}^{i,j})$, under our hardness assumption. As before, we adapt the argument from Theorem 6, using the fact that the lower bound depends only on the number of holes and not the number of pigeons. □

8. Conclusion

An obvious open problem is to prove our lower bounds in the dag-like case. One way to do this would be to show that the tree-like systems of depth $d + 1$, can polynomially simulate the depth-d dag-like system. In particular, is it true that AC^0_{d+1}-PK* can polynomially simulate AC^0_d-PK? We can ask the same question for the other proof systems studied in this paper. That is, can $\mathrm{ACC}^0_{d+1}[m]$-PK* polynomially simulate $\mathrm{ACC}^0_d[m]$-PK? Can G^*_{i+1} polynomially simulate G_i? Note that all of these simulations hold if we restrict to d the depth of the formula being proved or if we restrict its quantifier alternation depth to i.

Secondly, we would like to develop a new, general-purpose method for obtaining AC^0-Frege lower bounds for CNF formulas. For example, can we obtain a top-down strategy for the liar game formulation of AC^0-Frege for the PHP? Toward this end, we would like to know whether inapproximability results are enough to prove lower bounds for CNF formulas. For example, can we reduce the AC^0-Frege lower bound for some CNF formula to a natural hardness assumption about AC^0, such as the inapproximability of parity by AC^0 circuits? The only known proofs require structural information about AC^0, such as the fact that under a special family of restrictions, an AC^0 function reduces to a local function (a small-depth decision tree, or a function depending on only a constant number of variables).

Thirdly, in our last application we show that the G^*_i hierarchy does not collapse to G^*_1 unless SAT can be approximated by polynomial-size circuits. In contrast, it has been known that the S^i_2 hierarchy does not collapse to S^1_2 unless the polynomial hierarchy collapses. We would like to know how this assumptions compare. In particular, do polynomial-size circuits approximating SAT imply the collapse of the polynomial-time hierarchy?

Acknowledgements

Alexis Maciel was supported by NSF grant CCR-9877150. Toniann Pitassi was supported by an NSERC grant. She would like to gratefully acknowledge Maria Bonet for conversations on this subject many years ago.

References

[1] M. Ajtai. The complexity of the pigeonhole principle. In *Proc. 29th Ann. IEEE Symp. on Foundations of Computer Science*, pages 346–355, 1988.

[2] M. Bonet, C. Domingo, R. Gavalda, A. Maciel, and T. Pitassi. Non-automatizability of bounded-depth Frege proofs. In *Proc. 14th Ann. IEEE Conf. on Computational Complexity*, pages 15–23, 1999.

[3] S. Cook and T. Morioka. Quantified Propositional Calculus and a Second-Order Theory for NC1. Manuscript submitted for publication, April 2004. Preliminary version presented at SML, 2003.

[4] A. Haken. The intractability of resolution. *Theoretical Computer Science*, 39:297–308, 1985.

[5] J. Håstad. Almost optimal lower bounds for small depth circuits. In *Proc. 18th Ann. ACM Symp. on Theory of Computing*, pages 6–20, 1986.

[6] A. Haken and S. A. Cook. An exponential lower bound for the size of monotone real circuits. *Journal of Computer and System Sciences*, 58:326–335, 1999.

[7] J. Krajíček. Lower bounds to the size of constant-depth propositional proofs. *Journal of Symbolic Logic*, 59(1):73–86, 1994.

[8] J. Krajíček. *Bounded Arithmetic, Propositional Logic and Computational Complexity* Cambridge University Press, 1995.

[9] J. Krajíček and P. Pudlák. Quantified Propositional Calculi and Fragments of Bounded Arithmetic. *Zeitschrift f. Mathematkal Logik u. Grundlagen d. Mathematik*, 36:29-46, 1990.

[10] J. Krajíček, P. Pudlák and G. Takeuti. Bounded arithmetic and the polynomial hierarchy. *Annals of Pure and Applied Logic*, 52:143–153, 1991.

[11] J. Krajíček, P. Pudlák and A. Woods. Exponential lower bound to the size of bounded depth Frege proofs of the pigeonhole principle. *Random Structures and Algorithms*, 7:15–39, 1995.

[12] A. Maciel, T. Pitassi and A. Woods. A New Proof of the Weak Pigeonhole Principle. *Journal of Computer Systems Sciences*, 64:843–872, 2002.

[13] J.B. Paris, A.J. Wilkie and A.R. Woods. Provability of the pigeonhole principle and the existence of infinitely many primes. *Journal of Symbolic Logic*, 53:1235–1244, 1988.

[14] T. Pitassi, P. Beame and R. Impagliazzo. Exponential lower bounds for the pigeonhole principle. *Computational Complexity*, 97–140, 1993.

[15] P. Pudlák. Lower bounds for resolution and cutting plane proofs and monotone computations. *Journal of Symbolic Logic*, 62(3):981–998, September 1997.

[16] R. Smolensky. Algebraic methods in the theory of lower bounds for Boolean circuit complexity. In *Proc. 19th Ann. ACM Symp. on Theory of Computing*, 1987.

[17] R. Smolensky. On Representations by Low-Degree Polynomials. In *Proc. 34th Ann. Symp. on Foundations of Computer Science*, 1993.

Session 6:
Model Theory

A Characterisation of First-Order Constraint Satisfaction Problems

Benoit Larose
Department of Mathematics and Statistics
Concordia University
1455 de Maisonneuve West
Montréal, Qc
Canada, H3G 1M8
larose@mathstat.concordia.ca

Cynthia Loten
Royal Military College of Canada
PO Box 17000 Station "Forces"
Kingston, Ontario
Canada, K7K 7B4
cindy.loten@shaw.ca

Claude Tardif
Royal Military College of Canada
PO Box 17000 Station "Forces"
Kingston, Ontario
Canada, K7K 7B4
Claude.Tardif@rmc.ca

Abstract

We characterise finite relational core structures admitting finitely many obstructions, in terms of special near-unanimity functions, and in terms of dismantling properties of their square. As a consequence, we show that it is decidable to determine whether a constraint satisfaction problem is first-order definable: we show the general problem to be **NP***-complete, and give a polynomial-time algorithm in the case of cores.*

1. Introduction

This paper is concerned with the expressibility of constraint satisfaction problems (CSP's) in first-order logic. In a constraint satisfaction problem, one is given variables and constraints on these, and one must decide whether the variables can be assigned values that satisfy all constraints; this framework is quite general and flexible, and numerous examples occur naturally in combinatorics, graph theory, database theory, and so forth (see references below). The general problem is **NP**-complete, but one may obtain tractable cases by restricting the nature of the constraints. A natural and convenient approach to CSP's is to view them as generalised colouring problems (see for example [10]). Fix a relational structure $\mathbb{A}$ of signature σ, and define $\mathbb{A}$-CSP to be the class of all σ-structures $\mathbb{B}$ that admit a relation-preserving map (i.e. a *homomorphism*) from their universe to that of $\mathbb{A}$. The elements of the universe of the input structure $\mathbb{B}$ are the variables, the elements of the universe of $\mathbb{A}$ are the values and the constraints are determined by the relations; the homomorphism from $\mathbb{B}$ to $\mathbb{A}$ is the desired assignment of values. The nature of the target structure $\mathbb{A}$ determines the complexity of $\mathbb{A}$-CSP: for instance, a celebrated result of Hell and Nešetřil states that if $\mathbb{A}$ is a non-bipartite graph then $\mathbb{A}$-CSP is **NP**-complete, and otherwise it is in **P** [9]. It has been conjectured that this dichotomy should hold for all target structures [7]. A novel approach involving algebraic techniques, pioneered by Bulatov, Jeavons and Krokhin (see [2]), has shown promise, but the general conjecture remains open.

One family of well-studied tractable CSP's consists of the problems of so-called *bounded width* (see for example [1], [3], [6],[8], [12]). It is still unknown whether these problems can actually be recognised algorithmically. One subclass however, the problems of width 1, is decidable: these are the structures with tree duality [8]. A family $\mathcal{F}$ of σ-structures is called a *complete set of obstructions* for the σ-structure $\mathbb{A}$ if none of the members of $\mathcal{F}$ admits a homomorphism to $\mathbb{A}$ and for every σ-structure $\mathbb{B}$ that does not admit a homomorphism to $\mathbb{A}$ there exists some $\mathbb{C} \in \mathcal{F}$ which admits a homomorphism to $\mathbb{B}$. The structure $\mathbb{A}$ is said to have *tree duality* if it admits a complete set of obstructions consisting of trees (see 2.1 below), and *finitary duality* if it admits a finite complete set of obstructions. Given a structure $\mathbb{A}$, there is a structure $S(\mathbb{A})$ of the same type (easily constructed from $\mathbb{A}$) such that $\mathbb{A}$ has tree duality if and only

1043-6871/06 $20.00

if $S(\mathbb{A})$ admits a homomorphism to $\mathbb{A}$, and hence this property is decidable ([8], see also [6].)

If a structure has finitary duality then it is easy to see that the associated problem $\mathbb{A}$-CSP is definable in the existential positive fragment of first-order logic and in particular the problem $\mathbb{A}$-CSP is in AC^0. Atserias has shown that in fact, the structures with finitary duality are precisely those such that $\mathbb{A}$-CSP is first-order definable [1] (this is also a consequence of the more general result in [17].) It is known that if a structure has finitary duality then it also has tree duality [15]. Naturally the question arises as to whether one can recognise these structures algorithmically: in this paper we answer this in the affirmative, and give various characterisations of structures with a first-order definable associated CSP. As a consequence we obtain a decision procedure to recognise first-order definable CSP's. We now give an overview of our results; although our results are conceptually simple, their proofs use quotients, exponentiation and dismantlability in the context of general relational structures, hence to simply the discussion at this stage we illustrate our results with the case of digraphs.

Two σ-structures $\mathbb{A}$ and $\mathbb{B}$ are *homomorphically equivalent* if $\mathbb{A}$-CSP and $\mathbb{B}$-CSP coincide. Within a class of homomorphically equivalent structures, there is, up to isomorphism, a unique structure with universe of minimum size; such a structure is called a *core*. In section 2.2 we characterise σ-structures with finite duality in terms of the diameter of their critical (i.e. minimal) obstructions (Lemma 2.4). In section 3.2 we characterise those structures $\mathbb{A}$ which admit a complete set of obstructions all of whose members have at most n hyperedges with the use of special homomorphisms from the product structure $\mathbb{A}^{n+1}$ to $\mathbb{A}$ (Corollary 3.3): as a consequence we obtain that core structures with finitary duality are precisely those admitting a so-called 1-tolerant near-unanimity operation (Proposition 3.4). Note that there is no a priori bound on the arity of the operation and thus this result does not in itself yield a decision procedure. For two vertices u, v of a digraph H, we say that v *dominates* u if every outneighbour of u is also an outneighbour of v and every inneighbour of u is also an inneighbour of v. If there exists a sequence $H = H_0, H_1, \ldots, H_n = R$ of digraphs such that H_i is obtained from H_{i-1} by removing a dominated vertex for $i = 1, \ldots, n$, we say that H *dismantles to* R. In section 4.1 we define a similar concept for general structures. We then obtain the following result: for any core structure $\mathbb{A}$, the problem $\mathbb{A}$-CSP is first-order definable if and only if the product structure $\mathbb{A}^2$ dismantles to the diagonal (Theorem 4.7).

In particular, this result yields the following polynomial-time algorithm to recognise cores with a first-order definable CSP: remove greedily from A^2 any pair (a, b) with $a \neq b$ such that (a, b) is dominated; if at the end of the process only pairs (a, a) remain then $\mathbb{A}$-CSP is first-order definable, otherwise it is not. For a general structure $\mathbb{A}$, one must determine if some retract of $\mathbb{A}$ has the above property: this turns out to be **NP**-complete (Theorem 5.1).

We believe that, beyond the decidability issues, our characterisations of structures with a first-order definable CSP are of interest in themselves. Previously, Dalmau, Krokhin and Larose [5] had given a similar characterisation of posets and reflexive digraphs whose *retraction* problem was first-order definable, and these coincided with those structures which admitted a near-unanimity operation; in a sense the present result clarifies the connection for arbitrary relational structures. Dalmau and Krokhin have recently proved that CSP's admitting a 3-variable near-unanimity operation are in the complexity class **NL** [4] by showing the CSP has bounded path duality. Our results might give some insight into how one might extend this result to near-unanimity operations of arbitrary arity; it is still open whether the problem of recognising structures admitting such an operation is decidable (although the purely algebraic version has recently been solved in the affirmative by Maróti [14].)

2. Preliminaries

For basic notation and terminology with follow mainly [3] and [15]. A *vocabulary* is a finite set $\sigma = \{R_1, \ldots, R_m\}$ of *relation symbols*, each with an *arity* r_i assigned to it. A σ-structure is a relational structure $\mathbb{A} = \langle A; R_1(\mathbb{A}), \ldots, R_m(\mathbb{A})\rangle$ where A is a non-empty set called the *universe* of $\mathbb{A}$, and $R_i(\mathbb{A})$ is an r_i-ary relation on A for each i. The elements of $R_i(\mathbb{A})$, $1 \leq i \leq m$ will be called *hyperedges* of $\mathbb{A}$. For σ-structures $\mathbb{A}$ and $\mathbb{B}$, a *homomorphism* from $\mathbb{A}$ to $\mathbb{B}$ is a map $f : A \to B$ such that $f(R_i(\mathbb{A})) \subseteq R_i(\mathbb{B})$ for all $1 = 1, \ldots, m$, where for any relation $R \in \sigma$ of arity r we have

$$f(R) = \{(f(x_1), \ldots, f(x_r)) : (x_1, \ldots, x_r) \in R\}.$$

A σ-structure $\mathbb{B}$ is a *substructure* of a σ-structure $\mathbb{A}$ if $B \subseteq A$ and the identity map on B is a homomorphism from $\mathbb{B}$ to $\mathbb{A}$. For a subset B of A, the *substructure* $\mathbb{B}$ *of* $\mathbb{A}$ *induced by* B is the σ-structure with universe B with relations $R_i(\mathbb{B}) = R_i(\mathbb{A}) \cap B^{r_i}$ for every i. A substructure $\mathbb{B}$ of $\mathbb{A}$ is called a *retract* of $\mathbb{A}$ if there exists a homomorphism ρ from $\mathbb{A}$ to $\mathbb{B}$ whose restriction to B is the identity; the map ρ is then called a *retraction*. A structure $\mathbb{A}$ is called a *core* if it has no retract other than itself. It is well known (see [15]) that every (finite) σ-structure has a core which is unique up to isomorphism.

Let $\mathbb{A}$ be a σ-structure. We define the *incidence multigraph* $\mathrm{Inc}(\mathbb{A})$ of $\mathbb{A}$ as the bipartite multigraph with parts A and $\mathrm{Block}(\mathbb{A})$ which consists of all pairs (R, r) such that $R \in \sigma$ and $r \in R(A)$, and with edges $e_{a,i,B}$ joining $a \in A$ to $B = (R, (x_1, \ldots, x_r)) \in \mathrm{Block}(\mathbb{A})$ when $x_i = a$. This allows us to import some basic concepts from graph theory: the *distance* $d_{\mathbb{A}}(a, b)$ between two elements a and b of A is defined as half their distance in Inc($\mathbb{A}$), the *diameter* of $\mathbb{A}$ is defined as half the diameter of Inc($\mathbb{A}$), and the *girth* of $\mathbb{A}$ is defined as half the shortest length of a cycle in Inc($\mathbb{A}$). In particular, $\mathbb{A}$ has girth 1 if and only if Inc($\mathbb{A}$) has parallel edges, and infinite girth if and only if Inc($\mathbb{A}$) is acyclic. Notice in particular that tuples with repeated entries (such as (a, a, b)) create parallel edges and hence cycles; this property is not captured in the Gaifman graph. We'll require a finer notion of tree below and this explains why we choose this variant of a (multi)graph associated to a relational structure rather than the Gaifman graph.

Although this presentation of the girth differs from that given in [8], the concept is the same and we can use the following Erdős-type result.

Lemma 2.1 ([8] Theorem 5) *Let $\mathbb{A}$ and $\mathbb{B}$ be σ-structures such that there exist no homomorphism from $\mathbb{A}$ to $\mathbb{B}$. Then for any positive integer n there exists a σ-structure $\mathbb{A}_n$ of girth greater than n such that there exists a homomorphism from $\mathbb{A}_n$ to $\mathbb{A}$ but no homomorphism from $\mathbb{A}_n$ to $\mathbb{B}$.*

Note that a σ-structure of large girth must have large diameter unless it is acyclic.

A *loop* in a σ-structure $\mathbb{A}$ is an element $a \in A$ such that $(a, \ldots, a) \in R_i(\mathbb{A})$ for any i; equivalently, $a \in A$ is a loop if and only if for every σ-structure $\mathbb{B}$ the constant map $\mathbb{B} \to \mathbb{A}$ with value a is a homomorphism. In particular, the image of a loop under a homomorphism is itself a loop. For an integer n the *n-link* of type $\sigma = \{R_1, \ldots, R_m\}$ is the σ-structure

$$\mathbb{L}_n = \langle \{0, 1, \ldots, n\}; R_1(\mathbb{L}_n), \ldots, R_m(\mathbb{L}_n) \rangle,$$

such that $R_i(\mathbb{L}_n) = \cup_{j=1}^{n} \{j-1, j\}^{r_i}$ for $i = 1, \ldots, m$ (where r_i is the arity of the relation R_i). Note that every $i \in \{0, 1, \ldots, n\}$ is a loop in $\mathbb{L}_n$. A *link* in an arbitrary σ-structure is a homomorphic image of $\mathbb{L}_n$ for some n. The term "path" is more common than "link", but we chose the latter to make it clear that these are not trees in the sense defined below.

2.1 Trees

A σ-structure $\mathbb{T}$ is called a *σ-tree* (or *tree* for short) if Inc($\mathbb{T}$) is a tree, i.e. it is acyclic and connected. We require the following technical results:

Lemma 2.2 *For every σ-tree $\mathbb{T}$ with n hyperedges, there exists a sequence $\mathbb{T} = \mathbb{T}_n, \mathbb{T}_{n-1}, \ldots, \mathbb{T}_1$ of subtrees of $\mathbb{T}$ with the following properties: for each $j = 1, \ldots, n-1$*

1. *$\mathbb{T}_j$ has j hyperedges;*
2. *$\mathbb{T}_j$ is a subtree of $\mathbb{T}_{j+1}$;*
3. *if $(x_1, \ldots, x_r)$ is the hyperedge of $\mathbb{T}_{j+1}$ which does not belong to $\mathbb{T}_j$ then there exists a unique index i such that x_i is in the universe of $\mathbb{T}_j$.*

Proof. Let $P = u_0, u_1, \ldots, u_k$ be a path of maximal length in Inc($\mathbb{T}$), where $\mathbb{T} = (T, R_1, \ldots, R_m)$ has more than one hyperedge. If $u_0 = (R, (x_1)) \in$ Block($\mathbb{T}$), (R has to be a 1-ary relation of σ), we obtain a new tree $\mathbb{T}'$ from $\mathbb{T}$ by removing x_1 from R. If $u_0 \in T$, then $u_1 = (R, (x_1, \ldots, x_r)) \in$ Block($\mathbb{T}$), and we obtain a new tree $\mathbb{T}'$ by removing $(x_1, \ldots, x_r)$ from R and $\{x_1, \ldots, x_m\} \setminus \{u_2\}$ from T. Repeating this proceedure, we eventually obtain the desired decomposition. ∎

Lemma 2.3 *Let $\sigma = \{R_1, \ldots, R_m\}$ be a vocabulary. Then for any integer n the number of core σ-trees of diameter at most n is finite.*

Proof. We will show that the number t_n of core *rooted* trees in which the distance to the root is at most n is finite. Let m be the number of relations in σ and let r be the maximum arity of a relation in σ. We have $t_0 \leq 2^m$, with equality only if $r = 1$. Now suppose that t_{n-1} is finite. For a rooted tree $\mathbb{T}$ in which the distance to the root u is at most n, we can encode each hyperedge $(x_1, \ldots, x_{r'})$ to which u belongs by the name of the relation $R_i(\mathbb{T})$ containing it (there are at most m choices), the index i such that $u = x_i$ (there are at most r choices) and the trees rooted at $x_j, j \neq i$ branching away from u (there are at most t_{n-1}^{r-1} choices). If $\mathbb{T}$ is a core, no two hyperedges can have the same label and $\mathbb{T}$ is determined by its set of labels of hyperedges containing u. Therefore $t_n \leq 2^{m \cdot r \cdot t_{n-1}^{r-1}}$. ∎

2.2 Complete sets of obstructions

The σ-structure $\mathbb{B}$ is an *obstruction* for the σ-structure $\mathbb{A}$ if there is no homomorphism from $\mathbb{B}$ to $\mathbb{A}$. A family $\mathcal{F}$ of obstructions for $\mathbb{A}$ is called a *complete set of obstructions* if for every σ-structure $\mathbb{B}$ that does not admit a homomorphism to $\mathbb{A}$ there exists some $\mathbb{C} \in \mathcal{F}$ which admits a homomorphism to $\mathbb{B}$. The structure $\mathbb{A}$ is said to have *tree duality* if it admits a complete set of obstructions consisting of trees, and *finitary duality* if it admits a finite complete set of obstructions. According to [15], for every finite family $\mathcal{F}$ of σ-trees, there exists a σ-structure $\mathbb{A}_{\mathcal{F}}$ which admits $\mathcal{F}$ as a complete set of obstructions; and conversely every σ-structure $\mathbb{A}$ with finitary duality admits a finite complete set of obstructions consisting of trees. Thus the structures with finitary duality form a subclass of the structures with tree duality, and there is one such core structure for every finite set of tree obstructions.

An obstruction $\mathbb{B}$ for $\mathbb{A}$ is called *critical* if every proper substructure of $\mathbb{B}$ admits a homomorphism to $\mathbb{A}$. It is clear that a critical obstruction is a core, and that every obstruction contains, as a substructure, a critical obstruction.

Lemma 2.4 *A σ-structure $\mathbb{A}$ has finitary duality if and only if there is an upper bound on the diameter of its critical obstructions.*

Proof. Clearly, if $\mathbb{A}$ has finitary duality, then the maximum diameter of an obstruction in a finite complete set of obstructions for $\mathbb{A}$ is an upper bound on the diameter of all critical obstructions for $\mathbb{A}$. Conversely, suppose that the critical obsructions for $\mathbb{A}$ have diameter at most m. Let $\mathcal{F}$ be the set of core σ-trees of diameter at most m which do not admit a homomorphism to $\mathbb{A}$. By Lemma 2.3, $\mathcal{F}$ is finite. By Lemma 2.1, for any σ-structure $\mathbb{B}$ which does not admit a homomorphism to $\mathbb{A}$, there exists a structure $\mathbb{C}$ of girth at least $2m+2$ which admits a homomorphism to $\mathbb{B}$ but not to $\mathbb{A}$. A critical obstruction for $\mathbb{A}$ contained in $\mathbb{C}$ cannot contain a cycle hence it must be a tree $\mathbb{T}$ of diameter at most m. Therefore $\mathbb{T} \in \mathcal{F}$; this shows that $\mathcal{F}$ is a finite complete set of obstructions for $\mathbb{A}$.

■

For a σ-structure $\mathbb{A}$, the problem $\mathbb{A}$-CSP consists of determining whether an input structure $\mathbb{B}$ admits a homomorphism to $\mathbb{A}$. It is said to be *first-order definable* if there exists a first-order sentence Φ (in the language of σ) which is true on $\mathbb{B}$ if and only if $\mathbb{B}$ admits a homomorphism to $\mathbb{A}$. By a result of Atserias [1], $\mathbb{A}$-CSP is first-order definable if and only if $\mathbb{A}$ has finitary duality, hence we have the following equivalences:

Theorem 2.5 *Let $\mathbb{A}$ be a σ-structure. Then the following are equivalent.*

1. *$\mathbb{A}$-CSP is first-order definable;*
2. *$\mathbb{A}$ has finitary duality;*
3. *$\mathbb{A}$ has a finite complete set of obstructions consisting of trees;*
4. *The critical obstructions of $\mathbb{A}$ have bounded diameter.*

We are mostly interested in the "meta-problem" of deciding whether an input structure $\mathbb{A}$ has a first-order definable CSP. The equivalences of Theorem 2.5 are not a usable decision procedure, but they will be used in the next two sections to find such a procedure. As a benchmark we state here Feder and Vardi's decision procedure for tree duality. Given a structure $\mathbb{A} = \langle A; R_1(\mathbb{A}), \ldots, R_m(\mathbb{A})\rangle$, we define the structure $\mathcal{U}(\mathbb{A}) = \langle U; R_1(\mathcal{U}(\mathbb{A})), \ldots, R_m(\mathcal{U}(\mathbb{A}))\rangle$, where U is the set of all nonempty subsets of A, and for $i = 1, \ldots, m$, $R_i(\mathcal{U}(\mathbb{A}))$ is the set of all r_i-tuples $(X_1, \ldots, X_{r_i})$ such that for all $j \in \{1, \ldots, r_i\}$ and $x_j \in X_j$ there exist $x_k \in X_k, k \in \{1, \ldots, r_i\} \setminus \{j\}$ such that $(x_1, \ldots, x_{r_i}) \in R_i(\mathbb{A})$.

Theorem 2.6 ([8] Theorem 21) *A σ-structure $\mathbb{A}$ has tree duality if and only if there exists a homomorphism from $\mathcal{U}(\mathbb{A})$ to $\mathbb{A}$.*

This proves that determining whether a given structure $\mathbb{A}$ has tree duality is decidable, since a search for a homomorphism from $\mathcal{U}(\mathbb{A})$ to $\mathbb{A}$ can be done in finite time. In the next section, we provide similar "construction-and-homomorphism" characterisations of first-order definable constraint satisfaction problems.

3 Constructions

3.1 Quotients

Let $\mathbb{A} = \langle A; R_1(\mathbb{A}), \ldots, R_m(\mathbb{A})\rangle$ be a σ-structure and $\sim$ an equivalence relation on A. For $a \in A$ we denote $a/\sim$ the $\sim$-equivalence class containing a. The *quotient* $\mathbb{A}/\sim$ of $\mathbb{A}$ under $\sim$ is the σ-structure whose universe is the set of $\sim$-equivalence classes, where for $i = 1, \ldots, m$ we have $(C_1, \ldots, C_{r_i}) \in R_i(\mathbb{A}/\sim)$ if and only if there exist $a_j \in C_j$, $j = 1, \ldots, r_i$ such that $(a_1, \ldots, a_{r_i}) \in R_i(\mathbb{A})$. Note that the quotient map $q : \mathbb{A} \to \mathbb{A}/\sim$ where $q(a) = a/\sim$ is a homomorphism; in fact for every homomorphism $\phi : \mathbb{A} \to \mathbb{B}$, there is a natural equivalence $\sim$ (the "kernel" of ϕ) on A and an injective homomorphism $\psi : \mathbb{A}/\sim \to \mathbb{B}$ such that $\phi = \psi \circ q$.

Here we give a first application of quotients to reveal an important structural property of cores with tree duality. A σ-structure $\mathbb{A}$ is called *rigid* if the identity is the only homomorphism from $\mathbb{A}$ to itself.

Lemma 3.1 *Let $\mathbb{A}$ be a core with tree duality. Then $\mathbb{A}$ is rigid.*

Proof. Suppose that $\tau : \mathbb{A} \to \mathbb{A}$ is a homomorphism. Since $\mathbb{A}$ is a core, τ is an automorphism of $\mathbb{A}$ hence we can define an equivalence relation $\sim$ on A by putting $a \sim b$ if there exists an integer p such that $\tau^p(a) = b$. We will show that every tree which admits a homomorphism to $\mathbb{A}/\sim$ also admits a homomorphism to $\mathbb{A}$.

Let $\mathbb{T}$ be a tree which admits a homomorphism $\psi : \mathbb{T} \to \mathbb{A}/\sim$. Let $\mathbb{T} = \mathbb{T}_n, \mathbb{T}_{n-1}, \ldots, \mathbb{T}_1$ be the sequence of Lemma 2.2. For $k = 1, \ldots, n$, the restriction of ψ to the universe of $\mathbb{T}_k$ is a homomorphism $\psi_k : \mathbb{T}_k \to \mathbb{A}/\sim$; we recursively define a sequence $\phi_k : \mathbb{T}_k \to \mathbb{A}$ of homomorphisms such that $\psi_k = q \circ \phi_k$, where q is the quotient map from $\mathbb{A}$ to $\mathbb{A}/\sim$. First, $\mathbb{T}_1$ has just one hyperedge $(x_1, \ldots, x_{r_i}) \in R_i(\mathbb{T})$ for some i, and $(\psi(x_1), \ldots, \psi(x_{r_i})) \in R_i(\mathbb{A}/\sim)$. By definition of quotients this means that there exist $y_j \in \psi(x_j), j = 1, \ldots, r_i$

such that $(y_1, \dots, y_{r_i}) \in R_i(\mathbb{A})$, thus we can define $\phi_1 : \mathbb{T}_1 \to \mathbb{A}$ by $\phi_1(x_j) = y_j$. Now suppose that $\phi_{k-1} : \mathbb{T}_{k-1} \to \mathbb{A}/\sim$ is already defined. $\mathbb{T}_k$ is obtained from $\mathbb{T}_{k-1}$ by adding an hyperedge $(x_1, \dots, x_{r_i}) \in R_i(\mathbb{T})$ which has only one coordinate x_ℓ in the universe of $\mathbb{T}_{k-1}$. Again we have $(\psi(x_1), \dots, \psi(x_{r_i})) \in R_i(\mathbb{A}/\sim)$ and there exist $y_j \in \psi(x_j), j = 1, \dots, r_i$ such that $(y_1, \dots, y_{r_i}) \in R_i(\mathbb{A})$. Put $a = \phi_{k-1}(x_\ell) \in a/\sim = \psi(x_\ell)$. Then $y_\ell \sim a$ hence by the definition of $\sim$ there exists a power p such that $\tau^p(y_\ell) = a$. Since τ is a homomorphism, we then have $(\tau^p(y_1), \dots, \tau^p(y_{r_i})) \in R_i(\mathbb{A})$, and we can extend the definition of ϕ_{k-1} to that of $\phi_k : \mathbb{T}_k \to \mathbb{A}$ by putting $\phi_k(z) = \phi_{k-1}(z)$ if z is in the universe of $\mathbb{T}_{k-1}$, and $\phi_k(x_j) = \tau^p(y_j), j = 1, \dots, r_i$. Indeed ϕ_k is well defined since both definitions coincide on x_ℓ, it is a homomorphism since it preserves $(x_1, \dots, x_{r_i}) \in R_i(\mathbb{T})$ in addition to all the hyperedges preserved by ϕ_{k-1}, and $\phi_k(z) \in \psi_k(z)$ for all z in the universe of $\mathbb{T}_k$ whence $\psi_k(z) = q \circ \phi_k(z)$. In this way we eventually define a homomorphism $\phi = \phi_n$ from $\mathbb{T} = \mathbb{T}_n$ to $\mathbb{A}$.

Hence every tree which admits a homomorphism to $\mathbb{A}/\sim$ also admits a homomorphism to $\mathbb{A}$. Since $\mathbb{A}$ has tree duality this implies that $\mathbb{A}/\sim$ admits a homomorphism to $\mathbb{A}$. Since $\mathbb{A}$ is a core which admits a homomorphism to $\mathbb{A}/\sim$, this implies that $\sim$ cannot identify vertices, whence τ is the identity.

■

3.2 Products and powers

Given two σ-structures $\mathbb{A} = \langle A; R_1(\mathbb{A}), \dots, R_m(\mathbb{A})\rangle$ and $\mathbb{B} = \langle B; R_1(\mathbb{B}), \dots, R_m(\mathbb{B})\rangle$ their *product* is the σ-structure

$$\mathbb{A} \times \mathbb{B} = \langle A \times B; R_1(\mathbb{A} \times \mathbb{B}), \dots, R_m(\mathbb{A} \times \mathbb{B})\rangle,$$

where for $i = 1, \dots, m$, $R_i(\mathbb{A} \times \mathbb{B})$ consists of all tuples $((a_1, b_1), \dots, (a_{r_i}, b_{r_i}))$ such that $(a_1, \dots, a_{r_i}) \in R_i(\mathbb{A})$ and $(b_1, \dots, b_{r_i}) \in R_i(\mathbb{B})$. Both projections $\pi_1 : \mathbb{A} \times \mathbb{B} \to \mathbb{A}$ and $\pi_2 : \mathbb{A} \times \mathbb{B} \to \mathbb{B}$ are homomorphism and in general for any σ-structure $\mathbb{C}$ and any pair $\phi_1 : \mathbb{C} \to \mathbb{A}$, $\phi_2 : \mathbb{C} \to \mathbb{B}$ of homomorphisms there is a unique homomorphism $\phi : \mathbb{C} \to \mathbb{A} \times \mathbb{B}$ such that $\phi_1 = \pi_1 \circ \phi$ and $\phi_2 = \pi_2 \circ \phi$. The product is associative; the *n-th power* $\mathbb{A}^n$ of $\mathbb{A}$ is the product of n copies of $\mathbb{A}$. For any $n \geq 1$ an *n-ary operation on* $\mathbb{A}$ is a homomorphism from $\mathbb{A}^n$ to $\mathbb{A}$.

The *one-tolerant n-th power* ${}^1\mathbb{A}^n$ of $\mathbb{A}$ is the σ-structure $\langle A^n; R_1({}^1\mathbb{A}^n), \dots, R_m({}^1\mathbb{A}^n)\rangle$ where for $i = 1, \dots, m$, $R_i({}^1\mathbb{A}^n)$ consists of tuples $((a_{1,1}, \dots, a_{1,n}), \dots, (a_{r_i,1}, \dots, a_{r_i,n}))$ such that $|\{k : (a_{1,k}, \dots, a_{r_i,k}) \in R_i(\mathbb{A})\}| \geq n - 1$. In other words, ${}^1\mathbb{A}^n$ is obtained from $\mathbb{A}^n$ by adding to $R_i(\mathbb{A}^n)$ all hyperedges that are mapped to $R_i(\mathbb{A})$ by at least $n-1$ of the projections. In particular, the projections are not homomorphisms from ${}^1\mathbb{A}^n$ to $\mathbb{A}$ hence ${}^1\mathbb{A}^n$ does not necessarily admit a homomorphism to $\mathbb{A}$. However notice that removal of a coordinate is a homomorphism from ${}^1\mathbb{A}^{n+1}$ to ${}^1\mathbb{A}^n$.

Lemma 3.2 *There exists a homomorphism from ${}^1\mathbb{A}^{n+1}$ to $\mathbb{A}$ if and only if the critical obstructions of $\mathbb{A}$ have at most n hyperedges.*

Proof. Let $\mathbb{C}$ be a critical obstruction of $\mathbb{A}$ with m distinct hyperedges $e_1, \dots, e_m$, $m > n$. Then for $k = 1, \dots, m$, the σ-structure $\mathbb{C}_j$ obtained from $\mathbb{C}$ by removing e_k (without changing the universe) admits a homomorphism ϕ_k to $\mathbb{A}$. By definition of ${}^1\mathbb{A}^m$, the map $\phi = (\phi_1, \dots, \phi_m)$ is a homomorphism from $\mathbb{C}$ to ${}^1\mathbb{A}^m$. Therefore there is no homomorphism from ${}^1\mathbb{A}^m$ to $\mathbb{A}$, and in particular none from ${}^1\mathbb{A}^{n+1}$ to $\mathbb{A}$.

Conversely, suppose that there is no homomorphism from ${}^1\mathbb{A}^{n+1}$ to $\mathbb{A}$. Then there exists a critical obstruction $\mathbb{C}$ of $\mathbb{A}$ which admits a homomorphism ϕ to ${}^1\mathbb{A}^{n+1}$. For every coordinate $k = 1, \dots, n+1$, there exists an hyperedge e_k of $\mathbb{C}$ which is not respected by $\pi_k \circ \phi$, since $\pi_k \circ \phi$ is not a homomorphism from $\mathbb{C}$ to $\mathbb{A}$. By the definition of ${}^1\mathbb{A}^{n+1}$, e_k is respected by $\pi_j \circ \phi$ for every $j \neq k$, whence $e_j \neq e_k$ for $j \neq k$. Therefore $\mathbb{C}$ has at least $n+1$ hyperedges.

■

Corollary 3.3 *A σ-structure $\mathbb{A}$ has finitary duality if and only if there exists a positive integer n such that ${}^1\mathbb{A}^n$ admits a homomorphism to $\mathbb{A}$.*

Note that the homomorphisms from 1-tolerant powers of $\mathbb{A}$ to $\mathbb{A}$ are operations on $\mathbb{A}$. An operation $\phi : \mathbb{A}^n \to \mathbb{A}$ is called a *near unanimity operation* if it satisfies the identities

$$\phi(y, x, x, \dots, x) = \phi(x, y, x, \dots, x) = \cdots$$
$$\cdots = \phi(x, x, x, \dots, y) = x.$$

Proposition 3.4 *Let $\mathbb{A}$ be a core with finitary duality. Then every homomorphism from a 1-tolerant power of $\mathbb{A}$ to $\mathbb{A}$ is a near unanimity operation.*

Proof. Let $\phi : {}^1\mathbb{A}^n \to \mathbb{A}$ be a homomorphism. For every $y \in A$ and $k \in \{1, \dots, n\}$, consider the homomorphism $\psi_{y,k} : \mathbb{A} \to {}^1\mathbb{A}^n$ defined by $\psi_{y,k}(x) = (x_1, \dots, x_n)$ where $x_j = y$ if $j = k$ and $x_j = x$ otherwise. By Lemma 3.1, $\mathbb{A}$ is rigid whence the map $\phi \circ \psi_{y,k} : \mathbb{A} \to \mathbb{A}$ is the identity. Thus for every $x, y \in A$ and $k \in \{1, \dots, n\}$ we have $\phi(\psi_{y,k}(x)) = x$, and this is precisely the definition of a near unanimity operation.

■

Corollary 3.5 *Every core relational structure with a first-order definable CSP admits a near unanimity operation.*

3.3 Products of links and squares

Recall from Section 2 that the n-link $\mathbb{L}_n$ of type σ has universe $\{0,1,\ldots,n\}$. For a σ-structure $\mathbb{C}$, a map ϕ from its universe to $\{0,1,\ldots,n\}$ is a homomorphism from $\mathbb{C}$ to $\mathbb{L}_n$ if and only if $|\phi(x)-\phi(y)|\leq 1$ whenever x and y are in a common hyperedge.

Given a σ-structure $\mathbb{A}=\langle A;R_1(\mathbb{A}),\ldots,R_m(\mathbb{A})\rangle$, note that the product $\mathbb{L}_n\times\mathbb{A}^2$ has diameter at least n since for any $a,a',b,b'\in A$ the distance between $(0,a,b)$ and (n,a',b') is at least n. Let $\sim_n$ be the equivalence relation defined on $\mathbb{L}_n\times\mathbb{A}^2$ by

$$(k,a,b)\sim_n(k',a',b')\equiv\begin{cases}(k,a,b)=(k',a',b')\\ \text{or } k=k'=0 \text{ and } a=a'\\ \text{or } k=k'=n \text{ and } b=b'.\end{cases}$$

Note that $\mathbb{L}_n\times\mathbb{A}^2/\!\sim_n$ also has diameter at least n.

Lemma 3.6 *The substructures $\mathbb{B}_0$ and $\mathbb{B}_n$ of $\mathbb{L}_n\times\mathbb{A}^2/\!\sim_n$ induced by $B_0=\{(k,a,b)/\!\sim_n\colon k\neq 0\}$ and $B_n=\{(k,a,b)/\!\sim_n\colon k\neq n\}$ respectively both admit homomorphisms to $\mathbb{A}$.*

Proof. On B_0 we can define a map ϕ to A by $\phi((k,a,b)/\!\sim_n)=b$. We show that ϕ is a homomorphism from $\mathbb{B}_0$ to $\mathbb{A}$. For $R_i\in\sigma$ and $((k_1,a_1,b_1)/\!\sim_n,\ldots,(k_{r_i},a_{r_i},b_{r_i})/\!\sim_n)\in R_i(\mathbb{B}_0)$, there exist $(k'_j,a'_j,b'_j)\in(k_j,a_j,b_j)/\!\sim_n$, $j=1,\ldots,r_i$ such that $((k'_1,a'_1,b'_1),\ldots,(k'_{r_i},a'_{r_i},b'_{r_i}))\in R_i(\mathbb{L}_n\times\mathbb{A}^2)$. We then have that

$$(\phi((k_1,a_1,b_1)/\!\sim_n),\ldots,\phi((k_{r_i},a_{r_i},b_{r_i})/\!\sim_n))$$

is equal to $(b'_1,\ldots,b'_{r_i})$ which is in $R_i(\mathbb{A})$, thus ϕ is a homomorphism. Similarly, we can define a homomorphism $\psi:\mathbb{B}_n\to\mathbb{A}$ by $\psi((k,a,b)/\!\sim_n)=a$.

■

Proposition 3.7 *A σ-structure $\mathbb{A}$ has critical obstructions of bounded diameter if and only if there exists a positive integer n such that $\mathbb{L}_n\times\mathbb{A}^2/\!\sim_n$ admits a homomorphism to $\mathbb{A}$.*

Proof. By the previous lemma, any critical obstruction of $\mathbb{A}$ contained in $\mathbb{L}_n\times\mathbb{A}^2/\!\sim_n$ must contain an element with first coordinate 0 and an element with first coordinate n (the first coordinates are invariants of $\sim_n$-equivalence classes) thus have diameter at least n. Hence if n is larger than the diameter of all the critical obstructions of $\mathbb{A}$, then $\mathbb{L}_n\times\mathbb{A}^2/\!\sim_n$ admits a homomorphism to $\mathbb{A}$.

Now suppose that $\mathbb{A}$ has critical obstructions of arbitrary large diameter. We will show that for every integer n there exists an obstruction $\mathbb{C}$ of $\mathbb{A}$ which admits a homomorphism to $\mathbb{L}_n\times\mathbb{A}^2/\!\sim_n$. Let $\mathbb{C}=\langle C;R_1(\mathbb{C}),\ldots,R_m(\mathbb{C})\rangle$ be an obstruction of $\mathbb{A}$ with diameter at least $n+2$. Let x and y be elements of C at distance $n+2$, and $\mathbb{C}_x$, $\mathbb{C}_y$ the substructures of $\mathbb{C}$ induced respectively by $C\setminus\{x\}$ and $C\setminus\{y\}$. Fix homomorphisms $\alpha:\mathbb{C}_y\to\mathbb{A}$ and $\beta:\mathbb{C}_x\to\mathbb{A}$ and define $\kappa:C\to\{0,\ldots,n\}$ by

$$\kappa(z)=\begin{cases}0 \text{ if } z=x,\\ d_{\mathbb{C}}(x,z)-1 \text{ if } d_{\mathbb{C}}(x,z)\leq n+1 \text{ and } z\neq x,\\ n \text{ if } d_{\mathbb{C}}(x,z)\geq n+2;\end{cases}$$

note that κ is a homomorphism from $\mathbb{C}$ to $\mathbb{L}_n$. We fix an element $p\in A$ and define a map ϕ from C to the universe of $\mathbb{L}_n\times\mathbb{A}^2/\!\sim_n$ by

$$\phi(z)=\begin{cases}(\kappa(z),\alpha(z),\beta(z))/\!\sim_n \text{ if } z\neq x,y,\\ (\kappa(z),\alpha(z),p)/\!\sim_n \text{ if } z=x,\\ (\kappa(z),p,\beta(z))/\!\sim_n \text{ if } z=y.\end{cases}$$

We will show that ϕ is a homomorphism from $\mathbb{C}$ to $\mathbb{L}_n\times\mathbb{A}^2/\!\sim_n$.

Let $(z_1,\ldots,z_{r_i})$ be in $R_i(\mathbb{C})$ for some $R_i\in\sigma$. If $z_j\notin\{x,y\}$ for all $j\in\{1,\ldots,r_i\}$, then $(\phi(z_1),\ldots,\phi(z_{r_i}))=((\kappa(z_1),\alpha(z_1),\beta(z_1))/\!\sim_n,\ldots,(\kappa(z_{r_i}),\alpha(z_{r_i}),\beta(z_{r_i}))/\!\sim_n$ which belongs to $R_i(\mathbb{L}_n\times\mathbb{A}^2/\!\sim_n)$ since κ,α,β and the quotient map from $\mathbb{L}_n\times\mathbb{A}^2$ to $\mathbb{L}_n\times\mathbb{A}^2/\!\sim_n$ are homomorphisms. If there exists an index $\hat{j}$ such that $z_{\hat{j}}=x$, then $\kappa(z_j)=0$ for $j=1,\ldots,r_i$ whence $\phi(z_j)=(0,\alpha(z_j),\alpha(z_j))/\!\sim_n$ for $j=1,\ldots,r_i$ by definition of $\sim_n$; therefore $(\phi(z_1),\ldots,\phi(z_{r_i}))$ is equal to $((0,\alpha(z_1),\alpha(z_1))/\!\sim_n,\ldots,(0,\alpha(z_{r_i}),\alpha(z_{r_i}))/\!\sim_n)$ which is in $R_i(\mathbb{L}_n\times\mathbb{A}^2/\!\sim_n)$. Similarly if there exists an index $\hat{j}$ such that $z_{\hat{j}}=y$, then $(\phi(z_1),\ldots,\phi(z_{r_i}))=((n,\beta(z_1),\beta(z_1))/\!\sim_n,\ldots,(n,\beta(z_{r_i}),\beta(z_{r_i}))/\!\sim_n)\in R_i(\mathbb{L}_n\times\mathbb{A}^2/\!\sim_n)$. Thus ϕ is a homomorphism.

Since there exists a homomorphism from an obstruction of $\mathbb{A}$ to $\mathbb{L}_n\times\mathbb{A}^2/\!\sim_n$ we conclude that there is no homomorphism from $\mathbb{L}_n\times\mathbb{A}^2/\!\sim_n$ to $\mathbb{A}$.

■

By Theorem 2.5, Corollary 3.3 and Proposition 3.7 we have the following characterisations:

Theorem 3.8 *Let $\mathbb{A}$ be a σ-structure. Then the following are equivalent.*

1. *$\mathbb{A}$-CSP is first-order definable;*
2. *For some n there exists a homomorphism from ${}^1\mathbb{A}^n$ to $\mathbb{A}$;*
3. *For some n there exists a homomorphism from $\mathbb{L}_n\times\mathbb{A}^2/\!\sim_n$ to $\mathbb{A}$.*

At first glance our situation vis-a-vis the decidability question appears no better than before, but a closer look at the third condition in the above theorem reveals an upper bound on n: indeed, for $0 \le k \le n$, the restriction ϕ_k of a homomorphism $\phi : \mathbb{L}_n \times \mathbb{A}^2/{\sim_n} \to \mathbb{A}$ to $\{k\} \times \mathbb{A}^2/{\sim_n}$ corresponds to a homomorphism from $\mathbb{A}^2$ to $\mathbb{A}$, and there are at most $|A|^{|A|^2}$ of these. If for $k < k'$ we have $\phi_k = \phi_{k'}$, then for $n' = n - k' + k$ we can define a homomorphism $\phi' : \mathbb{L}_{n'} \times \mathbb{A}^2/{\sim_{n'}} \to \mathbb{A}$ by removing the useless middle part. Therefore to determine whether $\mathbb{A}$-CSP is first-order definable it suffices to search for a homomorphism $\phi : \mathbb{L}_n \times \mathbb{A}^2/{\sim_n} \to \mathbb{A}$ with $n \le |A|^{|A|^2}$, and this is a finite decision procedure.

We can refine this argument by defining a graph structure on the set of all homomorphisms from $\mathbb{A}^2$ to $\mathbb{A}$, where two homomorphisms ψ, ψ' are called *adjacent* if there exists a homomorphism $\phi : \mathbb{L}_1 \times \mathbb{A}^2 \to \mathbb{A}$ such that $\phi_0 = \psi$ and $\phi_1 = \psi'$. A homomorphism from $\mathbb{L}_n \times \mathbb{A}^2/{\sim_n}$ to $\mathbb{A}$ then corresponds to a link of length n between a homomorphism $\phi_0 : \mathbb{A}^2 \to \mathbb{A}$ which factors through the first projection and a homomorphism $\phi_n : \mathbb{A}^2 \to \mathbb{A}$ which factors through the second projection. Since undirected reachability can be solved in logarithmic space, in our exponential setting this means that the search can be performed in polynomial space. In the next section this idea is developed further and we prove that the problem of determining whether $\mathbb{A}$-CSP is first-order definable is actually in **NP**.

4 Dismantlability

4.1 Preliminaries

Let $\mathbb{A} = \langle A; R_1(\mathbb{A}), \ldots, R_m(\mathbb{A})\rangle$ be a σ-structure. For $x, y \in A$ we say that *y dominates x in* $\mathbb{A}$, if for every $R_i \in \sigma$, $j \in \{1, \ldots, r_i\}$ and $(x_1, \ldots, x_{r_i}) \in R_i(\mathbb{A})$ with $x_j = x$ we also have $(y_1, \ldots, y_{r_i}) \in R_i(\mathbb{A})$ with $y_j = y$ and $y_k = x_k$ for all $k \neq j$. For instance, if R_i is ternary and $(x, t, x) \in R_i(\mathbb{A})$, then for y to dominate x we must have $(y, t, x) \in R_i(\mathbb{A})$ and $(x, t, y) \in R_i(\mathbb{A})$, each of which also implies $(y, t, y) \in R_i(\mathbb{A})$. We say that *$x$ is dominated in* $\mathbb{A}$ if it is dominated by some element $y \in A \setminus \{x\}$. We say that $\mathbb{A}$ *dismantles to* its induced substructure $\mathbb{B}$ if there exists a sequence $x_1, \ldots, x_k$ of distinct elements of A such that $A \setminus B = \{x_1, \ldots, x_k\}$ and for each $1 \le i \le k$ the element x_i is dominated in the structure induced by $B \cup \{x_i, \ldots, x_k\}$. In other words, the structure $\mathbb{B}$ can be obtained from $\mathbb{A}$ by successively removing dominated elements; the sequence $x_1, \ldots, x_k$ is then called a *dismantling sequence*. Note that if $\mathbb{A}_x$ is the substructure of $\mathbb{A}$ induced by $A \setminus \{x\}$, where x is dominated by y in $\mathbb{A}$, then we can define a retraction $\rho : \mathbb{A} \to \mathbb{A}_x$ by putting $\rho(x) = y$ and $\rho(z) = z$ for all $z \neq x$. Using composition we then see that if $\mathbb{A}$ dismantles to $\mathbb{B}$ then $\mathbb{B}$ is a retract of $\mathbb{A}$ (the converse does not hold in general). Our first result shows that "dismantling $\mathbb{A}$ to $\mathbb{B}$" can be done greedily.

Lemma 4.1 *Let $\mathbb{A}, \mathbb{B}$ be σ-structures such that $\mathbb{A}$ dismantles to $\mathbb{B}$. Then for every dominated element $a \in A \setminus B$ of $\mathbb{A}$, the substructure $\mathbb{A}_a$ of $\mathbb{A}$ induced by $A \setminus \{a\}$ dismantles to $\mathbb{B}$.*

Proof. Let $x_1, \ldots, x_k$ be a dismantling sequence of $\mathbb{A}$ on $\mathbb{B}$. Note that for some index j we have $x_j = a$. We will show that by removing x_j and perhaps rearranging the sequence we get a dismantling sequence of $\mathbb{A}_a$ on $\mathbb{B}$. For $i = 1, \ldots, k$ let y_i be an element dominating x_i in the substructure $\mathbb{A}_i$ of $\mathbb{A}$ induced by $B \cup \{x_i, \ldots, x_k\}$. Note that for some indices i there may be many choices for y_i, and whenever $y_i \neq a$, y_i also dominates x_i in the substructure of $\mathbb{A}_a$ induced by $B \cup \{x_i, \ldots, x_k\} \setminus \{x_j\}$. Thus it suffices to show that for all $i \in \{1, \ldots, k\}$, we can select y_i other than a.

Let i be the smallest index such that $y_i = a$, and let b be an element dominating a in $\mathbb{A}$. Note that if $b \notin \{x_1, \ldots, x_{i-1}\}$, then b also dominates x_i in the substructure of $\mathbb{A}_a$ induced by $B \cup \{x_i, \ldots, x_k\} \setminus \{x_j\}$, hence we can select $y_i = b$ instead. Thus we can assume that $b = x_{i'}$ for some $i' < i$. We then define a finite increasing sequence $i_0, i_1, \ldots, i_\ell$ by putting $i_0 = i'$, and letting i_{p+1} be the index in $\{i_p + 1, \ldots, i - 1\}$ such that $y_{i_p} = x_{i_{p+1}}$ if such an index exists. Then x_i is dominated by a in $\mathbb{A}_i$, which is dominated by $b = x_{i_0}$ in $\mathbb{A}$. For $p = 0, \ldots, \ell - 1$, x_{i_p} is dominated by $y_{i_p} = x_{i_{p+1}}$ in $\mathbb{A}_{i_p}$, and x_{i_ℓ} is dominated by $y_{i_\ell} \neq a$ in $\mathbb{A}_{i_\ell}$. If $y_{i_\ell} \neq x_i$, then y_{i_ℓ} also dominates x_i in $\mathbb{A}_i$ hence we can select $y_i = y_{i_\ell}$ instead of $y_i = a$. If $y_{i_\ell} = x_i$, then x_i and $a = x_j$ dominate each other in $\mathbb{A}_i$. In this case, $x_1, \ldots, x_{i-1}$ is a dismantling sequence of $\mathbb{A}_a$ on its substructure induced by $B \cup \{x_i, \ldots, x_{j-1}\} \cup \{x_{j+1}, \ldots, x_k\}$, which is isomorphic to $\mathbb{A}_{i+1}$ via an isomorphism which fixes B, whence $\mathbb{A}_a$ dismantles to $\mathbb{B}$.

■

4.2 Exponentiation

Let $\mathbb{A}$ and $\mathbb{B}$ be two σ-structures. The *$\mathbb{A}$-th power of $\mathbb{B}$* is the σ-structure

$$\mathbb{B}^{\mathbb{A}} = \langle B^A; R_1(\mathbb{B}^{\mathbb{A}}), \ldots, R_m(\mathbb{B}^{\mathbb{A}})\rangle,$$

where B^A is the set of all maps from A to B, and for $i = 1, \ldots, m$ the relation $R_i(\mathbb{B}^{\mathbb{A}})$ consists of all hyperedges $(f_1, \ldots, f_{r_i})$ such that $(f_1(x_1), \ldots, f_{r_i}(x_{r_i})) \in R_i(\mathbb{B})$ whenever $(x_1, \ldots, x_{r_i}) \in R_i(\mathbb{A})$ (see [13]). This definition is derived from the following correspondence, whose proof is straightforward.

Lemma 4.2 *Let $\phi : \mathbb{A} \times \mathbb{C} \to \mathbb{B}$ be a homomorphism. Then the map $\psi : C \to B^A$ defined by $\psi(c) = f_c$, where $f_c(a) = \phi(a, c)$, is a homomorphism from $\mathbb{C}$ to $\mathbb{B}^{\mathbb{A}}$. Conversely, if $\psi : \mathbb{C} \to \mathbb{B}^{\mathbb{A}}$ is a homomorphism, then the map $\phi : A \times$*

$C \to B$ *defined by* $\phi(a, c) = \phi(c)(a)$ *is a homomorphism from* $\mathbb{A} \times \mathbb{C}$ *to* $\mathbb{B}$.

In particular the homomorphisms from $\mathbb{A}$ to itself can be viewed as homomorphisms from the product of $\mathbb{A}$ and a loop to $\mathbb{A}$, which then correspond to loops in $\mathbb{A}^{\mathbb{A}}$.

Now suppose that a is dominated by b in $\mathbb{A}$, and let ρ be the retraction which maps a to b and fixes every other element of A. Then, considered as an element of $\mathbb{A}^{\mathbb{A}}$, ρ is a "neighbour" of the identity in the sense that there exists a homomorphism ψ from the 1-link $\mathbb{L}_1$ to $\mathbb{A}^{\mathbb{A}}$ defined by $\psi(0) = \mathrm{id}_A$ and $\psi(1) = \rho$. The main result of this section is a generalisation of this observation to the dismantling process in general.

Lemma 4.3 *Let* $\mathbb{A}$ *be a* σ*-structure and let* $\mathbb{B}$ *be a substructure of* $\mathbb{A}$. *Then* $\mathbb{A}$ *dismantles to* $\mathbb{B}$ *if and only if there exist some* $n \geq 0$ *and a homomorphism* $P : \mathbb{L}_n \to \mathbb{A}^{\mathbb{A}}$ *such that*

(i) $P(0) = id_A$,

(ii) B *is fixed pointwise by* $P(t)$ *for every* $t = 0, \ldots, n$,

(iii) $P(n)$ *is a retraction onto* B.

We call two homomorphisms $f, g : \mathbb{A} \to \mathbb{A}$ *adjacent* if there is a homomorphism P from $\mathbb{L}_1$ to $\mathbb{A}^{\mathbb{A}}$ such that $P(0) = f$ and $P(1) = g$. Hence Lemma 4.3 states that $\mathbb{A}$ dismantles to $\mathbb{B}$ if and only if there is a link of homomorphisms fixing B pointwise which joins the identity on A to a retraction onto B. The proof will use the following property of composition in powers, whose proof is a straightforward application of the definition.

Lemma 4.4 *Let* $\mathbb{A}, \mathbb{B}, \mathbb{C}$ *be* σ*-structures. Then the map* $\phi : \mathbb{A}^{\mathbb{B}} \times \mathbb{B}^{\mathbb{C}} \to \mathbb{A}^{\mathbb{C}}$ *defined by* $\phi(f, g) = f \circ g$ *is a homomorphism. In particular for any integer* p, *the map* $\varepsilon_p : \mathbb{A}^{\mathbb{A}} \to \mathbb{A}^{\mathbb{A}}$ *defined by* $\varepsilon_p(f) = f^p$ *is a homomorphism.*

For every $f \in A^A$, and $a \in A$, there exist integers $0 \leq i < j \leq |A|$ such that we have $f^j(a) = f^i(a)$; we say that a has *finite period under* f if we can take $i = 0$. For $p = |A|!$, we then have $f^p(a) = a$ if a has finite period under f, and otherwise $f^p(a)$ has finite period under f. Thus f^p is a set-theoretic retraction of A onto the set of its elements of finite period under f. Therefore for $p = |A|!$, the homomorphism ε_p defined in Lemma 4.4 is a retraction of $\mathbb{A}^{\mathbb{A}}$ onto its substructure induced by the set-theoretic retractions of A.

Proof. [of Lemma 4.3] Suppose that $\mathbb{A}$ dismantles to $\mathbb{B}$, and let $x_1, \ldots, x_k$ be a dismantling sequence of $\mathbb{A}$ on $\mathbb{B}$. For $t = 1, \ldots, k$, let y_t be an element dominating x_t in the substructure of $\mathbb{A}$ induced by $B \cup \{x_i, \ldots, x_k\}$. We define a sequence $\rho_0, \rho_1, \ldots, \rho_k$ of retractions inductively by $\rho_0 = \mathrm{id}_A$, $\rho_t(z) = y_t$ if $\rho_{t-1}(z) = x_t$ and $\rho_t(z) = \rho_{t-1}(z)$ otherwise. Let $P : \mathbb{L}_k \to \mathbb{A}^{\mathbb{A}}$ be defined by $P(t) = \rho_t$. Then $P(0)$ is the identity, B is fixed by each $P(t)$, and $P(k)$ is a retraction onto B. We show that P is a homomorphism.

For $R_i \in \sigma$, let $(t_1, \ldots, t_{r_i})$ be an element of $R_i(\mathbb{L}_k)$. Then there exists an index $t \in \{1, \ldots, k\}$ and a subset J of $\{1, \ldots, r_i\}$ such that $t_j = t$ if $j \in J$ and $t_j = t - 1$ otherwise. We then have $(P(t_1), \ldots, P(t_{r_i})) = (f_1, \ldots, f_{r_i})$ where $f_j = \rho_t$ if $j \in J$ and $f_j = \rho_{t-1}$ otherwise. For every $(a_1, \ldots, a_{r_i}) \in R_i(\mathbb{A})$, we have $(\rho_{t-1}(a_1), \ldots, \rho_{t-1}(a_{r_i})) \in R_i(\mathbb{A})$, since ρ_{t-1} is a homomorphism. Now $(f_1(a_1), \ldots, f_{r_i}(a_{r_i}))$ coincides with $(\rho_{t-1}(a_1), \ldots, \rho_{t-1}(a_{r_i}))$ except for some possible coordinates in J where y_t replaces x_t. Since $\{\rho_{t-1}(a_1), \ldots, \rho_{t-1}(a_{r_i})\} \subseteq B \cup \{x_t \ldots, x_k\}$ and y_t dominates x_t in the substructure of $\mathbb{A}$ induced by that subset, we then have $(f_1(a_1), \ldots, f_{r_i}(a_{r_i})) \in R_i(\mathbb{A})$. Thus $(f_1, \ldots, f_{r_i}) \in R_i(\mathbb{A}^{\mathbb{A}})$. This shows that P is a homomorphism.

Conversely, suppose that $P : \mathbb{L}_n \to \mathbb{A}^{\mathbb{A}}$ is a homomorphism such that for $\phi_t = P(t), t = 0, \ldots, n$ we have $\phi_0 = \mathrm{id}_A$, B is fixed pointwise by each ϕ_t and ϕ_n is a retraction onto B. Put $p = |A|!$. We define three maps as follows.

(i) $P' : \mathbb{L}_n \to \mathbb{A}^{\mathbb{A}}$ is defined by $P'(t) = \rho_t := \phi_t^p$. Thus $P' = \varepsilon_p \circ P$, which is a homomorphism by Lemma 4.4.

(ii) $P'' : \mathbb{L}_n \to \mathbb{A}^{\mathbb{A}}$, where $P''(t) = \psi_t$ is defined recursively by $\psi_0 = \rho_0$ and $\psi_t = \psi_{t-1} \circ \rho_t$ for $t = 1, \ldots, n$. By Lemma 4.4, $\psi_t = \psi_{t-1} \circ \rho_t$ is adjacent to $\psi_{t-1} \circ \rho_{t-1} = \psi_{t-1}$, whence P'' is a homomorphism.

(iii) $P''' = \varepsilon_p \circ P'' : \mathbb{L}_n \to \mathbb{A}^{\mathbb{A}}$ is a homomorphism by Lemma 4.4.

Note that $P'''(0) = P''(0) = P'(0) = P(0) = \mathrm{id}_A$, and since every $P(t)$ fixes B, $P'''(n) = P''(n) = P'(n) = P(n)$ which is a retraction onto B. Also, for $t = 1, \ldots, n$, $\hat{\rho}_t := P'''(t)$ is a retraction whose image $\mathrm{im}(\hat{\rho}_t)$ is contained in that of $\hat{\rho}_{t-1}$. We can then show that every $a \in \mathrm{im}(\hat{\rho}_{t-1}) \setminus \mathrm{im}(\hat{\rho}_t)$ is dominated by $\hat{\rho}_t(a)$ in the substructure $\mathbb{A}_{t-1}$ of $\mathbb{A}$ induced by $\mathrm{im}(\hat{\rho}_{t-1})$. Indeed, for $R_i \in \sigma$ and $(a_1, \ldots, a_{r_i}) \in R_i(\mathbb{A}_{t-1})$ such that $a_j = a$ for some index j, we have that $(\hat{\rho}_{t-1}(a_1), \ldots, \hat{\rho}_{t-1}(a_{j-1}), \hat{\rho}_t(a_j), \hat{\rho}_{t-1}(a_{j+1}), \ldots, \hat{\rho}_{t-1}(a_{r_i}))$ is in $R_i(\mathbb{A})$ since $\hat{\rho}_t$ is adjacent to $\hat{\rho}_{t-1}$, whence $\hat{\rho}_t(a)$ dominates a in $\mathbb{A}_{t-1}$. Therefore $\mathbb{A}$ dismantles to its substructure induced by $\hat{\rho}_n(A) = B$.

■

4.3 $\mathbb{A}^{(\mathbb{A}^2)}$ and $(\mathbb{A}^2)^{(\mathbb{A}^2)}$

Here we interpret Proposition 3.7 in terms of exponential structures. For a σ-structure $\mathbb{A}$ we denote π_1 and π_2 the two projections of $\mathbb{A}^2$ on $\mathbb{A}$. The *diagonal* of $\mathbb{A}^2$ is its substructure $\Delta_{\mathbb{A}^2}$ induced by $\{(a,a) : a \in A\}$.

Lemma 4.5 *Let $\mathbb{A}$ be a σ-structure and n an integer. If there exists a homomorphism $P : \mathbb{L}_n \to \mathbb{A}^{(\mathbb{A}^2)}$ such that $P(0) = \pi_1$ and $P(n) = \pi_2$, then there exists a homomorphism from $\mathbb{L}_n \times \mathbb{A}^2/{\sim_n}$ to $\mathbb{A}$. If $\mathbb{A}$ is a core, the converse also holds.*

Lemma 4.6 *Let $\mathbb{A}$ be a σ-structure. If $\mathbb{A}^2$ dismantles to its diagonal, then for some n there exists a homomorphism $P : \mathbb{L}_n \to \mathbb{A}^{(\mathbb{A}^2)}$ such that $P(0) = \pi_1$ and $P(n) = \pi_2$. If $\mathbb{A}$ is a core, the converse also holds.*

Proof. [of Lemma 4.5] By Lemma 4.2 a homomorphism $P : \mathbb{L}_n \to \mathbb{A}^{(\mathbb{A}^2)}$ corresponds to the homomorphism $\phi : \mathbb{L}_n \times \mathbb{A}^2 \to \mathbb{A}$ defined by $\phi(i,a,b) = P(i)(a,b)$. If $P(0) = \pi_1$ and $P(n) = \pi_2$, then ϕ is constant on every $\sim_n$-equivalence class, hence we can define a homomorphism $\psi : \mathbb{L}_n \times \mathbb{A}^2/{\sim_n} \to \mathbb{A}$ by $\psi((t,a,b)/{\sim_n}) = \phi(t,a,b)$.

Conversely, any homomorphism $\psi : \mathbb{L}_n \times \mathbb{A}^2/{\sim_n} \to \mathbb{A}$ can be composed with the quotient map $q : \mathbb{L}_n \times \mathbb{A}^2 \to \mathbb{L}_n \times \mathbb{A}^2/{\sim_n}$ to give a homomorphism $q \circ \psi : \mathbb{L}_n \times \mathbb{A}^2 \to \mathbb{A}$. By Lemma 4.2, $q \circ \psi$ corresponds to a homomorphism $P : \mathbb{L}_n \to \mathbb{A}^{(\mathbb{A}^2)}$, and by definition of $\sim_n$ there exist homomorphisms ϕ_1, ϕ_2 from $\mathbb{A}$ to itself such that $P(0) = \phi_1 \circ \pi_1$ and $P(n) = \phi_2 \circ \pi_2$. If $\mathbb{A}$ is a core, then by Lemma 3.1, ϕ_1 and ϕ_2 are both the identity, whence $P(0) = \pi_1$ and $P(n) = \pi_2$.

■

Proof. [of Lemma 4.6] Suppose that $\mathbb{A}^2$ dismantles to its diagonal $\Delta_{\mathbb{A}^2}$. By Lemma 4.3, for some n there exists a homomorphism $P : \mathbb{L}_n \to (\mathbb{A}^2)^{(\mathbb{A}^2)}$ such that $P(0)$ is the identity and $P(n)$ is a retraction on $\Delta_{\mathbb{A}^2}$. We can then define a homomorphism $P' : \mathbb{L}_{2n} \to \mathbb{A}^{(\mathbb{A}^2)}$ by $P'(t) = \pi_1 \circ P(t)$ and $P'(2n-t) = \pi_2 \circ P(t)$ for $t = 0, \dots, n$. Indeed both definitions of $P'(n)$ coincide since $P(n)$ is a retraction on $\Delta_{\mathbb{A}^2}$, and since $P(0)$ is the identity, $P'(0) = \pi_1$ and $P'(2n) = \pi_2$.

Conversely, for every homomorphism $P : \mathbb{L}_n \to \mathbb{A}^{(\mathbb{A}^2)}$ such that $P(0) = \pi_1$ and $P(n) = \pi_2$, we can define a homomorphism $P' : \mathbb{L}_n \to (\mathbb{A}^2)^{(\mathbb{A}^2)}$ by $P'(t) = (P(t), \pi_2)$. Then $P'(0) = (\pi_1, \pi_2)$ is the identity and $P'(n) = (\pi_2, \pi_2)$ is a retraction on $\Delta_{\mathbb{A}^2}$. If $\mathbb{A}$ is a core, then since $\Delta_{\mathbb{A}^2}$ is isomorphic to $\mathbb{A}$ via the canonical isomorphism, the restriction of every $P(t)$ to $\Delta_{\mathbb{A}^2}$ must coincide with π_2 by Lemma 3.1. Hence for $t = 0, \dots, n$, $P'(t)$ fixes $\Delta_{\mathbb{A}^2}$. Therefore $\mathbb{A}^2$ dismantles to $\mathbb{A}$ by Lemma 4.3.

■

Let $\mathbb{A}$ be a relational structure such that $\mathbb{A}^2$ dismantles to $\Delta_{\mathbb{A}^2}$. Then by Lemma 4.6, $\mathbb{A}^{(\mathbb{A}^2)}$ contains a link between the two projections, thus for some n there exists a homomorphism from $\mathbb{L}_n \times \mathbb{A}^2/{\sim_n}$ to $\mathbb{A}$ by Lemma 4.5. Hence, by Theorem 3.8, $\mathbb{A}$-CSP is first-order definable. The converse does not hold in general. However, for any retract $\mathbb{B}$ of $\mathbb{A}$, $\mathbb{A}$-CSP is equivalent to $\mathbb{B}$-CSP. In particular, if $\mathbb{B}$ is the core of $\mathbb{A}$ and $\mathbb{A}$-CSP is first-order definable, then Theorem 3.8, Lemma 4.5 and Lemma 4.6 imply that $\mathbb{B}^2$ dismantles to $\Delta_{\mathbb{B}^2}$. Therefore we have proved the following:

Theorem 4.7 *A relational structure has a first-order definable CSP if and only if it has a retract whose square dismantles to its diagonal.*

5 The complexity of recognising first-order definable CSPs

Theorem 5.1 *The problem of determining whether a relational structure $\mathbb{A}$ has a first-order definable CSP is* **NP**-*complete.*

In fact, we will show the problem to be **NP**-complete even in the restricted case of directed graphs. We contrast this with the following result in the case of cores:

Theorem 5.2 *The problem of determining whether a relational structure $\mathbb{A}$ is a core with a first-order definable CSP can be solved in polynomial time.*

Proof. [of Theorem 5.1] Theorem 4.7 shows that the problem is in **NP**. We will show that 3-SAT reduces to the problem of determining whether a given digraph has first-order definable CSP. Let $\mathcal{I} = \bigwedge_{i=0}^{n-1} (L_{i,1} \vee L_{i,2} \vee L_{i,3})$ be an instance of 3-SAT, where each literal is one of the variables $x_1, \dots, x_m$ or its negation, and (without loss of generality) $L_{i,j} \neq L_{i,j'}$ when $j \neq j'$. We construct a digraph H such that $\mathcal{I}$ is satisfiable if and only if H has first-order definable CSP. The vertex-set of H is $\{0, \dots, n-1\} \times \{1,2,3\}$, and there is an arc from (i,j) to (i',j') if and only if $i < i'$ and $L_{i,j}$ is not the negation of $L_{i',j'}$.

Thus the map ϕ from H to the transitive tournament T_n on n vertices defined by $\phi(i,j) = i$ is a homomorphism. Furthermore it is not hard to see that for every tree A which admits a homomorphism $\psi : A \mapsto T_n$, there exists a homomorphism $\hat{\psi} : A \mapsto H$ such that $\psi = \phi \circ \hat{\psi}$. Thus the trees that map to H are precisely those which map to T_n.

Since T_n has finite duality [15], this means that H has first-order definable CSP if and only if T_n is the core of H by Theorem 2.5.

If $\mathcal{I}$ is satisfiable, then selecting for each i an index j_i such that L_{i,j_i} is true yields a homomorphic image $\{(i, j_i) : 1 \leq i \leq n\}$ of T_n in H. Conversely, if $\{(i, j_i) : 1 \leq i \leq n\}$ is a homomorphic image of T_n in H, then we can consistently deem the literals L_{i,j_i} to be true to find a satisfactory truth assignment of $\mathcal{I}$. Therefore $\mathcal{I}$ is satisfiable if and only if H has first-order definable CSP.

■

Proof. [of Theorem 5.2] We first test whether $\mathbb{A}^2$ dismantles to $\Delta_{\mathbb{A}^2}$. According to Lemma 4.1 this step can be performed in polynomial time using the greedy algorithm. If the answer is negative, then either $\mathbb{A}$ is not a core, or it is a core which does not have a first-order definable CSP. In any case, we output "no" and stop. If the answer is positive, then $\mathbb{A}$ does have first-order definable CSP, but it may not be a core. For each pair $a, b \in A, a \neq b$ we form the quotient $\mathbb{A}_{\{a,b\}}$ of $\mathbb{A}$ under the equivalence which identifies a and b. By Theorem 2.5, $\mathbb{A}$ has tree duality, hence the polynomial consistency-check algorithm (see [8]) detects whether $\mathbb{A}_{\{a,b\}}$ admits a homomorphism to $\mathbb{A}$. If such a homomorphism ϕ exists, then $\mathbb{A}$ admits a homomorphism to its proper substructure $\phi(\mathbb{A}_{\{a,b\}})$ hence it is not a core; we then output "no" and stop. If no homomorphism exists from any quotient $\mathbb{A}_{\{a,b\}}$ to $\mathbb{A}$, then $\mathbb{A}$ is a core. We then output "yes".

■

6. Conclusion

We have described a simple polynomial-time algorithm that determines if a finite relational structure is a core with first-order definable CSP, and have proved that deciding FO-definability is **NP**-complete. We have also given various characterisations of FO-definable structures in terms of sets of obstructions, and proved that core structures with finite duality admit a 1-tolerant near-unanimity operation.

Feder and Vardi's Theorem 2.6 shows that the problem of determining whether an input structure $\mathbb{A}$ has tree duality is decidable. In fact the proof of Theorem 5.1 also implies that this problem is NP-hard, but for the moment it is not known to belong to NP or even to P-space. It would be interesting to have these issues resolved.

In the case of first-order definable CSPs, we now have an algorithm which outputs a yes-no answer to the question as to whether an input structure $\mathbb{A}$ has a first-order definable CSP. Using Lemma 2.3, it is possible to modify it so that in the case where $\mathbb{A}$-CSP is first-order definable, it outputs a first-order sentence $\Phi_{\mathbb{A}}$ such that $\mathbb{B}$ admits a homomorphism to $\mathbb{A}$ if and only if $\Phi_{\mathbb{A}}$ is true on $\mathbb{B}$. However the upper bound on the length of $\Phi_{\mathbb{A}}$ involves a tower of exponents. It is not clear whether this is realistic; [16] reports cases where the length of $\Phi_{\mathbb{A}}$ can be logarithmic in terms of the size of $\mathbb{A}$, but there are no examples in the direction of the other extreme.

References

[1] A. Atserias, On Digraph Coloring Problems and Treewidth Duality, in *Proceedings of the Twentieth Annual IEEE Symp. on Logic in Computer Science*, LICS 2005 106–115, 2005.

[2] A. Bulatov, A. Krokhin, P. Jeavons. Constraint satisfaction problems and finite algebras. In *ICALP'00*, volume 1853 of *LNCS*, 272–282, 2000.

[3] V. Dalmau, P. Kolaitis, M. Vardi, Constraint satisfaction, bounded treewidth, and finite-variable logics, in *Constraint Programming '02, (LNCS 2002)* 310-326, 2002.

[4] V. Dalmau, A. Krokhin, Majority constraints have bounded path duality, preprint, 17 pages, 2006.

[5] V. Dalmau, A. Krokhin, B. Larose, First-order definable retraction problems for posets and reflexive graphs, in *Proceedings of the 19th IEEE Symposium on Logic in Computer Science (LICS 2004)*, IEEE, 232-241, 2004.

[6] V. Dalmau, J. Pearson, Closure Functions and Width 1 Problems, in *Proc. Principles and Practice of Constraint Programming - CP'99, 5th International Conference, Alexandria, Virginia*, Lecture Notes in Computer Science **1713** Springer 1999, 159–173.

[7] T. Feder, M. Y. Vardi, Monotone monadic SNP and constraint satisfaction, in *Proceedings of the 25rd Annual ACM Symposium on Theory of Computing (STOC)*, San Diego, California, (1993), 612–622.

[8] T. Feder, M. Y. Vardi, The Computational structure of monotone monadic SNP and constraint satisfaction: a study through datalog and group theory, *SIAM Journal of Computing* **28**, (1998), 57-104.

[9] P. Hell, J. Nešetřil, On the complexity of H-coloring, *J. Combin. Theory Ser. B* **48**, 1990, 92–110.

[10] P. G. Kolaitis, M. Y. Vardi, A game-theoretic approach to constraint satisfaction, in *7th National Conference on Artificial Intelligence*, 175–181, 2000.

[11] G. Kun, Cs. Szabó, Order varieties and monotone retractions of finite posets, *Order* **18**, 79-88, 2001.

[12] B. Larose, L. Zádori, Bounded width problems and algebras, *Algebra Universalis*, 25 pages, to appear.

[13] L. Lovász, Operations with structures, *Acta Math. Acad. Sci. Hungar* **18**, 1967, 321-328.

[14] M. Maróti, The existence of a near-unanimity term in a finite algebra is decidable, preprint, 13 pages, 2005.

[15] J. Nešetřil, C. Tardif, Duality theorems for finite structures (characterising gaps and good characterisations), *J. Combin. Theory Ser. B* **80**, 2000, 80–97.

[16] J. Nešetřil, C. Tardif, Short answers to exponentially long questions: Extremal aspects of homomorphism duality, *SIAM Journal on Discrete Mathematics*, 7 pages, to appear.

[17] B. Rossman, Existential Positive Types and Preservation under Homomorphisms, in *Proceedings of the Twentieth Annual IEEE Symp. on Logic in Computer Science, (LICS)*, 467–476, 2005.

First order formulas with modular predicates

Laura Chaubard
LIAFA, Université Paris VII and CNRS, Case 7014,
2 Place Jussieu, 75251 Paris Cedex 05, France.
Laura.Chaubard@liafa.jussieu.fr

Jean-Éric Pin
LIAFA, Université Paris VII and CNRS, Case 7014,
2 Place Jussieu, 75251 Paris Cedex 05, France.
Jean-Eric.Pin@liafa.jussieu.fr

Howard Straubing
Department of Computer Science, Boston College, Chestnut Hill, MA 02467, USA
straubin@cs.bc.edu

Abstract

Two results by Schützenberger (1965) and by McNaughton and Papert (1971) lead to a precise description of the expressive power of first order logic on words interpreted as ordered colored structures. In this paper, we study the expressive power of existential formulas and of Boolean combinations of existential formulas in a logic enriched by modular numerical predicates. We first give a combinatorial description of the corresponding regular languages, and then give an algebraic characterization in terms of their syntactic morphisms. It follows that one can effectively decide whether a given regular language is captured by one of these two fragments of first order logic. The proofs rely on nontrivial techniques of semigroup theory: stamps, derived categories and wreath products.

1. Introduction

There is by now an extensive literature on the expressive power of various fragments of first order logic interpreted on finite words. There are also known connections with several areas in mathematics and computer science, including finite semigroups, automata, descriptive set theory, complexity, circuits and communication complexity. Further, this research is a necessary step towards the study of richer structures like infinite words, trees or graphs. This paper is a contribution to this theory.

Let us briefly describe the framework of our results. We associate to each nonempty word $u = a_0 a_1 \dots a_{|u|-1}$ over the alphabet A a relational structure

$$\mathfrak{M}_u = \{(0, 1, \dots, |u| - 1), <, (\mathbf{a})_{a \in A}\}$$

where $<$ is the usual order on the domain and $\mathbf{a}$ is a predicate giving the positions i such that $a_i = a$. For instance, if $u = abbaaba$, then $\mathbf{a} = \{0, 3, 4, 6\}$ and $\mathbf{b} = \{1, 2, 5\}$. Given a formula φ, the language defined by φ is $L(\varphi) = \{u \in A^+ \mid \mathfrak{M}_u \text{ satisfies } \varphi\}$. Since languages may contain the empty word, we make the convention that a language L of A^* is defined by φ if $L(\varphi) = L \cap A^+$.

McNaughton and Papert [11] showed that a language is first-order definable (in the signature $\{<, (\mathbf{a})_{a \in A}\}$) if and only if it is star-free. The decidability of this class of regular languages, denoted by $\mathbf{FO}[<]$, follows from a celebrated result of Schützenberger [20]: a regular language is *star-free* if and only if its syntactic monoid is *aperiodic*. Thomas [27] (see also [13]) refined this correspondence between first order logic and star-free languages by showing that the concatenation hierarchy of star-free languages is, level by level, in correspondence with the Σ_n-hierarchy of first order formulas. However, little is known about the decidability of these classes. It is not very difficult to decide whether or not a given regular language belongs to $\mathbf{\Sigma_1}[<]$. The decidability of the Boolean closure of this class, denoted by $\mathcal{B}\mathbf{\Sigma_1}[<]$, relies on a nontrivial algebraic result of Simon [23]. The decidability of $\mathbf{\Sigma_2}[<]$ was also proved by algebraic methods [1, 17], but the decidability of the upper levels $\mathcal{B}\mathbf{\Sigma_2}[<]$, $\mathbf{\Sigma_3}[<]$ and beyond is a major open problem.

Several enrichments to the vocabulary $<$ were considered in the literature. Let $k \geq 0$. Recall that a k-ary *numerical predicate symbol* associates to each $n \geq 0$ a subset of

$\{0,\ldots,n-1\}^k$. We view $(i_1,\ldots,i_k) \in \{0,\ldots,n-1\}^k$ as a word $\delta_0 \cdots \delta_{n-1}$ over the alphabet $\Delta = 2^{\{1,\ldots,k\}}$ by setting $\delta_j = \{r \mid i_r = j\}$. Thus each numerical predicate symbol gives rise to a language in Δ^*. We say the numerical predicate symbol is *regular* if the corresponding language is regular. (Note that if $k = 0$, $\{0,\ldots,n-1\}^k$ is the one-element set $\{\emptyset\}$.)

Let $0 < d$, and $r \in \mathbb{Z}/d\mathbb{Z}$. We define two numerical predicate symbols (the *modular predicates*): The unary symbol MOD_r^d assigns to n the set $\{i < n \mid i \bmod d = r\}$, and the 0-ary symbol D_r^d assigns $\{\emptyset\}$ to n if $n \bmod d = r$, and $\emptyset$ otherwise. The associated languages are $(\emptyset^d)^*\emptyset^{r-1}\{1\}\emptyset^*$ and $(\emptyset^d)^*\emptyset^r$, respectively, so these are regular numerical predicates. Equivalently, we could introduce a constant symbol m denoting the last position in a string, in which case D_r^d is equivalent to $\text{MOD}_{r-1}^d m$. (This is the notation that we shall adopt below.)

We denote by $\mathbf{FO}[< + \text{MOD}]$ the logic obtained by adjoining all modular predicates. This signature was considered implicitly in automata theory and explicitly in a recent paper by Ésik and Ito [6]. It should not be confused with first order logic with modular quantifiers.

The logic $\mathbf{FO}[<+\text{REG}]$ is obtained by adjoining all regular numerical predicate symbols. This logic was considered in [2, 10, 12, 25] in connection with circuit complexity.

It is not difficult to see that $\mathbf{FO}[< + \text{MOD}] = \mathbf{FO}[< + \text{REG}]$. However, the lower levels of the Σ_n-hierarchy differ for the three signatures. The decidability of $\mathbf{\Sigma_1}[< + \text{REG}]$ and $\mathcal{B}\mathbf{\Sigma_1}[< + \text{REG}]$ was established in [10]. In this paper, we establish the decidability of the fragments $\mathbf{\Sigma_1}[<+\text{MOD}]$ and $\mathcal{B}\mathbf{\Sigma_1}[< + \text{MOD}]$, a problem left open in [6]. The situation is summarized in the table below:

	$<$	$< + \text{MOD}$	$< + \text{REG}$
Σ_1	DECIDABLE [13, 27]	DECIDABLE **New result**	DECIDABLE [8, 10, 21]
$\mathcal{B}\Sigma_1$	DECIDABLE [23, 27]	DECIDABLE **New result**	DECIDABLE [10]
$\vdots$			
FO	DECIDABLE [11, 20]	DECIDABLE [2, 25]	DECIDABLE [2, 25]

Our paper is organized as follows. Section 2 presents the necessary background to understand our proofs. Our main decidability results on fragments of first order logic are proved in Section 3 for $\mathbf{\Sigma_1}[< + \text{MOD}]$ and in Section 4 for $\mathcal{B}\mathbf{\Sigma_1}[< + \text{MOD}]$. In the last section, we summarize our results and compare them with other decidability results.

2. The algebraic approach

In this section, we survey the algebraic approach to automata theory that is needed to state our main results. We briefly present Eilenberg's variety theory [4], its extension to the ordered case [15] and its more recent generalization to stamps [5, 6, 7, 16, 26], in a form suitable to our purpose.

2.1 Semigroups, monoids and stamps

A *semigroup* is a set equipped with a binary associative operation, denoted multiplicatively, or additively when the semigroup is commutative. A *monoid* is a semigroup with a unit element. An element e of a semigroup is *idempotent* if $e^2 = e$. In a finite semigroup, every element x has a unique idempotent power, denoted by x^ω.

An element s of a semigroup S is said to be *regular* if and only if there exists an element $\bar{s}$ of S, called an *inverse* of s such that $s\bar{s}s = s$ and $\bar{s}s\bar{s} = \bar{s}$.

Given two monoids M and N, a *monoid morphism* is a map $\varphi : M \to N$ satisfying $\varphi(1) = 1$ and $\varphi(uv) = \varphi(u)\varphi(v)$ for all u, v in M. A monoid M is a *submonoid* of a monoid N if there exists an injective morphism from M into N. A monoid N is a *quotient* of a monoid M if there exists a surjective morphism from M onto N. A monoid M *divides* a monoid N if M is a quotient of a submonoid of N. The *product* of two monoids M_1 and M_2 is the set $M_1 \times M_2$ equipped with the product $(x_1, x_2)(y_1, y_2) = (x_1y_1, x_2y_2)$.

An *ordered* semigroup is a semigroup equipped with a partial order compatible with the operation of the semigroup. An *order ideal* I of an ordered semigroup $(S, \leq)$ is a subset of S such that if $x \in I$ and $y \leq x$ then $y \in I$.

Morphisms of ordered semigroups are order-preserving morphisms of semigroups. The notions of *ordered subsemigroup*, quotient and product are readily adapted from their unordered version and easily extended to the monoid case.

A *relational morphism* between two monoids M and N is a relation $\tau : M \to N$ which satisfies

(1) for every $s \in M$, $\tau(s) \neq \emptyset$,

(2) for every $s_1, s_2 \in M$, $\tau(s_1)\tau(s_2) \subseteq \tau(s_1s_2)$,

(3) $1 \in \tau(1)$.

A *stamp* is a morphism from a finitely generated free monoid onto a finite monoid. A stamp $\varphi : A^* \to M$ is said to be *trivial* if M is the trivial monoid. An *ordered stamp* is a stamp onto an ordered monoid.

Let $\varphi : A^* \to M$ be a stamp and let $Z = \varphi(A)$. Then Z is an element of the monoid $\mathcal{P}(M)$ of subsets of M, equipped with the product $XY = \{xy \mid x \in X, y \in Y\}$. Since $\mathcal{P}(M)$ is finite, Z has an idempotent power. This justifies the following definition: the *stability index* of a stamp $\varphi : A^* \to M$ is the least positive integer such that $\varphi(A^s) = \varphi(A^{2s})$. The set $\varphi(A^s)$ is a subsemigroup of M called the *stable semigroup of* φ and the monoid $\varphi(A^s) \cup \{1\}$ is called the *stable monoid of* φ.

2.2 Stamps and languages

Stamps and ordered stamps can be seen as language recognizers in the following way. Let $\varphi : A^* \to M$ be a stamp. A language L over A^* is *recognized by* the stamp φ if there exists a subset F of M such that $L = \varphi^{-1}(F)$. If M is ordered, we require F to be an order ideal of M. By extension, we say that the (ordered) monoid M recognizes L if there exists a stamp $\varphi : A^* \to M$ recognizing L.

A language is said to be *recognizable* if it is recognized by some finite monoid. Kleene's theorem asserts that recognizable and regular languages coincide.

Given a language L over A^*, we define the *syntactic congruence* $\sim_L$ and the *syntactic preorder* $\leq_L$ as follows:

(1) $u \sim_L v$ iff for all $x, y \in A^*, xvy \in L \Leftrightarrow xuy \in L$,

(2) $u \leq_L v$ iff for all $x, y \in A^*, xvy \in L \Rightarrow xuy \in L$.

The monoid $A^*/{\sim_L}$ is the *syntactic monoid* of L and is denoted by $M(L)$. It can be ordered with the partial order relation induced by $\leq_L$, to form the *ordered syntactic monoid* of L. The natural morphism $\eta_L : A^* \to M(L)$ is called the *syntactic (ordered) stamp* of L. The syntactic monoid of L is the smallest monoid (with respect to the division order on monoids) that recognizes L. In particular, a language is regular if and only if its syntactic monoid is finite.

From now on, all semigroups and monoids will be either finite or free.

2.3 The variety approach

The general idea of the variety theory is to classify regular languages through the algebraic properties of their syntactic invariants. For this purpose, Eilenberg originally considered classes of finite monoids defined by equations, called *varieties*. This gave an appealing framework in which to study classes of recognizable languages closed under Boolean operations, quotients, and inverse morphisms.

However, our classes $\mathbf{\Sigma}_1[<+\text{MOD}]$ and $\mathcal{B}\mathbf{\Sigma}_1[<+\text{MOD}]$ are not closed under inverse morphisms and the first one is not even closed under complement. Still, they are closed under inverses of *length-multiplying* morphisms and it is possible to adapt Eilenberg's variety theory to this weaker setting. The price to pay is the shift from the syntactic monoid to the syntactic stamp (for $\mathcal{B}\mathbf{\Sigma}_1[<+\text{MOD}]$) or to the syntactic ordered stamp (for $\mathbf{\Sigma}_1[<+\text{MOD}]$). The general framework for this study is the theory of $\mathcal{C}$-varieties, recently introduced by Straubing [26].

We first recall the classical notion of varieties. A *variety of finite monoids* is a class of (finite) monoids closed under division and finite product. Varieties of finite semigroups and of finite *ordered* monoids are defined analogously.

We now turn to varieties of stamps. Recall that a morphism $f : A^* \to B^*$ is *length-multiplying* (lm for short) if there exists an integer k such that the image of each letter of A is a word of B^k. A stamp $\varphi : A^* \to M$ *lm-divides* a stamp $\psi : B^* \to N$ if there is a pair (f, η) (called an lm-division), where $f : A^* \to B^*$ is an lm-morphism, $\eta : N \to M$ is a partial surjective monoid morphism, and $\varphi = \eta \circ \psi \circ f$. If f is the identity on A^*, the pair (f, η) is simply called a division. If φ and ψ are ordered stamps, that is, if M and N are ordered monoids, η is required to be order-preserving.

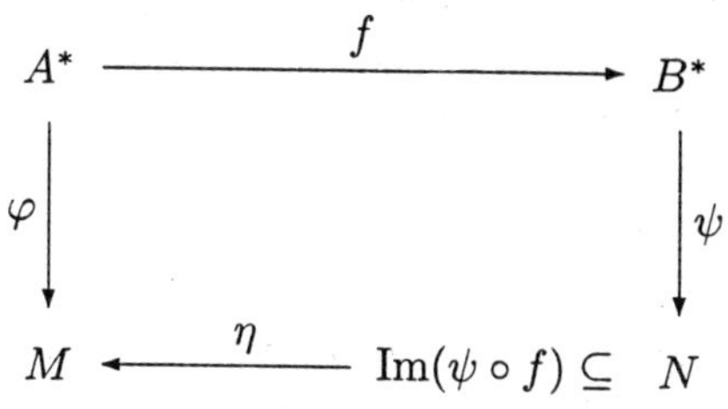

Figure 1. A division diagram.

The *product* of two stamps $\varphi_1 : A^* \to M_1$ and $\varphi_2 : A^* \to M_2$ is the stamp φ with domain A^* defined by $\varphi(a) = (\varphi_1(a), \varphi_2(a))$. The range of φ is a submonoid of $M_1 \times M_2$.

An *lm-variety of stamps* is a class of stamps containing the trivial stamps and closed under lm-division and finite products. The definition of a variety of ordered stamps is similar. Note that if $\mathbf{V}$ is a variety of finite (ordered) monoids, then the class of all (ordered) stamps whose range is in $\mathbf{V}$ forms an lm-variety of (ordered) stamps, also denoted by $\mathbf{V}$.

We now come to the definition of varieties of languages. A *positive Boolean algebra* is a set of languages that is closed under finite union and finite intersection. If it is also closed under complement, it is called a *Boolean algebra*. Given a language L and a word u, we set

$$u^{-1}L = \{v \in A^* \mid uv \in L\}$$
$$Lu^{-1} = \{v \in A^* \mid vu \in L\}$$

A *class of recognizable languages* $\mathcal{V}$ assigns to each finite alphabet A a set $\mathcal{V}(A^*)$ of recognizable languages of A^*. A *positive variety of languages* is a class of recognizable languages $\mathcal{V}$ such that for any alphabets A and B,

(1) $\mathcal{V}(A^*)$ is a positive Boolean algebra,

(2) if $L \in \mathcal{V}(A^*)$ and $a \in A$ then $a^{-1}L, La^{-1} \in \mathcal{V}(A^*)$,

(3) if $\varphi : A^* \to B^*$ is a morphism, $L \in \mathcal{V}(B^*)$ implies $\varphi^{-1}(L) \in \mathcal{V}(A^*)$.

A *variety of languages* is a positive variety $\mathcal{V}$ such that, for each alphabet A, $\mathcal{V}(A^*)$ is closed under complement.

Positive lm-varieties and *lm-varieties* of languages are defined in the same way by weakening Condition (3) to

(3′) if $\varphi : A^* \to B^*$ is an lm-morphism, $L \in \mathcal{V}(B^*)$ implies $\varphi^{-1}(L) \in \mathcal{V}(A^*)$.

Given a variety of finite monoids $\mathbf{V}$, the class $\mathcal{V}$ of all languages recognized by a monoid in $\mathbf{V}$ is a variety of languages. Eilenberg's theorem [4] asserts that the correspondence $\mathbf{V} \rightarrow \mathcal{V}$ is one-to-one and onto.

Similarly, if $\mathbf{V}$ is a variety of finite ordered monoids, the class $\mathcal{V}$ of all languages recognized by an ordered monoid in $\mathbf{V}$ is a positive variety of languages. It is proved in [15] that the correspondence $\mathbf{V} \rightarrow \mathcal{V}$ is one-to-one and onto.

Finally, given an lm-variety of (ordered) stamps $\mathbf{V}$, the class $\mathcal{V}$ of all languages recognized by a stamp in $\mathbf{V}$ is a (positive) lm-variety of languages. It is proved in [26] that the correspondence $\mathbf{V} \rightarrow \mathcal{V}$ is one-to-one and onto.

2.4 Examples

Example 2.1 The trivial variety of monoids $\mathbf{I}$ consists only of one monoid, the trivial monoid. The corresponding variety of languages $\mathcal{I}$ is defined, for every alphabet A, by $\mathcal{I}(A^*) = \{\emptyset, A^*\}$.

Example 2.2 A semigroup S is *locally trivial* if $eSe = \{e\}$ for each idempotent e of S. The class of *locally trivial* semigroups form a variety of semigroups, denoted by **LI**.

Example 2.3 Let us denote by $\mathbf{J}^+$ the class of all finite ordered monoids $(M, \leq)$ such that, for all $x \in M$, $x \leq 1$. One can show that $\mathbf{J}^+$ is a variety of ordered monoids and that a language belongs to $\mathcal{J}^+(A^*)$ if and only if it is a finite union of languages of the form $A^*a_1A^* \cdots a_kA^*$, where $k \geq 0$ and $a_1, \ldots, a_k$ are letters of A. Further, it is shown in [13] that $\mathcal{J}^+$ is equal to the class $\mathbf{\Sigma}_1[<]$.

Example 2.4 A monoid M is *$\mathcal{J}$-trivial* if division is a partial order on M, that is, if the conditions $uxv = y$ and $syt = x$ imply $x = y$. The class of *$\mathcal{J}$-trivial* monoids form a variety, denoted by $\mathbf{J}$. Simon's theorem [22] states that $\mathcal{J}(A^*)$ is the Boolean algebra generated by the languages of the form $A^*a_1A^* \cdots a_kA^*$, where $k \geq 0$ and $a_1, \ldots, a_k$ are letters of A. It follows from [27] that $\mathcal{J}$ is also equal to the class $\mathcal{B}\mathbf{\Sigma}_1[<]$.

Example 2.5 A monoid M is *aperiodic* if there exists an integer n such that, for every $x \in M$, $x^n = x^{n+1}$. The class of aperiodic monoids form a variety denoted by $\mathbf{A}$. The results of Schützenberger [20] and McNaughton and Papert [11] show that the corresponding variety of languages is the class of star-free languages, or in logical terms, the class $\mathbf{FO}[<]$.

Example 2.6 Let **MOD** be the class of all stamps $\varphi : A^* \rightarrow M$ such that M is a cyclic group and $\varphi(a) = \varphi(b)$ for all letters a, b in A. Then **MOD** is an lm-variety of stamps. For each alphabet A, a language of $\mathcal{M}od(A^*)$ is recognized by some stamp $\pi_n : A^* \rightarrow \mathbb{Z}/n\mathbb{Z}$ and hence is a finite union of languages of the form $(A^n)^*A^k$ with $0 \leq k < n$.

Example 2.7 Given a variety of finite semigroups $\mathbf{V}$, a stamp is said to be a *quasi-$\mathbf{V}$ stamp* if its stable subsemigroup belongs to $\mathbf{V}$. It is stated in [26] that the quasi-$\mathbf{V}$ stamps form an lm-variety, denoted by $\mathbf{QV}$. It was proved in [2] that $\mathbf{FO}[< + \text{MOD}]$ is the lm-variety of languages corresponding to $\mathbf{QA}$.

2.5 Identities

Both varieties of finite monoids and lm-varieties of stamps have equational characterizations [19, 9, 16]. The same result holds for their ordered counterparts. The formal definition of identities requires the introduction of profinite topologies. Here we consider a simpler notion, illustrated with a few basic examples, which implies the result.

We start by recalling an elementary fact about finite semigroups. Let x be an element of a finite semigroup S. Since S is finite, there exist integers $i, p > 0$ such that $x^{i+p} = x^i$. The subsemigroup of S generated by x is represented below.

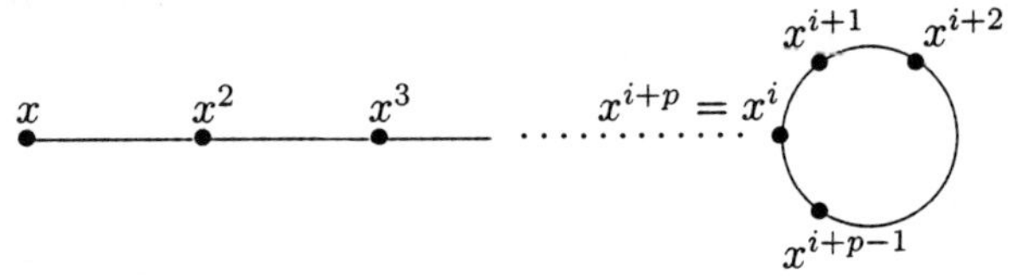

It is easy to see that the semigroup $\{x^i, \ldots, x^{i+p-1}\}$ is a cyclic group $G(x)$, whose identity is x^ω, the unique idempotent power of x.

An *ω-term* on an alphabet A is built from the letters of A using the usual concatenation product and two unary operators: $x \rightarrow x^\omega$ and $x \rightarrow x^{\omega-1}$. Thus, if $A = \{a, b, c\}$, abc, a^ω and $((ab^{\omega-1}c)^\omega ab)^\omega$ are examples of ω-terms.

Let $\varphi : A^* \rightarrow M$ be a stamp. The image $\varphi(t)$ of an ω-term t is defined recursively as follows. If t is a letter, then $\varphi(t)$ is already defined. If t and t' are ω-terms, then $\varphi(tt') = \varphi(t)\varphi(t')$. If $t = u^\omega$, then $\varphi(t)$ is the unique idempotent power of $\varphi(u)$. Finally if $t = u^{\omega-1}$, then $\varphi(t)$ is the inverse of $\varphi(u)^\omega\varphi(u)$ in the cyclic group $G(\varphi(u))$.

Let u, v be two ω-terms on a finite alphabet B. A stamp $\varphi : A^* \rightarrow M$ is said to *satisfy the lm-identity* $u = v$ if, for every lm-morphism $f \colon B^* \rightarrow A^*$, $\varphi \circ f(u) = \varphi \circ f(v)$. If M is ordered, we say that φ satisfies the lm-identity $u \leq v$ if, for every lm-morphism $f \colon B^* \rightarrow A^*$, $\varphi \circ f(u) \leq \varphi \circ f(v)$.

A monoid (ordered monoid) M satisfies the identity $u = v$ $(u \leq v)$ if for every morphism $\varphi \colon B^* \rightarrow M$, $\varphi(u) = \varphi(v)$ $(\varphi(u) \leq \varphi(v))$.

An lm-variety $\mathbf{V}$ satisfies a given lm-identity if every stamp in $\mathbf{V}$ satisfies this identity. The class of all stamps satisfying a given set of lm-identities is an lm-variety of stamps. Similarly the class of all (ordered) monoids satisfying a given set of identities is an variety of (ordered) monoids.

By extension, we say that a language L satisfies a monoid identity (lm-identity) if its syntactic monoid (ordered monoid, stamp, ordered stamp) satisfies this identity.

Example 2.8 As an lm-variety of stamps, **MOD** is defined by the single identity $x^{\omega-1}y = 1$.

The variety of finite aperiodic monoids **A** is defined by the identity $x^\omega = x^{\omega+1}$.

The variety of finite ordered monoids $\mathbf{J}^+$ is defined by the identity $x \leq 1$. The variety of finite monoids **J** is defined by the two identities $x^\omega = x^{\omega+1}$ and $(xy)^\omega = (yx)^\omega$.

3. Expressive power of $\Sigma_1[< + \text{MOD}]$

We first give a simple combinatorial description of the languages definable in $\Sigma_1[< + \text{MOD}]$.

Let us call *modular simple* a language of the form $(A^d)^*a_1(A^d)^*a_2(A^d)^* \cdots a_k(A^d)^*$, where $d > 0$, $k \geq 0$ and $a_1, a_2, \ldots, a_k \in A$.

Proposition 3.1 *A language is definable in* $\Sigma_1[<+\text{MOD}]$ *if and only if it is a finite union of modular simple languages.*

Proof. The language $(A^d)^*a_1(A^d)^*a_2(A^d)^* \cdots a_k(A^d)^*$ can be defined by the Σ_1-formula

$$\exists x_1 \ldots \exists x_k \ (x_1 < \ldots < x_k) \wedge (\mathbf{a}_1 x_1 \wedge \cdots \wedge \mathbf{a}_k x_k)$$
$$\wedge (\text{MOD}_0^d\, x_1 \wedge \text{MOD}_1^d\, x_2 \wedge \cdots \wedge \text{MOD}_{k-1}^d\, x_k \wedge \text{MOD}_{k-1}^d\, m)$$

This shows that any finite union of modular simple languages is definable in $\Sigma_1[< + \text{MOD}]$. To prove the result in the opposite direction, consider a Σ_1-formula $\psi = \exists x_1 \ldots \exists x_k\ \varphi(x_1, \ldots, x_k)$. We may assume that φ is in disjunctive normal form. Negations of atomic formulas can be eliminated by replacing $\neg(x = y)$ by $(x < y) \vee (y < x)$, $\neg(x < y)$ by $(x = y) \vee (y < x)$, $\neg(\text{MOD}_r^d\, x)$ by $\vee_{s \neq r} \text{MOD}_s^d\, x$ and $\neg(\mathbf{a}x)$ by $\vee_{b \neq a}(\mathbf{b}x)$. Further, by the Chinese remainder theorem, conjunctions of atomic formulas of the form $\text{MOD}_{r_0}^{d_0}\, m \wedge \bigwedge_{1 \leq i \leq n} \text{MOD}_{r_i}^{d_i}\, x_i$ can be replaced by disjunctions of formulas of the form $\text{MOD}_{s_0}^d\, m \wedge \bigwedge_{1 \leq i \leq n} \text{MOD}_{s_i}^d\, x_i$, where $d = \text{lcm}(d_i)$. Altogether, ψ is equivalent to a disjunction of formulas of the form $\exists x_1 \ldots \exists x_k\ (x_1 < \ldots < x_k) \wedge (\mathbf{a}_1 x_1 \wedge \cdots \wedge \mathbf{a}_k x_k) \wedge (\text{MOD}_{r_1}^d\, x_1 \wedge \cdots \wedge \text{MOD}_{r_k}^d\, x_k \wedge \text{MOD}_r^d\, m)$ defining the language $(A^d)^* A^{s_1} a_1 (A^d)^* A^{s_2} a_2 (A^d)^* \cdots\ a_k (A^d)^* A^s$ where, for $1 \leq i \leq k$, $s_1 + s_2 + \cdots + s_i \equiv r_i \pmod d$ and $r_k + s \equiv r \pmod d$. Finally, observing that $(A^d)^*A^r = [(A^d)^*(\cup_{a \in A} a)]^r (A^d)^*$, it suffices to use the distributivity of concatenation over union to conclude that the language $L(\psi)$ is a finite union of modular simple languages. □

The concatenation hierarchy of star-free languages mentioned in the introduction is defined by alternating two types of operations: the Boolean operations and the polynomial closure, that we now define. Given a class of languages $\mathcal{L}$, we denote by Pol($\mathcal{L}$) the *polynomial closure* of $\mathcal{L}$, which is the class of languages that are finite unions of languages of the form $L_0 a_1 L_1 a_2 \cdots a_k L_k$, where $L_0, \ldots, L_k \in \mathcal{L}$ and $a_1, \ldots, a_k$ are letters. We also denote by $\mathcal{B}$Pol($\mathcal{L}$) the Boolean closure of Pol($\mathcal{L}$).

It is shown in [13] that $\Sigma_1[<]$ is equal to Pol($\mathcal{I}$) where $\mathcal{I}$ is the trivial variety of languages. The next proposition shows that $\Sigma_1[< + \text{MOD}]$ is equal to Pol($\mathcal{M}od$).

Proposition 3.2 *A language belongs to Pol($\mathcal{M}od$) if and only if it is a finite union of modular simple languages.*

Proof. First, Pol($\mathcal{M}od$) clearly contains the modular simple languages. Conversely, any language of Pol($\mathcal{M}od$)(A^*) can be written as a finite union of languages of the form $L = L_0 a_1 L_1 a_2 \cdots a_k L_k$, where $a_1, \ldots, a_k$ are letters and $L_0, \ldots, L_k \in \mathcal{M}od(A^*)$. Thus each L_i is a finite union of languages of the form $(A^{n_i})^* A^k$, with $0 \leq k \leq n_i$. Let d be the least common multiple of the n_i. Setting $r_i = d/n_i$, we observe that $(A^{n_i})^* = \cup_{0 \leq k < r_i} (A^d)^* A^{kn_i}$. Applying the distributivity of concatenation over union, we may assume that all L_i are of the form $(A^d)^* A^k$. But $(A^d)^* A^k$ can be written as $\cup_{a_1 a_2 \cdots a_k \in A^k} (A^d)^* a_1 (A^d)^* a_2 \cdots a_k (A^d)^*$. It follows that any language of Pol($\mathcal{M}od$)(A^*) is a finite union of modular simple languages. □

Our decidability result for $\Sigma_1[< + \text{MOD}]$ relies on an algebraic characterization of the polynomial closure [16, 17]. However, the formulation of this general result requires us to introduce Mal'cev products of varieties and we prefer here a simpler formulation.

Proposition 3.3 *A language belongs to Pol($\mathcal{M}od$) if and only if its ordered syntactic stamp φ satisfies the following property: there exists a positive integer n such that the ordered monoid $\varphi((A^n)^*)$ satisfies the identity $x \leq 1$.*

Unfortunately, Proposition 3.3 does not provide a decidability criterion for Pol($\mathcal{M}od$). The next result fixes this problem.

Theorem 3.4 *A language belongs to Pol($\mathcal{M}od$) if and only if the stable ordered monoid of its ordered syntactic stamp satisfies the identity $x \leq 1$.*

Proof. By Proposition 3.3, it suffices to show that if $\varphi((A^n)^*)$ satisfies the identity $x \leq 1$ for some $n > 0$, then $\varphi((A^s)^*)$ satisfies the same identity. But since $\varphi(A^s) =$

$\varphi(A^{ns})$, $\varphi((A^s)^*) = \varphi((A^{ns})^*)$. It follows that $\varphi((A^s)^*)$ is a submonoid of $\varphi((A^n)^*)$ and thus satisfies the identity $x \leq 1$. □

Theorem 3.4 gives a decidable condition for testing membership in Pol($\mathcal{M}od$). But since we know that Pol($\mathcal{M}od$) is a positive lm-variety of languages, it is interesting to find the identities defining the corresponding variety of ordered stamps.

Theorem 3.5 *A language belongs to Pol($\mathcal{M}od$) if and only if its ordered syntactic stamp satisfies the lm-identities $x^{\omega-1}y \leq 1$ and $yx^{\omega-1} \leq 1$.*

Proof. Let L be a regular language, φ: $A^* \to M$ its ordered syntactic stamp, S its stable monoid and s its stability index.

First assume that L belongs to Pol($\mathcal{M}od$). Let x and y be two words in A^* of equal length and let $u = x^{(s-1)\omega}x^{\omega-1}y$. The length of u is a multiple of s and thus $\varphi(u)$ belongs to S. By Theorem 3.4, S satisfies the identity $x \leq 1$ and hence $\varphi(u) \leq 1$. But $\varphi(u) = \varphi(x^{\omega-1}y)$ and thus $\varphi(x^{\omega-1}y) \leq 1$. This proves that φ satisfies the lm-identities $x^{\omega-1}y \leq 1$. A symmetrical argument works for the second identity.

Conversely, assume that φ satisfies the lm-identities $x^{\omega-1}y \leq 1$ and $yx^{\omega-1} \leq 1$. We claim that $m \leq 1$ for all $m \in S$. The relation is trivial if $m = 1$. If $m \neq 1$, then $m \in \varphi(A^s) = T$. Since $T^2 = T$, it follows from [14, Chap. 1, Proposition 1.12] that $m = uev$ for some $u, e, v \in T$ with e idempotent. Thus there exist $x, y, z \in A^s$ such that $\varphi(y) = u$, $\varphi(x) = e$ and $\varphi(z) = v$. Since $|x| = |y| = |z|$, one has $\varphi(yx^{\omega-1}) \leq 1$ and $\varphi(x^{\omega-1}z) \leq 1$. It follows that $ue \leq 1$ and $ev \leq 1$, whence $m = uev = ueev \leq 1$. This proves the claim and shows, by Theorem 3.4, that L belongs to Pol($\mathcal{M}od$). □

The results of this section should be compared with the characterization of the class $\mathbf{\Sigma_1}[< + \text{REG}]$ which can be derived from the two papers [8, 21].

4. Expressive power of $\mathcal{B}\Sigma_1[< + \text{MOD}]$

In this section we give several characterizations of the class $\mathcal{B}\Sigma_1[< + \text{MOD}]$. Let us start with an immediate consequence of Proposition 3.1:

Proposition 4.1 *A language is definable in $\mathcal{B}\Sigma_1[<+\text{MOD}]$ if and only if it is a Boolean combination of modular simple languages.*

Our second characterization is based on properties of the wreath product. The non-specialist reader can skip the technical definitions given below, admit Theorem 4.2 and jump directly to Theorem 4.3.

The wreath product $N \circ K$ of two monoids N and K is defined on the set $N^K \times K$ by the following product:

$$(f_1, k_1)(f_2, k_2) = (f, k_1k_2), \text{ with } f(k) = f_1(k)f_2(kk_1)$$

This definition can be extended to varieties of stamps as follows. Let $\mathbf{V}, \mathbf{W}$ be two lm-varieties of stamps. A $(\mathbf{V}, \mathbf{W})$-product stamp is a stamp $\varphi : A^* \to M$ such that:

(1) M is a submonoid of a wreath product $N \circ K$, where N and K are finite monoids.

(2) Let $\pi : N \circ K \to K$ be the canonical projection morphism. Then the stamp $\pi \circ \varphi : A^* \to \pi(M)$ is in $\mathbf{W}$.

(3) For a in A, we can write $\varphi(a) = (f_a, \pi \circ \varphi(a))$ where f_a is in N^K. We now treat $K \times A$ as a finite alphabet and we define a stamp $\Phi : (K \times A)^* \to \text{Im}(\Phi) \subseteq N$ by $\Phi(k, a) = f_a(k)$. We require Φ to be in $\mathbf{V}$.

We define $\mathbf{V} * \mathbf{W}$ to be the class of all stamps that divide a $(\mathbf{V}, \mathbf{W})$-product stamp. The class $\mathbf{V} * \mathbf{W}$ is called the *wreath product* of the lm-varieties of stamps $\mathbf{V}$ and $\mathbf{W}$. It can be shown [3] that $\mathbf{V} * \mathbf{W}$ is an lm-variety of stamps containing $\mathbf{W}$. The wreath product is an associative operation on lm-varieties of stamps which extends the classical wreath product on Eilenberg's varieties.

The wreath product principle [6, 3] gives a description of languages recognized by a stamp of $\mathbf{V} * \mathbf{W}$. It is based on similar results for varieties of monoids [24, 18]. We only give here a simplified version for the case $\mathbf{W} = \mathbf{MOD}$. For each $n > 0$, let $B_n = \mathbb{Z}/n\mathbb{Z} \times A$ and $\sigma_n : A^* \to B_n^*$ be the sequential function defined by setting:

$$\sigma_n(a_1 \cdots a_k) = (0, a_1)(1, a_2) \cdots (k-1, a_k).$$

Theorem 4.2 *Let $\mathbf{V}$ be an lm-variety of stamps and let $\mathcal{U}$ be the lm-variety of languages associated with $\mathbf{V} * \mathbf{MOD}$. Then for every alphabet A, $\mathcal{U}(A^*)$ is the smallest positive Boolean algebra containing $\mathcal{M}od(A^*)$ and the languages of the form $\sigma_n^{-1}(V)$, where $n > 0$ and V is in $\mathcal{V}(B_n^*)$.*

Proof. The general Wreath Product Principle on stamps (WPP for short) [3] makes use of slightly more involved sequential functions that we shall introduce now. Given a stamp $\varphi : A^* \to M$ and an element m in M, we define the sequential function $\rho_m : A^* \to (M \times A)^*$ by setting:

$$\rho_m(a_1 \cdots a_n) = (m, a_1)(m\varphi(a_1), a_2) \cdots (m\varphi(a_1 \cdots a_{n-1}), a_n)$$

A sequential function ρ is said to be *associated with* φ if $\rho = \rho_m$ for some m in M. The WPP states that $\mathcal{U}(A^*)$ is the smallest positive Boolean algebra containing $\mathcal{M}od(A^*)$ and the languages of the form $\rho^{-1}(V)$, where ρ is a sequential function associated with a stamp $\varphi : A^* \to M$ in $\mathbf{MOD}$ and V is in $\mathcal{V}((M \times A)^*)$.

Notice first that, if $\varphi : A^* \to M$ is in **MOD** then M is a finite cyclic group, and one can thus assume that $M = \mathbb{Z}/n\mathbb{Z}$ for some positive integer n. We denote this group additively. Further, since φ is surjective, there exists a generator k of $\mathbb{Z}/n\mathbb{Z}$ such that $\varphi(A) = \{k\}$. Thus φ is isomorphic to the stamp $\pi_n : A^* \to \mathbb{Z}/n\mathbb{Z}$, defined by $\pi_n(A) = \{1\}$. Therefore $\mathcal{U}(A^*)$ is the smallest positive Boolean algebra containing $\mathcal{M}od(A^*)$ and the languages of the form $\rho^{-1}(V)$, where ρ is a sequential function associated with some stamp π_n and V is in $\mathcal{V}(B_n^*)$.

Now, let V be a language in $\mathcal{V}(B_n^*)$ and let $\rho_k : A^* \to B_n^*$ be the sequential function associated with π_n and an element k in $\mathbb{Z}/n\mathbb{Z}$. Define the lm-morphism $f_k \colon B_n^* \to B_n^*$ by $f_k(x, a) = (x + k, a)$, and let $V' = f_k^{-1}(V)$. Then V' is in $\mathcal{V}(B_n^*)$ and $\rho_k^{-1}(V) = \sigma_n^{-1}(V')$. Therefore, it is sufficient to consider sequential functions of the form σ_n, which concludes the proof. □

We now arrive at our second characterization of $\mathcal{B}\boldsymbol{\Sigma}_1[< + \text{MOD}]$.

Theorem 4.3 *A language is a Boolean combination of modular simple languages if and only if its syntactic stamp belongs to the lm-variety* $\mathbf{J} * \mathbf{MOD}$.

Proof. Let $\mathcal{U}$ be the lm-variety of languages corresponding to $\mathbf{J} * \mathbf{MOD}$. We first show that each language of $\mathcal{U}$ is a Boolean combination of modular simple languages. By Proposition 3.2, it suffices to show that $\mathcal{U}$ is contained in $\mathcal{B}$Pol($\mathcal{M}od$).

Let A be an alphabet. According to Theorem 4.2, $\mathcal{U}(A^*)$ is the smallest positive Boolean algebra containing $\mathcal{M}od(A^*)$ and the languages of the form $\sigma_n^{-1}(V)$, where $n > 0$ and V belongs to $\mathcal{J}(B_n^*)$. Since $\mathcal{M}od$ is contained in Pol($\mathcal{M}od$), it remains to prove that all languages of the form $\sigma_n^{-1}(V)$ are in $\mathcal{B}$Pol($\mathcal{M}od$). Further, since σ_n^{-1} commutes with Boolean operations, we may assume by Simon's theorem [22] that V is equal to $B_n^* b_1 B_n^* \cdots b_p B_n^*$ for some $b_1, \ldots, b_p \in B_n$. Setting $b_i = (r_i, a_i)$, we observe that

$$\sigma_n^{-1}(V) = (A^n)^* A^{r_1} a_1 (A^n)^* A^{s_2} a_2 \cdots (A^n)^* A^{s_p} a_p A^*,$$

with $s_i = r_i - (r_{i-1} + 1) \bmod n$, for $i = 2 \cdots p$. Since A^* and all languages of the form $(A^n)^* A^j$ are in $\mathcal{M}od(A^*)$, $\sigma^{-1}(V)$ belongs to Pol($\mathcal{M}od(A^*)$).

We now prove that any Boolean combination of modular simple languages is in $\mathcal{U}$. A simple computation shows that if

$$L = (A^d)^* a_1 (A^d)^* a_2 (A^d)^* \cdots\ a_k (A^d)^*$$

is a modular simple language of A^*, then

$$L = \sigma_d^{-1}(B_d^* b_1 B_d^* \cdots b_k B_d^*) \cap (A^d)^* A^k$$

with $b_i = (i-1, a_i)$ for $1 \leq i \leq k$. Since $B_d^* b_1 B_d^* \cdots b_k B_d^*$ is in $\mathcal{J}(B_d^*)$, L belongs to $\mathcal{U}(A^*)$. Finally, since $\mathcal{U}(A^*)$ is a Boolean algebra, any Boolean combination of modular simple languages of A^* is in $\mathcal{U}(A^*)$. □

It follows from Proposition 4.1 and Theorem 4.3 that deciding whether a given regular language is definable in $\mathcal{B}\boldsymbol{\Sigma}_1[< + \text{MOD}]$ amounts to showing that the lm-variety $\mathbf{J} * \mathbf{MOD}$ is decidable. The proof requires us to introduce derived categories [28]. In this paper, categories are viewed as generalizations of monoids since a one-object category is in fact a monoid.

Let C, D be two categories. A *division* of categories $\tau : C \to D$ is given by a mapping $\tau : Obj(C) \to Obj(D)$ and for each pair (u, v) of objects of C, by a relation $\tau : C(u, v) \to D(\tau(u), \tau(v))$ such that

(1) $\tau(x)\tau(y) \subseteq \tau(xy)$ for any consecutive arrows x, y,

(2) $\tau(x) \neq \emptyset$ for any arrow x,

(3) $1_{\tau(u)} \in \tau(1_u)$,

(4) $\tau(x) \cap \tau(y) \neq \emptyset$ implies $x = y$ for any coterminal arrows x, y of C.

If $\mathbf{V}$ is variety of monoids, we denote by $g\mathbf{V}$ the class of all categories that divide a monoid in $\mathbf{V}$ (regarded as a one-object category). By transitivity of division of categories, $g\mathbf{V}$ is always closed under division.

Let $\varphi : A^* \to M$ be a stamp. For each integer n, let $\pi_n : A^* \to \mathbb{Z}/n\mathbb{Z}$ be the stamp defined by $\pi_n(u) = |u| \bmod n$ and let φ_n be the relational morphism $\varphi_n = \pi_n \circ \varphi^{-1}$.

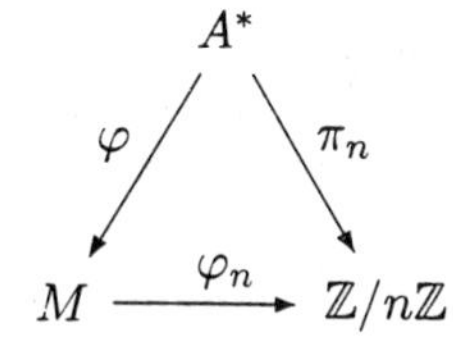

Let $C_n(\varphi)$ be the category whose objects are elements of $\mathbb{Z}/n\mathbb{Z}$ and whose arrows from object i to object j are the triples (i, m, j) where $j - i \in \varphi_n(m)$. Its composition rule is given by $(i, m_1, j)(j, m_2, k) = (i, m_1 m_2, k)$.

The next result is a special instance of the derived category theorem due to Tilson [28], but two modifications occur. First, Tilson's original definition of the derived category was different from ours, but this more complex definition is not required for relational morphisms onto a group. Second, Tilson's proof needs to be adapted to the context of stamps. Altogether, we obtain the following result:

Theorem 4.4 *A stamp* φ *is in* $\mathbf{J} * \mathbf{MOD}$ *if and only if there exists a positive integer* n *such that* $C_n(\varphi)$ *is in* $g\mathbf{J}$.

We shall now improve Theorem 4.4 by giving an explicit bound on the integer n. First, it was shown by Knast that a category belongs to $g\mathbf{J}$ if and only if, for each of its subgraphs of the form given in Figure 2, one has

$$(m_1 m_2)^\omega (m_3 m_4)^\omega = (m_1 m_2)^\omega m_1 m_4 (m_3 m_4)^\omega \quad (1)$$

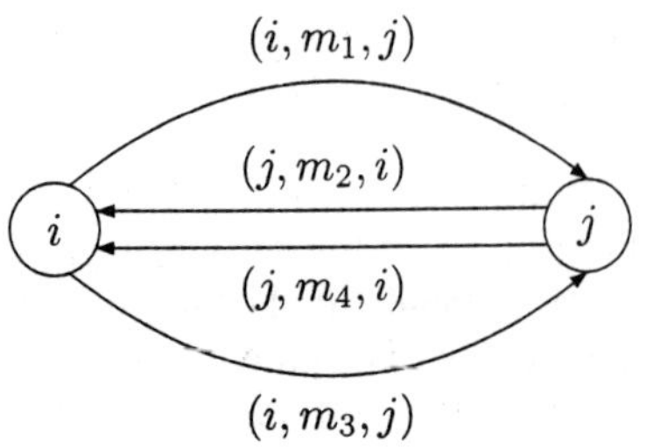

Figure 2. A Knast subgraph.

We now state our new characterization.

Theorem 4.5 *Let φ be a stamp of stability index s. Then φ belongs to $\mathbf{J} * \mathbf{MOD}$ if and only if $C_s(\varphi)$ is in $g\mathbf{J}$.*

Proof. First, if $C_s(\varphi)$ is in $g\mathbf{J}$, then φ belongs to $\mathbf{J} * \mathbf{MOD}$ by Theorem 4.4.

Now assume that $\varphi\colon A^* \rightarrow M$ belongs to $\mathbf{J} * \mathbf{MOD}$. Then, by Theorem 4.4, there exists a positive integer n such that $C_n(\varphi)$ is in $g\mathbf{J}$. We prove that $C_s(\varphi)$ is in $g\mathbf{J}$ by showing that it satisfies Knast's equation. Consider a Knast subgraph of $C_s(\varphi)$, with the notation in Figure 2. Set $k = j - i$. There exist words u_1, u_2, u_3, u_4 in A^* such that $\varphi(u_i) = m_i$ for $1 \leq i \leq 4$ and

$$|u_1| \equiv |u_3| \equiv -|u_2| \equiv -|u_4| \equiv k \bmod s.$$

Since M is a finite monoid, there exists an integer ω such that, for all $x \in M$, x^ω is idempotent. Further we can assume that ω is greater than s. Now setting

$$\begin{cases} v_1 = (u_1u_2)^\omega u_1, & v_2 = u_2(u_1u_2)^{\omega-1} \\ v_3 = (u_3u_4)^\omega u_3, & v_4 = u_4(u_3u_4)^{\omega-1} \end{cases}$$

we still have $|v_1| \equiv |v_3| \equiv -|v_2| \equiv -|v_4| \equiv k \bmod s$. Further $(\varphi(v_1), \varphi(v_2))$ and $(\varphi(v_3), \varphi(v_4))$ are pairs of mutually inverse elements of M. If $k \neq 0$, then for each i, $|v_i| \geq s$ and one can find an integer p_i such that

$$\begin{cases} |v_i| = p_i s + k\,, \quad p_i > 0, & \text{for } i = 1, 3 \\ |v_i| = p_i s - k\,, \quad p_i > 1, & \text{for } i = 2, 4 \end{cases}$$

By definition of s, we have $\varphi(A^s) = \varphi(A^{2s})$ and hence

$$\begin{cases} \varphi(A^{p_i s+k}) = \varphi(A^{np_i s+k}), & \text{for } i = 1, 3 \\ \varphi(A^{p_i s-k}) = \varphi(A^{np_i s-k}), & \text{for } i = 2, 4 \end{cases}$$

Thus, there exist words x_1, x_2, x_3, x_4 in A^* such that $\varphi(v_i) = \varphi(x_i)$ for $1 \leq i \leq 4$ and

$$\begin{cases} |x_i| = np_i s + k, & \text{for } i = 1, 3 \\ |x_i| = np_i s - k, & \text{for } i = 2, 4 \end{cases}$$

Therefore, $|x_1| \equiv |x_3| \equiv -|x_2| \equiv -|x_4| \equiv k \bmod n$, and $C_n(\varphi)$ contains the subgraph pictured in Figure 3.

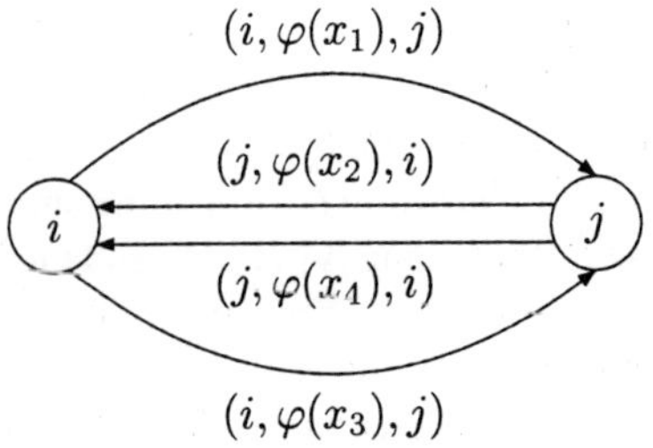

Figure 3. A subgraph of $C_n(\varphi)$.

Since $C_n(\varphi)$ is in $g\mathbf{J}$, it satisfies Knast's equation, that is,

$$\varphi(x_1x_2)^\omega\varphi(x_3x_4)^\omega = \varphi(x_1x_2)^\omega\varphi(x_1x_4)\varphi(x_3x_4)^\omega,$$

which finally yields Equation (1). Therefore, $C_s(\varphi)$ is in $g\mathbf{J}$.

We now treat the case where $k = 0$. If $u_1 = u_2 = u_3 = u_4 = 1$, Equation (1) holds trivially. Else, if $u_1 = u_2 = 1$ but $u_3u_4 \neq 1$, we set $x_1 = x_2 = 1$ and since $|v_3|, |v_4| \geq s$, we can take x_3, x_4 as above. Then, it is still true that $|x_1| \equiv |x_3| \equiv -|x_2| \equiv -|x_4| \equiv 0 \bmod n$ and that $C_n(\varphi)$ contains the subgraph pictured in Figure 3, which gives the result. The argument is symmetrical if $u_3 = u_4 = 1$. In all remaining cases, the words v_i have length greater or equal to s and the proof of the case $k \neq 0$ carries over. □

Corollary 4.6 *Given a regular language L, one can effectively decide whether L is definable in $\mathcal{B}\Sigma_1[< + \text{MOD}]$.*

Proof. It suffices to compute the syntactic stamp of L and its stability index s and check whether the derived category $C_s(\varphi)$ satisfies Knast's identity (1). □

5. Summary

We proved the decidability of the two classes $\Sigma_1[< + \text{MOD}]$ and $\mathcal{B}\Sigma_1[< + \text{MOD}]$. In algebraic terms, our results can be summarized as follows:

	$<$	$< + \text{MOD}$	$< + \text{REG}$
Σ_1	$\mathbf{J}^+$	$\mathbf{J}^+ * \mathbf{MOD}$	$\mathbf{J}^+ * \mathbf{LI} * \mathbf{MOD}$
$\mathcal{B}\Sigma_1$	$\mathbf{J}$	$\mathbf{J} * \mathbf{MOD}$	$\mathbf{J} * \mathbf{LI} * \mathbf{MOD}$
$\vdots$			
FO	$\mathbf{A}$	$\mathbf{A} * \mathbf{MOD}$	$\mathbf{A} * \mathbf{MOD}$

However, there are subtle differences between these two new results, as well as important features that distinguish them from the older results listed in the fourth column of the table. Indeed, given a stamp φ, one can decide whether φ belongs to the varieties of the fourth column by verifying that their stable (ordered) monoid satisfies certain conditions. This is due to the properties that the varieties $\mathbf{J}^+ * \mathbf{LI}$, $\mathbf{J} * \mathbf{LI}$ and $\mathbf{A}$ satisfy the condition $\mathbf{V} * \mathbf{LI} = \mathbf{V}$. It was observed both in [6] and in [12] that for varieties satisfying this condition, the decidability of $\mathbf{V}$ and $\mathbf{V}*\mathbf{MOD}$ are equivalent. The variety of ordered monoids $\mathbf{J}^+$ does not satisfy this condition, but it is a *local variety* in the sense of Tilson [28]: this still suffices to get the decidability of $\mathbf{J}^+ * \mathbf{MOD}$. The hardest case is $\mathbf{J} * \mathbf{MOD}$: the variety $\mathbf{J}$ is known to be nonlocal and Knast identities are required to get the decidability.

It would be interesting to obtain a purely model theoretic proof of our results.

References

[1] Mustapha Arfi. Opérations polynomiales et hiérarchies de concaténation. *Theoret. Comput. Sci.*, 91(1):71–84, 1991.

[2] David A. Mix Barrington, Kevin J. Compton, Howard Straubing, and Denis Thérien. Regular languages in NC^1. *J. Comput. Syst. Sci.*, 44:478–499, 1992.

[3] Laura Chaubard, Jean-Éric Pin, and Howard Straubing. Actions, wreath products of $\mathcal{C}$-varieties and concatenation product. *Theoret. Comput. Sci.*, 2006. to appear.

[4] Samuel Eilenberg. *Automata, languages, and machines. Vol. B*. Academic Press [Harcourt Brace Jovanovich Publishers], New York, 1976. With two chapters ("Depth decomposition theorem" and "Complexity of semigroups and morphisms") by Bret Tilson, Pure and Applied Mathematics, Vol. 59.

[5] Zoltán Ésik. Extended temporal logic on finite words and wreath products of monoids with distinguished generators. In Masami et al. Ito, editor, *Developments in language theory. 6th international conference, DLT 2002, Kyoto, Japan, September 18-21*, number 2450 in Lect. Notes Comp. Sci., pages 43–58, Berlin, 2002. Springer.

[6] Zoltán Ésik and Masami Ito. Temporal logic with cyclic counting and the degree of aperiodicity of finite automata. *Acta Cybernetica*, 16:1–28, 2003.

[7] Zoltán Ésik and Kim G. Larsen. Regular languages definable by lindström quantifiers. *Theor. Inform. Appl.*, 37:179–241, 2003.

[8] Christian Glaßer. Polylog-time reductions decrease dot-depth. In *STACS 2005*, volume 3404 of *Lect. Notes Comp. Sci.*, pages 170–181. Springer, Berlin, 2005.

[9] Michal Kunc. Equational description of pseudovarieties of homomorphisms. *Theoretical Informatics and Applications*, 37:243–254, 2003.

[10] Alexis Maciel, Pierre Péladeau, and Denis Thérien. Programs over semigroups of dot-depth one. *Theoret. Comput. Sci.*, 245(1):135–148, 2000.

[11] Robert McNaughton and Seymour Papert. *Counter-free automata*. The M.I.T. Press, Cambridge, Mass.-London, 1971. With an appendix by William Henneman, M.I.T. Research Monograph, No. 65.

[12] Pierre Péladeau, Howard Straubing, and Denis Thérien. Finite semigroup varieties defined by programs. *Theoret. Comput. Sci.*, 180(1-2):325–339, 1997.

[13] Dominique Perrin and Jean-Éric Pin. First order logic and star-free sets. *J. Comput. System Sci.*, 32:393–406, 1986.

[14] Jean-Éric Pin. *Varieties of formal languages*. North Oxford, London and Plenum, New-York, 1986. (Traduction de Variétés de langages formels).

[15] Jean-Éric Pin. A variety theorem without complementation. *Russian Mathematics (Izvestija vuzov.Matematika)*, 39:80–90, 1995.

[16] Jean-Éric Pin and Howard Straubing. Some results on $\mathcal{C}$-varieties. *Theoret. Informatics Appl.*, 39:239–262, 2005.

[17] Jean-Éric Pin and Pascal Weil. Polynomial closure and unambiguous product. *Theory Comput. Systems*, 30:1–39, 1997.

[18] Jean-Éric Pin and Pascal Weil. The wreath product principle for ordered semigroups. *Communications in Algebra*, 30:5677–5713, 2002.

[19] Jan Reiterman. The Birkhoff theorem for finite algebras. *Algebra Universalis*, 14(1):1–10, 1982.

[20] Marcel-Paul Schützenberger. On finite monoids having only trivial subgroups. *Information and Control*, 8:190–194, 1965.

[21] Victor L. Selivanov. Some hierarchies and reducibilities on regular languages. Technical Report 349, University of Würzburg, Germany, 2004.

[22] Imre Simon. *Hierarchies of Events with Dot-Depth One*. PhD thesis, University of Waterloo, Waterloo, Ontario, Canada, 1972.

[23] Imre Simon. Piecewise testable events. In H. Brackage, editor, *Proc. 2nd GI Conf.*, volume 33 of *Lecture Notes in Comp. Sci.*, pages 214–222. Springer Verlag, Berlin, Heidelberg, New York, 1975.

[24] Howard Straubing. Families of recognizable sets corresponding to certain varieties of finite monoids. *J. Pure Appl. Algebra*, 15(3):305–318, 1979.

[25] Howard Straubing. *Finite automata, formal logic, and circuit complexity*. Birkhäuser Boston Inc., Boston, MA, 1994.

[26] Howard Straubing. On logical descriptions of regular languages. In *LATIN 2002*, number 2286 in Lect. Notes Comp. Sci., pages 528–538, Berlin, 2002. Springer.

[27] Wolfgang Thomas. Classifying regular events in symbolic logic. *J. Comput. System Sci.*, 25(3):360–376, 1982.

[28] Bret Tilson. Categories as algebra: an essential ingredient in the theory of monoids. *J. Pure Appl. Algebra*, 48(1-2):83–198, 1987.

On tractability and congruence distributivity

Emil Kiss
Eötvös University
Department of Algebra and Number Theory
1117 Budapest, Pázmány Péter sétány 1/c
Hungary
ewkiss@cs.elte.hu

Matthew Valeriote
Department of Mathematics and Statistics
McMaster University
Hamilton, Ontario
L8S 4K1, Canada
matt@math.mcmaster.ca

Abstract

Constraint languages that arise from finite algebras have recently been the object of study, especially in connection with the Dichotomy Conjecture of Feder and Vardi. An important class of algebras are those that generate congruence distributive varieties and included among this class are lattices, and more generally, those algebras that have near-unanimity term operations. An algebra will generate a congruence distributive variety if and only if it has a sequence of ternary term operations, called Jónsson terms, that satisfy certain equations.

We prove that constraint languages consisting of relations that are invariant under a short sequence of Jónsson terms are tractable by showing that such languages have bounded width. Consequently, the class of instances of the constraint satisfaction problem arising from such a constraint language that fail to have solutions is definable in Datalog.

1. Introduction

The Constraint Satisfaction Problem (CSP) provides a framework for expressing a wide class of combinatorial problems. Given an instance of the CSP, the aim is to determine if there is a way to assign values from a fixed domain to the variables of the instance so that each of its constraints is satisfied. While the entire collection of CSPs forms an **NP**-complete class of problems, a number of subclasses have been shown to be tractable (i.e., to lie in **P**). A major focus of research in this area is to determine the subclasses of the CSP that are tractable.

One way to define a subclass of the CSP is to restrict the constraint relations that occur in an instance to a given finite set of relations over a fixed, finite domain, called a constraint language. A central problem is to classify the constraint languages that give rise to tractable subclasses of the CSP. Currently, all constraint languages that have been investigated have been shown to give rise to a subclass of the CSP that is either **NP**-complete or in **P**. It is conjectured in [10] that this dichotomy holds for all subclasses arising from finite constraint languages.

In some special cases, the conjectured dichotomy has been verified. For example, the work of Schaefer [18] and of Bulatov [1] establish this over domains of sizes 2 and 3 respectively. For constraint languages over larger domains a number of significant results have been obtained [5, 6, 9].

One method for establishing that the subclass of the CSP associated with a finite constraint language is tractable is to establish a type of local consistency property for the instances in the subclass. In [11] Feder and Vardi introduce a notion of the width of a constraint language and show that languages of bounded width give rise to tractable subclasses of the CSP. There is a natural connection between these subclasses of the CSP and definability within Datalog.

In work by Jeavons and his co-authors an approach to classifying the tractable constraint languages via algebraic methods has been proposed and applied with great success [5]. In essence, their work allows one to associate a finite algebraic structure to each constraint language and then to analyze the complexity of the corresponding subclass of the CSP in purely algebraic terms.

In this paper, we employ the algebraic approach to analyzing constraint languages and with it are able to identify a new, general class of tractable constraint languages. These languages arise from finite algebras that generate congruence distributive varieties, or equivalently, that have a sequence of special term operations, called Jónsson terms, that satisfy certain equations. Theorem 4.1 establishes the tractability of these languages by showing that they are of bounded width. Consequently, the class of instances of the CSP arising from such a constraint language that fail to have a solution is definable in Datalog.

2. Preliminaries

In this section we introduce the necessary terminology and results on the CSP and from universal algebra that will be needed to prove the main result (Theorem 4.1) of this paper.

In the following discussion we will employ standard terminology and notation when dealing with n-tuples and relations over sets. In particular, if $\vec{a}$ is a tuple over the sequence of domains A_i, $1 \leq i \leq n$, (i.e., is a member of $\prod_{1 \leq i \leq n} A_i$) and I is a subset of $\{1, 2, \ldots, n\}$ then $\mathrm{proj}_I(\vec{a})$ denotes the tuple $(a_i : i \in I) \in \prod_{i \in I} A_i$ over the sequence of domains $(A_i : i \in I)$ and is called the restriction (or the projection) of $\vec{a}$ to I. We extend this projection function to arbitrary relations over the A_i. The ith element of the tuple $\vec{a}$ will be denoted by $\vec{a}(i)$.

For R and S binary relations on a set A, we define the relational product of R and S to be the binary relation consisting of all pairs (a, b) for which there is some c with $(a, c) \in R$ and $(c, b) \in S$.

2.1. The Constraint Satisfaction Problem

Definition 2.1 *An instance of the constraint satisfaction problem is a triple $P = (V, A, \mathcal{C})$ with*

- *V a non-empty, finite set of variables,*
- *A a non-empty, finite set (or domain),*
- *$\mathcal{C}$ a set of constraints $\{C_1, \ldots, C_q\}$ where each C_i is a pair $(\vec{s}_i, R_i)$ with*
  - *$\vec{s}_i$ a tuple of variables of length m_i, called the scope of C_i, and*
  - *R_i an m_i-ary relation over A, called the constraint relation of C_i.*

Given an instance P of the CSP we wish to answer the following question:

> Is there a solution to P, i.e., is there a function $f : V \to A$ such that for each $i \leq q$, the m_i-tuple $f(\vec{s}_i) \in R_i$?

Note that if the variables of P are linearly ordered, then by permuting and identifying indices of some of the constraints of P, we can obtain an instance having the same set of solutions as P and such that the scope of each of its constraints is a strictly increasing sequence of elements from V.

In general, the class of CSPs is **NP**-complete (see [14]), but by restricting the nature of the constraint relations that are allowed to appear in an instance of the CSP, it is possible to find natural subclasses of the CSP that are tractable.

Definition 2.2 *Let A be a domain and Γ a set of finitary relations over A. CSP(Γ) denotes the collection of all instances of the CSP with domain A and with constraint relations coming from Γ. Γ is called the constraint language of the class CSP(Γ).*

Definition 2.3 *Call a finite constraint language Γ tractable if the class of problems CSP(Γ) is tractable (i.e., lies in* **P***). If Γ is infinite and each finite subset Γ' of Γ is tractable then we say that Γ is tractable. If the entire class CSP(Γ) is in* **P** *then we say that Γ is globally tractable.*

Γ is said to be **NP***-complete if for some finite subset Γ' of Γ, the class of problems CSP(Γ') is* **NP***-complete.*

A key problem in this area is to classify the (globally) tractable constraint languages. Note that in this paper we will assume that $\mathbf{P} \neq \mathbf{NP}$. Feder and Vardi [11] conjecture that every finite constraint language is either tractable or is **NP**-complete.

We will find it convenient to extend the above notions of instances of the CSP and constraint languages to a multi-sorted setting. This approach has been used on a number of occasions, in particular in [3].

Definition 2.4 *A multi-sorted instance of the constraint satisfaction problem is a pair $P = (\mathcal{A}, \mathcal{C})$ where*

- *$\mathcal{A} = (A_1, A_2, \ldots, A_n)$ is a sequence of finite, non-empty sets, called the domains of P, and*
- *$\mathcal{C}$ is a set of constraints $\{C_1, \ldots, C_q\}$ where each C_i is a pair (S_i, R_i) with*
  - *S_i a non-empty subset of $\{1, 2, \ldots, n\}$ called the scope of C_i, and*
  - *R_i an $|S_i|$-ary relation over $(A_j : j \in S_i)$, called the constraint relation of C_i.*

In this case, a solution to P is an n-tuple $\vec{a}$ over the sequence $(A_i : 1 \leq i \leq n)$ such that $\mathrm{proj}_{S_j}(\vec{a}) \in R_j$ for each $1 \leq j \leq q$. Clearly, each standard instance of the CSP can be expressed as an equivalent multi-sorted instance.

In addition to the set of solutions of an instance of the CSP, one can also consider partial solutions of the instance.

Definition 2.5 *For P as in the previous definition and I a subset of $\{1, 2, \ldots, n\}$, the set of partial solutions of P over I, denoted P_I, is the set of solutions of the instance $P' = (\mathcal{A}', \mathcal{C}')$ where $\mathcal{A}' = (A_i : i \in I)$ and $\mathcal{C} = \{C_1', \ldots, C_q'\}$ with $C_j' = (I \cap S_j, \mathrm{proj}_{(I \cap S_j)}(R_j))$ for $1 \leq j \leq q$.*

Clearly if the set of partial solutions of an instance over some subset of coordinates is empty then the instance has no solutions.

Definition 2.6 *Let C be a finite set (or sequence) of finite, non-empty sets. A (multi-sorted) constraint language over C is a collection of finitary relations over the sets in C. Given a multi-sorted constraint language Γ over C, the class CSP(Γ) consists of all multi-sorted instances of the CSP whose domains come from C and whose constraint relations come from Γ. Γ_C denotes the set of all finitary relations over the members of C.*

In a natural way, the notions of tractability and **NP**-completeness can be extended to multi-sorted constraint languages.

Definition 2.7 *A relation R over the sets A_i, $1 \leq i \leq n$, is subdirect if for all $1 \leq i \leq n$, $\mathrm{proj}_{\{i\}}(R) = A_i$. We call a multi-sorted instance P of the CSP subdirect if each of its constraint relations is.*

As noted in the introduction, one approach to proving the tractability of a constraint language Γ is to apply a notion of local consistency to the instances in CSP(Γ) to determine if the instances have solutions. We present a notion of width, called relational width, developed by Bulatov and Jeavons [4] that, for finite constraint languages, is closely related to the notion of width defined by Feder and Vardi (see [15]).

Definition 2.8 *Let $\mathcal{A} = (A_1, \ldots, A_n)$ be a sequence of finite, non-empty sets, let $P = (\mathcal{A}, \mathcal{C})$ be an instance of the CSP and let $k > 0$. We say that P is k-minimal if:*

1. *For each subset I of $\{1, 2, \ldots, n\}$ of size at most k, there is some constraint (S, R) in $\mathcal{C}$ such that $I \subseteq S$, and*
2. *If (S_1, R_1) and (S_2, R_2) are constraints in $\mathcal{C}$ and $I \subseteq S_1 \cap S_2$ has size at most k then $\mathrm{proj}_I(R_1) = \mathrm{proj}_I(R_2)$.*

It is not hard to show that the second condition of this definition is equivalent to having the set of partial solutions P_I of P equal to $\mathrm{proj}_I(R_i)$ for all subsets I of size at most k and all i with $I \subseteq S_i$.

In [4] it is shown that for a fixed k, there is a polynomial time algorithm that converts a given instance of the CSP into an equivalent one (i.e., that has the same solution set) that is also k-minimal.

Definition 2.9 *Let $k > 0$. A constraint language Γ has relational width k if whenever P is a k-minimal instance of CSP(Γ) whose constraint relations are all non-empty then P has a solution. We say that Γ has finite relational width if it has relational width k for some $k > 0$.*

The following theorem records some relevant facts about this notion.

Theorem 2.10 *Let Γ be a constraint language.*

1. *([4]) If Γ is of finite relational width then it is globally tractable.*
2. *If Γ is finite, then it has finite relational width if and only if it is of bounded width (according to the Feder-Vardi definition). It follows, in this case, that the class of instances from CSP(Γ) that fail to have a solution is definable within Datalog.*

A proof of the equivalence of bounded width and finite relational width for finite constraint languages can be found in [16, 15]. We will use this theorem to establish the global tractability of languages that arise in the particular algebraic context set out in Section 3.

2.2. Algebras

There are a number of standard sources for the basics of universal algebra, for example [7] and [17]. The books [12, 8] provide details on the more specialized aspects of the subject that we will use in this paper.

Definition 2.11 *An algebra $\mathbf{A}$ is a pair (A, F) where A is a non-empty set and F is a (possibly infinite) collection of finitary operations on A. The operations in F are called the basic operations of $\mathbf{A}$. A term operation of an algebra $\mathbf{A}$ is a finitary operation on A that can be obtained by repeated compositions of the basic operations of $\mathbf{A}$.*

We assume some familiarity with the standard algebraic operations of taking subalgebras, homomorphic images and cartesian products. Note that in order to sensibly take a homomorphic image of an algebra, or the cartesian product of a set of algebras or to speak of terms and equations of an algebra we need to have some indexing of the basic operations of the algebras. Algebras that have the same indexing are said to be similar (or of the same similarity type).

When necessary, we distinguish between an algebra and its underlying set, or universe. A subuniverse of an algebra (A, F) is a subset of A that is invariant under F. Note that we allow empty subuniverses but not algebras with empty universes.

Definition 2.12 *A variety of algebras is a collection of similar algebras that is closed under the taking of cartesian products, subalgebras and homomorphic images. If $\mathcal{K}$ is a class of similar algebras then $\mathsf{V}(\mathcal{K})$ denotes the smallest variety that contains $\mathcal{K}$.*

Theorem 2.13 (Birkhoff) *A class $\mathcal{V}$ of similar algebras is a variety if and only if $\mathcal{V}$ can be axiomatized by a set of equations.*

It turns out that for a class $\mathcal{K}$ of similar algebras, $\mathsf{V}(\mathcal{K}) = \mathsf{HSP}(\mathcal{K})$, i.e., the class of homomorphic images of subalgebras of cartesian products of members of $\mathcal{K}$.

Definition 2.14 *Let* $\mathbf{A}$ *be an algebra.*

1. *An equivalence relation* θ *on* A *is a congruence of* $\mathbf{A}$ *if it is invariant under the basic operations of* $\mathbf{A}$.
2. *The congruence lattice of* $\mathbf{A}$, *denoted* $\mathrm{Con}\,(\mathbf{A})$, *is the lattice of all congruences of* $\mathbf{A}$, *ordered by inclusion.*
3. 0_A *and* 1_A *denote the smallest and largest congruences of the algebra* $\mathbf{A}$.

The congruence lattice of an algebra is a very useful invariant and the types of congruence lattices that can appear in a variety govern many properties of the algebras in the variety. One particularly relevant and important property of congruence lattices is that of distributivity.

Definition 2.15 *An algebra* $\mathbf{A}$ *is said to be congruence distributive if its congruence lattice satisfies the distributive law for congruence meet and join. A class of algebras is congruence distributive if all of its members are.*

Definition 2.16 *For* $k > 0$, *we define* $CD(k)$ *to be the class of all algebras* $\mathbf{A}$ *that have a sequence of ternary term operations* $p_i(x, y, z)$, $0 \le i \le k$, *that satisfies the identities:*

$$\begin{aligned} p_0(x,y,z) &= x \\ p_k(x,y,z) &= z \\ p_i(x,y,x) &= x \text{ for all } i \\ p_i(x,x,y) &= p_{i+1}(x,x,y) \text{ for all } i \text{ even} \\ p_i(x,y,y) &= p_{i+1}(x,y,y) \text{ for all } i \text{ odd} \end{aligned}$$

A sequence of term operations of an algebra $\mathbf{A}$ that satisfies the above equations will be referred to as Jónsson terms of $\mathbf{A}$. The following celebrated theorem of Jónsson relates congruence distributivity to the existence of Jónsson terms.

Theorem 2.17 (Jónsson) *An algebra* $\mathbf{A}$ *generates a congruence distributive variety if and only if there is some* $k > 0$ *such that* $\mathbf{A}$ *is in* $CD(k)$. *In this case, all algebras in* $\mathsf{V}(\mathbf{A})$ *lie in* $CD(k)$.

Definition 2.18 *For* $k > 1$, *define* $\mathcal{V}_k$ *to be the variety of all algebras that have as basic operations a sequence of* $k + 1$ *ternary operations* $p_i(x, y, z)$, *for* $0 \le i \le k$, *that satisfy the equations from Definition 2.16.*

Note that an algebra is in $CD(1)$ if and only if it has size 1 and is in $CD(2)$ if and only if it has a majority term operation (i.e., a term operation $m(x, y, z)$ that satisfies the equations $m(x, x, y) = m(x, y, x) = m(y, x, x) = x$).

Some of the main results and conjectures dealing with the CSP can be expressed in terms of Tame Congruence Theory, a deep theory of the local structure of finite algebras developed by Hobby and McKenzie. Details of this theory may be found in [12] or [8]. The connection between the CSP and Tame Congruence Theory was made by Bulatov, Jeavons, and Krokhin [5] and we will touch on it in the next subsection. In this paper we will only introduce some of the basic terminology of the theory and will omit most details.

In Tame Congruence Theory, five local types of behaviour of finite algebras are identified and studied. The five types are, in order:

1. the unary type,
2. the affine or vector-space type,
3. the 2 element Boolean type,
4. the 2 element lattice type,
5. the 2 element semi-lattice type.

We say that an algebra $\mathbf{A}$ omits a particular type if, locally, the corresponding type of behaviour does not occur in $\mathbf{A}$. A class of algebras $\mathcal{C}$ is said to omit a particular type if all finite members of $\mathcal{C}$ omit that type.

In [12], characterizations of finite algebras that generate varieties that omit the unary type or both the unary and affine type are given. The characterizations are similar to that given by Jónsson of the congruence distributive varieties. It easily follows from the characterizations that if $\mathbf{A}$ is a finite algebra that generates a congruence distributive variety then the variety omits both the unary and affine types.

To close this subsection we note a special property of the term operations of the algebras in $\mathcal{V}_k$ for all $k > 1$.

Definition 2.19 *An* n*-ary operation* $f(x_1, \ldots, x_n)$ *on a set* A *is idempotent if* $f(a, a, \ldots, a) = a$ *for all* $a \in A$. *An algebra is idempotent if all of its term operations are idempotent.*

Note that idempotency is hereditary in the sense that if a function is the composition of some idempotent operations then it too is idempotent. In another sense, if $\mathbf{A}$ is idempotent then all algebras in $\mathsf{V}(\mathbf{A})$ are idempotent, since this condition can be described equationally. Finally, note that Jónsson terms are idempotent and so all algebras in $\mathcal{V}_k$ for $k > 1$ are idempotent.

2.3. Algebras and the CSP

The natural duality between sets of relations (constraint languages) over a set A and sets of operations (algebras) on A has been studied by algebraists for some time. Jeavons and his co-authors [13] have shown how this link between constraint languages and algebras can be used to transfer questions about tractability into equivalent questions about algebras. In this subsection we present a concise overview of this connection.

Definition 2.20 *Let A be a non-empty set.*

1. *Let R be an n-ary relation over A and $f(\bar{x})$ an m-ary function over A for some n, $m \geq 0$. We say that R is invariant under f and that f is a polymorphism of R if for all $\vec{a}_i \in R$, for $1 \leq i \leq m$, the n-tuple $f(\vec{a}_1, \ldots, \vec{a}_m) \in R$ whose i-th coordinate is equal to $f(\vec{a}_1(i), \ldots, \vec{a}_m(i))$.*
2. *For Γ a set of relations over A, $\mathrm{Pol}\,(\Gamma)$ denotes the set of functions on A that are polymorphisms of all the relations in Γ.*
3. *For F a set of finitary operations on A, $\mathrm{Inv}(F)$ denotes the set of all finitary relations on A that are invariant under all operations in F.*
4. *For Γ a constraint language over A, $\langle\Gamma\rangle$ denotes $\mathrm{Inv}(\mathrm{Pol}\,(\Gamma))$ and $\mathbf{A}_\Gamma$ denotes the algebra $(A, \mathrm{Pol}\,(\Gamma))$.*
5. *For $\mathbf{A} = (A, F)$, an algebra over A, $\Gamma_\mathbf{A}$ denotes the constraint language $\mathrm{Inv}(F)$.*
6. *We call a finite algebra $\mathbf{A}$ tractable (**NP**-complete) if the constraint language $\Gamma_\mathbf{A}$ is.*
7. *We say that a finite algebra $\mathbf{A}$ is of finite relational width (bounded width) if each finite constraint language contained in $\Gamma_\mathbf{A}$ is.*

Note that if $\mathbf{A}$ is an algebra, then $\mathrm{Inv}(\mathbf{A})$ coincides with the set of all subuniverses of finite cartesian powers of $\mathbf{A}$.

Theorem 2.21 *([13]) Let Γ be a constraint language on a finite set. If Γ is tractable then so is $\langle\Gamma\rangle$. If $\langle\Gamma\rangle$ is **NP**-complete then so is Γ.*

In algebraic terms, Theorem 2.21 states that a constraint language Γ is tractable (or **NP**-complete) if and only if the algebra $\mathbf{A}_\Gamma$ is. So, the problem of characterizing the tractable constraint languages can be reduced to the problem of characterizing the tractable finite algebras. In a further step, Bulatov, Jeavons and Krokhin [5] provide a reduction down to idempotent algebras. For this class of algebras, they propose the following characterization of tractability.

Conjecture 2.22 *Let $\mathbf{A}$ be a finite idempotent algebra. Then $\mathbf{A}$ is tractable if and only if the variety $\mathsf{V}(\mathbf{A})$ omits the unary type.*

They show that when this condition fails, the algebra is **NP**-complete [5]. They also show that if $\mathbf{A}$ is a finite, idempotent algebra then $\mathsf{V}(\mathbf{A})$ omits the unary type if and only if the class $\mathsf{HS}(\mathbf{A})$ does. This conjecture has been verified for a number of large classes of algebras. For example, results of Schaefer [18] and Bulatov [1] provide a verification for algebras whose universes have size 2 and 3 respectively.

A conjecture similar to 2.22 has been proposed by Larose and Zádori [16] for constraint languages of bounded width.

Conjecture 2.23 *Let $\mathbf{A}$ be a finite idempotent algebra. Then $\mathbf{A}$ is of bounded width if and only if $\mathsf{V}(\mathbf{A})$ omits the unary and affine types.*

In [16] Larose and Zádori verify one direction of this conjecture, namely that if $\mathsf{V}(\mathbf{A})$ fails to omit the unary or affine types then $\mathbf{A}$ is not of bounded width. Note that in [2], Bulatov proposes a conjecture that is parallel to 2.23. Larose and the second author have noted [19] that, as with the unary type, one need only check in $\mathsf{HS}(\mathbf{A})$ to determine if $\mathsf{V}(\mathbf{A})$ omits the unary and affine types when $\mathbf{A}$ is finite and idempotent.

The main result of this paper can be regarded as providing some evidence in support of Conjecture 2.23. Theorem 4.1 establishes that if $\mathbf{A}$ is a finite member of $CD(3)$ then any finite constraint language contained in $\Gamma_\mathbf{A}$ is of bounded width and hence tractable.

3. Algebras in $CD(3)$

Recall that the variety $\mathcal{V}_3$ consists of all algebras $\mathbf{A}$ having four basic operations $p_i(x, y, z)$, $0 \leq i \leq 3$ that satisfy the equations of Definition 2.16. Since the equations dictate that p_0 and p_3 are projections onto x and z respectively, they will play no role in the analysis of algebras in $CD(3)$.

3.1. Jónsson ideals

For $\mathbf{A}$ an algebra in $\mathcal{V}_3$, define $x \cdot y$ to be the binary term operation $p_1(x, y, y)$ of $\mathbf{A}$. Note that the Jónsson equations imply that $x \cdot y = p_2(x, y, y)$ as well. This "multiplication" will play a crucial role in the proof of the main theorem of this paper.

Definition 3.1 *For X a subset of an algebra $\mathbf{B} \in \mathcal{V}_3$ let $J(X)$ be the smallest subuniverse Y of $\mathbf{B}$ containing X and satisfying the following closure property: if x is in Y and $u \in B$ then $u \cdot x$ is also in Y.*

We will call $J(X)$ the Jónsson ideal of $\mathbf{B}$ generated by X. The concept of a Jónsson ideal was developed in [19] for any algebra that generates a congruence distributive variety and was used in that paper to establish some intersection properties of subalgebras that are related to relational width.

Definition 3.2 *A finite algebra $\mathbf{B} \in \mathcal{V}_3$ will be called Jónsson trivial if it has no proper non-empty Jónsson ideals.*

Note that **B** is Jónsson trivial if and only if $J(\{b\}) = B$ for all $b \in B$. Also note that if **B** is Jónsson trivial then every homomorphic image of it is, as well.

We now define a notion of distance in an algebra that will be applied to Jónsson trivial algebras to establish some useful features of the subalgebras of their cartesian products.

Definition 3.3 *Let* **A** *and* **B** *be arbitrary similar algebras and* **S** *a subdirect subalgebra of* $\mathbf{A} \times \mathbf{B}$.

1. *Let* $S_0 = 0_A$ *and* S_1 *be the relation on* A *defined by:*

$$(a, c) \in S_1 \iff (a, b), (c, b) \in S \text{ for some } b \in B.$$

2. *For* $k > 0$, *let* $S_{k+1} = S_k \circ S_1$.
3. *For* a, $b \in A$, *we write* $d(a, b) = k$ *if the pair* (a, b) *is in* S_k *and not in* S_{k-1} *and will say that the distance between* a *and* b *relative to* S *is* k. *If no such* k *exists,* $d(a, b)$ *is said to be undefined.*
4. *If* $d(a, b)$ *is defined for all* a *and* $b \in A$ *we say that* **A** *is connected with respect to* **S**.

Proposition 3.4 *Let* **A**, **B** *and* **S** *be as in the definition.*

1. *For each* $k \geq 0$, *the relation* S_k *is a reflexive, symmetric subalgebra of* $\mathbf{A}^2$.
2. *If* **A** *is an idempotent algebra and* $c \in A$ *then for any* $k \geq 0$, *the set of all elements* a *with* $d(a, c) \leq k$ *is a subuniverse of* **A**.
3. *If* **A** *is a simple algebra then either* $d(a, b)$ *is undefined for all* $a \neq b \in A$ *(equivalently* $S_1 = 0_A$*) or* **A** *is connected with respect to* **S**.

Lemma 3.5 *Let* **A** *and* **B** *be finite algebras in* $\mathcal{V}_3$ *and* **S** *a subdirect subalgebra of* $\mathbf{A} \times \mathbf{B}$. *Suppose that* **A** *is connected with respect to* **S**. *Then for every* $x, y, z \in A$ *we have*

$$d(x \cdot y, z) \leq \max\left(\left\lceil \frac{d(x, y) + 1}{2} \right\rceil, d(y, z)\right).$$

PROOF: Let $d(y, z) = m$, $d(x, y) = n$ and choose elements $a_i \in A$ for $0 \leq i \leq n$ with $x = a_0$, $a_n = y$ and $(a_i, a_{i+1}) \in S_1$ for $0 \leq i < n$. For k the largest integer below $[(n + 1)/2]$ we get that $d(x, a_k)$ and $d(a_k, y)$ are both at most k. Therefore if $d = \max(k, m)$, then the pairs (x, a_k), (y, a_k), (y, z) are in S_d, and so

$$(p_2(x, y, y), p_2(a_k, a_k, z)) \in S_d .$$

But $p_2(x, y, y) = x \cdot y$ and $p_2(a_k, a_k, z) = z$, proving the lemma. •

Corollary 3.6 *For* **A**, **B** *and* **S** *as in the previous lemma, suppose that* $d(a, b) \leq n$ *for all* a, $b \in A$. *Let* $m \geq [(n + 1)/2]$ *be any integer and* $c \in A$. *Then the set of all elements of* A *whose distance from* c *is at most* m *is a Jónsson ideal of* **A**.

PROOF: As noted earlier the set $I = \{a \in A : d(a, c) \leq m\}$ is a subuniverse of **A** since **A** is idempotent. We need only show that I is closed under multiplication on the left. So, suppose that $a \in I$ and $u \in A$. Since $d(u, c) \leq n$, we have $d(u \cdot a, c) \leq \max(m, d(a, c)) \leq m$ by the previous lemma. •

Corollary 3.7 *Let* **A** *and* **B** *be finite members of* $\mathcal{V}_3$ *such that* **A** *is Jónsson trivial and connected with respect to some subdirect subalgebra* **S** *of* $\mathbf{A} \times \mathbf{B}$. *Then* $d(a, b) \leq 1$ *for all* a, $b \in A$ *(or equivalently,* $S_1 = A^2$*).*

PROOF: Suppose that the maximum distance n between the points of A is at least 2 and that a, $b \in A$ with $d(a, b) = n$. Then m, the largest integer below $[(n + 1)/2]$ is less than n. From the previous lemma, the set of all elements $u \in A$ with $d(a, u) \leq m$ is a proper Jónsson ideal of **A**, contradicting that **A** is Jónsson trivial. •

Lemma 3.8 *Let* **A**, **B** *be finite members of* $\mathcal{V}_3$ *with* **A** *Jónsson trivial and simple and let* **S** *be a subdirect subalgebra of* $\mathbf{A} \times \mathbf{B}$. *Then either* $S = A \times B$, *or* S *is the graph of an onto homomorphism from* **B** *to* **A**.

PROOF: As **A** is simple, then either $S_1 = 0_A$ or **A** is connected with respect to **S**. In the former case, we conclude that S is the graph of an onto homomorphism from **B** to **A** and in the latter, it follows from the previous corollary that $S_1 = A^2$.

For $a \in A$, let $S_a = \{b \in B : (a, b) \in S\}$ and choose a with $|S_a|$ maximal. Let I denote the set of those elements x of A for which $S_x = S_a$. To complete the proof we will need to demonstrate that $I = A$ and $S_a = B$. To show that $I = A$ it will suffice to prove that it is a Jónsson ideal of **A**.

Indeed, let $u \in A$ and $c \in I$ be arbitrary. Then $(u, c) \in S_1$ (since $S_1 = A^2$) and therefore there is a $b \in B$ such that (u, b) and (c, b) are in S. Note that since $c \in I$ then $b \in S_a$. If d is any element of S_a then $c \in I$ implies that $(c, d) \in S$, so we get that

$$(p_2(u, c, c), p_2(b, b, d)) = (u \cdot c, d) \in S.$$

Since this holds for every $d \in S_a$, we conclude that $u \cdot c \in I$. Finally, since S is subdirect it follows that $S_a = B$. •

We apply this lemma to obtain a simple description of subdirect products of finite, simple, Jónsson trivial members of $\mathcal{V}_3$ and then show how to use this description to prove that certain k-minimal instances of the CSP have solutions, when $k \geq 3$.

Lemma 3.9 *Let $\mathbf{A}_i$, for $1 \le i \le n$, be finite members of $\mathcal{V}_3$ with $\mathbf{A}_1$ Jónsson trivial. Let* **S** *be a subdirect product of the $\mathbf{A}_i$'s such that for all $1 < i \le n$, the projection of S onto coordinates 1 and i is equal to $A_1 \times A_i$. Then $S = A_1 \times D$, where $D = \text{proj}_{\{2 \le i \le n\}}(S)$.*

PROOF: We prove this by induction on n. For $n = 2$, the result follows by our hypotheses. Consider the case $n = 3$ and let **D** be the projection of **S** onto $\mathbf{A}_2 \times \mathbf{A}_3$. Let $(u, v) \in D$ and let $I_{(u,v)} = \{a \in A_1 : (a, u, v) \in S\}$. Our goal is to show that $I_{(u,v)} = A_1$ and we can accomplish this by showing that it is a non-empty Jónsson ideal. Clearly $I_{(u,v)}$ is a non-empty subuniverse of $\mathbf{A}_1$ since all algebras involved are idempotent.

Let $a \in I_{(u,v)}$, $b \in A_1$ and choose elements $y \in A_3$ and $x \in A_2$ with (b, u, y) and $(a, x, y) \in S$. By our hypotheses, these elements exist. Applying p_2 to these elements, along with (a, u, v), we get the element $(b \cdot a, u, v)$, showing that $b \cdot a \in I_{(u,v)}$. Thus $I_{(u,v)}$ is a Jónsson ideal.

Now, consider the general case and suppose that the result holds for products of fewer than n factors. Let $\mathbf{S}_1 = \text{proj}_{\{1 \le i < n\}}(S)$ and $\mathbf{S}_2 = \text{proj}_{\{2 \le i < n\}}(S)$. Then **S** is isomorphic to a subdirect product of $\mathbf{A}_1$, $\mathbf{S}_2$ and $\mathbf{A}_n$ and, by induction, $S_1 = A_1 \times S_2$. Then, applying the result with $n = 3$ to this situation, we conclude that $S = A_1 \times D$, as required. •

Corollary 3.10 *Let $\mathbf{A}_i$ be finite, simple, Jónsson trivial members of $\mathcal{V}_3$, for $1 \le i \le n$, and let* **S** *be a subdirect product of the $\mathbf{A}_i$'s. If, for all $1 \le i < j \le n$, the projection of S onto $A_i \times A_j$ is not the graph of a bijection then $S = \prod_{1 \le i \le n} A_i$.*

PROOF: For $1 \le i < j \le n$, we have, by Lemma 3.8 that either the projection of S onto $A_i \times A_j$ is the graph of a bijection between the two factors (since they are both simple) or is the full product. The former case is ruled out by assumption and so we are in a position to apply the previous lemma inductively to reach the desired conclusion. •

Definition 3.11 *A subdirect product* **S** *of the algebras $\mathbf{A}_i$, $1 \le i \le n$, is said to be almost trivial if, after suitably rearranging the coordinates, there is a partition of $\{1, 2, \dots, n\}$ into intervals I_j, $1 \le j \le p$, such that $S = \text{proj}_{I_1}(S) \times \cdots \times \text{proj}_{I_p}(S)$ and, for each j, if $I_j = \{i : u \le i \le v\}$ then there are bijections $\pi_i : A_u \to A_i$, for $i \in I_j$ such that $\text{proj}_{I_j}(S) = \{(a, \pi_{u+1}(a), \dots, \pi_v(a)) : a \in A_u\}$.*

Corollary 3.12 *Let $\mathbf{A}_i$ be finite, simple, Jónsson trivial members of $\mathcal{V}_3$, for $1 \le i \le n$, and let* **S** *be a subdirect product of the $\mathbf{A}_i$'s. Then* **S** *is almost trivial.*

PROOF: For $1 \le i, j \le n$, set $i \sim j$ if $i = j$ or the projection of S onto A_i and A_j is equal to the graph of a bijection between these two factors. In this case, let $\pi_{i,j}$ denote this bijection.

It is not hard to see that $\sim$ is an equivalence relation on the set $\{1, 2, \dots, n\}$ and, by applying Lemma 3.8, if $i \not\sim j$ then the projection of S onto A_i and A_j is equal to $A_i \times A_j$. By using the bijections $\pi_{i,j}$ and Corollary 3.10 it is elementary to show that **S** is indeed almost trivial. •

For $\mathcal{A}$ a finite sequence of finite algebras, $P = (\mathcal{A}, \mathcal{C})$ denotes a multi-sorted instance of the CSP whose domains are the universes of the algebras in $\mathcal{A}$ and whose constraint relations are subuniverses of cartesian products of members from $\mathcal{A}$.

Theorem 3.13 *Let $\mathcal{A}$ be a finite sequence of finite, simple, Jónsson trivial members of $\mathcal{V}_3$ and let $P = (\mathcal{A}, \mathcal{C})$ be a subdirect, k-minimal instance of the CSP for some $k \ge 3$. If the constraint relations of P are all non-empty then P has a solution.*

Definition 3.11 and analogs of Corollary 3.12 and Theorem 3.13 can be found at the end of Section 3.3 in [3]. The proof of Corollary 3.4 given in that paper can be used to prove our Theorem 3.13. As we shall see, this theorem will form the base of the inductive proof of our main result.

3.2. The reduction to Jónsson trivial algebras

The goal of this subsection is to show how to reduce a k-minimal instance P of the CSP whose domains all lie in $\mathcal{V}_3$ and whose constraint relations are all non-empty to another k-minimal, subdirect instance P' whose domains are all Jónsson trivial and whose constraint relations are non-empty. In order to accomplish this, we will need to work with a suitably large $k \ge 3$.

To start, let $\mathcal{A} = (\mathbf{A}_1, \dots, \mathbf{A}_n)$ be a sequence of finite algebras from $\mathcal{V}_3$ and let $M = \max\{|A_i| : 1 \le i \le n\}$. Let $k > 0$ and $P = (\mathcal{A}, \mathcal{C})$ be a k-minimal instance of the CSP with $\mathcal{C}$ consisting of the constraints $C_i = (S_i, R_i)$, $1 \le i \le m$. By taking suitable subalgebras of the $\mathbf{A}_i$ we may assume that P is subdirect and, of course, we also assume that the R_i are all non-empty. In addition, k-minimality assures that we may assume that the scope of each constraint of P consists of at least k variables and that no two constraints have the same k-element set as their scopes.

Since P is k-minimal then its system of partial solutions over k-element sets satisfies an important compatibility property. Namely, if I and K are k-element sets of coordinates then $\text{proj}_{(I \cap K)}(P_I) = \text{proj}_{(I \cap K)}(P_K)$. In this section we will denote P_I by $\Lambda(I)$ and call this function the k-system (of partial solutions) determined by P. Since P is subdirect then for all I, $\Lambda(I)$ will be a subdirect product of the algebras $\mathbf{A}_i$, for $i \in I$.

We wish to consider the situation in which some $\mathbf{A}_i$, say $\mathbf{A}_1$, has a proper Jónsson ideal J. The main result of this subsection is that if the scopes of the constraints of P all have size at most k (and hence exactly k), or if $k \geq M^2$ then we can reduce the question of the solvability of P to the solvability of a k-minimal instance with $\mathbf{A}_1$ replaced by J. Doing so will allow us to proceed by induction to reduce our original instance down to one whose domains are all Jónsson trivial.

So, let J be a proper non-empty Jónsson ideal of $\mathbf{A}_1$ and define Λ_J to be the following function on the set of k-element subsets of $\{1, 2, \ldots, n\}$:

- If I is a k-element set that includes 1 then define $\Lambda_J(I)$ to be $\{\vec{a} \in \Lambda(I) : \vec{a}(1) \in J\}$.
- If $1 \notin I$, define $\Lambda_J(I)$ to be the set of all $\vec{a} \in \Lambda(I)$ such that for all $i \in I$ the restriction of $\vec{a}$ to $I \setminus \{i\}$ can be extended to an element of $\Lambda_J(\{1\} \cup (I \setminus \{i\}))$.

Lemma 3.14 *If $k \geq 3$ then*

1. *$\Lambda_J(I)$ is non-empty for all I and if $1 \in I$ then the projection of $\Lambda_J(I)$ onto the first coordinate is equal to J.*
2. *For I, K, k-element subsets of $\{1, 2, \ldots, n\}$, $\mathrm{proj}_{(I \cap K)}(\Lambda_J(I)) = \mathrm{proj}_{(I \cap K)}(\Lambda_J(K))$.*

Corollary 3.15 *If all of the constraints of P have scopes of size k then there is a k-minimal instance P_J of the constraint satisfaction problem over the domains $\mathbf{J}$ and the $\mathbf{A}_i$, for $2 \leq i \leq n$, whose constraint relations are all non-empty and whose solution set is contained in the solution set of P.*

PROOF: It follows from our assumptions on the sizes of the scopes of the constraints of P that the constraints can be indexed by the k-element subsets of $\{1, 2, \ldots, n\}$ and that for such a subset I, the constraint C_I is of the form (I, R_I) where R_I is a subdirect product of the algebras $\mathbf{A}_i$, for $i \in I$.

We set P_J to be the instance of the CSP over the domains $\mathbf{J}$ and the $\mathbf{A}_i$, for $2 \leq i \leq n$, that has, for each k-element subset I of $\{1, 2, \ldots, n\}$, the constraint $C'_I = (I, R'_I)$, where $R'_I = \Lambda_J(I)$. It follows by construction and from the previous lemma that P_J is a k-minimal instance of the CSP whose constraint relations are all non-empty and whose solutions are also solutions of P. •

The previous corollary can be used to establish the tractability of the constraint languages arising from finite members of $\mathcal{V}_3$, while the following lemma will be used to prove that these languages are in fact globally tractable.

Lemma 3.16 *Assume that $k \geq M^2$ and let $C = (S, R)$ be a constraint of P. Then there is a subuniverse R_J of R such that for all k-element subsets I of S, the projection of R onto I is equal to $\Lambda_J(I)$.*

Corollary 3.17 *If $k \geq M^2$ then there is a k-minimal instance P_J of the constraint satisfaction problem over $\mathbf{J}$ and the $\mathbf{A}_i$, for $2 \leq i \leq n$, whose constraint relations are all non-empty and whose solution set is contained in the solution set of P.*

PROOF: From the preceding lemma it follows that the instance P_J over the domains $\mathbf{J}$ and the $\mathbf{A}_i$, for $2 \leq i \leq n$, with constraints $C' = (S, R_J)$, for each constraint $C = (S, R)$ of P, is k-minimal and has all of its constraint relations non-empty. Since the constraint relations of P_J are subsets of the corresponding constraint relations of P then the result follows. •

Theorem 3.18 *Let $\mathcal{A} = (\mathbf{A}_1, \ldots, \mathbf{A}_n)$ be a sequence of finite algebras from $\mathcal{V}_3$ and let $P = (\mathcal{A}, \mathcal{C})$ be a k-minimal instance of the CSP whose constraint relations are non-empty. If $k \geq 3$ and the sizes of the scopes of the constraints of P are bounded by k or if $k \geq M^2$, where $M = \max\{|A_i| : 1 \leq i \leq n\}$, then there is a subdirect k-minimal instance P' of the CSP over Jónsson trivial subalgebras of the $\mathbf{A}_i$ such that the constraint relations of P' are non-empty and the solution set of P' is contained in the solution set of P.*

PROOF: This theorem is proved by repeated application of Corollaries 3.15 and 3.17. •

3.3. The reduction to simple algebras

In this subsection we show, for $k \geq 3$, how to reduce a k-minimal instance of the CSP whose domains are Jónsson trivial members of $\mathcal{V}_3$ and whose constraint relations are all non-empty to one which has in addition, domains that are simple algebras. Our development closely follows parts of the proof of Theorem 3.1 in [3].

Definition 3.19 *Let $\mathbf{A}_i$, $1 \leq i \leq m$, be similar algebras and let $\Theta = (\theta_1, \ldots, \theta_m)$ be a sequence of congruences $\theta_i \in \mathrm{Con}\,(\mathbf{A}_i)$.*

1. *$\prod_{i=1}^{m} \theta_i$ denotes the congruence on $\prod_{i=1}^{m} \mathbf{A}_i$ that identifies two m-tuples $\vec{a}$ and $\vec{b}$ if and only if $(a_i, b_i) \in \theta_i$ for all i.*
2. *If I is a subset of $\{1, 2, \ldots, m\}$ and $\mathbf{R}$ is a subalgebra of $\prod_{i \in I} \mathbf{A}_i$ then $\mathbf{R}/\Theta$ denotes the quotient of $\mathbf{R}$ by the restriction of the congruence $\prod_{i \in I} \theta_i$ to R.*

Let $\mathcal{A} = (\mathbf{A}_1, \ldots, \mathbf{A}_n)$ be a sequence of finite, Jónsson trivial members of $\mathcal{V}_3$ and let $P = (\mathcal{A}, \mathcal{C})$ be a subdirect, k-minimal instance of the CSP whose constraint relations are all non-empty. Let $\mathcal{C} = \{C_1, C_2, \ldots, C_m\}$ where, for $1 \le i \le m$, $C_i = (S_i, R_i)$ for some subset S_i of $\{1, 2, \ldots, n\}$ and some subuniverse R_i of $\prod_{i \in S_i} \mathbf{A}_i$. Suppose that one of the $\mathbf{A}_i$ is not simple, say for $i = 1$, and let θ_1 be a maximal proper congruence of $\mathbf{A}_1$.

Recall that for $I \subseteq \{1, 2, \ldots, n\}$, P_I denotes the set of partial solutions of P over the variables I. If $|I| \le k$ then since P is k-minimal, P_I is non-empty and is a subdirect subuniverse of $\prod_{i \in I} \mathbf{A}_i$.

Since the algebra $\mathbf{A}_1/\theta_1$ is a simple, Jónsson trivial algebra then it follows by Lemma 3.8 that for $2 \le i \le n$, $P_{\{1,i\}}/(\theta_1 \times 0_{A_i})$ is either the graph of a homomorphism π_i from $\mathbf{A}_i$ onto $\mathbf{A}_1/\theta_1$ or is equal to $A_1/\theta_1 \times A_i$. Let W consist of 1 along with the set of all i for which the former holds. For $2 \le i \le n$, let θ_i be the kernel of the map π_i if $i \in W$, and 0_{A_i} otherwise.

Let $\Theta = (\theta_1, \ldots, \theta_n)$ and set $P/\Theta = (\mathcal{A}/\Theta, \mathcal{C}/\Theta)$ where $\mathcal{A}/\Theta = (\mathbf{A}_1/\theta_1, \ldots, \mathbf{A}_n/\theta_n)$ and $\mathcal{C}/\Theta$ consists of the constraints $C_i/\Theta = (S_i, R_i/\Theta)$, for $1 \le i \le m$.

Note that since P is subdirect and k-minimal then so is P/Θ and that each $\mathbf{A}_i/\theta_i$ is Jónsson trivial, since this property is preserved by taking quotients.

Lemma 3.20 *If the instance P/Θ has a solution, then there is some k-minimal instance $P' = (\mathcal{A}', \mathcal{C}')$ such that*

- *$\mathcal{A}' = (\mathbf{A}'_1, \ldots, \mathbf{A}'_n)$, where for each $1 \le i \le n$, $\mathbf{A}'_i$ a subalgebra of $\mathbf{A}_i$.*
- *A'_1 is a proper subset of A_1,*
- *$\mathcal{C}' = \{C'_1, \ldots, C'_m\}$ where, for each $1 \le i \le m$, $C'_i = (S_i, R'_i)$ for some non-empty subuniverse R'_i of R_i.*

Hence, any solution of P' is a solution of P.

4. Proof of the main result

In the preceding section we established techniques for reducing k-minimal instances of the CSP over domains from $\mathcal{V}_3$ to more manageable instances. The following theorem employs these techniques to establish the finite relational width of constraint languages arising from finite algebras in $CD(3)$.

Let $\mathbf{A}$ be a finite algebra in $CD(3)$. Then $\mathbf{A}$ has term operations $p_1(x, y, z)$ and $p_2(x, y, z)$ that satisfy the equations:

$$\begin{aligned} p_i(x, y, x) &= x \ , i = 1, 2 \\ p_1(x, x, y) &= x \\ p_1(x, y, y) &= p_2(x, y, y) \\ p_2(x, x, y) &= y \end{aligned}$$

Associated with $\mathbf{A}$ is the constraint language $\Gamma_{\mathbf{A}} = \mathrm{Inv}(\mathbf{A})$, consisting of all relations invariant under the basic operations of $\mathbf{A}$.

Theorem 4.1 *If Γ is a subset of $\Gamma_{\mathbf{A}}$ whose relations all have arity k or less, for some $k \ge 3$, then Γ has relational width k. If $M = |A|^2$ then $\Gamma_{\mathbf{A}}$ has relational width M.*

Corollary 4.2 *If Γ is a finite subset of $\Gamma_{\mathbf{A}}$ then Γ is tractable and the class of instances of CSP(Γ) that fail to have a solution is definable within Datalog. $\Gamma_{\mathbf{A}}$ is globally tractable.*

PROOF: (of the Theorem) We may assume in fact that $\mathbf{A} = (A, p_0, p_1, p_2, p_3)$, where $p_0(x, y, z) = x$ and $p_3(x, y, z) = z$ for all x, y, $z \in A$ since if we can establish the theorem for this sort of algebra, it will then apply to all algebras with universe A that have the p_i as term operations.

Our assumption on $\mathbf{A}$ places it in the variety $\mathcal{V}_3$ and so the results from the previous section apply. Let Γ be a subset of $\Gamma_{\mathbf{A}}$. If Γ is finite, let k be the maximum of 3 and the arities of the relations in Γ and replace Γ by Γ_k, the set of all relations in $\Gamma_{\mathbf{A}}$ of arity k or less. Establishing relational width k for this enlarged Γ will, of course, be a stronger result. If Γ is not finite, replace it by $\Gamma_{\mathbf{A}}$ and set $k = |A|^2$. We will show that in either case, Γ has relational width k.

Our goal is to show that if P is a k-minimal instance of $CSP(\Gamma)$ whose constraint relations are all non-empty then P has a solution. We may express P in the form $(\mathcal{A}, \mathcal{C})$ where $\mathcal{A} = (\mathbf{A}, \mathbf{A}, \ldots, \mathbf{A})$ is a sequence of length n, for some $n > 0$, and where $\mathcal{C}$ is a set of constraints of the form $C = (S, R)$, for some non-empty subset S of $\{1, 2, \ldots, n\}$ and some non-empty subuniverse R of $\mathbf{A}^{|S|}$.

In order to apply the results from the previous section as seamlessly as possible, we enlarge our language Γ to a closely related, but larger, multi-sorted language. Let $\mathcal{H}$ be the set of all quotients of subalgebras of $\mathbf{A}$. Note that $\mathcal{H}$ is finite and all algebras in it have size at most $|A|$. If $\Gamma = \Gamma_k$, replace it with the set of all subuniverses of l-fold products of algebras from $\mathcal{H}$, for all $1 \le l \le k$, and otherwise, replace it by the set of all subuniverses of finite products of algebras from $\mathcal{H}$. In both cases, we have extended our original constraint language. P can now be viewed as a k-minimal instance of $CSP(\Gamma)$, the class of multi-sorted CSPs whose instances have domains from $\mathcal{H}$ and whose constraint relations are from Γ.

We now prove that every k-minimal instance of $CSP(\Gamma)$ whose constraint relations are non-empty has a solution. If this is not so, let Q be a counter-example such that the sum of the sizes of the domains of Q is as small as possible. Note that independent of this size, no domain of Q is bigger than $|A|$ since they all come from $\mathcal{H}$. Also note that Q must be subdirect.

From Theorem 3.18 it follows that all of the domains of Q are Jónsson trivial. Then, from Lemma 3.20 we can deduce that all of the domains of Q are simple. If not, then either there is a proper quotient of Q that is k-minimal and that does not have a solution, or the k-minimal instance produced by the lemma cannot have a solution. In either case, we contradict the minimality of Q. Thus Q is a subdirect, k-minimal instance of $CSP(\Gamma)$ whose domains are all simple and Jónsson trivial and whose constraint relations are all non-empty. From Theorem 3.13 we conclude that in fact Q has a solution. This contradiction completes the proof of the theorem. •

5. Conclusion and Acknowledgments

The main result of this paper establishes that for certain constraint languages Γ that arise from finite algebras that generate congruence distributive varieties, the problem class $CSP(\Gamma)$ is tractable. This class of constraint languages includes those that are compatible with a majority operation but also includes some languages that were not previously known to be tractable.

We feel that the proof techniques employed in this paper may be useful in extending our results to include all constraint languages that arise from finite algebras that generate congruence distributive varieties and perhaps beyond.

Problem 1: Extend the algebraic tools developed to handle algebras in $CD(3)$ to algebras in $CD(n)$ for any $n > 3$. In particular, generalize the notion of a Jónsson ideal to this wider setting.

We note that in [19] some initial success at extending the notion of a Jónsson ideal has been obtained.

The bound on relational width established for the languages addressed in this paper seems to depend on the size of the underlying domain of the language. Nevertheless, we are not aware of any constraint language that has finite relational width that is not of relational width 3.

Problem 2: For each $n > 3$, produce a constraint language Γ_n that has relational width n and not $n-1$. As a strengthening of this problem, find Γ_n that in addition have compatible near unanimity operations.

The first author acknowledges the support of the Hungarian National Foundation for Scientific Research (OTKA), grants no. T043671 and T043034, while the second, the support of the Natural Sciences and Engineering Research Council of Canada. Support of the Isaac Newton Institute for Mathematical Sciences and the organizers of the Logic and Algorithms programme is also gratefully acknowledged.

References

[1] A. Bulatov. A dichotomy theorem for constraints on a three-element set. In *Proceedings of the 43rd IEEE Symposium on Foundations of Computer Science*, pages 649–658. IEEE Computer Society, 2002.

[2] A. Bulatov. A graph of a relational structure and constraint satisfaction problems. In *Proceedings of the 19th Annual IEEE Symposium on Logic in Computer Science, 2004*, pages 448–457. IEEE, 2004.

[3] A. Bulatov. Combinatorial problems raised from 2-semilattices. *Journal of Algebra*, 298(2):321–339, 2006.

[4] A. Bulatov and P. Jeavons. Algebraic structures in combinatorial problems. submitted for publication.

[5] A. Bulatov, P. Jeavons, and A. Krokhin. Classifying the complexity of constraints using finite algebras. *SIAM J. Comput.*, 34(3):720–742 (electronic), 2005.

[6] A. A. Bulatov. Tractable conservative constraint satisfaction problems. In P. G. Kolaitis, editor, *Proceedings of the Eighteenth Annual IEEE Symp. on Logic in Computer Science, LICS 2003*, pages 321–. IEEE Computer Society Press, June 2003.

[7] S. Burris and H. P. Sankappanavar. *A course in universal algebra*, volume 78 of *Graduate Texts in Mathematics*. Springer-Verlag, New York, 1981.

[8] M. Clasen and M. Valeriote. Tame congruence theory. In *Lectures on algebraic model theory*, volume 15 of *Fields Inst. Monogr.*, pages 67–111. Amer. Math. Soc., Providence, RI, 2002.

[9] V. Dalmau. Generalized majority-minority operations are tractable. In P. Panangaden, editor, *Proceedings of the Twentieth Annual IEEE Symp. on Logic in Computer Science, LICS 2005*, pages 438–447. IEEE Computer Society Press, June 2005.

[10] T. Feder and M. Y. Vardi. Monotone monadic snp and constraint satisfaction. In *STOC '93: Proceedings of the twenty-fifth annual ACM symposium on Theory of computing*, pages 612–622, New York, NY, USA, 1993. ACM Press.

[11] T. Feder and M. Y. Vardi. The computational structure of monotone monadic SNP and constraint satisfaction: a study through Datalog and group theory. *SIAM J. Comput.*, 28(1):57–104 (electronic), 1999.

[12] D. Hobby and R. McKenzie. *The structure of finite algebras*, volume 76 of *Contemporary Mathematics*. American Mathematical Society, Providence, RI, 1988.

[13] P. Jeavons. On the algebraic structure of combinatorial problems. *Theoret. Comput. Sci.*, 200(1-2):185–204, 1998.

[14] P. Jeavons, D. Cohen, and M. C. Cooper. Constraints, consistency and closure. *Artificial Intelligence*, 101(1-2):251–265, 1998.

[15] B. Larose. Some notes on bounded widths. unpublished, 2004.

[16] B. Larose and L. Zádori. Bounded width problems and algebras. Accepted by Algebra Universalis, 2006.

[17] R. McKenzie, G. McNulty, and W. Taylor. *Algebras, Lattices, Varieties Volume 1*. Wadsworth and Brooks/Cole, Monterey, California, 1987.

[18] T. J. Schaefer. The complexity of satisfiability problems. In *Conference Record of the Tenth Annual ACM Symposium on Theory of Computing (San Diego, Calif., 1978)*, pages 216–226. ACM, New York, 1978.

[19] M. Valeriote. A subalgebra intersection property for congruence distributive varieties. submitted for publication, 2005.

PSPACE Bounds for Rank-1 Modal Logics

Lutz Schröder
Department of Computer Science, Universität Bremen
and DFKI-Lab Bremen

Dirk Pattinson
Department of Computer Science
University of Leicester

Abstract

For lack of general algorithmic methods that apply to wide classes of logics, establishing a complexity bound for a given modal logic is often a laborious task. The present work is a step towards a general theory of the complexity of modal logics. Our main result is that all rank-1 logics enjoy a shallow model property and thus are, under mild assumptions on the format of their axiomatization, in PSPACE. This leads not only to a unified derivation of (known) tight PSPACE-bounds for a number of logics including K, coalition logic, and graded modal logic (and to a new algorithm in the latter case), but also to a previously unknown tight PSPACE-bound for probabilistic modal logic, with rational probabilities coded in binary. This generality is made possible by a coalgebraic semantics, which conveniently abstracts from the details of a given model class and thus allows covering a broad range of logics in a uniform way.

1. Intoduction

Modal logics are attractive from a computational point of view, as they often combine expressiveness with decidability. For many modal logics not involving dynamic features, satisfiability is known to be in $PSPACE$. This is typically proved for one logic at a time, e.g. by modifications of the witness algorithm for the modal logic K [4], but also using markedly different methods such as in the constraint-based $PSPACE$-algorithm for graded modal logic [31]. A first glimpse of a generalisable method was given in [34], where various epistemic logics, equipped with a neighborhood frame semantics, were shown to be in NP and $PSPACE$, respectively (with the K axiom being responsible for $PSPACE$-hardness; recent work [11] shows that negative introspection brings the complexity back down to NP). Nevertheless, there is to date no generally applicable theorem that allows establishing $PSPACE$-bounds for large classes of modal logics in a uniform way.

Here, we generalise the methods of [34] to obtain $PSPACE$ bounds for rank-1 modal logics (those axiomatisable by formulae whose nesting depth of modalities equals one) in a systematic way. Although limited to rank 1, our approach covers numerous relevant and non-trivial examples. E.g., our results recover known $PSPACE$ bounds for standard modal logics such as K and also for a range of non-normal modal logics such as graded modal logic [31] and coalition logic [23]. Moreover, our method goes beyond re-proving known results in a uniform fashion: we obtain a previously unknown $PSPACE$-bound for probabilistic modal logic [17, 13], with rational probabilities coded in binary. These logics are far from exotic: graded modal logic plays a role e.g. in decision support and knowledge representation [33, 19], and probabilistic modal logic has appeared in connection with model checking [17] and in modelling economic behaviour [13].

The key to the generality is to parametrise the theory over the type of systems defining the semantics, using coalgebraic methods. Coalgebra conveniently abstracts from the details of a concrete class of models by encoding it as an endofunctor on the category of sets. As specific instances, one obtains e.g. Kripke frames, (monotone) neighbourhood frames [12], game frames [23], probabilistic transition systems and automata [24, 3], weighted automata, linear automata [6], and multigraphs [9]. Despite the broad range of systems covered by the coalgebraic approach, a substantial body of concepts and non-trivial results has emerged, encompassing e.g. generic notions of bisimilarity and coinduction [2], corecursion [32], duality, and ultrafilter extensions [15]. Coalgebraic modal logic features in actual specification languages such as the object oriented specification language CCSL [26] and CoCasl [18].

The coalgebraic study of computational aspects of modal logic was initiated in [30], where the finite model property and associated $NEXPTIME$-bounds were proved. Here, we push this further by proving a coalgebraic shallow model property. Our $PSPACE$-algorithm traverses a shallow model, stripping off one layer of modalities in every step. This requires converting the axiomatisation of a given logic into a set of logical rules that obeys a specific closure condition, and a general construction to perform this conversion

1043-6871/06 $20.00 © 2006 IEEE

is provided. The algorithm runs in *PSPACE*, provided the induced set of rules has a polynomial bound on matchings, which is the case for all examples we are aware of.

2. Coalgebraic Modal Logic

We briefly recapitulate the basics of the coalgebraic interpretation of modal logic.

Definition 2.1. [27] Let $T : \mathbf{Set} \to \mathbf{Set}$ be a functor, referred to as the *signature functor*, where **Set** is the category of sets. A *T-coalgebra* $A = (X, \xi)$ is a pair (X, ξ) where X is a set (of *states*) and $\xi : X \to TX$ is a function called the *transition* function.

We view coalgebras as generalised transition systems: the transition function delivers a structured set of successors and observations for a state. Mutatis mutandis, we can in fact allow T to take proper classes as values, as we never iterate T or otherwise assume that TX is a set; details are left implicit. This allows us to treat more examples, in particular Pauly's coalition logic (Example 2.5.7 below).

Assumption 2.2. We can assume w.l.o.g. that T preserves injective maps [1]. For convenience of notation, we will in fact sometimes assume that $TX \subseteq TY$ in case $X \subseteq Y$. Moreover, we assume w.l.o.g. that T is non-trivial, i.e. $TX = \emptyset \implies X = \emptyset$ (otherwise, $TX = \emptyset$ for all X).

Modal logic in the form considered here has been introduced as a specification logic for coalgebraically modelled reactive systems in [22], generalising previous results [14, 25, 16, 20]. The coalgebraic semantics is based on predicate liftings, which abstract from the concrete interpretation of modal operators in the same way that the signature functor abstracts from a concrete class of models.

Definition 2.3. A *predicate lifting* for a functor T is a natural transformation $\lambda : 2 \to 2 \circ T^{op}$, where 2 denotes the contravariant powerset functor $\mathbf{Set}^{op} \to \mathbf{Set}$.

A coalgebraic semantics for a modal logic consists of a signature functor and an assignment of a predicate lifting to every modal operator; we write $[\lambda]$ for a modal operator that is interpreted using the lifting λ. Thus, a set Λ of predicate liftings for T determines the syntax of a modal logic $\mathcal{L}(\Lambda)$. Formulae $\phi, \psi \in \mathcal{L}(\Lambda)$ are defined by the grammar

$$\phi ::= \bot \mid \phi \wedge \psi \mid \neg\phi \mid [\lambda]\,\phi,$$

where λ ranges over Λ. Disjunctions $\phi \vee \psi$, truth $\top$, and other boolean operations are defined as usual. The *rank* of a formula is its maximal nesting depth of modal operators; note however that the notion of *rank*-1 *axiom* employed in [21, 8, 15, 30], replaced below by the notion of one-step rule, is stricter than 'formula of rank 1' in that it disallows non-trivial subformulae of rank 0.

The satisfaction relation $\models_C$ between states x of a T-coalgebra $C = (X, \xi)$ and $\mathcal{L}(\Lambda)$-formulae is defined inductively, with the usual clauses for the boolean operations. The clause for the modal operator $[\lambda]$ is

$$x \models_C [\lambda]\phi \iff \xi(x) \in \lambda_C([\![\phi]\!]_C),$$

where $[\![\phi]\!]_C = \{x \in X \mid x \models_C \phi\}$. We drop the subscripts C when C is clear from the context.

From a coalgebraic perspective, the logics $\mathcal{L}(\Lambda)$ have pleasant properties. Behaviourally equivalent states (i.e. states identified by some pair of morphisms) have the same theory [22], and we can – in case T is accessible – always find enough (polyadic) modal operators to distinguish non-equivalent states [29]. In the interest of readability, we restrict our attention to unary modalities for the purpose of this work. However, we remark that our treatment extends to the polyadic case in a straightforward manner. Our main interest is in the (local) *satisfiability problem* for $\mathcal{L}(\Lambda)$:

Definition 2.4. An $\mathcal{L}(\Lambda)$-formula ϕ is *satisfiable* if there exist a T-coalgebra C and a state x in C such that $x \models_C \phi$.

For a more detailed discussion of global and local consequence and weak and strong completeness in a coalgebraic context see [30]. Many modal logics (including probabilistic modal logic and graded modal logic) fail to be compact and hence do not admit finitary *strongly* complete proof systems. The following examples show that the coalgebraic approach subsumes a large class of modal logics.

Example 2.5. [22, 8, 30]

1. Let $\mathcal{P}$ be the covariant powerset functor. Then $\mathcal{P}$-coalgebras are graphs, thought of as transition systems or indeed Kripke frames. The predicate lifting λ defined by

$$\lambda_X(A) = \{B \in \mathcal{P}(X) \mid B \subset A\}$$

gives rise to the standard box modality $\Box = [\lambda]$. This translates verbatim to the finitely branching case, captured by the (accessible) finite powerset functor $\mathcal{P}_{fin}$.

2. Coalgebras for the functor $N = 2 \circ 2^{op}$ (composition of the contravariant powerset functor with itself) are neighbourhood frames, the canonical semantic domain of non-normal logics [7]. The coalgebraic semantics induced by the predicate lifting λ defined by

$$\lambda_X(A) = \{\alpha \in N(X) \mid A \in \alpha\}$$

is just the neighbourhood semantics for $\Box = [\lambda]$.

3. Similarly, coalgebras for the subfunctor of N given by the upwards closed subsets of 2^X are monotone neighbourhood frames [12]. Putting $\Box = [\lambda]$, with λ defined as above, gives the standard interpretation of the $\Box$-modality of monotone modal logic.

4. It is straightforward to extend a given coalgebraic modal logic for T with a set U of *propositional symbols*. This is captured by passing to the functor $T'X = TX \times \mathcal{P}(U)$ and extending the set of predicate liftings by the liftings λ^a, $a \in U$, defined by

$$\lambda^a_X(A) = \{(t, B) \in TX \times \mathcal{P}(U) \mid a \in B\}.$$

Since λ^a is independent of its argument, the induced modal 'operator' can be written as just the propositional symbol a, with the expected meaning.

5. The *finite multiset* (or *bag*) functor $\mathcal{B}$ maps a set X to the set of maps $b : X \to \mathbb{N}$ with finite support. The action on morphisms $f : X \to Y$ is given by $\mathcal{B}f : \mathcal{B}X \to \mathcal{B}Y, b \mapsto \lambda y. \sum_{f(x)=y} b(x)$. Coalgebras for $\mathcal{B}$ are directed graphs with $\mathbb{N}$-weighted edges, often referred to as *multigraphs* [9], and provide a coalgebraic semantics for *graded modal logic* (GML): One defines a set of predicate liftings $\{\lambda^k \mid k \in \mathbb{N}\}$ by

$$\lambda^k_X(A) = \{b : X \to \mathbb{N} \in \mathcal{B}(X) \mid \textstyle\sum_{a \in A} b(a) > k\}.$$

The arising modal operators are precisely the modalities $\Diamond_k$ of GML [9], i.e. $x \models \Diamond_k\phi$ iff ϕ holds for more than k successor states of x, taking into account multiplicities. (GML is more standardly interpreted over Kripke frames, where $\Diamond_k\phi$ reads 'there are more than k successors satisfying ϕ'. Both interpretations induce the same notion of satisfiability [30].) Note that $\Diamond_k$ is monotone, but fails to be normal unless $k = 0$. (Recall that a diamond-like operator $\Diamond$ is called *monotone* if it satisfies $\Diamond(a \wedge b) \to \Diamond a$, and *normal* if it satisfies $\Diamond(a \vee b) \to \Diamond a \vee \Diamond b$). A non-monotone variation of GML arises when negative multiplicities are admitted.

6. The *finite distribution functor* D_ω maps a set X to the set of probability distributions on X with finite support. Coalgebras for the functor $T = D_\omega \times \mathcal{P}(U)$, where U is a set of propositional symbols, are probabilistic transition systems (also called *probabilistic type spaces* [13]) with finite branching degree.
The natural predicate liftings for T are the propositional symbols (Item 4 above) and the liftings λ^p defined by

$$\lambda^p(A) = \{P \in D_\omega X \mid PA \geq p\},$$

where $p \in [0, 1] \cap \mathbb{Q}$. This yields the modalities $L_p = [\lambda^p]$ of *probabilistic modal logic (PML)* [17, 13], where $L_p\phi$ reads 'ϕ holds in the next step with probability at least p'. (In general [13], probabilistic type spaces can have arbitrary branching degree, but since PML has the finite model property, this has no bearing on satisfiability.) PML is non-normal ($L_p(a \vee b) \to L_pa \vee L_pb$ is not valid for $p > 0$).

7. A coalgebraic semantics for *coalition logic* [23] is given by the class-valued signature functor T defined by

$$TX = \{(S_1, \ldots, S_n, f) \mid \emptyset \neq S_i \in \mathbf{Set}, f : \prod_{i \in N} S_i \to X\}$$

where $N = \{1, \ldots, n\}$ is a fixed set of *agents*. Thus, the elements of TX are *strategic games* with set X of states, i.e. tuples consisting of nonempty sets S_i of *strategies* for all agents i, and an *outcome function* $(\prod S_i) \to X$. Then, a T-coalgebra is a *game frame* [23]. Subsets $C \subseteq N$ are called *coalitions*. We denote the set $\prod_{i \in C} S_i$ by S_C, and for $\sigma_C \in S_C, \sigma_{\bar{C}} \in S_{\bar{C}}$, where $\bar{C} = N - C$, $(\sigma_C, \sigma_{\bar{C}})$ denotes the obvious element of $\prod_{i \in N} S_i$. The modalities $[C]$ of coalition logic are captured as $[C] = [\lambda^C]$ by the predicate liftings λ^C, given by

$$\lambda^C_X(A) = \{(S_1, \ldots, S_n, f) \in TX \mid \\ \exists \sigma_C \in S_C. \forall \sigma_{\bar{C}} \in S_{\bar{C}}. f(\sigma_C, \sigma_{\bar{C}}) \in A\}.$$

Intuitively, $[C]\phi$ means that coalition C can force ϕ.

All the above examples can be canonically extended to systems that process inputs from a set I by passing from the signature functor T to the functor T^I. Similarly, output of elements of O is modelled by extending the functor T to the assignment $X \mapsto O \times TX$. We refer to [8] for a detailed account of the induced logics.

3. Proof Systems For Coalgebraic Modal Logic

Our decision procedure for rank-1 logics relies on a complete axiomatisation in a certain format. Deduction for modal logics with coalgebraic semantics has been considered in [21, 8, 15, 30]. It has been shown that every modal logic over coalgebras can be axiomatised in rank 1 using either rank-1 axioms or rules leading from rank 0 to rank 1 [30], essentially because functors, as opposed to comonads, only encode the one-step behaviour of systems. Here, we focus on rules. The crucial ingredients for the shallow model construction and the ensuing *PSPACE* algorithm are novel notions of *resolution closure* and *strict one-step completeness* of rule sets.

For the remainder of the paper, we assume given a functor T and a set Λ of predicate liftings for T. We recall a few basic notions from propositional logic, as well as notation for coalgebraic modal logic introduced in [21, 8]:

Definition 3.1. We denote the set of propositional formulae over a set V by $\mathsf{Prop}(V)$. Here, we regard $\neg$ and $\wedge$ as the basic connectives, with all other connectives defined in the standard way. A *literal* over V is either an element of V or the negation of such an element. We use variables ϵ etc. to denote either nothing or $\neg$, so that a literal over V has the general form ϵa, $a \in V$. A *clause* is a finite, possibly empty, disjunction of literals. The set of all clauses over V is denoted by $\mathsf{Cl}(V)$. Although we regard clauses as formulae rather than sets of literals, we shall sometimes use terminology such as 'a literal is contained in a clause' or 'a clause contains another', with the obvious meaning. We denote by $\mathsf{Up}(V)$ the set $\{[\lambda]a \mid \lambda \in \Lambda, a \in V\}$.

If the elements of V are, or have an interpretation as, subsets of a given set X, then $\phi \in \mathsf{Prop}(V)$ can be interpreted as a subset $[\![\phi]\!]_X$ of X; we write $X \models \phi$ if $[\![\phi]\!]_X = X$. Similarly, if $a \in V$ is interpreted as a subset A of X, then we interpret $[\lambda]a \in \mathsf{Up}(V)$ as the subset $[\![[\lambda]a]\!] = \lambda_X(A)$ of TX. This can be iterated, leading to interpretations $[\![\phi]\!] \subset TX$ of $\phi \in \mathsf{Up}(\mathsf{Prop}(V))$ etc.

In case the elements of V are formulae in $\mathcal{L}(\Lambda)$, we also regard propositional formulae over V as formulae in $\mathcal{L}(\Lambda)$. We sometimes explicitly designate V as consisting of *propositional variables*; propositional variables retain their status across further applications of Up and Prop (e.g. if V is a set of propositional variables, then V and not $\mathsf{Prop}(V)$ is the set of propositional variables for $\mathsf{Up}(\mathsf{Prop}(V))$). Given a set L, an *L-substitution* is a substitution σ of the propositional variables by elements of L; for a formula ϕ over V, we call $\phi\sigma$ an *L-instance* of ϕ. If $L \subset \mathcal{P}(X)$ for some X, then we also refer to σ as an *L-valuation.*

Definition 3.2. A *(one-step) rule* R over a set V of propositional variables is a rule ϕ/ψ, where $\phi \in \mathsf{Prop}(V)$ and $\psi \in \mathsf{Cl}(\mathsf{Up}(V))$. We silently identify rules under α-equivalence. The rule R is *sound* if, whenever $\phi\sigma$ is valid for an $\mathcal{L}(\Lambda)$-substitution σ, then $\psi\sigma$ is valid. Moreover, R is *one-step sound* if for each set X and each $\mathcal{P}(X)$-valuation τ, $X \models \phi\tau$ implies $TX \models \psi\tau$.

Out hitherto informal use of the term *rank*-1 *logic* formally means *axiomatisable by one-step rules* (equivalently by rank-1-axioms [30]). The class of rank-1 logics includes many interesting cases (Example 3.17), but excludes logics whose axiomatisation needs nested modalities, e.g. $S4$.

Remark 3.3. We can always assume that every propositional variable a appearing in the premise ϕ of a one-step rule appears also in the conclusion: otherwise, we can eliminate a by passing from ϕ to $\phi[\top/a] \vee \phi[\bot/a]$.

Proposition 3.4. *Every one-step sound rule is sound.*

The converse holds under additional assumptions [29]; note however that the obviously sound rule $\bot/\bot$ is one-step sound iff $T\emptyset = \emptyset$ (as is the case e.g. for PML).

A given set $\mathcal{R}$ of one-step sound rules induces a proof system for $\mathcal{L}(\Lambda)$ as follows.

Definition 3.5. Let $\mathcal{R}_C$ denote the set of rules obtained by extending $\mathcal{R}$ with the *congruence rule*

$$(C)\ \frac{a \leftrightarrow b}{[\lambda]a \to [\lambda]b}.$$

(This rule of course implies a rule where $\to$ is replaced by $\leftrightarrow$, which however does not fit the format for one-step rules.) The set of *derivable* formulae is the smallest set closed under propositional entailment and the rules in $\mathcal{R}_C$, with propositional variables instantiated to formulae in $\mathcal{L}(\Lambda)$.

It is easy to see that this proof system is sound. Completeness requires 'enough' rules in the following sense.

Definition 3.6. The set $\mathcal{R}$ is *(strictly) one-step complete* if, for each set X and each finite $\mathfrak{A} \subset \mathcal{P}(X)$, whenever $TX \models \chi$ for $\chi \in \mathsf{Cl}(\mathsf{Up}(\mathfrak{A}))$, then χ is *(strictly) derivable*; i.e. χ is propositionally entailed by clauses $\psi\tau$, where ϕ/ψ is in $\mathcal{R}$ and τ is a $\mathsf{Prop}(\mathfrak{A})$-valuation (an $\mathfrak{A}$-valuation) such that $X \models \phi\tau$.

The distinctive feature of *strict* one-step completeness is that strict derivation precludes intermediate reasoning over $\mathsf{Up}(\mathsf{Prop}(\mathfrak{A}))$. This plays a central role in the shallow model construction to be presented in Section 4.

Remark 3.7. It is easy to see that in the definition of one-step completeness, it does not matter whether elements of $\mathsf{Prop}(\mathfrak{A})$ are regarded as formulae or as subsets of X.

Lemma and Definition 3.8. *If $\mathcal{R}$ is strictly one-step complete, then for each set X, each $\phi \in \mathsf{Prop}(\mathsf{Up}(V))$, and each $\mathcal{P}(X)$-valuation τ such that $TX \models \phi\tau$, ϕ is* strictly congruence derivable, *i.e. propositionally entailed by clauses $\psi\sigma$, where ϕ/ψ is in $\mathcal{R}_C$ (Definition 3.5) and σ is a V-substitution such that $X \models \phi\sigma\tau$.*

Remark 3.9. It is implicitly shown in [30] that the set of all one-step sound rules is always strictly one-step complete and that the proof system induced by a one-step complete set of rules is *weakly complete*, i.e. proves all valid formulae.

Proposition 3.10. *A set $\mathcal{R}$ of one-step rules is (strictly) one-step complete iff for all* finite *sets X and all subsets $\mathfrak{A} \subset \mathcal{P}X$ that generate $\mathcal{P}(X)$ as a boolean algebra, χ is (strictly) derivable under $\mathcal{R}$ whenever $TX \models \chi$ for $\chi \in \mathsf{Cl}(\mathsf{Up}(\mathfrak{A}))$.*

Strictly one-step complete sets of rules are generally more complicated than one-step complete sets of rules or axioms [21, 30]. In our terminology, part of the effort of [34] and [23] is devoted to finding strictly one-step complete sets of rules. We now develop a systematic procedure for turning one-step complete rule sets into strictly one-step complete ones. For the following, recall that given clauses ϕ and ψ containing literals a and $\neg a$, respectively, a *resolvent* of ϕ and ψ *(at a)* is obtained by removing a and $\neg a$ from the clause $\phi \vee \psi$. A set Φ of clauses is called *resolution closed* if, for $\phi, \psi \in \Phi$, all resolvents of ϕ and ψ are in Φ.

Definition 3.11. A set $\mathcal{R}$ of one-step rules is *resolution closed* if it satisfies the following requirement. Let $R_1, R_2 \in \mathcal{R}$, where $R_1 = \phi_1/\psi_1$ and $R_2 = \phi_2/\psi_2$. We can assume that R_1 and R_2 have disjoint sets of propositional variables. Let $[\lambda]a$ be in ψ_1, and let $\neg[\lambda]b$ be in ψ_2 for some $\lambda \in \Lambda$, so that we have a resolvent ψ of ψ_1 and $\psi_2[a/b]$ at $[\lambda]a$. Then $\mathcal{R}$ is required to contain a rule $R = \phi/\psi$ such that ϕ is propositionally entailed by $\phi_1 \wedge \phi_2[a/b]$; in this case, R is called a *resolvent* of R_1 and R_2.

Remark 3.12. One can construct resolution closed sets by iterated addition of missing resolvents. Here, an obvious choice for a resolvent ϕ/ψ as above is to take ϕ as $\phi_1 \wedge \phi_2[a/b]$, with a eliminated according to Remark 3.3 if a is not contained in ψ; it is clear that $\phi_1 \wedge \phi_2[a/b]/\psi$ is one-step sound if R_1 and R_2 are one-step sound.

Remark 3.13. One should not confuse the terminology introduced above with existing resolution-based approaches to decision procedures for modal logic (e.g. [10]), which rely on translating modal logic into first-order logic.

Lemma 3.14. *Let V be a set of propositional variables, let $\psi \in \mathsf{Cl}(V)$, and let $\Phi \subset \mathsf{Cl}(V)$ be resolution closed. Then Φ propositionally entails ψ iff ψ contains a clause in Φ.*

Theorem 3.15. *If $\mathcal{R}$ is one-step complete and resolution closed, then $\mathcal{R}$ is strictly one-step complete.*

Proof. (Sketch) Let $\mathfrak{A} \subset \mathcal{P}X$, and let $\gamma \in \mathsf{Cl}(\mathsf{Up}(\mathfrak{A}))$ such that $TX \models \gamma$. By one-step completeness, γ is propositionally entailed by the set of clauses

$$\Psi = \{\psi\sigma \mid \phi/\psi \in \mathcal{R}, \sigma \text{ a } \mathsf{Prop}(\mathfrak{A})\text{-valuation}, X \models \phi\sigma\}.$$

Resolution closedness of $\mathcal{R}$ implies that Ψ is resolution closed. By Lemma 3.14, it follows that γ contains, and hence is propositionally entailed by, a clause $\psi\sigma$ in Ψ, where necessarily $\sigma(v) \in \mathfrak{A}$ for variables v of ψ. □

In summary, strictly one-step complete rule sets can be constructed by resolving the rules of a one-step complete axiomatisation against each other. Below, we give examples of strictly one-step complete systems obtained in this way. In order to simplify the presentation for the case of graded modal logic and probabilistic modal logic, we use the following notation. If ϕ_i is a formula, $r_i \in \mathbb{Z}$ for all $i \in I$, and $k \in \mathbb{Z}$, we abbreviate

$$\sum_{i \in I} r_i\phi_i \geq k \equiv \bigwedge_{r(J)<k} \Big(\bigwedge_{j\in J} \phi_j \to \bigvee_{j \notin J} \phi_j\Big),$$

where $r(J) = \sum_{j\in J} r_j$. Moreover, if $r \in \mathbb{Z} - \{0\}$ and ϕ is a formula, then we put

$$sgn(r)\phi = \begin{cases} \phi & r > 0 \\ \neg\phi & r < 0. \end{cases}$$

The formula $\sum_{i\in I} r_i a_i \geq k$ translates into the arithmetic of characteristic functions as suggested by the notation:

Lemma 3.16. *An element $x \in X$ belongs to the interpretation of $\sum_{i\in I} r_i a_i \geq k$ under a $\mathcal{P}(X)$-valuation σ iff*

$$\sum_{i\in I} r_i \mathbb{1}_{\sigma(a_i)}(x) \geq k,$$

where $\mathbb{1}_A : X \to \{0, 1\}$ is the characteristic function of $A \subseteq X$.

In all examples, the resolution process, applied to known one-step complete rule sets, can be kept under control; by Theorem 3.15, the resulting rule sets are strictly one-step complete.

Example 3.17. 1. The empty set of rules is one-step complete for neighbourhood frame semantics (Example 2.5.2). This set is trivially resolution closed.

2. (Monotone modal logic) The one-step rule

$$(M)\ \frac{a \to b}{\Box a \to \Box b}$$

is one-step complete for monotone neighbourhood frame semantics (Example 2.5.2), and clearly resolution closed.

3. (Standard modal logic K) The one-step rules

$$\frac{a}{\Box a} \qquad \frac{a \wedge b \to c}{\Box a \wedge \Box b \to \Box c}$$

are one-step complete for Kripke semantics (Example 2.5.1), i.e. for the modal logic K [21]. The resolution closure $\mathcal{R}$ of these rules consists of the rules

$$\frac{\bigwedge_{i=1}^n a_i \to b}{\bigwedge_{i=1}^n \Box a_i \to \Box b}$$

for all $n \in \mathbb{N}$ (here, strict one-step completeness is also easily seen directly).

4. (Coalition logic) In Lemma 6.1 of [23], the following set of one-step rules for coalition logic (Example 2.5.7), numbered as in loc. cit., is implicit:

$$(1)\ \frac{\bigvee_{i=1}^n \neg a_i}{\bigvee_{i=1}^n \neg[C_i]a_i} \quad (2)\ \frac{a}{[C]a} \quad (3)\ \frac{a \vee b}{[0]a \vee [N]b}$$

$$(4)\ \frac{\bigwedge_{i=1}^n a_i \to b}{\bigwedge_{i=1}^n [C_i]a_i \to [\bigcup C_i]b}$$

where $n \geq 0$, and rules (1) and (4) are subject to the side condition that the C_i are pairwise disjoint. This set of rules extends the axiomatisation of coalition logic, which one easily proves to be one-step complete given the results of [23]. The rules are moreover 'nearly' resolution closed (full resolution closure is not needed in [23] due to a slightly different notion of closed rule sets). Resolving rule (4) with rules (2) and (3), one obtains the rule schema

$$(4')\ \frac{\bigwedge_{i=1}^n a_i \to b \vee \bigvee_{j=1}^m c_j}{\bigwedge_{i=1}^n [C_i]a_i \to [D]b \vee \bigvee_{j=1}^m [N]c_j}$$

where $m, n \geq 0$, subject to the side condition that the C_i are pairwise disjoint subsets of D; this subsumes rules (2)–(4) above. The set consisting of the rules (1) and (4') is easily seen to be resolution closed.

5. (Graded modal logic) Using Proposition 3.10, one shows directly that the one-step rules

$$(W)\ \Diamond_{k+1}a \to \Diamond_k a \qquad (A_1)\ \frac{b \to \bigvee_{i=1}^m a_i}{\Diamond_{\sum_{i=1}^m k_i} b \to \bigvee_{i=1}^m \Diamond_{k_i} a_i}$$

$$(A_2)\ \frac{\bigwedge_{\substack{1\leq i,j\leq n\\ i\neq j}} (\neg b_i \vee \neg b_j) \quad \bigwedge_{j=1}^n (b_j \to a)}{\bigwedge_{j=1}^n \Diamond_{k_j} b_j \to \Diamond_k a} \ (\textstyle\sum_{j=1}^n (k_j+1)=k+1),$$

where $m \geq 0$, $n \geq 1$, are one-step complete for GML (Example 2.5.5). All these rules are subsumed by the rule schema

$$(G)\ \frac{\sum_{i=1}^m a_i - \sum_{j=1}^n b_j \geq 0}{\bigwedge_{j=1}^n \Diamond_{l_j} b_j \to \bigvee_{i=1}^m \Diamond_{k_i} a_i},$$

where $n, m \geq 0$ and $n+m \geq 1$, subject to the side condition $\sum_{j=1}^n (l_i+1) \geq 1+\sum_{i=1}^m k_i$. Soundness of this rule is seen analogously as for similar rules in probabilistic modal logic [13]. It is easy to see that the rule schema is closed under resolution.

6. (Probabilistic modal logic) By reformulating the one-step complete set of axioms for probabilistic modal logic given in [8] as one-step rules and subsequently applying resolution, one obtains the rules

$$(P_k)\ \frac{\sum_{i=1}^m a_i - \sum_{j=1}^n b_j \geq k}{\bigwedge_{j=1}^n L_{q_j} b_j \to \bigvee_{i=1}^m L_{p_i} a_i},$$

where $m, n \geq 0$, $m+n \geq 1$, and $k \in \mathbb{Z}$, subject to the side condition

$$\begin{aligned} &\textstyle\sum_{i=1}^m p_i - \sum_{j=1}^n q_j \leq k, \text{ and} \\ &\text{if } m = 0 \text{ then } -\textstyle\sum_{j=1}^n q_j < k. \end{aligned}$$

This rule schema subsumes the axiomatisation in loc. cit. and hence is one-step complete. Using Lemma 3.16, one can show directly that (P_k) is one-step sound in the same way as for the axiomatisation in [8]. Moreover, it is easy to see that the rule schema is resolution closed: the required resolvent of an instance of (P_k) and an instance of (P_l) is obtained as an instance of (P_{k+l}).

4. The Shallow Model Construction

We now present the announced generic shallow model construction, which is based on strictly one-step complete axiomatisations. The construction is performed along with the proof of a recursive characterisation of satisfiable formulae which generalises results from [34] (where the use of axiomatisations is implicit in certain lemmas).

Definition 4.1. A set Σ of formulae is called *closed* if it is closed under subformulae and under *normalised negation* $\sim$, where $\sim\phi$ is defined to be ψ in case ϕ is of the form $\neg\psi$, and $\neg\phi$ otherwise. The smallest closed set containing a given formula ϕ is denoted $\Sigma(\phi)$. A subset H of Σ is called a *Σ-Hintikka set* if $\bot \notin H$ and, for $\phi \wedge \psi \in \Sigma$, $\phi \wedge \psi \in H$ iff $\phi, \psi \in H$, and, for $\neg\phi \in \Sigma$, $\neg\phi \in H$ iff $\phi \notin H$.

For a formula $\chi \in \mathsf{Prop}(V)$ and a Σ-substitution σ, we define satisfaction of $\chi\sigma$ in H ($H \models \chi\sigma$) inductively by

$$\begin{aligned} H \models (\chi_1 \wedge \chi_2)\sigma \quad &:\Longleftrightarrow\quad H \models \chi_1\sigma \text{ and } H \models \chi_2\sigma \\ H \models (\neg\chi)\sigma \quad &:\Longleftrightarrow\quad H \not\models \chi\sigma \\ H \models a\sigma \quad &:\Longleftrightarrow\quad \sigma(a) \in H \\ H \not\models \bot. \end{aligned}$$

This is well-defined because H is Hintikka.

Lemma 4.2. *Let Σ be closed, let H be a Σ-Hintikka set, and let $\phi, \psi \in \mathsf{Prop}(V)$. Then $H \models \phi \vee \psi$ iff $H \models \phi$ or $H \models \psi$.*

Lemma 4.3 (Soundness of propositional reasoning for Hintikka sets)**.** *Let Σ be closed, and let H be a Σ-Hintikka set. Let $\phi, \psi \in \mathsf{Prop}(V)$, and let σ be a Σ-substitution. If $H \models \phi\sigma$ and ϕ propositionally entails ψ, then $H \models \psi\sigma$.*

The following result generalises Propositions 3.2, 3.5, 3.8, 3.13, and 3.16 (but not 3.10 and 3.18, which concern logics outside rank 1) of [34] and Lemma 6.1 of [23].

Theorem 4.4. *Let $\mathcal{R}$ be strictly one-step complete. Then $\phi \in \mathcal{L}(\Lambda)$ is satisfiable iff $\phi \in H$ for some Hintikka set $H \subset \Sigma(\phi)$ such that, for every clause $\rho = \bigvee_{i=1}^n \epsilon_i[\lambda_i]\rho_i$ over $\Sigma(\phi)$ with $H \not\models \rho$ and for each rule $\psi/\bigvee_{i=1}^n(\epsilon_i[\lambda_i]a_i)$ in $\mathcal{R}_C$, the formula $\neg\psi[\rho_i/a_i]_{i=1,\dots,n}$ is satisfiable.*

Proof. *'Only if':* Take H to be the intersection of $\Sigma(\phi)$ with the theory of a state satisfying ϕ.

'If': For each formula $\chi \equiv \neg\psi[\rho_i/a_i]_{i=1,\dots,n}$ as in the statement, there exists a coalgebra $C_\chi = (X_\chi, \xi_\chi)$ and a state x_χ in C_χ such that $x_\chi \models_{C_\chi} \chi$; we can assume that the X_χ are pairwise disjoint. Define the sets X and $\hat\rho$ by

$$X = \{x_0\} \cup \bigcup_\chi X_\chi \quad \text{and} \quad \hat\rho = A_\rho \cup \bigcup_\chi [\![\rho]\!]_{C_\chi},$$

where x_0 is a fresh element, $\rho \in \Sigma(\phi)$, and $A_\rho = \{x_0\}$ if $\rho \in H$, $A_\rho = \emptyset$ otherwise. We define a coalgebra structure ξ on X as follows. For $x \in X_\chi$, we put $\xi(x) = \xi_\chi(x) \in TX_\chi \subset TX$ (cf. Assumption 2.2). Then for $[\lambda]\rho \in \Sigma(\phi)$,

$$\xi(x) \in \lambda\hat\rho \iff x \models_{C_\chi} [\lambda]\rho, \tag{1}$$

because by naturality $(\lambda\hat\rho) \cap TX_\chi = \lambda(\hat\rho \cap X_\chi) = \lambda[\![\rho]\!]_{C_\chi}$. Moreover, we will show that there exists $\xi(x_0) \in TY \subset TX$, where Y is the set of all x_χ, such that for $[\lambda]\rho \in \Sigma(\phi)$,

$$\xi(x_0) \in \lambda\hat\rho \iff [\lambda]\rho \in H. \tag{2}$$

By structural induction, (1) and (2) then imply

$$x \models_C \rho \iff x \models_{C_X} \rho \text{ for } x \in X_X, \text{ and}$$
$$x_0 \models_C \rho \iff \rho \in H$$

for all $\rho \in \Sigma(\phi)$. In particular, $x_0 \models \phi$, and we are done.

It remains to prove that $\xi(x_0)$ satisfying (2) exists. Assume the contrary. Let V be the set of propositional variables b_ρ, where $[\lambda]\rho \in \Sigma(\phi)$ for some λ. Let $\theta \in \mathsf{Cl}(\mathsf{Up}(V))$ consist of the literals $\neg[\lambda]b_\rho$ for $[\lambda]\rho \in H$ and $[\lambda]b_\rho$ for $\neg[\lambda]\rho \in H$. By assumption, $TY \models \theta\tau^Y$, where τ^Y is the $\mathcal{P}(Y)$-valuation taking b_ρ to $\hat{\rho} \cap Y = \{x_X \mid x_X \models_{C_X} \rho\}$. By Lemma 3.8, it follows that θ is strictly congruence derivable from those $\zeta \in \mathsf{Prop}(V)$ such that $Y \models \zeta\tau^Y$.

From the derivation of θ, it now follows that $H \models \theta\sigma$, where σ is the $\Sigma(\phi)$-substitution taking b_ρ to ρ (note that $\theta\sigma$ is a propositional formula over atoms $[\lambda]\rho \in \Sigma(\phi)$), by Lemma 4.2 a contradiction to the construction of θ: by Lemma 4.3, the propositional steps are sound over H; it remains to be shown that if the derivation of θ uses a rule $R \equiv \psi/\bigvee_{i=1}^n(\epsilon_i[\lambda_i]a_i)$ in $\mathcal{R}_C$, instantiated for a V-substitution η, then the conclusion of $R\eta\sigma$ is satisfied over H. Assume the contrary. By Lemma 4.2, it follows that $\epsilon_i[\lambda_i]\sigma(\eta(a_i)) \notin H$ for all i. By construction, we have $x_\chi \models_{C_X} \chi$ for $\chi \equiv \neg\psi\eta\sigma$. But since $R\eta$ appears in the derivation of θ, $Y \models \psi\eta\tau^Y$ and hence $x_\chi \in [\![\psi\eta\tau^X]\!]$, where τ^X is the $\mathcal{P}(X_X)$-valuation taking b_ρ to $[\![\rho]\!]_{C_X}$. Since $[\![\psi\eta\tau^X]\!] = [\![\psi\eta\sigma]\!]_{C_X}$, we have arrived at a contradiction. □

As a corollary to the above proof, we obtain that coalgebraic modal logic has the shallow model property. The formulation of this property requires the following notion.

Definition 4.5. A *supporting Kripke frame* of a T-coalgebra (X, ξ) is a Kripke frame (X, R) such that for each $x \in X$,

$$\xi(x) \in T\{y \mid xRy\} \subset TX.$$

As clauses suffice for satisfiability checking, we obtain

Corollary 4.6 (Shallow model property). *Every satisfiable $\mathcal{L}(\Lambda)$-formula ϕ is satisfiable in a* shallow model, *i.e. in a T-coalgebra (X, ξ) that has a supporting Kripke frame which consists of a tree of depth at most the rank of ϕ and of branching degree at most 2^n, where n is the number of subformulae of ϕ, and possibly an additional* final *state $x_\top$, i.e. for all x, $xRx_\top$, and $x_\top Rx$ implies $x = x_\top$.*

(The state $x_\top$ may arise from the rule $\bot/\bot$, cf. Sect. 3.)

5. A Generic PSPACE Algorithm

The shallow model result (Theorem 4.4) will be exploited to design a decision procedure in the spirit of [34]. Since resolution closed rule sets are in general infinite, this requires ensuring that we never need to instantiate literals in the conclusions of rules with identical formulae: otherwise, an infinite number of rules could match a single given clause over a Hintikka set. This is formally captured as follows.

Definition 5.1. We call a clause over L *reduced* if all its literals are distinct. An L-instance $\phi\sigma/\psi\sigma$ of a rule $\phi/\psi \in \mathcal{R}$ is *reduced* if the clause $\psi\sigma$ is reduced. Finally, $\mathcal{R}$ is *closed under reduction* if for every V-instance $\phi\sigma/\psi\sigma$ of a rule ϕ/ψ over V in $\mathcal{R}$, there exists a reduced V-instance $\phi'\sigma'/\psi'\sigma'$ of a rule $\phi'/\psi' \in \mathcal{R}$ such that $\psi\sigma$ and $\psi'\sigma'$ are propositionally equivalent and and $\phi'\sigma'$ is propositionally entailed by $\phi\sigma$.

I.e. a rule set is reduced if every instance of a rule that duplicates literals in the conclusion can be replaced by a reduced instance of a different rule. Not all the rule sets discussed in Example 3.17 satisfy this property, but they can easily be extended to reduction closed sets: just add a rule ϕ'/ψ' for every rule ϕ/ψ over V in $\mathcal{R}$ and every V-substitution σ, where ϕ' is some suitably chosen propositional equivalent of $\phi\sigma$ and ψ' is obtained from $\psi\sigma$ by removing duplicate literals. It is clear that the new rules remain one-step sound. Note that there is no need to preserve closure under resolution when passing to a reduced rule set, as Theorem 4.4 requires only strict one-step completeness, which is preserved under extending the rule set.

Example 5.2. 1. The strictly one-step complete rule sets of Examples 3.17.1–4 (including monotone modal logic, K, and coalition logic) are easily seen to be closed under reduction, essentially because in all relevant rule schemas, the premise is a clause of the same general format as the conclusion.

2. (Graded modal logic) The rule schema (G) of Example 3.17.5 fails to be closed under reduction, as duplicating literals in the conclusion substantially affects both the premise and the side condition. We can close (G) under reduction as described above; this results in the rule schema

$$(G') \quad \frac{\sum_{i=1}^n r_i a_i \geq 0}{\bigvee_{i=1}^n sgn(r_i)\Diamond_{k_i} a_i},$$

where $n \geq 1$ and $r_1, \dots, r_n \in \mathbb{Z} - \{0\}$, subject to the side condition $\sum_{r_i<0} r_i(k_i + 1) \geq 1 + \sum_{r_i>0} r_i k_i$.

3. (Probabilistic modal logic) The rule schema (P_k) of Example 3.17.6 fails to be closed under reduction. Closure under reduction as described above leads to the rule schema

$$(P'_k) \quad \frac{\sum_{i=1}^n r_i a_i \geq k}{\bigvee_{1\leq i\leq n} sgn(r_i) L_{p_i} a_i}$$

where $n \geq 1$ and $r_1, \ldots, r_n \in \mathbb{Z} - \{0\}$, subject to the side condition

$$\sum_{i=1}^{n} r_i p_i \leq k, \text{ and}$$
$$\text{if } \forall i.\, r_i < 0 \text{ then } \sum_{i=1}^{n} r_i p_i < k.$$

As instances of the congruence rule never contain duplicate literals, we have the following trivial fact.

Lemma 5.3. *If $\mathcal{R}$ is closed under reduction, then so is $\mathcal{R}_C$.*

Thus the following is immediate from Theorem 4.4.

Corollary 5.4. *Let $\mathcal{R}$ be strictly one-step complete and closed under reduction. Then $\phi \in \mathcal{L}(\Lambda)$ is satisfiable iff $\phi \in H$ for some Hintikka set $H \subset \Sigma(\phi)$ such that, for every* reduced *clause $\rho = \bigvee_{i=1}^{n} \epsilon_i[\lambda_i]\rho_i$ over $\Sigma(\phi)$ with $H \not\models \rho$ and for each rule $\psi / \bigvee_{i=1}^{n}(\epsilon_i[\lambda_i]a_i)$ in $\mathcal{R}_C$, the formula $\neg\psi[\rho_i/a_i]_{i=1,\ldots,n}$ is satisfiable.*

In the implementation of the algorithm suggested by Corollary 5.4, we need to pass around matches of rules with given clauses. Since rules, in particular their premises, are generally too large to pass around directly, we assume that every rule (i.e. every instance of a rule scheme) is given by a *code*, i.e. a string over some alphabet which identifies the rule; when rules appear as data, they are always represented by their code. Moreover, we assume that propositional variables a_i in rules are uniformly represented by indices that point to literals $\epsilon_i[\lambda_i]a_i$ of the conclusion.

Definition 5.5. We say that a rule $R \in \mathcal{R}$ *matches* a reduced clause $\rho \equiv \bigvee_{i=1}^{n} \epsilon_i[\lambda_i]\phi_i$ if the conclusion of R is of the form $\bigvee_{i=1}^{n} \epsilon_i[\lambda_i]a_i$. By the above variable convention, the instantiation $\psi[\phi_i/a_i]_{i=1,\ldots,n}$ of a conjunct ψ of the premise of R can be computed in polynomial time from ψ and ρ; we denote the result by $\psi[\rho]$. Two matching rules are *equivalent* if their premises are propositionally equivalent; equivalence classes $[R]$ are called *$\mathcal{R}$-matchings*. The code of R is also a *code* for $[R]$.

We fix some size measures for complexity purposes:

Definition 5.6. The size $size(a)$ of an integer a is $\lceil \log_2(|a| + 1) \rceil$, where $\lceil r \rceil = \min\{z \in \mathbb{Z} \mid z \geq r\}$ as usual. The size $size(p)$ of a rational number $p = a/b$, with a, b relatively prime, is $1 + size(a) + size(b)$. The *size* $|\phi|$ of a formula ϕ over V is defined by counting 1 for each propositional variable, boolean operator, or modal operator, and additionally the size of each index of a modal operator. (In the examples, indices are either numbers, with sizes as above, or subsets of $\{1, \ldots, n\}$, assumed to be of size n.)

In particular, indices of graded or probabilistic modal operators are coded in binary.

Example 5.7. For the rules of Examples 3.17 and 5.2, we just take the parameters of a rule as its code in the obvious way. E.g. the code of an instance of (P'_k) as displayed in Example 5.2.3 consists of n, k, the r_i, and the p_i. The size of the code is determined by the sizes of these numbers plus separating letters, say, $\sum(1+size(a_i))+\sum(1+size(p_i))+size(n)+size(k)+1$. Note that not all such codes represent instances of (P'_k).

The following decision procedure on an alternating Turing machine generalises the algorithms in [34], given a strictly one-step complete and reduction closed set $\mathcal{R}$.

Algorithm 5.8. (Decide satisfiability of $\phi \in \mathcal{L}(\Lambda)$)

1. (Initialise) Construct the set $\Sigma(\phi)$.
2. (Existential) Guess a Hintikka set $H \subset \Sigma(\phi)$ with $\phi \in H$.
3. (Universal) Guess a reduced clause $\bot \neq \rho \in \Sigma(\phi)$ with $H \not\models \rho$ and an $\mathcal{R}_C$-matching $[R]$ of ρ.
4. (Existential) Guess a clause γ from the conjunctive normal form (CNF) of the premise of R and recursively check that $\neg\gamma[\rho]$ is satisfiable.

The algorithm succeeds if all possible choices at steps marked *universal* lead to successful termination, and for all steps marked *existential*, there exists a choice leading to successful termination.

Correctness of the algorithm is guaranteed by Corollary 5.4. Note that the algorithm terminates successfully in Step 3 if there are no rules matching clauses over H. In particular, the algorithm terminates either in Step 2 or in Step 3 if ϕ has rank 0. We emphasise that in Step 3, it suffices to guess one code for each matching.

The crucial requirement for the effectivity of Algorithm 5.8 is that Steps 3 and 4 can be performed in polynomial time, i.e. by suitable nondeterministic polynomial-time multivalued functions (NPMV) [5]. We recall that a function $f : \Sigma^* \to \mathcal{P}(\Delta^*)$, where Σ and Δ are alphabets, is NPMV iff

1. there exists a polynomial p such that $|y| \leq p(|x|)$ for all $y \in f(x)$, where $|\cdot|$ denotes size, and
2. the graph $\{(x, y) \mid y \in f(x)\}$ of f is in *NP*.

Thus, the following conditions guarantee that Algorithm 5.8 has polynomial running time:

Definition 5.9. A set $\mathcal{R}$ of rules is called *PSPACE-tractable* if there exists a polynomial p such that all $\mathcal{R}$-matchings of a reduced clause ρ over $\mathcal{L}(\Lambda)$ have a code of size at most $p(|\rho|)$, and it can be decided in *NP*

1. whether a given code is the code of some rule in $\mathcal{R}$;
2. whether a rule matches a given reduced clause; and

3. whether a clause belongs to the CNF of the premise of a given rule.

Theorem 5.10 (Space Complexity). *Let $\mathcal{R}$ be strictly one-step complete, closed under reduction, and PSPACE-tractable. Then the satisfiability problem for $\mathcal{L}(\Lambda)$ is in PSPACE.*

Remark 5.11. A more careful analysis of Algorithm 5.8 reveals that it suffices for the decision problems in Definition 5.9 to be in PH, the polynomial time hierarchy. In our examples, however, the complexity is in fact P rather than NP. We expect that this situation is typical, with the crucial condition for $PSPACE$-tractability being the polynomial bound on $\mathcal{R}$-matchings. We are not aware of any natural examples of intractable rule sets (contrived examples are easy to construct, e.g. by using hard side conditions).

The next lemma, which follows directly from size estimates in linear integer programming [28], is crucial for establishing $PSPACE$-tractability in the examples. Following usual practice, we take the *size* $|W|$ of a rational inequality $W \equiv (\sum_{i=1}^{n} u_i x_i \text{ op } u_0)$, op $\in \{<, \leq, >, \geq\}$, to be $1 + n + \sum_{i=0}^{n} size(u_i)$.

Lemma 5.12. *There exists a polynomial p such that for every rational linear inequality W and every solution $r_0, \dots, r_n \in \mathbb{Z}$ of W, there exists a solution $r'_0, \dots, r'_n \in \mathbb{Z}$ of W such that $size(r'_i) \leq p(|W|)$ for all i, and the formulae $\sum_{i=1}^{n} r_i a_i \geq r_0$ and $\sum_{i=1}^{n} r'_i a_i \geq r'_0$ are propositionally equivalent.*

We now illustrate how Theorem 5.10 allows us to establish $PSPACE$ bounds for many modal logics in a uniform way. In particular, we obtain a new (tight) $PSPACE$ bound for probabilistic modal logic.

Example 5.13. Conditions 1 and 2 of Definition 5.9 are immediate for all the rule sets of Example 3.17 — the decision problems in question involve no more than checking computationally harmless side conditions in the case of Condition 1 (disjointness and containment of finite sets, linear inequalities), and comparing clauses of polynomial (in fact, linear) size in the case of Condition 2. Moreover, Condition 3 is immediate in those cases where the premises of rules are just single clauses. This leaves only GML and PML; but the definition of $\sum_{i \in I} r_i a_i \geq k$ is already in CNF, and checking whether a given clause belongs to this CNF is clearly in P.

It remains to establish the polynomial bound on the matchings. For GML and PML, this is guaranteed by Lemma 5.12. In all other cases, every reduced clause ρ matches at most one rule, whose code has size linear in the size of ρ.

We thus have obtained $PSPACE$-tractability and hence decidability in $PSPACE$ for all logics in Example 3.17. The logic of neighbourhood frames and monotone modal logic are of lesser interest here, as the corresponding modal logics are in NP [34]. We briefly comment on the algorithms and bounds for the other cases.

1. For the modal logic K (Example 3.17.3), Algorithm 5.8 is essentially the witness algorithm [34, 4], with reduced clauses violated by H corresponding to *demands*.

2. For coalition logic (Example 3.17.4), we arrive, due to minor differences of the rule sets, at a slight variant of Pauly's $PSPACE$-algorithm [23].

3. For graded modal logic, we obtain a new algorithm which confirms the known $PSPACE$ bound [31]. One might claim that the new algorithm is not only nicely embedded into a unified framework, but also conceptually simpler than the constraint-based algorithm of [31] (which corrects an erroneous algorithm previously given elsewhere).

4. For probabilistic modal logic, we obtain a new algorithm which yields a previously unknown $PSPACE$-bound (to our knowledge, the best previously published bound for PML is $EXPTIME$ [30]). The bound is tight, as PML contains the $PSPACE$-complete logic KD as a fragment (embedded by mapping $\Box$ to L_1).

6. Conclusion

Generalising results of [34], we have shown that coalgebraic modal logic has the shallow model property, and we have presented a generic $PSPACE$ algorithm for satisfiability based on depth-first exploration of shallow models. We have thus

- reproduced the *witness algorithm* for K [4]
- obtained a slight variant of the known $PSPACE$ algorithm for coalition logic [23]
- obtained a new $PSPACE$ algorithm for graded modal logic, recovering the known $PSPACE$ bound [31]
- obtained a novel $PSPACE$ bound for probabilistic modal logic [17, 13].

In all these cases, the bound obtained is tight.

The crucial prerequisite for the generic algorithm is an axiomatisation by so-called one-step rules (going from rank 0 to rank 1) obeying two closedness conditions: closedness under resolution and under removal of duplicate literals. In the examples, it has not only turned out that is it feasible to keep this closure process under control, but also that the axiomatisations obtained have pleasingly compact presentations — often, one ends up with a single rule schema. Nevertheless, it remains desirable to prove a $PSPACE$ bound relying on purely semantic conditions such as the ones appearing in [30]; this is the subject of further research, as is the extension of the theory beyond rank 1 by means of comonads and the treatment of iteration, possibly using automata theoretic methods [35, 36].

Ongoing work indicates that every modal logic can be equipped with a coalgebraic semantics, provided it is axiomatisable in rank 1 and satisfies the congruence rule. This means in particular that the method employed here applies to every such modal logic, i.e. one obtains a purely syntactic criterion (tractability of a certain closure of the axiomatisation) for rank-1 modal logics to be in *PSPACE*.

Acknowledgements. The authors wish to thank Alexander Kurz for useful discussions, Erwin R. Catesbeiana for the rule leading to final states, and the Department of Computer Science at the University of Bremen for funding a visit of the second author.

References

[1] M. Barr. Terminal coalgebras in well-founded set theory. *Theoret. Comput. Sci.*, 114:299–315, 1993.

[2] F. Bartels. Generalised coinduction. *Math. Struct. Comput. Sci.*, 13:321–348, 2003.

[3] F. Bartels, A. Sokolova, and E. de Vink. A hierarchy of probabilistic system types. In *Coalgebraic Methods in Computer Science*, volume 82 of *ENTCS*. Elsevier, 2003.

[4] P. Blackburn, M. de Rijke, and Y. Venema. *Modal Logic*. Cambridge, 2001.

[5] R. Book, T. Long, and A. Selman. Quantitative relativizations of complexity classes. *SIAM J. Computing*, 13:461–487, 1984.

[6] J. W. Carlyle and A. Paz. Realizations by stochastic finite automata. *J. Comput. System Sci.*, 5:26–40, 1971.

[7] B. Chellas. *Modal Logic*. Cambridge, 1980.

[8] C. Cîrstea and D. Pattinson. Modular construction of modal logics. In *Concurrency Theory*, volume 3170 of *LNCS*, pages 258–275. Springer, 2004.

[9] G. D'Agostino and A. Visser. Finality regained: A coalgebraic study of Scott-sets and multisets. *Arch. Math. Logic*, 41:267–298, 2002.

[10] H. De Nivelle, R. A. Schmidt, and U. Hustadt. Resolution-based methods for modal logics. *Logic J. IGPL*, 8:265–292, 2000.

[11] J. Halpern and L. C. Rêgo. Closing the NP-PSPACE gap in the satisfiability problem for modal logic. Available on arXiv, http://arxiv.org/abs/cs/0603019, 2006.

[12] H. H. Hansen and C. Kupke. A coalgebraic perspective on monotone modal logic. In *Coalgebraic Methods in Computer Science*, volume 106 of *ENTCS*, pages 121–143. Elsevier, 2004.

[13] A. Heifetz and P. Mongin. Probabilistic logic for type spaces. *Games and Economic Behavior*, 35:31–53, 2001.

[14] B. Jacobs. Towards a duality result in the modal logic of coalgebras. In *Coalgebraic Methods in Computer Science*, volume 33 of *ENTCS*. Elsevier, 2000.

[15] C. Kupke, A. Kurz, and D. Pattinson. Ultrafilter extensions for coalgebras. In *Algebra and Coalgebra in Computer Science*, volume 3629 of *LNCS*, pages 263–277. Springer, 2005.

[16] A. Kurz. Specifying coalgebras with modal logic. *Theoret. Comput. Sci.*, 260:119–138, 2001.

[17] K. Larsen and A. Skou. Bisimulation through probabilistic testing. *Inform. Comput.*, 94:1–28, 1991.

[18] T. Mossakowski, L. Schröder, M. Roggenbach, and H. Reichel. Algebraic-coalgebraic specification in CoCASL. *J. Logic Algebraic Programming*, 67:146–197, 2006.

[19] H. J. Ohlbach and J. Koehler. Modal logics, description logics and arithmetic reasoning. *Artif. Intell.*, 109:1–31, 1999.

[20] D. Pattinson. Semantical principles in the modal logic of coalgebras. In *Symposium on Theoretical Aspects of Computer Science*, volume 2010 of *LNCS*, pages 514–526. Springer, 2001.

[21] D. Pattinson. Coalgebraic modal logic: Soundness, completeness and decidability of local consequence. *Theoret. Comput. Sci.*, 309:177–193, 2003.

[22] D. Pattinson. Expressive logics for coalgebras via terminal sequence induction. *Notre Dame J. Formal Logic*, 45:19–33, 2004.

[23] M. Pauly. A modal logic for coalitional power in games. *J. Logic Comput.*, 12:149–166, 2002.

[24] M. Rabin. Probabilistic automata. *Inform. Control*, 6:220–245, 1963.

[25] M. Rößiger. Coalgebras and modal logic. In *Coalgebraic Methods in Computer Science*, volume 33 of *ENTCS*. Elsevier, 2000.

[26] J. Rothe, H. Tews, and B. Jacobs. The Coalgebraic Class Specification Language CCSL. *J. Universal Comput. Sci.*, 7:175–193, 2001.

[27] J. Rutten. Universal coalgebra: A theory of systems. *Theoret. Comput. Sci.*, 249:3–80, 2000.

[28] A. Schrijver. *Theory of linear and integer programming*. Wiley Interscience, 1986.

[29] L. Schröder. Expressivity of coalgebraic modal logic: the limits and beyond. In *Foundations of Software Science And Computation Structures*, volume 3441 of *LNCS*, pages 440–454. Springer, 2005.

[30] L. Schröder. A finite model construction for coalgebraic modal logic. In L. Aceto and A. Ingólfsdóttir, editors, *Foundations Of Software Science And Computation Structures*, volume 3921 of *LNCS*, pages 157–171. Springer, 2006.

[31] S. Tobies. *PSPACE* reasoning for graded modal logics. *J. Logic Comput.*, 11:85–106, 2001.

[32] D. Turi and G. Plotkin. Towards a mathematical operational semantics. In *Logic in Computer Science*, pages 280–291. IEEE, 1997.

[33] W. van der Hoek and J.-J. Meyer. Graded modalities in epistemic logic. In *Logical foundations of computer science*, volume 620 of *LNCS*, pages 503–514. Springer, 1992.

[34] M. Vardi. On the complexity of epistemic reasoning. In *Logic in Computer Science*, pages 243–251. IEEE, 1989.

[35] M. Y. Vardi. Why is modal logic so robustly decidable? In *Descriptive Complexity and Finite Models*, volume 31 of *DIMACS Ser. Discrete Math. Theoret. Comput. Sci.*, pages 149–184. AMS, 1996.

[36] Y. Venema. Automata and fixed point logics: a coalgebraic perspective. *Inform. Comput.* To appear.

Invited Talk

Avoiding Determinization*

Orna Kupferman†
Hebrew University

Abstract

Automata on infinite objects are extensively used in system specification, verification, and synthesis. While some applications of the automata-theoretic approach have been well accepted by the industry, some have not yet been reduced to practice. Applications that involve determinization of automata on infinite words have been doomed to belong to the second category. This has to do with the intricacy of Safra's optimal determinization construction, the fact that the state space that results from determinization is awfully complex and is not amenable to optimizations and a symbolic implementation, and the fact that determinization requires the introduction of acceptance conditions that are more complex than the Büchi acceptance condition. Examples of applications that involve determinization and belong to the unfortunate second category include model checking of ω-regular properties, decidability of branching temporal logics, and synthesis and control of open systems.

We offer an alternative to the standard automata-theoretic approach. The crux of our approach is avoiding determinization. Our approach goes instead via universal co-Büchi automata. Like nondeterministic automata, universal automata may have several runs on every input. Here, however, an input is accepted if all of the runs are accepting. We show how the use of universal automata simplifies significantly known complementation constructions for automata on infinite words, known decision procedures for branching temporal logics, known synthesis algorithms, and other applications that are now based on determinization. Our algorithms are less difficult to implement and have practical advantages like being amenable to optimizations and a symbolic implementation.

*The Safraless plot described in this paper is based on joint work with Moshe Y. Vardi, appearing in [21, 24].

†Address:School of Computer Science and Engineering, Hebrew University, Jerusalem 91904, Israel. Email: orna@cs.huji.ac.il. Supported in part by BSF grant 9800096 and by a grant from Minerva.

1 Introduction

Finite automata on infinite objects were first introduced in the 60's. Motivated by decision problems in mathematics and logic, Büchi, McNaughton, and Rabin developed a framework for reasoning about infinite words and infinite trees [4, 28, 36]. The framework has proved to be very powerful. Automata, and their tight relation to second-order monadic logics were the key to the solution of several fundamental decision problems in mathematics and logic [47]. Today, automata on infinite objects are used for specification and verification of nonterminating systems [49, 27, 51]. The automata-theoretic approach separates the logical and the combinatorial aspects of reasoning about systems. The translation of specifications to automata handles the logic and shifts all the combinatorial difficulties to automata-theoretic problems.

While some applications of the automata-theoretic approach have been well accepted by the industry, some have not yet been reduced to practice. As we detail below, applications that involve determinization is of automata on infinite words have been doomed to belong to the second category. This has to do with the intricacy of Safra's optimal determinization construction, the fact that the state space that results from determinization is awfully complex and is not amenable to optimizations and a symbolic implementation, and the fact that determinization requires the introduction of acceptance conditions that are more complex than the Büchi acceptance condition.

Let us examine some examples, and let us start with perhaps the most successful and influential application of automata theory in formal verification : linear time model checking [51]. In the automata-theoretic approach to model checking, we check the correctness of a system with respect to a specification by checking containment of the language of the system in the language of an automaton that accepts exactly all computations that satisfy the specification. In order to check the latter, we check that the intersection of the system with an automaton that accepts exactly all the computations that violate the specification is empty. For instance, LTL model checking usually proceeds by translating the negation of an LTL formula into a Büchi automaton.

Difficulties start when properties are specified by ω-regular automata. Then, one needs to complement the property automaton. Efforts for developing complementation constructions for nondeterministic Büchi automata started early in the 60s. Büchi suggested a complementation construction that involved a doubly-exponential blow-up in the state space. Thus, complementing an automaton with n states resulted in an automaton with $2^{2^{O(n)}}$ states [4]. Büchi's motivation was decidability of S1S. In the mid 80s, when complementation became of practical interest in formal verification, and complexity-theoretic considerations started to play a greater role, the problem was re-examined and a construction with $2^{O(n^2)}$ states was suggested in [42].

Only in [40], however, Safra introduced an optimal determinization construction, which also enabled a $2^{O(n \log n)}$ complementation construction, matching the known lower bound [30]. Safra's determinization construction is beautiful. In order to obtain the optimal bound, Safra defined each state of the deterministic automaton to be a tree of subset constructions that cleverly maintains the essential information about all possible runs (unlike automata on finite words, the set of states reachable in all possible runs does not provide sufficient information, as we also need information about the set of states that have been visited along each run). While being the heart of many complexity results in verification, the construction in [40] is complicated and difficult to implement. Efforts to implement it [46, 2] have to cope with the awfully complex state space of the deterministic automaton, which is amenable to optimizations and a symbolic representation. Almost 20 years have passed since the introduction of Safra's construction, and no implementation that can handle automata with more than 8 states exists.

Due to the lack of a simple complementation construction, users are typically required to specify the property by deterministic Büchi automata (it is easy to complement a deterministic automaton [26]), or to supply the automaton for the negation of the property [16]. Similarly, specification formalisms like ETL [53], which have automata within the logic, involve complementation of automata, and the difficulty of complementing Büchi automata is an obstacle to practical use [3]. In fact, even when the properties are specified in LTL, complementation is useful: the translators from LTL into automata have reached a remarkable level of sophistication (cf. [43, 11]). Even though complementation of the automata is not explicitly required, the translations are so involved that it is useful to checks their correctness, which involves complementation[1]. Complementation is interesting in practice also because it enables refinement and optimization techniques that are based on language containment rather than simulation. Thus, an effective algorithm for the complementation of Büchi automata is of significant practical value.

Let us move on to another important application — decidability of branching temporal logics. Using automata on infinite trees, Rabin was able to prove the decidability of SnS, the monadic theory of infinite trees. In fact, SnS decidability was the motivation for extending the automata-theoretic framework to infinite trees [36]. The complexity of SnS decidability is known to be nonelementary [29]. Thus, while decidability of many logics has been established by demonstrating an effective reduction to SnS, this approach was no longer appealing when decidability became of practical interest in areas such as formal verification and AI [12, 19]. This is when the original automata-theoretic idea was revived: by going from various logics to automata directly, decision procedures of elementary complexity were obtained for many logics, e.g., [44, 45, 50].

By the mid 1980s, the focus was on using automata to obtain tighter upper bounds. Safra's optimal determinization construction has led to a breakthrough progress also in the branching setting. Indeed, the translation of branching temporal logic formulas to automata on infinite trees typically involves determinization of automata on infinite words that are associated with linear requirements in the formula. More progress was attained by improved algorithms for the nonemptiness problem of nondeterministic tree automata [8, 35]. The introduction of alternating automata on infinite trees [9, 31] simplified this approach further. In the now standard approach for checking whether a formula ψ is satisfiable, one constructs an alternating parity tree automaton $\mathcal{A}_\psi$ that accepts all (or enough) tree models of ψ (the translation from formulas to alternating parity tree automata is simple and well known, c.f., [9, 25]), and then checks that the language of $\mathcal{A}_\psi$ is nonempty.

While the above approach yielded significantly improved upper bounds (in some cases reducing the upper time bound from octuply exponential [45] to singly exponential [48]), it proved to be not too amenable to implementation. First, checking the nonemptiness of alternating parity tree automata requires their translation to nondeterministic parity tree automata. Such removal of alternation involves determinization of word automata, and thus involves Safra's construction[2]. Second, the best-known algorithms for nonemptiness of nondeterministic parity tree automata are exponential [17]. Implementing them on top of the messy state space that results from Safra's determinization is practically impossible.

As a final example, consider the synthesis problem for

[1]For an LTL formula ψ, one typically checks that both the intersection of $\mathcal{A}_\psi$ with $\mathcal{A}_{\neg\psi}$ and the intersection of their complementary automata are empty.

[2]An alternative construction for removal of alternation is described in [33]. Like Safra's construction, however, this construction is very complicated and we know of no implementation of it.

linear specifications. When a system is reactive, it interacts with the environment, and a correct system should satisfy the specification with respect to all environments. As argued in [1, 6, 35], the right way to approach synthesis of reactive systems is to consider the situation as a (possibly infinite) game between the environment and the system. A correct system can be then viewed as a winning strategy in this game. The traditional algorithm for finding a winning strategy for the system transforms the specification into a parity automaton over trees that embody all the possible inputs to the system. The system is realizable precisely when this tree automaton is not empty [35]. A finite generator of an infinite tree accepted by this automaton can be viewed as a finite-state system realizing the specification. This is closely related to the approach taken, e.g., in [38], to solve Church's solvability problem [5].

In spite of the rich theory developed for system synthesis, little of this theory has been reduced to practice. Some people argue that this is because the realizability problem for LTL specifications is 2EXPTIME-complete [35, 39], but this argument is not compelling. First, experience with verification shows that even nonelementary algorithms can be practical, since the worst-case complexity does not arise often (c.f., the model-checking tool MONA [7]). Furthermore, in some sense, synthesis is not harder than verification. Indeed, realizable specifications for which the solution of the synthesis problem is doubly exponential, require systems of doubly exponential size for their realization [39]. While the verification of such systems is linear in the size of the system, is doubly exponential in the specification. We believe that, as with satisfiability, the main reason for the lack of practical impact of synthesis theory is the fact the generation of the tree automaton uses Safra's determinization construction, and the check for its emptiness requires an execution of a parity-tree-automata emptiness algorithm on top of its messy state space. The lack of a simple implementation is not due to a lack of need: implementations of realizability algorithms exist, but they have to either restrict the specification to one that generates "easy to determinize" automata [41, 52] or give up completeness [15].

In this work we offer an alternative to the standard automata-theoretic approach. The crux of our approach is avoiding the use of Safra's construction. Instead, we use universal automata. Like nondeterministic automata, universal automata may have several runs on every input. Here, however, an input is accepted if all of the runs are accepting. Universal automata are sufficiently strong to play the role that deterministic automata play in the current algorithms. Complementing a nondeterministic automaton can be done by dualizing its acceptance condition and viewing it as a universal automaton. In addition, universal automata have the desired property, enjoyed by deterministic automata but not by nondeterministic automata, of having the ability to run over all branches of an input tree – this is required for both satisfiability and synthesis. Using universal automata, we can also avoid the parity acceptance condition. For complementation, dualizing the Büchi acceptance condition, one gets the co-Büchi condition. This observation is helpful also in the context of synthesis, as a universal co-Büchi automaton for a required behavior ψ can be obtained by dualizing a nondeterministic Büchi automaton for $\neg\psi$. For satisfiability, we show that an alternating parity tree automaton can be reduced[3] to a universal co-Büchi tree automaton.

By analyzing runs of universal co-Büchi word automata, we are able to translate them to nondeterministic Büchi automata. Such a translation completes a complementation construction for nondeterministic Büchi word automata. An analysis of runs of universal co-Büchi tree automata is more sophisticated, and it enables us to reduce universal co-Büchi tree automata to nondeterministic Büchi tree automata. Such a reduction completes a solution for the decidability and synthesis problems. Our translations and reductions are significantly simpler than the standard approach, making them less difficult to implement, both explicitly and symbolically. These advantages are obtained with no increase in the complexity (in fact, in some cases, the complexity is improved). In addition, they give rise to several significant optimizations and heuristics.

The idea of avoiding determinization was first suggested in the context of complementation in [18], which described a $2^{O(n \log n)}$ Safraless complementation construction. The analysis of runs of universal co-Büchi automata that we do here is similar to the progress-measures introduced there. Unfortunately, the complementation construction in [18] is complicated and we know of no implementation of it. We believe that the simplicity of our approach follows from the fact we explicitly use universal co-Büchi automata as an intermediate step (in fact, as described in [21], it is possible to decompose our construction further and use alternating weak automata as another intermediate step). A more recent effort to avoid determinization in the context of synthesis is described in [14]. There, the challenge is to cope with the fact that when objectives in two-player games are ω-regular, current solutions construct the product of the game with a deterministic automaton for the objective. Instead, Henzinger and Piterman suggest to leave the objective automaton nondeterministic, but to restructure its state space and transitions so that taking its product with the system does solve the original game. The construction of "good-for-games automata" involves an inevitable exponential blow up, but is much simpler than Safra's determinization.

[3] We use "reduce A_1 to A_2", rather than "translate A_1 to A_2" to indicate that A_1 need not be equivalent to A_2, yet the language of $\mathcal{A}_1$ is empty iff the language of $\mathcal{A}_2$ is empty.

2 Safraless Complementation

Given an alphabet Σ, an *infinite word over* Σ is an infinite sequence $w = \sigma_0 \cdot \sigma_1 \cdot \sigma_2 \cdots$ of letters in Σ. We denote by w^l the suffix $\sigma_l \cdot \sigma_{l+1} \cdot \sigma_{l+2} \cdots$ of w. An *automaton on infinite words* is $\mathcal{A} = \langle \Sigma, Q, Q_{in}, \rho, \alpha \rangle$, where Σ is the input alphabet, Q is a finite set of states, $\rho : Q \times \Sigma \to 2^Q$ is a transition function, $Q_{in} \subseteq Q$ is a set of initial states, and α is an acceptance condition (a condition that defines a subset of Q^ω). Intuitively, $\rho(q, \sigma)$ is the set of states that $\mathcal{A}$ can move into when it is in state q and it reads the letter σ. Since the transition function of $\mathcal{A}$ may specify many possible transitions for each state and letter, $\mathcal{A}$ is not *deterministic*. If ρ is such that for every $q \in Q$ and $\sigma \in \Sigma$, we have that $|\rho(q, \sigma)| = 1$, then $\mathcal{A}$ is a deterministic automaton.

A *run* of $\mathcal{A}$ on w is a function $r : \mathbb{N} \to Q$ where $r(0) \in Q_{in}$ (i.e., the run starts in an initial state) and for every $l \geq 0$, we have $r(l+1) \in \rho(r(l), \sigma_l)$ (i.e., the run obeys the transition function). Acceptance is defined according to the set $Inf(r)$ of states that r visits *infinitely often*, i.e., $Inf(r) = \{q \in Q : r(l) = q \text{for infinitely many } l \in \mathbb{N}\}$. As Q is finite, it is guaranteed that $Inf(r) \neq \emptyset$. The way we refer to $Inf(r)$ depends on the acceptance condition of $\mathcal{A}$. In *Büchi automata*, $\alpha \subseteq Q$, and r is accepting iff $Inf(r) \cap \alpha \neq \emptyset$. Dually, in *co-Büchi automata*, $\alpha \subseteq Q$, and r is accepting iff $Inf(r) \cap \alpha = \emptyset$.

Since $\mathcal{A}$ is not deterministic, it may have many runs on w. In contrast, a deterministic automaton has a single run on w. There are two dual ways in which we can refer to the many runs. When $\mathcal{A}$ is a *nondeterministic* automaton, it accepts an input word w iff there exists an accepting run of $\mathcal{A}$ on w. When $\mathcal{A}$ is a *universal* automaton, it accepts an input word w iff all the runs of $\mathcal{A}$ on w are accepting.

We denote each of the different types of automata (some will be defined only in the sequel) by three letter acronyms in $\{D, N, U, A\} \times \{B, C, P, R, S\} \times \{W, T\}$, where the first letter describes the branching mode of the automaton (deterministic, nondeterministic, universal, or alternating), the second letter describes the acceptance condition (Büchi, co-Büchi, parity, Rabin, or Streett), and the third letter describes the object over which the automaton runs (words or trees). For example, APT stands for an alternating parity tree automaton and UCW stands for a universal co-Büchi word automaton.

Our Safraless complementation construction proceeds as follows. In order to complement an NBW, first dualize the transition function and the acceptance condition, and then translate the resulting UCW automaton back to an NBW. By [32], the dual automaton accepts the complementary language, and therefore, so does the nondeterministic automaton we end up with. Thus, rather than determinization, complementation is based on a translation of universal automata to nondeterministic ones. We now give the technical details of the construction.

Consider a UCW $\mathcal{A} = \langle \Sigma, Q, Q_{in}, \delta, \alpha \rangle$. The runs of $\mathcal{A}$ on a word $w = \sigma_0 \cdot \sigma_1 \cdots$ can be arranged in an infinite DAG (directed acyclic graph) $G = \langle V, E \rangle$, where

- $V \subseteq Q \times \mathbb{N}$ is such that $\langle q, l \rangle \in V$ iff some run of $\mathcal{A}$ on w has $q_l = q$. For example, the first level of G contains the vertices $Q_{in} \times \{0\}$.
- $E \subseteq \bigcup_{l \geq 0} (Q \times \{l\}) \times (Q \times \{l+1\})$ is such that $E(\langle q, l \rangle, \langle q', l+1 \rangle)$ iff $\langle q, l \rangle \in V$ and $q' \in \delta(q, \sigma_l)$.

Thus, G embodies exactly all the runs of $\mathcal{A}$ on w. We call G the *run* DAG of $\mathcal{A}$ on w, and we say that G is *accepting* if all its paths satisfy the acceptance condition α. Note that $\mathcal{A}$ accepts w iff G is accepting. We say that a vertex $\langle q', l' \rangle$ is a *successor* of a vertex $\langle q, l \rangle$ iff $E(\langle q, l \rangle, \langle q', l' \rangle)$. We say that $\langle q', l' \rangle$ is *reachable* from $\langle q, l \rangle$ iff there exists a sequence $\langle q_0, l_0 \rangle, \langle q_1, l_1 \rangle, \langle q_2, l_2 \rangle, \ldots$ of successive vertices such that $\langle q, l \rangle = \langle q_0, l_0 \rangle$, and there exists $i \geq 0$ such that $\langle q', l' \rangle = \langle q_i, l_i \rangle$. For a set $S \subseteq Q$, we say that a vertex $\langle q, l \rangle$ of G is an *S-vertex* if $q \in S$.

Consider a (possibly finite) DAG $G' \subseteq G$. We say that a vertex $\langle q, l \rangle$ is *finite* in G' if only finitely many vertices in G' are reachable from $\langle q, l \rangle$. For a set $S \subseteq Q$, we say that a vertex $\langle q, l \rangle$ is *S-free* in G' if all the vertices in G' that are reachable from $\langle q, l \rangle$ are not S-vertices. Note that, in particular, an S-free vertex is not an S-vertex. We say that a level l of G' is of *width* $d \geq 0$ if there are d vertices of the form $\langle q, l \rangle$ in G'. Finally, the *width* of G' is the maximal $d \geq 0$ such that there are infinitely many levels l of width d. The *α-less* width of a level of $\mathcal{G}$ is defined similarly, restricted to vertices $\langle q, l \rangle$ for which $q \notin \alpha$. Note that the width of G is at most n and the α-less width of G_r is at most $n - |\alpha|$.

Runs of UCW were studied in [21]. For $x \in \mathbb{N}$, let $[x]$ denote the set $\{0, 1, \ldots, x\}$, and let $[x]^{odd}$ and $[x]^{even}$ denote the set of odd and even members of $[x]$, respectively. A *co-Büchi-ranking* for G (*C-ranking*, for short) is a function $f : V \to [2n]$ that satisfies the following two conditions:

1. For all vertices $\langle q, l \rangle \in V$, if $f(\langle q, l \rangle)$ is odd, then $q \notin \alpha$.
2. For all edges $\langle \langle q, l \rangle, \langle q', l+1 \rangle \rangle \in E$, we have $f(\langle q', l+1 \rangle) \leq f(\langle q, l \rangle)$.

Thus, a C-ranking associates with each vertex in G a rank in $[2n]$ so that the ranks along paths do not increase, and α-vertices get only even ranks. We say that a vertex $\langle q, l \rangle$ is an *odd vertex* if $f(\langle q, l \rangle)$ is odd. Note that each path in G eventually gets trapped in some rank. We say that the C-ranking f is an *odd C-ranking* if all the paths of G eventually get trapped in an odd rank. Formally, f is odd iff for all paths $\langle q_0, 0 \rangle, \langle q_1, 1 \rangle, \langle q_2, 2 \rangle, \ldots$ in G, there is $l \geq 0$

such that $f(\langle q_l, l\rangle)$ is odd, and for all $l' \geq l$, we have $f(\langle q_{l'}, l'\rangle) = f(\langle q_l, l\rangle)$. Note that, equivalently, f is odd if every path of G has infinitely many odd vertices.

Lemma 2.1 [21] *The following are equivalent.*

1. *All the paths of G have only finitely many α-vertices.*
2. *There is an odd C-ranking for G.*

Proof: Assume first that there is an odd C-ranking for G. Then, every path in G eventually gets trapped in an odd rank. Hence, as α-vertices get only even ranks, all the paths of G visit α only finitely often, and we are done.

For the other direction, given an accepting run DAG G, we define an infinite sequence $G_0 \supseteq G_1 \supseteq G_2 \supseteq \ldots$ of DAGs inductively as follows.

- $G_0 = G$.
- $G_{2i+1} = G_{2i} \setminus \{\langle q, l\rangle \mid \langle q, l\rangle \text{ is finite in } G_{2i}\}$.
- $G_{2i+2} = G_{2i+1} \setminus \{\langle q, l\rangle \mid \langle q, l\rangle \text{ is } \alpha\text{-free in } G_{2i+1}\}$.

It is shown in [21] that for every $i \geq 0$, the transition from G_{2i+1} to G_{2i+2} involves the removal of an infinite path from G_{2i+1}. Since the width of G_0 is bounded by n, it follows that the width of G_{2i} is at most $n - i$. Hence, G_{2n} is finite, and G_{2n+1} is empty. In fact, as argued in [13], the α-less width of G_{2i} is at most $n - (|\alpha| + i)$, implying that $G_{2(n-|\alpha|)+1}$ is already empty. Since $|\alpha| \geq 1$, we can therefore assume that G_{2n-1} is empty.

Each vertex $\langle q, l\rangle$ in G has a unique index $i \geq 1$ such that $\langle q, l\rangle$ is either finite in G_{2i} or α-free in G_{2i+1}. Thus, the sequence of DAGs induces a function $rank : V \to [2n-2]$, defined as follows.

$$rank(q, l) = \left[\begin{array}{ll} 2i & \text{If } \langle q, l\rangle \text{ is finite in } G_{2i}. \\ 2i+1 & \text{If } \langle q, l\rangle \text{ is } \alpha\text{-free in } G_{2i+1}. \end{array} \right.$$

It is shown in [21] that the function $rank$ is an odd C-ranking. □

We now use C-ranking in order to translate UCWs to NBWs.

Theorem 2.2 [21] *Let $\mathcal{A}$ be a* UCW *with n states. There is an* NBW *$\mathcal{A}'$ with $2^{O(n \log n)}$ states such that $L(\mathcal{A}') = L(\mathcal{A})$.*

Proof: Let $\mathcal{A} = \langle \Sigma, Q, Q_{in}, \delta, \alpha\rangle$. When $\mathcal{A}'$ reads a word w, it guesses an odd C-ranking for the run DAG G of $\mathcal{A}$ on w. At a given point of a run of $\mathcal{A}'$, it keeps in its memory a whole level of G and a guess for the rank of the vertices at this level. In order to make sure that all the paths of G visit infinitely many odd vertices, $\mathcal{A}'$ remembers the set of states that owe a visit to an odd vertex.

Before we define $\mathcal{A}'$, we need some notations. A *level ranking* for $\mathcal{A}$ is a function $g : Q \to [2n-2]$, such that if $g(q)$ is odd, then $q \notin \alpha$. Let $\mathcal{R}$ be the set of all level rankings. For a subset S of Q and a letter σ, let $\delta(S, \sigma) = \bigcup_{s \in S} \delta(s, \sigma)$. Note that if level l in G, for $l \geq 0$, contains the states in S, and the $(l+1)$-th letter in w is σ, then level $l+1$ of G contains the states in $\delta(S, \sigma)$.

For two level rankings g and g' in $\mathcal{R}$ and a letter σ, we say that g' *covers* $\langle g, \sigma\rangle$ if for all q and q' in Q, if $q' \in \delta(q, \sigma)$, then $g'(q') \leq g(q)$. Thus, if g describes the ranks of the vertices of level l, and the $(l+1)$-th letter in w is σ, then g' is a possible level ranking for level $l+1$. Finally, for $g \in \mathcal{R}$, let $odd(g) = \{q : g(q) \in [2n-2]^{odd}\}$. Thus, a state of Q is in $odd(g)$ if has an odd rank.

Now, $\mathcal{A}' = \langle \Sigma, Q', Q'_{in}, \delta', \alpha'\rangle$, where

- $Q' = 2^Q \times 2^Q \times \mathcal{R}$, where a state $\langle S, O, g\rangle \in Q'$ indicates that the current level of the DAG contains the states in S, the set $O \subseteq S$ contains states along paths that have not visited an odd vertex since the last time O has been empty, and g is the guessed level ranking for the current level.
- $Q'_{in} = \{Q_{in}\} \times \{\emptyset\} \times \mathcal{R}$.
- δ' is defined, for all $\langle S, O, g\rangle \in Q'$ and $\sigma \in \Sigma$, as follows.
  - If $O \neq \emptyset$, then $\delta'(\langle S, O, g\rangle, \sigma) = \{\langle \delta(S, \sigma), \delta(O, \sigma) \setminus odd(g'), g'\rangle : g' \text{ covers } \langle g, \sigma\rangle\}$.
  - If $O = \emptyset$, then $\delta'(\langle S, O, g\rangle, \sigma) = \{\langle \delta(S, \sigma), \delta(S, \sigma) \setminus odd(g'), g'\rangle : g' \text{ covers } \langle g, \sigma\rangle\}$.
- $\alpha' = 2^Q \times \{\emptyset\} \times \mathcal{R}$.

Consider a state $\langle S, O, g\rangle \in Q'$. Since $O \subseteq S$, there are at most 3^n pairs S and O that can be members of the same state. In addition, since there are at most $(2n-1)^n$ level rankings, the number of states in $\mathcal{A}'$ is at most $3^n \cdot (2n-1)^n$, which is $2^{O(n \log n)}$ □

Corollary 2.3 *Let $\mathcal{A}$ be an NBW with n states. There is an NBW $\tilde{\mathcal{A}}$ with $2^{O(n \log n)}$ states such that $L(\tilde{\mathcal{A}}) = \Sigma^\omega \setminus L(\mathcal{A})$.*

2.1 Remarks

2.1.1 A tighter construction Both Safra's construction and our construction results in $\tilde{\mathcal{A}}$ with $2^{O(n \log n)}$ states, matching Michel's lower bound. A careful analysis, however, of the exact blow-up in Safra's and Michel's bounds reveals an exponential gap in the constants hiding in the $O()$ notations: while the upper bound on the number of states in Safra's complementary automaton is n^{2n}, Michel's lower bound involves only an $n!$ blow up, which is roughly $(n/e)^n$. The construction above does better: since $(1+\frac{x}{n})^n = e^x$, the $3^n \cdot (2n-1)^n$ bound in Theorem 2.2 is equal to $(6n)^n/\sqrt{e}$. This is still far from Michel's lower bound.

In [10] we improved the construction further and described a construction that results in an NBW with at most $(0.96n)^n$ states. The idea is as follows. Let k be the maximal odd rank that some vertex in G has. There is a level l in G such that all the odd ranks below k appear in all the levels above l. Intuitively, it follows from the fact that odd ranks correspond to vertices that are α-free, and there is a level l that has an α-free vertex in all the intermediate DAGs G_i, for each odd i below k. This observation suggests that the NBW $\mathcal{A}'$ can guess the level l and restrict the level rankings g that are guessed for the levels above it to level rankings in which all odd ranks below k appear. In addition, in a state $\langle S, O, g\rangle$, the level ranking g need not refer to states not in S. The above considerations significantly reduce the the number of potential level rankings, and lead to the $(0.96n)^n$ bound.

We note that the lower bound for NBW complementation was recently tightened too: a new technique by Yan implies a $(0.76n)^n * poly(n)$ lower bound [54]. Thus, there is still a gap between the upper and lower bounds, but it is less significant than the gap between Safra's and Michel's bound.

2.1.2 Finding the minimal rank required A drawback of our construction in Theorem 2.2 is that it never performs better than its worst-case complexity. Indeed, the $3^n \cdot (2n-1)^n$ blow-up is introduced regardless of the structure of $\mathcal{A}$ and would occur even if, say, $\mathcal{A}$ is a deterministic automaton. In order to circumvent such an unnecessary blow up, we suggest to first calculate the *minimal rank required for* $\mathcal{A}$ (formally defined below), and then to construct $\mathcal{A}'$ with respect to this rank.

For every $j \in [n]$, we define the NBW $\mathcal{A}'_j$ as a restriction of $\mathcal{A}'$ from Theorem 2.2 to states $\langle S, O, g\rangle$ in which $g : Q \to [2j-2]$. Thus, $\mathcal{A}'_j$ restricts the runs of $\mathcal{A}'$ to guess only ranks smaller than $2j-2$. It is easy to see that for every j, the language of $\mathcal{A}'_j$ is contained in the language of $\mathcal{A}'$. On the other hand, the language of $\mathcal{A}'_j$ contains only these words in $L(\mathcal{A}')$ for which G_{2j+1} is empty. The minimal rank required for $\mathcal{A}$ is the minimal $j \in [n]$ for which $L(\mathcal{A}) \subseteq L(\mathcal{A}'_j)$.

As demonstrated in the experimental results in [13], this minimal rank is often significantly smaller than n. Also, the size of $\mathcal{A}'_j$ is only $3^n(2j-1)^n$. As discussed in [21], the problem of finding the minimal rank required for $\mathcal{A}$ is PSPACE-complete.

2.1.3 An incremental approach As stated above, the problem of finding the minimal rank required for $\mathcal{A}$ requires space that is polynomial in $\mathcal{A}$. Nevertheless, the automaton $\mathcal{A}$ is typically small, and the bottle-neck of the computation is usually the application of $\mathcal{A}'$ (e.g., taking its product with a system with a large state space). Thus, finding the minimal rank j required for $\mathcal{A}$ and using $\mathcal{A}'_j$ instead of $\mathcal{A}'$ may be of great practical importance.

Moreover, for the language-containment application, one need not calculate the minimal required rank and can check the containment of S in $\mathcal{A}$ by checking the emptiness of $S \cap \mathcal{A}'_j$ for increasing j's. In Section 4.1.2, we describe the incremental approach in more detail. There, we also note that it is possible to take advantage of the work done during the emptiness test of $S \cap \mathcal{A}'_j$, when testing emptiness of $S \cap \mathcal{A}'_{j'}$, for $j' > j$.

2.1.4 More heuristics In [13], we used the fact that the state space of $\mathcal{A}'$ is simple and suggested an arsenal of optimization techniques that can be applied to it. The optimizations make use of the fact that the construction of $\mathcal{A}'$ from $\mathcal{A}$ may use an intermediate alternating week automaton, and are applied on both the intermediate automaton and the final NBW. The optimizations involve techniques of rank reduction (described above), height reductions (repeatedly removing a minimal strongly connected component, as long as such a removal does not change the language of the intermediate automaton), as well as direct and fair simulation. As detailed in [13], the construction and the optimizations have been implemented and they significantly reduce the size of the state space of $\mathcal{A}'$.

2.1.5 Safraless complementation of nondeterministic Rabin and Streett automata In [23], we extended the ranking technique to Rabin and Streett automata, and use the analysis in order to describe simple complementation constructions for NRW and NSW. Thus, also in these classes, it is possible to avoid determinization and complement automata by dualizing them to universal automata.

3 Safraless Decision Procedures

The key idea in [21] is that when all the paths of a DAG have only finitely many α-vertices, and finite vertices are removed, the removal of α-free vertices results in a DAG with a strictly smaller width. Consequently, when the width of the DAG is bounded by some $k \geq 1$ (and in the case of a run DAG of a UCW with n states we know that $k \leq n$), iterative removal of finite and α-free vertices results in an empty DAG after at most k iterations. This is why every vertex can be associated with a finite rank bounded by $2k$, and the translation of UCWs to NBWs proceeds by letting the NBW guess the ranks.

In order to solve the satisfiability problem for branching temporal logics, we reduce the satisfiability problem to the emptiness problem of UCTs. We then solve the emptiness problem for UCTs by reducing them to NBTs. Runs of a UCT can also be arranged in a run DAG, and as in the linear case, when all the paths of the DAG have only finitely many α-vertices, and finite vertices are removed, the removal of α-free vertices results in a DAG with a strictly smaller width. In the case of tree automata, however, one crucial factor is missing: we do not have a bound on the width of the run DAG. Indeed, since the UCT runs on trees whose width is not bounded, the width of the run DAG is not bounded either.

The way we solve this problem is as follows. Recall that our motivation is the satisfiability problem. Therefore, we do not have to construct an NBT $\mathcal{A}'$ that is equivalent to the UCT $\mathcal{A}$, and we only need an NBT that is emptiness-equivalent to the UCT (that is, $L(\mathcal{A}') \neq \emptyset$ iff $L(\mathcal{A}) \neq \emptyset$). Accordingly, the NBTs we construct are parameterized by a parameter k and the NBT $\mathcal{A}'_k$ accepts only trees whose accepting run graph (graph, rather than a DAG, as we have to refer to its size and not to its width) has at most k vertices. By a bounded model property for UCTs, we know that $L(\mathcal{A}) \neq \emptyset$ iff $L(\mathcal{A}'_k) \neq \emptyset$ for $k = n^{2n+3}$. The bounded model property relies on Safra's determinization construction (k above depends on the number of states in a DSW equivalent to an NBW induced by $\mathcal{A}$), but it is only the correctness of the our construction that relies on Safra's construction: once we have k, the construction is independent of the intricacy of Safra's construction.

Below we describe the construction briefly. The full details, as well as the definitions of trees, alternating tree automata, and run graphs, can be found in [24]. The input to the satisfiability problem is a μ-calculus formula ψ [19]. The formula ψ can be translated to an APT with no blow up [9]. Such translations exist for several other branching temporal logics [25]. Thus, the problem we need to solve is APT emptiness, and we start with a reduction of APT emptiness to UCT emptiness.

UCTs are a special case of APTs and are strictly less expressive than APTs. The emptiness problem for APTs can be still easily reduced to the emptiness problem for UCTs. The idea is to enrich the alphabet of the APT by a "strategy component" — information on how nondeterminizm is going to be resolved in the current transition. Then, guesses of the alternating automaton are reduced to guesses about the input letter, and the automaton becomes universal, over a richer alphabet. In addition, by changing the state space of the automaton, the parity condition is replaced by a co-Büchi condition. Formally, we have the following.

Theorem 3.1 [24] *Let $\mathcal{A}$ be an APT with n states, transition function of size m, and index h. There is a UCT $\mathcal{A}'$ with $O(nh)$ states and alphabet of size $2^{O(m)}$ such that $L(\mathcal{A}) \neq \emptyset$ iff $L(\mathcal{A}') \neq \emptyset$.*

As explained above, in order to reduce the UCT to an NBT, we first need a bounded-model property for UCTs, which also implies a bound on the size of an accepting run graph. Let $det(n) = n^{2n+2}$.

Theorem 3.2 [24] *A UCT $\mathcal{A}$ with n states is not empty iff $\mathcal{A}$ has an accepting run graph with at most $n \cdot det(n)$ vertices.*

By translating the UCT to an NBT that accepts exactly all trees whose accepting run graph has at most $n \cdot det(n)$ vertices, we finally get the following.

Theorem 3.3 [24] *Let $\mathcal{A}$ be a UCT with n states. There is an NBT $\mathcal{A}'$ over the same alphabet such that $L(\mathcal{A}') \neq \emptyset$ iff $L(\mathcal{A}) \neq \emptyset$, and the number of states in $\mathcal{A}'$ is $2^{O(n^2 \log n)}$.*

Combining Theorems 3.1 and 3.3, we get the desired reduction from the nonemptiness problem for APT to the nonemptiness problem for NBT:

Theorem 3.4 [24] *Let $\mathcal{A}$ be an APT with n states, transition function of size m, and index h. There is an NBT $\mathcal{A}'$ with $2^{O(n^2h^2 \log nh)}$ states and alphabet of size $2^{O(m)}$ such that $L(\mathcal{A}) \neq \emptyset$ iff $L(\mathcal{A}') \neq \emptyset$.*

The complexity of the nonemptiness algorithm for APT that follows coincides with the known one. The main advantage of our approach is the fact it avoids Safra's determinization and the need to solve parity games on top of it, and the fact it enables an incremental and symbolic implementation. We will get back to this point in Section 4.

We note that an improvement of the upper bound of NBW determinization would lead to an improvement in the complexity of our decision procedure. Indeed, $det(n)$ is the blow up that determinization involves, and it affects the range of ranks that the NBT has to guess. In fact, the bound described here is better than the one in [24], and the improvement is due to Piterman's recent determinization construction [34].

4 Safraless LTL Realizability and Synthesis

Given an LTL formula ψ over the sets I and O of input and output signals, the *realizability problem* for ψ is to decide whether there is a *strategy* $f : (2^I)^* \to 2^O$, generated by a transducer[4] such that all the computations of the system generated by f satisfy ψ [35]. Formally, a computation $\rho \in (2^{I \cup O})^\omega$ is generated by f if $\rho = (i_0 \cup o_0), (i_1 \cup o_1), (i_2 \cup o_2), \ldots$ and for all $j \geq 1$, we have $o_j = f(i_0 \cdot i_1 \cdots i_{j-1})$.

[4]It is known that if some transducer that generates f exists, then there is also a finite-state transducer.

The traditional algorithm for solving the realizability problem translates the LTL formula into an NBW, applies Safra's construction in order to get a DPW $\mathcal{A}_\psi$ for it, expands $\mathcal{A}_\psi$ to a DPT $\mathcal{A}_{\forall\psi}$ that accepts all the trees all of whose branches satisfy ψ, and then checks the nonemptiness of $\mathcal{A}_{\forall\psi}$ with respect to *I-exhaustive* $2^{I\cup O}$-labeled 2^I-trees, namely $2^{I\cup O}$-labeled 2^I-trees that contain, for each word $w \in (2^I)^\omega$, at least one path whose projection on 2^I is w [35]. Thus, the algorithm applies Safra's determinization construction, and has to solve the nonemptiness problem for DPT. For ψ of length n, the DPW $\mathcal{A}_\psi$ has $2^{2^{O(n \log n)}}$ states and index $2^{O(n)}$. This is also the size of the DPT $\mathcal{A}_{\forall\psi}$, making the overall complexity doubly-exponential, which matches the lower bound in [39]. We now show how UCW can be used instead of DPW. Intuitively, universal automata have the desired property, enjoyed also by deterministic automata but not by nondeterministic automata, of having the ability to run over all branches of an input tree. In addition, since complementation of LTL is trivial, the known translations of LTL into NBW can be used in order to translate LTL into UCW. Formally, we have the following.

Theorem 4.1 [24] *The realizability problem for an LTL formula can be reduced to the nonemptiness problem for a UCT with exponentially many states.*

Proof: A strategy $f : (2^I)^* \to 2^O$ can be viewed as a 2^O-labeled 2^I-tree. We define a UCT $\mathcal{S}_\psi$ such that $\mathcal{S}_\psi$ accepts a 2^O-labeled 2^I-tree $\langle T, \tau\rangle$ iff τ is a good strategy for ψ.

Let $\mathcal{A}_{\neg\psi} = \langle 2^{I\cup O}, Q, q_{in}, \delta, \alpha\rangle$ be an NBW for $\neg\psi$ [51]. Thus, $\mathcal{A}_{\neg\psi}$ accepts exactly all the words in $(2^{I\cup O})^\omega$ that do not satisfy ψ. Then, $\mathcal{S}_\psi = \langle 2^O, 2^I, Q, q_{in}, \delta', \alpha\rangle$, where for every $q \in Q$ and $o \in 2^O$, we have $\delta'(q, o) = \bigwedge_{i\in 2^I} \bigwedge_{q'\in\delta(q,i\cup o)} (i, q')$. Thus, from state q, reading the output assignment $o \in 2^O$, the automaton $\mathcal{S}_\psi$ branches to each direction $i \in 2^I$, with all the states q' to which δ branches when it reads $i \cup o$ in state q. It is not hard to see that $\mathcal{S}_\psi$ accepts a 2^O-labeled 2^I-tree $\langle T, \tau\rangle$ iff for all the paths $\{\varepsilon, i_0, i_0 \cdot i_1, i_0 \cdot i_1 \cdot i_2, \ldots\}$ of T, the infinite word $(i_0 \cup \tau(\varepsilon)), (i_1 \cup \tau(i_0)), (i_2 \cup \tau(i_0 \cdot i_1)), \ldots$ is not accepted by $\mathcal{A}_{\neg\psi}$; thus all the computations generated by τ satisfy ψ. Since the size of $\mathcal{A}_{\neg\psi}$ is exponential in the length of ψ, so is $\mathcal{S}_\psi$, and we are done. □

For an LTL formula of length n, the size of the automaton S_ψ is $2^{O(n)}$, making the overall complexity doubly-exponential, matching the complexity of the traditional algorithm , as well as the lower bound [39].

The *synthesis problem* for an LTL formula ψ is to find a a transducer that generates a strategy realizing ψ. Known algorithms for the nonemptiness problem can be easily extended to return a transducer [37]. The algorithm we present here also enjoys this property, thus it can be used to solved not only the realizability problem but also the synthesis problem (as well as related richer problems, like supervisory-control and synthesis with incomplete information). While our Safraless approach simplifies the algorithms and improves the complexity of the decidability problems, the fact it uses a simplified class of automata (that is, co-Büchi rather than parity) causes the constructions to have more states than these constructed by the traditional algorithm. We believe, however, that this drawback is compensated by the practical advantages, discussed below, of our approach.

4.1 Remarks

4.1.1 A symbolic implementation Safra's determinization construction involves complicated data structures: each state in the deterministic automaton is associated with a labeled ordered tree. Consequently, there is no symbolic implementation of decision procedures that are based on Safra's determinization and NPT. Our construction, on the other hand, can be implemented symbolically. Indeed, the state space of the NBT constructed in Theorem 3.3 consists of sets of states and a ranking function, it can be encoded by Boolean variables, and the NBT's transitions can be encoded by relations on these variables and a primed version of them. The fixpoint solution for the nonemptiness problem of NBT (c.f., [50]) then yields a symbolic solution to the original UCT nonemptiness problem. Moreover, when applied for the solution of the realizability problem, the BDDs that are generated by the symbolic decision procedure can be used to generate a symbolic witness strategy. In [15], the authors suggest a symbolic solution for the LTL synthesis problem. However, the need to circumvent Safra's determinization causes the algorithm in [15] to be complete only for a subset of LTL. Our approach circumvents Safra's determinization without giving up completeness.

4.1.2 An incremental approach Our construction is based on the fact we can bound the maximal rank that a vertex of G can get by $k = n \cdot det(n)$ — the bound on the size of the run graphs of $\mathcal{A}$. Often, the bound on the maximal rank much smaller. Accordingly, as in the linear case, we suggest to regard k as a parameter in the construction, start with a small parameter, and increase it if necessary. Let us describe the incremental algorithm that follows in more detail.

Consider the construction described in Theorem 3.3. Starting with a UCT $\mathcal{A}$ with state space Q, we constructed an NBT $\mathcal{A}'$ with state space $2^Q \times 2^Q \times \mathcal{R}$, where $\mathcal{R}$ is the set of functions $f : Q \to [k]$ in which $f(q)$ is even for all $q \in \alpha$. For $l \leq k$, let $\mathcal{R}[l]$ be the restriction of $\mathcal{R}$ to functions with range $[l]$, and let $\mathcal{A}'[l]$ be the NBT $\mathcal{A}'$ with k being replaced by l. Recall that the NBT $\mathcal{A}'[l]$ is empty iff all the run graphs of $\mathcal{A}$ of size at most l are not accepting. Thus, coming to check the emptiness of $\mathcal{A}$, a possible heuristic would be to proceed as follows: start with a small l and check the nonemptiness of $\mathcal{A}'[l]$. If $\mathcal{A}'[l]$ is not empty, then $\mathcal{A}$ is not empty, and we can terminate with a "nonempty" output. Otherwise, increase l, and repeat the procedure. When $l = k$ and $\mathcal{A}'[l]$ is still empty, we can terminate with an "empty" output.

It is important to note that it is possible to take advantage of the work done during the emptiness test of $\mathcal{A}'[l_1]$, when testing emptiness of $\mathcal{A}'[l_2]$, for $l_2 > l_1$. To see this, note that the state space of $\mathcal{A}'[l_2]$ consists of the union of $2^Q \times 2^Q \times \mathcal{R}[l_1]$ (the state space of $\mathcal{A}'[l_1]$) with $2^Q \times 2^Q \times (\mathcal{R}[l_2] \setminus \mathcal{R}[l_1])$ (states whose $f \in \mathcal{R}[l_2]$ has a state that is mapped to a rank greater than l_1). Also, since ranks can only decrease, once the NBT $\mathcal{A}'[l_2]$ reaches a state of $\mathcal{A}'[l_1]$, it stays in such states forever. So, if we have already checked the nonemptiness of $\mathcal{A}'[l_1]$ and have recorded the classification of its states to empty and nonempty, the additional work needed in the nonemptiness test of $\mathcal{A}'[l_2]$ concerns only states in $2^Q \times 2^Q \times (\mathcal{R}[l_2] \setminus \mathcal{R}[l_1])$.

The incremental approach circumvents the fact that the blow-up that is introduced in the translation of a UCT to an NBT occurs for all UCT. With the incremental algorithm, the blow occurs only in the worst case. As shown in [13], experimental results show that in the case of word automata the construction typically ends up with a small k.

4.1.3 Ranks for generalized universal co-Büchi automata

In [22, 20], we extended the ranking analysis to universal *generalized co-Büchi* word and tree automata. Consequently, we can handles LTL formulas by translating them to nondeterministic generalized Büchi automata. This leads to an exponential improvement in the complexity of the algorithm. Since our Safraless approach uses a "Safraful" bound on the size of run graph, the extension to generalized co-Büchi automata required, on top of the above analysis of runs, also an extension of Safra's determinization construction to nondeterministic generalized Büchi automata. The extension leads to an exponential improvement (with respect to an approach that first translates the generalized Büchi automaton to a Büchi automaton) in that construction.

4.1.4 Compositional Synthesis

A drawback of current theory of system synthesis is that it assumes that one gets a comprehensive set of temporal assertions as a starting point. This cannot be realistic in practice. A more realistic approach would be to assume an *evolving* formal specification: temporal assertions can be added, deleted, or modified. Accordingly, there is a need to develop compositional synthesis algorithms. Such algorithms can, for example, refine designs when provided with additional temporal properties.

In [20], we describe such an algorithm. Given a specification ψ, we first check its realizability. Suppose now that we get an additional specification ψ'. We can, of course, simply check the realizability of $\psi \wedge \psi'$ from scratch. Instead, we suggest to first check also the realizability of ψ'. We then show how, thanks to the simple structure of the NBT obtained in the Safraless approach, much of the work used in checking the realizability of ψ and ψ' in isolation can be reused in checking the realizability of $\psi \wedge \psi'$.

References

[1] M. Abadi, L. Lamport, and P. Wolper. Realizable and unrealizable concurrent program specifications. In *Proc. 16th ICALP*, LNCS 372, pages 1–17, 1989.

[2] C. Schulte Althoff, W. Thomas, and N. Wallmeier. Observations on determinization of Büchi automata. In *Proc. 10th ICIAA*, LNCS 3845, pages 262–272, 2005.

[3] R. Armoni, L. Fix, A. Flaisher, R. Gerth, B. Ginsburg, T. Kanza, A. Landver, S. Mador-Haim, E. Singerman, A. Tiemeyer, M.Y. Vardi, and Y. Zbar. The ForSpec temporal logic: A new temporal property-specification logic. In *Proc. 8th TACAS*, LNCS 2280, pages 296–211, 2002.

[4] J.R. Büchi. On a decision method in restricted second order arithmetic. In *Proc. International Congress on Logic, Method, and Philosophy of Science. 1960*, pages 1–12, Stanford, 1962. Stanford University Press.

[5] A. Church. Logic, arithmetics, and automata. In *Proc. International Congress of Mathematicians, 1962*, pages 23–35. Institut Mittag-Leffler, 1963.

[6] D.L. Dill. *Trace theory for automatic hierarchical verification of speed independent circuits.* MIT Press, 1989.

[7] J. Elgaard, N. Klarlund, and A. Möller. Mona 1.x: new techniques for WS1S and WS2S. In *Proc. 10th CAV*, LNCS 1427, pages 516–520, 1998.

[8] E.A. Emerson and C. Jutla. The complexity of tree automata and logics of programs. In *Proc. 29th FOCS*, pages 328–337, White Plains, October 1988.

[9] E.A. Emerson and C. Jutla. Tree automata, μ-calculus and determinacy. In *Proc. 32nd FOCS*, pages 368–377, 1991.

[10] E. Friedgut, O. Kupferman, and M.Y. Vardi. Büchi complementation made tighter. In *Proc. 2nd ATVA*, LNCS 3299, pages 64–78, 2004.

[11] C. Fritz and T. Wilke. State space reductions for alternating Büchi automata: Quotienting by simulation equivalences. In *Proc. 22th FST&TCS*, LNCS 2556, pages 157–169, 2002.

[12] G. De Giacomo and M. Lenzerini. Concept languages with number restrictions and fixpoints, and its relationship with μ-calculus. In *Proc. 11th ECAI-94*, pages 411–415, 1994.

[13] S. Gurumurthy, O. Kupferman, F. Somenzi, and M.Y. Vardi. On complementing nondeterministic Büchi automata. In *Proc. 12th CHARME*, LNCS 2860, pages 96–110, 2003.

[14] T.A. Henzinger and N. Piterman. Solving games without determinization, *Submitted*, 2006.

[15] A. Harding, M. Ryan, and P. Schobbens. A new algorithm for strategy synthesis in ltl games. In *Proc. 11th TACAS*, LNCS 3440, pages 477–492, 2005.

[16] G. Holzmann. *Design and Validation of Computer Protocols*. Prentice-Hall International Editions, 1991.

[17] M. Jurdzinski. Small progress measures for solving parity games. In *17th STACS*, LNCS 1770, pages 290–301, 2000.

[18] N. Klarlund. Progress measures for complementation of ω-automata with applications to temporal logic. In *Proc. 32nd FOCS*, pages 358–367, 1991.

[19] D. Kozen. Results on the propositional μ-calculus. *Theoretical Computer Science*, 27:333–354, 1983.

[20] O. Kupferman, N. Piterman, and M.Y. Vardi. Safraless compositional synthesis. In *Proc. 18th CAV*, LNCS, 2006.

[21] O. Kupferman and M.Y. Vardi. Weak alternating automata are not that weak. *ACM TOCL*, 2(2):408–429, July 2001.

[22] O. Kupferman and M.Y. Vardi. From complementation to certification. In *Proc. 10th TACAS*, LNCS 2988, pages 591–606, 2004.

[23] O. Kupferman and M.Y. Vardi. Complementation constructions for nondeterministic automata on infinite words. In *Proc. 11th TACAS*, LNCS 3440, pages 206–221, 2005.

[24] O. Kupferman and M.Y. Vardi. Safraless decision procedures. In *Proc. 46th FOCS*, pages 531–540, 2005.

[25] O. Kupferman, M.Y. Vardi, and P. Wolper. An automata-theoretic approach to branching-time model checking. *Journal of the ACM*, 47(2):312–360, March 2000.

[26] R.P. Kurshan. Complementing deterministic Büchi automata in polynomial time. *Journal of Computer and System Science*, 35:59–71, 1987.

[27] R.P. Kurshan. *Computer Aided Verification of Coordinating Processes*. Princeton Univ. Press, 1994.

[28] R. McNaughton. Testing and generating infinite sequences by a finite automaton. *I& C*, 9:521–530, 1966.

[29] A. R. Meyer. Weak monadic second order theory of successor is not elementary recursive. In *Proc. ICALP*, LNCS 453, pages 132–154, 1975.

[30] M. Michel. Complementation is more difficult with automata on infinite words. CNET, Paris, 1988.

[31] D.E. Muller and P.E. Schupp. Alternating automata on infinite trees. In *Automata on Infinite Words*, LNCS 192, pages 100–107, 1985.

[32] D.E. Muller and P.E. Schupp. Alternating automata on infinite trees. *Theoretical Computer Science*, 54:267–276, 1987.

[33] D.E. Muller and P.E. Schupp. Simulating alternating tree automata by nondeterministic automata: New results and new proofs of theorems of Rabin, McNaughton and Safra. *Theoretical Computer Science*, 141:69–107, 1995.

[34] N. Piterman. From nondeterministic Büchi and Streett automata to deterministic parity automata. In *25th LICS*, 2006.

[35] A. Pnueli and R. Rosner. On the synthesis of a reactive module. In *Proc. 16th POPL*, pages 179–190, 1989.

[36] M.O. Rabin. Decidability of second order theories and automata on infinite trees. *Trans. AMS*, 141:1–35, 1969.

[37] M.O. Rabin. Weakly definable relations and special automata. In *Proc. Symp. Math. Logic and Foundations of Set Theory*, pages 1–23, 1970.

[38] M.O. Rabin. Automata on infinite objects and Church's problem. *Amer. Mathematical Society*, 1972.

[39] R. Rosner. *Modular Synthesis of Reactive Systems*. PhD thesis, Weizmann Institute of Science, Rehovot, Israel, 1992.

[40] S. Safra. On the complexity of ω-automata. In *Proc. 29th FOCS*, pages 319–327, 1988.

[41] R. Sebastiani and S. Tonetta. "more deterministic" vs. "smaller" büchi automata for efficient ltl model checking. In *Proc. 12th CHARME*, LNCS 2860, pages 126–140, 2003.

[42] A.P. Sistla, M.Y. Vardi, and P. Wolper. The complementation problem for Büchi automata with applications to temporal logic. *Theoretical Computer Science*, 49:217–237, 1987.

[43] F. Somenzi and R. Bloem. Efficient Büchi automata from LTL formulae. In *Proc. 12th CAV*, LNCS 1855, pages 248–263, 2000.

[44] R.S. Street and E.A. Emerson. An elementary decision procedure for the μ-calculus. In *Proc. 11th ICALP*, LNCS 172, pages 465–472, 1984.

[45] R.S. Streett. Propositional dynamic logic of looping and converse. *Information and Control*, 54:121–141, 1982.

[46] S. Tasiran, R. Hojati, and R.K. Brayton. Language containment using non-deterministic omega-automata. In *Proc. 8th CHARME*, LNCS 987, pages 261–277, 1995.

[47] W. Thomas. Automata on infinite objects. *Handbook of Theoretical Computer Science*, pages 133–191, 1990.

[48] M.Y. Vardi. Reasoning about the past with two-way automata. In *Proc. 25th ICALP*, LNCS 1443, pages 628–641, 1998.

[49] M.Y. Vardi and P. Wolper. An automata-theoretic approach to automatic program verification. In *Proc. 1st LICS*, pages 332–344, 1986.

[50] M.Y. Vardi and P. Wolper. Automata-theoretic techniques for modal logics of programs. *Journal of Computer and System Science*, 32(2):182–221, April 1986.

[51] M.Y. Vardi and P. Wolper. Reasoning about infinite computations. *I& C*, 115(1):1–37, November 1994.

[52] G. Wang, A. Mishchenko, R. Brayton, and A. Sangiovanni-Vincentelli. Synthesizing FSMs according to co-Büchi properties. Technical report, UC Berkeley, 2005.

[53] P. Wolper. Temporal logic can be more expressive. *I& C*, 56(1–2):72–99, 1983.

[54] Q. Yan. Lower bounds for complementation of ω-automata via the full automata technique. In *Proc. 33rd ICALP*, LNCS 4052, pages 589–600, 2006.

Session 7:
Temporal Logics and Automata

From Nondeterministic Büchi and Streett Automata to Deterministic Parity Automata

Nir Piterman
Ecole Polytechnique Fédéral de Lausanne (EPFL)

Abstract

In this paper we revisit Safra's determinization constructions. We show how to construct deterministic automata with fewer states and, most importantly, parity acceptance conditions. Specifically, starting from a nondeterministic Büchi automaton with n states our construction yields a deterministic parity automaton with n^{2n+2} states and index $2n$ (instead of a Rabin automaton with $(12)^n n^{2n}$ states and n pairs). Starting from a nondeterministic Streett automaton with n states and k pairs our construction yields a deterministic parity automaton with $n^{n(k+2)+2}(k+1)^{2n(k+1)}$ states and index $2n(k+1)$ (instead of a Rabin automaton with $(12)^{n(k+1)}n^{n(k+2)}(k+1)^{2n(k+1)}$ states and $n(k+1)$ pairs). The parity condition is much simpler than the Rabin condition. In applications such as solving games and emptiness of tree automata handling the Rabin condition involves an additional multiplier of $n^2 n!$ (or $(n(k+1))^2(n(k+1))!$ in the case of Streett) which is saved using our construction.

1 Introduction

One of the fundamental questions in the theory of automata is determinism vs. nondeterminism. Another related question is the question of complementation. That is, given some machine (in some complexity class) can we produce a machine (in the same class) that accepts the complement language? The problems of determinization and complementation are strongly related. Indeed, if the machine is deterministic we just have to dualize its answer. If the machine is nondeterministic we do not have a simple solution.

In the theory of finite automata on finite words the relation between nondeterministic and deterministic automata is well understood. We know that there exists an efficient procedure that gets a nondeterministic automaton with n states and constructs a deterministic automaton with 2^n states accepting the same language [26]. This construction is also tight (cf. [8]). By dualizing the acceptance condition of the deterministic automaton we get an automaton for the complement language, which is again tight (cf. [8]).

In his proof that satisfiability of S1S is decidable, Büchi introduces nondeterministic automata on infinite words [2]. Büchi takes a 'normal' finite automaton and runs it on infinite words. A run of such an automaton is an infinite sequence of states, instead of a finite sequence. The set of states *recurring* infinitely often is used to define the acceptance condition. A run is accepting according to the *Büchi condition* if the set of recurring states intersects the set of accepting states.

In the case of finite automata on infinite words determinization and complementation are much more involved. Given a deterministic Büchi automaton one can easily construct a nondeterministic Büchi automaton for the complement language [17]. However, deterministic Büchi automata are not closed under complementation [18]. This forced the introduction of more complex acceptance conditions such as Rabin, Streett, and parity. A Rabin acceptance condition is a set of pairs of subsets of the states. A run is accepting according to a Rabin condition if there exists a pair $\langle E, F\rangle$ such that the set of recurring states does not intersect E but does intersect F. The Streett condition is the dual of Rabin. A run is accepting according to a Streett condition if for every pair $\langle E, F\rangle$ we have that if F intersects the set of recurring states so must E. A parity condition gives a priority to every state and a run is accepting if the minimal recurring priority is even. The number of priorities is the *index* of the parity condition. Rabin and Streett conditions are more general than parity in the following sense. A parity condition of index $2k$ can be written as a Rabin (or Streett) condition with k pairs (without modifying the structure of the automaton). A Rabin or Streett condition with k pairs is equivalent to a parity condition of index $2k+1$ using a gadget with $k^2k!$ states. All three conditions are strong enough to allow determinization [34].

In the case of automata on infinite words determinization and complementation are no longer so strongly coupled. Determinization can be used for complementation by dualizing the acceptance condition of the deterministic automaton. However, there are complementation constructions that are much simpler than determinization. Specifically, Büchi showed that the class of languages recognized by nondeterministic Büchi automata is closed under complement without determinization [2]. Sistla, Vardi, and Wolper suggested a single exponential complementation construction [33], however with a quadratic exponent. This was followed by a complementation construction by Klarlund [13] and a very elegant complementation via alternating automata by Kupferman and Vardi [15]. The latter construction was recently improved to give a complement automaton with at most $(0.96n)^n$ states [7], which is currently the best complementation construction. See also [34].

Determinization constructions for automata on infinite words followed a similar path[1]. McNaughton showed a determinization construction that is doubly exponential and results in an automaton with the Muller acceptance condition [20]. Safra gives a determinization construction which takes a nondeterministic Büchi automaton with n states and returns a deterministic Rabin automaton with at most $(12)^n n^{2n}$ states and n pairs [28]. An alternative determinization with a similar upper bound that also results in a deterministic Rabin automaton was given by Muller and Schupp [22]. Michel showed that this is essentially optimal and that the best possible upper bound for determinization and complementation is $n!$ [21, 19].

Safra's idea is to use a tree of subset constructions. The root of the tree is the classical subset construction for automata on finite words. In every transition, a node with set of states S spawns a new son that includes all the accepting states in S. Thus, all the states in a leaf are the endpoints of runs that agree (more or less) on the number of times they have visited the acceptance set. In order to keep the tree finite, we ensure that every state is followed in at most one branch of the tree, we keep the copy in the oldest branch. Furthermore, whenever all the states followed by some node have visited the acceptance set, the node is marked as accepting and all its descendants are removed. The Rabin acceptance condition associates a pair with every node in the tree. There should be some node that is erased from the tree at most finitely often and marked accepting infinitely often for a run to be accepting.

The fact that stronger acceptance conditions are introduced raises the question of determinization of automata using these conditions. Rabin and parity automata can be easily converted to Büchi automata. Given a Rabin automaton with n states and k pairs there exists an equivalent nondeterministic Büchi automaton with $n(k+1)$ states. Applying Safra's determinization on top of this automaton produces a deterministic Rabin automaton with $(12)^{n(k+1)}(n(k+1))^{2n(k+1)}$ states and $n(k+1)$ pairs. For Streett automata, going through nondeterministic Büchi automata is far from optimal. A nondeterministic Streett automaton with n states and k pairs can be converted to a nondeterministic Büchi automaton with $n2^k$ states [3], which is optimal [31]. Combining this conversion with the determinization results in a doubly exponential deterministic automaton. In order to handle Streett automata, Safra generalized his determinization construction [30]. Given a Streett automaton with n states and k pairs he constructs a Rabin automaton with $(nk)^{O(nk)}$ states and $O(nk)$ pairs. As Streett automata are more general than Büchi automata, the lower bound shows that this is essentially optimal.

We mentioned that the Rabin and Streett conditions are duals; the dual of the parity condition is parity again. Sometimes, given a nondeterministic automaton, we need to generate a deterministic automaton for the complementary language, a process called *co-determinization* (e.g., for converting alternating tree automata to nondeterministic tree automata). While complementing a deterministic automaton can be easily done by dualizing the acceptance condition, such a dualization for a Rabin or Streett automaton results in an automaton of the second type. Thus, co-determinization of a Büchi (or Streett) automaton results in a deterministic Streett automaton. Translating from Streett to Rabin or parity is exponential, we add a gadget with $k^2k!$ states where k is the number of pairs of the Streett condition [30]. The translation of Rabin to Streett or parity is dual and has exactly the same complexity.

Determinization has many uses other than complementation. Indeed, Rabin uses McNaughton's determinization of Büchi automata to complement nondeterministic Rabin tree automata [25].[2] A node in an infinite tree belongs to infinitely many branches. A tree automaton has to choose states that handle all branches in a single run. In many cases, we want all branches of the tree to belong to some word language. If we have a deterministic automaton for this word language, we run it in all directions simultaneously. This kind of reasoning enables conversion of alternating tree automata to nondeterministic tree automata and complementation of nondeterministic tree automata (cf. [25, 34, 35]).

Deterministic automata are used also for solving games and synthesizing strategies. In the context of games, the opponent may be able to choose between different options. Using a deterministic automaton we can follow the game step by step and monitor the goal of the game. For example, in order to solve a game in which the goal is an LTL formula, one first converts the LTL formula to a deterministic automaton and then solves the resulting Rabin game [24] (cf. [14, 4]). Using Safra's determinization, reasoning about tree automata reduces to reasoning about nondeter-

[1] Incidentally, both determinization constructions provided the best upper bound for complementation at the time of their introduction.

[2] Rabin uses this complementation in order to prove that satisfiability of S2S is decidable [25]. This is essentially the same use that Büchi had for the complementation of Büchi automata. In the context of tree automata one has to use a more general acceptance condition.

ministic Rabin tree automata and reasoning about general games reduces to reasoning about Rabin games. Some of these applications use co-determinization, the deterministic automaton for the complementary language.

In this paper we revisit Safra's determinization constructions. We show that we can further compact the tree structure used by Safra to get a smaller representation of the deterministic automata. By using dynamic node names instead of the static names used by Safra we can construct directly a deterministic parity automaton. Specifically, starting from a nondeterministic Büchi automaton with n states, we end up with a deterministic parity automaton with n^{2n+2} states and index $2n$ (instead of Rabin automaton with $(12)^n n^{2n}$ states and n pairs). Starting from a Streett automaton with n states and index k, we end up with a deterministic parity automaton with $n^{n(k+2)+2}(k+1)^{2n(k+1)}$ states and index $2n(k+1)$ (instead of Rabin automaton with $(12)^{n(k+1)}n^{n(k+2)}(k+1)^{2n(k+1)}$ states and $n(k+1)$ pairs). For both constructions, complementation is done by considering the same automaton with a dual parity condition.

Though dividing the number of states by 12^n is not negligible, the main importance of our result is in the fact that the resulting automaton is a parity automaton instead of Rabin. Solving Rabin games (equivalently, emptiness of nondeterministic Rabin tree automata) is NP-complete in the number of pairs [6]. Solution of parity games is in NP∩co-NP. The current best upper bound for solving Rabin games is $mn^{k+1}k!$ where m is the number of transitions, n the number of states, and k the number of pairs [23]. Using our determinization construction instead of reasoning about Rabin conditions we can consider parity conditions. The best upper bound for solving parity games is $mn^{k/2}$ [10] (cf. [1, 11] for other solutions). That is, we save a multiplier of at least $kk!$.

The gain by using our determinization is even greater when we consider applications that use co-determinization. As Streett is the dual of Rabin it follows that solving Streett games is co-NP-complete. Even if we ignore the computational difficulty, the Rabin acceptance condition at least allows using memoryless strategies. That is, when reasoning about Rabin games (or Rabin tree automata) the way to resolve nondeterminism relies solely on the current location. This is not the case for Streett. In order to solve Streett games we require exponential memory [5, 9]. Applications like nondeterminization of alternating tree automata use co-determinization but require the result to be a Rabin or parity automaton. Hence, the resulting deterministic Streett automaton has to be converted to a parity automaton. Again, the price tag of this conversion is a blowup of $k^2k!$ where k is the number of pairs. As the complexity of reasoning about parity games is $mn^{k/2}$, the extra multiplier grows to $(k^2k!)^k$.

Recently, Kupferman and Vardi showed that they can check the emptiness of an alternating parity tree automaton without directly using Safra's determinization [16]. Their construction can be used for many game / tree automata applications that require determinization. However, Kupferman and Vardi use Safra's determinization to get a bound on the size of the minimal model of the alternating tree automaton. Given such a bound, they can check emptiness by restricting the search to small models. Our improved construction implies that the complexity of their algorithm reduces from $(12)^{n^2}n^{4n^2+2n}(n!)^{2n}$ to n^{4n^2+2n}.

2 Nondeterministic Automata

Given a finite set Σ, a *word* over Σ is a finite or infinite sequence of symbols from Σ. We denote by Σ^* the set of finite sequences over Σ and by Σ^ω the set of infinite sequences over Σ. Given a word $w = \sigma_0\sigma_1\sigma_2\cdots \in \Sigma^* \cup \Sigma^\omega$, we denote by $w[i,j]$ the word $\sigma_i \cdots \sigma_j$.

A *nondeterministic automaton* is $N = \langle \Sigma, S, \delta, s_0, F\rangle$, where Σ is a finite alphabet, S is a finite set of states, $\delta : S \times \Sigma \rightarrow 2^S$ is a transition function, $s_0 \in S$ is an initial state, and F is an acceptance condition to be defined below. A *run* of N on a word $w = w_0w_1\cdots$ is an infinite sequence of states $s_0s_1\cdots \in S^\omega$ such that s_0 is the initial state and forall $j \geq 0$ we have $s_{j+1} \in \delta(s_j, w_j)$. For a run $r = s_0s_1\cdots$, let $inf(r) = \{s \in S \mid s = s_i \text{ for infinitely many } i\text{'s}\}$ be the set of all states occurring infinitely often in the run. We consider four acceptance conditions. A *Rabin* condition F is a set of pairs $\{\langle E_1, F_1\rangle, \ldots, \langle E_k, F_k\rangle\}$ where forall i we have $E_i \subseteq S$ and $F_i \subseteq S$. We call k the *index* of the Rabin condition. A run is *accepting* according to the Rabin condition F if there exists some i such that $inf(r) \cap E_i = \emptyset$ and $inf(r) \cap F_i \neq \emptyset$. That is, the run visits finitely often states from E_i and infinitely often states from F_i. The *Streett* condition is the dual of the Rabin condition. Formally, a *Streett* condition F is also a set of pairs $\{\langle R_1, G_1\rangle, \ldots, \langle R_k, G_k\rangle\}$ where forall i we have $R_i \subseteq S$ and $G_i \subseteq S$. We call k the *index* of the Streett condition. A run is *accepting* according to the Streett condition F if for every i either $inf(r) \cap G_i = \emptyset$ or $inf(r) \cap R_i \neq \emptyset$. That is, the run either visits G_i finitely often or visits R_i infinitely often. As a convention for pairs in a Rabin condition we use E and F and for pairs in a Streett condition we use R and G. A *parity* condition F is a partition $\{F_0, \ldots, F_k\}$ of S. We call k the *index* of the parity condition. A run is *accepting* according to the parity condition F if for some even i we have $inf(r) \cap F_i \neq \emptyset$ and forall $i' < i$ we have $inf(r) \cap F_{i'} = \emptyset$. A *Büchi* condition F is a subset of S. A run is *accepting* according to the Büchi condition F if $inf(r) \cap F \neq \emptyset$. That is, the run visits infinitely often states from F. A word w is *accepted* by N if there exists some accepting run of N over w. The *language* of N is the set of words accepted by N. Formally, $L(N) = \{w \mid w \text{ is accepted by } N\}$. Two automata are *equivalent* if they accept the same language.

Given a set of states $S' \subseteq S$ and a letter $\sigma \in \Sigma$, we denote by $\delta(S', \sigma)$ the set $\bigcup_{s \in S'} \delta(s, \sigma)$. Similarly, for a word $w \in \Sigma^*$ we define $\delta(S', w)$ in the natural way: $\delta(S', \epsilon) = S'$ and $\delta(S', w\sigma) = \delta(\delta(S', w), \sigma)$. For two states s and t and $w \in \Sigma^*$, we say that t is *reachable from* s *reading* w if $t \in \delta(\{s\}, w)$.

An automaton is *deterministic* if for every state $s \in S$ and letter $\sigma \in \Sigma$ we have $|\delta(s, \sigma)| = 1$. In that case we write $\delta : S \times \Sigma \to S$.

We use acronyms in $\{N, D\} \times \{R, S, P, B\} \times \{W\}$ to denote automata. The first symbol stands for the branching mode of the automaton: N for nondeterministic and D for deterministic. The second symbol stands for the acceptance condition of the automaton: R for Rabin, S for Streett, P for parity, and B for Büchi. The last symbol stands for the object the automaton is reading, in our case W for words. For example, a DRW is a deterministic Rabin word automaton and a NBW is a nondeterministic Büchi word automaton.

3 Determinization of Büchi Automata

In this section we give a short exposition of Safra's determinization [28] and show how to improve it. We replace the constant node names with dynamic names, which allow us to simulate the *index appearance record* construction within the deterministic automaton. We get a deterministic automaton with fewer states and in addition a parity automaton instead of Rabin.

3.1 Safra's Construction

Here we describe Safra's determinization construction [28, 29]. The construction takes an NBW and constructs an equivalent DRW. Safra constructs a tree of subset constructions. Every node in the tree is labeled by the states it follows. The labels of siblings are disjoint and the label of a node is a strict superset of the labels of its descendants. The sons are ordered according to their age. The transition of a tree replaces the label of every node by the set of possible successors. If the label now includes some accepting states, we add a new son to the node with all these accepting states. Intuitively, the states that label the sons of a node have already visited an accepting state. Thus, the states in the label of a node that are not in the labels of its descendants are states that still owe a visit to the acceptance set. We move states occurring in more than one node to older siblings. If the label of a node becomes equal to the union of labels of its descendants then we mark this node as accepting and remove all its descendants. If some node remains eventually always in the tree and is marked accepting infinitely often, the run is accepting. Formally, we have the following.

Let $\mathcal{N} = \langle \Sigma, S, \delta, s_0, \mathcal{F} \rangle$ be an NBW with $|S| = n$. Let $V = [n]$. We first define Safra trees.

A *Safra tree* t over S is $\langle N, r, p, \psi, l, E, F \rangle$ where the components of t are as follows.

- $N \subseteq V$ is a set of nodes.
- $r \in N$ is the root node.
- $p : N \to N$ is the parent function defined over $N - \{r\}$, defining for every $v \in N - \{r\}$ its parent $p(v)$.
- ψ is a partial order defining "older than" on siblings (i.e., children of the same node).
- $l : N \to 2^S$ is a labeling of the nodes with subsets of S. The label of every node is a proper superset of the union of the labels of its sons. The labels of two siblings are disjoint.
- $E, F \subseteq V$ are two disjoint subsets of V. They are used to define the Rabin acceptance condition.

The following claim is proven in [28, 29, 12, 16].

Claim 3.1 *The number of nodes in a Safra tree is at most* n. *The number of Safra trees over* $\mathcal{N}$ *is not more than* $(12)^n n^{2n}$.

Proof: As the labels of siblings are disjoint and the union of labels of children is a proper subset of the label of the parent it follows that every node is the minimal (according to the subset order on the labels) to contain (at least) some state $s \in S$. It follows that there are at most n nodes.

The number of ordered trees on n nodes is the $n-1$th Catalan number. We know that $Cat(n) = \frac{(2n)!}{n!(n+1)!}$ and $Cat(n-1) \leq 4^n$. We represent the naming of nodes by $f : [n] \to [n]$ that associates the ith node with its name $f(i)$. There are at most n^n such functions. The labeling function is $l : S \to [n]$ where $l(s) = i$ means that s belongs to the ith node and all its ancestors. Finally, we represent E and F by a function $a : V \to \{0, 1, 2\}$ such that $a(i) = 0$ means that $i \notin E \cup F$, $a(i) = 1$ means that $i \in E$, and $a(i) = 2$ means that $i \in F$. There are at most 3^n such functions.

To summarize, the number of trees is at most $4^n \cdot 3^n \cdot n^n \cdot n^n = (12)^n n^{2n}$. □

We construct the DRW $\mathcal{D}$ equivalent to $\mathcal{N}$. Let $\mathcal{D} = \langle \Sigma, D, \rho, d_0, \mathcal{F}' \rangle$ where the components of $\mathcal{D}$ are as follows.

- D is the set of Safra trees over S. For a state $d \in D$ we denote by a d subscript the components of d. For example, N_d is the set of nodes of d and l_d is the labeling of d.
- d_0 is the tree with a single node 1 labeled by $\{s_0\}$ where E is $V - \{1\}$ and F is the empty set.
- Let $\mathcal{F}' = \{\langle E_1, F_1 \rangle, \ldots, \langle E_n, F_n \rangle\}$ be the Rabin acceptance condition where $E_i = \{d \in D \mid i \in E_d\}$ and $F_i = \{d \in D \mid i \in F_d\}$.

- For every tree $d \in D$ and letter $\sigma \in \Sigma$ the transition $d' = \rho(d, \sigma)$ is the result of the following transformations on d. We use temporarily the set of names V' disjoint from V.
  1. For every node v with label S' replace S' by $\delta(S', \sigma)$ and set E and F to the empty set.
  2. For every node v with label S' such that $S' \cap \mathcal{F} \neq \emptyset$, create a new node $v' \in V'$ which becomes the youngest child of v. Set its label to be $S' \cap \mathcal{F}$.
  3. For every node v with label S' and state $s \in S'$ such that s also belongs to the label of an older sibling v' of v, remove s from the label of v and all its descendants.
  4. Remove all nodes with empty labels.
  5. For every node v whose label is equal to the union of the labels of its children, remove all descendants of v. Add v to F.
  6. Add all unused names to E.
  7. Change the nodes in V' to nodes in V.

Theorem 3.2 [28] $L(\mathcal{D}) = L(\mathcal{N})$.

For other expositions of this determinization we refer the reader to [12, 19, 27].

3.2 From NBW to DPW

We now present our construction. Intuitively, we take Safra's construction and replace the constant node name with a dynamic one that decreases as nodes below it get erased from the tree (called number below). Using the new names we can give up the "older than" relation. The smaller the name of a node, the older it is. Furthermore, the names give a natural parity order on good and bad events. Erasing a node is a bad event (which forces all nodes with greater name to change their name). Finding that the label of some name is equal to the union of labels of its descendants is a good event. The key observation is that a node can change its name at most a finite number of times without being erased. It follows, that the names of all nodes that stay eventually in the tree get constant. Thus, bad events happen eventually only to nodes that get erased from the tree. Then we can monitor good events that happen to the nodes with constant names and insist that they happen infinitely often. Formally, we have the following.

Let $\mathcal{N} = \langle \Sigma, S, \delta, s_0, \mathcal{F} \rangle$ be an NBW with $|S| = n$. For the sake of the proof we would like to treat the nodes as entities. Hence, we distinguish between the set of nodes $V = [2n]$ of a tree and their numbers that may change and range over $[n]$. All important information (tree structure, label) can be associated with the numbers and in practice the names are not needed.

A *compact Safra tree* t over S is $\langle N, M, 1, p, l, e, f \rangle$ where the components of t are as follows.

- $N \subseteq V$ is a set of nodes.
- $M : N \to [n]$ is the numbering function.
- $1 \in N$ such that $M(1) = 1$ is the root node.
- $p : N \to N$ is the parent function.
- $l : N \to 2^S$ is a labeling of the nodes with subsets of S. The label of every node is a proper superset of the union of the labels of its sons. The labels of two siblings are disjoint.
- $e, f \in [n+1]$ are used to define the parity acceptance condition. The number e is used to memorize the minimal node that changed its name and f the minimal node that is equivalent to its descendants.

Notice that we give up the "older than" relation and replace the sets E and F by numbers e and f. We require that the numbering M is a bijection from N to $[|N|]$. That is, the numbers of the nodes in N are consecutive starting from the root, which is numbered 1.

The following claim is proven much like the similar proof for Safra trees.

Claim 3.3 *The number of compact Safra trees over S is not more than n^{2n+2}.*

Proof: Just like Safra trees there are at most n nodes. We use only the numbers of the nodes. The parenthood relation is represented by a function $p : [n] \to [n]$. As in Safra trees, every node has at least one unique state in S that belongs to it. We add the function $l : S \to [n]$ that associates a state with the minimal node (according to the descendant order in the tree) to which it belongs. Finally, there are n options for e and f each. It follows that there are at most $n \cdot n \cdot n^n \cdot n^n = n^{2n+2}$ different compact Safra trees.[3] □

We construct the DPW $\mathcal{D}$ equivalent to $\mathcal{N}$. Let $\mathcal{D} = \langle \Sigma, D, \rho, d_0, \mathcal{F}' \rangle$ where the components of $\mathcal{D}$ are as follows.

- D is the set of compact Safra trees over S.
- d_0 is the tree with a single node 1 labeled $\{s_0\}$ and numbered 1 where $e = 2$ and $f = 1$.
- The parity acceptance condition $\mathcal{F}' = \langle F_0, \ldots, F_{2n-1} \rangle$ is defined as follows.
  - $F_0 = \{d \in D \mid f = 1\}$
  - $F_{2i+1} = \{d \in D \mid e = i + 2 \text{ and } f \geq e\}$
  - $F_{2i+2} = \{d \in D \mid f = i + 2 \text{ and } e > f\}$

  Note that we do not consider the case $e = 1$. In this case the label of the root is empty. This is a rejecting sink state.[4]

[3] We note that there is much order in the numbering of the nodes which we have not used to reduce the number of states. We know that the numbers respect the parenthood relation. If we add order to the sons of a node (which practically comes for free: the number of ordered trees on n nodes is 4^n and the number of unordered trees is 3^n) then the numbers respect this order as well.

[4] We note that the information contained in e, f is used solely to define the parity condition. Thus, instead of maintaining both e and f ($(n+1)^2$ options) we could maintain the result of the analysis using one value

- For every tree $d \in D$ and letter $\sigma \in \Sigma$ the transition $d' = \rho(d, \sigma)$ is the result of the following transformations on d.
  1. For every node v with label S' replace S' by $\delta(S', \sigma)$.
  2. For every node v with label S' such that $S' \cap \mathcal{F} \neq \emptyset$, create a new son $v' \notin N$ of v. Set its label to $S' \cap \mathcal{F}$. Set its number to the minimal value greater than all used numbers. We may have to use temporarily numbers in the range $[(n+1)..(2n)]$.
  3. For every node v with label S' and state $s \in S'$ such that s belongs also to some sibling v' of v such that $M(v') < M(v)$, remove s from the label of v and all its descendants.
  4. For every node v whose label is equal to the union of the labels of its children, remove all descendants of v. Call such nodes *green*. Set f to the minimum of $n+1$ and the numbers from green nodes. Notice that all nodes in $[(n+1)..(2n)]$ cannot be green.
  5. Remove all nodes with empty labels. Set e to the minimum of $n+1$ and the numbers from nodes removed during all stages of the transformation. Notice that by the definition of the parity condition, a green node that is removed does not lead to visits in even priorities.
  6. Let Z denote the set of nodes removed during all previous stages of the transformation. For every node v let $rem(v)$ be $|\{v' \in Z \mid M(v') < M(v)\}|$. That is, we count how many nodes are removed during the transformation and have smaller number than the number of v. For every node v such that $l(v) \neq \emptyset$ we change the number of v to $M(v) - rem(v)$. It is simple to see that the resulting numbers are consecutive again and in the range $[n]$.[5]

We show that the two automata are equivalent. The proof is an adaptation of Safra's proof [28].

Theorem 3.4 $L(\mathcal{D}) = L(\mathcal{N})$.

Proof: Consider $w \in L(\mathcal{N})$. We have to show $w \in L(\mathcal{D})$. Let $r = s_0 s_1 \cdots$ be an accepting run of $\mathcal{N}$ on w. Let $r' = d_0 d_1 \cdots$ be the run of $\mathcal{D}$ on w and let $d_i = \langle N_i, M_i, 1, p_i, l_i, e_i, f_i \rangle$. It is simple to see that forall $i \geq 0$ we have $s_i \in l_i(1)$. If step 4 is applied infinitely often to node 1 (equivalently, $f = 1$ infinitely often, or during the transformation of the trees the label of 1 equals the labels of its sons) then r' visits F_0 infinitely often.

Otherwise, from some point onwards in r' we have step 4 is not applied to node 1. Let j_1 be this point. There exists a point $j' > j_1$ such that $s_{j'} \in \mathcal{F}$. It follows that forall $j > j'$ we have s_j belongs to some son v_1 of 1. Notice, that just like in Safra's case, the run r may start in some son of 1 and move to a son with a smaller number. However, this can happen finitely often and hence we treat v_1 as constant. The number $M(v_1)$ may decrease finitely often until it is constant. Let o_1 be such that forall $o > o_1$ we have $a_1 = M_o(v_1)$. As $M_o(v_1) = a_1$ forall $o > o_1$ it follows that $e_o > a_1$ forall $o > o_1$.

Suppose that step 4 is applied to v_1 infinitely often (equivalently, $f \leq a_1$ infinitely often). It follows that for every odd $p < 2a_1 - 2$ we have F_p is visited finitely often and either F_{2a_1-2} is visited infinitely often or there exists some even $p' < 2a_1 - 2$ such that $F_{p'}$ is visited infinitely often. In this case $\mathcal{D}$ accepts w.

Otherwise, step 4 is applied to v_1 finitely often. We construct by induction a sequence $v_1, \ldots, v_k$ such that eventually $v_1, \ldots, v_k$ do not change their numbers and r belongs to all of them. As the number of active nodes in a tree (nodes v such that $l(v) \neq \emptyset$) is bounded by n we can repeat the process only finitely often. Hence, w is accepted by $\mathcal{D}$.

In the other direction, consider $w \in L(\mathcal{D})$. Let $r' = d_0 d_1 \cdots$ be the accepting run of $\mathcal{D}$ on w where $d_i = \langle N_i, M_i, 1, p_i, l_i, f_i, e_i \rangle$. Let F_{2b} be the minimal set to be visited infinitely often. It follows that eventually always $e_i > b + 1$ and infinitely often $f_i = b + 1$.

We first prove two claims.

Claim 3.5 *For every $i \in \mathbb{N}$, $j \in [n]$, and every state $s \in l_i(j)$ we have s is reachable from s_0 reading $w[0, i-1]$.*

Proof: We prove the claim for all $j \geq 1$ by induction on i. Clearly, it holds for $i = 0$. Suppose that it holds for i. As $l_{i+1}(j) \subseteq \delta(l_i(j'), w_i)$ for some j' it follows that every state in $l_{i+1}(j)$ is reachable from s_0 reading $w[0, i]$. □

Claim 3.6 *Consider $i, i' \in \mathbb{N}$ such that $i < i'$, $d_i, d_{i'} \in F_{2j}$ for some j, and forall $j' \leq 2j$ and forall $i < a < i'$ we have $d_a \notin F_{j'}$. Then there exists a node v such that $M_a(v) = j + 1$ forall $i \leq a \leq i'$ and every state s in $l_{i'}(v)$ is reachable from some state in $l_i(v)$ reading $w[i, i' - 1]$ with a run that visits $\mathcal{F}$.*

Proof: There exists some node v such that $M_i(v) = j + 1$ (as $d_i \in F_{2j}$). By assumption, for every $j' < 2j$ the set $F_{j'}$ is not visited between i and i'. Hence, for every node v' such that $M_i(v) \leq j + 1$ we have that $M_a(v') = M_i(v')$ forall $i \leq a \leq i'$. That is, between i and i' all nodes whose

ranging between 0 and $2n-1$ ($2n$ options). This would reduce the number of states to $2n^{2n+1}$.

[5]Suppose that two nodes are numbered $p' > p$ before the number change and p'' after the number change. This implies that $p - p''$ nodes with number smaller than p are removed and $p' - p''$ nodes with number smaller than p' are removed. Thus, the number of nodes removed whose number is between p and p' is $p' - p$, which implies that the node numbered p itself is removed.

number is at most $j + 1$ do not change their numbers. In particular, forall $i \leq a \leq i'$ we have $M_a(v) = j + 1$. If $i' = i + 1$ then all the states in $l_{i'}(v)$ are in $\mathcal{F}$ and we are done. Otherwise, $i' > i + 1$. We show that for every $i \leq a < i'$ and every descendant v' of v, every state in $l_a(v')$ is reachable from some state in $l_i(v)$ along a run visiting $\mathcal{F}$. As v is a leaf in d_i for $a = i$ this is obviously true. Suppose it is true for a and prove for $a + 1$. We know that for every descendant v' of v either $l_{a+1}(v') \subseteq \delta(l_a(v), w_a) \cap \mathcal{F}$ or for some descendant v'' of v we have $l_{a+1}(v') \subseteq \delta(l_a(v''), w_a)$ (v'' may be v'). As during the transformation from $d_{i'-1}$ to $d_{i'}$ the label $l_{i'}(v)$ equals the union of labels of sons of v the claim follows. □

We construct an infinite tree with finite branching degree. The root of the tree corresponds to the initial state of $\mathcal{N}$. Every node in the tree is labeled by some state of $\mathcal{N}$ and a time stamp i. An edge between the nodes labeled (s, i) and (t, j) corresponds to a run starting in s, ending in t, reading $w[i, j - 1]$, and visiting $\mathcal{F}$. From König's lemma this tree contains an infinite branch. The composition of all the run segments in this infinite branch is an infinite accepting run of $\mathcal{N}$ on w.

Let $(s_0, 0)$ label the root of T. Let i_0 be the maximal location such that forall $j < 2b$ the set F_j is not visited after i_0. Let v be the node such that forall $i > i_0$ we have $M_i(v) = b + 1$. Let i_1 be the minimal location such that $i_1 > i_0$ and $f_{i_1} = b + 1$ (that is step 4 was applied to v). For every state s in $l_{i_1}(v)$ we add a node to T, label it by (s, i_1) and connect it to the root. We extend the tree by induction. We have a tree with leafs labeled by the states in $l_a(v)$ stamped by time a, and $f_a = b+1$ (step 4 was applied to v). That is, for every state s in $l_a(v)$ there exists a leaf labeled (s, a). We know that F_{2b} is visited infinitely often. Hence, there exists $a' > a$ such that $f_{a'} = b + 1$ (step 4 is applied to v). For every state s' in $l_{a'}(v)$ we add a node to T and label it (s', a'). From Claim 3.6 there exists a state s in $l_a(v)$ such that s' is reachable from s reading $w[a, a' - 1]$ with a run that visits $\mathcal{F}$. We connect (s', a') to (s, a).

From Claim 3.5 it follows that every edge $(s_0, 0), (s', i')$ corresponds to some run starting in s_0, ending in s', and reading $w[0, i' - 1]$. From Claim 3.6, every other edge in the tree $(s, a), (s', a')$ corresponds to some run starting in s, ending in s', reading $w[a, a' - 1]$, and visiting $\mathcal{F}$. From König's lemma there exists an infinite branch in the tree. This infinite branch corresponds to an accepting run of $\mathcal{N}$ on w. □

Theorem 3.7 *For every NBW $\mathcal{N}$ with n states there exists a DPW $\mathcal{D}$ with n^{2n+2} states and index $2n$ such that $L(\mathcal{D}) = L(\mathcal{N})$.*

We note that this improves Safra's construction in two ways. First, we reduce the number of states from $(12)^n n^{2n}$ to n^{2n+2}. Second, our automaton is a parity automaton which is amenable to simpler algorithms. Many times we are interested in a deterministic automaton for the complement language, a process called co-determinization. The natural complement of a DRW is a DSW. However,the Streett acceptance condition is less convenient in many applications (due to the fact that Streett acceptance conditions require memory). Thus, the complement automaton is usually converted to a DPW using the IAR construction [30]. In such a case, one would have to multiply the number of states by $k^2k!$ where k is the number of Rabin pairs. A similar effect occurs when using deterministic automata in the context of games. Solution of Rabin games incurs an additional multiplier of $k^2k!$. Obviously, with our construction this penalty is avoided.

4 Determinization of Streett Automata

In this section we give a short exposition of Safra's determinization of Streett automata [30] and show how to improve it. Again, we replace the constant node names with dynamic names. We get a deterministic automaton with fewer states and in addition a parity automaton instead of Rabin. The intuition is similar to the construction in Section 3.

4.1 Safra's Construction

Here we describe Safra's determinization for Streett Automata [30]. The construction takes an NSW and constructs an equivalent DRW.

As mentioned, in the case of Streett automata, determinization via conversion to Büchi automata is less than optimal. Safra generalizes his construction to work for Streett automata. The idea is still to use a set of subset constructions. Let $\mathcal{S} = \langle \Sigma, S, \delta, s_0, \mathcal{F} \rangle$ be an NSW where $\mathcal{F} = \{\langle R_1, G_1 \rangle, \ldots, \langle R_k, G_k \rangle\}$. We say that a run r of $\mathcal{S}$ is accepting according to the *witness set* $J \subseteq [k]$ if for every $j \in J$ we have $inf(r) \cap R_j \neq \emptyset$ and for every $j \notin J$ we have $inf(r) \cap G_j = \emptyset$. It is easy to construct an NBW whose language is all words accepted according to witness set J. The NBW has two parts. In the first part it waits until all visits to G_j for $j \notin J$ have occurred. Then it moves nondeterministically to the second part where it waits for visits to R_j foreach $j \in J$ according to their order and disallows visits to G_j for every $j \notin J$. If the automaton loops through all $j \in J$ infinitely often the run is accepting. Unfortunately, the number of possible witness sets is exponential.

Safra's construction arranges all possible runs of the NSW and all relevant witness sets in a tree structure. A state is again a tree of subset constructions. Every node in a tree represents a process that is monitoring some witness set and checking this witness set. The node for witness set

J follows some set of states. It waits for visits to R_j for every $j \in J$ (in descending order), if this happens without visiting G_j for $j \notin J$ then the node succeeds and starts all over again.

A *Streett Safra tree* is a tree whose nodes are labeled by subsets of the states in S. The labels of siblings are disjoint and the labels of sons form a partition of the label of the parent. In addition every node is annotated by a subset $J \subseteq [k]$. The annotation of a son misses at most one element from the annotation of the parent. Every node that is not a leaf has at least one son whose annotation is a strict subset. In addition, children are ordered according to their age.

The root node monitors the set $[k]$ as a possible witness set. If some node is annotated with J and has a child annotated $J - \{j\}$ this means that the child has given up on the hope that R_j will occur. If a node has given up on R_j but visits G_j then the states visiting G_j have no place in this node and they are moved to a new sibling. Similarly, if a node has given up on R_j and visits R_j then the states visiting R_j have no place in this node and they are moved to a new sibling. Whenever the label of a node gets empty it is removed from the tree. If all the states followed by a node completed a cycle through its witness set, all the descendants of this node are removed and it is marked accepting. The Rabin condition associates a pair with every node. A run is accepting if some node is erased finitely often and marked accepting infinitely often. Formally, we have the following.

Let $\mathcal{S} = \langle \Sigma, S, \delta, s_0, \mathcal{F} \rangle$ be an NSW where $\mathcal{F} = \{\langle R_1, G_1 \rangle, \ldots, \langle R_k, G_k \rangle\}$ and $|S| = n$. Let $m = n(k+1)$ and $V = [m]$. We first define Streett Safra trees.

A *Streett Safra tree* t over S is $\langle N, r, p, \psi, l, h, E, F \rangle$ where the components of t are as follows.

- $N \subseteq V$ is the set of nodes.
- $r \in N$ is the root node.
- $p : N \to N$ is the parent function defined over $N - \{r\}$, defining for every $v \in N - \{r\}$ its parent $p(v)$.
- ψ is a partial order defining "older than" on siblings (i.e., children of the same node).
- $l : N \to 2^S$ is a labeling of nodes with subsets of S. The label of every node is equal to the union of the labels of its sons. The labels of two siblings are disjoint.
- $h : N \to 2^{[k]}$ annotates every node with a set of indices from $[k]$. The root is annotated by $[k]$. The annotation of every node is contained in that of its parent and it misses at most one element from the annotation of the parent. Every node that is not a leaf has at least one son with strictly smaller annotation.
- $E, F \subseteq V$ are two disjoint subsets of V. They are used to define the Rabin acceptance condition.

The following claim is proven in [30, 32].

Claim 4.1 *The number of nodes in a Streett Safra tree is at most $n(k+1)$. The number of Streett Safra trees over S is at most $(12)^{n(k+1)} n^{n(k+2)} (k+1)^{2n(k+1)}$.*

We construct the DRW $\mathcal{D}$ equivalent to $\mathcal{S}$. Let $\mathcal{D} = \langle \Sigma, D, \rho, d_0, \mathcal{F}' \rangle$ where the components of $\mathcal{D}$ are as follows.

- D is the set of Streett Safra trees over S.
- d_0 is the tree with a single node 1 labeled by $\{s_0\}$ where E is $V - \{1\}$ and F is the empty set.
- Let $\mathcal{F}' = \{\langle E_1, F_1 \rangle, \ldots, \langle E_m, F_m \rangle\}$ be the Rabin acceptance condition where $E_i = \{d \in D \mid i \in E_d\}$ and $F_i = \{d \in D \mid i \in F_d\}$.
- For every tree $d \in D$ and letter $\sigma \in \Sigma$ the transition $d' = \rho(d, \sigma)$ is the result of the following (recursive) transformation applied on d starting from the root. Before we start, we set E and F to the empty set and replace the label of every node v by $\delta(l(v), \sigma)$. We use temporarily the set of names V' disjoint from V.
  1. If v is a leaf such that $h(v) = \emptyset$ stop.
  2. If v is a leaf such that $h(v) \neq \emptyset$, add to v a new youngest son $v' \in V'$. Set $l(v') = l(v)$ and $h(v') = h(v) - \{max(h(v))\}$.
  3. Let $v_1, \ldots, v_l$ be the sons of v (ordered from oldest to youngest) and let $j_1, \ldots, j_l$ be the indices such that $j_i \in h(v) - h(v_i)$ (note that $|h(v) - h(v_i)| \leq 1$; in case that $h(v) = h(v_i)$ we have $j_i = 0$). Apply the procedure recursively on $v_1, \ldots, v_l$ (including sons created in step 2 above).
     For every son v_i and every state $s \in l(v_i)$ do the following.
     (a) If $s \in R_{j_i}$, remove s from the label of v_i and all its descendants. Add a new youngest son $v' \in V'$ to v. Set $l(v') = \{s\}$ and $h(v') = h(v) - \{max(\{0\} \cup (h(v) \cap \{1, \ldots, j_i - 1\}))\}$.
     (b) If $s \in G_{j_i}$, remove s from the label of v_i and all its descendants. Add a new youngest son $v' \in V'$ to v. Set $l(v') = \{s\}$ and $h(v') = h(v) - \{j_i\}$.[6]
  4. If a state s appears in $l(v_i)$ and $l(v_{i'})$ and $j_i < j_{i'}$ then remove s from the label of $v_{i'}$ and all its descendants.
  5. If a state s appears in $l(v_i)$ and $l(v_{i'})$ and $j_i = j_{i'}$ then remove s from the label of the younger sibling and all its descendants.
  6. Remove sons with empty label.

[6]We note that in Safra's original construction [30, 32] the rank of the new node is set to $h(v') = h(v) - \{max(h(v))\}$. In case that both G_{j_i} and R_{j_i} are visited infinitely often this may lead to the following situation. Suppose that the node v has a son v' that is waiting for a visit to R_{j_i} where j_i is not the maximum in $h(v)$. In the case that G_{j_i} is visited, the runs are moved to new siblings that await $max(h(v))$ again. This way, the run may cycle infinitely often between $max(h(v))$ and j_i, leading to incompleteness of the construction.

7. If all sons are annotated by $h(v)$ remove all the sons and all their descendants. Add v to F.

Finally, we add all unused names to E, remove unused names from F, and change the nodes in V' to nodes in V.

Theorem 4.2 [30] $L(\mathcal{D}) = L(\mathcal{N})$.

For other expositions of this determinization we refer the reader to [12, 32].

4.2 From NSW to DPW

We now present our construction. Let $\mathcal{S} = \langle \Sigma, S, \delta, s_0, \mathcal{F} \rangle$ be an NSW where $\mathcal{F} = \{\langle R_1, G_1 \rangle, \ldots, \langle R_k, G_k \rangle\}$ and $|S| = n$. Denote $m = n(k+1)$. For the sake of the proof, we distinguish between the set of nodes $V = [2m]$ of a tree and their numbers that range over $[m]$. All important information (tree structure, label) can be associated with the numbers and in practice names are not needed.

A *compact Streett Safra tree* t over S is $\langle N, M, 1, p, l, h, e, f \rangle$ where the components of t are as follows.

- $N \subseteq V$ is a set of nodes.
- $M : N \to [m]$ is the numbering function.
- $1 \in N$ such that $M(1) = 1$ is the root node.
- $p : N \to N$ is the parent function.
- $l : N \to 2^S$ is a labeling of the nodes with subsets of S. The label of every node is equal to the union of the labels of its sons. The labels of two siblings are disjoint.
- $h : N \to 2^{[k]}$ annotates every node with a set of indices from $[k]$. The root is annotated by $[k]$. The annotation of every node is contained in that of its parent and it misses at most one element from the annotation of the parent. Every node that is not a leaf has at least one son with strictly smaller annotation.
- $e, f \in [m+1]$ are used to define the parity acceptance condition.

Notice that we give up the "older than" relation and replace the sets E and F by numbers e and f. The numbering M is a bijection from N to $[|N|]$. That is, the numbers of nodes in N are consecutive starting from the root, which is numbered 1.

The following claim is proven much like the similar proof for Streett Safra trees.

Claim 4.3 *The number of compact Streett Safra trees over $\mathcal{S}$ is not more than $n^{n(k+2)+2}(k+1)^{2n(k+1)}$.*

We construct the DPW $\mathcal{D}$ equivalent to $\mathcal{S}$. Let $\mathcal{D} = \langle \Sigma, D, \rho, d_0, \mathcal{F}' \rangle$ where the components of $\mathcal{D}$ are as follows.

- D is the set of compact Streett Safra trees over $\mathcal{S}$.
- d_0 is the tree with a single node 1 labeled $\{s_0\}$, numbered 1, and annotated $[k]$. We set $e = 2$ and $f = 1$.
- The parity acceptance condition $\mathcal{F}' = \langle F_0, \ldots, F_{2m-1} \rangle$ is defined as follows.
  - $F_0 = \{d \in D \mid f = 1\}$
  - $F_{2i+1} = \{d \in D \mid e = i+2 \text{ and } f \geq e\}$
  - $F_{2i+2} = \{d \in D \mid f = i+2 \text{ and } e > f\}$

  As before, we do not handle the case where $e = 1$.
- For every tree $d \in D$ and letter $\sigma \in \Sigma$ the transition $d' = \rho(d, \sigma)$ is the result of the following (recursive) transformation applied on d starting from the root. Before we start, we set e and f to $m+1$ and replace the label of every node v by $\delta(l(v), \sigma)$.
  1. If v is a leaf such that $h(v) = \emptyset$ stop.
  2. If v is a leaf such that $h(v) \neq \emptyset$, add to v a new son v'. Set $l(v') = l(v)$, $h(v') = h(v) - \{max(h(v))\}$, and set $M(v')$ to the minimal value greater than all used numbers. We may use temporarily numbers out of the range $[m]$.
  3. Let $v_1, \ldots, v_l$ be the sons of v (ordered according to their numbers) and let $j_1, \ldots, j_l$ be the indices such that $j_i = max((h(v) \cup \{0\}) - h(v_i))$ (note that $|h(v) - h(v_i)| \leq 1$; in case that $h(v) = h(v_i)$ we have $j_i = 0$). Apply the procedure recursively on $v_1, \ldots, v_l$ (including sons created in step 2 above).

     For every son v_i and every state $s \in l(v_i)$ do the following.
     (a) If $s \in R_{j_i}$, remove s from the label of v_i and all its descendants. Add a new son v' to v. Set $l(v') = \{s\}$, $h(v') = h(v) - \{max(\{0\} \cup (h(v) \cap \{1, \ldots, j_i - 1\}))\}$, and set $M(v')$ to the minimal value larger than all used numbers.
     (b) If $s \in G_{j_i}$, remove s from the label of v_i and all its descendants. Add a new son v' to v. Set $l(v') = \{s\}$, $h(v') = h(v) - \{j_i\}$, and set $M(v')$ to the minimal value larger than all used numbers.
  4. If a state s appears in $l(v_i)$ and $l(v_{i'})$ and $j_i < j_{i'}$ then remove s from the label of $v_{i'}$ and all its descendants.
  5. If a state s appears in $l(v_i)$ and $l(v_{i'})$, $j_i = j_{i'}$, and $M(v_i) < M(v_{i'})$ then remove s from the label of $v_{i'}$ and all its descendants.
  6. Remove sons with empty label. Set e to the minimum of its previous value and the minimal number from the removed descendant.
  7. If all sons are annotated by $h(v)$ remove all sons and all their descendants. Set e to the minimum of its previous value and the minimal number from the removed descendant. Set f to the minimum of its previous value and the number of v.

Let Z denote the set of nodes removed during this recursive procedure. For every node v let $rem(v)$ be

$|\{v' \in Z \mid M(v') < M(v)\}|$. That is, we count how many nodes got removed during the recursive transformation and their number is smaller than the number of v. For every node v such that $l(v) \neq \emptyset$ we change the number of v to $M(v) - empty(v)$. The resulting numbers are consecutive again and in the range $[m]$.

We show that the two automata are equivalent. The proof is an adaptation of Safra's proof [30].

Theorem 4.4 $L(\mathcal{D}) = L(\mathcal{S})$.

Theorem 4.5 *For every NSW $\mathcal{S}$ with n states and index k there exists a DPW $\mathcal{D}$ with $n^{n(k+2)+2}(k+1)^{2n(k+1)}$ states and index $2n(k+1)$ such that $L(\mathcal{D}) = L(\mathcal{N})$.*

As before, when compared to Safra's construction, we reduce the number of states and get a parity automaton. The advantages are similar to those described in Section 3.

5 Acknowledgments

I thank T.A. Henzinger for fruitful discussions, O. Kupferman and M.Y. Vardi for discussions on Safra's construction and comments on an earlier version, and Y. Lustig for comments on an earlier version.

References

[1] H. Björklund, S. Sandberg, and S. Vorobyov. A discrete subexponential algorithm for parity games. In *20th STACS*, LNCS 2607, pp 663–674. Springer-Verlag, 2003.

[2] J. Büchi. On a decision method in restricted second order arithmetic. In *Proc. International Congress on Logic, Method, and Philosophy of Science. 1960*, pp 1–12, 1962.

[3] Y. Choueka. Theories of automata on ω-tapes: A simplified approach. *JCSS*, 8:117–141, 1974.

[4] L. de Alfaro, T. Henzinger, and R. Majumdar. From verification to control: dynamic programs for omega-regular objectives. In *16th LICS*, pp 279–290, 2001.

[5] S. Dziembowski, M. Jurdzinski, and I. Walukiewicz. How much memory is needed to win infinite games. In *12th LICS*, pp 99–110, 1997.

[6] E. Emerson and C. Jutla. The complexity of tree automata and logics of programs. In *29th FOCS*, pp 328–337, 1988.

[7] E. Friedgut, O. Kupferman, and M. Vardi. Büchi complementation made tighter. In *2nd ATVA*, LNCS 3299, pp 64–78. Springer-Verlag, 2004.

[8] J. Hopcroft, R. Motwani, and J. Ullman. *Introduction to Automata Theory, Languages, and Computation*. 2000.

[9] F. Horn. Streett games on finite graphs. In *2nd GDV*, 2005.

[10] M. Jurdzinski. Small progress measures for solving parity games. In *17th STACS*, LNCS 1770, pp 290–301. Springer-Verlag, 2000.

[11] M. Jurdziński, M. Paterson, and U. Zwick. A deterministic subexponential algorithm for solving parity games. In *SODA*, 2006.

[12] C. Jutla. Determinization and memoryless winning strategies. *IC*, 133(2):117–134, 1997.

[13] N. Klarlund. Progress measures for complementation of ω-automata with applications to temporal logic. In *32nd FOCS*, pp. 358–367, 1991.

[14] O. Kupferman and M. Vardi. Freedom, weakness, and determinism: from linear-time to branching-time. In *13th LICS*, pp 81–92, 1998.

[15] O. Kupferman and M. Vardi. Weak alternating automata are not that weak. *ACM TCL*, 2(2):408–429, 2001.

[16] O. Kupferman and M. Vardi. Safraless decision procedures. In *46th FOCS*, 2005.

[17] R. Kurshan. Complementing deterministic Büchi automata in polynomial time. *JCSS*, 35:59–71, 1987.

[18] L. Landweber. Decision problems for ω–automata. *MST*, 3:376–384, 1969.

[19] C. Löding. Methods for the transformation of ω-automata: Complexity and connection to second-order logic. MSc thesis, Kiel, 1998.

[20] R. McNaughton. Testing and generating infinite sequences by a finite automaton. *IC*, 9:521–530, 1966.

[21] M. Michel. Complementation is more difficult with automata on infinite words. CNET, Paris, 1988.

[22] D. Muller and P. Schupp. Simulating alternating tree automata by nondeterministic automata: New results and new proofs of theorems of Rabin, McNaughton and Safra. *TCS*, 141:69–107, 1995.

[23] N. Piterman and A. Pnueli. Faster solution of rabin and streett games. In *21st LICS*. 2006.

[24] A. Pnueli and R. Rosner. On the synthesis of a reactive module. In *16th POPL*, pp 179–190, 1989.

[25] M. Rabin. Automata on infinite objects and Church's problem. *AMS*, 1972.

[26] M. Rabin and D. Scott. Finite automata and their decision problems. *IBM JRD*, 3:115–125, 1959.

[27] M. Roggenbach. Determinization of Büchi-automata. In *Automata, Logics, and Infinite Games: A Guide to Current Research*, LNCS 2500, pp 43–60. Springer-Verlag, 2001.

[28] S. Safra. On the complexity of ω-automata. In *29th FOCS*, pp 319–327, 1988.

[29] S. Safra. *Complexity of automata on infinite objects*. PhD thesis, Weizmann Institute, 1989.

[30] S. Safra. Exponential determinization for ω-automata with strong-fairness acceptance condition. In *24th STOC*, 1992.

[31] S. Safra and M. Vardi. On ω-automata and temporal logic. In *21st STOC*, pp 127–137, 1989.

[32] S. Schwoon. Determinization and complementation of streett automata. In *Automata, Logics, and Infinite Games: A Guide to Current Research*, LNCS 2500, pp 79–91, 2001.

[33] A. Sistla, M. Vardi, and P. Wolper. The complementation problem for Büchi automata with applications to temporal logic. In *10th ICALP*, LNCS 194, pp 465–474, 1985.

[34] W. Thomas. Automata on infinite objects. *Handbook of TCS*, pp 165–191, 1990.

[35] M. Vardi. Reasoning about the past with two-way automata. In *25th ICALP*, LNCS 1443, pp 628–641, 1998.

Memoryful Branching-Time Logic

Orna Kupferman
Hebrew University*

Moshe Y. Vardi
Rice University and Microsoft Research†

Abstract

Traditional branching-time logics such as CTL* are memoryless: once a path in the computation tree is quantified at a given node, the computation that led to that node is forgotten. Recent work in planning suggests that CTL* cannot easily express temporal goals that refer to whole computations. Such goals require memoryful quantification of paths. With such a memoryful quantification, $E\psi$ holds at a node s of a computation tree if there is a path π starting at the root of the tree and going through s such that π satisfies the linear-time formula ψ. We define the memoryful branching-time logic mCTL* and study its expressive power and algorithmic properties.

We show that mCTL* is as expressive, but exponentially more succinct, than CTL*, and that the ability of mCTL* to refer to the present is essential for this equivalence. From the algorithmic point of view, while the satisfiability problem for mCTL* is 2EXPTIME-complete — not harder than that of CTL*, its model-checking problem is EXPSPACE-complete — exponentially harder than that of CTL*. The upper bounds are obtained by extending the automata-theoretic approach to handle memoryful quantification, and are much more efficient than these obtained by translating mCTL* to branching logics with past. The EXPSPACE lower bound for the model-checking problem applies already to formulas of restricted form (in particular, to $AGE\psi$, which is useful for specifying possibility properties), and implies that reasoning about a memoryful branching-time logic is harder than reasoning about the linear-time logic of its path formulas.

*Address: School of Computer Science and Engineering, Jerusalem 91904, Israel. Email: orna@cs.huji.ac.il. Supported in part by BSF grant 9800096, and by a grant from Minerva.

†Address: Department of Computer Science, Houston, TX 77251-1892, U.S.A. Email: vardi@cs.rice.edu. Supported in part by NSF grants CCR-9988322, CCR-0124077, CCR-0311326, and ANI-0216467, by BSF grant 9800096, and by Texas ATP grant 003604-0058-2003. Part of this work was done while the author was visiting the Isaac Newton Institute for Mathematical Science, as part of a Special Programme on Logic and Algorithm.

1 Introduction

Since the introduction of temporal logic into computer science by Pnueli in [28], the family of temporal logics has been widely accepted as an appropriate formal framework for the description of dynamic behavior, cf. [22]. Within this family, the branching-time logic CTL* has emerged as one of the more expressive logics [9], unifying the linear-time logic LTL [28] and the branching-time logic CTL [7]. The modal fixpoint logic [15] is more expressive than CTL*, but it is in some sense a low-level logic, making it an "unfriendly" logic for users, whereas CTL* can express complex properties of computation trees in a natural fashion. While the appropriateness of a branching-time logic for practical formal verification is under debate [34], CTL* is the right logic for applications that require computation-tree reasoning.

An example of an application that requires computation-tree reasoning is sanity checks for the modeling of a system: verification is done with respect to a mathematical model of the system, and it is important to check that the model, whose generation typically involves abstraction and reduction techniques, is correct. In order to check that the model does not disable essential behaviors of the system, one has to check *possibility properties* [19], which require computations of the model to be extendible to computations exhibiting the behaviors.

Another example of a setting in which computation-tree reasoning is required is *automated task planning*, a major research area in Artificial Intelligence, where given a description of a dynamic domain and of the basic actions that can be performed on it, and given a goal that defines a success condition to be achieved, one has to find a suitable plan, that is, a description of the actions to be executed on the domain in order to achieve the goal. "Classical" planning concentrates on the so called "reachability" goals, that is, on goals that define a set of final desired states to be reached (e.g., the red block is above the yellow block). Quite often, practical applications require plans that deal with goals that are more general than sets of final states. Several planning approaches have been recently proposed, where *temporal logic* formulas are used as goal languages, thus allowing

1043-6871/06 $20.00 © 2006 IEEE

for goals that define conditions on the whole plan execution paths, i.e., on the sequences of states resulting from the execution of plans (see, e.g., [1]). Most of these approaches use LTL as the goal language. The linear-temporal logic LTL allows one to express reachability goals (e.g., Fq — reach q), maintainability goals (e.g., Gq — maintain q), as well as goals that combine reachability and maintainability requirements (e.g., FGq — reach a set of states where q can be maintained), and Boolean combinations of these goals.

In *planning in nondeterministic domains* [5], actions are allowed to have different outcomes, and it is not possible to know at planning time which of the different possible outcomes will actually take place. Nondeterminism in action outcome is necessary for modeling in a realistic way several practical domains (e.g., robotics, autonomous controllers, etc.). For instance, in a realistic robotic application one has to take into account that actions like "pick up object" might result in a failure (e.g., if the object slips out of the robot's hand). Planning in nondeterministic domains is essentially the same as *synthesis of open systems* [30], the only difference is that in planning there is emphasis on describing the domain using a modelling language, cf. [13].

A consequence of nondeterminism is that the execution of a plan may lead to more than one possible execution path. Therefore, one has to distinguish between the case the given goal has to be satisfied by all possible execution paths ("strong" planning) and the case where the goal has to be satisfied only by some possible execution path ("weak" planning). In the case of an LTL goal φ, strong planning corresponds to interpreting the formula in a universal way, as the CTL* formula as $A\varphi$, while weak planning corresponds to interpret it in an existential way, as the CTL* formula $E\varphi$. (Synthesis corresponds to strong planning).

Weak and strong plans are two very extreme ways of satisfiability of an LTL formula. In practical applications, it might be impossible to achieve goals in a strong way: for instance, in the robotic application it might be impossible to fulfill a given task if objects keep slipping from the robot's hand. On the other hand, weak plans are too unreliable, since they achieve the goal only under overly optimistic assumptions on the outcomes of action executions. In the case of reachability goals, *strong cyclic planning* [4] has been shown to provide a viable compromise between weak and strong planning. Formally, a plan is strong cyclic if each possible partial execution of the plan can always be extended to an execution that reaches some goal state. Strong cyclic planning allows for plans that encode iterative trial-and-error strategies, like "pick up an object until succeed". The execution of such strategies may loop forever only in the case the action "pick up object" continuously fails, and a failure in achieving the goal in the case of such an unfair execution is usually acceptable. This "always possibly" approach corresponds to Lamport's possibility properties mentioned above.

Inspired by the work on strong cyclic planning, Pistore and Vardi went on to explore the different degrees in which an LTL formula φ can be satisfied that exist between the strong goal $A\varphi$ and the weak goal $E\varphi$ [27]. They showed that a two-player game can model the spectrum between strong and weak planning. Player A chooses action outcomes in order to make goal φ fail, while player E chooses action outcomes in order to satisfy the goal φ. The degree of strength of the temporal requirement is determined by the structure of the game: who makes the first move and how many turns. Pistore and Vardi then proposed a logic based on these path games, using path quantifiers $\mathcal{A}$ and $\mathcal{E}$, which can express the spectrum between strong and weak planning. (Such *path games* have also been studied in [2].)

While the Pistore-Vardi logic is a branching-time logic, quite close to CTL*, it is different from CTL*. In CTL*, a path quantifier turns a path formula into a pure state formula. Thus, for example, the formula $AGE\varphi$ holds at a start state s_0 if for every state s reachable from s_0 there is a path starting at s that satisfies φ; the truth of $E\varphi$ depends only on the state in which it is evaluated. In contrast, in the Pistore-Vardi logic the formula $\mathcal{AE}\varphi$ holds at a start state s_0 if for every state s reachable from s_0 there is a path starting at s_0 and continuing through s that satisfies φ; the truth of $\mathcal{E}\varphi$ in a state depends also on the path that leads to that state. In other words, while CTL* path quantifiers are *memoryless*, the path quantifiers $\mathcal{A}$ and $\mathcal{E}$ are *memoryful*[1]. The Pistore-Vardi logic, however, does not have a standard logical syntax; for example, it is not closed under conjunction and disjunction[2].

We propose in this paper a memoryful variant of CTL*, which unifies CTL* and the Pistore-Vardi logic. We name the new logic mCTL*. Semantically, mCTL* is obtained from CTL* by reinterpreting the path quantifiers of the logic to be memoryful[3]. With memoryful quantification, $E\varphi$ holds at a node s of a computation tree if there is a path π starting at the root of the tree and going through s such that π satisfies the linear-time formula φ. Syntactically, we add a special proposition *present*, which is needed to emulate the ability of CTL* to talk about the "present". One of our main results is that the addition of *present* is needed to make mCTL* at least as expressive as CTL*. (As in [2], one can translate mCTL* to CTL* via path logic, but this translation is of nonelementary complexity.) We note that

[1] It is shown in [2] that the Pistore-Vardi logic is expressible in CTL*, but only a non-elementary translation, which goes through *path logic* [14], is known.

[2] The idea of memoryful quantification relative to the present has been studied in the context of *Ockhamist temporal logic*, cf. [3], but has not been explored in the context of CTL*, and that study does not refer to algorithmic properties.

[3] Strictly speaking, mCTL* covers only the finite-alternation fragment of the Pistore-Vardi logic, leaving out the infinite-alternation fragment.

present is not required to easily express the Pistore-Vardi logic in mCTL*; the strong cyclic goal of $\mathcal{AE}\varphi$ is expressed in mCTL* by the formula $AGE\varphi$.) We show that memoryful quantification can be expressed in CTL* extended with the ability to refer to the *linear past* [16]. We note that the proposition *present* of mCTL* is different from the "*Now*" used in [12], in the context of branching temporal logics with past. While the "*Now*" in [12] is a unary temporal operator, which chops away the past, our *present* is an atomic proposition that holds in the present.

We then examine two decision problems related to mCTL*: satisfiability and model checking. We first show that satisfiability of mCTL* is 2EXPTIME-complete, which is the same complexity as that of CTL* [10, 35]. We then show that model checking mCTL* is significantly harder than model checking CTL*. Model checking mCTL* is EXPSPACE-complete, while model checking CTL* is PSPACE-complete [11]. Establishing the two upper bounds via an automata-theoretic framework is quite nontrivial. The standard approach to mCTL* satisfiability would reduce it to emptiness of two-way alternating tree automata [33]. This approach would yield a 2EXPTIME bound for satisfiability, but not the EXPSPACE bound for model checking. Instead, we offer an extension of the automata-theoretic approach to model checking [17], and describe *hesitant alternating automata with satellites*. We show that this framework can establish both upper bounds.

Since our lower-bound proof uses an m$^-$CTL* formula corresponding to Lamport's possibility properties, it also settles an open question regarding the complexity of model checking of such properties, as well as that of the Pistore-Vardi logic. In addition, our results, together with the linear translation of mCTL* to CTL* with linear past, imply new results about the complexity of branching temporal logic with past [20, 12, 23]. Our results show that the transition from memoryless to memoryful quantifiers is significant. We can now see that the significant complexity gap between CTL* satisfiability, which is 2EXPTIME-complete, and CTL* model checking, which is PSPACE-complete, is due to quantifier memorylessness, which helps model checking [11] but not satisfiability [35]. We discuss this point more in Section 5.

Due to the lack of space, this version does not include all the proofs. A full version can be found at the authors' home pages.

2 The Temporal Logic Memoryful CTL*

The branching-time logic *memoryful CTL** (mCTL*, for short) combines both branching-time and linear-time operators [9]. A path quantifier E ("for some path") can prefix an assertion composed of an arbitrary combination of the linear-time operators X ("next time") and U ("until"). The syntax of mCTL* is similar to the syntax of CTL*: there are two types of formulas in mCTL*: *state formulas*, whose satisfaction is related to a specific state, and *path formulas*, whose satisfaction is related to a specific path. The only difference in the syntax between the two logics is the fact mCTL* formulas may refer to a special atomic proposition *present*, which holds only in the present. An mCTL* formula φ is *closed* if all the occurrences of *present* are in a scope of a path quantifier. The logic mCTL* consists of closed mCTL* state formulas. We define the *size* $|\varphi|$ of φ as the number of state and path subformulas that φ has.

The semantics of mCTL* is defined with respect to *computation trees*. Given a finite set D of *directions*, a *D-tree* is a set $T \subseteq D^*$ such that if $x \cdot d \in T$ where $x \in D^*$ and $d \in D$, then also $x \in T$. The elements of T are called *nodes*, and the empty word ε is the *root* of T. The prefix relation induces a partial order $\leq$ between nodes of T. Thus, for two nodes x and y, we say that $x \leq y$ iff there is some $z \in D^*$ such that $y = x \cdot z$. For every $x \in T$, the nodes $x \cdot d$, for $d \in D$, are the *successors* of x. A node is a *leaf* if it has no successors. For a node $x \in T$, an *x-path* of T is a minimal set $\pi \subseteq T$ such that $x \in \pi$ and for every $y \in \pi$, either y is a leaf or there exists a unique $d \in D$ such that $y \cdot d \in \pi$. When $x = \varepsilon$, we say that π is a *path*. For a path π and a node $x \in \pi$, the *suffix* of π that starts at x is the x-path $\pi \cap \{y : x \leq y\}$.

Given an alphabet Σ, a *Σ-labeled D-tree* is a pair $\langle T, \tau \rangle$ where T is a D-tree and $\tau : T \rightarrow \Sigma$ maps each node of T to a letter in Σ. Of special interest to us are Σ-labeled trees in which $\Sigma = 2^{AP}$ for some set AP of atomic propositions. We call such Σ-labeled trees *computation trees*. A computation tree is often given by means of a *Kripke structure* $K = \langle AP, W, R, w_{in}, L \rangle$, where AP is the set of atomic propositions, W is a set of states, $R \subseteq W \times W$ is a total transition relation , w_{in} is an initial state, and $L : W \rightarrow 2^{AP}$ maps each state to the set of atomic propositions true in that state. A *path* in K is an infinite sequence of states, $\pi = w_0, w_1, \ldots$ such that $\langle w_i, w_{i+1} \rangle \in R$ for every $i \geq 0$. We define the size $\|K\|$ of K as $|W| + |R|$. The Kripke structure K induces a computation tree $\langle T_K, \tau_K \rangle$ that corresponds to the unwinding of K from w_{in}.

The logics mCTL* and CTL* differ in the semantics of path quantification. Consider a computation tree. In CTL*, path quantification ranges over paths that start in the current node. In mCTL*, path quantification ranges over paths that start at the root and visit the current node. For example, the CTL* formula $AGE\psi$, for a linear formula ψ holds in a root of a computation tree if a computation satisfying ψ starts from every node in the tree. When viewed as an mCTL* formula, it holds in a computation tree if for every node x of the tree, the path from the root to x can be extended to a path satisfying ψ. As discussed in Section 1, this corresponds to strong cyclic plans [4]. In particular, when $\varphi = Fp$, it states that p has either occurred in the past or is possible in the future. This corresponds to Lamport's possibility properties [19]. Thus, when evaluating path formulas, one cannot ignore the past and satisfaction may depend on the events that have taken place since the beginning of the execution and until the present. Below we define the semantics of mCTL* formally.

Consider a computation tree $\langle T, \tau \rangle$. For two nodes x and c in T and an mCTL* formula φ, we use $x, c \models \varphi$ to indicate that x satisfies φ with c being the present. Similarly, $\pi, x, c \models \psi$, for a path formula ψ, iff the suffix of the path π that starts at x satisfies ψ with c being the present. Formally, we have the following (with respect to given T and τ).

- $x, c \models$ **true** and $x, c \not\models$ **false**, for all x, c in T.
- $x, c \models p$, for $p \in AP$, iff $p \in \tau(x)$.
- $x, c \models present$ iff $x = c$.
- $x, c \models \neg\varphi_1$ iff $x, c \not\models \varphi_1$.
- $x, c \models \varphi_1 \vee \varphi_2$ iff $x, c \models \varphi_1$ or $x, c \models \varphi_2$.
- $x, c \models E\psi$ iff there exists a path π such that $x \in \pi$ and $\pi, \varepsilon, x \models \psi$.
- $\pi, x, c \models \varphi$ for a state formula φ, iff $x, c \models \varphi$.
- $\pi, x, c \models \neg\psi_1$ iff $\pi, x, c \not\models \psi_1$.
- $\pi, x, c \models \psi_1 \vee \psi_2$ iff $\pi, x, c \models \psi_1$ or $\pi, x, c \models \psi_2$.
- $\pi, x, c \models X\psi$ iff $\pi, x \cdot d, c \models \psi$, where $d \in D$ is such that $x \cdot d \in \pi$.
- $\pi, x, c \models \psi_1 U \psi_2$ iff π contains a node $y \geq x$ such that $\pi, y, c \models \psi_2$, and $\pi, z, c \models \psi_1$ for all $x \leq z < y$.

Note that while in CTL* path quantification ranges over paths that start in the current node, here path quantification ranges over paths that start at the root and visit the current node. Thus, when evaluating path formulas, one cannot ignore the past and satisfaction may depend on the events that have taken place since the beginning of the execution and until the present. Note also that formulas of the form $E\psi$ "reset the present"; thus the satisfaction of $E\psi$ with respect to x, c is independent of c, and the present is set to x. It follows the truth value of a closed mCTL* formula in node x is independent of the present. Accordingly, we use the notation $x \models \varphi$ to indicate that an mCTL* formula φ is satisfied in node x. We say that a computation tree $\langle T, \tau \rangle$ satisfies an mCTL* formula φ iff $\varepsilon \models \varphi$.

Note that by letting path quantification range over paths that start at the root, an mCTL* formula can refer to events that happen in the past. Unlike, however, branching-time logics whose syntax contain explicit past-time operators, here the ability to refer to the past is limited. Note also that the Pistore-Vardi logic can be easily expressed in mCTL*.

The logic m$^-$CTL* is a fragment of mCTL* in which the atomic proposition *present* is not allowed. As we show in Section 3, m$^-$CTL* cannot emulate the ability of CTL* to refer to the present, and is strictly weaker than mCTL*.

Examples Consider the mCTL* formula $AGE(GF grasp \rightarrow F pick)$ that describes a desired behavior of a robot. The formula states that each node in the computation tree belong to a computation π such that if the robot tries to grasp an object infinitely often, it eventually picks it. Note that the robot may have picked the object before the present. Likewise, the mCTL* formula $AG(pickA \rightarrow EF pickB)$ states that whenever a node x is labeled by *pickA*, then some computation that goes through x has a node labeled *pickB*. Thus, whenever the robot picks A, either it has picked B in the past, or it is possible for it to pick B in the future. Note that the specification of this property in CTL* is much more complicated.

The formula $AG(grant \rightarrow EF(req \wedge F(ack \wedge F present)))$ demonstrates how mCTL* formulas can use the ability to refer to the present with *present* in order to refer to the past. Indeed, the formula states that whenever a node x is labeled with *grant*, the path from the root to x has a node labeled with *req*, followed by a node labeled with *ack*, followed by the present. Thus, grants are given only if a request was issued and then acknowledged in the past.

Finally, The formula $AG(ack \rightarrow EF(req \wedge F(present \wedge F grant)))$ gives a different view of the same sequence of events and demonstrates how mCTL* formulas can refer to both the past and the future. Indeed, the formula states that whenever a node x is labeled with *ack*, the path from the root to x has a node labeled with *req* and some path that starts in x has a node labeled with *grant*. Thus, acknowledgments are given only if a request was issued in the past and is going to be granted in the future. □

The definition of mCTL* leads to natural theoretical and practical questions: in the theoretical front, we would like to study how the transition to a memoryful path quantification influences the expressive power of the logic, its connection to logics with past, and to standard CTL*, as well as the necessity of the atomic proposition *present*. In the practical front, we would like to study how the transition influences the complexity of the satisfiability and the model-checking problems. The latter is of particular interest as model-checking algorithms for CTL* are based on a bottom-up reasoning, where internal state formulas are evaluated first and replaced by new atomic propositions [11]. Such reasoning cannot be applied with a memoryful path quantification.

3 Expressiveness

In this section we discuss the expressive power of mCTL* and m$^-$CTL*. We say that two branching temporal logic formulas φ_1 and φ_2 are equivalent if for every computation trees $\langle T, tau \rangle$ and node $x \in T$, we have $x \models \varphi_1$ iff $x \models \varphi_2$.

We start by comparing mCTL* with CTL*:

Theorem 3.1 *mCTL* and CTL* are equally expressive.*

As detailed in the proof, while the blow up in translating a CTL* formula to an mCTL* formula is linear (we replace each subformula of the form $E\xi$ by the formula $EF(present \wedge \xi)$), the translation in the other direction goes via monadic path logic [14, 2] and is of nonelementary complexity.

Theorem 3.2 *mCTL* is at least exponentially more succinct than CTL*.*

The formula used in the proof of Theorem 3.2 is similar to the one used in [12] for proving the succinctness of LTL+past with respect to LTL. In particular, while the formula does not use the proposition *present*, it makes use of the ability of mCTL* to refer to the past. We now show that if we extend CTL* with past temporal operators, the translation is linear. Let $\text{CTL}^\star_{lp}$ and $\text{CTL}^\star_{lp^-}$ denote the extension of CTL* with past operators, with and without *present*, respectively, where formulas are interpreted over computation trees, thus past is linear [16].

Theorem 3.3 *Every mCTL* (resp. m⁻CTL*) formula has an equivalent $\text{CTL}^\star_{lp}$ (resp. $\text{CTL}^\star_{lp^-}$) formula of linear length.*

We note that the complexity of the model-checking and the satisfiability problems for $\text{CTL}^\star_{lp}$ (with or without *present*) is open [16] (see also [20]), thus Theorem 3.3 does not lead to a model-checking or decidability procedure. In fact, the translation, together with the lower bounds we describe in Section 4 for mCTL* and mCTL*improves the known lower bounds known for $\text{CTL}^\star_{lp}$ and $\text{CTL}^\star_{lp^-}$.

Recall that the proposition *present* emulates the ability of CTL* to talk about the present. Indeed, the translation we described, of CTL* formulas to mCTL* formulas, uses *present*. In the full version, we show that the CTL formula $\psi = EF(EXp \wedge EX\neg p)$ has no equivalent $\text{m}^-\text{CTL}^\star$ formula. Thus, the use of *present* is essential, and $\text{m}^-\text{CTL}^\star$ is strictly weaker than mCTL* (and thus, also CTL*).

Theorem 3.4 *There is a CTL formula with no equivalent m⁻CTL* formula.*

The fact that $\text{m}^-\text{CTL}^\star$ loses track of the present whenever path quantification is applied weakens its branching nature. This is reflected in the fact that the CTL formula we have used in the proof of Theorem 3.4 is similar to the formula with which Milner shows the differences between trace equivalence and bisimulation [24]. This weakness of $\text{m}^-\text{CTL}^\star$ motivates us to focus, in the rest of this paper, on the logic mCTL*. In addition, as we show in Section 4.4, the EXPSPACE lower bound for mCTL* model checking holds also for $\text{m}^-\text{CTL}^\star$.

4 Decision Procedures

In this section we study the model-checking and satisfiability problems for mCTL*. We show that while the satisfiability problem is not harder than the one for CTL*, the model-checking problem is exponentially harder. For the upper bounds, we need to develop an automata-theoretic approach for memoryful branching temporal logic. For that, we start with definitions of alternating automata and introduce *alternating automata with satellites*. We then translate mCTL* formulas to such automata.

4.1 Alternating automata

Automata over infinite trees (tree automata) run over Σ-labeled D-trees that have no leaves [32]. *Alternating tree automata* generalize nondeterministic tree automata and were first introduced in [26]. Here we define *symmetric* alternating automata, which cannot distinguish between the different successors of a node, and send copies to the successors in either a universal or an existential manner [37].

Let $\Omega = \{\Box, \Diamond\}$, and let $\mathcal{B}^+(\Omega \times Q)$ be the set of positive Boolean formulas over $\Omega \times Q$; i.e., Boolean formulas built from elements in $\Omega \times Q$ using $\wedge$ and $\vee$, where we also allow the formulas **true** and **false** and, as usual, $\wedge$ has precedence over $\vee$. For a set $S \subseteq \Omega \times Q$ and a formula $\theta \in \mathcal{B}^+(\Omega \times Q)$, we say that S *satisfies* θ iff assigning **true** to elements in S and assigning **false** to elements in $(\Omega \times Q) \setminus S$ makes θ true.

In a symmetric alternating automaton, the transition function δ maps q and σ to a formula in $\mathcal{B}^+(\Omega \times Q)$. Intuitively, an atom $\langle \Box, q \rangle$ corresponds to copies of the automaton in state q, sent to all the successors of the current node. An atom $\langle \Diamond, q \rangle$ corresponds to a copy of the automaton in state q, sent to some successor of the current node.

Formally, a symmetric automaton is a tuple $\mathcal{A} = \langle \Sigma, Q, \delta, q_{in}, \alpha \rangle$ where Σ is the input alphabet, Q is a finite set of states, $\delta : Q \times \Sigma \to \mathcal{B}^+(\Omega \times Q)$ is a transition function, $q_{in} \in Q$ is an initial state, and α specifies the acceptance condition (a condition that defines a subset of Q^ω). Let $T = D^*$. A *run* of a symmetric alternating automaton $\mathcal{A}$ on an input Σ-labeled D-tree $\langle T, \tau \rangle$ is a $(D^* \times Q)$-labeled $\mathbb{N}$-tree $\langle T_r, r \rangle$ that satisfies the following:

1. $\varepsilon \in T_r$ and $r(\varepsilon) = (\varepsilon, q_{in})$.
2. Let $y \in T_r$ with $r(y) = (x, q)$ and $\delta(q, V(x)) = \theta$. Then there is a (possibly empty) set $S \subseteq \Omega \times Q$, such that S satisfies θ, and for all $(c, s) \in S$, the following hold:
   - If $c = \Box$, then for each $d \in D$, there is $j \in \mathbb{N}$ such that $y \cdot j \in T_r$ and $r(y \cdot j) = (x \cdot d, s)$.
   - If $c = \Diamond$, then for some $d \in D$, there is $j \in \mathbb{N}$ such that $y \cdot j \in T_r$ and $r(y \cdot j) = (x \cdot d, s)$.

Each infinite path ρ in $\langle T_r, r\rangle$ is labeled by a word in Q^ω. Let $inf(\rho)$ denote the set of states in Q that appear in $r(\rho)$ infinitely often. A run $\langle T_r, r\rangle$ is accepting iff all its infinite paths satisfy the acceptance condition. In *Büchi* automata, $\alpha \subseteq Q$, and an infinite path ρ satisfies α iff $inf(\rho) \cap \alpha \neq \emptyset$. In *co-Büchi* automata, $\alpha \subseteq Q$, and an infinite path ρ satisfies α iff $inf(\rho) \cap \alpha = \emptyset$.

An automaton accepts a tree iff there exists an accepting run on it. The language of $\mathcal{A}$, denoted $\mathcal{L}(\mathcal{A})$, is the set of all labeled trees that $\mathcal{A}$ accepts. The *nonemptiness problem* is to decide, given $\mathcal{A}$, whether $\mathcal{L}(\mathcal{A}) \neq \emptyset$. When $|\Sigma| = 1$, we refer to the problem as *1-letter nonemptiness*. The *complement* of an automaton $\mathcal{A}$ is an automaton $\tilde{\mathcal{A}}$ that accepts exactly all the tress that $\mathcal{A}$ rejects.

Symmetric automata are powerful enough for deciding satisfiability of CTL* formulas. Given a CTL* formula φ, we translate it to a symmetric automaton $\mathcal{A}_\phi$ that accepts tree models of φ. Then to decide satisfiability we have to check that $\mathcal{A}_\varphi$ is non-empty, cf. [17]. As the translation is exponential and the emptiness test is exponential, we get a doubly exponential upper bound, which is asymptotically optimal [35]. To decide satisfiability of mCTL*, we need an extension of symmetric automata to *two-way* automata [33]. This approach would yield a 2EXPTIME bound for satisfiability, but not the EXPSPACE bound for model checking. The reason is that mCTL* is interpreted over unfolding of programs. This requires us to convert two-way automata to one-way automata, involving another exponential blow-up. Thus, just the construction of automata is doubly exponential. Instead, we offer an extension of the automata-theoretic approach to model checking [17], and describe *hesitant alternating automata with satellites*. We show that this framework can establish upper bounds both for satisfiability and model checking.

In [17], the authors introduce *hesitant alternating automata* (HAAs, for short) and show that CTL* formulas can be translated to such automata. An HAA is an alternating automaton $\mathcal{A} = \langle \Sigma, Q, \delta, q_0, \alpha\rangle$, where $\alpha = \langle G, B\rangle$ with $G \subseteq Q$ and $B \subseteq Q$. That is, the acceptance condition of HAAs consists of a pair of sets of states. As in weak alternating automata [25], there exists a partition of Q into disjoint sets $Q_1, \ldots, Q_m$ and a partial order $\leq$ on these sets such that transitions lead to sets that are lower in the partial order. Formally, for every $q \in Q_i$ and $q' \in Q_j$ for which q' occurs in $\delta(q, \sigma)$, for some $\sigma \in \Sigma$, we have $Q_j \leq Q_i$. In addition, each set Q_i is classified as either *transient* ($\delta(q, \sigma)$ contains no states of Q_i), *existential* ($\delta(q, \sigma)$ only contains disjunctively related states of Q_i), or *universal* ($\delta(q, \sigma)$ only contains conjunctively related elements of Q_i). It follows that every infinite path π of a run $\langle T_r, r\rangle$ gets trapped within some existential or universal set Q_i. The path then satisfies an acceptance condition $\langle G, B\rangle$ if and only if either Q_i is an existential set and $inf(\pi) \cap G \neq \emptyset$, or Q_i is a universal set and $inf(\pi) \cap B = \emptyset$.

Given a transition function δ, let $\tilde{\delta}$ denote the dual function of δ. That is, for every q and σ with $\delta(q, \sigma) = \theta$, let $\tilde{\delta}(q, \sigma) = \tilde{\theta}$, where $\tilde{\theta}$ is obtained from θ by switching $\Box$ and $\Diamond$, switching $\vee$ and $\wedge$, and switching **true** and **false**. If, for example, $\theta = \Box p \vee (\textbf{true} \wedge \Diamond q)$ then $\tilde{\theta} = \Diamond p \wedge (\textbf{false} \vee \Box q)$,

Lemma 4.1 [25, 17] *Given an HAA* $\mathcal{A} = \langle \Sigma, Q, \delta, q_{in}, \langle G, B\rangle\rangle$, *the alternating automaton* $\tilde{\mathcal{A}} = \langle \Sigma, Q, \tilde{\delta}, q_{in}, \langle B, G\rangle\rangle$ *is an HAA that complements* $\mathcal{A}$.

A *satellite* for an HAA $\mathcal{A} = \langle \Sigma, Q, \delta, q_{in}, \alpha\rangle$ is a deterministic word automaton $\mathcal{U} = \langle \Sigma, Q', \delta', q'_{in}\rangle$ with no acceptance condition. For a node $x = d_0 \cdots d_k$ of a Σ-labeled D-tree $\langle T, \tau\rangle$, let $word\_to(x) = \tau(\varepsilon) \cdot \tau(d_0) \cdot \tau(d_0 \cdot d_1) \cdot \tau(d_0 \cdot d_1 \cdots d_{k-1})$ be the word that labels the path from the root to x. When the HAA reads a node x of the input tree, its transitions may depend on $\delta'(q_{in}, word\_to(x))$, namely on the state in which $\mathcal{U}$ would have been if we had run it along the paths of the tree. Formally, the transition function of $\mathcal{A}$ is $\delta : Q \times \Sigma \times Q' \to \mathcal{B}^+(\Omega \times Q)$, and is such that when $\mathcal{A}$ is in state q as it reads the node x, it proceeds according to $\delta(q, \tau(x), \delta'(q'_{in}, word\_to(x)))$. Technically, an HAA with a satellite is equivalent to the HAA obtained by taking the product of $\mathcal{A}$ and $\mathcal{U}$: the new state space is $Q \times Q'$, and whenever the product is in state $\langle q, q'\rangle$ and reads a node x, the transition from $\langle q, q'\rangle$ is obtained from $\delta(q, \tau(x), q')$ by replacing each atom $\Box s$ or $\Diamond s$ by $\Box(s, \delta'(q', \tau(x)))$ or $\Diamond(s, \delta'(q', \tau(x)))$, respectively. The acceptance condition of the product HAA is induced by F. The partition of the state space to sets, the partial order on the sets, and their classification into transient, universal, and existential are induced by these in $\mathcal{A}$.

Note that satellites are only a convenient way to describe HAA in which the state space can be partitioned to two components, one of which is deterministic, independent of the other, has no influence on the acceptance, and runs on all the branches of the tree. In particular, Lemma 4.1 holds also for HAA with satellites. It is sometimes convenient to describe the HAA and its satellite separately. In addition to clarity, the separation to $\mathcal{A}$ and $\mathcal{U}$ enables a tighter analysis of the complexity of the nonemptiness problem. Recall that the solution of the emptiness problem for alternating automata involves alternation removal, which results in a nondeterministic automaton with exponentially many states. While the product of an HAA with n states and a satellite with n' states has nn' states, there is a need to pay the exponential price of alternation removal in the process of the nonemptiness check only for $\mathcal{A}$. Formally, we have the following.

Theorem 4.2 *The nonemptiness problem for an HAA with* n *states and a satellite with* n' *states can be solved in time* $2^{O(n \log n' + n^2 \log n)}$.

Proof: Let $\mathcal{A}$ be an HAA with n states, and let $\mathcal{U}$ be its satellite with n' states. We first claim that $\mathcal{A}$ is not empty iff it accepts a tree of branching degree n. The proof of the claim is similar to the linear branching degree property of μ-calculus [7, 31]. Now, we can translate $\mathcal{A}$ to a nondeterministic parity tree automaton $\mathcal{A}'$ over trees of branching degree n, with $n^{O(n)}$ states, index $O(n)$, and with the same satellite $\mathcal{U}$. By taking the product of $\mathcal{A}'$ and $\mathcal{U}$, we get a nondeterministic parity automaton with $n'n^{O(n)}$ states, index $O(n)$, and no satellite. Checking the nonemptiness of such an NPT requires time $n'^{O(n)}n^{O(n^2)} = 2^{O(n \log n' + n^2 \log n)}$ [10, 30]. □

Theorem 4.3 *The 1-letter nonemptiness problem for an HAA with n states, depth m, and a satellite with n′ states can be solved in space* $O(m \log^2(nn'))$.

Proof: Let $\mathcal{A}$ be an HAA with n states and depth m, and let $\mathcal{U}$ be its satellite with n' states. We can translate $\mathcal{A}$ to an HAA with nn' states, depth m, and no satellite. By [17], checking the 1-letter nonemptiness of such an HAA requires space $O(m \log^2(nn'))$. □

4.2 From mCTL* to HAA

In this section we describe a translation of mCTL* formulas to HAA. In the sequel, we use the translation in order to obtain satisfiability and model-checking decision procedures for mCTL*.

We first need some definitions. For an mCTL* formula ψ, let $sf(\psi)$ be the set of state subformulas of ψ. For two formulas θ and φ of ψ, we say that θ is *maximal* in φ if θ is a strict state subformula of φ and there exists no state formula "between them", namely, there exists no strict subformula ξ of φ such that θ is a strict subformula of ξ. We denote by $max(\varphi)$ the set of all formulas maximal in φ. For example, $max(A((X\neg p)U(EXq))) = \{\neg p, EXq\}$. Consider an mCTL* formula ψ and a computation tree $\langle T, \tau \rangle$. We say that a $2^{sf(\psi)}$-labeled tree $\langle T, g \rangle$ is *sound* for ψ if for all $x \in T$ and $\theta \in sf(\psi)$, we have that $x, \epsilon \models \theta$ iff $\theta \in g(x)$. Thus, a node x is labeled by exactly all the formulas in $sf(\psi)$ that are satisfied in x, with ϵ being the present (note that the fact ϵ is the present is important only for $\theta = present$).

Theorem 4.4 *Given an mCTL* formula* ψ, *we can construct an HAA* $\mathcal{A}_\psi$ *with* $2^{O(|\psi|)}$ *states, depth* $O(|\psi|)$, *and a satellite with* $2^{2^{O(|\psi|)}}$ *states, such that* $\mathcal{A}_\psi$ *runs on* $2^{sf(\psi)}$*-labeled trees and accepts exactly all trees that are sound for* ψ *and satisfy* ψ.

Proof: We first define the satellite $\mathcal{U}$ for $\mathcal{A}_\psi$. Consider a subformula of ψ of the form $E\xi$. Let $\mathcal{U}_\xi = \langle 2^{sf(\psi)}, Q_\xi, M_\xi, Q_\xi^{in}, \alpha_\xi \rangle$ be a nondeterministic Büchi automaton on infinite words such that $\mathcal{U}_\xi$ accepts exactly all the computations satisfying ξ [36]. Note that $\mathcal{U}_\xi$ regards the formulas maximal in φ as atomic propositions ($\mathcal{U}_\xi$ ignores the other formulas in $sf(\psi)$). Let $\mathcal{U}_\xi^d = \langle 2^{sf(\psi)}, 2^{Q_\xi}, M_\xi^d, \{Q_\xi^{in}\} \rangle$ be the deterministic automaton with no acceptance condition obtained by applying the subset construction to $\mathcal{U}_\xi$. Thus, for all $S \in 2^{Q_\xi}$ and $\sigma \in 2^{sf(\psi)}$, we have that $M_\xi^d(S, \sigma) = \bigcup_{s \in S} M_\xi(s, \sigma)$. Now, the satellite $\mathcal{U} = \langle 2^{sf(\psi)}, Q', \delta', q'_{in} \rangle$ is the crossproduct of all the automata $\mathcal{U}_\xi^d$ above (for all the subformulas $E\xi$ of ψ). Intuitively, $\mathcal{U}$ supplies to $\mathcal{A}_\psi$ the information required in order to evaluate path formulas on paths that start in the root of the tree and visit the current node. When there is a need to check that $E\xi$ holds in some node x, the automaton $\mathcal{A}_\psi$ guesses a state q that is a member of the current state $S \in 2^{Q_\xi}$ of $\mathcal{U}_\xi^d$ (recall that 2^{Q_ξ} is a component in the state space of the satellite) and it executes $\mathcal{U}_\xi^q$ along some x-path. The position in which $\mathcal{A}_\psi$ starts the execution of $\mathcal{U}_\xi^q$ is the only position in which the atomic proposition *present* holds. Note that a correct guess of q and a successful run of $\mathcal{U}_\xi^q$ along some x-path are possible iff there is a path that visits x and satisfies ξ, which corresponds to the semantics of $E\xi$.

As in the case of the HAA for CTL* [17], we construct $\mathcal{A}_\psi$ by induction on the structure of ψ. With each subformula φ of ψ, we associate an HAA $\mathcal{A}'_\varphi$ composed from HAAs associated with formulas maximal in φ. We assume that the state sets of composed HAAs are disjoint (otherwise, we rename states). The HAA $\mathcal{A}'_\varphi$ assumes that the tree is sound for the formulas in $max(\varphi)$ and only checks the satisfaction of φ under this assumption. We then define $\mathcal{A}_\psi$ as the intersection of $\mathcal{A}'_\psi$ with an automaton that checks, by sending copies to the different $\mathcal{A}'_\varphi$ automata, that the input tree is indeed sound with respect to ψ.

- If $\varphi = p$ for $p \in AP$ or $p = present$, then $\mathcal{A}'_\varphi$ is the one-state HAA that goes to **true** when it reads σ with $p \in \sigma$ and goes to **false** otherwise.
- If $\varphi = \neg\varphi_1$, then $\mathcal{A}'_\varphi$ is $\tilde{\mathcal{A}}_{\varphi_1}$ — the HAA obtained by dualizing the HAA $\mathcal{A}_{\varphi_1}$ for φ_1. If $\varphi = \varphi_1 \vee \varphi_2$, then $\mathcal{A}'_\varphi$ has an initial state that sends all the copies sent by $\mathcal{A}'_{\varphi_1}$ or all the copies sent by $\mathcal{A}'_{\varphi_2}$.
- If $\varphi = E\xi$, where ξ is an mCTL* path formula, we proceed as follows. Let $\mathcal{U}_\xi = \langle 2^{sf(\psi)}, Q_\xi, M_\xi, Q_\xi^{in}, \alpha_\xi \rangle$. Recall that the state space Q' of the satellite $\mathcal{U}$ is the product of the state spaces of the deterministic automata for the path formulas. Thus, each state $q' \in Q'$ has a component for each of these automata, and in particular for $\mathcal{U}_\xi^d$. Consider a state $q' \in Q'$. Let $q'_{|\xi}$ be the state of $\mathcal{U}_\xi^d$ in q'. Note that $q'_{|\xi} \in 2^{Q_\xi}$. Then, $\mathcal{A}'_\varphi =$

$\langle 2^{sf(\psi)}, Q_\xi, \delta', q_{in}, \langle \alpha_\xi, \emptyset \rangle \rangle$ is defined so that from its initial state q_{in}, it consults the satellite's state q' and executes $\mathcal{U}_\xi$ along a single path, starting from some state in q'_ξ. The proposition *present* holds exactly at the node in which the execution of $\mathcal{U}_\xi$ starts, thus its first transition assumes that *present* holds. Formally, for all $\sigma \in 2^{sf(\psi)}$ and $q' \in Q'$, we have $\delta'(q_{in}, \sigma, q') = \bigvee_{s \in q'_{|\xi}} \bigvee_{s' \in M_\xi(s, \sigma \cup \{present\})} \Diamond s'$. Also, for all $q \in Q_\xi$, we have $\delta'(q, \sigma, q') = \bigvee_{q_i \in M_\xi(q,\sigma)} \Diamond q_i$. If $M_\xi(q, \sigma) = \emptyset$, then $\delta(q, \sigma, q') = \mathbf{false}$. Note that the only transition in which the input from the satellite is taken into an account is the transition from q_{in}, where $\mathcal{A}'_\varphi$ chooses a state from $q_{|\xi}$ to proceed with. Note also that Q_ξ constitutes a single existential set. The HAA $\mathcal{A}'_\varphi$ accepts a $2^{sf()}$-labeled tree from node x iff x satisfies φ, assuming the input tree is sound for the formulas in $max(\varphi)$. The states in Q_ξ constitute an existential set of the HAA.

We now add to $\mathcal{A}'_\psi$ transitions that check that the input tree is indeed sound for ψ, thus the letter read at node x describes the set of formulas satisfied in x. For this purpose, we add a new state q_{check}. Whenever $\mathcal{A}_\psi$ is in state q_{check} and reads a letter σ, it sends copies sent from the initial states of the HAA $\mathcal{A}'_{\varphi_i} = \langle 2^{sf(\psi)}, Q^i, \delta^i, q^i_{in}, \langle G^i, B^i \rangle \rangle$, for all $\varphi_i \in \sigma$, sends copies sent from the initial states of the HAA $\tilde{\mathcal{A}}'_{\varphi_i} = \langle 2^{sf(\psi)}, \tilde{Q}^i, \tilde{\delta}^i, q^i_{in}, \langle B^i, G^i \rangle \rangle$, for all $\varphi_i \notin \sigma$, (and also sends a copy that stays in q_{check} to all the successors). Formally, for all $\sigma \in 2^{sf(\psi)}$ and $q' \in Q'$, we have $\delta(q_{check}, \sigma, q') = \Box q_{check} \wedge \bigwedge_{\varphi_i \in \sigma} \delta^i(q^i_{in}, \sigma, q') \wedge \bigwedge_{\varphi_i \notin \sigma} \tilde{\delta}^i(q^i_{in}, \sigma, q')$.

The HAA $\mathcal{A}_\psi = \langle 2^{sf(\psi)}, Q, \delta, q_{in}, \langle G, B \rangle \rangle$ is such that Q is the union of $\{q_{in}, q_{check}\}$ with the union of the state spaces of $\mathcal{A}'_\theta$, for $\theta \in sf(\psi)$. The initial state q_{in} checks for the satisfaction of ψ and for the soundness with respect to ψ, thus $\delta(q_{in}, \sigma, q') = \delta^\psi(q^\psi_{in}, \sigma, q') \wedge \delta(q_{check}, \sigma, q')$, where δ^ψ and q^ψ_{in} are the transition function and initial state of $\mathcal{A}'_\psi$. Finally, $G = \bigcup_{\varphi_i \in sf(\psi)} G^i$ and $B = \bigcup_{\varphi_i \in sf(\psi)} B^i$. The state q_{in} is transient and the state q_{check} constitute a singleton universal set of the HAA.

The arguments about the correctness of the construction, its size, and its depth, are similar to these in [17], and are given in the full version. □

4.3 Satisfiability

Theorem 4.5 *The satisfiability problem for mCTL* is 2EXPTIME-complete.*

Proof: We start with the upper bound. Consider an mCTL* formula ψ. By Theorem 4.4, there is an HAA $\mathcal{A}_\psi$ with $2^{O(|\psi|)}$ states, depth $O(|\psi|)$, and a satellite with $2^{2^{O(|\psi|)}}$ states such that $\mathcal{L}(\mathcal{A}_\psi)$ is exactly the set of $2^{sf(\psi)}$-labeled trees that are sound for ψ and satisfy ψ. The HAA $\mathcal{A}_\psi$ is nonempty iff ψ is satisfiable. By Theorem 4.2, the nonemptiness of $\mathcal{A}_\psi$ can be decided in time $2^{2^{O(|\psi|)}}$, so we are done.

It is left to prove the lower bound. By Theorem 3.1, each CTL* formula can be linearly translated to an equivalent mCTL* formula. The lower bound then follows from the fact CTL* satisfiability is 2EXPTIME-hard [35]. □

Note that the application of the 2EXPTIME lower bound of CTL* satisfiability is not possible for m$^-$CTL*, and the exact complexity of the satisfiability problem for this logic is left open.

4.4 Model checking

For CTL*, the automata-theoretic approach is similar for satisfiability and model checking: the HAA for a CTL* formula ψ accepts exactly all 2^{AP}-labeled trees that satisfy ψ, so satisfiability is reduced to emptiness and model checking to 1-letter emptiness of the product of the HAA with the system [17]. In the case of mCTL*, the need to execute the word automata for the path formulas from the root of the tree, has forced us to define the HAA with respect to $2^{sf(\psi)}$-labeled trees. While this was not a problem for satisfiability, it is a problem for model checking, where we need to take the product of the HAA with a Kripke structure that is labeled by 2^{AP}. Fortunately, this is not a real problem, as it is possible to guess an extension of the 2^{AP}-labeling to a $2^{sf(\psi)}$-labeling, and then let the HAA check the soundness of the guess.

Theorem 4.6 *Given an mCTL* formula ψ, we can construct an HAA $\mathcal{A}^{AP}_\psi$ with $2^{O(|\psi|)}$ states, depth $O(|\psi|)$, and a satellite with $2^{2^{O(|\psi|)}}$ states, such that $\mathcal{A}^{AP}_\psi$ runs on 2^{AP}-labeled trees and accepts exactly all trees that satisfy ψ.*

Proof: The construction is similar to the one described in Theorem 4.4, only that we have to adjust the HAA and its satellite to the alphabet 2^{AP}. Intuitively, instead of having the input tree labeled by subsets of $sf(\psi)$, we let the satellite guess the richer labels, and then let the HAA check the guess. Thus, the satellite is nondeterministic — on top of its deterministic transition we add a guess of the subset of $sf(\psi)$ to be read in the successor node. Yet, running the HAA on a 2^{AP}-labeled tree, and letting it check the guesses, guarantees that $word\_to(x)$ can be viewed as a word in $(2^{sf(\psi)})^*$ rather than a word in $(2^{AP})^*$. Accordingly, $\delta'(q_{in}, word\_to(x))$ is a singleton, as in the case of a deterministic satellite.

Formally, if in the construction in Theorem 4.4 we ended up with a satellite $\mathcal{U} = \langle 2^{sf(\psi)}, Q', \delta', q'_{in} \rangle$ and

HAA $\mathcal{A}_\psi = \langle 2^{sf(\psi)}, Q, \delta, q_{in}, \langle G, B \rangle \rangle$, now we have a satellite $\mathcal{U}_{AP} = \langle 2^{AP}, Q' \times 2^{sf(\psi)}, \delta'_{AP}, q'_{in} \rangle$ where for all $\langle q', \sigma \rangle \in Q' \times 2^{sf(\psi)}$ and $\sigma' \in 2^{AP}$, we have $\delta'_{AP}(\langle q', \sigma \rangle, \sigma') = \{\delta'(q', \sigma)\} \times 2^{sf(\psi)}$, and $\mathcal{A}_\psi^{AP} = \langle 2^{AP}, Q, \delta^{AP}, q_{in}, \langle G, B \rangle \rangle$, where for all $q \in Q, \sigma' \in 2^{AP}$, and $\langle q', \sigma \rangle \in Q' \times 2^{sf(\psi)}$, we have $\delta^{AP}(q, \sigma', \langle q', \sigma \rangle) = \delta(q, \sigma, q') \wedge \bigwedge_{\varphi_i \in \sigma} \delta^i(q^i_{in}, \sigma, q') \wedge \bigwedge_{\varphi_i \notin \sigma} \bar{\delta}^i(q^i_{in}, \sigma, q')$. □

Theorem 4.7 *The model-checking problem for mCTL* is EXPSPACE-complete, even for formulas of the form $AGE\xi$, where ξ is an LTL formula.*

Proof: We start with the upper bound. Consider an mCTL* formula ψ. By Theorem 4.4, there is an HAA $\mathcal{A}_\psi$ with $2^{O(|\psi|)}$ states, depth $O(|\psi|)$, and a satellite with $2^{2^{O(|\psi|)}}$ states, such that $\mathcal{L}(\mathcal{A}_\psi)$ is exactly the set of computation trees satisfying ψ. Consider a Kripke structure K. By [17], K satisfies ψ iff the 1-letter HAA obtained by taking the product of K with $\mathcal{A}_\psi$ is not empty. The product has $|K|2^{O(|\psi|)}$ states, depth $O(|\psi|)$, and a satellite with $2^{2^{O(|\psi|)}}$ states. Thus, by Theorem 4.3, its 1-letter nonemptiness problem can be solved in space $|\psi| \log^2(|K| 2^{2^{O(|\psi|)}}) = |\psi|(\log^2 |K| + 2^{O(|\psi|)} \log |K| + 2^{O(\psi)})$. Note that the complexity is only logarithmic in the size of the structure, and the exponential dependency is in the length of the formula, which is usually much smaller.

In order to prove the EXPSPACE lower bound, we do a reduction from the *exponential tiling* problem [21]. In this problem we are given a fixed set T of tiles, two relations $H, V \subseteq T \times T$, an integer n, a tuple of n tiles $\langle t_0, \ldots, t_{n-1} \rangle \in T^n$, and a tile $t_{fin} \in T$. The problem is to decide whether there is $m \geq 0$ such that it is possible to tile a $(2^n \times m)$-square so that horizontal neighbors belong to H, vertical neighbors belong to V, the first n tiles in the first row are $t_0, \ldots, t_{n-1}$, and the first tile in the last row is t_{fin}. Given an instance $\mathcal{T}$ of the tiling problem, we construct an mCTL* formula φ over a fixed set AP of atomic propositions such that a legal tiling for $\mathcal{T}$ exists iff the universal model M_{AP} for AP (that is, a clique in which each node is labeled by a different subset of AP) satisfies φ. The formula φ is of length polynomial in $\mathcal{T}$, and the size of M_{AP} is fixed, so we actually prove that the EXPSPACE lower bound holds for structures of a fixed size. Essentially, the formula φ describes a path that encodes a legal tiling. It is easy to describe all the conditions for such a tiling, except for the condition about vertical neighbors, which are exponentially far. This is where the memoryfulness of φ comes into the picture. By pointing to a tile in the present (using *present*), we can relate it with the tile below it. For the detailed proof, see the full version. Finally, in order to prove the lower bound for formulas of the form $AGE\xi$, we use the fact that pointing to the present with *present* can be emulated by pointing to a location in the computation in which some special event occurs. For the detailed proof, see the full version. □

Note that the lower-bound proof applies already for an mCTL* formula of the form $AGE\xi$, for an LTL formula ξ. Thus, the EXPSPACE lower bound applies also for model checking of the less expressive m⁻CTL*, the Pistore-Vardi logic, and Lamport's possibility properties. In addition, together with Theorem 3.3, it implies an EXPSPACE lower bound for the model-checking problem of $\text{CTL}^\star_{lp}$, a problem that was left open in [16] (see also [20]).

5 Discussion

We introduced and studied mCTL* — a variant of CTL* in which path quantification ranges over paths that start in the beginning of the execution of the system and go through the present. We argued for the appropriateness of mCTL* for sanity checks and for planning in nondeterministic domains, and showed that memoryful path quantification can lead to formulas that are exponentially more succinct. Studying the algorithmic properties of memoryful path quantification, we showed that while the transition from memoryless to memoryful path quantification does not make the satisfiability problem harder, it does make the model-checking problem exponentially harder.

Our complexity results shed some new light on the old debate on the relative merits of linear vs. branching time, cf. [18, 29, 34]. One position in favor of branching time argues that a branching-time logic such as CTL* subsumes the expressive power of linear-time logic, without increasing the complexity of model checking [11]. The analysis in [19, 27] show that true computation-tree reasoning requires memoryful path quantification. As we showed here, this results in an exponential increase in the complexity of model checking. Thus the expressiveness of branching-time logic does not come for free.

The fragment CTL of CTL* has received a lot of attention, and its model-checking problem can be solved in linear time [8]. One can also define the logics mCTL and m⁻CTL, which is the memoryful counterparts of CTL. Unfortunately, mCTL and m⁻CTL are not of much interest. As we show in the full version, their expressive power is very limited (essentially, the fact its path formulas cannot contain a Boolean assertion containing *present* makes mCTL as expressive as m⁻CTL, where present is lost with each application of a temporal operator), and still, their model-checking problem is at least NP-hard.

Acknowledgement We thank Philippe Schnoebelen for helpful discussions regarding the succinctness of $\text{CTL}^\star_{lp}$.

References

[1] F. Bacchus and F. Kabanza. Planning for temporally extended goals. *Ann. of Mathematics and Artificial Intelligence*, 22:5–27, 1998.

[2] D. Berwanger, E. Grädel, and S. Kreutzer. Once upon a time in a west - determinacy, definability, and complexity of path games. In *Proc. 10th LPR*, LNCS 2850, pages 229–243, 2003.

[3] M. Brown and V. Goranko. An extended branching-time ockhamist temporal logic. *Journal of Logic, Language and Information*, 8(2):143–166, 1999.

[4] A. Cimatti, M. Roveri, and P. Traverso. Automatic OBDD-based generation of universal plans in non-deterministic domains. In *Proc. 15th AAAI*, pages 875–881, 1998.

[5] A. Cimatti, M. Roveri, and P. Traverso. Strong planning in non-deterministic domains via model checking. In *Proc. of 4th AIPS*, pages 36–43, 1998.

[6] E.M. Clarke and I.A. Draghicescu. Expressibility results for linear-time and branching-time logics. LNCS 354, pages 428–437, 1988.

[7] E.M. Clarke and E.A. Emerson. Design and synthesis of synchronization skeletons using branching time temporal logic. In *Proc. Workshop on Logic of Programs*, LNCS 131, pages 52–71, 1981.

[8] E.M. Clarke, E.A. Emerson, and A.P. Sistla. Automatic verification of finite-state concurrent systems using temporal logic specifications. *ACM TOPLAS*, 8(2):244–263, 1986.

[9] E.A. Emerson and J.Y. Halpern. Sometimes and not never revisited: On branching versus linear time. *JACM*, 33(1):151–178, 1986.

[10] E.A. Emerson and C. Jutla. The complexity of tree automata and logics of programs. In *Proc. 29th FOCS*, pages 328–337, 1988.

[11] E.A. Emerson and C.-L. Lei. Modalities for model checking: Branching time logic strikes back. In *Proc. 20th POPL*, pages 84–96, 1985.

[12] N. Markey F. Laroussinie and Ph. Schnoebelen. Temporal logic with forgettable past. In *Proc. 17th LICS*, pages 383–392, 2002.

[13] M. Fox, D. Long, and K. Halsey. An investigation into the expressive power of PDDL2.1. In *Proc. 16th ECAI*, pages 328–342, 2004.

[14] T. Hafer and W. Thomas. Computation tree logic CTL* and path quantifiers in the monadic theory of the binary tree. In *Proc. 14th ICALP*, LNCS 267, pages 269–279, 1987.

[15] D. Kozen. Results on the propositional μ-calculus. *TCS*, 27:333–354, 1983.

[16] O. Kupferman and A. Pnueli. Once and for all. In *Proc. 10th LICS*, pages 25–35, 1995.

[17] O. Kupferman, M.Y. Vardi, and P. Wolper. An automata-theoretic approach to branching-time model checking. *JACM*, 47(2):312–360, 2000.

[18] L. Lamport. Sometimes is sometimes "not never" - on the temporal logic of programs. In *Proc. 7th POPL*, pages 174–185, 1980.

[19] L. Lamport. Proving possibility properties. *TCS*, 206(1-2):341–352, 1998.

[20] F. Laroussinie and Ph. Schnoebelen. Specification in CTL+past for verification in CTL. *I& C*, 156(1-2):236–263, 2000.

[21] H.R. Lewis. Complexity of solvable cases of the decision problem for the predicate calculus. In *Foundations of Computer Science*, volume 19, pages 35–47, 1978.

[22] Z. Manna and A. Pnueli. *The Temporal Logic of Reactive and Concurrent Systems: Specification*. Springer, 1992.

[23] N. Markey. Temporal logic with past is exponentially more succinct. *EATCS Bulletin*, 79:122–128, 2003.

[24] R. Milner. *A Calculus of Communicating Systems*, LNCS 92, 1980.

[25] D.E. Muller, A. Saoudi, and P. E. Schupp. Weak alternating automata give a simple explanation of why most temporal and dynamic logics are decidable in exponential time. In *Proc. 3rd LICS*, pages 422–427, 1988.

[26] D.E. Muller and P.E. Schupp. Alternating automata on infinite trees. *TCS*, 54:267–276, 1987.

[27] M. Pistore and M. Vardi. The planning spectrum – one, two, three, infinity. In *Proc. 18th LICS*, pages 234–243, 2003.

[28] A. Pnueli. The temporal logic of programs. In *Proc. 18th FOCS*, pages 46–57, 1977.

[29] A. Pnueli. Linear and branching structures in the semantics and logics of reactive systems. In *Proc. 12th ICALP*, LNCS 194, pages 15–32, 1985.

[30] A. Pnueli and R. Rosner. On the synthesis of a reactive module. In *Proc. 16th POPL*, pages 179–190, 1989.

[31] R.S. Streett and E.A. Emerson. An automata theoretic decision procedure for the propositional μ-calculus. *I& C*, 81(3):249–264, 1989.

[32] W. Thomas. Automata on infinite objects. *Handbook of Theoretical Computer Science*, pages 133–191, 1990.

[33] M.Y. Vardi. Reasoning about the past with two-way automata. In *25th ICALP*, LNCS 1443, pages 628–641, 1998.

[34] M.Y. Vardi. Branching vs. linear time: Final showdown. In *7th TACAS*, LNCS 2031, pages 1–22, 2001.

[35] M.Y. Vardi and L. Stockmeyer. Improved upper and lower bounds for modal logics of programs. In *Proc 17th STOC*, pages 240–251, 1985.

[36] M.Y. Vardi and P. Wolper. Reasoning about infinite computations. *I&C*, 115(1):1–37, November 1994.

[37] T. Wilke. CTL$^+$ is exponentially more succinct than CTL. In *19th FST& TCS*, LNCS 1738, pages 110–121, 1999.

[38] P. Wolper. Temporal logic can be more expressive. In *Proc. 22nd FOCS*, pages 340–348, 1981.

Faster Solutions of Rabin and Streett Games*

Nir Piterman†
EPFL - I&C - MTC
Lausanne, Switzerland

Amir Pnueli
Weizmann Institute of Science
Rehovot, Israel

Abstract

In this paper we improve the complexity of solving Rabin and Streett games to approximately the square root of previous bounds. We introduce direct Rabin and Streett ranking that are a sound and complete way to characterize the winning sets in the respective games. By computing directly and explicitly the ranking we can solve such games in time $O(mn^{k+1}kk!)$ *and space* $O(nk)$ *for Rabin and* $O(nkk!)$ *for Streett where* n *is the number of states,* m *the number of transitions, and* k *the number of pairs in the winning condition. In order to prove completeness of the ranking method we give a recursive fixpoint characterization of the winning regions in these games. We then show that by keeping intermediate values during the fixpoint evaluation, we can solve such games symbolically in time* $O(n^{k+1}k!)$ *and space* $O(n^{k+1}k!)$. *These results improve on the current bounds of* $O(mn^{2k}k!)$ *time in the case of direct (symbolic) solution or* $O(m(nk^2k!)^k)$ *in the case of reduction to parity games.*

1 Introduction

One of the most ambitious and challenging problems in reactive system construction is the automatic synthesis of programs and (digital) designs from logical specifications. First identified as Church's problem [4], several methods have been proposed for its solution (cf. [2, 23]). The two prevalent approaches to solving the synthesis problem are by reducing it to the emptiness problem of tree automata, and viewing it as the solution of a two-person game. These two problems are essentially equivalent with efficient reductions between them [28].

A *two-player game* is a finite or infinite directed graph where the vertices are partitioned between the two players. A *play* proceeds by moving a token between the vertices of the graph. If the token is found on a vertex of player 0, she chooses an outgoing edge and moves the token along that edge. If the token is found on a vertex of player 1, she gets to choose the outgoing edge. The result is an infinite sequence of vertices. In order to determine the winner in a play we consider the *infinity set*, the set of states occurring infinitely often in the play. Then, there are several methods to define acceptance conditions that determine which infinity sets are winning for which player.

Two of the most natural such acceptance conditions are *Rabin* [22] and *Streett* [25]. Both conditions are defined using a set of pairs of subsets of the vertices of the graph. In order to win the Rabin condition over $\{\langle G_1, R_1\rangle, \ldots, \langle G_k, R_k\rangle\}$ the infinity set has to intersect G_i and not intersect R_i for some i. The Streett winning condition is the dual of the Rabin condition. In order to win the Streett condition over $\{\langle G_1, R_1\rangle, \ldots, \langle G_k, R_k\rangle\}$ the infinity set has to either be disjoint from G_i or to intersect R_i for every i. Both Rabin and Streett acceptance conditions are as general as every other *ω-regular* acceptance condition. That is, if the winning condition is defined using some automaton over infinite words (cf. [26]) or as the set of possible infinity sets (*Muller* condition) there is a way to augment the game with a *deterministic monitor* such that the winning condition over the states of the monitor is either Rabin or Streett. Another general acceptance condition is the *parity* acceptance condition [8]. In the parity condition , every vertex has a priority and a play is won if the minimal priority visited infinitely often is even. We mention parity games because our algorithms are derived from similar algorithms that solve parity games.

Rabin conditions arise naturally when the winning condition is supplied in the form of a nondeterminitic Büchi automaton over infinite words. In such a case, the standard approach to solving the game is by converting the nondeterminitic Büchi automaton to a deterministic Rabin automaton [24]. A solution to the Rabin game is then used to solve the original game.

Streett conditions arise naturally when considering synthesis of controllers from temporal logic specifications. In

*This research was supported in part by the Israel Science Foundation (grant no.106/02-1), European community project Prosyd, and the John von-Neumann Minerva center for Verification of Reactive Systems.

†Part of this research was performed while this author was visiting the Weizmann Institute.

many such cases, the controller has to supply *strong fairness*, that is, if some transition / resource is enabled / requested infinitely often it should be taken / granted infinitely often. These kind of requirements translate naturally to Streett conditions.

In [20] we presented a framework for synthesizing a design from a temporal logic specification by converting it into a two-player game, where the synthesized design plays against an adversary environment, striving to maintain the temporal specification. In that paper, we assumed that both the environment and the design are only constrained by *justice* (weak fairness) requirements. As a result of this restricting hypothesis, the resulting games were generalized Street games with $k = 1$. A strong motivation for the research reported in this paper is to remove this fairness restriction and allow *compassion* (strong fairness) both in the environment and the synthesized design. This can give rise to Street games with arbitrary k.

Consider for example the following specification of an arbiter. The arbiter controls the grant signals for n clients. Each client, has a request signal r_i which it may raise at will. Once raised, the agent may withdraw the request but only after at least one cycle. The controller has to allocate grants (permission to access a shared resource) among the clients, so that no two clients may access the resource at the same time (*mutual exclusion*) and so that every client that requests the resource infinitely often is granted the resource infinitely often. The natural translation of this scenario into a game results in a Streett game with one strong fairness requirement for every client.

Rabin and Streett games are known to be NP-complete and co-NP-complete respectively [7]. Emerson and Jutla [7] and independently Pnueli and Rosner [21] proposed algorithms that solve Rabin and Streett games in time $O((nk)^{3k})$ where n is the number of vertices and k the number of pairs. This was later improved by Kupferman and Vardi to $O(mn^{2k}k!)$ where m is the number of edges [17]. Recently, a different solution with the same complexity was given by Horn [12].[1] It is also possible to solve Rabin and Streett games by reducing them to parity games [8]. This reduction is by adding a deterministic monitor with $k^2k!$ states. The resulting parity game has $nk^2k!$ states and $2k$ priorities. Using the best current solution to parity game [13], we can solve Rabin and Streett games in time $O((nk^2k!)^k)$ (enumerative algorithm).

As Rabin and Streett conditions are duals, it is enough to reason about one of them in order to *decide* the winner in a game. A player is winning according to the Streett condition iff the other player is losing according to the Rabin condition and vice versa. In order to *synthesize* programs it is not sufficient to know who is the winner; we also need the *winning strategy*. That is, what is the sequence of moves that the winning player has to perform in order to ensure her win. In order to produce the winning strategy we have to reason separately about Rabin and Streett games. This way, we can produce the winning strategy for the player that interests us (be she Rabin or Streett). It is well known that winning strategies in Rabin games are *memoryless*, i.e., depend only on the current position in the game [6]. On the other hand, winning strategies in Streett games may require exponential memory [5, 12]. It follows, that the way to produce the winning strategy may be very different.

Solutions for parity games passed also a long line of improvements. For many years, the best solution to parity games had been the symbolic fixpoint evaluation algorithm of Emerson and Lei [9, 8]. The complexity of solving a parity game using this approach is mn^k where k is the number of priorities. One major improvement of the classical algorithm has been the observation of Long et al. that by saving intermediate values of the fixpoint computation the run time can be improved to the square root, i.e., $O(n^{\frac{k}{2}})$ [18]. Long et al. show that by storing intermediate values of the fixpoint computation they can start fixpoint evaluations from better approximations. Unfortunately, the space complexity is also $O(n^{\frac{k}{2}})$.

Jurdziński matched the smaller upper bound while reducing space complexity to linear [13]. His algorithm computes the winning region in a parity game by computing ranks for each vertex. Every vertex with a finite rank is winning and all the rest are losing. The direct rank computation can be accomplished in time $O(mn^{\frac{k}{2}})$. A disadvantage of this approach is that it cannot be applied symbolically. Thus, forcing enumerative handling of each vertex.

Here we generalize these two approaches to Rabin and Streett games. We give an enumerative algorithm that solves Rabin and Streett games in time $O(mn^{k+1}kk!)$ and $O(mn^kkk!)$ respectively and space $O(nk)$ and $O(nkk!)$ respectively. We give a symbolic algorithm that solves Rabin and Streett games in time $O(n^{k+1}k!)$ and space $O(n^{k+1}k!)$.

We introduce Rabin and Streett ranking which resemble Jurdziński's ranking in that every winning state has a finite rank and the ranking induces a winning strategy.[2] The direct computation of these ranks requires the square root of the time of previous algorithms. Recall that in the worst case a strategy to win a Streett game may require a memory of size $k!$ [5, 12]. Thus, it seems that the memory consumption is close to optimal.

In order to prove completeness of the ranking method we introduce recursive fixpoint algorithms that compute the winning regions in Rabin and Streett games[1]. These algorithms match the best previous upper bounds of $O(mn^{2k}k!)$

[1]These solutions, as well as our recursive fixpoint algorithm (in Section 5), are related to McNaughton's solution of Muller games [19] when specialized to Rabin and Streett conditions. See also expositions in [29, 5].

[2]Our Rabin and Streett ranking may be actually Klarlund and Kozen's Rabin measures when restricted to a finite domain [15, 16].

time and resemble the fixpoint characterization of parity games [8].

We then combine the fixpoint characterization of the winning regions and Long et al.'s method of fixpoint acceleration [18]. We show that by storing intermediate values of the fixpoints in our algorithm we can accelerate the fixpoint computation by starting the computation of fixpoints from better approximations. The result is a symbolic algorithm that matches the time of the enumerative algorithm.

From our algorithms it follows that Rabin and Streett games are in fact parity games with different orders on the pairs. This has been implicit in the conversion of Rabin and Streett games to parity games, as well as in the solution of Kupferman and Vardi for Rabin games [17]. We are the first to take advantage of this connection to improve the run time of the algorithms for Rabin and Streett games almost to a factor of $k!$. In subsequent work we show that this can be applied to every other solution of parity games (e.g., [27, 1, 14]).

2 Games

A *game* is a tuple $G = \langle V, E, W\rangle$ where V is the set of states of the game, V is partitioned to V_0 and V_1 the sets of states of player 0 and player 1 respectively, $E \subseteq V \times V$ is the transition relation, and $W \subseteq V^\omega$ is the winning condition of player 0. We assume that for every $v \in V$ there exists some state $v' \in V$ such that $(v, v') \in E$.

A *play* in G is a maximal (hence infinite) sequence of locations $p = v_0 v_1 \cdots$ such that forall $i \geq 0$ we have $(v_i, v_{i+1}) \in E$. For a play p we define $inf(p)$ to be the set of states occurring infinitely often in p. Formally, $inf(p) = \{v \mid v = v_i \text{ for infinitely many } is\}$. A play p is winning for player 0 if $p \in W$. Otherwise, player 1 wins.

A strategy for player 0 is a partial function $f : V^* \times V_0 \to V$ such that whenever $f(pv)$ is defined $(v, f(pv)) \in E$. We say that a play $p = v_0 v_1 \cdots$ is *f-conform* if whenever $v_i \in V_0$ we have $v_{i+1} = f(v_0 \cdots v_i)$. The strategy f is *winning from* v if every f-conform play that starts in v is winning for player 0. We say that *player 0 wins* from v if she has a winning strategy. The *winning region* of player 0, is the set of states from which player 0 wins. We denote the winning region of player 0 by W_0. A strategy, winning strategy, win, and winning region are defined dually for player 1. We *solve* a game by computing the winning regions W_0 and W_1. For the kind of games handled in this paper W_0 and W_1 form a partition of V [11].

In this paper we solve Rabin and Streett games. Both Rabin and Streett conditions are defined by a set of pairs of subsets of states. Formally, a Rabin condition is $\alpha = \{\langle G_1, R_1\rangle, \ldots, \langle G_k, R_k\rangle\}$ where forall i we have G_i and R_i are subsets of V. The Rabin condition α defines the set W of infinite sequences $p \in V^\omega$ such that for some i we have $inf(p)$ intersects G_i and $inf(p)$ does not intersect R_i. A Streett condition is $\alpha = \{\langle G_1, R_1\rangle, \ldots, \langle G_k, R_k\rangle\}$. The Streett condition α defines the set W of infinite sequences $p \in V^\omega$ such that forall i we have $inf(p)$ intersects G_i implies $inf(p)$ intersects R_i. The Streett condition is the dual of the Rabin condition; when a play is winning according to the Rabin condition it is losing according to the Streett condition and vice versa. It follows that when the winning condition for player 0 is the Rabin condition α then the Streett condition α is the winning condition for player 1. In order to partition the set of states to the winning regions it is enough to consider one of the two conditions. For example, we compute the winning region of player 0 according to the Rabin condition and its complement is the winning region for player 1 according to the Streett condition. However, when we are interested also in the winning strategy, we may be required to solve separately the Rabin and the Streett winning conditions according to the winning strategy we wish to construct. We abuse notation and write $G = \langle V, E, \alpha\rangle$ for a Rabin or Streett condition α.

3 Rabin and Streett Ranking

In this section we show how to define Rabin and Streett ranking. We prove that our ranking induces a winning strategy for player 0 and that it is defined on the winning region. Intuitively, the ranking measures the distance towards achieving small milestones during a play. By reducing the distance to these milestones we get to them, which eventually leads us to winning the game.

3.1 Rabin Ranking

Consider a game $G=\langle V, E, \alpha\rangle$ where $\alpha=\{\langle G_1, R_1\rangle, \ldots, \langle G_k, R_k\rangle\}$ is a Rabin winning condition. Player 0 wins an infinite play p if there exists $\langle G_i, R_i\rangle \in \alpha$ such that $inf(p) \cap G_i \neq \emptyset$ and $inf(p) \cap R_i = \emptyset$. We now define formally the range of the ranking function and the ranking function itself.

Let $\Pi(k)$ denote the set of permutations over $[1..k]$. Given a permutation $\pi = j_1 j_2 \cdots j_k \in \Pi(k)$ we denote j_i by π_i. The *Rabin domain* for α over V is $D_R(\alpha, V) = \{i_0 j_1 i_1 j_2 \cdots j_k i_k \mid i_0 \cdots i_k \in [0..n]^{k+1} \text{ and } j_1 \cdots j_k \in \Pi(k)\} \cup \{\infty\}$. That is, the domain contains the interleaving of a $k+1$ tuple of integers with a permutation over $[1..k]$. Every integer is bounded by n. For simplicity of notations we write D_R and Π instead of $D_R(\alpha, V)$ and $\Pi(k)$. Given $d = i_0 j_1 \cdots j_k i_k \in D_R$ we denote by $\pi(d)$ the permutation $j_1 \cdots j_k$ and by $m(d)$ the tuple $i_0 \cdots i_k \in [0..n]^k$. We order D_R according to the lexicographic ordering with ∞ as maximal element.

A *Rabin ranking* over V is $r : V \to D_R$. Intuitively, the ranking $i_0 j_1 \cdots j_k i_k$ fixes an order $j_1 \cdots j_k$ on the Rabin pairs. This is the order of importance between the pairs. It means that it is most important to visit G_{j_1} while avoiding R_{j_1}. We are also happy if we avoid R_{j_1} and R_{j_2} and visit G_{j_2} infinitely often and so on. A visit to R_{j_l} is allowed only by changing the importance order of the pairs that are less important than j_l (and j_l itself). We allow the order to change only to lower orders (according to the lexicographic ordering on permutations). This means that R_{j_l} can be visited only finitely often. The value i_l in the sequence $i_0 \cdots i_k$ measures the worst possible number of steps until a visit to G_{j_l} (while avoiding $R_{j_{l'}}$ forall $l' \leq l$). Whenever we visit G_{j_l} we are so happy that we allow to change the order of the less important pairs and to increase the distance to Gs for less important pairs. Finally, i_0 is intuitively the number of times that R_{j_1} may be visited (forcing a change to a lower permutation). Formally, we have the following.

Given a node $v \in V$ and a Rabin ranking r we denote by $best(v)$ the minimal rank of a successor of v in case that $v \in V_0$ or the maximal rank of a successor of v in case that $v \in V_1$. Formally,

$$best(v) = \begin{cases} min_{(v,w)\in E}(r(w)) & v \in V_0 \\ max_{(v,w)\in E}(r(w)) & v \in V_1 \end{cases}$$

We say that a Rabin ranking is *good* if for every state v such that $r(v) \neq \infty$ we have $best(v)$ is *better* than $r(v)$. Let $r(v) = i_0 j_1 i_1 \cdots i_k$ and and $best(v) = i'_0 j'_1 i'_1 \cdots i'_k$. We say that $best(v)$ is *better* than $r(v)$ if $i_0 > i'_0$ or $i_0 = i'_0$ and $best(v)$ is *better*$_1$ than $r(v)$. We say that $best(v)$ is *better*$_l$ than $r(v)$ if one of the following holds.

- $j_l > j'_l$.
- $j_l = j'_l$, $v \models \overline{R}_{j_l}$, and $i_l > i'_l$.
- $j_l = j'_l$, $v \models \overline{R}_{j_l}$, and $v \models G_{j_l}$.
- $j_l = j'_l$, $v \models \overline{R}_{j_l}$, $i_l = i'_l$, and $best(v)$ is better$_{l+1}$ than $r(v)$.

If one of the first three conditions holds we say that $best(v)$ is *strictly better*$_l$ than $r(v)$. It is simple to see that if $v \in V_1$ and $best(v)$ is better than $r(v)$ then for every node w such that $(v, w) \in E$ we have $r(w)$ is better than $r(v)$. This follows from $r(w)$ being at most $best(v)$.

We show that Rabin ranking is sound and complete. We show soundness by proving that the strategy of choosing the minimal possible successor is winning for player 0. Consider a play where player 0 uses this strategy. It follows that the sequence of ranks gets better and better (i.e., the rank of every state is better than that of its predecessor). The only way to create an infinite sequence of ranks that get better is by allowing the suffix of the rank to increase (i.e., leave the prefix $i_0 \cdots j_l$ fixed and increase $i_l j_{l+1} \cdots j_k i_k$). By the definition of better, the only way to increase the suffix of the rank is for some l to have that the rank is strictly better$_l$. There is some minimal l for which the ranks get strictly better$_l$ infinitely often. Consider the point in the play from which the ranks are always better$_l$ and infinitely often strictly better$_l$. In order to visit R_{j_l} the rank has to be strictly better$_{l'}$ for some $l' < l$ and this is impossible. Thus, R_{j_l} is never visited beyond this point. In order to allow infinitely many strictly better$_l$, it has to be the case that G_{j_l} is visited infinitely often. Formally, we have the following.

Claim 1 *Given a good Rabin ranking r, player 0 wins the Rabin game from every state v such that $r(v) \neq \infty$.*

Proof: Consider the following strategy. From a state $v \in V_1$ choose the successor w such that $r(w)$ is minimal. We show that this strategy is winning.

Consider an infinite play $v_0 v_1 \cdots$ that conforms to this strategy. Let $r_0 r_1 \cdots$ denote the sequence of ranks such that $r_m = r(v_m)$ and $r_m = i_0^m j_1^m i_1^m \cdots j_k^m i_k^m$. From the definition of good ranking it follows that it is always the case that r_{m+1} is better than r_m. Let l be the minimal value such that there exist infinitely many m such that r_{m+1} is strictly better$_l$ than r_m. There exists m' such that forall $m > m'$ and forall $l' < l$ we have r_{m+1} is not strictly better$_{l'}$ from r_m. So for all $l' < l$ and forall $m > m'$ we have $j_{l'}^m = j_{l'}^{m+1}$, $v_m \models \overline{R}_{j_{l'}^m}$, and $i_{l'}^m = i_{l'}^{m+1}$. Similarly, there exists $u \in [1..k]$ and $m'' > m'$ such that forall $m > m'$ we have $j_l^m = u$. Consider the pair $\langle G_u, R_u \rangle$ and the suffix of the play starting from m''. For every $m > m''$ we have r_{m+1} is better than r_m, hence $v_m \models \overline{R}_u$. Furthermore, whenever r_{m+1} is strictly better$_u$ than r_m then either $i_u^m > i_u^{m+1}$ or $v_m \models G_u$. We conclude that the play is winning according to the pair $\langle G_u, R_u \rangle$. □

We show completeness by proving that the algorithm in Fig. 3 induces a good Rabin ranking on the entire winning set of player 0. Intuitively, a state gets a ranking according to the first time it is discovered by the least fixpoints in the algorithm. The values j_l and i_l are determined by lth nested call to `Rabin`. Every least fixpoint is in a loop that goes over all the pairs that are still free. The pair used in this loop gives the value j_l. Then the number of iteration of the least fixpoint gives value i_l. In order for a state to be discovered its successors have to already be discovered, which implies that successors have a better rank.

Theorem 2 *Player 0 wins the Rabin game from v iff there exists a good Rabin ranking such that $r(v) \neq \infty$.*

3.2 Streett Ranking

Consider a game $G{=}\langle V, E, \alpha \rangle$ where $\alpha{=}\{\langle G_1, R_1 \rangle, \ldots, \langle G_k, R_k \rangle\}$ is a Streett winning condition. Player 0 wins an infinite play p if forall i we have $inf(p) \cap G_i \neq \emptyset$ implies $inf(p) \cap R_i \neq \emptyset$. We now define formally the range of the ranking function and the ranking function itself.

The *Streett domain* for α over V is $[0..n]^k \cup \{\infty\}$, denoted by $D_S(\alpha, V)$. We order $D_S(\alpha, V)$ according to the lexicographic order with ∞ as maximal element. Given $m \in D_s(\alpha, V)$ we denote by m_l the lth entry in m. Consider the set $\Pi(k)$. Let $\pi = j_1 \cdots j_k \in \Pi(k)$ be some permutation. We define what it means to increase the lth entry in π. We increase the lth entry by leaving the first $l-1$ entries unchanged. For the lth entry we choose the next available value among the rest of the entries. If the lth entry is already the maximal among these entries then we go back to the minimal. For the entries $l+1, ..., k$ we take the unused entries in increasing order. Let $\pi = j_1 \cdots j_k$. We set $inc_l(\pi)$ to be the permutation $j_1 \cdots j_{l-1} j'_l \cdots j'_k$ such that if $j_l = max(j_l, \dots j_k)$ then $j'_l = min(j_l, \cdots, j_k)$ and if $j_l < max(j_l, \dots, j_k)$ then j'_l is set to the minimal value in $j_l, \dots, j_k$ such that $j'_l > j_l$. Then, we order $\{j_l, \dots, j_k\} - \{j'_l\}$ in increasing order and this completes the permutation. For example, $inc_k(\pi)$ is π, $inc_1(123)$ is 213, and $inc_2(123)$ is 132. As before, we write D_s and Π instead of $D_s(\alpha, V)$ and $\Pi(k)$.

A *Streett ranking* over V is $r : V \times \Pi \rightarrow D_s$. That is, with every state $v \in V$ and every permutation $\pi \in \Pi$ we associate a rank in D_s. Intuitively, the ranking $r(v, \pi) = i_1 \cdots i_k$ is a rank according to the order π on the pairs. As before, it is most important to visit R_{j_1}. We are also happy if we avoid G_{j_1} and visit R_{j_2} and so on. Intuitively, i_l counts how many visits to G_{j_l} are possible until a visit to R_{j_l}. In particular, either G_{j_l} is visited finitely often, or after every visit to G_{j_l} there is a visit to R_{j_l}. Whenever we visit R_{j_l} we switch to pursue a visit to $R_{j_{l'}}$ for one of the next 'less important' pairs. We do this by replacing the permutation π by a permutation π' that agrees with π on the $l-1$ first entries. Thus, we continue to avoid $G_{j_{l''}}$ for $l'' < l$ and visit (infinitely often) $R_{j_{l'}}$ for $l' \geq l$. Formally, we have the following.

For every state v and permutation π, we denote by $best(v, \pi)$ the rank of the minimal successor of v in case that $v \in V_0$ or the rank of the maximal successor of V in case that $v \in V_1$. Let $\pi = j_1 \cdots j_k$, if $v \in R_{j_l}$ for some l then we consider the rank of the successors according to the permutation $inc_l(\pi)$. Formally,

$$best(v,\pi) = \begin{cases} min_{(v,w)\in E}(r(w, inc_l(\pi))) & v \in V_0 \text{ and } v \in R_{j_l} \\ min_{(v,w)\in E}(r(w,\pi)) & v \in V_0 \text{ and } \forall l.\ v \notin R_{j_l} \\ max_{(v,w)\in E}(r(w, inc_l(\pi))) & v \in V_1 \text{ and } v \in R_{j_l} \\ max_{(v,w)\in E}(r(w,\pi)) & v \in V_1 \text{ and } \forall l.\ v \notin R_{j_l} \end{cases}$$

We say that a Streett ranking is *good* if for every state v and $\pi \in \Pi$ such that $r(v, \pi) \neq \infty$ we have $best(v, \pi)$ is *better* than $r(v, \pi)$. Let $\pi = j_1 \cdots j_k$, $r(v, \pi) = i_1 \cdots i_k$, and $best(v, \pi) = i'_1 \cdots i'_k$. We say that $best(v, \pi)$ is *better* than $r(v, \pi)$ if it is *better*$_1$ than $r(v, \pi)$. We say that $best(v, \pi)$ is *better*$_l$ than $r(v, \pi)$ if one of the following holds.

- $i_l > i'_l$.
- $v \models R_{j_l}$ and $best(v, inc_l(\pi)) \neq \infty$.
- $i_l = i'_l$, $v \models \neg G_{j_l}$, and $best(v, \pi)$ is better$_{l+1}$ than $r(v, \pi)$.

Finally, $best(v, \pi)$ is *better*$_{k+1}$ than $r(v, \pi)$ if $best(v, \pi) \neq \infty$. It is simple to see that if $v \in V_1$ and $best(v, \pi)$ is better than $r(v, \pi)$ then for every node w such that $(v, w) \in E$ we have $r(w, \pi)$ is better than $r(v, \pi)$.

We show that Streett ranking is sound and complete. We show soundness by proving that the rank induces a winning strategy. Player 0 uses a permutation in Π_k as memory value. As long as the memory value is π, player 0 uses the ranking $r(\cdot, \pi)$ to determine her next move. While playing with memory $\pi = j_1 \cdots j_k$, player 0 tries to minimize the rank $r(\cdot, \pi)$. Whenever the set R_{j_l} is visited, player 0 chooses the least j' in $j_{l+1}, \dots, j_k$ that is greater than j_l (if no such value exists then the minimal in $j_{l+1}, \dots, j_k$) and changes her memory value to $j_1 \cdots j_{l-1} j', j'_{l+1} \cdots j'_k$ where $j'_{l+1} \cdots j'_k$ are the remaining pairs in increasing order. Consider a play where player 0 uses this strategy. It follows that as long as the memory does not change all parts G of pairs are not visited. One option is to eventually remain with constant memory, which implies that $G_{l'}$ forall l' are visited finitely often. Otherwise, the memory changes infinitely often. There is a point l for which the memory changes around point l infinitely often. It follows that all $G_{l'}$ for $l' < l$ are visited finitely often and all $R_{l''}$ for $l'' \geq l$ are visited infinitely often. Formally, we have the following.

Claim 3 *Given a good Streett ranking r, player 0 wins the Streett game from every state v such that for some permutation $\pi \in \Pi$ we have $r(v, \pi) \neq \infty$.*

Proof: We construct a strategy that uses as memory a permutation from Π. The initial value of this memory is a permutation π such that $r(v, \pi) \neq \infty$. We define the strategy.

From a state $v \in V_0$ with memory $\pi \in \Pi$ apply *policy*$_1$. Let $\pi = j_1 \cdots j_k$, $r(v, \pi) = i_1 \cdots i_k$, and $best(v, \pi) = i'_1 \cdots i'_k$. In order to apply *policy*$_l$ we do the first possible option of the following.

- If $i'_l < i_l$ then choose w for which $r(w, \pi) = best(v, \pi)$.
- If $v \models R_{j_l}$, update the memory to $\pi' = inc_l(\pi)$. Choose some successor w such that $r(w, inc_l(\pi)) = best(v, \pi)$.
- If $i'_l = i_l$ and $v \models \overline{R}_{j_l}$ then apply policy$_{l+1}$.

In order to apply policy $k+1$ we simply choose some successor w for which $r(w, \pi) = best(v, \pi)$. It is simple to see that if the Streett ranking is good then from a state v and permutation π such that $r(v, \pi)$ is finite it is possible to apply this strategy. We have to show that this strategy is winning.

Consider an infinite play $v_0 v_1 \cdots$ that conforms to this strategy and let $\pi_0 \pi_1 \cdots$ be the sequence of memory values that is used in the application of the strategy. Let $\pi_m = j_1^m \cdots j_k^m$. Let $r_0 r_1 \cdots$ denote the sequence of ranks such that $r_m = r(v_m, \pi_m)$ and let $r_m = i_1^m \cdots i_k^m$. We have to show that $v_0 v_1 \cdots$ is winning for player 0.

Let l be the minimal value such that there are infinitely many locations such that policy$_l$ is applied while policy$_{l+1}$ is not applied (that is, one of the first two options in policy$_l$ is chosen). There exists m' such that forall $m > m'$ it is always the case that policy$_l$ is applied (sometimes by calling policy$_{l+1}$). It follows that there exist values $j_1 \cdots j_{l-1}$ such that forall $m > m'$ we have $j_1^m \cdots j_{l-1}^m = j_1 \cdots j_{l-1}$. From the definition of good ranking and the strategy it follows that forall $m > m'$, forall $u < l$ we have $v_m \notin G_{j_u}$. Hence, all the pairs $\langle G_{j_u}, R_{j_u} \rangle$ for $u < l$ are satisfied. Consider the values $j_l \cdots j_k$. As policy$_l$ is applied infinitely often it follows that for every $u \geq l$ we have R_{j_u} is visited infinitely often. It follows that also the pairs $\langle G_u, R_u \rangle$ for $u \geq l$ are satisfied and the play is winning for player 0. □

We show completeness by proving that the algorithm in Fig. 4 induces a good Streett ranking on the entire winning region of player 1. As before, a state gets a ranking according to the first time it is discovered by the least fixpoints in the algorithm. This time, because of the change of order of least and greatest fixpoints every state is included in the computation of the greatest fixpoints for every possible choice of pairs. Thus, for a given permutation π, the rank of v associated with π is the time of discovery of v when the maximal fixpoints are working on the permutation π. As before, at the time of discovery of a state, its successors have already been discovered, which implies that successors have a better rank.

Theorem 4 *Player 1 wins the Streett game from v iff there exists a good Streett ranking and permutation π such that $r(v, \pi) \neq \infty$.*

4 Computing Ranks Explicitly

So far we have established the existence of good ranking systems for Rabin and Streett games. We do not know yet how to compute such rankings. In this section we generalize Jurdziński's explicit ranking computation of parity games to Rabin and Streett ranking [13]. As in the case of parity, the minimal good ranking is a least fixpoint of a monotone operator on a complete lattice. By Knaster-Tarski theorem there exists a least good ranking and there exists a simple lifting algorithm that computes it. From previous section it follows that the least good ranking is defined on the winning region. Etessami et al. show exactly how to encode Jurdziński's algorithm to get the stated time and space bounds [10]. We extend their efficient implementation to the more general case of Rabin and Streett rankings.

Consider the set of possible Rabin rankings $r : V \longrightarrow D_R$. We say that $r_1 \sqsubseteq r_2$ if for every $v \in V$ we have $r_1(v) \leq r_2(v)$. The resulting structure is a complete lattice. We use $r_1 \sqsubset r_2$ to denote $r_1 \sqsubseteq r_2$ and $r_1 \neq r_2$. We now define the lifting operator. Given a ranking $r : V \longrightarrow D_R$ and a state $v \in V$ we set $prog(r, v)$ to be the least value $d \in D_R$ such that $best(v)$ is better than d. We define $lift(r, v)$ to be the following function.

$$lift(r,v)(u) = \begin{cases} r(u) & u \neq v \\ max\{r(u), prog(r,u)\} & u = v \end{cases}$$

The operator *lift* is monotone according to $\sqsubseteq$. Furthermore, every good Rabin ranking r is a pre-fixpoint with respect to $lift(r, v)$ for all states $v \in V$ and every pre-fixpoint with respect to $lift(r, v)$ for all states $v \in V$ is a good Rabin ranking.

Similarly, consider the set of possible Streett rankings $r : V \times \Pi \longrightarrow D_S$. We say that $r_1 \sqsubseteq r_2$ if for every $v \in V$ and every $\pi \in \Pi$ we have $r_1(v, \pi) \leq r_2(v, \pi)$. The resulting structure is a complete lattice. We use $r_1 \sqsubset r_2$ to denote $r_1 \sqsubseteq r_2$ and $r_1 \neq r_2$. The Streett lifting operator is defined analogously to the above. Given a ranking $r : V \times \Pi \longrightarrow D_S$, a state $v \in V$, and a permutation $\pi \in \Pi$ we set $prog(r, v, \pi)$ to be the least value $d \in D_S$ such that $best(v, \pi)$ is better than d. The ranking $lift(r, v, \pi)$ is the following ranking.

$$lift(r,v,\pi)(u) = \begin{cases} r(u,\pi') & u \neq v \text{ or } \pi \neq \pi' \\ max\{r(u,\pi), prog(r,u,\pi)\} & u = v \text{ and } \pi = \pi' \end{cases}$$

Again, the operator *lift* is monotone according to $\sqsubseteq$. Every good Streett ranking r is a pre-fixpoint with respect to $lift(r, v, \pi)$ for all states $v \in V$ and permutations $\pi \in \Pi$ and every pre-fixpoint with respect to $lift(r, v, \pi)$ for all $v \in V$ and $\pi \in \Pi$ is a good Streett ranking.

By the Knaster-Tarski theorem the least pre-fixpoint (either for Streett or Rabin) exists and it can be computed by the algorithm in Fig. 1. Let $r0$ denote the following ranking. In the case of Rabin $r0$ is the ranking such that for every $v \in V$ we have $\pi(r(v)) = 12 \cdots k$ and $m(r(v)) = 0 \cdots 0$. In the case of Streett $r0$ is the ranking such that for every $v \in V$ and $\pi \in \Pi$ we have $r(v, \pi) = 0 \cdots 0$. We use the notations $lift(r, v, \pi)$ for both Rabin and Streett. In the case of Rabin we mean $lift(r, v)$.

```
RankingLifting
  Let r := r0;
  While (∃v,π s.t.  r ⊏ lift(r,v,π))
    Let r := lift(r,v,π);
  End -- While(...)
End -- RankingLifting
```

Figure 1. The lifting algorithm.

The procedure in Fig. 1 misses most of the implementation details. A naïve approach to choosing the next $v \in V$

and $\pi \in \Pi$ for performing lifting can take $O(nk!)$ for one lift. Etessami et al. supplied the necessary details for the case of parity games with 3 winning conditions [10]. In Fig. 2 we generalize their implementation to the case of Rabin and Streett ranks. As before, we handle both Rabin and Streett together. In order to handle Rabin one has to ignore the permutation π component when appropriate. Here $C(v,\pi)$ denotes the number of successors w of v such that $r(w,\pi) = \mathit{best}(v,\pi)$ and $B(v,\pi)$ denotes $\mathit{best}(v,\pi)$.

```
foreach v ∈ V and π ∈ Π do
   B(v,π) := 0; C(v,π) := |{w : (v,w) ∈ δ}| ;
   r(v,π) := 0;
L := {v ∈ V | q ∉ L(v) and p ∈ L(v)};
while L ≠ ∅ do
   let v ∈ L;L := L \ {v};
   t := r(v);
   B(v) := best(v); C(v) := cnt(v);
   r(v) := incr_v(best(v));
   P := {w ∈ V | (w,v) ∈ ρ};
   foreach w ∈ P such that w ∉ L do
      if (w ∈ V_0 and t = B(w) and C(w) > 1)
         C(w) := C(w)−1;
      if (w ∈ V_0 and t = B(w) and C(w) = 1)
         L := L ∪ {w};
      if (w ∈ V_1 and t = B(w))
         C(w) := C(w)+1;
      if (w ∈ V_1 and t > B(w))
         L := L ∪ {w};
   endforeach
endwhile
```

Figure 2. Efficient computation of ranks.

Theorem 5 *Rabin and Streett games can be solved in time $O(mn^{k+1}kk!)$ and space $O(nk)$ for Rabin and time $O(mn^kkk!)$ and space $O(nkk!)$ for Streett where n is the number of states, m is the number of edges, and k is the number of pairs.*

Proof: We start with Rabin. The space required is $O(nk)$ as we have to store the ranking for each state $v \in V$ and an entry $d \in D_R$ requires $O(k)$ space. The lifting operator can work in time $O(k \cdot \mathit{out{-}deg}(v))$, where $\mathit{out{-}deg}(v)$ is the out-degree of v. Every state can be lifted at most $|D_R|$ times. The total run time is bounded by

$$O\left(\sum_{v\in V} k \cdot \mathit{out{-}deg}(v) \cdot |D_R|\right) = O(km|D_R|)$$

As $|D_R| = n^{k+1}k!$ the bound follows.

For the case of Streett, the space required is $O(nkk!)$ as we have to store a value $d \in D_S$ for each state $v \in V$ and every permutation $\pi \in \Pi$. An entry $d \in D_S$ requires $O(k)$ space. The lifting operator can work in time $O(k \cdot \mathit{out{-}deg}(v))$. Every state and permutation can be lifted at most $|D_S|$ times. The total run time is bounded by

$$O\left(\sum_{v\in V}\sum_{\pi\in\Pi} k \cdot \mathit{out{-}deg}(v) \cdot |D_S|\right) = O(kmk!|D_S|)$$

As $|D_S| = n^k$ the bound follows. □

As in Jurdziński's original algorithm this algorithm cannot be applied symbolically (see Section 7).

5 Recursive Algorithm

In this section we present recursive fixpoint algorithms for computing the winning sets in Rabin and Streett games. These algorithms form part of the proof of completeness of our ranking systems. There are other algorithms based on similar ideas that solve Rabin and Street games with the same complexity [17, 12]. However, we find our algorithms significantly different in one major aspect: Our algorithms are in fact a recipe for a very clean symbolic computation of the winning regions. This advantage of our algorithms led us to two results. First, our algorithms provide proofs for the completeness of the ranking system presented above. Second, the cleanliness of our algorithms enables us to use optimization techniques that were developed for symbolic fixpoint computations. The applicability of these symbolic fixpoint computation optimizations was overlooked/impossible in other solutions to Rabin and Streett games.

We comment that, as Rabin and Streett conditions are duals, the algorithms are dual. This suggests that in order to prove their correctness we could prove that both algorithms are sound and that they are dual. In order to prove that the two algorithms are dual, one would have to flatten the recursive function calls. We find it simpler to prove soundness and completeness separately.

5.1 Rabin Games

We give a recursive algorithm that solves Rabin games. Let $G=\langle V,E,\alpha\rangle$ where $\alpha=\{\langle G_1,R_1\rangle,\ldots,\langle G_k,R_k\rangle\}$ is a Rabin winning condition. An infinite play p is winning according to α if there exists some i such that $inf(p)\cap G_i \neq \emptyset$ and $inf(p) \cap R_i = \emptyset$. Intuitively, the algorithm chooses a first pair $\langle G,R\rangle$ from α, it collects recursively all the states that win according to the rest of the pairs while avoiding R. We now add states that can visit G infinitely often or get to the previously computed states. We repeat the process for the choice of other pairs as first pair. Here `cpred` denotes the control predecessor $\bigcirc\!\!\!\!\diamond$. The loop `GreatestFix(Z)` starts by setting Z to the set of all states and terminates once two consecutive rounds compute the same set of states. The loop `LeastFix(Z)` starts by setting Z to the empty set of states and terminates once two consecutive rounds compute the same set of states. Given a pair $\langle g, r\rangle$ we denote by g the set of states in g and by $\overline{r}$ the set of states in $V-R$. We freely confuse between set notation and Boolean algebra notation. Thus, given sets a and b the set $a\&b$ is the intersection of a and b and $a|b$ is the disjunction of a and b. Similarly, `true` and `false` denote the sets V and $\emptyset$ respectively.

```
Func main_Rabin(Set);
LeastFix(Z)
 My p1 := cpred(Z);
 Z := Rabin(Set,true,p1);
End -- LeastFix(Z)
Return Z;
End -- Func main_Rabin(Set)

Func Rabin(Set,seqnr,right);
 My U := 0;
 Foreach (<g,r> in Set)
  My nSet := Set-<g,r>;
  GreatestFix(Y)
   My p2 := right |
  seqnr & r̄ & g & cpred(Y);
    LeastFix(X)
     My p3 := p2 |
      seqnr & r̄ & cpred(X);
      If (|nSet|=0)
       X := p3;
      Else
       X := Rabin(nSet,
              seqnr & r̄,p3);
      End -- If (|nset|=0)
     End -- LeastFix(X)
     Y := X;
  End -- GreatestFix(Y)
  U := U | Y;
 End -- Foreach (<g,r>
 Return U;
End -- Func Rabin
```

Figure 3. Recursive Algorithm for Rabin.

Theorem 6 *The algorithm in Fig. 3 computes the winning set of player 0 according to the Rabin winning condition.*

We show by induction on the number of pairs in S that the function `Rabin` computes the set of states winning for player 0 by either reaching previously computed winning states, supplying a pair $\langle G, R\rangle$ or by avoiding R forever while fulfilling one of the other pairs.

5.2 Streett Games

We give a recursive algorithm that solves Streett games. Let $G=\langle V, E, \alpha\rangle$ where $\alpha=\{\langle G_1, R_1\rangle, \ldots, \langle G_k, R_k\rangle\}$ is a Streett winning condition. An infinite play p is winning according to α if forall i we have $inf(p) \cap G_i \neq \emptyset$ implies $inf(p) \cap R_i \neq \emptyset$. Intuitively, the algorithm chooses a pair $\langle G, R\rangle$ in α, it collects all states that eventually avoid G states while making sure recursively that all other pairs are satisfied. We then add states that can visit R infinitely often and do the same for all other pairs.

```
Func main_Streett(Set)
 If (|nSet|=0)
    Return m_Streett(true,false);
 Return Streett(Set,true,false);
End -- Func main_Streett(Set)

Func Streett(Set,seqng,right)
 GreatestFix(Z)
  Foreach (<g,r> in Set)
   My nSet := Set-<g,r>;
   My p1 := right |
     seqp & r & cpred(Z);
   LeastFix(Y)
    My p2 := p1 |
        seqng & cpred(Y);
    If (|nSet|=0)
     Y := m_Streett(
           seqng & ḡ,p2);
    Else
     Y := Streett(nSet,
           seqng & ḡ,p2);
    End -- If (|nSet|=0)
   End -- LeastFix(Y)
   Z := Y;
  End -- Foreach (<g,r>
 End -- GreatestFix(Z)
 Return Z;
End -- Streett

Func m_Streett(seqng,right)
GreatestFix(X)
 X := right |
      seqng & cpred(X);
End -- GreatestFix(X)
Return X;
End -- m_Streett
```

Figure 4. Recursive Algorithm for Streett.

Theorem 7 *The algorithm in Fig. 4 computes the winning* *set of player 0 according to the Streett winning condition.*

We show by induction on the number of pairs in S that the function `Streett` computes the set of states winning for player 0 by either reaching previously computed winning states, or by visiting all Rs in S infinitely often, or by choosing some pair, avoiding G and winning recursively according to the other pairs.

From Theorems 6 and 7 it is easy to derive the following bounds. A greatest or least fixpoint collects at least one state in every iteration and hence cannot be repeated more than n times. The inner most fixpoint can be computed in time proportional to m where m is the number of transitions.

Corollary 8 *Rabin and Streett games can be solved symbolically in time $O(mn^{2k}k!)$ where n is the number of states, m is the number of transitions, and k is the number of pairs of the winning condition.*

We stress that these algorithms are not important by themselves. Indeed, the same complexity is achieved by other similar algorithms [17, 12]. They are used to establish the results in Sections 3 and 6.

6 Fast Symbolic Computation

In this section we generalize the method of Long et al. for accelerating the evaluation of fixpoints [18]. Long et al. show that by maintaining the intermediate values of the fixpoint, they can use these values to start the computation of future fixpoints not from minimal or maximal values but rather from better approximations. They show that with these approximations the worst time complexity of the fixpoint computation is reduced to the square root of the original. Unfortunately, the memory consumption amounts to the other square root.

The acceleration works very similarly for Rabin and Streett games. We explain it here for the case of Rabin. The case of Streett is identical but for the order of the indices. Consider the algorithm in Fig. 3. We add a counter to each of the fixpoints. To each of the minimal fixpoints we add a counter i. It is initialized to 0 in the first visit to the command `LeastFix` and incremented by 1 in every subsequent visit. Similarly, to each of the maximal fixpoint we add a counter p. It is initialized to 0 in the first visit to the command `GreatestFix` and incremented by 1 in every subsequent visit. Consider an active copy of the function `Rabin` with $l-1$ copies of `Rabin` on the store. Suppose that the active copy of `Rabin` is found in line 4. Let $i_0 \cdots i_{l-1}$ be the values of the counters i associated with the least fixpoints in the copies of `Rabin` on the stack (where i_0 is the counter in the function `main_Rabin`). Let $p_1 \cdots p_l$ be the values of the counters p associated with the greatest fixpoints in the copies of `Rabin` on the stack. Let $j_1 \cdots j_l$ denote the number of pairs handled by the different copies of `Rabin`. We set $Y(i_0, \cdots i_{l-1}, p_1 \cdots p_l, j_1 \cdots j_l)$ to be the value of Y when the counter p is set to p_l. When the active copy of `Rabin` is found in line 6 then the sequence $i_0 \cdots i_l$ includes also the value of the counter i in the active copy of `Rabin`. We set $X(i_0 \cdots i_l, p_1 \cdots p_l, j_1 \cdots j_l)$ to be the value of X when the counter i is set to i_l.

Given sequences $\alpha = i_0 \cdots i_{l-1}$, $\beta = p_1 \cdots p_l$, and $\gamma = j_1 \cdots j_l$ and $\alpha' = i'_0 \cdots i'_{l-1}$, $\beta' = p'_1 \cdots p'_l$, and $\gamma' = j'_1 \cdots j'_l$ we say that $\alpha\beta\gamma <_\nu \alpha'\beta'\gamma'$ if $\alpha = \alpha'$, $\gamma = \gamma'$ and $\beta < \beta'$ according to the lexicographic order. Similarly, given $\alpha = i_0 \cdots i_l$, $\beta = p_1 \cdots p_l$, and $\gamma = j_1 \cdots j_l$ and $\alpha' = i'_0 \cdots i'_l$, $\beta' = p'_1 \cdots p'_l$, and $\gamma' = j'_1 \cdots j'_l$ we say that $\alpha\beta\gamma <_\mu \alpha'\beta'\gamma'$ if $\beta = \beta'$, $\gamma = \gamma'$ and $\alpha < \alpha'$ according to the lexicographic order. For a fixed $\alpha = i_0 \cdots i_{l-1}$ and $\gamma = j_1 \cdots j_l$, the ordering $<_\nu$ is a total order on l-tuples. Similarly, for a fixed $\beta = j_1 \cdots j_l$ and $\gamma = j_1 \cdots j_l$, the ordering $<_\mu$ is a total order on l-tuples.

For every $\alpha = i_0 \cdots i_{l-1}$, $\beta = p_0 \cdots p_{l-1}$, and $\gamma = j_1 \cdots j_l$ the maximal value p such that $Y(\alpha, \beta p, \gamma)$ is defined is a greatest fixpoint value. Long et al. show that $Y(\alpha, \beta p, \gamma)$ is contained in every set $Y(\alpha, \beta', \gamma)$ such that $\beta' < \beta p$. It follows that the computation of $Y(\alpha, \beta 0, \gamma)$ (which leads to the computation of $Y(\alpha, \beta p, \gamma)$) can start from the minimal set $Y(\alpha, \beta', \gamma)$ such that $\beta' < \beta 0$. Consider now the values of the inner-most greatest fixpoint. That is, the values $Y(\alpha, \beta, \gamma)$ where $|\beta| = k$. It follows that for every value of α and γ there are at most n different values for $Y(\alpha, \beta, \gamma)$.

Dually, for every $\alpha = i_0 \cdots i_{l-1}$, $\beta = p_0 \cdots p_l$, and $\gamma = j_1 \cdots j_l$ the maximal value i such that $X(\alpha i, \beta, \gamma)$ is defined is a least fixpoint value. Long et al. show that $X(\alpha i, \beta, \gamma)$ contains every set $X(\alpha', \beta, \gamma)$ such that $\alpha' < \alpha i$. It follows that the computation of $X(\alpha 0, \beta, \gamma)$ (which leads to the computation of $X(\alpha i, \beta, \gamma)$ can start from the maximal set $X(\alpha', \beta, \gamma)$ such that $\alpha' < \alpha 0$). Consider now the values of the inner-most least fixpoint. That is, the values $X(\alpha, \beta, \gamma)$ where $|\alpha| = k$. If follows that for every value of β and γ there are at most n different values for $X(\alpha, \beta, \gamma)$.

The computation of the inner-most least fixpoint dominates the computation time. It follows that the computation can be concluded in time $O(n^{k+1}k!)$. However, we have to store the Y values for every possible value of α and γ. Notice, that the β values are implicit in every point of the computation. We just have to store the best value for α and γ. Similarly, we store the X values for every possible value of β and γ. Thus, the memory required by the algorithm is $O(n^{k+1}k!)$. Formally, we have the following.

Theorem 9 *Rabin and Streett games can be solved in time $O(n^{k+1}k!)$ and space $O(n^{k+1}k!)$ where n is the number of states and k is the number of pairs of the winning condition.*

On the one hand, the space complexity of the algorithm makes it prohibitively expensive. Implementing an efficient memory system that supports this algorithm makes it less attractive in practice. On the other hand, if we want to use the intermediate fixpoint values for construction of the winning strategy then memorizing some of the intermediate values is necessary anyway.

7 Conclusions

We show how to define Rabin and Streett ranking, which are a sound and complete way to characterize the winning regions in the respective games. We show that by computing the ranking directly we can solve these games faster. Our algorithms improve the time to solve these kind of games to approximately the square root of previous bounds.

In order to prove completeness of the ranking method, we provide recursive fixpoint algorithms for solving Rabin and Streett games. We then further show that by accelerating the fixpoint computation we get algorithms that match the run time of our explicit algorithm at the price of increasing the space complexity.

Both the enumerative and symbolic algorithms are borrowed from algorithms for solving parity games. This raises the question whether other algorithms for parity games (e.g., [27, 1, 14]) can be used in a similar fashion. In subsequent work we show that every solution to parity games that works in time $t(m, n, k)$ can be generalized to solve Rabin and Streett games in time $k!t(m, n, 2k)$.

We mentioned that the direct rank computation cannot be implemented symbolically. This is similar to Jurdziński's algorithm [13]. Bustan et al. suggested to use Algebraic Decision Diagrams (ADDs) to represent Jurdziński's ranking symbolically [3]. We cannot say whether this would be applicable in our case as well.

Acknowledgments

We thank an anonymous referee for explaining the connection with McNaughton's, Zielonka, and Klarlund and Kozen's work.

References

[1] H. Björklund, S. Sandberg, and S. Vorobyov. A discrete subexponential algorithm for parity games. In *20th STACS*, LNCS 2607, pp. 663–674. Springer-Verlag, 2003.

[2] J. Büchi and L. Landweber. Solving sequential conditions by finite-state strategies. *TAMS*, 138:295–311, 1969.

[3] D. Bustan, O. Kupferman, and M. Vardi. A measured collapse of the modal μ-calculus alternation hierarchy. In *Proc. 21st STACS*, LNCS 2996, pp. 522–533. 2004.

[4] A. Church. Logic, arithmetic and automata. In *Proc. 1962 Int. Congr. Math.*, pages 23–25, Upsala, 1963.

[5] S. Dziembowski, M. Jurdzinski, and I. Walukiewicz. How much memory is needed to win infinite games. In *12th LICS*, pp. 99–110, 1997.

[6] E. Emerson. Automata, tableaux and temporal logics. In *ICLP*, LNCS 193, pp 79–88. Springer-Verlag, 1985.

[7] E. Emerson and C. Jutla. The complexity of tree automata and logic of programs. In *29th FOCS*, pp. 328–337, 1988.

[8] E. Emerson and C. Jutla. Tree automata, μ-calculus and determinacy. In *32nd FOCS*, pp. 368–377, 1991.

[9] E. A. Emerson and C. L. Lei. Efficient model-checking in fragments of the propositional modal μ-calculus. In *1st LICS*, pp. 267–278, 1986.

[10] K. Etessami, T. Wilke, and R. A. Schuller. Fair simulation relations, parity games, and state space reduction for Büchi automata. In *28th ICALP*, LNCS 2076, pp. 694–707. 2001.

[11] Y. Gurevich and L. Harrington. Automata, trees and games. In *14th STOC*, pp. 60–65, 1982.

[12] F. Horn. Streett games on finite graphs. In *2nd GDV*, 2005.

[13] M. Jurdzinski. Small progress measures for solving parity games. In *17th STACS*, LNCS 1770, pp. 290–301. 2000.

[14] M. Jurdziński, M. Paterson, and U. Zwick. A deterministic subexponential algorithm for solving parity games. In *SODA*, 2006.

[15] N. Klarlund. Progress measures, immediate determinacy, and a subset construction for tree automata. *APAL*, 69(2–3):243–268, 1994.

[16] N. Klarlund and D. Kozen. Rabin measures. *Chicago JTCS*, 1995.

[17] O. Kupferman and M. Vardi. Weak alternating automata and tree automata emptiness. In *30th STOC*, pp. 224–233, 1998.

[18] D. Long, A. Brown, E. Clarke, S. Jha, and W. Marrero. An improved algorithm for the evaluation of fixpoint expressions. In *6th CAV*, LNCS 818, pp. 338–350, 1994.

[19] R. McNaughton. Infinite games played on finite graphs. *APAL*, 65(2):149–184, 1993.

[20] N. Piterman, A. Pnueli, and Y. Sa'ar. Synthesis of Reactive(1) Designs. In *7th VMCAI*, LNCS 3855, pp 364–380, 2006.

[21] A. Pnueli and R. Rosner. On the synthesis of a reactive module. In *16th POPL*, pp. 179–190, 1989.

[22] M. Rabin. Decidability of second order theories and automata on infinite trees. *TAMS*, 141:1–35, 1969.

[23] M. Rabin. *Automata on Infinite Objects and Churc's Problem*, volume 13 of *Regional Conference Series in Mathematics*. AMS, 1972.

[24] S. Safra. On the complexity of ω-automata. In *29th FOCS*, pp. 319–327, 1988.

[25] R. Streett. Propositional dynamic logic of looping and converse is elementarily decidable. *IC*, 54:121–141, 1982.

[26] W. Thomas. Automata on infinite objects. In *Handbook of TCS*, volume B, chapter 4, pp. 165–191. MIT Press, 1990.

[27] J. Voge and M. Jurdzinski. A discrete strategy improvement algorithm for solving parity games. In *12th CAV*, LNCS 1855, Springer-Verlag, pp. 202–215, 2000.

[28] T. Wilke. Alternating tree automata, parity games, and modal μ-calculus. *Bull. Soc. Math. Belg.*, 8(2), May 2001.

[29] W. Zielonka. Infinite games on finitely coloured graphs with applications to automata on infinite trees. *TCS*, 200(1–2):135–183, 1998.

Bounds in ω-regularity

Mikołaj Bojańczyk
Warsaw University and LIAFA, Paris
bojan@mimuw.edu.pl

Thomas Colcombet
CNRS/IRISA, Rennes
colcombe@irisa.fr

Abstract

We consider an extension of ω-regular expressions where two new variants of the Kleene star L^* are added: L^B and L^S. These exponents act as the standard star, but restrict the number of iterations to be bounded (for L^B) or to tend toward infinity (for L^S). These expressions can define languages that are not ω-regular.

We develop a theory for these languages. We study the decidability and closure questions. We also define an equivalent automaton model, extending Büchi automata. This culminates with a — partial — complementation result.

1 Introduction

In this paper we introduce a new kind of language of infinite words. The new languages – called ωBS-regular languages – are defined using an extended form of ω-regular expressions. The extended expressions can define properties such as "words of the form $(a^*b)^\omega$ where the size of a^*b blocks is bounded". As witnessed by this example, ωBS-regular languages are a proper extension of ω-regular languages.

The expressions for ωBS-regular languages are obtained from the usual ω-regular expressions by adding two new variants of the Kleene star L^*. These are called the bounded exponent L^B and the strongly unbounded exponent L^S. The idea behind B is that the language L in the expression L^B must be iterated a bounded number of times. For instance, the language from the first paragraph is described by the expression $(a^Bb)^\omega$. The idea behind S is that the iterations of the language L must tend toward infinity (i.e. have no bounded subsequence). This is not the same as being unbounded, which is more easily satisfied. In particular, the complement of the language $(a^Bb)^\omega$ is the language

$$(a+b)^*a^\omega + ((a+b)^*a^Sb)^\omega$$

and not the (smaller) language

$$(a+b)^*a^\omega + (a^Sb)^\omega .$$

For instance, the word $aba^1baba^2baba^3baba^4b\cdots$ belongs to the first but not the second.

This paper is devoted to developing a theory for those new languages.

The most important concept is a new type of automaton over infinite words, called a bounding automaton. Bounding automata can be used as an alternative definition of the new languages. However, the translations between bounding automata and ωBS regular expressions are more involved than in the case of regular languages.

A bounding automaton is a finite automaton equipped with a finite number of counters. These couters can be incremented and reset, but not read. The counter values are used in the acceptance condition, which depends on their asymptotic values (whether counter values are bounded or tend toward infinity). We show that bounding automata recognize exactly the languages that can be defined using ωBS-regular expressions. Thanks to simple automata constructions, we obtain closure of ωBS-regular languages under union, intersection and projection.

Unfortunately, ωBS-regular languages are not closed under complementation, nor can the bounding automata be determinized. The following language witnesses the first statement as it is ωBS-regular, but its complement is not:

> Words of the form $a^{n_1}ba^{n_2}b\cdots$ where $n_1, n_2, \ldots$ can be split in two subsequences: one bounded, the other tending toward infinity.

Failure of complementation is bad news, especially from a logical point of view. However, we are able to identify two fragments of ωBS-regular languages that complement each other. We show that the complement of a language that only talks about bounded sequences is a language that only talks about sequences tending toward infinity; and vice versa. The difficult proof of this complementation result is the technical core of the paper.

Finally, we present a logic that expresses ωBS-regular languages. As is well known, languages defined by

Work supported by the EU-TNR network GAMES. The first author also supported by MNII grant 4 T11C 042 25 and a scholarship of the Foundation for Polish Science

1043-6871/06 $20.00 © 2006 IEEE

ω-regular expressions are exactly the ones definable in monadic second-order logic. What extension logic corresponds to ωBS-regular expressions? One avenue is to add a new quantifier, called the bounding quantifier $\mathbb{B}$. A formula $\mathbb{B}X.\ \phi(X)$ is true if the size of sets satisfying $\phi(X)$ is bounded. Every ωBS-regular language can be defined in monadic second-order logic extended with $\mathbb{B}$. Due to failure of complementation, the converse does not hold.

Related work This work tries to continue the long lasting tradition of logic/automata correspondences [10] initiated by Büchi [4, 5] and continued by Rabin [7]. We believe that bounding properties extend the received notion of regularity and that languages defined by our extended expressions have every right to be called regular, even though they are not captured by Büchi automata. For instance, every ωBS-regular language L has a finite number of quotients $w^{-1}L, Lw^{-1}$. (Moreover, the right quotients Lw^{-1} are regular languages of finite words.) Unfortunately, our results fall short of these grand expectations, since we do not have a full complementation result.

The quantifier $\mathbb{B}$ in the logic that describes ωBS-regular languages was already introduced in [2]. Although [2] went beyond words and considered infinite trees, the satisfiability algorithm worked for a more restricted fragment of the logic with no (not even partial) complementation result. In particular, no appropriate notion of automata or regular expression was proposed.

Boundedness properties have been considered in model-checking. For instance, [3] considered systems described by push-down automata whose stack size is unbounded.

Our work on bounds can also be related to cardinality restrictions. In[6], Klaedtke and Ruess considered an extension of monadic second-order logic with cardinality extensions of the form

$$|X_1| + \cdots + |X_n| \leq |Y_1| + \cdots + |Y_m| \,.$$

In general, such cardinality constraints (even $|X| \leq |Y|$) lead to undecidability. Even though cardinality constraints can express all ωBS-regular languages, the decidable fragments considered in [6] are insufficient for our purposes.

Structure of the paper. In Section 2, we formally define the ωBS-regular expressions that are the subject of this paper. We introduce two restricted types of expressions (where the B and S exponents are prohibited, respectively) and overview the closure properties of the respective expressions. In Section 3, we introduce our automata models and show that they are equivalent to the regular expressions. In Section 4, we state the main technical result, which concerns closure under complementation. In Section 5, we show how our results can be applied to obtain a decision procedure for satisfiability in an extension of monadic second-order logic.

2 Regular expressions with bounds

In this section we define the different variants of ωBS-regular expressions, overview the results concerning them and show the strictness of their inclusions.

2.1 Definition

To the standard operations used in ω-regular expressions, we add two variants of the Kleene star $*$: the B and S exponents. These are used to constrain the number of iterations. When the B exponent is used, the number of iteration has to be bounded. When the S exponent is used, it has to tend toward infinity. For instance, the expression $(a^B b)^\omega$ represents the words in $(a^* b)^\omega$ where the size of sequences of consecutive a's is bounded. Similarly, the expression $(a^S b)^\omega$ requires the size of maximal sequences of consecutive a's to tend toward infinity. These new expressions are called ωBS-regular expression.

In the following we will say that a sequence of naturals is *strictly unbounded* if it tends toward the infinite, i.e. has no bounded subsequence. This behavior is denoted by the letter S, while the bounded behavior is denoted by B.

In order to formally define ωBS-regular expressions, we first use BS-regular expressions, which describe infinite sequences of finite words. Our ωBS-regular expressions are built on top of BS-regular expression just as ω-regular expressions are built on top of regular expressions. A BS-*regular expression* has the following syntax (a being some letter of the given finite alphabet Σ, and M ranging over the regular languages of finite words over Σ):

$$e = \ \emptyset \ \mid \ a \ \mid \ e.e \ \mid \ e+e \ \mid \ M \rhd e \ \mid \ e^* \ \mid \ e^B \ \mid \ e^S \,.$$

Except for the two extra exponents B and S and the $\rhd$ operator, these expressions coincide syntactically with the standard regular expressions. However, the semantics cannot be given in terms of languages of finite words. Instead, a BS-regular expression is evaluated to a language of sequences; by *sequence* we mean an element of $(\Sigma^*)^\omega$. We will denote by $\vec{u}$ the sequence $(u_1, u_2, \ldots)$.

The semantic of BS-regular expressions is defined as follows.

- $\emptyset$ is the empty language of sequences.
- a for $a \in \Sigma$ is the language containing the single sequence $(a, a, \ldots)$.
- The *concatenation* of sequence languages is defined by
$$K.L = \{(u_1v_1, u_2v_2 \ldots) \ : \ \vec{u} \in K, \vec{v} \in L\} \,.$$
- The *mix* of sequence languages (which is *not* the union) is
$$K + L = \{\vec{w} \ : \ \vec{u}, \vec{v} \in K \cup L, \ \forall i. w_i \in \{u_i, v_i\}\} \,.$$

- The *finite mix* $M \rhd L$ for M a regular language of finite words, is the set of sequences obtained by taking a sequence from L and replacing a finite number of coordinates with a word from M. This operator is redundant as established in Proposition 2.4.

- The $*$-*exponent* of a language of sequences is defined by grouping words into blocks:

$$L^* = \{(u_1 \dots u_{f(1)-1}, u_{f(1)} \dots u_{f(2)-1}, \dots) : \vec{u} \in L,\ f \text{ nondecreasing}\}.$$

- The *bounded exponent* L^B of a language of sequences is defined like L^* but we additionally require the values $f(i+1) - f(i)$ to be bounded, i.e. only factorizations of bounded size are allowed.

- The *strictly unbounded exponent* L^S of a language of sequences is defined like L^* but we additionally require the values $f(i+1) - f(i)$ to be strictly unbounded, i.e. the size of the concatenations used in the factorization must tend toward the infinite.

Languages of sequences obtained by nesting these operations — i.e. the language of sequences obtained by evaluating BS-regular expressions — are called *BS-regular languages*. The *B-regular* (resp. *S-regular*) languages correspond to the particular case where the exponent S (resp. B) is not used. When the context is clear, we do not distinguish between an expression and the corresponding language.

For instance the BS-regular (also B-regular) expression a^B represents the sequences of words from a^* where the number of a's is bounded:

$$a^B = \{(a^{f(1)}, a^{f(2)}, \dots) : f \text{ is bounded}\}$$

The sequence language $a^B.(b.a^B)^S$ consists of sequences where the number of consecutive a's is bounded, while the number of b's in each word of the sequence is strictly unbounded.

In this definition, we override the symbols $+, ., *$ from regular expressions. However, there is a strong link between the two semantics. If one takes a standard regular expression defining a language of finite words L and evaluates it as a BS-regular expression, the resulting language of sequences is simply $\{\vec{u} : \forall i. u_i \in L\}$.

Before proceeding to the definition of ωBS-regular languages, we first emphasize some closure properties of BS-regular languages.

Fact 2.1 Every BS-regular language satisfies $L = L + L$. Furthermore, for $\vec{u}$ in L and f a strictly unbounded sequence of naturals, the sequence $(u_{f(1)}, u_{f(2)}, \dots)$ also belongs to L. In particular, L is closed under taking subsequences.

Proof
Structural induction. □

We are now ready to introduce the ωBS-regular expressions. These describe languages of ω-words. From a sequence with nonempty words on infinitely many coordinates, we can construct an ω-word by concatenation of all the words:

$$(u_1, u_2, \dots)^\omega = u_1 u_2 \dots$$

This operation is naturally extended to languages of sequences by taking the ω power of every sequence in the language.

Definition 2.2 An *ωBS-regular language* is a finite union (denoted $+$) of languages of the form $M.L^\omega$, where M is a regular language of finite words and L is BS-regular. When only B-regular (resp. S-regular) languages are used for L then the resulting language is called *ωB-regular* (resp. *ωS-regular*).

This definition differs from the definition of ω-regular expressions only in that the ω is applied to BS-regular languages of sequences instead of regular word languages. As one may expect, the standard class of ω-regular languages corresponds to the case of ωBS-regular languages where neither B nor S is used.

For instance, the expression $(a^B.b)^\omega$ defines the language of ω-words containing an infinite number of b's where the possible number of consecutive a's is bounded. The language $(a^S.b)^\omega$ corresponds to the case where the length of maximal consecutive sequences of a's tends toward infinity. The language $(a+b)^*a^\omega + ((a^*.b)^*.a^S.b)^\omega$ is a bit more involved. It corresponds to the language of words where either there are finitely many b's, or the number of consecutive a's is unbounded but not necessarily strictly unbounded. This is the complement of the language $(a^B.b)^\omega$.

Fact 2.3 Emptiness is decidable for ωBS-regular languages.

Proof
An ωBS-regular language is nonempty if and only if one of the languages $M.L^\omega$ is such that the regular language M is nonempty and the BS-regular language L admits infinitely many nonempty words in a sequence. The latter can be shown decidable by structural induction. Essentially it amounts to finding a letter in the BS-expression, and verifying that none of the subexpressions containing this letter is concatenated with an empty language. □

The finite mix operator $\rhd$ will turn out to be a convenient technical device. However, it is not necessary for describing ωBS-regular languages, as stated by:

Proposition 2.4 Every ωBS-regular expression (resp. ωB-regular and ωS-regular ones) is equivalent to one without $\triangleright$ operator.

Note that this proposition does not mean that finite mix can be eliminated from BS-regular languages of sequences. For instance, the finite mix operator is necessary to define the set of sequences $a \triangleright b$ where a finite number of a's is used. However, after the ω power is applied, the expression $(a \triangleright b)^\omega$ can be rewritten into – and this is the subject of Proposition 2.4 – the expression $(a+b)^*b^\omega$.

2.2 Summary: The diamond

In this section we present Figure 1, which summarizes the technical contributions of this paper. We call this figure *the diamond*. Though not all the material necessary to understand this figure has been yet provided, we give it here as a reference and guide to what follows.

The diamond illustrates the four variants of languages of ω-words we consider: ω-regular, ωB-regular, ωS-regular and ωBS-regular languages. The inclusions between those four classes give a diamond shape. We show in Section 2.3 that the inclusions in the diamond are indeed strict.

To each class of languages corresponds a family of automata. The automata come in two variants: "normal automata", and the equivalent "hierarchical automata". The exact definition of these automata as well as the corresponding equivalences are the subject of Section 3 and Theorem 3.1.

All the classes are closed under union by definition. It is also easy to show that the classes are closed under projection, i.e. images under a letter to letter morphism (operation denoted by π in the figure). From the equivalence of the different families of languages with families automata we obtain closure by intersection for the four classes; see Corollary 3.2. For the closure under complement, things are not so nice. Indeed in Section 2.3 we show that ωBS-regular language are not closed under complement. However, some complementation results are still possible. Namely Theorem 4.1 establishes that complementing an ωB-regular language gives an ωS-language, and vice-versa. This is by far the most involved result of this work and we only sketch some ideas about its proof.

In Section 5 we will show how the closure results can be used to partially answer the satisfiability problem for an extension of monadic second-order logic. For this purpose, we establish Proposition 5.3 stating the closure of ωS-regular languages under a less standard operation called $\mathbb{U}$.

2.3 Limits of the diamond

In this section we show that all the inclusions depicted in the diamond are strict. Moreover, we show that there exists an ωBS-regular language whose complement is not ωBS-regular.

We start by a simple lemma.

Lemma 2.5 Every ωB-regular language over the alphabet $\{a,b\}$ which contains a word with an infinite number of b's contains a word in $(a^B b)^\omega$.

Proof
We show by a simple structural induction that a B-regular language of sequences L satisfies:

- if L contains a sequence in a^*, it contains a sequence in a^B, and,
- if L contains a sequence in $(a^*b)^+a^*$, it contains a sequence in $(a^Bb)^+a^B$.

The statement of the lemma follows. □

Corollary 2.6 The language $(a^Sb)^\omega$ is not ωB-regular. The language $(a^Bb)^\omega$ is not ωS-regular.

Proof
The language $(a^Sb)^\omega$ contains a word with an infinite number of b's, but its intersection with $(a^Bb)^\omega$ is empty. Being ωB-regular for this language would contradict Lemma 2.5.

For the second part, assume that the language $(a^Bb)^\omega$ is ωS-regular, then so is the language $(a^Bb)^\omega + (a+b)^*a^\omega$. Using Theorem 4.1, its complement $((a^*b)^*a^Sb)^\omega$ would be ωB-regular. But this is not possible, by the same argument as above. A proof that does not use complementation – along the same lines as in the first part – can also be given.
□

We now proceed to show that ωBS-regular languages are not closed under complement. We start with a similar lemma.

Lemma 2.7 Every ωBS-regular language over the alphabet $\{a,b\}$ that contains a word with an infinite number of b's also contains a word in $(a^Bb + a^Sb)^\omega$.

Proof
As for Lemma 2.5, we show the following properties of a BS-regular language of sequences L by a simple structural induction:

- if L contains a sequence in a^*, it contains a sequence in $a^B + a^S$, and,
- if L contains a sequence in $(a^*b)^+a^*$, it contains a sequence in $(a^Bb + a^Sb)^+(a^B + a^S)$.

The result directly follows. □

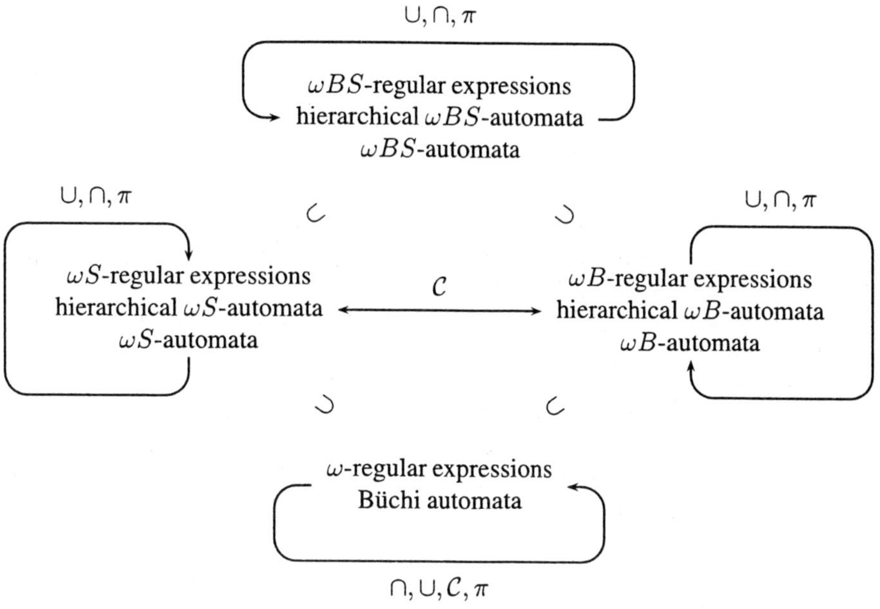

Figure 1. The diamond

Corollary 2.8 The complement of $L = (a^B b + a^S b)^\omega$ is not ωBS-regular.

Proof
The complement of L contains the word

$$a^1\ ba^1ba^2\ ba^1ba^2ba^3\ ba^1ba^2ba^3ba^4b\ \ldots\ ,$$

and consequently, assuming it is ωBS-regular, one can apply Lemma 2.7 on it. It follows that the complement of L should intersect L. Obviously a contradiction. □

3 Automata

In this section we introduce new types of automata over infinite words, called ωBS-automata, and show their equivalence with ωBS-regular expressions.

3.1 Statement of the equivalences

The key equivalence result of this section is the following one.

Theorem 3.1
The following properties of a language of ω-words L are equivalent:

1. *L is ωBS-regular (resp. ωB-regular, resp. ωS-regular),*
2. *L is accepted by a hierarchical ωBS-automaton (resp. a hierarchical ωB-automaton, resp. a hierarchical ωS-automaton),*
3. *L is accepted by an ωBS-automaton (resp. an ωB-automaton, resp. an ωS-automaton).*

The necessary definitions are in the two subsequent sections, the first one defining the most general form of ωBS-automata, the second introducing their hierarchical form.

We mention here, somewhat ahead of time, an important application of this theorem: the closure under intersection of all the classes of languages.

Corollary 3.2 The classes of ωBS-regular, ωB-regular and ωS-regular languages are closed under intersection.

Proof
The corresponding automata are closed under intersection.
□

3.2 General form of ωBS-automata

An *ωBS-automaton*, like any finite automaton, has an *input alphabet* Σ, a finite set of *states* Q and an *initial state* $q_I \in Q$. The automaton also has a set of *counters* Γ, which is partitioned into a set Γ_B of *bounding counters* (we also say *B-counters* or *counters of type B*) and a set Γ_S of *unbounding counters* (we also say *S-counters* or *counters of* *type* S). With every letter $a \in \Sigma$ the automaton associates its *transition relation*:

$$\delta_a \subseteq Q \times \{\mathrm{i}, \mathrm{r}, \epsilon\}^\Gamma \times Q \,.$$

The intuition is that in a transition the automaton decides what do with each counter: whether to increment it (i), reset it (r), or leave it unchanged (ϵ). When the automaton only has counters of type B (resp. of type S), then the automaton is called an ωB-*automaton* (resp. an ωS-*automaton*). The counter values are never read by the automaton; they are only used for the acceptance condition.

A *run* ρ of an ωBS-automaton over some ω-word $a_1 a_2 \dots$ is a sequence of transitions $\rho = t_1 t_2 \cdots$ such that for every i, t_i belongs to δ_{a_i}, the source state of t_1 is q_I and for each i, the target state of the transition t_i is the same as the source state of the transition t_{i+1}. During such a run, the automaton updates the values of the counters. Initially, all counters have the value 0. A counter $c \in \Gamma$ is incremented when the transition assigns i to it, it is reset to 0 when the transition assigns r to it and it is left unchanged otherwise. For a run ρ, we denote by $c(\rho)$ the sequence of values that the counter c assumes *just before being reset*. This sequence can be finite if the counter is reset only a finite number of times, or it can be infinite. A *run* ρ is *accepting* if for every counter c, the sequence $c(\rho)$ is infinite and furthermore, if c is of type S then $c(\rho)$ is strongly unbounded and if c is of type B then $c(\rho)$ is bounded.

As an example, consider the following automaton with a single counter of type B (the counter action is in the parenthesis):

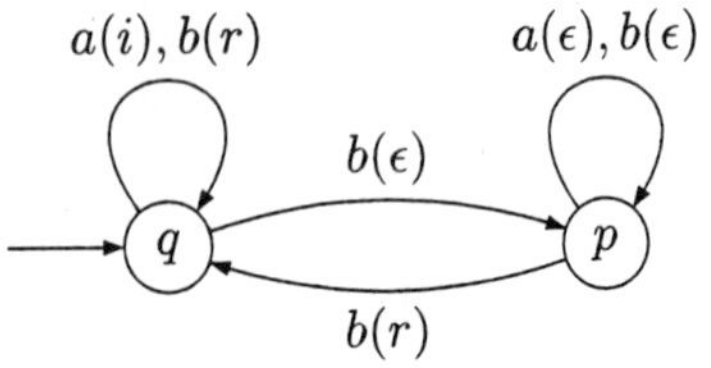

This automaton accepts the language $(a^B b(a^* b)^*)^\omega$. If the counter is of type S, then the same automaton accepts the language $(a^S b(a^* b)^*)^\omega$.

Though we do not prove it here, it should be fairly clear that no deterministic ωBS-automaton can accept these languages. For this reason, we are doomed to working with non-deterministic automata. This is one of the reasons why the complementation result is difficult.

3.3 Hierarchical automata

Hierarchical ωBS-automata are a more structured version of ωBS-automata where the counters are required to be nested. They are more closely related to ωBS-regular expressions than the general form of ωBS-automata.

An ωBS-automaton is called *hierarchical* if its set of counters is $\Gamma = \{1, \dots, n\}$ and whenever a counter $i > 1$ is incremented or reset, the counters $1 \dots i-1$ are reset. It is convenient to define for a hierarchical automaton its *counter type*, defined as a word in $\{B + S\}^*$. The length of this word is the number of counters; its i-th letter is the type of counter i.

According to this definition, a transition (q, v, r) in a hierarchical automaton can be of three forms:

- either $v(l) = \epsilon$ for every $l = 1, \dots, n$, or;
- there is some k such that $v(l) = r$ for $l = 1, \dots, k$, and $v(l) = \epsilon$ for $l = k+1, \dots, n$, or;
- there is some k such that $v(l) = r$ for $l = 1, \dots, k-1$, $v(k) = i$ and $v(l) = \epsilon$ for $l = k+1, \dots, n$.

4 Complementation

The main technical result of this paper is the following complementation theorem:

Theorem 4.1
The complement of an ωS-regular language is ωB-regular. The complement of an ωB-regular language is ωS-regular.

The proof of this result is long. Here, we just try to give some ideas underlying the proof. For the sake of the explanation, we only consider the case of complementing an ωS-regular language.

First consider the simple case of a language described by an ωS-automaton $\mathcal{A}$ which has a single counter, and such that in every run, between two resets, the increments of the counter are consecutive. This means that in every run, between two resets of the counter, the counter is first left unchanged during a while, then during the n-next following steps the counter is always incremented, then it is not incremented anymore before reaching the second reset. We call *increment interval* an interval of positions in the word corresponding to a maximal sequence of increments.

We now describe an ωB-automaton $\mathcal{B}$ accepting the complement of the language recognised by $\mathcal{A}$. It uses a single B-counter which beats as a clock dividing the input ω-word into pieces of bounded size (independantly from any run of $\mathcal{A}$). We say that an interval of positions in the word is *short* (with respect to this clock) if there is at most one beat of the clock in it. If the clock beats every n steps, then short intervals have length at most $n-1$. Reciprocally, if an interval has length at most n, then it is short with respect to every clock beating with a tempo greater than n. Using those remarks, we can see the notion of being short as a fair approximation of the length of an interval.

The complement automaton $\mathcal{B}$ works by guessing the beats of a clock using non-determinism together with a B-counter, and then checks the following fact: every run of $\mathcal{A}$ which contains an infinite number of resets, contains an infinite number of short increment intervals. Once the clock is fixed, checking this is definable in monadic second-order logic. Using this remark it is simple to construct $\mathcal{B}$.

It is easy to see that if $\mathcal{B}$ accepts an ω-word, then it is not accepted by $\mathcal{A}$. The converse implication requires to remark the following: if no run of $\mathcal{A}$ is accepting, then there exists a natural N such that in every run of $\mathcal{A}$ doing an infinite number of resets, there is less than N increments between two resets infinitely often. Such a property can be established using Ramsey-like arguments.

Let us turn now to the more general case of complementing a single counter ωS-automaton (we do not constrain anymore the increments to be contiguous). Our technique uses Simon's factorisation theorem for finite semigroups [9], and reduces the problem to a bounded number of instances of the above construction. In this case, the complement ωB-automaton uses one counter for each level of the factorisation, the result being a structure of nested clocks beating with different 'granularity'. As above, once the beats of the clocks are fixed, checking if a run makes few increments is approximable in monadic second-order logic. This makes it implementable by an ωB-automaton.

Finally, for treating the general case of ωS-automata, we use automata in their hierarchical form and perform an induction on the number of counters.

5 Monadic second-order logic with bounds

In this section, we introduce the logic MSOLB. This is a strict extension of monadic second-order logic (MSOL), where the new quantifier $\mathbb{U}$ is added (the original definition in [2] uses the quantifier $\mathbb{B}$ which is the negation of $\mathbb{U}$). This quantifier expresses the fact that a property is satisfied by arbitrarily large sets. We are interested in satisfiability: the decision problem whether there exists an ω-word modeling a given formula of MSOLB. We are not able to solve this problem in its full generality. However, the diamond properties allow us to provide an interesting partial solution.

In Section 5.1 we introduce formally the logic MSOLB. In Section 5.2 we explain how ωBS-regular languages can be used to deal with intersection, complementation and existential quantification in a decision procedure for satisfiability. In Section 5.3 we deal with the quantifier $\mathbb{U}$. Finally, in Section 5.4 we present an application of this logic to ω-automatic structures.

5.1 The logic

Recall that monadic second-order logic is an extension of first-order logic by set quantification. Hence a formula of this logic is made of atomic predicates, boolean connectives ($\wedge, \vee, \neg$), first-order quantification ($\exists x.\varphi$ and $\forall x.\varphi$) and monadic second-order quantification ($\exists X.\varphi$ and $\forall X.\varphi$) together with the membership predicate $x \in X$. Over ω-words the universe is the set $\mathbb{N}$ of positions, while the atomic predicates used are: a binary predicate $x \leq y$ for order on positions, and for each letter a of the alphabet, a unary predicate $a(x)$ that tests if a position x has the label a.

In the logic MSOLB we add a new quantifier: the *existential unbounding quantifier* $\mathbb{U}$ which has the following semantics:

$$\mathbb{U}X.\varphi := \forall N \in \mathbb{N}.\ \exists X.\ (\varphi \wedge |X| \geq N)\ .$$

The quantified variable X is a set variable and $|X|$ denotes its cardinality. Informally speaking, $\mathbb{U}X.\varphi(X)$ says that the formula $\varphi(X)$ is true for sets X of arbitrarily large cardinality. If $\varphi(X)$ is true for some infinite set X, then $\mathbb{U}X.\varphi(X)$ is immediately true.

From this quantifier, we can construct other meaningful quantifiers:

- The quantifier $\mathbb{A}$ — *the universal above quantifier* — is the dual of $\mathbb{U}$, i.e. $\mathbb{A}X.\varphi$ is a shortcut for $\neg\mathbb{U}X.\neg\varphi$. It is satisfied if all the sets X above a given threshold of cardinality satisfy property φ.
- Finally, the *bounding quantifier* $\mathbb{B}$ is syntactically equivalent to the negation of the $\mathbb{U}$ quantifier. This quantifier was the first chronologically studied[2]. It says that a formula $\mathbb{B}X.\varphi$ holds if there is a bound on the cardinality of sets satisfying property φ.

Over finite structures, MSOLB and MSOL are equivalent: the quantifiers $\mathbb{U}$ is always false over finite structures and consequently can be removed. Over infinite words, MSOLB defines strictly more languages than MSOL. For instance the formula

$$\mathbb{B}X.\ [\forall x \in X.a(x)] \wedge [\forall x \leq y \leq z.x, z \in X \rightarrow y \in X]$$

corresponds over $\{a, b\}^\omega$ to the language $(a^B.b)^\omega$. Indeed, the formula says there is a bound on the size of contiguous segments made of a's. As we have seen, this language is not regular. Hence, this formula is not equivalent to any MSOL formula. This motivates the following decision problem:

> Is a given formula of MSOLB satisfied over some infinite word?

We do not know the answer to this question in its full generality. However, using the diamond (Figure 1), we can solve this question for a certain class of formulas. This is the subject of the next section.

5.2 A decidable fragment of MSOLB

The classical approach for solving satisfiability of monadic second-order logic is to translate formulas into automata. To every operation in the logic corresponds a language operation. As automata happen to be closed under those operations, and emptiness is decidable for automata, the satisfaction problem is decidable for MSOL. We use the same approach for MSOLB. Unfortunately, our automata are not closed under complement, hence we do not solve the whole logic.

Those operations are summarized in the logical view of the diamond, i.e. Figure 2. Closures under $\vee$ and $\wedge$ are a direct consequence of closure under $\cup$ and $\cap$. Closure under $\exists$ corresponds to closure under projection, which is straightforward for non-deterministic automata. Negation $\neg$ is obtained by the closure under complementation. Closures under universal quantification follow as duals of the existential quantifications. Closure under $\mathbb{U}$ of ωS-regular langages is the subject of Section 5.3, while closure under $\mathbb{A}$ is obtained by duality. We did not represent the closure under the $\mathbb{B}$ quantifier on this picture. It would go from ωS-regular languages to ωB-regular languages.

Since emptiness for BS-regular languages is decidable by Fact 2.3, we obtain:

Theorem 5.1
The satisfiability problem is decidable for the following formulas:

- B-formulas. *These include all of MSOL, are closed under* $\vee, \wedge, \forall, \exists$ *and* $\mathbb{A}$. *Moreover, the negation of an S-formula is a B-formula.*
- S-formulas. *These include all of MSOL, are closed under* $\vee, \wedge, \forall, \exists$ *and* $\mathbb{U}$. *Moreover, the negation of a B-formula is an S-formula.*
- BS-formulas. *These include all B-formulas and S-formulas, and are closed under* $\vee, \wedge, \exists$ *and* $\mathbb{U}$.

All ωBS-regular languages can be described by an MSOLB formulas:

Fact 5.2 Every ωBS-regular language (resp. ωB-regular, resp. ωS-regular) is definable by a BS-formula (resp. a B-formula, resp. an S-formula).

Proof
Guess a run of the automaton, and check that this run is accepting using the new quantifiers. □

The converse fails for ωBS-regular language since these languages are not closed under complementation. But it holds for ωB-regular and ωS-regular languages.

5.3 Closure under existential unbounding quantification

Here we show that the classes of ωS- and ωBS-regular languages are closed under application of the quantifier $\mathbb{U}$. This closure is settled by Proposition 5.3.

Before we proceed, we describe the quantifier $\mathbb{U}$ as a language operation, in the same way as existential quantification corresponds to projection. Let Σ be an alphabet, and consider a language $L \subseteq (\Sigma \times \{0,1\})^\omega$. Given a word $w \in \Sigma^\omega$ and a set $X \subseteq \mathbb{N}$, let $w[X] \in (\Sigma \times \{0,1\})^\omega$ be the word obtained from w by setting the second coordinate to 1 on the positions from X and to 0 on the other positions. We then define $\mathbb{U}(L)$ to be the set of those words $w \in \Sigma^\omega$ such that for every $N \in \mathbb{N}$ there is a set $X \subseteq \mathbb{N}$ of at least N elements such that $w[X]$ belongs to L.

Proposition 5.3 Both ωS and ωBS-regular languages are closed under the operation $\mathbb{U}(L)$.

We begin with a simple auxiliary result. A *partial sequence* over an alphabet Σ is a word in $\perp^*\Sigma^\omega$. A partial sequence is *defined* on the positions where it does not have value $\perp$. We say two partial sequences *meet* if there is some position where they are both defined and have the same letter.

Lemma 5.4 Let I be an infinite set of partial sequences over a finite alphabet. There is a partial sequence in I that meets infinitely many partial sequences from I.

Proof
Let Σ be the finite alphabet. A *constrainer* for I is an infinite word c over $P(\Sigma)$ such that the i-th position of every sequence in I is either undefined or belongs to c_i. The size of a constrainer is the maximal size of a set it uses infinitely.

The proof is by induction over the size of a constrainer for I. This is sufficient since every set I admits the constrainer that has Σ on every coordinate. If I admits a constrainer of size 1 then we are done. Take a set I with a constrainer c of size n. Take some sequence s in I. If s meets infinitely many sequences from I, then we are done. Otherwise let $J \subseteq I$ be the (infinite) set of sequences that do not meet s. Then one can verify that d is a constrainer for J, where d is defined by $d_i = c_i \setminus \{s_i\}$. Moreover, d is of size $n-1$. □

Let L be a language of infinite words over $\Sigma \times \{0,1\}$ recognized by an ωBS-automaton. We want to show that the language $\mathbb{U}(L)$ is also recognized by a bounding automaton. Consider the following language:

$$K = \{w[X] : w[Y] \in L, \text{ for some } X \subseteq Y\}.$$

This language is downward closed in the sense that if $w[X]$ belongs to K, then $w[Y]$ belongs to K for every $Y \subseteq X$.

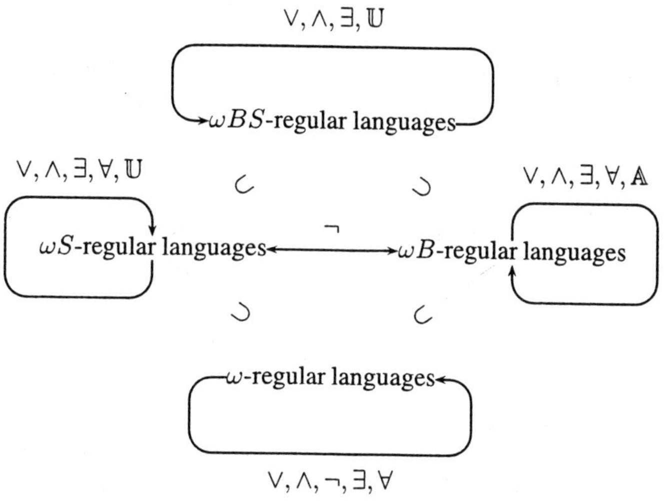

Figure 2. Logical view of the diamond

Furthermore, clearly $\mathbb{U}(L) = \mathbb{U}(K)$. Moreover, if L is recognized by a ωBS-automaton (resp. ωS-automaton), then so is K. Let $\mathcal{A}$ be an ωBS-automaton recognizing K. We will construct a ωBS-automaton recognizing $\mathbb{U}(K)$.

Given a word $w \in \Sigma^\omega$, a sequence of sets $X_1, X_2, \ldots \subseteq \mathbb{N}$ is *an unbounding witness* for K if for every i, the word $w[X_i]$ belongs to K and the sizes of the sets are unbounded. An unbounding witness is *sequential* if there is a sequence of numbers $a_1 < a_2 < \cdots$ such that all members of X_i are between a_i and a_{i+1}.

The following lemma is a simple application of the property of K being downward closed.

Lemma 5.5 A word admitting an unbounding witness for K admits a sequential one.

Let $X_1, X_2, \ldots$ be a sequential unbounding witness and let $a_1 < a_2 \cdots$ be the appropriate sequence of numbers. Let $\rho_1, \rho_2, \ldots$ be accepting runs of the automaton $\mathcal{A}$ over the words $w[X_1], w[X_2], \ldots$ Such runs exist by definition of unbounding witness. The sequence $X_1, X_2, \ldots$ is a *good witness* if every two runs ρ_i and ρ_j agree on almost all positions.

Lemma 5.6 A word belongs to $\mathbb{U}(K)$ if and only if it admits a good witness.

Proof

By Lemma 5.5, a word belongs to $\mathbb{U}(K)$, if and only if it admits a sequential witness. For every i, let s_i be the partial sequence that has $\perp$ on positions before a_{i+1} and agrees with ρ_i after a_{i+1}. By applying Lemma 5.4 to the set $\{s_1, s_2 \ldots\}$, we can find a run ρ_i and a set $J \subseteq \mathbb{N}$ such that for every $j \in J$, the runs ρ_i and ρ_j agree on some position x_j after a_{j+1}. For $j \in J$, let ρ'_j be a run that is defined as ρ_j on positions before x_j and is defined as ρ_i on positions after x_j. Since modifying the counter values over a finite set of positions does not violate the acceptance condition, the run ρ'_j is also an accepting run over the word $w[X_j]$. For every $j, k \in J$, the runs ρ'_j and ρ'_k agree on almost all positions (i.e. positions after both x_j and x_k). Therefore the witness obtained by using only the sets X_j with $j \in J$ is a good witness. □

Lemma 5.7 Words admitting a good witness can be recognized by a bounding automaton.

Proof

Given a word w, the automaton is going to guess a sequential witness

$$a_1 < a_2 < \cdots \qquad X_1, X_2, \ldots \subseteq \mathbb{N}$$

and a run ρ of $\mathcal{A}$ over w and verify the following properties:

- The run ρ is accepting;
- There is no bound on the size of the X_i's;
- For every i, some run over $w[X_i]$ agrees with ρ on almost all positions.

The first property can be obviously verified by a ωBS-automaton. For the second property, the automaton nondeterministically chooses a subsequence of $X_1, X_2, \ldots$ where the sizes are strongly unbounded. The third property is a regular property. The statement of the lemma then follows by closure of bounding automata under projection and intersection. □

5.4 An example: unbounded out-degree

Let $\varphi(X, Y)$ be a formula of MSOLB with two free set variables. This formula can be seen as an edge relation on sets. We show here that MSOLB can be used to say that this edge relation has unbounded out-degree.

We begin by defining the notion of an X-witness. This is a set witnessing that there are many successors of the set X under φ. (The actual successors of X form a set of sets, something MSOLB cannot talk about directly.) An X-*witness* is a set Y such that every two elements $x, y \in Y$ can be separated by a successor of X, that is:

$$\forall x, y \in Y\ \exists Z.\varphi(X, Z) \wedge (x \in Z \Leftrightarrow y \notin Z) .$$

(Therefore being an X-witness can be defined by an MSOLB formula.) We claim that the graph of φ has unbounded out-degree if and only if there are X-witnesses of arbitrarily large cardinality (for different sets X). This claim follows from the following fact:

Fact 5.8 If X has more than 2^n successors, then it has an X-witness of size at least n. If X has n successors, then all X-witnesses have size at most 2^n.

Proof
For the first statement, we first show that X has at least n successors that are boolean independent (none is a boolean combination of the others). From n boolean independent successors one can then construct by induction an X-witness of size n.

For the second statement, consider X with n successors as well as an X-witness. To each element w of the X-witness, associate the characteristic function of '$w \in Y$' for Y ranging over the successors of X. If the X-witness had more than 2^n elements, then at least two would give the same characteristic function, contradicting the definition of an X-witness. □

An ω-automatic graph is one where each vertex is a set of naturals, and the edge relation is defined by a formula $\varphi(X, Y)$ of MSOL over the naturals with successor (see [1]). In this particular case, the existence of arbitrarily large X-witnesses is expressed by a formula that belongs to one of the classes with decidable satisfiability from Theorem 5.1. This shows:

Proposition 5.9 It is decidable if an ω-automatic graph has unbounded out-degree.

6 Future work

We conclude the paper with some open questions.

As we have defined them, ωBS-regular languages are not closed under complementation. Can we find a larger class that is? What are the appropriate automata?

Are there natural deterministic automata? The automata in this paper seem to be inherently nondeterministic.

Our complementation proof is very complicated. It would be worthwhile to find a simpler version. In particular, the computational complexity of the construction could be reduced. In the present version, a single complementation step gives a non-elementary blowup of the automaton's state space.

Are there other meaningful and decidable extensions of monadic second-order logic? For instance does adding the predicate "the set of positions X is ultimately periodic" lead to an undecidable logic? (This predicate can be used to define the language $(ab^B)^\omega$.)

Is there an algebraic model for ωBS-regular languages? Can ω-semigroups be appropriately extended? Is there a link with tropical semirings [8]?

Is there a corresponding (decidable) temporal logic?

References

[1] A. Blumensath and E. Grädel. Finite presentations of infinite structures: Automata and interpretations. *Theory of Computing Systems*, 37:641 – 674, 2004.

[2] M. Bojańczyk. A bounding quantifier. In *Computer Science Logic*, volume 3210 of *Lecture Notes in Computer Science*, pages 41–55, 2004.

[3] A. Bouquet, O. Serre, and I. Walukiewicz. Pushdown games with unboundedness and regular conditions. In *Foundations of Software Technology and Theoretical Computer Science*, volume 2914 of *Lecture Notes in Computer Science*, pages 88–99, 2003.

[4] J. R. Büchi. Weak second-order arithmetic and finite automata. *Z. Math. Logik Grundl. Math.*, 6:66–92, 1960.

[5] J. R. Büchi. On a decision method in restricted second-order arithmetic. In *Proc. 1960 Int. Congr. for Logic, Methodology and Philosophy of Science*, pages 1–11, 1962.

[6] F. Klaedtke and H. Ruess. Parikh automata and monadic second–order logics with linear cardinality constraints. Technical Report 177, Institute of Computer Science at Freiburg University, 2002.

[7] M. O. Rabin. Decidability of second-order theories and automata on infinite trees. *Transactions of the AMS*, 141:1–23, 1969.

[8] I. Simon. Recognizable sets with multiplicites in the tropical semiring. In *Mathematical Foundations of Computer Science*, volume 324 of *Lecture Notes in Computer Science*, pages 107 – 120, 1988.

[9] I. Simon. Factorization forests of finite height. *Theoretical Computer Science*, 72:65 – 94, 1990.

[10] W. Thomas. Languages, automata, and logic. In G. Rozenberg and A. Salomaa, editors, *Handbook of Formal Language Theory*, volume III, pages 389–455. Springer, 1997.

Session 8:
Lambda Calculus

Head Normal Form Bisimulation for Pairs and the $\lambda\mu$-Calculus (Extended Abstract)

Soren B. Lassen
Google, Inc.
soren@google.com

Abstract

Böhm tree equivalence up to possibly infinite η expansion for the pure λ-calculus can be characterized as a bisimulation equivalence. We call this co-inductive syntactic theory extensional head normal form bisimilarity *and in this paper we extend it to the λFP-calculus (the λ-calculus with functional and surjective pairing) and to two untyped variants of Parigot's $\lambda\mu$-calculus. We relate the extensional head normal form bisimulation theories for the different calculi via Fujita's extensional CPS transform into the λFP-calculus. We prove that extensional hnf bisimilarity is fully abstract for the pure λ-calculus by a co-inductive reformulation of Barendregt's proof for Böhm tree equivalence up to possibly infinite η expansion. The proof uses the so-called Böhm-out technique from Böhm's proof of the Separation Property for the λ-calculus. Moreover, we extend the full abstraction result to extensional hnf bisimilarity for the λFP-calculus. For the "standard" $\lambda\mu$-calculus, the Separation Property fails, as shown by David and Py, and for the same reason extensional hnf bisimilarity is not fully abstract. However, an "extended" variant of the $\lambda\mu$-calculus satisfies the Separation Property, as shown by Saurin, and we show that extensional hnf bisimilarity is fully abstract for this extended $\lambda\mu$-calculus.*

1 Introduction

The goal of the work presented in this paper is to understand the computational behaviour of the untyped λ-calculus with pairs and the untyped $\lambda\mu$-calculus [16] and to find principles for reasoning about program behaviour and equivalence. In particular, we wish to learn the properties of two recent contributions to these calculi. One is Fujita's untyped adaptation [7] of Hofmann and Streicher's extensional CPS transform [9] of the λ-calculus and $\lambda\mu$-calculus into the λ-calculus with pairs. The other is Saurin's extension of the untyped $\lambda\mu$-calculus in [20].

We use the programming language semantics tools of structural operational semantics (SOS), continuation passing style (CPS) transform, and bisimulation equivalences. We take head reduction to head normal form (hnf) as our operational semantics, defined as big-step SOS evaluation relations, we use Fujita's extensional CPS transform, and we use the bisimulation characterization of Böhm tree equivalence up to possibly infinite η expansion from [12] as our bisimulation equivalence.

We give new definitions of solvability, head normal forms (hnfs), and head evaluation for the calculi and we present new co-inductive theories called extensional hnf bisimilarity. For the λFP-calculus and the extended $\lambda\mu$-calculus we prove that extensional hnf bisimilarity coincides with solvable equivalence. Furthermore, we relate extensional hnf bisimilarity for the λFP-calculus to extensional hnf bisimilarity for the other calculi via extensional CPS transforms.

Böhm tree equivalence up to possibly infinite η-expansion (or Nakajima tree equivalence) is a powerful syntactic characterization of the theory of solvable equivalence for the pure "sensible" λ-calculus [2]. It can be formulated co-inductively as a syntactic bisimulation equivalence, without reference to Böhm trees, based on head reduction to head normal form (hnf) [12]. We call this characterization *extensional hnf bisimilarity*. It is the greatest symmetric term relation $\eqsim$ such that, whenever $t \eqsim t'$, either t and t' have no hnfs or t and t' both have hnfs that η-expand to hnfs

$$\lambda x_1 \ldots x_m.\, y\, t_1 \ldots t_n, \quad \lambda x_1 \ldots x_m.\, y\, t'_1 \ldots t'_n,$$

respectively, where $m, n \geq 0$ and $t_1 \eqsim t'_1, \ldots, t_n \eqsim t'_n$.

This bisimulation characterization of solvable equivalence is useful because it makes it possible to prove program equivalences by the powerful and convenient bisimulation proof method. See [12, 14, 13] for examples of normal form bisimulation proofs of program equivalences.

Outline Section 2 describes related work. Sections 3 and 4 present the pure λ-calculus and the λFP-calculus and solvability, hnfs, head evalutation, extensional hnf bisimilarity,

1043-6871/06 $20.00

and Fujita's CPS transform. Section 5 outlines the congruence proof for extensional hnf bisimilarity for the λFP-calculus. Section 6 outlines full abstraction proofs for the pure λ-calculus and the λFP-calculus. The proofs present the "Böhm-out" technique in a novel co-inductive fashion. Sections 7 and 8 extend solvability, head normal forms, head evaluation, extensional hnf bisimilarity, and the CPS transform to the standard $\lambda\mu$-calculus and the extended $\lambda\mu$-calculus. We show that extensional hnf bisimilarity *is not* fully abstract for the standard $\lambda\mu$-calculus, using an example by David and Py, and we extend the Böhm-out technique to prove that extensional hnf bisimilarity *is* fully abstract for the extended $\lambda\mu$-calculus

2 Related work

Sangiorgi [19] first gave a bisimulation characterization of Lévy-Longo tree equivalence, which he called open applicative bisimulation. The hnf bisimulation characterization of Böhm tree equivalence (up to infinite η-expansion) was introduced by Lassen [12] and by David [5]. Eager normal form bisimulation [13] is a recent variant of hnf bisimulation for the call-by-value λ-calculus.

Most of the literature about the λ-calculus with surjective/explicit/functional pairs (see the survey in [21]) is about reduction, confluence, and conversion. Our definitions of head normal forms, head evaluation, solvability, solvable equivalence, and bisimilarity appear to be new.

Parigot introduced the standard $\lambda\mu$-calculus as a term assignment system for classical logic. David and Py [6] defined solvability, head normal forms, head reduction, and solvable equivalence for the untyped standard $\lambda\mu$-calculus. Saurin introduced the untyped extended $\lambda\mu$-calculus and defined head reduction and head normal forms. (Saurin names the calculus $\Lambda\mu$ and he uses a slightly different syntax.) We introduce alternative definitions of head normal forms and head evaluation that are better suited for hnf bisimulation. Our "big-step" definition of head evaluation is reminiscent of Ong and Stewart's evaluation semantics for a typed call-by-value $\lambda\mu$-calculus in [15]. Our definition of solvability is new.

David and Py established a "computational equivalence" result [6] for the standard $\lambda\mu$-calculus which amounts to an applicative bisimulation characterization of solvable equivalence [1].

CPS Translation Theorems relate the extensional hnf bisimulation theories for the λFP-calculus and the other calculi via Fujita's CPS transform. This is parallel to Boudol's correspondence result between Lévy-Longo tree equivalence and Böhm tree equivalence via Plotkin's call-by-name CPS transform [4] and Lassen's correspondence result between eager normal form (call-by-value) bisimilarity and hnf bisimilarity via Plotkin's call-by-value CPS transform [13] (Plotkin defined the CPS transforms in [17]).

Our syntactic congruence proof for extensional hnf bisimilarity for the λFP-calculus is novel. The Main Lemma only shows that bisimilarity is substitutive, not compatible. Compatibility is then derived from the definition of bisimilarity. Otherwise the congruence proof is similar to the congruence proofs for Lévy-Longo tree equivalence and Böhm tree equivalence in [12], which can be viewed as more intuitive (and symmetric) variant of Howe's congruence proof method [10]. Congruence of extensional hnf bisimilarity for the $\lambda\mu$-calculus is derived via the CPS transform, as in [13].

Our full abstraction proof for the pure λ-calculus is a co-inductive reformulation of the full abstraction proofs by Wadsworth, Hyland, and Barendregt [22, 11, 2]. It uses the Böhm-out technique from Böhm's proof of the Separation Property [3], a.k.a. Böhm's Theorem. Our extension of the proof to the λFP-calculus is new. Our proof for the extended $\lambda\mu$-calculus combines the new co-inductive Böhm-out formulation with elements from Saurin's proof of the Separation Property [20].

3 The λ-calculus

Let x, y, z range over variables. The terms of the pure λ-calculus are given by the grammar:

TERMS $t ::= x \mid \lambda x. t \mid t_1\, t_2$

Application associates to the left and λ-abstraction extends as far to the right as possible, so $\lambda x. t_1\, t_2\, t_3 = \lambda x. ((t_1\, t_2)\, t_3)$.

Let $\mathrm{FV}(t)$ denote the set of free variables in t. We identify terms up to renaming of bound variables. Let $t_1[t_2/x]$ denote the capture-free substitution of t_2 for all free occurrences of x in t_1.

Even though we will not be concerned with reduction and conversion, we list the usual β and η equations for the λ-calculus:

$$(\lambda x. t_1)\, t_2 =_\beta t_1[t_2/x] \qquad (\beta)$$

$$\lambda x. t\, x =_\eta t, \text{ if } x \notin \mathrm{FV}(t) \qquad (\eta)$$

The β equation will form the basis for the evaluation relation below and both equations will be satisfied by extensional hnf bisimilarity.

Rather than the usual definition of head reduction and the derived definition of head normal forms as the normal forms of head reduction, here we first define the head normal forms (hnfs) and then define a head evaluation relation between terms and hnfs.

HNFS $h ::= f \mid \lambda x. h$

λ-FREE HNFS $f ::= x \mid f\, t$

That is, hnfs are terms of the form $\lambda x_1 \ldots x_m. y\, t_1 \ldots t_n$.

The head evaluation relation between terms t and hnfs h, written $t \rightsquigarrow h$, is defined inductively in the style of big-step structural operational semantics, except that we define head evaluation also for open terms.

$$\text{(E1)}\ \frac{}{x \rightsquigarrow x}$$

$$\text{(E2)}\ \frac{t \rightsquigarrow h}{\lambda x.\, t \rightsquigarrow \lambda x.\, h}$$

$$\text{(E3)}\ \frac{t_1 \rightsquigarrow f}{t_1\, t_2 \rightsquigarrow f\, t_2}$$

$$\text{(E4)}\ \frac{t_1 \rightsquigarrow \lambda x.\, h_1 \quad h_1[t_2/x] \rightsquigarrow h}{t_1\, t_2 \rightsquigarrow h}$$

This definition is convenient for our uses. The head evaluation relation can also be defined in terms of conventional head reduction to hnf.

We say that a term t *has a hnf* if $t \rightsquigarrow h$ for some h. Not all terms have a hnf. For instance, $\Omega = (\lambda x.\, x\, x)\,(\lambda x.\, x\, x)$ has no hnf.

For the pure λ-calculus, a closed term t is *solvable* iff $t\,\vec{t} =_\beta \lambda x.\, x$, for some closed arguments $\vec{t}$ (zero or more arguments) [2].

Lemma 1 (Wadsworth [22]). *A closed term is solvable iff it has a hnf.*

A term relation R is *semi sensible* iff, whenever t and t' are closed terms and $t\ R\ t'$, t is solvable iff t' is solvable. A semi sensible relation is *sensible* iff it relates all unsolvable terms, that is, it satisfies the equation:

$$t =_\Omega \Omega, \quad \text{if } t \text{ is unsolvable} \qquad (\Omega)$$

Definition 1. Let *solvable equivalence* be the greatest compatible semi sensible relation. (A term relation is compatible if it is closed under all term contructors.) It relates terms t and t' iff, for all term contexts C (term with any number of holes $[\,]$) such that $C[t]$ and $C[t']$ are closed, $C[t]$ is solvable iff $C[t']$ is solvable.

Given a term relation R, let $M(R)$ be the relation between hnfs defined inductively by the rules:

$$\text{(M1)}\ \frac{}{x\ M(R)\ x}$$

$$\text{(M2)}\ \frac{f\ M(R)\ f'}{f\,t\ M(R)\ f'\,t'}\ \text{if } t\ R\ t'$$

$$\text{(M3)}\ \frac{h\ M(R)\ h'}{\lambda x.\, h\ M(R)\ \lambda x.\, h'}$$

$$\text{(M4)}\ \frac{f\,x\ M(R)\ h}{f\ M(R)\ \lambda x.\, h}\ \text{if } x \notin \mathrm{FV}(f)$$

$$\text{(M5)}\ \frac{h\ M(R)\ f\,x}{\lambda x.\, h\ M(R)\ f}\ \text{if } x \notin \mathrm{FV}(f)$$

In other words, $h\ M(R)\ h'$ if $h = \lambda x_1 \ldots x_m. y\, t_1 \ldots t_n$ and $h' = \lambda x_1 \ldots x_{m+k}. y\, t'_1 \ldots t'_{n+k}$ and

$$t_1\ R\ t'_1, \ldots, t_n\ R\ t'_n, x_{m+1}\ R\ t_{n+1}, \ldots, x_{m+k}\ R\ t_{n+k}$$

and similarly if h has more leading lambdas than h'.

Definition 2. Given a term relation R, let $B(R)$ be the term relation defined as follows:

$t\ B(R)\ t'$ iff
 $(i)\ \forall h.\, t \rightsquigarrow h \Rightarrow \exists h'.\, t' \rightsquigarrow h' \;\&\; h\ M(R)\ h'$ and
 $(ii)\ \forall h'.\, t' \rightsquigarrow h' \Rightarrow \exists h.\, t \rightsquigarrow h \;\&\; h\ M(R)\ h'$

A term relation R is a *hnf bisimulation up to* η [12] iff it is a post-fixpoint of B, that is, $R \subseteq B(R)$. Let *extensional hnf bisimilarity*, $\precapprox$, be the greatest fixpoint of B which, by the Tarski-Knaster fixpoint theorem, exists and is the greatest hnf bisimulation up to η.

For example, we can show co-inductively that extensional hnf bisimilarity satisfies the well-known infinite η-expansion equation:

$$\lambda x.\, x \precapprox J, \text{ where } J = \Theta\, \lambda xyz.\, y\, x\, z \qquad (1)$$

(Θ denotes Turing's fixpoint combinator) by checking that $\{(\lambda x.\, x, J), (z, J\, z) \mid z \text{ is a variable}\}$ is a hnf bisimulation up to η.

It is immediate from the definition that extensional hnf bisimilarity is semi sensible and it is easy to show that extensional hnf bisimilarity is an equivalence relation (reflexive, transitive, symmetric) and, using properties of head evaluation, that it includes the β, η, and Ω equations and satisfies the following extensionality property (see [2]):

$$t\, x \precapprox t'\, x \;\Rightarrow\; t \precapprox t', \quad \text{if } x \notin \mathrm{FV}(t) \cup \mathrm{FV}(t') \qquad (\textit{ext})$$

It follows from the definitions that extensional hnf bisimilarity is the same as Böhm tree equivalence up to possibly infinite η expansion. Barendregt showed that this is a congruence and that it is fully abstract with respect to (coincides with) solvable equivalence. A direct co-inductive congruence proof for extensional hnf bisimilarity is given in [12]. Later in this paper we will give a new congruence proof and outline a new co-inductive formulation of the full abstraction proof.

4 The λFP-calculus

We now consider the λFP-calculus which is an extension of the λ-calculus with functional and surjective pairing:

$$\text{TERMS}\ t ::= x \mid \lambda x.\, t \mid t_1\, t_2 \mid \langle t_1, t_2\rangle \mid \pi_1\, t \mid \pi_2\, t$$

The β equation from the pure λ-calculus together with the projection equation:

$$\pi_i\ \langle t_1, t_2\rangle =_\pi t_i, \quad \text{if } i \in \{1,2\} \qquad (\pi)$$

and two commutation (or "functional pairing") equations [21]:

$$\pi_i\,(t_1\, t_2) =_{\pi_\nu} (\pi_i\, t_1)\, t_2, \quad \text{if } i \in \{1,2\} \qquad (\pi_\nu)$$
$$\pi_i\, \lambda x.\, t =_{\pi_\lambda} \lambda x.\, \pi_i\, t, \quad \text{if } i \in \{1,2\} \qquad (\pi_\lambda)$$

form the basis for the evaluation relation below. Extensional hnf bisimilarity for the λFP-calculus, which we define below, satisfies all these equations as well as the η equation from the pure λ-calculus and the surjective pairing equation:

$$\langle \pi_1\, t, \pi_2\, t\rangle =_{\text{sp}} t \qquad (\text{sp})$$

One motivation for studying the λ-calculus with pairs is that it is the target of Fujita's continuation passing style (CPS) transform of the pure λ-calculus [7]. Following Danvy and Hatcliff [8], we change Fujita's transform slightly by adding an η redex to the variable case.

$$\begin{aligned}
\text{cps}(x) &= \lambda a.\, x\, a \\
\text{cps}(\lambda x.\, t) &= \lambda a.\, (\lambda x.\ \text{cps}(t))\, (\pi_1\, a)\, (\pi_2\, a) \\
\text{cps}(t_1\, t_2) &= \lambda a.\ \text{cps}(t_1)\ \langle \text{cps}(t_2), a\rangle
\end{aligned}$$

where a is a fresh variable that does not occur free in the source terms. Fujita [7] has investigated relationships between reductions and equations in the source and target calculi with respect to his transform. In Section 5 we report a new CPS Translation Theorem that relates extensional hnf bisimilarity in the λ-calculus and the λFP-calculus.

We define the head normal forms as follows:

HNFS $h ::= f \mid \lambda x.\, h$

λ-FREE HNFS $f ::= p[x] \mid f\, t$

PROJECTION CONTEXTS $p ::= [] \mid \pi_1\, p \mid \pi_2\, p$

To differentiate λ-terms and hnfs in the pure λ-calculus from the new definitions for the λFP-calculus, we will refer to the former as *pure terms* and *pure hnfs* in the sequel.

These operations are used in the definitions of head evaluation and $M(R)$ below.

We define head evaluation from terms to hnfs by the rules:

$$(\text{E1})\ \frac{}{p[x] \rightsquigarrow p[x]}$$

$$(\text{E2})\ \frac{p[t] \rightsquigarrow h}{p[\lambda x.\, t] \rightsquigarrow \lambda x.\, h}$$

$$(\text{E3})\ \frac{p[t_1] \rightsquigarrow f}{p[t_1\, t_2] \rightsquigarrow f\, t_2}$$

$$(\text{E4})\ \frac{p[t_1] \rightsquigarrow \lambda x.\, h_1 \quad h_1[{}^{t_2}\!/\!_x] \rightsquigarrow h}{p[t_1\, t_2] \rightsquigarrow h}$$

$$(\text{E5})\ \frac{p[t_i] \rightsquigarrow h}{p[\pi_i\ \langle t_1, t_2\rangle] \rightsquigarrow h}\ \text{if } i \in \{1,2\}$$

For the λFP-calculus, we define a closed term t to be solvable iff $p[t]\, \vec{t} =_{\beta\pi\pi_\nu\pi_\lambda} \lambda x.\, x$, for some projection context p and closed arguments $\vec{t}$. For example, Ω and $\langle \Omega, \Omega\rangle$ are unsolvable, but $t = \langle \lambda x.\, x, \Omega\rangle$ is solvable, even though t does not have a hnf, because $\pi_1\, t =_\pi \lambda x.\, x$.

Lemma 2. *A closed term t is solvable iff there is a projection context p such that $p[t]$ has a hnf.*

As for the pure λ-calculus, we say that a relation R on λFP-terms is semi sensible iff, whenever R relates two closed terms t and t', t is solvable iff t' is solvable. Solvable equivalence is again the greatest compatible semi-sensible relation.

For the λFP-calculus we extend the definition of $M(R)$ by generalizing (M1) as follows:

$$(\text{M1})\ \frac{}{p[x]\ M(R)\ p[x]}$$

In the definition of $B(R)$ we will also use the notation $t \rightsquigarrow_p h$, defined by

$$t \rightsquigarrow_p \lambda\vec{x}.\, p'[y]\, \vec{t} \ \text{ iff } \ p[t] \rightsquigarrow \lambda\vec{x}.\, p[p'[y]]\, \vec{t}.$$

For example, $\langle \pi_1\, h, \pi_2\, h\rangle \rightsquigarrow_{\pi_1[]} h$.

Definition 3. Given a term relation R, let $B(R)$ be the term relation defined as follows:

$$\begin{aligned}
&t\ B(R)\ t' \text{ iff} \\
&\quad (i)\ \forall p, h.\ p[t] \rightsquigarrow h \Rightarrow \\
&\qquad\qquad \exists p', h'.\ p[t'] \rightsquigarrow_{p'} h'\ \&\ h\ M(R)\ h' \text{ and} \\
&\quad (ii)\ \forall p, h'.\ p[t'] \rightsquigarrow h' \Rightarrow \\
&\qquad\qquad \exists p', h.\ p[t] \rightsquigarrow_{p'} h\ \&\ h\ M(R)\ h'
\end{aligned}$$

Again a relation R is a hnf bisimulation up to η iff $R \subseteq B(R)$ and extensional hnf bisimilarity, $\precsim$, is the greatest fixpoint of B.

Extensional hnf bisimilarity relates terms up to infinite sp-expansion, as illustrated by

$$\lambda x.\, x \approx L, \text{ where } L = \Theta\, \lambda x.\, y\langle \pi_1\, y, x\,(\pi_2\, y)\rangle \qquad (2)$$

which follows immediately from the fact that $\approx$ is a fixpoint of B. This example motivates the subtleties in the definition of $B(R)$ in Definition 3.

Just like for the pure λ-calculus, extensional hnf bisimilarity is a semi sensible equivalence relation and includes the Ω equation (for the new definition of solvability) and satisfies the extensionality property ***ext***. Moreover, it includes extensional hnf bisimilary for the pure λ-calculus and includes the β, η, π, π_ν, π_λ, and sp equations.

Remark 1. The definitions of hnfs, head evaluation, solvability, $M(-)$, $B(-)$, and extensional hnf bisimilarity all cleanly extend those for the pure λ-calculus. In particular, two pure λ-terms are extensional hnf bisimilar in the pure λ-calculus (Definition 2) iff they are extensional hnf bisimilar in the λFP-calculus (Definition 3). This is a general property of normal form bisimulation theories. The same is true for extensional hnf bisimilarity for the standard $\lambda\mu$-calculus in Section 7 and again for the extended $\lambda\mu$-calculus in Section 8. The whnf bisimulation equivalence for a nondeterministic λ-calculus with ambiguous choice in [14] exhibits the same property relative to whnf bisimilarity for the pure deterministic λ-calculus.

5 Congruence and CPS Translation Theorem

We now want to show that extensional hnf bisimilarity for the λFP-calculus is a congruence. To this end we define, for any given term relation R, its substitutive hnf-closure $S(R)$ to be the term relation defined inductively by the rules:

$$\text{(S1)}\ \frac{}{t\ S(R)\ t'}\ \text{if } t\ R\ t'$$

$$\text{(S2)}\ \frac{h\ M(S(R))\ h'}{h\ S(R)\ h'}$$

$$\text{(S3)}\ \frac{t_1\ S(R)\ t_1' \quad t_2\ S(R)\ t_2'}{t_1[{}^{t_2}\!/\!{}_x]\ S(R)\ t_1'[{}^{t_2'}\!/\!{}_x]}$$

Lemma 3 (Main Lemma). *If R is a hnf bisimulation up to η, so is $S(R)$.*

Proof outline. We instrument the head evaluation relation $t \rightsquigarrow h$ with a natural number n, written $t \overset{n}{\rightsquigarrow} h$, where n counts the number of β-reductions (rule (E5)) used in the derivation of $t \rightsquigarrow h$.

Now, under the assumption that $R \subseteq B(R)$, we prove

$$\begin{aligned} &t\ S(R)\ t' \ \&\ p[t] \overset{n}{\rightsquigarrow} h \Rightarrow \\ &\quad \exists p', h'.\, p[t'] \rightsquigarrow_{p'} h' \ \&\ h\ M(S(R))\ h' \end{aligned}$$

by induction (1) on n and (2) on the derivation of $t\ S(R)\ t'$, ordered lexicographically. The argument resembles the congruence proofs in [12, 14]. This establishes part (i) of the inclusion $S(R) \subseteq B(S(R))$, cf. Definition 3. Part (ii) is symmetrical. □

Theorem 4. *Extensional hnf bisimilarity is a congruence for the* λFP*-calculus.*

Proof. We know that extensional hnf bisimilarity is an equivalence relation (reflexive, transitive, and symmetric), so we just need to show that it is compatible, namely:

$$t \approx t' \ \Rightarrow\ \lambda x.\, t \approx \lambda x.\, t' \qquad \text{(C1)}$$

$$t_1 \approx t_1' \ \&\ t_2 \approx t_2' \ \Rightarrow\ t_1\, t_2 \approx t_1'\, t_2' \qquad \text{(C2)}$$

$$t_1 \approx t_1' \ \&\ t_2 \approx t_2' \ \Rightarrow\ \langle t_1, t_2\rangle \approx \langle t_1', t_2'\rangle \qquad \text{(C3)}$$

$$t \approx t' \ \Rightarrow\ \pi_i\, t \approx \pi_i\, t', \text{ if } i \in \{1,2\} \qquad \text{(C4)}$$

For (C1), $t \approx t'$ implies $\lambda x.\, t\ B(\approx)\ \lambda x.\, t'$ directly, without the Main Lemma, as follows. Suppose $p[\lambda x.\, t] \rightsquigarrow h$. This must be derived from (E2), so $h = \lambda x.\, h_0$ for some h_0 such that $p[t] \rightsquigarrow h_0$. If $t \approx t'$, $p[t'] \rightsquigarrow_{p'} h_0'$ for some p' and hnf h_0' such that $h_0\ M(\approx)\ h_0'$. By (E2), $p[\lambda x.\, t'] \rightsquigarrow_{p'} \lambda x.\, h_0'$ and, by (M3), $h = \lambda x.\, h_0\ M(\approx)\ \lambda x.\, h_0'$. This establishes part (i) of $\lambda x.\, t\ B(\approx)\ \lambda x.\, t'$. Part (ii) is symmetrical.

Since extensional hnf bisimilarity is a hnf bisimulation up to η, the Main Lemma entails that its substitutive hnf closure is a hnf bisimulation up to η and thus contained in extensional hnf bisimilarity, by co-induction. We conclude that extensional hnf bisimilarity is substitutive:

$$t_1 \approx t_1' \ \&\ t_2 \approx t_2' \ \Rightarrow\ t_1[{}^{t_2}\!/\!{}_x] \approx t_1'[{}^{t_2'}\!/\!{}_x]$$

The clauses (C2), (C3), and (C4) follow from substitutivity and reflexivity. □

Theorem 5 (CPS Translation). *$t \approx t'$ in the pure λ-calculus iff* $\mathrm{cps}(t) \approx \mathrm{cps}(t')$ *in the* λFP*-calculus.*

The proof is analogous to the proof of the CPS Translation Theorem for Plotkin's CPS transform, eager normal form bisimilarity up to η, and extensional hnf bisimilarity in [13]: The proof relies on a CPS Simulation Theorem that relates head evaluation of terms t in the pure λ-calculus and head evaluation of $\mathrm{cps}(t)$ in the λFP-calculus, then both the 'if' and 'only if' directions of the CPS Translation Theorem are established by exhibiting hnf bisimulations up to η.

Since $\mathrm{cps}(-)$ is compositional and extensional hnf bisimilarity is a congruence for the λFP-calculus, we conclude:

Corollary 6. *Extensional hnf bisimilarity is a congruence for the pure λ-calculus.*

6 Böhm-out and full abstraction

In this section, we show that extensional hnf bisimilarity is fully abstract with respect to solvable equivalence. Our proof is based on the classical proofs [22, 11, 2] but we use a co-inductive formulation of the Böhm-out technique that elucidates the argument. We first prove full abstraction for the pure λ-calculus and then describe how the proof extends to the λFP-calculus. In Section 8 we adapt the proof to the $\lambda\mu$-calculus.

Let Λ be the set of all pure λ-terms. Then $\Lambda \times \Lambda$ is the universal relation on pure λ-terms. Two closed pure hnfs h and h' are *equivalent*, written $h \sim h'$, iff $h\ M(\Lambda \times \Lambda)\ h'$. For arbitrary closed pure λ-terms t and t' we define $t \sim t'$ iff $t\ B(\Lambda \times \Lambda)\ t'$, that is either both t and t' are unsolvable or both are solvable and have equivalent hnfs.

Lemma 7. *$t \sim t'$, for all closed pure solvably equivalent λ-terms t and t'.*

The *permutator* P_n and *projection* U^n_i, for $0 \le i \le n$, are the terms:

$$\mathsf{P}_n = \lambda x_1 \ldots x_n x_{n+1}.\, x_{n+1}\, x_1 \ldots x_n$$
$$\mathsf{U}^n_i = \lambda x_1 \ldots x_n.\, x_i$$

Collectively, we call permutators and projections *discriminator terms*. Let δ range over these and let Δ range over applicative contexts with discriminator arguments:

DISCRIMINATORS $\delta ::= \mathsf{P}_n \mid \mathsf{U}^n_i$

DISCRIMINATION CONTEXTS $\Delta ::= [\,] \mid \Delta\, \delta$

Now we define a "Böhm-out" relation $\approx$. For closed pure λ-terms t and t',

$$t \approx t' \text{ iff } \forall \Delta.\ \Delta[t] \sim \Delta[t']$$

On open terms we define $\approx$ as the limit of an increasing sequence of relations, $\approx = \bigcup_{n<\omega} \approx_n$, where $t \approx_n t'$ iff

$$\forall \{x_1, \ldots, x_m\} \supseteq \text{FV}(t) \cup \text{FV}(t').\ \forall n_1, \ldots, n_m \ge n.$$
$$t[\mathsf{P}_{n_1}/x_1] \ldots [\mathsf{P}_{n_m}/x_m] \approx t'[\mathsf{P}_{n_1}/x_1] \ldots [\mathsf{P}_{n_m}/x_m].$$

Lemma 8 (Böhm-out). *$\approx$ is a hnf bisimulation up to η.*

Proof outline. We must show that $\approx\ \subseteq B(\approx)$, that is, $t \approx_n t'$ implies $t\ B(\approx)\ t'$, for all $n < \omega$ and terms t, t'. We show that $t \rightsquigarrow h$ implies there exist h' and n' such that $t' \rightsquigarrow h'$ and $h\ M(\approx_{n'})\ h'$. The choice of n' depends on n and the structure of h. By symmetry we conclude that $t\ B(\approx)\ t'$, as required. □

Theorem 9 (Full abstraction [2]). *Extensional hnf bisimilarity coincides with solvable equivalence for the pure λ-calculus.*

Proof. Extensional hnf bisimilarity is included in solvable equivalence because it is semi sensible and congruent. Conversely, since solvable equivalence is included in $\sim$ and is congruent, it is easy to see that solvable equivalence is included in $\approx$ which, by the Böhm-out Lemma and co-induction, is included in extensional hnf bisimilarity. □

The definitions and lemmas extend to the λFP-calculus, if we let terms and hnfs range over λFP-terms and hnfs and we use $M(\Lambda\text{FP} \times \Lambda\text{FP})$ and $B(\Lambda\text{FP} \times \Lambda\text{FP})$ in the definition of $\sim$, where ΛFP is the set of all λFP-terms and M and B are the extended relational operators from Section 4.

We extend the definition of discriminators:

DISCRIMINATORS $\delta ::= \mathsf{P}_n \mid \overline{p}[\mathsf{U}^n_i]$

where $\overline{p}$ is the right-inverse of the projection context p, satisfying $p[\overline{p}[t]] =_\pi t$, defined as:

$$\overline{[\,]} = [\,]$$
$$\overline{p[\pi_1\,[\,]]} = \langle \overline{p}, \Omega \rangle$$
$$\overline{p[\pi_2\,[\,]]} = \langle \Omega, \overline{p} \rangle$$

The definitions of discrimination contexts, Δ, and the Böhm-out relation, $\approx$, are unchanged and the structure of the proof of the Böhm-out Lemma is the same as for the pure λ-calculus.

Theorem 10 (Full abstraction). *Extensional hnf bisimilarity coincides with solvable equivalence for the λFP-calculus.*

Theorems 5, 9, and 10 entail that Fujita's CPS transform of the λ-calculus is fully abstract.

7 The standard $\lambda\mu$-calculus

We now consider the untyped $\lambda\mu$-calculus [16]. Let a and b range over "names".

TERMS $t ::= x \mid \lambda x.\, t \mid t_1\, t_2 \mid \mu a.\, [b]t$

Naming and μ-abstraction extend as far to the right as possible, so $\mu a.\, [b]t_1\, t_2 = \mu a.\, [b](t_1\, t_2)$.

We refer to this restricted syntax, where μ-abstraction and naming are coupled in a single syntactic construction $\mu a.\, [b]t$, as *standard*. It is some times useful to consider named terms as a separate syntactic category so that we can regard μ-abstractions as terms of the form $\mu a.\, \tau$ where τ is a *named term*:

NAMED TERMS $\tau ::= [a]t$

If ϕ is a syntactic phrase, notation $\phi[a \Leftarrow t]$ denotes the capture-free substitution of $[a](t'[a \Leftarrow t]\, t)$ for every occurrence of a named subterm of the form $[a]t'$ in ϕ. Notation

$\phi[^a\!/\!_b]$ denotes the capture-free substitution of a for all free occurrences of b in ϕ. We write $\text{FN}(\phi)$ for the set of free names in ϕ and we say ϕ is *closed* when $\text{FN}(\phi) = \text{FV}(\phi) = \emptyset$ and ϕ is *variable-closed* if $\text{FV}(\phi) = \emptyset$.

Apart from the β and η equations from the pure λ-calculus, the standard $\lambda\mu$-calculus has the following additional equations:

$$(\mu a.\,\tau)\,t =_\mu \mu a.\,\tau[a{\Leftarrow}t], \text{ if } a \notin \text{FN}(t) \qquad (\mu)$$

$$\mu a.\,[b]\mu a'.\,\tau =_\rho \mu a.\,\tau[^b\!/\!_{a'}] \qquad (\rho)$$

$$\mu a.\,[a]t =_\theta t, \text{ if } a \notin \text{FN}(t) \qquad (\theta)$$

Fujita extended his extensional CPS transform to the standard $\lambda\mu$-calculus by the following additional clauses:

$$\text{cps}(\mu a.\,\tau) = \lambda a.\ \text{cps}(\tau)$$
$$\text{cps}([a]t) = \text{cps}(t)\,a$$

(For convenience, we include the names from the $\lambda\mu$-calculus in the set of variables in the λFP-calculus.)

We define hnfs for the standard $\lambda\mu$-calculus as follows:

HNFS $h ::= g \mid \mu a.\,[b]g$

μ-FREE HNFS $g ::= f \mid \lambda x.\,h$

λ-FREE HNFS $f ::= x \mid f\,t$

Furthermore, we let γ range over *named hnfs*:

NAMED HNFS $\gamma ::= [a]g$

Definition 4. The syntactic operation $\underline{[a]}h$ maps a hnf h to a named hnf:

$$\underline{[a]}g = [a]g$$
$$\underline{[a]}\mu b.\,\gamma = \gamma[^a\!/\!_b]$$

We define head evaluation to hnf by rules (E1) through (E4) from Section 3 plus the following additional rules:

$$\text{(E5)}\ \frac{t_1 \rightsquigarrow \mu a.\,\gamma \quad \mu a.\,\gamma[a{\Leftarrow}t_2] \rightsquigarrow h}{t_1\,t_2 \rightsquigarrow h} \text{ if } a \notin \text{FN}(t_2)$$

$$\text{(E6)}\ \frac{t \rightsquigarrow h}{\mu a.\,[b]t \rightsquigarrow \mu a.\,\underline{[b]}h}$$

Let us say that a closed term in the standard $\lambda\mu$-calculus is solvable iff $t\,\vec{t} =_{\beta\mu\rho\theta} \lambda x.\,x$, for some closed arguments $\vec{t}$.

Lemma 11. *A closed standard $\lambda\mu$-term is solvable iff it has a hnf.*

Given this definition of solvability, the definition of a semi sensible relation is the same as before and solvable equivalence is the greatest compatible semi sensible relation.

Definition 5. Define the syntactic operations $h\underline{[a{\Leftarrow}x]}$ on hnfs h as follows:

$$f\underline{[a{\Leftarrow}x]} = f[a{\Leftarrow}x]$$
$$(\lambda y.\,h)\underline{[a{\Leftarrow}x]} = \lambda y.\,h\underline{[a{\Leftarrow}x]}, \text{ if } x \neq y$$
$$(\mu b.\,[a']g)\underline{[a{\Leftarrow}x]} = \mu b.\,\underline{[a']}(g\underline{[a{\Leftarrow}x]}), \text{ if } a' \neq a \neq b$$
$$(\mu b.\,[a]f)\underline{[a{\Leftarrow}x]} = \mu b.\,[a](f[a{\Leftarrow}x]\,x), \text{ if } a \neq b$$
$$(\mu b.\,[a]\lambda y.\,h)\underline{[a{\Leftarrow}x]} = \mu b.\,\underline{[a]}(h[^x\!/\!_y]\underline{[a{\Leftarrow}x]}), \text{ if } a \neq b$$

We extend the definition of $M(R)$ from the pure λ-calculus with three additional rules (M6) through (M8) and also define an auxiliary relation $N(R)$ on named hnfs:

$$\text{(M6)}\ \frac{\gamma\ N(R)\ \gamma'}{\mu a.\,\gamma\ M(R)\ \mu a.\,\gamma'}$$

$$\text{(M7)}\ \frac{\gamma\ N(R)\ [a]g}{\mu a.\,\gamma\ M(R)\ g} \text{ if } a \notin \text{FN}(g)$$

$$\text{(M8)}\ \frac{[a]g\ N(R)\ \gamma}{g\ M(R)\ \mu a.\,\gamma} \text{ if } a \notin \text{FN}(g)$$

$$\text{(N1)}\ \frac{f\ M(R)\ f'}{[a]f\ N(R)\ [a]f'}$$

$$\text{(N2)}\ \frac{\underline{[a]}(h\underline{[a{\Leftarrow}x]})\ N(R)\ \underline{[a]}(h'\underline{[a{\Leftarrow}x]})}{[a]\lambda x.\,h\ N(R)\ [a]\lambda x.\,h'}$$

$$\text{(N3)}\ \frac{\underline{[a]}(h\underline{[a{\Leftarrow}x]})\ N(R)\ [a](f[a{\Leftarrow}x]\,x)}{[a]\lambda x.\,h\ N(R)\ [a]f}$$

$$\text{(N4)}\ \frac{[a](f[a{\Leftarrow}x]\,x)\ N(R)\ \underline{[a]}(h\underline{[a{\Leftarrow}x]})}{[a]f\ N(R)\ [a]\lambda x.\,h}$$

For illustration, observe how $x\ M(\{(y,y)\})\ h$, where $h = \mu a.\,[a]\lambda y.\,\mu b.\,[a]x$, and compare to:

$$x =_{\rho\theta} \mu a.\,[a]\mu b.\,[a]x =_\eta \mu a.\,[a]\lambda y.\,(\mu b.\,[a]x)\,y =_\mu h.$$

Given the definitions of hnfs, evaluation, and $M(R)$ for the standard $\lambda\mu$-calculus, the definition of $B(R)$, hnf bisimulation up to η, and extensional hnf bisimilarity are unchanged.

Extensional hnf bisimilarity for the standard $\lambda\mu$-calculus is a semi sensible equivalence relation that includes the Ω equation (for the new definition of solvability) and satisfies the extensionality property ***ext***. It includes extensional hnf bisimilarity for the pure λ-calculus and the β, η, μ, ρ, and θ equations.

The CPS Translation Theorem from the pure λ-calculus can be extended to the standard $\lambda\mu$-calculus.

Theorem 12 (CPS Translation). *$t \approx t'$ in the standard $\lambda\mu$-calculus iff $\text{cps}(t) \approx \text{cps}(t')$ in the λFP-calculus.*

Corollary 13. *Extensional hnf bisimilarity is a congruence for the standard* $\lambda\mu$*-calculus.*

Full abstraction fails for extensional hnf bisimilarity and for Fujita's CPS transform of the standard $\lambda\mu$-calculus, as witnessed by David and Py's counter-example to the Separation Property:

$$\begin{aligned} 0 &= \lambda x.\, \lambda y.\, y \\ 1 &= \lambda x.\, \lambda y.\, x \\ U_0 &= \mu b.\, [a]0 \\ W &= \lambda x.\, \mu a.\, [a]x\,(\mu b.\, [a]x\, U_0\, y)\, U_0 \end{aligned}$$

David and Py [6] showed that $W[{}^0\!/\!_y]$ is solvably equivalent to $W[{}^1\!/\!_y]$, via a context lemma. However, $\mu b.\, [a]x\, U_0\, 0$ is not extensional hnf bisimilar (nor solvably equivalent) to $\mu b.\, [a]x\, U_0\, 1$ and therefore $W[{}^0\!/\!_y]$ is not extensional hnf bisimilar to $W[{}^1\!/\!_y]$.

Saurin [20] recovered the Separation Property for the $\lambda\mu$-calculus by considering an extended syntax. This suggests that full abstraction is attainable for the extended $\lambda\mu$-calculus. In the next section we extend the definitions of head normal forms, head evaluation, solvable equivalence, and extensional hnf bisimulation to the extended $\lambda\mu$-calculus and prove full abstraction by adapting the Böhm-out technique to the extended $\lambda\mu$-calculus.

8 The extended $\lambda\mu$-calculus

Saurin extended the standard $\lambda\mu$-calculus by relaxing the syntactic coupling between μ-abstraction to naming:

$$\textsc{Terms}\ t \ ::=\ x \mid \lambda x.\, t \mid t_1\, t_2 \mid \mu a.\, t \mid [a]t$$

and relaxed the μ and ρ equations correspondingly:

$$(\mu a.\, t_1)\, t_2 =_\mu \mu a.\, t_1[a{\Leftarrow}t_2], \ \text{ if } a \notin \text{FN}(t_2) \qquad (\mu)$$

$$[a]\mu b.\, t =_\rho t[{}^a\!/\!_b] \qquad (\rho)$$

The β, η, and θ equations remain the same as in the standard $\lambda\mu$-calculus.

In the sequel "the $\lambda\mu$-calculus" and "$\lambda\mu$-terms" refer to the extended syntax.

The evaluation relation below is based on the β, μ, and ρ equations plus the equations:

$$[a_1][a_2]\lambda x.\, t =_{\kappa_1} [a_2]\lambda x.\, \mu b.\, [a_1][b]t, \ \text{ if } a_1 \neq b \notin \text{FN}(t) \qquad (\kappa_1)$$

$$([a]\lambda x.\, t_1)\, t_2 =_{\kappa_2} [a]\lambda x.\, \mu b.\, ([b]t_1)\, t_2, \ \text{ if } x \notin \text{FV}(t_2) \text{ and } b \notin \text{FN}(t_1) \cup \text{FN}(t_2) \qquad (\kappa_2)$$

which can be derived from the β, η, μ, and ρ equations.

We extend Fujita's CPS transform as follows:

$$\begin{aligned} \text{cps}(\mu a.\, t) &= \lambda a.\ \text{cps}(t) \\ \text{cps}([b]t) &= \lambda a.\ \text{cps}(t)\, b\, a \end{aligned}$$

where a is a fresh variable that does not occur free in the source terms. (The added η redex in the transform of named terms is analogous to the η redex in the variable case.)

We define the hnfs for the $\lambda\mu$-calculus as follows:

$$\begin{aligned} &\textsc{Hnfs}\ h \ ::=\ g \mid \mu a.\, h \\ &\mu\text{-FREE HNFS}\ g \ ::=\ f \mid \lambda x.\, h \mid [a]\lambda x.\, h \\ &\lambda\text{-FREE HNFS}\ f \ ::=\ x \mid f\, t \mid [a]f \end{aligned}$$

Definition 6. Now the syntactic operations $\underline{[a]}h$ and $h\underline{[a{\Leftarrow}x]}$ map hnfs h to hnfs as follows:

$$\begin{aligned} &\underline{[a]}f = [a]f \\ &\underline{[a]}\lambda x.\, h = [a]\lambda x.\, h \\ &\underline{[a]}[a_2]\lambda x.\, h = [a_2]\lambda x.\, \mu b.\, \underline{[a]}(\underline{[b]}h), \ \text{ if } a \neq b \notin \text{FN}(h) \\ &\underline{[a]}\mu b.\, h = h[{}^a\!/\!_b] \end{aligned}$$

$$\begin{aligned} &f\underline{[a{\Leftarrow}x]} = f[a{\Leftarrow}x] \\ &(\lambda y.\, h)\underline{[a{\Leftarrow}x]} = \lambda y.\, h\underline{[a{\Leftarrow}x]}, \ \text{ if } x \neq y \\ &([b]\lambda y.\, h)\underline{[a{\Leftarrow}x]} = [b]\lambda y.\, h\underline{[a{\Leftarrow}x]}, \ \text{ if } a \neq b, x \neq y \\ &([a]\lambda y.\, h)\underline{[a{\Leftarrow}x]} = \underline{[a]}(h[{}^x\!/\!_y]\underline{[a{\Leftarrow}x]}) \\ &(\mu b.\, h)\underline{[a{\Leftarrow}x]} = \mu b.\, h\underline{[a{\Leftarrow}x]}, \ \text{ if } a \neq b \end{aligned}$$

We extend head evaluation to the extended $\lambda\mu$-calculus by replacing the rules (E5) and (E6) from the standard $\lambda\mu$-calculus by the following rules:

$$\text{(E5)}\ \frac{t_1 \rightsquigarrow \mu a.\, h_1 \quad h_1\underline{[a{\Leftarrow}t_2]} \rightsquigarrow h}{t_1\, t_2 \rightsquigarrow \mu a.\, h} \ \text{ if } a \notin \text{FN}(t_2)$$

$$\text{(E6)}\ \frac{t_1 \rightsquigarrow [a]\lambda x.\, h_1 \quad (\underline{[b]}h_1)\, t_2 \rightsquigarrow h}{t_1\, t_2 \rightsquigarrow [a]\lambda x.\, \mu b.\, h}$$
$$\text{if } x \notin \text{FV}(t_2), b \notin \text{FN}(t_1) \cup \text{FN}(t_2)$$

$$\text{(E7)}\ \frac{t \rightsquigarrow h}{\mu a.\, t \rightsquigarrow \mu a.\, h}$$

$$\text{(E8)}\ \frac{t \rightsquigarrow h}{[a]t \rightsquigarrow \underline{[a]}h}$$

Let a closed $\lambda\mu$-term t be solvable iff

$$([a] \ldots ([a]t\, \vec{t_0})\, \vec{t_1} \ldots)\, \vec{t_m} =_{\beta\mu\rho} \lambda x.\, x$$

for some name a and closed arguments $\vec{t_0}, \vec{t_1}, \ldots, \vec{t_m}$.

Lemma 14. *A closed* $\lambda\mu$*-term is solvable iff it has a hnf.*

As before, a relation R on $\lambda\mu$-terms is semi sensible iff, whenever R relates two closed terms t and t', t is solvable iff t' is solvable. Solvable equivalence is the greatest semi sensible relation.

If we revisit David and Py's example from Section 7, we observe that $W[{}^0\!/\!_y]$ and $W[{}^1\!/\!_y]$ are not solvably equivalent in the $\lambda\mu$-calculus, because taking

$$C = \mu a.\,([a][\,]\,\mu b.\,\lambda z.\,[b]z)\,1\,0$$

we get $C[W] \rightsquigarrow \mu a.\,[a]y$ and therefore $C[W[{}^0\!/\!_y]]\,\Omega$ has hnf $\mu a.\,[a]\lambda y.\,y$ whereas $C[W[{}^1\!/\!_y]]\,\Omega$ has no hnf.

We extend the definition of $M(R)$ from the pure λ-calculus with the additional rules:

$$\text{(M6)}\ \frac{h\ M(R)\ h'}{\mu a.\,h\ M(R)\ \mu a.\,h'}$$

$$\text{(M7)}\ \frac{h\ M(R)\ \underline{[a]}g}{\mu a.\,h\ M(R)\ g}\ \text{if } a \notin \text{FN}(g)$$

$$\text{(M8)}\ \frac{\underline{[a]}g\ M(R)\ h}{g\ M(R)\ \mu a.\,h}\ \text{if } a \notin \text{FN}(g)$$

$$\text{(M9)}\ \frac{f\ M(R)\ f'}{[a]f\ M(R)\ [a]f'}$$

$$\text{(M10)}\ \frac{\underline{\underline{[a](h\lfloor a \Leftarrow x\rfloor)}}\ M(R)\ \underline{\underline{g\lfloor a \Leftarrow x\rfloor}}}{[a]\lambda x.\,h\ M(R)\ g}\ \text{if } x \notin \text{FV}(g)$$

$$\text{(M11)}\ \frac{\underline{\underline{g\lfloor a \Leftarrow x\rfloor}}\ M(R)\ \underline{\underline{[a](h\lfloor a \Leftarrow x\rfloor)}}}{g\ M(R)\ [a]\lambda x.\,h}\ \text{if } x \notin \text{FV}(g)$$

Given the definitions of hnfs, evaluation, and $M(R)$ for the $\lambda\mu$-calculus, the definition of $B(R)$, hnf bisimulation up to η, and extensional hnf bisimilarity are the same as for the pure λ-calculus.

Extensional hnf bisimilarity for the extended $\lambda\mu$-calculus includes extensional hnf bisimilarity for the standard $\lambda\mu$-calculus (which in turn includes extensional hnf bisimilarity for the pure λ-calculus). Moreover, it is a semi sensible equivalence relation and includes the Ω equation (for the new definition of solvability) and satisfies the extensionality property ***ext***.

The CPS Translation Theorem can be extended to the extended $\lambda\mu$-calculus:

Theorem 15 (CPS Translation). *$t \precsim t'$ in the extended $\lambda\mu$-calculus iff $\text{cps}(t) \precsim \text{cps}(t')$ in the* λFP-*calculus.*

Corollary 16. *Extensional hnf bisimilarity is a congruence for the extended $\lambda\mu$-calculus.*

We now show that extensional hnf bisimilarity is fully abstract with respect to solvable equivalence for the $\lambda\mu$-calculus. The proof extends our co-inductive proof from Section 6 with a $\lambda\mu$-variant of the Böhm-out technique. We use the "sub-term selectors" from Saurin's proof of the Separation Property for the $\lambda\mu$-calculus but we eschew the "parametric pairs" and "fst-transform".

Let $\Lambda\mu$ be the set of all $\lambda\mu$-terms. Two variable-closed hnfs h and h' are equivalent, $h \sim h'$, iff $h\ M(\Lambda\mu \times \Lambda\mu)\ h'$. For arbitrary variable-closed $\lambda\mu$-terms t and t', $t \sim t'$ iff $t\ B(\Lambda\mu \times \Lambda\mu)\ t'$.

Lemma 17. *$t \sim t'$, for all variable-closed solvably equivalent $\lambda\mu$-terms t and t'.*

We define the *μ-permutator* $\mathbf{Q}_m$, for $m \geq 0$, to be the $\lambda\mu$-term:

$$\mathbf{Q}_m = \mu a_1.\ \ldots \mu a_m.\,\lambda x.\,[a_m]\ldots[a_1]x$$

We define the *sub-term selector* $\mathbf{\Phi}^{m,n}_{i,j}$, for $i \geq 1, j \geq 1, m \geq 0, n \geq 0$, and $(m+1,n) \geq (i,j)$ lexicographically (that is, $m \geq i$ or $m+1 = i$ and $j \geq n$), to be the $\lambda\mu$-term:

$$\begin{aligned}\mathbf{\Phi}^{m,n}_{i,j} &= \mu a_1 \ldots \mu a_{i-1}.\,\lambda x_1 \ldots \lambda x_j.\\ &\qquad \mu a_i \ldots \mu a_m.\,\lambda y_1 \ldots \lambda y_n.\,x_j,\ \text{if } m \geq i\\ \mathbf{\Phi}^{m,n}_{m+1,j} &= \mu a_1 \ldots \mu a_m.\,\lambda y_1 \ldots \lambda y_n.\,y_j,\ \text{if } n \geq j\end{aligned}$$

We call μ-permutators and sub-term selectors discriminator terms and we define discrimination contexts as follows:

$$\textsc{Discriminators}\ \delta ::= \mathbf{Q}_m \mid \mathbf{\Phi}^{m,n}_{i,j}$$

$$\textsc{Discrimination contexts}\quad \Delta ::= [\,] \mid \Delta\,\delta \mid [a]\Delta \mid [a](\mu a.\,\Delta)\,\delta$$

We define the Böhm-out relation $\approx$ for variable-closed $\lambda\mu$-terms t and t' as follows:

$$t \approx t'\ \text{ iff }\ \forall \Delta.\ \Delta[t] \sim \Delta[t']$$

On open $\lambda\mu$-terms $\approx\ = \bigcup_{n<\omega} \approx_n$, where $t \approx_n t'$ iff

$$\forall \{x_1,\ldots,x_m\} \supseteq \text{FV}(t) \cup \text{FV}(t').\ \forall n_1,\ldots,n_m \geq n.\\ t[{}^{\mathbf{Q}_{n_1}}\!/\!_{x_1}]\ldots[{}^{\mathbf{Q}_{n_m}}\!/\!_{x_m}] \approx t'[{}^{\mathbf{Q}_{n_1}}\!/\!_{x_1}]\ldots[{}^{\mathbf{Q}_{n_m}}\!/\!_{x_m}].$$

Lemma 18 (Böhm-out). *$\approx$ is a hnf bisimulation up to η.*

The structure of the proof is the same as in the proof of the Böhm-out Lemma for the pure λ-calculus

Theorem 19 (Full abstraction). *Extensional hnf bisimilarity coincides with solvable equivalence for the extended $\lambda\mu$-calculus.*

Theorems 15, 19, and 10 entail that the CPS transform of the extended $\lambda\mu$-calculus is fully abstract.

Acknowledgements Kristian Støvring pointed out errors in drafts of this paper and helped me find literature on the λ-calculus with surjective pairing. I thank the referees for helpful comments and Alexis Saurin and Paul Blain Levy for discussions about this work.

References

[1] S. Abramsky. The lazy lambda calculus. In D. Turner, editor, *Research Topics in Functional Programming*, pages 65–116. Addison-Wesley, 1990.

[2] H. P. Barendregt. *The Lambda Calculus: Its Syntax and Semantics*. Number 103 in Studies in Logic and the Foundations of Mathematics. North-Holland, revised edition, 1984.

[3] C. Böhm. Alcune proprieta delle forme $\beta\eta$-normali nel λK-calculus. Pubblicazioni 696, Instituto per le Applicazioni del Calcolo, Roma, 1968.

[4] G. Boudol. On the semantics of the call-by-name CPS transform. *Theoretical Computer Science*, 234:309–321, 2000.

[5] R. David. Computing with Böhm trees. *Fundamenta Informaticae*, 45:53–77, 2001.

[6] R. David and W. Py. $\lambda\mu$-calculus and Böhm's theorem. *Journal of Symbolic Logic*, 66(1):407–413, 2001.

[7] K. Fujita. A sound and complete CPS-translation for $\lambda\mu$-calculus. In *TLCA*, volume 2701 of *Lecture Notes in Computer Science*, pages 120–134. Springer-Verlag, 2003.

[8] J. Hatcliff and O. Danvy. Thunks and the λ-calculus. *Journal of Functional Programming*, 7(3):303–319, 1997.

[9] M. Hofmann and T. Streicher. Continuation models are universal for $\lambda\mu$-calculus. In *Proc. 12th Annual IEEE Symposium on Logic in Computer Science*, pages 387–395, 1997.

[10] D. J. Howe. Proving congruence of bisimulation in functional programming languages. *Information and Computation*, 124(2):103–112, 1996.

[11] J. M. E. Hyland. A syntactic characterisation of the equality in some models for the lambda calculus. *Journal of the London Mathematical Society*, 12(3):361–370, 1976.

[12] S. B. Lassen. Bisimulation in untyped lambda calculus: Böhm trees and bisimulation up to context. In *MFPS XV*, volume 20 of *Electronic Notes in Theoretical Computer Science*, pages 346–374. Elsevier, 1999.

[13] S. B. Lassen. Eager normal form bisimulation. In *Proc. 20th Annual IEEE Symposium on Logic in Computer Science*, pages 345–354, 2005.

[14] S. B. Lassen. Normal form simulation for McCarthy's amb. In *MFPS XXI*, volume 155 of *Electronic Notes in Theoretical Computer Science*, pages 445–465. Elsevier, 2005.

[15] C.-H. L. Ong and C. A. Stewart. A curry-howard foundation for functional computation with control. In *Proc. 24th ACM Symposium on Principles of Programming Languages*, 1997.

[16] M. Parigot. $\lambda\mu$-calculus: An algorithmic interpretation of classical natural deduction. In A. Voronkov, editor, *Proceedings Intl. Conf. on Logic Programming and Automated Reasoning, LPAR'92, St Petersburg*, volume 624 of *Lecture Notes in Computer Science*, pages 190–201. Springer-Verlag, 1992.

[17] G. D. Plotkin. Call-by-name, call-by-value and the λ-calculus. *Theoretical Computer Science*, 1:125–159, 1975.

[18] G. E. Révész. Categorical combinators with explicit products. *Fundamenta Informaticae*, 22:153–166, 1995.

[19] D. Sangiorgi. The lazy lambda calculus in a concurrency scenario. *Information and Computation*, 111(1):120–153, 1994.

[20] A. Saurin. Separation with streams in the $\lambda\mu$-calculus. In *Proc. 20th Annual IEEE Symposium on Logic in Computer Science*, pages 356–365, 2005.

[21] K. Støvring. Extending the extensional lambda calculus with surjective pairing is conservative. *Logical Methods in Computer Science*, 2(2:1):1–14, 2006.

[22] C. P. Wadsworth. The relation between computational and denotational properties for Scott's D_∞-models of the lambda-calculus. *SIAM Journal on Computing*, 5(3):488–521, 1976.

A proof of strong normalisation using domain theory

Thierry Coquand
Chalmers Tekniska Högskola
Gothenburg
coquand@cs.chalmers.se

Arnaud Spiwack
Ecole Normale Supérieure de Cachan
Arnaud.Spiwack@dptinfo.ens-cachan.fr

Abstract

U. Berger, [11] significantly simplified Tait's normalisation proof for bar recursion [27], see also [9], replacing Tait's introduction of infinite terms by the construction of a domain having the property that a term is strongly normalizing if its semantics is $\neq\perp$. The goal of this paper is to show that, using ideas from the theory of intersection types [2, 6, 7, 21] and Martin-Löf's domain interpretation of type theory [18], we can in turn simplify U. Berger's argument in the construction of such a domain model. We think that our domain model can be used to give modular *proofs of strong normalization for various type theory. As an example, we show in some details how it can be used to prove strong normalization for Martin-Löf dependent type theory extended with bar recursion, and with some form of proof-irrelevance.*

1 Introduction

In 1961, Spector [25] presented an extension of Gödel's system T by a new schema of definition called bar recursion. With this new schema, he was able to give an interpretation of Analysis, extending Gödel's Dialectica interpretation of Arithmetic, and completing preliminary results of Kreisel [17]. Tait proved a normalisation theorem for Spector's bar recursion, by embedding it in a system with infinite terms [27]. In [9], an alternative form of bar recursion was introduced. This allowed to give an interpretation of Analysis by modified realisability, instead of Dialectica interpretation. The paper [9] presented also a normalisation proof for this new schema, but this proof, which used Tait's method of introducing infinite terms, was quite complex. It was simplified significantly by U. Berger [11, 12], who used instead a modification of Plotkin's computational adequacy theorem [22], and could prove *strong* normalisation. In a way, the idea is to replace infinite terms by elements of a domain interpretation. This domain has the property that a term is strongly normalisable if its semantics is $\neq\perp$

The main contribution of this paper is to show that, using ideas from intersection types [2, 6, 7, 21] and Martin-Löf's domain interpretation of type theory [18], one can in turn simplify further U. Berger's argument. Contrary to [11], we build a domain model for an *untyped* programming language. A noteworthy feature of this domain model is that it is in a natural way a *complete* lattice, and in particular it has a *top* element which can be seen as the interpretation of a top-level exception in programming language. We think that this model can be the basis of *modular* proofs of strong normalisation for various type systems. As a main application, we show that Martin-Löf dependent type theory extended with various form of bar recursion has the strong normalisation property. To illustrate further the modularity of this approach, we show the strong normalisation property when adding some form of proof-irrelevance to our type theory [28].

2 An Untyped Programming Language

Our programming language is untyped λ-calculus extended with constants, and has the following syntax.

$$M, N ::= x \mid \lambda x.M \mid M\ N \mid c \mid f$$

There are two kinds of constants: *constructors* $c, c', \ldots$ and *defined constants* $f, g, \ldots$. We use $h, h', \ldots$ to denote a constant which may be a constructor or defined. Each constant has an *arity*, but can be partially applied. We write $\mathsf{FV}(M)$ for the

1043-6871/06 $20.00

set of free variables of M. We write $N(x = M)$ the result of substituting the free occurences of x by M in N. and may write it $N[M]$ if x is clear from the context. We consider terms up to α-conversion.

The computation rules of our programming language are the usual β-reduction and *ι-reduction* defined by a set of rewrite rules of the form

$$f\, p_1 \ldots p_k \to M$$

where k is the arity of f and $\mathsf{FV}(M) \subseteq \mathsf{FV}(f\; p_1 \ldots p_k)$. In this rewrite rule, $p_1, \ldots, p_k$ are *constructor patterns i.e.* terms of the form

$$p ::= x \mid c\, p_1 \ldots p_l$$

where l is the arity of c. Like in [11], we assume our system of constant reduction rules to be *left linear*, i.e. a variable occurs at most once in the left hand side of a rule, and *mutually disjoint*, i.e. the left hand sides of two disjoint rules are non-unifiable. We write $M \to M'$ if M reduces in one step to M' by β, ι-reduction and $M =_{\beta,\iota} M'$ if M, M' are convertible by β, ι conversion. It follows from our hypothesis on our system of reduction rules that β, ι-reduction is confluent. We write $\to (M)$ the set of terms M' such that $M \to M'$.

We work with a given set of constants, that are listed in the appendix, but our arguments are general and make use only of the fact that the reduction system is left linear and mutually disjoint. We call UPL, for Untyped Programming Language, the system defined by this list of constants and ι-reduction rules. The goal of the next section is to define a domain model for UPL that has the property that M is strongly normalizing if $[\![M]\!] \neq \perp$.

3 A domain for strong normalization

3.1 Formal Neighbourhoods

Definition 1 *The* Formal Neighbourhoods *are given by the following grammar:*

$$U, V ::= \nabla \mid c\, U_1 \ldots U_k \mid U \to V \mid U \cap V$$

On these neighbourhoods we introduce a *formal inclusion* $\subseteq$ relation defined inductively by the rules of Figure 1. In these rules we use the formal equality relation $U = V$ defined to be $U \subseteq V$ and $V \subseteq U$. We let $\mathcal{M}$ be the set of neighbourhoods quotiented by the formal equality. The terminology "formal neighborhoods" comes from [17, 23, 18].

$$\begin{array}{rcl} \nabla \cap U & = & \nabla \\ c\, U_1 \ldots U_k \cap c'\, V_1 \ldots V_l & = & \nabla \\ c\, U_1 \ldots U_k \cap V \to W & = & \nabla \\ (U \to V_1) \cap (U \to V_2) & = & U \to (V_1 \cap V_2) \end{array}$$

$$c\, U_1 \ldots U_k \cap c\, V_1 \ldots V_k = c\, (U_1 \cap V_1) \ldots (U_k \cap V_k)$$

$$\frac{U_1 \subseteq U_2 \quad U_2 \subseteq U_3}{U_1 \subseteq U_3} \qquad \frac{}{U \subseteq U}$$

$$\frac{U \subseteq V_1 \quad U \subseteq V_2}{U \subseteq V_1 \cap V_2} \qquad \frac{}{V_1 \cap V_2 \subseteq V_i}$$

$$\frac{U_2 \subseteq U_1 \quad V_1 \subseteq V_2}{U_1 \to V_1 \subseteq U_2 \to V_2}$$

Figure 1. Formal inclusion

Lemma 1 *The formal inclusion and equality are both* decidable *relations, and $\mathcal{M}$ is a poset for the formal inclusion relation, and $\cap$ defines a binary meet operation on $\mathcal{M}$. We have $c\ U_1 \ldots U_k \neq c'\ V_1 \ldots V_l$ if $c \neq c'$ and $c\, U_1 \ldots U_k = c\, V_1 \ldots V_k$ if and only if $U_1 = V_1, \ldots, U_k = V_k$. An element in $\mathcal{M}$ is either ∇ or of the form $c\ U_1 \ldots U_k$ or of the form $(U_1 \to V_1) \cap \ldots \cap (U_n \to V_n)$ and this defines a partition of $\mathcal{M}$. Furthermore the following "continuity condition" holds: if I finite set and $\bigcap_{i \in I}(U_i \to V_i) \subseteq U \to V$ then the set $J = \{i \in I \mid U \subseteq U_i\}$ is not empty and $\bigcap_{i \in J} V_i \subseteq V$.*

Similar results are proved in [4, 2, 7, 6, 18]. For the proof one can introduce the set of neighborhood in "normal form" by the grammar

$$\begin{array}{lcl} W, W' & ::= & \nabla \mid c\, W_1\ \ldots\ W_k \mid I \\ I & ::= & (W_1 \to W_1') \cap \cdots \cap (W_n \to W_n') \end{array}$$

and define directly the operation $\cap$ and the relation $\subseteq$ on this set.

We associate to $\mathcal{M}$ a type system defined in Figure 2 (when unspecified, k is the arity of the related constant). It is a direct extension of the type systems considered in [4, 2, 7, 6, 18]. The typing rules for the constructors and defined constants appear to be new however. Notice that the typing of the function symbols is very close to a recursive definition of the function itself. Also, we make use of the fact that, as a consequence of Lemma 1, one can define when a constructor pattern matches an element of $\mathcal{M}$.

An important consequence of the continuity condition of Lemma 1 is the following result.

$$\frac{x : U \in \Gamma}{\Gamma \vdash_{\mathcal{M}} x : U}$$

$$\frac{}{\Gamma \vdash_{\mathcal{M}} c : U_1 \to \ldots \to U_k \to c\, U_1 \ldots U_k}$$

$$\frac{\Gamma, x{:}U \vdash_{\mathcal{M}} M : V}{\Gamma \vdash_{\mathcal{M}} \lambda x.M : U \to V}$$

$$\frac{\Gamma \vdash_{\mathcal{M}} N : U \to V \quad \Gamma \vdash_{\mathcal{M}} M : U}{\Gamma \vdash_{\mathcal{M}} N\, M : V}$$

$$\frac{\Gamma \vdash_{\mathcal{M}} M : U \quad \Gamma \vdash_{\mathcal{M}} M : V}{\Gamma \vdash_{\mathcal{M}} M : U \cap V}$$

$$\frac{\Gamma \vdash_{\mathcal{M}} M : V \quad V \subseteq U}{\Gamma \vdash_{\mathcal{M}} M : U}$$

$$\frac{f\, p_1 \ldots p_k \to M \quad p_i(W_1, \ldots, W_n) = U_i \quad \Gamma, x_1{:}W_1, \ldots, x_n{:}W_n \vdash_{\mathcal{M}} M : V}{\Gamma \vdash_{\mathcal{M}} f : U_1 \to \ldots \to U_k \to V}$$

$$\frac{\text{for any } U_1, \ldots, U_k \text{ such that no rewriting rules of } f \text{ matches } U_1, \ldots, U_k}{\Gamma \vdash_{\mathcal{M}} f : U_1 \to \ldots \to U_k \to \nabla}$$

Figure 2. Types with intersection in $\mathcal{M}$

Lemma 2 *If $\Gamma \vdash_{\mathcal{M}} \lambda x.N : U \to V$ then $\Gamma, x{:}U \vdash_{\mathcal{M}} N : V$.*

3.2 Reducibility candidates

Definition 2 *$\mathcal{S}$ (the set of simple terms) is the set of terms that are neither an abstraction nor a constructor headed term, nor a partially applied destructor headed term* (i.e. *$f\ M_1\ \ldots\ M_n$ is simple if n is greater or equal to the arity of f).*

Definition 3 *A* reducibility candidate *X is a set of terms with the following properties:*

(CR1) $X \subseteq \mathsf{SN}$

(CR2) $\to (M) \subseteq X$ *if* $M \in X$

(CR3) $M \in X$ *if* $M \in \mathcal{S}$ *and* $\to (M) \subseteq X$

It is clear that the reducibility candidates form a complete lattice w.r.t. the inclusion relation. In particular, there is a *least* reducibility candidate R_0, which can be inductively defined as the set of terms $M \in \mathcal{S}$ such that $\to (M) \subseteq R_0$. For instance, if M is a variable x, then we have $M \in R_0$ since $M \in \mathcal{S}$ and $\to (M) = \emptyset$.

We define two operations on sets of terms, which preserve the status of candidates. If c is a constructor of arity k and $X_1, \ldots, X_k$ are sets of terms then the set $c\ X_1 \ldots X_k$ is inductively defined to be the set of terms M of the form $c\, M_1 \ldots M_k$, with $M_1 \in X_1 \ldots M_k \in X_k$ or such that $M \in \mathcal{S}$ and $\to (M) \subseteq c\, X_1 \ldots X_k$. If X and Y are sets of terms, $X \to Y$ is the set of terms N such that $N\ M \in Y$ if $M \in X$.

Lemma 3 *If X and Y are reducibility candidates then so are $X \cap Y$ and $X \to Y$. If $X_1, \ldots, X_k$ are reducibility candidates then so is $c\, X_1 \ldots X_k$.*

Definition 4 *The function $[-]$ associates a reducibility candidate to each formal neighbourhood.*

- $[\nabla] \triangleq R_0$
- $[c\, U_1 \ldots U_k] \triangleq c\, [U_1] \ldots [U_k]$
- $[U \to V] \triangleq [U] \to [V]$
- $[U \cap V] \triangleq [U] \cap [V]$

Lemma 4 *If $U \subseteq V$ for the formal inclusion relation then $[U] \subseteq [V]$ as sets of terms.*

This follows from the fact that all the rules of Figure 1 are valid when we interpret formal neighbourhoods as reducility candidates.

Theorem 5 *If $\vdash_{\mathcal{M}} M : U$ then $M \in [U]$. In particular M is strongly normalising.*

As usual, we prove that if $x_1 : U_1, \ldots, x_n : U_n \vdash_{\mathcal{M}} M : U$ and $M_1 \in [U_1], \ldots, M_n \in [U_n]$ then $M(x_1 = M_1, \ldots, x_n = M_n) \in [U]$. This is direct by induction on derivations using Lemma 4.

3.3 Filter Domain

Definition 5 *An* I-filter[1] *over $\mathcal{M}$ is a subset $\alpha \subseteq \mathcal{M}$ with the following closure properties:*

- *if $U, V \in \alpha$ then $U \cap V \in \alpha$*
- *if $U \in \alpha$ and $U \subseteq V$ then $V \in \alpha$*

It is clear that the set D of all I-filters over $\mathcal{M}$ ordered by the set inclusion is a complete algebraic domain. The finite elements of D are exactly $\emptyset$ and the principal I-filters $\uparrow U \triangleq \{V \mid U \subseteq V\}$. The

[1]This terminology, coming from [6], stresses the fact that the empty set is also an I-filter.

element $\top = \uparrow \nabla$ is the greatest element of D and the least element is $\bot = \emptyset$.

We can define on D a binary application operation

$$\alpha\, \beta \triangleq \{V \mid \exists U, U \to V \in \alpha \wedge U \in \beta\}$$

We have always $\alpha\ \ \bot = \bot$ and $\top\ \beta = \top$ if $\beta \neq \bot$. We write $\alpha_1 \ldots \alpha_n$ for $(\ldots(\alpha_1\ \alpha_2)\ \ldots)\ \alpha_n$.

3.4 Denotational semantics of UPL

As usual, we let $\rho, \nu, \ldots$ to range over *environments*, i.e. mapping from variables to D.

Definition 6 *If M is a term of UPL, $[\![M]\!]_\rho$ is the I-filter of neighborhoods U such that $x_1{:}V_1, \ldots, x_n{:}V_n \vdash_{\mathcal{M}} M : U$ for some $V_i \in \rho(x_i)$ with $\mathsf{FV}(M) = \{x_1, \ldots, x_n\}$.*

A direct consequence of this definition and of Theorem 5 is then

Theorem 6 *If there exists ρ such that $[\![M]\!]_\rho \neq \bot$ then M is strongly normalising.*

Notice also that we have $[\![M]\!]_\rho = [\![M]\!]_\nu$ as soon as $\rho(x) = \nu(x)$ for all $x \in \mathsf{FV}(M)$. Because of this we can write $[\![M]\!]$ for $[\![M]\!]_\rho$ if M is closed. If c is a constructor, we write simply c for $[\![c]\!]$.

Lemma 7 *We have $c\ \alpha_1 \ldots \alpha_k \neq c'\ \beta_1 \ldots \beta_l$ if $c \neq c'$ and $c\ \alpha_1 \ldots \alpha_k = c\ \beta_1 \ldots \beta_k$ if and only if $\alpha_1 = \beta_1 \ldots \alpha_k = \beta_k$, whenever $\alpha_i \neq \bot$, $\beta_j \neq \bot$. An element of D is either $\bot$, or $\top$ or of the form $c\,\alpha_1\ \ldots\ \alpha_k$ with c of arity k and $\alpha_i \neq \bot$ or is a sup of elements of the form $\uparrow (U \to V)$. This defines a partition of D.*

As a consequence of Lemma 7, it is possible to define when a constructor pattern matches an element of D. The next result expresses the fact that we have defined in this way a *strict model* of UPL.

Theorem 8

$$\begin{array}{lcl} [\![x]\!]_\rho & = & \rho(x) \\ [\![N\ M]\!]_\rho & = & [\![N]\!]_\rho\ [\![M]\!]_\rho \\ [\![\lambda x.M]\!]_\rho\ \alpha & = & [\![M]\!]_{(\rho, x:=\alpha)} \quad \text{if } \alpha \neq \bot\ (*) \end{array}$$

If $f\ p_1\ \ldots\ p_k \to M$ and $\alpha_i = [\![p_i]\!]_\rho$ then $[\![f]\!]\ \alpha_1 \ldots \alpha_k = [\![M]\!]_\rho$. If there is no rule for f which matches $\alpha_1, \ldots, \alpha_k$ and $\alpha_1, \ldots, \alpha_k$ are $\neq \bot$ then $[\![f]\!]\ \alpha_1 \ldots \alpha_k = \top$. Finally, if for all $\alpha \neq \bot$ we have $[\![M]\!]_{(\rho,x:=\alpha)} = [\![N]\!]_{(\nu,y:=\alpha)}$ then $[\![\lambda x.M]\!]_\rho = [\![\lambda y.N]\!]_\nu$.

The property $(*)$ follows from Lemma 2.

Corollary 9 $[\![N(x = M)]\!]_\rho = [\![N]\!]_{(\rho, x = [\![M]\!]_\rho)}$

We have for instance $[\![\mathsf{less}]\!]\ (\mathsf{S}\top)\ (\mathsf{S}\top) = \top$, but also $[\![\mathsf{less}]\!]\ \mathsf{nat}\ \mathsf{nat} = \top$. This illustrates the fact that $\top$ can be thought of as the semantics of a top level "error" element.

4 Application to Type Theory

4.1 Typing rules

We follow [19] and present dependent type theory in a Logical Framework extended with some constants. We have three syntactical categories, for *types* $A, B, \ldots$, for *terms* $M, N, \ldots$ and for *contexts* $\Gamma, \Delta, \ldots$ We have a special type Set of (data) types, i.e. primitive types given with constructors. We have also a constructor Fun of arity 2 and we write $(x{:}A) \to B$ instead of $\mathsf{Fun}\ A\ (\lambda x.B)$, and $A \to B$ instead of $\mathsf{Fun}\ A\ (\lambda x.B)$ if x is not free in B. The syntax of the Logical Framework is

$$\begin{array}{lcll} A & ::= & \mathsf{Set} \mid El\ M \mid (x{:}A) \to A & \textit{types} \\ M & ::= & x \mid M\ M \mid \lambda x.M & \textit{terms} \\ \Gamma & ::= & () \mid \Gamma, x{:}A & \textit{contexts} \end{array}$$

The general typing rules of the Logical Framework are presented in figure 3[2]. There are five kinds of judgement Δ correct, $\Delta \vdash A$, $\Delta \vdash M : A$, $\Delta \vdash A_1 = A_2$ and $\Delta \vdash M_1 = M_2 : A$. We write $\Gamma \vdash J$ where J can have the form $A, A = B, M : A, M_1 = M_2 : A$. The constants are the ones of our language UPL, and the typing rules of these constants are also given in the appendix.

The system is designed in such a way that the following lemmas can be directly proved by induction on derivation. For a detailed metatheory of a similar system, see [16].

If γ is a substitution, we write $\gamma : \Delta \to \Gamma$ to express that we have $\Delta \vdash x\gamma : A\gamma$ for all $x{:}A$ in Γ.

Lemma 10 *If Δ correct and $\gamma : \Delta \to \Gamma$ and $\Gamma \vdash J$ then $\Delta \vdash J\gamma$.*

[2] In this presentation, we consider λ-terms up to α-conversion. This system is quite close to the substitution calculus of P. Martin-Löf [15]. We note however that the following judgement is derivable

$$A{:}\mathsf{Set}, P{:}A \to \mathsf{Set} \vdash \lambda x.\lambda x.x : (x{:}A) \to P\ x \to P\ x$$

while it is not in the substitution calculus (as noticed in [20]).

rules for contexts

$$\frac{}{()\ \textsf{correct}} \qquad \frac{\Gamma\ \textsf{correct} \quad \Gamma \vdash A}{\Gamma, x{:}A\ \textsf{correct}}$$

rules for types

$$\frac{\Gamma\ \textsf{correct}}{\Gamma \vdash \textsf{Set}} \qquad \frac{\Gamma \vdash M : \textsf{Set}}{\Gamma \vdash \textsf{El}\, M} \qquad \frac{\Gamma, x{:}A \vdash B}{\Gamma \vdash (x{:}A) \to B}$$

rules for terms

$$\frac{\Gamma\ \textsf{correct} \quad (x{:}A) \in \Gamma}{\Gamma \vdash x{:}A} \qquad \frac{\Gamma, x{:}A \vdash M : B}{\Gamma \vdash \lambda x.M : (x{:}A) \to B} \qquad \frac{\Gamma \vdash N : (x{:}A) \to B \quad \Gamma \vdash M : A}{\Gamma \vdash N\, M : B[M]}$$

type equality rule

$$\frac{\Gamma \vdash M : A \quad \Gamma \vdash A = B}{\Gamma \vdash M : B}$$

substitution rule

$$\frac{\Gamma, x{:}A \vdash B \quad \Gamma \vdash M_1 = M_2 : A}{\Gamma \vdash B[M_1] = B[M_2]}$$

conversion rules

$$\frac{\Gamma \vdash A}{\Gamma \vdash A = A} \qquad \frac{\Gamma \vdash A = B}{\Gamma \vdash B = A} \qquad \frac{\Gamma \vdash A = B \quad \Gamma \vdash B = C}{\Gamma \vdash A = C}$$

$$\frac{\Gamma \vdash M : A}{\Gamma \vdash M = M : A} \qquad \frac{\Gamma \vdash M = N : A}{\Gamma \vdash N = M : A} \qquad \frac{\Gamma \vdash M = N : A \quad \Gamma \vdash N = P : A}{\Gamma \vdash M = P : A}$$

$$\frac{\Gamma \vdash M = N : A \quad \Gamma \vdash A = B}{\Gamma \vdash M = N : B}$$

$$\frac{\Gamma\ \textsf{correct}}{\Gamma \vdash \textsf{Set} = \textsf{Set}} \qquad \frac{\Gamma \vdash M_1 = M_2 : \textsf{Set}}{\Gamma \vdash \textsf{El}\, M_1 = \textsf{El}\, M_2} \qquad \frac{\Gamma \vdash A_1 = A_2 \quad \Gamma, x{:}A_1 \vdash B_1 = B_2}{\Gamma \vdash (x{:}A_1) \to B_1 = (x{:}A_2) \to B_2}$$

$$\frac{\Gamma, x{:}A \vdash M_1 = M_2 : B}{\Gamma \vdash \lambda x.M_1 = \lambda x.M_2 : (x{:}A) \to B}$$

$$\frac{\Gamma, x{:}A \vdash B \quad \Gamma \vdash N_1 = N_2 : (x{:}A) \to B \quad \Gamma \vdash M_1 = M_2 : A}{\Gamma \vdash N_1\, M_1 = N_2\, M_2 : B[M_1]}$$

$$\frac{\Gamma, x{:}A \vdash N : B \quad \Gamma \vdash M : A}{\Gamma \vdash (\lambda x.N)\, M = N[M] : B[M]} \qquad \frac{\Gamma \vdash A \quad \Gamma \vdash M : (x{:}A) \to B}{\Gamma \vdash M = \lambda x.M\, x : (x{:}A) \to B}$$

$$\frac{\Gamma \vdash M : A \quad M \to_{\iota} N \quad \text{(toplevel reduction)}}{\Gamma \vdash M = N : A}$$

Figure 3. Logical Framework

Lemma 11 *If* $\Gamma \vdash (x{:}A_1) \to B_1 = (x{:}A_2) \to B_2$ *then* $\Gamma \vdash A_1 = A_2$ *and* $\Gamma, x{:}A_1 \vdash B_1 = B_2$.

Lemma 12 *If* $\Gamma \vdash A = B$ *then* $\Gamma \vdash A$ *and* $\Gamma \vdash B$. *If* $\Gamma \vdash M_1 = M_2 : A$ *then* $\Gamma \vdash M_1 : A$ *and* $\Gamma \vdash M_2 : A$. *If* $\Gamma \vdash M : A$ *then* $\Gamma \vdash A$. *If* $\Gamma \vdash M = N : A$ *then* $\Gamma \vdash A$.

Corollary 13 *If* $\Gamma \vdash M : A$ *and* $M \to M'$ *then* $\Gamma \vdash M' : A$

Corollary 14 *If* $\Gamma \vdash M : A$ *and* $\Gamma \vdash M' : A$ *and* $M =_{\beta,\iota} M'$ *then* $\Gamma \vdash M = M' : A$

This is direct from Corollary 13 and the Church-Rosser property of β, ι reduction.

Notice that, because of the conversion rule, the strengthening property, stating that $\Gamma \vdash J$ follows from $\Gamma, x{:}A \vdash J$ if x is not free in J, is not clear *a priori*. It is actually a consequence of the normalisation property.

4.2 PER Models of type theory

A *partial equivalence relation* on D is a subset $X \subseteq \mathsf{D}$ with an equivalence relation $=_X$ on X. We write $u_1 = u_2 \in X$ instead of $u_1 =_X u_2$. We let PER(D) be the collection of all partial equivalence relation on D. If F is a function from X to PER(D) such that $F(u_1) = F(u_2)$ whenever $u_1 = u_2 \in X$ we write $F : X \to \mathsf{PER(D)}$. If $X \in \mathsf{PER(D)}$ and $F : X \to \mathsf{PER(D)}$ we define $\Pi(X, F) \in \mathsf{PER(D)}$ by

$v \in \Pi(X, F)$ if and only if $u_1 = u_2 \in X$ implies $v\ u_1 = v\ u_2 \in F(u_1)$

$v_1 = v_2 \in \Pi(X, F)$ if and only if $v_1\ u = v_2\ u \in F(u)$ for all $u \in X$

These constructions are standard [5].

Definition 7 A PER model *of our type theory consists of a pair* T, I *with* $T \in \mathsf{PER(D)}$ *and* $I : T \to \mathsf{PER(D)}$ *is such that*

1. $\mathsf{Set} \in T$
2. *if* $U_1 = U_2 \in T$ *and* $u_1 = u_2 \in I(U)$ *implies* $F_1\ u_1 = F_2\ u_2 \in T$ *then* $\mathsf{Fun}\ U_1\ F_1 = \mathsf{Fun}\ U_2\ F_2 \in T$ *and* $I(\mathsf{Fun}\ U_1\ F_1) = I(\mathsf{Fun}\ U_2\ F_2) = \Pi(I(U_1), \lambda u.I(F_1\ u))$
3. $\mathsf{El}\ u_1 = \mathsf{El}\ u_2 \in T$ *if* $u_1 = u_2 \in I(\mathsf{Set})$.
4. $[\![A]\!] \in T$ *and* $h \in I([\![A]\!])$ *whenever* $\vdash h{:}A$ *is a typing rule for the constant* h.

If Δ is a context we write $\rho \Vdash \Delta$ to express that $[\![A]\!]_\rho \in T$ and $\rho(x) \in I([\![A]\!]_\rho)$ for $x{:}A$ in Δ and we write $\rho_1 = \rho_2 \Vdash \Delta$ to express that $[\![A]\!]_{\rho_1} = [\![A]\!]_{\rho_2} \in T$ and $\rho_1(x) = \rho_2(x) \in [\![A]\!]_{\rho_1}$ for $x{:}A$ in Δ.

The next result states the soundness of PER semantics for the type system. We assume given a PER model T, I of our type theory. The proof is direct by induction on derivations using Theorem 8 and Lemma 9.

Theorem 15 *Assume* $\rho_1 = \rho_2 \Vdash \Delta$. *If* $\Delta \vdash A$ *then* $[\![A]\!]_{\rho_1} = [\![A]\!]_{\rho_2} \in T$. *If* $\Delta \vdash M{:}A$ *then* $[\![A]\!]_{\rho_1} = [\![A]\!]_{\rho_2} \in T$ *and* $[\![M]\!]_{\rho_1} = [\![M]\!]_{\rho_2} \in I([\![A]\!]_{\rho_1})$.

A *totality relation* on D is a partial equivalence relation X such that $u \neq \perp$ if $u \in X$ and $\top \in X$. We let TR(D) be the collection of all totality relations.

Lemma 16 *If* $X \in \mathsf{TR(D)}$ *and* $F : X \to \mathsf{TR(D)}$ *then* $\Pi(X, F) \in \mathsf{TR(D)}$.

We have $\top \in X$. If $v \in \Pi(X, F)$ then $v\ \top \in F(\top)$ and so $v\ \top \neq \perp$ and $v \neq \perp$ holds. If $u \in X$ then $u \neq \perp$ so that $\top\ u = \top \in F(u)$. This shows $\top \in \Pi(X, F)$.

The next theorem has a subtle proof, but it is standard [1, 8, 24]. The main idea is to define the pair T, I by an inductive process, using Lemma 7 to ensure the consistency of this definition.

Theorem 17 *The filter model* D *of UPL can be extended to a model of our type theory, in such a way that* $T \in \mathsf{TR(D)}$ *and* $I : T \to \mathsf{TR(D)}$.

For instance the element nat is in T and $I(\mathsf{nat})$ is the PER containing the elements $\mathsf{S}^k\ 0$ and $\mathsf{S}^k\ \top$. Similarly, Void will be in T and $I(\mathsf{Void})$ contains only $\top$.

The verifications of condition 4 of Definition 7 for the constants Φ and Ψ are similar to the ones in [11], and it is crucial at this point that we are using a domain model. These constants make also the system proof-theoretically strong, at least the strength of second-order arithmetic.

Corollary 18 *If* $\vdash A$ *then* $[\![A]\!] \neq \perp$. *If* $\vdash M : A$ *then* $[\![M]\!] \neq \perp$.

By combining Corollary 18 with Theorem 6 we get

Theorem 19 *If* $\vdash A$ *then* A *is strongly normalisable. If* $\vdash M : A$ *then* M *is strongly normalisable.*

4.3 Decidability properties

In order to get decidability of conversion, we use a technique introduced in [14] and first define the η-expansion $\eta\ A\ M$ in a syntactical way.

$$\eta\ \mathsf{Set}\ M = M \qquad \eta\ (\mathsf{El}\ B)\ M = M$$
$$\eta\ (\mathsf{Fun}\ A\ F)\ M =$$
$$\lambda x.\eta\ (F\ (\eta\ A\ x))\ (M\ (\eta\ A\ x))$$

Lemma 20 *If* $\Gamma \vdash M : A$ *then* $\Gamma \vdash M = \eta\ A\ M : A$

The intuition behind the next statement is clear: if we work only with the η-expansions of the terms, we don't need the η-conversion rule. For a precise proof, we rely on the soundness of a particular PER model for our type system.

Lemma 21 *If* $\vdash M_1 = M_2 : A$ *then we have* $\eta\ A\ M_1 =_{\beta,\iota} \eta\ A\ M_2$

For the proof we use the following PER model. The domain D is the set of all terms, with β,ι-conversion as equality. The PER Set is interpreted by the conversion: we have $M_1 = M_2 : \mathsf{Set}$ if and only if $M_1 = M_2$, and for any M the PER $\mathsf{El}\ M$ is also the conversion. A constant h defined to be of type A is interpreted by $\eta\ A\ h$, and one can check that $\eta\ A\ f$ satisfies the same equality as f. For instance, Rec is interpreted as $\lambda C.\lambda a.\lambda b.\lambda n.\mathsf{Rec}\ (\lambda x.C\ x)\ a\ (\lambda x.\lambda y.b\ x\ y)\ n$. The soundness of the type theory w.r.t. this interpretation gives the result.

Theorem 22 *If* $\vdash M_1 : A$ *and* $\vdash M_2 : A$ *then* $\vdash M_1 = M_2 : A$ *if and only if* $\eta\ A\ M_1 =_{\beta,\iota} \eta\ A\ M_2$.

This follows from Lemmas 20 and 21 and Corollary 14.

Corollary 23 *If* $\vdash M_1 : A$ *and* $\vdash M_2 : A$ *then* $\vdash M_1 = M_2 : A$ *is decidable.*

Indeed, by the theorem we are reduced to check $\eta\ A\ M_1 =_{\beta,\iota} \eta\ A\ M_2$. This is decidable since both $\eta\ A\ M_1$ and $\eta\ A\ M_2$ are strongly normalisable, and β,ι reduction is confluent.

Corollary 24 *If* A *is in* β*-normal form then* $\vdash A$ *is decidable. If* $\vdash A$ *and* M *is in* β*-normal form then* $\vdash M : A$ *is decidable.*

4.4 Proof irrelevance

We add two new constants Prf and O with the rules

$$\frac{\Gamma \vdash M : \mathsf{Set}}{\Gamma \vdash \mathsf{Prf}\ M} \qquad \frac{\Gamma \vdash M : \mathsf{Prf}\ N}{\Gamma \vdash \mathsf{O} : \mathsf{Prf}\ N}$$
$$\frac{\Gamma \vdash M_1 = M_2 : \mathsf{Set}}{\Gamma \vdash \mathsf{Prf}\ M_1 = \mathsf{Prf}\ M_2}$$
$$\frac{\Gamma \vdash M_1 : \mathsf{Prf}\ N \qquad \Gamma \vdash M_2 : \mathsf{Prf}\ N}{\Gamma \vdash M_1 = M_2 : \mathsf{Prf}\ N}$$

We can read the judgement $\mathsf{O} : \mathsf{Prf}\ A$ as claiming that the proposition A is *true*: we know that A has a proof but the proof has been hidden.

Notice that the strengthening property does not hold for this system. We shall be interested however only in terms that do not contain O. This element is only here in order to prove the decidability of the conversion relation and it is not needed in order to have a strongly normalising proof-irrelevant theory.

The PER model extends directly to this system by interpreting O by $\top$ and letting $I([\![\mathsf{Prf}\ A]\!])$ be the set $I([\![\mathsf{El}\ A]\!])$ with the universal equivalence relation. One can show the soundness of this PER model w.r.t. the typing rules and it follows that strong normalisation still holds for this system.

This PER model validates also the following rule.

$$\frac{\Gamma \vdash M : \mathsf{El}\ A}{\Gamma \vdash M : \mathsf{Prf}\ A}$$

For proving the decidability of convertibility, we update the definition of $\eta\ A\ M$ by taking $\eta\ (\mathsf{Prf}\ B)\ M = \mathsf{O}$. It is then still the case that $\vdash M_1 = M_2 : A$ if and only if $\eta\ A\ M_1 =_{\beta,\iota} \eta\ A\ M_2$ if $\vdash M_1 : A$ and $\vdash M_2 : A$.

Theorem 25 *If* A *is in* β*-normal form and does not contain* O *then* $\vdash A$ *is decidable. If* $\vdash A$ *and* M *is in* β*-normal form and does not contain* O *then* $\vdash M : A$ *is decidable.*

5 Conclusion

We have built a filter model D for an untyped calculus having the property that a term is strongly normalisable whenever its semantics is $\neq\perp$, and then used this to give various *modular* proofs of strong normalization. While each part uses essentially variation on standard materials, our use of filter models seems to be new and can be seen as an application of computing science to proof theory. It is interesting that we are naturally lead in this way to consider a domain with a top element. We have shown on some examples that this can be used to prove strong normalisation theorem in a modular way, essentially by reducing this problem to show the soundness of a PER semantics over the domain D. As suggested to us by Andreas Abel, it seems likely that Theorem 5 has a purely combinatorial proof, similar in complexity to the one for simply typed λ-calculus. There should be no problem to use our model to give a simple normalisation proof of system F extended with bar recursion. For this, we don't need to work with PERs, but it would be enough to work with *totality predicates* that are subsets $X \subseteq \mathsf{D}$ such that $\top \in X$ and $u \neq \perp$ if $u \in X$. It is then direct that totality predicates are closed under arbitrary non empty intersections. By working in the D-set model instead of the PER model over D [26, 3], one should be able to get also strong normalisation theorems for various impredicative type theories extended with bar recursion.

For proving normalisation for *predicative* type systems, the use of the model D is proof-theoretically too strong: the PER are relations over filters, that are themselves sets of formal neighborhoods, and so are essentially third-order objects. For applications not involving strong schemas like bar recursion, it is possible however to work instead only with the definable elements of the set D, and PER becomes second-order objects, as usual. It is then natural to extend our programming language with an extra element $\top$ that plays the role of a top-level error.

A natural extension of this work would be also to state and prove a *density* theorem for our denotational semantics, following [13]. The first step would be to define when a formal neighborhood is of a given type.

In [6, 21], for untyped λ-calculus without constants, it is proved that a term M is strongly normalizing if *and only if* $[\![M]\!] \neq \perp$. This does not hold here since we have for instance 0 nat strongly normalizing, but $[\![0\ \mathsf{nat}]\!] = \perp$. However, it may be possible to find a natural subset of term M for which the equivalence between M is strongly normalizing and $[\![M]\!] \neq \perp$ holds.

A more natural extension of a system with dependent types with some form of bar recursion would be to add a constant for the double negation shift [25], which would be a constant of type

$$((n : \mathsf{nat}) \to \neg(\neg F\ n)) \to \neg\neg((n : \mathsf{nat}) \to F\ n)$$

with suitable computation rules, for $F : \mathsf{nat} \to \mathsf{Set}$. We leave this for further work.

Most of our results hold without the hypotheses that the rewriting rules are mutually disjoint. We only have to change the typing rules for a constant f in Figure 2 by the uniform rule: $\Gamma \vdash_{\mathcal{M}} f : U_1 \to \ldots \to U_k \to V$ if *for all* rules $f\ p_1 \ldots p_k \to M$ and *for all* $W_1, \ldots, W_n$ such that $p_i(W_1, \ldots, W_n) = U_i$ we have $\Gamma, x_1 : W_1, \ldots, x_n : W_n \vdash_{\mathcal{M}} M : V$. (This holds for instance trivially in the special case where no rules for f matches $U_1, \ldots, U_n$.) For instance, we can add a constant $+$ with rewrite rules

$$\begin{array}{ccccc} + & n & 0 & \to & n \\ + & 0 & n & \to & n \\ + & n & (\mathsf{S}\ m) & \to & \mathsf{S}\ (+\ n\ m) \\ + & (\mathsf{S}\ n) & m & \to & \mathsf{S}\ (+\ n\ m) \end{array}$$

and Theorem 6 is still valid with this extension.

Appendix: the language UPL

The constructors Set, nat, Void, Unit, 0, [] (arity 0), list, El, S (arity 1) and cons, Fun (arity 2).

The defined constants of the language UPL are isZero, less, length, concat, get, Rec, Φ, Ψ. The arities are clear from the following ι-rules.

$\mathsf{Rec}\ M\ N\ 0 \to N$
$\mathsf{Rec}\ M\ N\ (\mathsf{S}\ P) \to M\ P\ (\mathsf{Rec}\ M\ N\ P)$
$\mathsf{isZero}\ 0 \to \mathsf{Unit}$
$\mathsf{isZero}\ (\mathsf{S}\ P) \to \mathsf{Void}$
$\mathsf{less}\ P\ 0 \to 0$
$\mathsf{less}\ 0\ (\mathsf{S}\ P) \to \mathsf{S}\ 0$
$\mathsf{less}\ (\mathsf{S}\ P)\ (\mathsf{S}\ Q) \to \mathsf{less}\ P\ Q$
$\mathsf{get}\ a\ (\mathsf{cons}\ x\ L)\ (\mathsf{S}\ N) \to \mathsf{get}\ L\ N$
$\mathsf{get}\ a\ (\mathsf{cons}\ x\ L)\ (0) \to x$
$\mathsf{get}\ a\ []\ N \to a$
$\mathsf{length}\ [] \to 0$
$\mathsf{length}\ (\mathsf{cons}\ P\ L) \to \mathsf{S}\ (\mathsf{length}\ L)$
$\mathsf{concat}\ []\ x \to \mathsf{cons}\ x\ []$
$\mathsf{concat}\ (\mathsf{cons}\ P\ L)\ x \to \mathsf{cons}\ P\ (\mathsf{concat}\ L\ x)$
$\Phi\ M\ N\ L\ R \to$
$M\ (\lambda x.\Psi\ M\ N\ L\ R\ x\ (\mathsf{less}\ x\ (\mathsf{length} L)))$
$\Psi\ M\ N\ L\ R\ Q\ 0 \to \mathsf{get}\ R\ L\ Q$
$\Psi\ M\ N\ L\ R\ Q\ (\mathsf{S}\ \_) \to$
$N\ Q\ (\lambda x.\Phi\ M\ N\ (\mathsf{concat}\ x\ L))\ R$

Finally the typing rules for constants are the following

nat :	Set
0 :	nat
S :	nat $\rightarrow$ nat
Rec :	$((n : \mathsf{nat}) \rightarrow C\ n \rightarrow (C\ (\mathsf{S}\ n))) \rightarrow$ $C\ 0 \rightarrow (n : \mathsf{nat}) \rightarrow C\ n$ $[C : \mathsf{nat} \rightarrow \mathsf{Set}]$
isZero :	nat $\rightarrow$ Set
list :	Set $\rightarrow$ Set
[] :	list A $[A : \mathsf{Set}]$
cons :	$A \rightarrow$ list $A \rightarrow$ list A $[A : \mathsf{Set}]$
Void :	Set
Unit :	Set
0 :	Unit
get :	$A \rightarrow$ list $A \rightarrow$ nat $\rightarrow A$ $[A : \mathsf{Set}]$
length :	list $A \rightarrow$ nat $[A : \mathsf{Set}]$
less :	nat $\rightarrow$ nat $\rightarrow$ nat $[A : \mathsf{Set}]$
concat :	list $A \rightarrow A \rightarrow$ list A $[A : \mathsf{Set}]$
Φ :	$((\mathsf{nat} \rightarrow A) \rightarrow \mathsf{nat}) \rightarrow$ $(\mathsf{nat} \rightarrow (A \rightarrow \mathsf{nat}) \rightarrow A) \rightarrow$ list $A \rightarrow A \rightarrow$ nat $[A : \mathsf{Set}]$
Ψ :	$((\mathsf{nat} \rightarrow A) \rightarrow \mathsf{nat}) \rightarrow$ $(\mathsf{nat} \rightarrow (A \rightarrow \mathsf{nat}) \rightarrow A) \rightarrow$ list $A \rightarrow A \rightarrow$ nat $\rightarrow$ nat $\rightarrow$ nat $[A : \mathsf{Set}]$

The rules for Φ and Ψ are the rules for a variation of bar recursion. We do not comment further on these rules, since they are essentially the same as the ones given in [11], with the get function suitably modified to take into account the empty type, which is not present in the system [11].

The rule cons : $A \rightarrow$ list $A \rightarrow$ list A $[A : \mathsf{Set}]$ for instance means that we have

$$\frac{\vdash A : \mathsf{Set}}{\vdash \mathsf{cons} : A \rightarrow \mathsf{list}\ A \rightarrow \mathsf{list}}$$

and similarly for the other constants.

Acknowledgement

Thanks to Mariangiola Dezani-Ciancaglini for the reference to the paper [6].

References

[1] P. Aczel Frege structures and the notions of proposition, truth and set. *The Kleene Symposium*, pp. 31–59, Stud. Logic Foundations Math., 101, North-Holland, Amsterdam-New York, 1980.

[2] Y. Akama. SN Combinators and Partial Combinatory Algebras. LNCS 1379, p. 302-317, 1998.

[3] Th. Altenkirch. *Constructions, Inductive Types and Strong Normalization.* PhD thesis, University of Edinburgh, 1993.

[4] R. Amadio and P.L. Curien. *Domains and Lambda-Calculi.* Cambridge tracts in theoretical computer science, 46, (1997).

[5] D. Aspinall. Subtyping Dependent Types. CSL'94, LNCS 933, 1994.

[6] S. van Bakel. Complete restrictions of the Intersection Type Discipline. Theoretical Computer Science, 102:135-163, 1992.

[7] H. Barendregt, M. Coppo and M. Dezani-Ciancaglini. A filter lambda model and the completeness of type assignment. *J. Symbolic Logic* 48 (1983), no. 4, 931–940 (1984).

[8] M. Beeson. *Foundations of constructive mathematics. Metamathematical studies.* Ergebnisse der Mathematik und ihrer Grenzgebiete (3) [Results in Mathematics and Related Areas (3)], 6. Springer-Verlag, Berlin, 1985.

[9] S. Berardi, M. Bezem and Th. Coquand. On the computational content of the axiom of choice. Journal of Symbolic Logic 63 (2), 600-622, 1998.

[10] U. Berger and P. Oliva. Modified Bar Recursion and Classical Dependent Choice. Logic Colloquium '01, 89–107, Lect. Notes Log., 20, Assoc. Symbol. Logic, Urbana, IL, 2005.

[11] U. Berger. Continuous Semantics for Strong Normalisation. LNCS 3526, 23-34, 2005.

[12] U. Berger. A Computational Interpretation of Open Induction. Proceeding of LICS 2004.

[13] U. Berger. Continuous Functionals of Dependent and Transfinite Types. in *Models and Computability*, London Mathematical Society, Lecture Note Series, p. 1–22, 1999.

[14] Th. Coquand, R. Pollack and M. Takeyama. A Logical Framework with Dependently Typed Record. Fundam. Inform. 65 (1-2), p. 113-134, 2005.

[15] D. Fridlender. A proof-irrelevant model of Martin-Lf's logical framework. Math. Structures Comput. Sci. 12 (2002), no. 6, 771–795.

[16] R Harper, F Pfenning. On equivalence and canonical forms in the LF type theory ACM Transactions on Computational Logic, p. 61–101, 2005.

[17] G. Kreisel. Interpretation of analysis by means of constructive functionals of finite types. In *Constructivity in Mathematics*, North-Holland, 1958.

[18] P. Martin-Löf. Lecture note on the domain interpretation of type theory. *Workshop on Semantics of Programming Languages, Chalmers*, (1983).

[19] B Nordstrom, K Petersson, JM Smith. Martin-Löf Type Theory. Handbook of Logic in Computer Science, 2000.

[20] R. Pollack. Closure Under Alpha-Conversion. TYPES 1993, Lecture Notes in Computer Science 806, p. 313-332, 1993.

[21] G. Pottinger. A type assignment for the strongly normalizable terms. in: J.P. Seldin and J.R. Hindley (eds.), *To H. B. Curry: essays on combinatory logic, lambda calculus and formalism*, Academic Press, London, pp. 561-577, 1980.

[22] G. Plotkin. LCF considered as a programming language. *Theoretical Computer Science*, 5:223-255, 1977.

[23] D. Scott. Lectures on a mathematical theory of computation. Theoretical foundations of programming methodology (Munich, 1981), 145–292, NATO Adv. Study Inst. Ser. C: Math. Phys. Sci., 91, Reidel, Dordrecht, 1982.

[24] D. Scott. Combinators and classes. *λ-calculus and computer science theory*, pp. 1–26. Lecture Notes in Comput. Sci., Vol. 37, Springer, Berlin, 1975.

[25] C. Spector. Provably recursive functionals of analysis: a consistency proof of analysis by an extension of principles in current intuitionistic mathematics. In F.D.E.Dekker, editor, Recursive Function Theory, 1962

[26] Th. Streicher. *Semantics of Type Theory.* in the series Progress in Theoretical Computer Science. Basel: Birkhaeuser. XII, 1991.

[27] W.W. Tait. Normal form theorem for bar recursive functions of finite type. *Proceedings of the Second Scandinavian Logic Symposium*, North-Holland, 1971.

[28] B. Werner. A Proof-Irrelevant Type Theory. Unpublished manuscript, 2003.

Boolean algebras for lambda calculus*

G. Manzonetto[†°] and A. Salibra[°]
† Laboratoire PPS (Université Paris 7)
2 place Jussieu (case 7014)
72251 Paris Cedex 05, France
gmanzone@dsi.unive.it
° Università Ca'Foscari di Venezia
Dipartimento di Informatica
Via Torino 155, 30172 Venezia, Italy
salibra@dsi.unive.it

Abstract

In this paper we show that the Stone representation theorem for Boolean algebras can be generalized to combinatory algebras. In every combinatory algebra there is a Boolean algebra of central elements *(playing the role of idempotent elements in rings), whose operations are defined by suitable combinators. Central elements are used to represent any combinatory algebra as a Boolean product of directly indecomposable combinatory algebras (i.e., algebras which cannot be decomposed as the Cartesian product of two other nontrivial algebras). Central elements are also used to provide applications of the representation theorem to lambda calculus. We show that the* indecomposable semantics *(i.e., the semantics of lambda calculus given in terms of models of lambda calculus, which are directly indecomposable as combinatory algebras) includes the continuous, stable and strongly stable semantics, and the term models of all semisensible lambda theories. In one of the main results of the paper we show that the indecomposable semantics is equationally incomplete, and this incompleteness is as wide as possible: for every recursively enumerable lambda theory $\mathcal{T}$, there is a continuum of lambda theories including $\mathcal{T}$ which are omitted by the indecomposable semantics.*

1 Introduction

The lambda calculus is not a true equational theory since the variable-binding properties of lambda abstraction prevent variables in lambda calculus from operating as real algebraic variables. Consequently the general methods that have been developed in universal algebra, for defining the semantics of an arbitrary algebraic theory for instance, are not directly applicable. There have been several attempts to reformulate the lambda calculus as a purely algebraic theory. The earliest, and best known, algebraic models are Curry's combinatory algebras [14]. Combinatory algebras have a simple purely equational characterization and were used to provide an intrinsic first-order, but not equational, characterization of the models of lambda calculus, as a special class of combinatory algebras called λ-models [2, Def. 5.2.7].

Topology is at the center of the known approaches to giving models of the untyped lambda calculus. The first model, found by Scott in 1969 in the category of algebraic lattices, was successfully used to show that all unsolvable λ-terms can be consistently equated. After Scott, a large number of mathematical models for lambda calculus, arising from syntax-free constructions, have been introduced in various categories of domains and were classified into semantics according to the nature of their representable functions, see e.g. [1, 2, 5, 6, 23]. Scott's continuous semantics [27] is given in the category whose objects are complete partial orders and morphisms are Scott continuous functions. The stable semantics (Berry [8]) and the strongly stable semantics (Bucciarelli-Ehrhard [10]) are a strengthening of the continuous semantics, introduced to capture the notion of "sequential" Scott continuous function. All these semantics are structurally and equationally rich [7, 18, 19] in the sense that it is possible to build up $2^{\aleph_0}$ λ-models in each of them inducing, through the kernel congruence relation of the interpretation function, pairwise distinct lambda theories. Nevertheless, the above denotational semantics are equationally *incomplete*: they do not match all possible operational semantics of lambda calculus. The problem of the equational incompleteness was positively solved by Honsell-Ronchi della Rocca [16] for the continuous semantics and by Bastonero-Gouy [4, 15] for the stable semantics. In [25, 26] Salibra has shown in a uniform way that all semantics (including the strongly stable semantics), which involve monotonicity with respect to some partial order and have a bottom element, fail to induce a continuum of lambda theories.

*Work partially supported by the Equipe PPS of the University Paris 7-Denis Diderot, and by MIUR Cofin'04 FOLLIA Project.

Salibra [20, 26, 24] has recently launched a research program for exploring lambda calculus and combinatory logic using techniques of universal algebra. In [20] Lusin and Salibra have shown that a lattice identity is satisfied by all congruence lattices of combinatory algebras iff it is trivial (i.e, true in all lattices). As a consequence, it is not possible to apply to combinatory algebras the nice results developed in universal algebra (see [12, 21]) in the last thirty years, which essentially connect lattice identities satisfied by all congruence lattices of algebras in a variety, and Mal'cev conditions (that characterize properties in varieties by the existence of suitable terms involved in certain identities). Thus there is a common belief that lambda calculus and combinatory logic are algebraically pathological.

On the contrary, in this paper we show that combinatory algebras satisfy interesting algebraic properties. One of the milestones of modern algebra is the Stone representation theorem for Boolean algebras, which was generalized by Peirce to commutative rings with unit and next by Comer to the class of algebras with Boolean factor congruences (see [13, 17, 22]). By applying a theorem by Vaggione [30], we show that Comer's generalization of Stone representation theorem holds also for combinatory algebras: any combinatory algebra is isomorphic to a weak Boolean product of directly indecomposable combinatory algebras (i.e., algebras which cannot be decomposed as the Cartesian product of two other nontrivial algebras). Another way to express the representation theorem is in terms of sheaves: any combinatory algebra is isomorphic to the algebra of global sections of a sheaf of indecomposable combinatory algebras over a Boolean space.

The proof of the representation theorem for combinatory algebras is based on the fact that every combinatory algebra has *central elements*, i.e., elements which define a direct decomposition of the algebra as the Cartesian product of two other combinatory algebras, just like idempotent elements in rings or complemented elements in bounded distributive lattices. Central elements in universal algebra were introduced by Vaggione in [29] and were used to investigate the closure of varieties of algebras under Boolean products. In this paper we show that central elements in a combinatory algebra constitute a Boolean algebra, whose Boolean operations can be defined by suitable combinators. This result highlights a connection between propositional classic logic and combinatory logic. What is the real meaning of this flavour of classic logic within combinatory logic remains to be investigated in the future. What we would like to emphasize here is that central elements have been shown fundamental in the application of the representation theorem to lambda calculus, as it will be explained in the next paragraph.

The representation theorem can be roughly summarized as follows: the directly indecomposable combinatory algebras are the 'building blocks' in the variety of combinatory algebras. On the other hand, the result of incompleteness [26], stating that any semantics of lambda calculus given in terms of partial orderings with a bottom element is incomplete, removes the belief that partial orderings are intrinsic to λ-models. It would be interesting to find new Cartesian closed categories, where the partial orderings play no role and the reflexive objects are directly indecomposable as combinatory algebras. In this paper we investigate the class of all models of lambda calculus, which are directly indecomposable as combinatory algebras (*indecomposable semantics*, for short). We show that the indecomposable semantics includes the continuous, stable and strongly stable semantics, and the term models of all semisensible lambda theories (theories which do not equate solvable and unsolvable terms). In one of the main results of the paper we show that the indecomposable semantics is incomplete, and this incompleteness is as wide as possible: for every recursively enumerable lambda theory $\mathcal{T}$, there is a continuum of lambda theories including $\mathcal{T}$ which are omitted by the indecomposable semantics.

It is unknown, in general, whether the set of lambda theories, which are representable in a semantics of lambda calculus, is a lattice with respect to the inclusion ordering. In the last result of the paper we show that the set of lambda theories representable in each of the classic semantics of lambda calculus is not closed under finite intersection, so that it cannot constitute a sublattice of the lattice of all lambda theories.

2 Notation and basic definitions

We will generally use the notation of Barendregt's classic work [2] for lambda calculus and combinatory logic and the notation of Burris and Sankappanavar [12] for universal algebra.

2.1 The untyped lambda calculus

Λ and Λ^o are, respectively, the set of λ-terms and of closed λ-terms.

We will denote $\alpha\beta$-conversion by $\lambda\beta$. A *lambda theory* is a congruence on Λ (with respect to the operators of abstraction and application) which contains $\lambda\beta$; it can also be seen as a (specific) set of equations between λ-terms. The set of all lambda theories is naturally equipped with a structure of complete lattice, hereafter denoted by $\lambda\mathcal{T}$, with meet defined as set theoretical intersection. The join of two lambda theories $\mathcal{T}$ and $\mathcal{S}$ is the least equivalence relation including $\mathcal{T} \cup \mathcal{S}$. It is clear that $\lambda\beta$ is the least element of $\lambda\mathcal{T}$, while the inconsistent lambda theory $\Lambda \times \Lambda$ is the top element of $\lambda\mathcal{T}$.

The lambda theory generated (or axiomatized) by a set of equations is the least lambda theory containing it. As a matter of notation, $\mathcal{T} \vdash M = N$ stands for $M = N \in \mathcal{T}$; this is also written as $M =_{\mathcal{T}} N$. A lambda theory $\mathcal{T}$ is consistent if there exists at least an equation $M = N$ such that $\mathcal{T} \nvdash M = N$.

Solvable λ-terms can be characterized as follows: a λ-term M is solvable if, and only if, it has a *head normal form*, that is, $M =_{\lambda\beta} \lambda x_1 \dots x_n.yM_1 \dots M_k$ for some $n, k \geq 0$ and λ-terms $M_1, \dots, M_k$. $M \in \Lambda$ is *unsolvable* if it is not solvable.

$\mathcal{H}$ is the lambda theory generated by equating all the unsolvable λ-terms, while $\mathcal{H}^*$ is the unique maximal consistent lambda theory such that $\mathcal{H} \subseteq \mathcal{H}^*$. A lambda theory $\mathcal{T}$ is called *semisensible* [2, Def. 4.1.7(iii)] if $\mathcal{T} \nvdash M = N$ whenever M is solvable and N is unsolvable. $\mathcal{T}$ is semisensible iff $\mathcal{T} \subseteq \mathcal{H}^*$. A lambda theory $\mathcal{T}$ is *sensible* if $\mathcal{H} \subseteq \mathcal{T}$ (see Section 10.2 and Section 16.2 in [2]).

2.2 Combinatory algebra

An *applicative structure* is an algebra with a distinguished 2-ary function symbol which we call *application*. We may write it infix as $s \cdot t$, or even drop it entirely and write st. As usual, application associates to the left; stu means $(st)u$.

Curry discovered that a particularly simple applicative structure has tremendous expressive power [14]: a *combinatory algebra* $\mathbf{C} = (C, \cdot, \mathbf{k}, \mathbf{s})$ is an applicative structure for a signature with two constants $\mathbf{k}$ and $\mathbf{s}$, such that $\mathbf{k}xy = x$ and $\mathbf{s}xyz = xz(yz)$ for all x, y, and z. See elsewhere [14] for a full treatment.

Call $\mathbf{k}$ and $\mathbf{s}$ the *basic combinators*. In the equational language of combinatory algebras the derived combinators $\mathbf{i}$ and $\mathbf{1}$ are defined as $\mathbf{i} \equiv \mathbf{skk}$ and $\mathbf{1} \equiv \mathbf{s}(\mathbf{ki})$. It is not hard to verify that every combinatory algebra satisfies the identities $\mathbf{i}x = x$ and $\mathbf{1}xy = xy$.

We say that $c \in C$ *represents* a function $f : C \to C$ (and that f is *representable*) if $cz = f(z)$ for all $z \in C$. Call $c, d \in C$ *extensionally equal* when they represent the same function in C. For example c and $\mathbf{1}c$ are always extensionally equal. (We use $\mathbf{1}$ below to select a canonical representative inside a class of extensionally equivalent elements.)

For each variable x we define a transformation λx^* of the set of combinatory terms as follows: $\lambda x^*.x = \mathbf{i}$. Let t be a combinatory term different from x. If x does not occur in t, define $\lambda x^*.t = \mathbf{k}t$. Otherwise, t must be of the form rs where s and r are combinatory terms, at least one of which contains x; in this case define $\lambda x^*.t = \mathbf{s}(\lambda x^*.r)(\lambda x^*.s)$. It is well known that x does not occur in $\lambda x^*.t$ and that, for every combinatory algebra $\mathbf{C}$ and combinatory term u, we have:

$$\mathbf{C} \models (\lambda x^*.t)u = t[x := u],$$

where the combinatory term $t[x := u]$ is obtained by substituting u for x in t.

If t is a combinatory term and $x_1, x_2 \dots, x_n$ $(n \geq 2)$ are variables, then $\lambda x_1 x_2 \dots x_n^*.t$ is defined by induction as follows: $\lambda x_1 x_2 \dots x_n^*.t \equiv \lambda x_1^*.(\lambda x_2 \dots \lambda x_n^*.t)$.

2.3 Lambda model

The axioms of an elementary subclass of combinatory algebras, called λ-*models* or models of the lambda calculus, were expressly chosen to make coherent the definition of interpretation of λ-terms (see [2, Def. 5.2.7]). Let $\mathbf{C}$ be a λ-model and let $\bar{c}$ be a new symbol for each $c \in C$. Extend the language of the lambda calculus by adding $\bar{c}$ as a new constant symbol for each $c \in C$. Let $\Lambda^o(C)$ be the set of closed λ-terms with constants from C. The interpretation of terms in $\Lambda^o(C)$ with elements of C can be defined by induction as follows (for all $M, N \in \Lambda^o(C)$ and $c \in C$):

$$|\bar{c}| = c; \ |(MN)| = |M|\,|N|; \ |\lambda x.M| = \mathbf{1}m,$$

where $m \in C$ is any element representing the following function $f : C \to C$:

$$f(c) = |M[x := \bar{c}]|, \quad \text{for all } c \in C.$$

The *Meyer-Scott axiom* is the most important axiom in the definition of a λ-model. In the first-order language of combinatory algebras it takes the following form

$$\forall x \forall y (\forall z (xz = yz) \Rightarrow \mathbf{1}x = \mathbf{1}y).$$

The combinator $\mathbf{1}$ becomes an inner choice operator, that makes coherent the interpretation of an abstraction λ-term.

Each λ-model $\mathbf{C}$ induces a lambda theory, denoted here by $Th(\mathbf{C})$, and called *the equational theory of* $\mathbf{C}$. Thus, $M = N \in Th(\mathbf{C})$ if, and only if, M and N have the same interpretation in $\mathbf{C}$.

Definition 1 *Given a lambda theory $\mathcal{T}$, a λ-model* $\mathbf{C}$ represents (or induces) $\mathcal{T}$ *if* $\mathcal{T} = Th(\mathbf{C})$.

The *term model* $\mathcal{M}_{\mathcal{T}}$ of a lambda theory $\mathcal{T}$ (see [2, Def. 5.2.11]) consists of the set of the equivalence classes of λ-terms modulo the lambda theory $\mathcal{T}$ together with the operation of application on the equivalence classes. By [2, Cor. 5.2.13(ii)] $\mathcal{M}_{\mathcal{T}}$ is a λ-model which represents the lambda theory $\mathcal{T}$.

We define various notions of representability of theories in classes of models.

Definition 2 *Given a class $\mathbb{C}$ of λ-models and a lambda theory $\mathcal{T}$,*

1. $\mathbb{C}$ represents $\mathcal{T}$ *if there is some* $\mathcal{M} \in \mathbb{C}$ *representing* $\mathcal{T}$.

2. $\mathbb{C}$ omits $\mathcal{T}$ *if there is no* $\mathcal{M} \in \mathbb{C}$ *representing* $\mathcal{T}$.

3. $\mathbb{C}$ *is* complete *for the set* $S \subseteq \lambda\mathcal{T}$ *of lambda theories if* $\mathbb{C}$ *represents all elements of* S.

4. $\mathbb{C}$ *is* incomplete *if it omits a consistent lambda theory.*

2.4 Algebra

A congruence θ on an algebra $\mathbf{A}$ is an equivalence relation which is compatible with respect to the basic operation of the algebra. Write Con$\mathbf{A}$ for the set of congruences of $\mathbf{A}$. This has a natural complete lattice structure by inclusion of sets (considering θ as a subset of $A \times A$, so the meet is just set-intersection).

θ is *trivial* if it is the top or bottom element in the natural inclusion ordering; write these $\nabla^{\mathbf{A}}$ (equal to $A \times A$) and $\Delta^{\mathbf{A}}$ (equal to $\{(a, a) \mid a \in A\}$) respectively. Also, given $a, b \in A$ write $\theta(a, b)$ for the least congruence relating a and b.

Given two congruences σ and τ on the algebra $\mathbf{A}$, we can form the *relative product*:

$$\tau \circ \sigma = \{(a, c) \mid a\sigma b\tau c, \text{for some } b \in A\}.$$

This is a compatible relation on $\mathbf{A}$, but not necessarily a congruence.

An algebra $\mathbf{A}$ is *simple* when its only congruences are $\Delta^{\mathbf{A}}$ and $\nabla^{\mathbf{A}}$.

An algebra $\mathbf{A}$ is a *subdirect product* of the algebras $(\mathbf{B}_i : i \in I)$ if there exists an embedding f of $\mathbf{A}$ into the direct product $\Pi_{i \in I}\mathbf{B}_i$ such that the projection $\pi_i \circ f : \mathbf{A} \to \mathbf{B}_i$ is onto for every $i \in I$. We write $\mathbf{A} \leq \Pi_{i \in I}\mathbf{B}_i$ if $\mathbf{A}$ is a subdirect product of the algebras $(\mathbf{B}_i : i \in I)$.

Call a nonempty class K of algebras of the same similarity type a *variety* if it is closed under subalgebras, homomorphic images and direct products. By Birkhoff's theorem (see [21]) a class of algebras is a variety if, and only if, it is an equational class (that is, it is axiomatized by a set of equations).

2.5 Factor congruence

Call θ a *factor congruence* when there exists another congruence $\overline{\theta}$ such that $\theta \cap \overline{\theta} = \Delta^{\mathbf{A}}$ and $\nabla^{\mathbf{A}} = \theta \circ \overline{\theta}$. In this case call θ and $\overline{\theta}$ a *pair of complementary factor congruences.*

It is easy to see that $\mathbf{A}$ has a pair $(\theta, \overline{\theta})$ of complementary factor congruences precisely when it is isomorphic to $\mathbf{B} \times \mathbf{C}$ (with $\mathbf{B}$ isomorphic to $\mathbf{A}/\theta$ and $\mathbf{C}$ isomorphic to $\mathbf{A}/\overline{\theta}$).

So factor congruences are another way of saying 'this algebra is a direct product of simpler algebras'.

The set of factor congruences of $\mathbf{A}$ is not, in general, a sublattice of Con$\mathbf{A}$. $\Delta^{\mathbf{A}}$ and $\nabla^{\mathbf{A}}$ are the *trivial* factor congruences, corresponding to $\mathbf{A} \cong 1 \times \mathbf{A}$; of course, 1 is isomorphic to $\mathbf{A}/\nabla^{\mathbf{A}}$ and $\mathbf{A}$ is isomorphic to $\mathbf{A}/\Delta^{\mathbf{A}}$.

An algebra $\mathbf{A}$ is *directly indecomposable* when $\mathbf{A}$ admits only the two trivial factor congruences ($\Delta^{\mathbf{A}}$ and $\nabla^{\mathbf{A}}$), while $\mathbf{A}$ is *directly decomposable* when $\mathbf{A}$ admits nontrivial factor congruences.

Clearly, a simple algebra is directly indecomposable, though there are algebras which are directly indecomposable but not simple (they just have congruences which do not split the algebra up neatly as a Cartesian product).

It is useful to characterize factor congruences in terms of algebra homomorphisms satisfying certain equalities (the next step will be to express the equalities in the equational language of the algebra itself).

A decomposition operation (see [21, Def. 4.32]) for an algebra $\mathbf{A}$ is a function $f : A \times A \to A$ such that

- $f(x, x) = x$;
- $f(f(x, y), z) = f(x, z) = f(x, f(y, z))$;
- f is an algebra homomorphism from $\mathbf{A} \times \mathbf{A}$ into $\mathbf{A}$.

By [21, Thm. 4.33] there exists a bijective correspondence between pairs of complementary factor congruences and decomposition operations, and thus between decomposition operations and factorizations $\mathbf{A} \cong \mathbf{B} \times \mathbf{C}$.

By this intuition we see that the binary relations θ and $\overline{\theta}$ defined by

$$x \, \theta \, y \text{ iff } f(x, y) = y; \quad x \, \overline{\theta} \, y \text{ iff } f(x, y) = x,$$

are a pair of complementary factor congruences, and conversely we see that for every pair θ and $\overline{\theta}$ of complementary factor congruences, the map f defined by

$$f(x, y) = u \text{ iff } x \, \theta \, u \, \overline{\theta} \, y, \tag{1}$$

is a decomposition operation. Notice that for any x and y there is just one element u such that $x \, \theta \, u \, \overline{\theta} \, y$.

The reader can easily verify these facts, or find proofs elsewhere [21].

An algebra has *Boolean factor congruences* if the factor congruences form a Boolean sublattice of the congruence lattice. Most known examples of varieties in which all algebras have Boolean factor congruences are those with *factorable congruences*, that is, varieties in which every congruence θ on $\mathbf{A} \times \mathbf{B}$ is a product congruence $\theta_1 \times \theta_2$ of two congruences $\theta_1 \in$ Con$\mathbf{A}$ and $\theta_2 \in$ Con$\mathbf{B}$. Recall that $(b, c) \, \theta_1 \times \theta_2 \, (b', c')$ iff $b \, \theta_1 \, b'$ and $c \, \theta_2 \, c'$.

2.6 Boolean product

The Boolean product construction (see [12, Chapter IV]) provides a method for translating numerous fascinating properties of Boolean algebras into other varieties of algebras. Actually the construction that we call "Boolean product" has been known for several years as "the algebra of global sections of sheaves of algebras over Boolean spaces" (see [13, 17]); however the definition of the latter was unnecessarily involved. We recall that a Boolean space is a compact, Hausdorff and totally disconnected topological space.

A *weak Boolean product* of an indexed family $(\mathbf{A}_i : i \in I)$ of algebras is a subdirect product $\mathbf{A} \leq \Pi_{i \in I} \mathbf{A}_i$, where I can be endowed with a Boolean space topology so that

(i) the set $\{i \in I : a_i = b_i\}$ is open for all $a, b \in A$, and

(ii) if $a, b \in A$ and N is a clopen subset of I, then the element c, defined by $c_i = a_i$ for every $i \in N$ and $c_i = b_i$ for every $i \in I - N$, belongs to A.

A *Boolean product* is just a weak Boolean product such that the set $\{i \in I : a_i = b_i\}$ is clopen for all $a, b \in A$.

3 The Stone representation theorem for combinatory algebras

The axioms characterizing the variety of combinatory algebras are suggested by an analysis of recursive processes, not by logic (as for Boolean algebras and Heyting algebras) or by algebra (as for groups and rings). Combinatory algebras are never commutative, associative, finite and recursive, so that there is a common belief that these algebras are algebraically pathological.

On the contrary, in this section we show that combinatory algebras satisfy interesting algebraic properties: the Stone representation theorem for Boolean algebras admits a generalization to combinatory algebras.

3.1 Stone and Peirce

The Stone representation theorem for Boolean rings (the observation that Boolean algebras could be regarded as rings is due to Stone) admits a generalization, due to Peirce, to commutative rings with unit (see [22] and [17, Chapter V]). To make the reader familiar with the argument, we give in this subsection an outline of Peirce construction.

Let $\mathbf{A} = (A, +, \cdot, 0, 1)$ be a commutative ring with unit, and let $E(A) = \{a \in A : a \cdot a = a\}$ be the set of idempotent elements of A. We define a structure of Boolean algebra on $E(A)$ as follows, for all $a, b \in E(A)$:

- $a \wedge b = a \cdot b$;
- $a \vee b = a + b - (a \cdot b)$;
- $a^- = 1 - a$.

Then it is possible to show that every idempotent element $a \neq 0, 1$ defines a pair $\theta(a, 1)$, $\theta(a, 0)$ of nontrivial complementary factor congruences, where $\theta(a, 1)$ is the least congruence containing the pair $(a, 1)$ and similarly for the other congruence $\theta(a, 0)$. In other words, the ring $\mathbf{A}$ can be decomposed in a non trivial way as $\mathbf{A} = \mathbf{A}/\theta(a, 1) \times \mathbf{A}/\theta(a, 0)$. If $E(A) = \{0, 1\}$, then A is directly indecomposable. Then the Peirce theorem for commutative rings with unit can be stated as follows: every commutative ring with unit is isomorphic to a Boolean product of directly indecomposable rings. If $\mathbf{A}$ is a Boolean ring, then we get the Stone representation theorem for Boolean algebras, because the ring of truth values is the unique directly indecomposable Boolean ring.

The remaining part of this section is devoted to the proof of the representation theorem for combinatory algebras.

3.2 The Boolean algebra of central elements

Combinatory logic and lambda calculus internalize many important things (computability theory, for example). 'To be directly decomposable' is another internalizable property of these formalisms, as it will be shown in this subsection.

In the equational language of combinatory algebras the combinators $\mathbf{t}, \mathbf{f}$ representing the booleans are defined by $\mathbf{t} \equiv \mathbf{k}$ and $\mathbf{f} \equiv \mathbf{ki}$. The booleans satisfy the identities $\mathbf{t}xy = x$ and $\mathbf{f}xy = y$.

The combinators $\mathbf{t}$ and $\mathbf{f}$ correspond to the constants 0 and 1 in a commutative ring with unit, while, as it will be shown below, the so-called central elements of a combinatory algebra correspond to idempotent elements in a ring. Central elements in universal algebra were introduced by Vaggione in [29].

Definition 3 *Let* $\mathbf{A}$ *be a combinatory algebra. We say an element* $e \in A$ *is* central *when it satisfies the following equations, for all* $x, y, z, t \in A$:

(i) $exx = x$.

(ii) $e(exy)z = exz = ex(eyz)$.

(iii) $e(xy)(zt) = exz(eyt)$.

(iv) $e = e\mathbf{tf}$.

The set of central elements of $\mathbf{A}$ will be denoted by $E(\mathbf{A})$.

Every combinatory algebra admits at least two central elements, namely the combinators $\mathbf{t}$ and $\mathbf{f}$. Now we show that central elements, as idempotent elements in a ring, decompose a combinatory algebra $\mathbf{A}$ as a Cartesian product: if $e \in E(\mathbf{A})$, then $\mathbf{A} = \mathbf{A}/\theta(e, \mathbf{t}) \times \mathbf{A}/\theta(e, \mathbf{f})$. This will be shown in the next proposition via decomposition operators.

The use of decomposition operators to characterize central elements is new.

Fix some combinatory algebra.

Proposition 4 *There is a (natural) bijective correspondence between central elements and decomposition operators.*

Proof. Given a central element e we obtain a decomposition operator by taking $f_e(x, y) = exy$. It is a simple exercise to show that axioms (i)-(iii) of a central element make f_e a decomposition operator.

Conversely, given a decomposition operator f, we have to show that the element $f(\mathbf{t}, \mathbf{f})$ is central. From Section 2.5 we have that $f(\mathbf{t}, \mathbf{f})$ is the unique element u satisfying $\mathbf{t}\ \theta\ u\ \overline{\theta}\ \mathbf{f}$, where θ and $\overline{\theta}$ are the pair of complementary factor congruences associated with the decomposition operator f. Then, from the property of congruence of θ and $\overline{\theta}$ it follows, for all x, y:

$$\mathbf{t}xy\ \theta\ f(\mathbf{t}, \mathbf{f})xy\ \overline{\theta}\ \mathbf{f}xy,$$

that implies $x\ \theta\ f(\mathbf{t}, \mathbf{f})xy\ \overline{\theta}\ y$. Since by definition $f(x, y)$ is the unique element satisfying $x\ \theta\ f(x, y)\ \overline{\theta}\ y$, then we obtain

$$f(x, y) = f(\mathbf{t}, \mathbf{f})xy \quad (2)$$

Finally, the identities defining f as decomposition operator make $f(\mathbf{t}, \mathbf{f})$ a central element.

It is easy to verify that these correspondences form the two sides of a bijection. If e is central, then the central element $f_e(\mathbf{t}, \mathbf{f})$ is equal to e, because $f_e(\mathbf{t}, \mathbf{f}) = e\mathbf{t}\mathbf{f} = e$ by Def. 3(iv). If f is a decomposition operator, then by (2) we have that $f_{f(\mathbf{t},\mathbf{f})}(x, y) = f(\mathbf{t}, \mathbf{f})xy = f(x, y)$ for all x, y. ■

For every central element e, we denote respectively by f_e and by $(\theta_e, \overline{\theta}_e)$ the decomposition operator and the pair of complementary factor congruences determined by e.

Corollary 5 *If e is central, then we have:*

1. $x\ \theta_e\ exy\ \overline{\theta}_e\ y$;
2. $x\ \theta_e\ y$ *iff* $exy = y$; $\quad x\ \overline{\theta}_e\ y$ *iff* $exy = x$;
3. *The congruence θ_e is generated by the pair $(e, \mathbf{t})$ (i.e., $\theta_e = \theta(e, \mathbf{t})$);*
4. *The congruence $\overline{\theta}_e$ is generated by the pair $(e, \mathbf{f})$ (i.e., $\overline{\theta}_e = \theta(e, \mathbf{f})$).*

We now show that the partial ordering over central elements, defined by

$$d \leq e \text{ iff } \theta_d \subseteq \theta_e \quad (3)$$

is a Boolean ordering. The combinators $\mathbf{t}$ and $\mathbf{f}$ are respectively the bottom element and the top element of this ordering, while the combinators $\lambda xy^*.xty$ and $\lambda x^*.x\mathbf{f}\mathbf{t}$ (recall that λxy^* is defined in Section 2.2) represent respectively the meet operation and the complementation.

Theorem 6 *Let $\mathbf{A}$ be a combinatory algebra. Then the algebra $\mathbf{E}(\mathbf{A}) = (E(\mathbf{A}), \wedge, ^-)$ of central elements of $\mathbf{A}$, defined by*

$$e \wedge d = e\mathbf{t}d; \quad e^- = e\mathbf{f}\mathbf{t},$$

is a Boolean algebra.

Proof. We first show that the factor congruences of $\mathbf{A}$ form a Boolean sublattice of the congruence lattice Con$\mathbf{A}$. Let $\mathbf{A} = \mathbf{B} \times \mathbf{C}$ be a decomposition of $\mathbf{A}$ as the direct product of two combinatory algebras $\mathbf{B}$ and $\mathbf{C}$. It is easy to show, by using the equations defining central elements, that $E(\mathbf{A}) = E(\mathbf{B}) \times E(\mathbf{C})$, i.e., every central element of $\mathbf{A}$ can be decomposed as a pair of central elements of $\mathbf{B}$ and $\mathbf{C}$. In the terminology of universal algebra this means that $\mathbf{A}$ has no 'skew factor congruences'. We get the conclusion from [9, Prop. 1.3], where it is shown that an algebra $\mathbf{A}$ has no skew factor congruences if, and only if, the factor congruences of $\mathbf{A}$ form a Boolean sublattice of the congruence lattice Con$\mathbf{A}$.

It follows that the partial ordering on central elements, defined in (3), is a Boolean ordering. We have to show now that, for all central elements d, e, the elements $e^- = e\mathbf{f}\mathbf{t}$ and $e \wedge d = e\mathbf{t}d$ are central and are respectively associated with the pairs $(\overline{\theta}_e, \theta_e)$ and $(\theta_e \cap \theta_d, \overline{\theta}_e \vee \overline{\theta}_d)$ of complementary factor congruences (recall that e is associated with the pair $(\theta_e, \overline{\theta}_e)$).

We check the details for $e\mathbf{f}\mathbf{t}$. By Cor. 5(1) we have that $e\mathbf{f}\mathbf{t}$ is the unique element u such that $\mathbf{t}\ \overline{\theta}_e\ u\ \theta_e\ \mathbf{f}$. By (1) in Section 2.5 this means that $e\mathbf{f}\mathbf{t} = g(\mathbf{t}, \mathbf{f})$ for the decomposition operator g associated with the pair $(\overline{\theta}_e, \theta_e)$ of complementary factor congruences. We have the conclusion that $e\mathbf{f}\mathbf{t}$ is central associated with the pair $(\overline{\theta}_e, \theta_e)$ as in the proof of Prop. 4.

We now consider $e \wedge d = e\mathbf{t}d$. First of all, we show that $e\mathbf{t}d = d\mathbf{t}e$. By Cor. 5(1) we have that $\mathbf{t}\ \theta_e\ e\mathbf{t}d\ \overline{\theta}_e\ d$, while $\mathbf{t}\ \theta_e\ d\mathbf{t}e\ \overline{\theta}_e\ d$ can be obtained as follows: $\mathbf{t} =$ (by Def. 3(i)) $d\mathbf{t}\mathbf{t}\ \theta_e$ (by $\mathbf{t}\theta_e e$) $d\mathbf{t}e\ \overline{\theta}_e$ (by $e\overline{\theta}_e\mathbf{f}$) $d\mathbf{t}\mathbf{f} =$ (by Def. 3(iv)) d. Since there is a unique element u such that $\mathbf{t}\ \theta_e\ u\ \overline{\theta}_e\ d$, then we have the conclusion $d\mathbf{t}e = e\mathbf{t}d$. We now show that $e\mathbf{t}d$ is the central element associated with the factor congruence $\theta_e \cap \theta_d$, i.e.,

$$\mathbf{t}\ (\theta_e \cap \theta_d)\ e\mathbf{t}d\ (\overline{\theta}_e \vee \overline{\theta}_d)\ \mathbf{f}.$$

From $d\mathbf{t}e = e\mathbf{t}d$ we easily get that $\mathbf{t}\ \theta_e\ e\mathbf{t}d$ and $\mathbf{t}\ \theta_d\ e\mathbf{t}d$, that is, $\mathbf{t}\ (\theta_e \cap \theta_d)\ e\mathbf{t}d$. Finally, by Cor. 5 we have: $e\mathbf{t}d\ \overline{\theta}_e\ d = d\mathbf{t}\mathbf{f}\ \overline{\theta}_d\ \mathbf{f}$, i.e., $e\mathbf{t}d\ (\overline{\theta}_e \vee \overline{\theta}_d)\ \mathbf{f}$. ■

We now provide the promised representation theorem. If I is a maximal ideal of the Boolean algebra $E(\mathbf{A})$, then $\cup I$ denotes the congruence on $\mathbf{A}$ defined by

$$x\ (\cup I)\ y \text{ iff } x\ \theta_e\ y \text{ for some } e \in I.$$

By a *Peirce variety* (see [30]) we mean a variety of algebras for which there are two constants $0, 1$ and a term $u(x, y, z, v)$ such that the following identities hold: $u(x, y, 0, 1) = x$ and $u(x, y, 1, 0) = y$.

Theorem 7 (Representation Theorem) *Let* $\mathbf{A}$ *be a combinatory algebra and* X *be the Boolean space of maximal ideals of the Boolean algebra* $\mathbf{E}(\mathbf{A})$ *of central elements. Then the map*

$$f : A \to \Pi_{I \in X}(A/\cup I),$$

defined by

$$f(x) = (x/\cup I : I \in X),$$

gives a **weak** *Boolean product representation of* $\mathbf{A}$*, where the quotient algebras* $\mathbf{A}/\cup I$ *are directly indecomposable.*

Proof. By Thm. 6 the set of factor congruences of $\mathbf{A}$ constitutes a Boolean sublattice of Con$\mathbf{A}$. Then by [13] f gives a weak Boolean product representation of $\mathbf{A}$. The quotient algebras $\mathbf{A}/\cup I$ are directly indecomposable by [30, Thm. 8], because the variety of combinatory algebras is a Peirce variety if we define $1 \equiv \mathbf{t}$, $0 \equiv \mathbf{f}$ and $u = \lambda xyzv^*.zyx$. ∎

The map f of the above theorem does not give in general a Boolean product representation. This follows from two results due to Vaggione [29] and to Plotkin-Simpson [28]. Vaggione has shown that, if a variety has factorable congruences (i.e., every congruence in a product is a product of congruences) and every member of the variety can be represented as a Boolean product of directly indecomposable algebras, then the variety is a discriminator variety (see [12] for the terminology). Discriminator varieties satisfy very strong algebraic properties, in particular they are congruence permutable (i.e., the join of two congruences is just their composition). Plotkin and Simpson have shown that the property of having permutable congruences is inconsistent with combinatory logic.

4 The algebraic incompleteness of lambda calculus

The representation theorem of combinatory algebras can be roughly summarized as follows: the directly indecomposable combinatory algebras are the 'building blocks' in the variety of combinatory algebras. Then it is natural to investigate the class of models of lambda calculus, which are directly indecomposable as combinatory algebras (*indecomposable semantics*, for short). In this section we show that the indecomposable semantics includes: the continuous, stable and strongly stable semantics, and the term models of all semisensible lambda theories. However, in one of the main results of the paper we give a proof, based on central elements, that the indecomposable semantics is incomplete, and this incompleteness is as wide as possible: for every recursively enumerable lambda theory $\mathcal{T}$, there is a continuum of lambda theories including $\mathcal{T}$ which are omitted by the indecomposable semantics. In the last result of the paper we show that the set of lambda theories induced by each of the known semantics is not closed under finite intersection, so that it cannot constitute a sublattice of the lattice of lambda theories.

4.1 Internalizing 'indecomposable'

We have shown how to internally represent a factor congruence as a central element. Now we show how to represent the logical assertion that the only factor congruences of a combinatory algebra are trivial.

We recall that an algebra $\mathbf{A}$ is *directly indecomposable* when it is not trivial and it is not isomorphic to a product of two nontrivial algebras (i.e., there is not a pair of nontrivial complementary factor congruences). A combinatory algebra $\mathbf{A}$ is directly indecomposable if $E(\mathbf{A}) = \{\mathbf{t}, \mathbf{f}\}$.

For two combinatory terms t and u, define the pair $[t, u] \equiv \lambda z^*.ztu$ and, for every sequence $t_1, \ldots, t_n$ ($n \geq 3$), define $[t_1, \ldots, t_n] \equiv [t_1, [t_2, \ldots, t_n]]$.

Define the following combinatory terms:

- $\mathbf{Z} \equiv \lambda e^*.[\lambda x^*.exx, \lambda xyz^*.e(exy)z, \lambda xyz^*.exz, \lambda xyzu^*.e(xy)(zu), e\mathbf{t}\mathbf{f}]$;
- $\mathbf{U} \equiv \lambda e^*.[\lambda x^*.x, \lambda xyz^*.exz, \lambda xyz^*.ex(eyz), \lambda xyzu^*.exz(eyu), e]$.

Lemma 8 *The class* CA_{DI} *of the directly indecomposable combinatory algebras is a universal class (i.e., it is an elementary class which can be axiomatized by universal sentences).*

Proof. By Def. 3 we have that e is central if, and only if, the equation $\mathbf{Z}e = \mathbf{U}e$ holds. Then the class CA_{DI} is axiomatized by the following universal formula ϕ:

$$\phi \equiv \forall e((\mathbf{Z}e = \mathbf{U}e \to e = \mathbf{t} \vee e = \mathbf{f}) \wedge \neg(\mathbf{t} = \mathbf{f})).$$

∎

Corollary 9 *The class* CA_{DI} *of the directly indecomposable combinatory algebras is closed under subalgebras and ultraproducts.*

4.2 Algebraic incompleteness

The closure of the class of directly indecomposable combinatory algebras under subalgebras is the key trick in the proof of the algebraic incompleteness theorem.

Lemma 10 *Given a lambda theory* $\mathcal{T}$ *the following conditions are equivalent:*

(i) The term model $\mathcal{M}_\mathcal{T}$ of $\mathcal{T}$ is directly decomposable.

(ii) All λ-models representing $\mathcal{T}$ are directly decomposable.

(iii) The indecomposable semantics omits $\mathcal{T}$.

Proof. (ii ⇔ iii): By Def. 2.

(i ⇒ ii): Recall that a λ-model **C** represents a lambda theory $\mathcal{T}$ (i.e., $Th(\mathbf{C}) = \mathcal{T}$) if, and only if, the term model $\mathcal{M}_\mathcal{T}$ of $\mathcal{T}$ is a subalgebra of **C**. Then the conclusion follows from Corollary 9. ∎

In every model of lambda calculus the interpretation of the combinators **t** and **f** is equal respectively to that of the λ-terms $\boldsymbol{T} \equiv \lambda xy.x$ and $\boldsymbol{F} \equiv \lambda xy.y$. It follows that the λ-terms $\boldsymbol{T}$ and $\boldsymbol{F}$ can cover the role of trivial central elements in every model of lambda calculus.

Theorem 11 (The algebraic Incompleteness Theorem) *The indecomposable semantics is incomplete.*

Proof. By Lemma 10 it is sufficient to define a lambda theory whose term model is directly decomposable. Let $\Omega \equiv (\lambda x.xx)(\lambda x.xx)$ be the usual looping term of lambda calculus. Consider two arbitrary consistent lambda theories $\mathcal{T}$ and $\mathcal{S}$ satisfying the following conditions:

$$\mathcal{T} \vdash \Omega = \boldsymbol{T}; \quad \mathcal{S} \vdash \Omega = \boldsymbol{F}.$$

$\mathcal{T}$ and $\mathcal{S}$ exist because Ω is an easy term (see [2, Prop. 15.3.9]), i.e., it can be equated consistently with any other closed term. It is a simple exercise to verify that the lambda theory $\mathcal{T} \cap \mathcal{S}$ contains all equations (i)-(iv) of Def. 3 for $e = \Omega$, making the equivalence class of Ω a nontrivial central element in the term model of $\mathcal{T} \cap \mathcal{S}$. ∎

We have shown that theories exist with no indecomposable models, so that any class of models which excludes decomposable models cannot be complete.

In the following theorem we show that, although the class of directly indecomposable λ-models is incomplete, it is so wide to include all term models of the semisensible lambda theories.

We recall from Section 2.3 that the term model $\mathcal{M}_\mathcal{T}$ of a lambda theory $\mathcal{T}$ is a model of lambda calculus and that the elements of $\mathcal{M}_\mathcal{T}$ are equivalence classes of λ-terms modulo $\mathcal{T}$.

Lemma 12 *Let $e \in \mathcal{M}_\mathcal{T}$ be a nontrivial central element in the term model of a lambda theory $\mathcal{T}$. Then, every λ-term belonging to the equivalence class e is unsolvable.*

Proof. By Cor. 5 the congruences $\theta_e = \theta(e, \boldsymbol{T})$ and $\overline{\theta}_e = \theta(e, \boldsymbol{F})$ on the term model of $\mathcal{T}$ are nontrivial. Then, for every λ-term $M \in e$, the lambda theories $\mathcal{T}_1$ and $\mathcal{T}_2$, generated respectively by $\mathcal{T} \cup \{\boldsymbol{F} = M\}$ and $\mathcal{T} \cup \{\boldsymbol{T} = M\}$, are consistent. Assume, by the way of contradiction, that M is solvable. By [2, Lemma 10.4.1(i)] it is consistent to equate two solvable λ-terms only if they are equivalent according to [2, Def. 10.2.9]. Then the λ-term M should be equivalent to $\boldsymbol{F}$ and $\boldsymbol{T}$. By Remark 10.2.20(ii) in [2] this is possible only if the head variable of Mxy, where x and y are distinct variables, is equal to x and to y at the same time. This contradiction provides the conclusion of the lemma. ∎

Theorem 13 *The indecomposable semantics is complete for the set of semisensible lambda theories.*

Proof. The conclusion of the theorem follows if we show that the term model of every semisensible lambda theory is directly indecomposable. Assume, by the way of contradiction, that there is a semisensible lambda theory $\mathcal{T}$ such that the term model $\mathcal{M}_\mathcal{T}$ of $\mathcal{T}$ admits e as a nontrivial central element. Since the term model $\mathcal{M}_\mathcal{T}$ satisfies the identity $exx = x$ (see Def. 3), then $\mathcal{T} \vdash Mxx = x$ for all λ-terms $M \in e$. By Lemma 12 $M \in e$ is unsolvable. Then the unsolvable λ-term Mxx is provably equal in $\mathcal{T}$ to the solvable λ-term x. This contradicts the hypothesis. ∎

4.3 Continuous, stable and strongly stable semantics

We recall that an algebra is *simple* when it has just two congruences (so that every simple algebra is directly indecomposable).

In the next two theorems we give simple proofs of incompleteness for the classic semantics of lambda calculus.

Theorem 14 (Honsell-Ronchi della Rocca [16]) *The semantics of lambda calculus given in terms of continuous models is incomplete.*

Proof. Let **C** be a continuous model of lambda calculus. The function g, defined by: $g(x) = c$ if $x \not\leq b$ and $g(x) = \bot$ otherwise, is Scott continuous for every arbitrary element c. We now show that **C** is simple as a combinatory algebra. Let θ be a congruence on **C** such that $a \ \theta \ b$ with $a \neq b$. We have $a \not\leq b$ or $b \not\leq a$. Suppose that we are in the first case. Since the continuous function g is representable in the model, then we have: $\bot = g(a) \ \theta \ g(b) = c$. By the arbitrariness of c we get that θ is trivial, so that **C** is simple. The conclusion of the theorem follows from the algebraic incompleteness theorem (see Thm. 11), because every simple combinatory algebra is directly indecomposable. ∎

The continuous function g of the above proof is neither stable nor strongly stable (see [5] for a full treatment of stable and strongly stable semantics).

Theorem 15 (Gouy-Bastonero [15, 4]; Salibra [25, 26]) *The semantics of lambda calculus given in terms of stable or strongly stable models, and whose underlying domain is algebraic, is incomplete.*

Proof. Let $\mathbf{C}$ be a (strongly) stable model of lambda calculus. Take $a, b \in \mathbf{C}$ such that $a \neq b$. We have $a \not\leq b$ or $b \not\leq a$. Suppose that we are in the first case. Then there is a compact element d of $\mathbf{C}$ such that $d \leq a$ and $d \not\leq b$. The step function f defined by : $f(x) = c$ if $x \geq d$ and $f(x) = \bot$ otherwise, is stable, and strongly stable for every element c. This function f can be used to show that every congruence on $\mathbf{C}$ is trivial as in the proof of Thm. 14. Then the conclusion is again a consequence of the algebraic incompleteness theorem. ∎

We do not know whether the stable and strongly stable models, whose underlying domains are *not* algebraic, are directly indecomposable as combinatory algebras.

Given a class $\mathbb{C}$ of λ-models, we denote by $\lambda\mathbb{C}$ the set of lambda theories which are representable in $\mathbb{C}$ (see Section 2.3). It is unknown, in general, whether $\lambda\mathbb{C}$ is a lattice with respect to the inclusion ordering of sets and whether $\lambda\mathbb{C}$ is a sublattice of the lattice $\lambda\mathcal{T}$ of lambda theories. In the remaining part of this subsection we show that, for each of the classic semantics of lambda calculus, the set $\lambda\mathbb{C}$ is not closed under finite intersection, so that it is not a sublattice of the lattice $\lambda\mathcal{T}$ of lambda theories.

Theorem 16 *Let $\mathbb{C}$ be a class of directly indecomposable models of lambda calculus. If there are two consistent lambda theories $\mathcal{T}, \mathcal{S} \in \lambda\mathbb{C}$ such that*

$$\mathcal{T} \vdash \Omega = \boldsymbol{T}; \quad \mathcal{S} \vdash \Omega = \boldsymbol{F},$$

then $\lambda\mathbb{C}$ is not closed under finite intersection, so it is not a sublattice of $\lambda\mathcal{T}$.

Proof. The term model of $\mathcal{T} \cap \mathcal{S}$ admits a nontrivial central element Ω, so that it is directly decomposable. It follows that $\mathcal{T} \cap \mathcal{S} \notin \lambda\mathbb{C}$. ∎

We recall that the graph λ-models (see, for example, [6, 11]) and the filter λ-models (see, for example, [3]) are classes of models within the continuous semantics.

Corollary 17 *Let $\mathbb{C}$ be one of the following semantics: graph semantics, filter semantics, continuous semantics, stable semantics, strongly stable semantics (these last two semantics restricted to models whose underlying domain is algebraic). Then $\lambda\mathbb{C}$ is not a sublattice of $\lambda\mathcal{T}$.*

Proof. Semantic proofs that Ω is an easy term were given in each of the semantics specified in the statement of the theorem (see [5]). Then the conclusion follows from Thm. 16, because the models in each of these semantics are directly indecomposable as combinatory algebras. ∎

4.4 Concerning the number of decomposable models

Now we show that the incompleteness of the indecomposable semantics is as wide as possible.

The proof of following lemma is similar to that of [2, Prop. 17.1.9], where the case $k = 1$ (due to Visser) is shown, and it is omitted.

Lemma 18 *Suppose $\mathcal{T}$ is a recursively enumerable* (r.e.) *lambda theory and fix arbitrary terms M_i, N_i for $1 \leq i \leq k$ which are not provably equal in $\mathcal{T}$, that is, such that $\mathcal{T} \nvdash M_i = N_i$ for all i. Then there exists a term M such that*

$$\mathcal{T} \cup \{M = P\} \nvdash M_i = N_i, \text{ for all } i \text{ and all closed terms } P.$$

Then the following theorem is a corollary of the algebraic incompleteness theorem.

Theorem 19 *Let $\mathcal{T}$ be an r.e. lambda theory. Then, the interval $[\mathcal{T}) = \{\mathcal{S} : \mathcal{T} \subseteq \mathcal{S}\}$ contains a subinterval $[\mathcal{S}_1, \mathcal{S}_2] = \{\mathcal{S} : \mathcal{S}_1 \subseteq \mathcal{S} \subseteq \mathcal{S}_2\}$, constituted by a continuum of lambda theories, satisfying the following conditions:*

- *$\mathcal{S}_1$ and $\mathcal{S}_2$ are r.e. lambda theories;*
- *Every $\mathcal{S} \in [\mathcal{S}_1, \mathcal{S}_2]$ is omitted by the indecomposable semantics (in particular, $\mathcal{S}$ is omitted by the continuous, stable and strongly stable semantics).*

Proof. The proof is divided into claims.

We first construct $\mathcal{S}_1$. We recall that a λ-term Q is $\mathcal{T}$-*easy* when, for every fixed closed λ-term P, the lambda theory generated by $\mathcal{T} \cup \{Q = P\}$ is consistent.

Claim 20 *There exists a $\mathcal{T}$-easy λ-term Q.*

By Lemma 18.

Claim 21 *$\mathcal{T} \nvdash Q = \boldsymbol{T}$ and $\mathcal{T} \nvdash Q = \boldsymbol{F}$.*

Trivial, because Q is $\mathcal{T}$-easy.

Let $\mathcal{S}_1 = \mathcal{T}_1 \cap \mathcal{T}_2$, where $\mathcal{T}_1$ and $\mathcal{T}_2$ are the consistent lambda theories generated respectively by $\mathcal{T} \cup \{Q = \boldsymbol{T}\}$ and $\mathcal{T} \cup \{Q = \boldsymbol{F}\}$.

Claim 22 *The lambda theory $\mathcal{S}_1$ is r.e. and contains $\mathcal{T}$.*

$\mathcal{S}_1$ is r.e., because it is the intersection of two r.e. lambda theories. The other property follows from $\mathcal{T} \subseteq \mathcal{T}_1 \cap \mathcal{T}_2 = \mathcal{S}_1$.

Claim 23 *The term model of $\mathcal{S}_1$ has a non trivial central element e.*

Let $e = [Q]_{\mathcal{S}_1}$ be the equivalence class of the lambda term Q. It is easy to show that e satisfies the equations of Def. 3. Moreover, e is not trivial because $\mathcal{S}_1 \nvdash Q = \boldsymbol{T}$ and $\mathcal{S}_1 \nvdash Q = \boldsymbol{F}$.

We now define the lambda theory $\mathcal{S}_2$.

Claim 24 *There exists an r.e. lambda theory $\mathcal{S}_2$, which is a proper extension of $\mathcal{S}_1$, such that $\mathcal{S}_2 \nvdash Q = \boldsymbol{T}$ and $\mathcal{S}_2 \nvdash Q = \boldsymbol{F}$.*

We apply Lemma 18 to the lambda theory $\mathcal{S}_1$ and to the equations $Q = \boldsymbol{T}$ and $Q = \boldsymbol{F}$. We get a $\mathcal{S}_1$-easy term R such that $\mathcal{S}_1 \cup \{R = P\} \nvdash Q = \boldsymbol{T}$ and $\mathcal{S}_1 \cup \{R = P\} \nvdash Q = \boldsymbol{F}$, for all lambda terms P. Let $\mathcal{S}_2 = \mathcal{S}_1 \cup \{R = \lambda x.x\}$. $\mathcal{S}_2$ is a proper extension of $\mathcal{S}_1$ because otherwise R would not be a $\mathcal{S}_1$-easy term.

Claim 25 *The equivalence class of Q is a non trivial central element of the term model of $\mathcal{S}_2$.*

The term model $\mathcal{M}_{\mathcal{S}_2}$ of $\mathcal{S}_2$ is a homomorphic image of the term model $\mathcal{M}_{\mathcal{S}_1}$ of $\mathcal{S}_1$. Then, every equation satisfied by $\mathcal{M}_{\mathcal{S}_1}$ is also satisfied by $\mathcal{M}_{\mathcal{S}_2}$. In particular, the equations characterizing Q as a central element. Finally, $[Q]_{\mathcal{S}_2}$ is nontrivial as a central element because $\mathcal{S}_2 \nvdash Q = \boldsymbol{T}$ and $\mathcal{S}_2 \nvdash Q = \boldsymbol{F}$.

Claim 26 *For every lambda theory $\mathcal{S}$ such that $\mathcal{S}_1 \subseteq \mathcal{S} \subseteq \mathcal{S}_2$ the equivalence class of Q is non trivial central element of the term model of $\mathcal{S}$.*

We get the conclusion of the theorem because the interval $[\mathcal{S}_1, \mathcal{S}_2]$ has a continuum of elements (see [2, Cor. 17.1.11]). ∎

Acknowledgments

Many thanks to Chantal Berline and Jamie Murdoch Gabbay for helpful comments and suggestions.

References

[1] S. Abramsky. Domain theory in logical form. *Annals of Pure and Applied Logic*, 51:1–77, 1991.

[2] H. P. Barendregt. *The Lambda calculus: Its syntax and semantics*. North-Holland, Amsterdam, 1984.

[3] H. P. Barendregt, M. Coppo, and M. Dezani-Ciancaglini. A filter lambda model and the completeness of type assignment. *Journal of Symbolic Logic*, 48(4):931–940, 1983.

[4] O. Bastonero and X. Guoy. Strong stability and the incompleteness of stable models of λ-calculus. *Annals of Pure and Applied Logic*, 100:247–277, 1999.

[5] C. Berline. From computation to foundations via functions and application: The λ-calculus and its webbed models. *Theoretical Computer Science*, 249:81–161, 2000.

[6] C. Berline. Graph models of λ-calculus at work, and variations. *Math. Struct. for Comput. Sci.*, 16:1–37, 2006.

[7] C. Berline and A. Salibra. Easiness in graph models. *Theoretical Computer Science*, 354:4–23, 2006.

[8] G. Berry. Stable models of typed lambda-calculi. In *In Proceedings of the Fifth Colloquium on Automata, Languages and Programming, LNCS 62*, Berline, 1978. Springer-Verlag.

[9] D. Bigelow and S. Burris. Boolean algebras of factor congruences. *Acta Sci. Math.*, 54:11–20, 1990.

[10] A. Bucciarelli and T. Ehrhard. Sequentiality and strong stability. In *Sixth Annual IEEE Symposium on Logic in Computer Science*, pages 138–145. IEEE Computer Society Press, 1991.

[11] A. Bucciarelli and A. Salibra. Sensible graph theories of lambda calculus. In *19th Annual IEEE Symposium on Logic in Computer Science (LICS'04)*, pages 276–285. IEEE Computer Society Publications, 2004.

[12] S. Burris and H. P. Sankappanavar. *A course in universal algebra*. Springer-Verlag, Berlin, 1981.

[13] S. Comer. Representations by algebras of sections over boolean spaces. *Pacific J. Math.*, 38:29–38, 1971.

[14] H. B. Curry and R. Feys. *Combinatory Logic, Vol. I*. North-Holland, Amsterdam, 1958.

[15] X. Gouy. Etude des théories équationnelles et des propriétés algébriques des modéles stables du λ-calcul, 1995. Thèse, Université de Paris 7.

[16] F. Honsell and S. R. D. Rocca. An approximation theorem for topological lambda models and the topological incompleteness of lambda calculus. *Journal of Computer and System Sciences*, 45:49–75, 1992.

[17] P. T. Johnstone. *Stone spaces*. Cambridge University Press, 1982.

[18] R. Kerth. Isomorphism and equational equivalence of continuous lambda models. *Studia Logica*, 61:403–415, 1998.

[19] R. Kerth. On the construction of stable models of λ-calculus. *Theoretical Computer Science*, 269:23–46, 2001.

[20] S. Lusin and A. Salibra. The lattice of lambda theories. *Journal of Logic and Computation*, 14:373–394, 2004.

[21] R. N. McKenzie, G. F. McNulty, and W. F. Taylor. *Algebras, Lattices, Varieties, Volume I*. Wadsworth Brooks, Monterey, California, 1987.

[22] R. S. Peirce. *Modules over commutative regular rings*. Memoirs Amer. Math. Soc., 1967.

[23] G. D. Plotkin. Set-theoretical and other elementary models of the λ-calculus. *Theoretical Computer Science*, 121:351–409, 1993.

[24] A. Salibra. On the algebraic models of lambda calculus. *Theoretical Computer Science*, 249:197–240, 2000.

[25] A. Salibra. A continuum of theories of lambda calculus without semantics. In *16th Annual IEEE Symposium on Logic in Computer Science*, pages 334–343. IEEE Computer Society Press, 2001.

[26] A. Salibra. Topological incompleteness and order incompleteness of the lambda calculus. LICS'01 Special Issue. Number 4, pages 379–401. ACM Transactions on Computational Logic, 2003.

[27] D. S. Scott. Continuous lattices. In *Toposes, algebraic geometry and logic*, Berlin, 1972. Springer-Verlag.

[28] P. Selinger. Order-incompleteness and finite lambda reduction models. *Theoretical Computer Science*, 309:43–63, 2003.

[29] D. Vaggione. V with factorable congruences and $V = \Pi\Gamma^a(V_{DI})$ imply V is a discriminator variety. *Acta Sci. Math.*, 62:359–368, 1996.

[30] D. Vaggione. Varieties in which the pierce stalks are directly indecomposable. *Journal of Algebra*, 184:424–434, 1996.

Normalisation is Insensible to λ-term Identity or Difference

Makoto Tatsuta
National Institute of Informatics
2-1-2 Hitotsubashi, 101-8430 Tokyo, Japan
e-mail: tatsuta@nii.ac.jp

Mariangiola Dezani-Ciancaglini
Dipartimento di Informatica
corso Svizzera 185, 10149 Torino, Italy
e-mail: dezani@di.unito.it

Abstract

This paper analyses the computational behaviour of λ-term applications. The properties we are interested in are weak normalisation (i.e. there is a terminating reduction) and strong normalisation (i.e. all reductions are terminating).

One can prove that the application of a λ-term M to a fixed number n of copies of the same arbitrary strongly normalising λ-term is strongly normalising if and only if the application of M to n different arbitrary strongly normalising λ-terms is strongly normalising. I.e. one has that $M\underbrace{X\ldots X}_{n}$ is strongly normalising, for an arbitrary strongly normalising X, if and only if $MX_1\ldots X_n$ is strongly normalising for arbitrary strongly normalising $X_1,\ldots,X_n$. The analogous property holds when replacing strongly normalising by weakly normalising.

As an application of the result on strong normalisation the λ-terms whose interpretation is the top element (in the environment which associates the top element to all variables) of the Honsell-Lenisa model turn out to be exactly the λ-terms which, applied to an arbitrary number of strongly normalising λ-terms, always produces strongly normalising λ-terms. This proof uses a finitary logical description of the model by means of intersection types. This answers an open question stated by Dezani, Honsell and Motohama.

1 Introduction

In the present paper we analyse when a weakly or strongly normalising λ-term preserves this property under application to a fixed or arbitrary number of λ-terms having the same property. The rather surprising result is the independence of this property from the arguments being copies of the same λ-term or being arbitrary λ-terms.

As the first simple illustration we consider the *head normalisation* or solvability property without restrictions on the arguments. We recall that a λ-term M is solvable if M reduces to a λ-term of the shape $\lambda x_1\ldots\lambda x_p.yM_1\ldots M_m$ [2, 6]. So the question when the application of M to arbitrary λ-terms has head normal form can be simply answered by cases on the head variable y. If y is free, then for all integers n and all λ-terms $X_1,\ldots,X_n$ the λ-term $MX_1\ldots X_n$ reduces to an head normal form with the same head variable y. Instead, if y is bound, i.e. there is an index i such that $x_i{=}y$, then $MX_1\ldots X_n$ reduces to an head normal form for all λ-terms $X_1,\ldots,X_n$ only if $n < i$. In fact when $n \geq i$ we can choose $X_i = (\lambda x.xx)(\lambda x.xx)$ and clearly $MX_1\ldots X_n$ is an unsolvable term. Since we use only one argument (i.e. the i-th argument) as an immediate consequence we get that:

$$(1)\qquad \forall\ \lambda\text{-term } X.M\underbrace{X\ldots X}_{n} \text{ is solvable iff}$$
$$\forall\ \lambda\text{-terms } X_1,\ldots,X_n.MX_1\ldots X_n \text{ is solvable.}$$

So we claim that head normalisation is insensible to having in applications the same repeated argument or different arguments, when the arguments are arbitrary λ-terms.

Instead, if we require the arguments to be also head normalising λ-terms, we loose this property. As a counter-example, consider the combinator $\mathbf{B} = \lambda xyz.x(yz)$ and $n = 2$. The application $\mathbf{B}\Delta(\mathbf{K}\Delta)$, where $\Delta = \lambda x.xx$ and $\mathbf{K} = \lambda xy.x$, reduces to $\lambda z.\Delta\Delta$, but there is no solvable X such that $\mathbf{B}XX$ is unsolvable. In fact let $\lambda x.X'$ be the head normal form of X. If the head variable of X' is x, then $\mathbf{B}XX$ reduces to $\lambda z.Y$ and the head variable of Y is z. Otherwise, if the head variable of X' is different from x — let it be y —, then $\mathbf{B}XX$ reduces to a λ-term whose head variable is y. So in both cases $\mathbf{B}XX$ is a solvable term.

We recall that a λ-term is *weakly normalising* if it has a finite reduction sequence to normal form, and it is *strongly normalising* if all reduction sequences are finite [2, 6]. We denote by WN and SN the sets of weakly normalising and strongly normalising λ-terms, respectively.

The main result of the paper is that weak normalisation and strong normalisation are insensible to having the same repeated argument or different arguments in WN and SN, respectively, i.e. we get:

$$(2)\qquad \forall\, X \in \mathsf{WN}.M\underbrace{X\ldots X}_{n} \in \mathsf{WN} \text{ iff}$$
$$\forall\, X_1,\ldots,X_n \in \mathsf{WN}.MX_1\ldots X_n \in \mathsf{WN}$$

1043-6871/06 $20.00

$$(3) \qquad \forall\, X \in \mathsf{SN}. M \underbrace{X \ldots X}_{n} \in \mathsf{SN} \text{ iff}$$
$$\forall\, X_1, \ldots, X_n \in \mathsf{SN}. M X_1 \ldots X_n \in \mathsf{SN}$$

We will show the following statements:

if $M[x_i := X, x_j := X] \in \mathsf{WN}$ (resp. SN) for all $X \in \mathsf{WN}$ (resp. SN) and for all i, j $(1 \leq i, j \leq n)$, then $M[x_1 := X_1, \ldots, x_n := X_n] \in \mathsf{WN}$ (resp. SN) for all $X_1, \ldots, X_n \in \mathsf{WN}$ (resp. SN).

We call these statements "Substitution Theorems", since they allow to substitute different λ-terms in WN (resp. SN), instead of the same λ-term in WN (resp. SN) for different variables, preserving the weak (strong) normalisation property. We will get both claims (2) and (3) as corollaries of the corresponding "Substitution Theorems".

For dealing with weak normalisation, we start from the analysis of substitutions of β-normal forms inside β-normal forms done in [4]. Our key result is that if there are $X_1, \ldots, X_n \in \mathsf{WN}$ such that $MX_1 \ldots X_n \notin \mathsf{WN}$, then the β-normal form of M has a particular shape. Moreover, from the same assumption we have that at most two λ-terms X_i, X_j need to be chosen appropriately, while all other λ-terms are arbitrary. We can observe that we can choose $X_i = X_j$ and this allows us to conclude the proof of (2).

For strong normalisation the situation is more involved, since we cannot forget reductions. We then consider Klop's extended λ-calculus [9] (a generalisation of Nederpelt's calculus [10]), where all reductions are non erasing. More precisely we use the variant of Klop's λ-calculus discussed in [3]: we call it λ^*-calculus. In λ^*-calculus a redex $(\lambda x.M)N$, with x not in the free variables of M, reduces to the pair $[M, N]$, instead of reducing to M. In this way no subterm is discarded, and strong normalisation coincides with weak normalisation as proved in [3].

Let κ-normal forms be the normal forms of λ^*-calculus: we generalise to κ-normal forms the analysis of substitutions for λ-calculus done in the weak normalisation case. This generalisation is not trivial and requires to associate to each κ-normal form a set of β-normal forms in λ-calculus. In this way we are able to show (3).

As an application of (3) we will prove the completeness of an inductive definition of strongly normalising and persistently strongly normalising λ-terms, where a λ-term M is persistently strongly normalising if for all n and all $X_1, \ldots, X_n \in \mathsf{SN}$ we get $MX_1 \ldots X_n \in \mathsf{SN}$. This inductive definition, which generalises the inductive definition of strongly normalising λ-terms given in [11], is interesting in itself. By means of this inductive definition, we can show that the persistently strongly normalising λ-terms are exactly the λ-terms which Honsell-Lenisa model [7] interprets as the top element, in the environment which associates the top element to all variables. Since for this proof we use a finitary logical description of Honsell-Lenisa model through intersection types, we will also obtain a characterisation of persistently strongly normalising λ-terms by means of typing. Such a characterisation was stated as an open problem in the conclusion of [4].

The present paper is organised as follows: Section 2 shows the "Substitution Theorem" for weak normalisation using a detailed analysis on how variables are substituted inside β-normal forms. Section 3 introduces the λ^*-calculus and associates to each λ^*-term a set of λ-terms. This allows us to prove the "Substitution Theorem" for strong normalisation. Section 4 presents the inductive definition of persistently strongly normalising terms and proves its soundness and completeness by using the "Substitution Theorem" for strong normalisation. Section 5 discusses Honsell-Lenisa model, and shows the characterisation of persistently strongly normalising λ-terms in that model via intersection types.

2 Weak Normalisation

We assume the standard definitions of λ-calculus and β-reduction, see [2], [6].

We use $x, y, z, w, t, u, v, \ldots$ to range over variables, and $M, N, L, P, X, Y, \ldots$ to range over λ-terms. We denote by Λ the set of λ-terms. In writing λ-terms we use vector notation as in [2], i.e. $\vec{M}$ denotes the sequence $M_1, M_2, \ldots, M_n$ for $n \geq 0$ and $\vec{M}$ is empty when $n = 0$; $\lambda \vec{x}.M\vec{N}$ is short for $\lambda x_1 \ldots x_n.MN_1 \ldots N_m$, where $\vec{x}$ is $x_1, \ldots, x_n$ and $\vec{N}$ is $N_1, \ldots, N_m$. If $\mathcal{A}$ is a set of λ-terms, $\vec{M} \in \mathcal{A}$ means $N \in \mathcal{A}$ for all $N \in \vec{M}$. By $M[x_1 := N_1, \ldots, x_n := N_n]$ and $M[\vec{x} := \vec{N}]$ we denote simultaneous capture-free substitutions. We use $\mathrm{lh}(\ )$ to denote the vector length. We assume the Barendregt convention [2] (page 26), i.e. that all names of bound variables are different from each other and different from those of the free variables.

For reduction: $\rightarrow_\beta$ is one step of β-reduction, and $\rightarrow^*_\beta$ is the reflexive transitive closure of the relation $\rightarrow_\beta$. We use $=$ to denote syntactical equality.

We recall that a λ-term is *weakly normalising* if it has a finite reduction sequence to normal form. Let WN be the *set of weakly normalising* λ-terms.

We want to show the following theorem, which allows us to substitute different λ-terms in WN, instead of the same λ-term in WN, for different variables preserving the weak normalisation property.

Theorem 2.1 (Substitution Theorem for WN**)**

1. *If* $M[x_i := X, x_j := X] \in \mathsf{WN}$ *for all* $X \in \mathsf{WN}$ *and for all* i, j $(1 \leq i, j \leq n)$*, then* $M[x_1 := X_1, \ldots, x_n := X_n] \in \mathsf{WN}$ *for all* $X_1, \ldots, X_n \in \mathsf{WN}$.
2. *If* $M[x_1 := X, \ldots, x_n := X] \in \mathsf{WN}$ *for all* $X \in \mathsf{WN}$*, then* $M[x_1 := X_1, \ldots, x_n := X_n] \in \mathsf{WN}$ *for all* $X_1, \ldots, X_n \in \mathsf{WN}$.

To this aim, following essentially [4], we say that a λ-term M is *persistently weakly normalising* if for all n and for all $X_1, \ldots, X_n \in \mathsf{WN}$ we get $MX_1 \ldots X_n \in \mathsf{WN}$. We denote by PWN the set of persistently weakly normalising λ-terms. A useful relation between WN and PWN is that the application of a λ-term in WN to a λ-term in PWN is a λ-term in WN. The proof is given in [4].

Lemma 2.2 *If $M \in \mathsf{WN}$ and $N \in \mathsf{PWN}$ then $MN \in \mathsf{WN}$.*

In the following, we do not allow α-conversion on β-normal forms: this allows us to identify bound variables by their names. Although we use this convention in our proofs, our results hold also for usual λ-calculus with α-conversion. We recall that a β-normal form has the shape $\lambda\overrightarrow{x}.y\overrightarrow{M}$. We denote by β-NF the set of β-normal forms.

We start by introducing the notions of *controls* and of *adjacent controls*. These notions simplify the notions of replacement paths and adjacent replacement paths of [4], respectively. Our aim is to understand which λ-terms we can substitute for free variables in normal forms in order to get non weakly normalising λ-terms. We consider some examples, where we use $\Delta = \lambda z.zz$. If $N_0 = xx$, we can choose $X = \Delta$, obtaining $N_0[x := X] = \Delta\Delta$. Instead, if $N_1 = x(\lambda x_1.x_1y)$, a suitable choice is $X = \lambda u.u\Delta$ and $Y = \Delta$, since $N_1[x := X, y := Y] = (\lambda u.u\Delta)(\lambda x_1.x_1\Delta) \to_\beta (\lambda x_1.x_1\Delta)\Delta \to_\beta \Delta\Delta$. It is important to notice that Δ is substituted for the (bound) variable x_1, since $\lambda u.u\Delta$ is substituted for the (free) variable x. Really we can substitute an arbitrary λ-term X_1 for x_1 in N_1 just by putting $X = \lambda u.uX_1$. We can then say that the (free) variable x *controls* the (bound) variable x_1 (notation $x \rightsquigarrow x_1$) in N_1. As another example we consider $N_2 = x(\lambda x_1.x_1(\lambda x_2.x_2y))$, for which a suitable choice is $X = \lambda v.v(\lambda u.u\Delta)$ and $Y = \Delta$. In N_2 the (free) variable x controls the (bound) variable x_1, and the (bound) variable x_1 controls the (bound) variable x_2: by transitivity the (free) variable x controls the (bound) variable x_2. Also in this example we can substitute an arbitrary λ-term X_2 for x_2 in N_2 just by putting $X = \lambda v.v(\lambda u.uX_2)$. In the above examples the two variable occurrences which "produce" $\Delta\Delta$ are xx, x_1y and x_2y, respectively. We can find appropriate substitutions also when the variable occurrences are separated by applications and/or abstractions, the necessary and sufficient requirement being that they occur as function and as argument, respectively. In this case we say that their controls are *adjacent*. For example, let $N_3 = xz(\lambda t.y)$: the controls $x \rightsquigarrow x$ and $y \rightsquigarrow y$ are adjacent in N_3. A suitable choice for N_3 is $X = \lambda uv.vu\Delta$ and $Y = \Delta$.

Definition 2.3 (Control) *1. The relation x* controls *y ($x \rightsquigarrow y$) in $N \in \beta$-NF is the smallest reflexive and transitive relation such that if $x\overrightarrow{L}(\lambda\overrightarrow{t}y.M)$ is a subterm of N then $x \rightsquigarrow y$ in N.*

2. If x controls y in $N \in \beta$-NF, then $x \rightsquigarrow y$ is a control *in $N \in \beta$-NF.*

Notice that if $x \rightsquigarrow y$ is a control in N then x occurs in N and y is bound in N, but y could not occur in N.

Example 2.4 *The set of controls in $N = \lambda y.x(\lambda v.vvy)(\lambda t.t(\lambda uz.xz))$ is $x \rightsquigarrow x$, $y \rightsquigarrow y$, $v \rightsquigarrow v$, $t \rightsquigarrow t$, $u \rightsquigarrow u$, $z \rightsquigarrow z$, $x \rightsquigarrow v$, $x \rightsquigarrow t$, $t \rightsquigarrow u$, $t \rightsquigarrow z$, $x \rightsquigarrow u$, $x \rightsquigarrow z$.*

Definition 2.5 *1. Two controls $x \rightsquigarrow z$ and $y \rightsquigarrow t$ in $N \in \beta$-NF are* adjacent *for $\{x, y\}$ in N if x, y are free in N and N contains a subterm of the shape $z\overrightarrow{M}(\lambda\overrightarrow{u}.t\overrightarrow{L})$.*

2. There are adjacent controls for $\overrightarrow{x}$ in $N \in \beta$-NF if there are adjacent controls for $\{x_i, x_j\}$ in N where $x_i, x_j \in \overrightarrow{x}$.

Notice that in the point (1) of the previous definition we do not require x, y, z, t be different variable names, so the set $\{x, y\}$ can contain only one element and the two controls can coincide. Moreover notice that x, y, z, t occur in N.

Example 2.6 *If N is defined as in Example 2.4, then the pairs of adjacent controls for $\{x\}$ are: $x \rightsquigarrow x$ and $x \rightsquigarrow v$, $x \rightsquigarrow v$ and $x \rightsquigarrow v$, $x \rightsquigarrow x$ and $x \rightsquigarrow t$, $x \rightsquigarrow t$ and $x \rightsquigarrow x$, $x \rightsquigarrow x$ and $x \rightsquigarrow z$.*

The first relation between adjacent controls and weak normalisation is stated in the following lemma, which is Lemma A.13 of [4] modulo the obvious mapping between controls and replacement paths.

Lemma 2.7 *If there are adjacent controls for $\{x\}$ in $N \in \beta$-NF, then there is $X \in \beta$-NF such that $N[x := X] \notin \mathsf{WN}$.*

Example 2.8 *If N is defined as in Example 2.4, and $X = \lambda w.w\Delta$ and $\Delta = \lambda r.rr$, then $N[x := X] = \lambda y.X(\lambda v.vvy)(\lambda t.t(\lambda uz.xz)) \to_\beta \lambda y.(\lambda v.vvy)\Delta(\lambda t.t(\lambda uz.xz)) \to_\beta \lambda y.\Delta\Delta y(\lambda t.t(\lambda uz.xz))$.*

From the previous lemma we get:

Lemma 2.9 *If N is in β-NF and for all $X \in \mathsf{WN}$ we have $N[x := X, y := X] \in \mathsf{WN}$, then there are no adjacent controls for $\{x, y\}$ in N.*

PROOF. Assume that there are adjacent controls for $\{x, y\}$ in N, then there are adjacent controls for $\{x\}$ in $N[y := x]$. By Lemma 2.7, there is $X \in \mathsf{WN}$ such that $N[y := x][x := X] \notin \mathsf{WN}$, that is, $N[x := X, y := X] \notin \mathsf{WN}$, and this gives a contradiction. □

The key result for proving the "Substitution Theorem" is the reverse of Lemma 2.9. The formulation of the following lemma underlines that, in order to characterise the β-normal forms which remain in WN after variable substitutions, we need also to characterise the β-normal forms which remain in PWN after variable substitutions.

Lemma 2.10 (Key Lemma) *1. If there are no adjacent controls for $\overrightarrow{x}$ in $N \in \beta$-NF, then $N[\overrightarrow{x} := \overrightarrow{X}] \in \mathsf{WN}$ for all $\overrightarrow{X} \in \mathsf{WN}$.*

2. *If* $N = \lambda\vec{y}.z\vec{L} \in \beta$-NF, *and there are no adjacent controls for* $\vec{x}, \vec{y}$ *in* $\vec{L}$, *and* $z \notin \vec{x}, \vec{y}$, *then* $N[\vec{x} := \vec{X}] \in$ PWN *for all* $\vec{X} \in$ WN.

PROOF. We show (1) and (2) simultaneously by induction on N. Let $\vec{x} = x_1, \ldots, x_n$ and $N = \lambda\vec{y}.z\vec{L}$.

If $z \notin \vec{x}$ we have $N[\vec{x} := \vec{X}] = \lambda\vec{y}.z\vec{L}[\vec{x} := \vec{X}]$. Since there are no adjacent controls for $\vec{x}$ in $\vec{L}$, by induction hypothesis on (1) $\vec{L}[\vec{x} := \vec{X}] \in$ WN, so we are done for (1). Moreover, if $z \notin \vec{y}$, there are no adjacent controls for $\vec{x}, \vec{y}$ in $\vec{L}$ and $\mathrm{lh}(\vec{y}) = \mathrm{lh}(\vec{Y})$, we have $N[\vec{x} := \vec{X}]\vec{Y}\vec{Z} = z\vec{L}[\vec{x} := \vec{X}][\vec{y} := \vec{Y}]\vec{Z}$ for all $\vec{Y}, \vec{Z} \in$ WN. By induction hypothesis on (1) $\vec{L}[\vec{x} := \vec{X}][\vec{y} := \vec{Y}] \in$ WN, and therefore we conclude (2).

If $z = x_h$ $(1 \leq h \leq n)$ we have $N[\vec{x} := \vec{X}] = \lambda\vec{y}.X_h\vec{L}[\vec{x} := \vec{X}]$. Let $Q = \lambda\vec{u}.v\vec{P} \in \vec{L}$ with $\mathrm{lh}(\vec{u}) = m$. We can observe that $v \notin \vec{x}, \vec{u}$, since otherwise $x_h \rightsquigarrow x_h$ and $v \rightsquigarrow v$ or $x_h \rightsquigarrow x_h$ and $x_h \rightsquigarrow v$ would be adjacent controls for $\vec{x}$ in N. Moreover, there are no adjacent controls $u_i \rightsquigarrow w_1$ and $u_j \rightsquigarrow w_2$ for $\{u_i, u_j\}$ $(1 \leq i, j \leq m)$ in $\vec{P}$, since otherwise $x_h \rightsquigarrow w_1$ and $x_h \rightsquigarrow w_2$ would be adjacent controls for $\{x_h\}$ in N. Lastly, there are no adjacent controls $x_i \rightsquigarrow w_1$ and $u_j \rightsquigarrow w_2$ for $\{x_i, u_j\}$ $(1 \leq j \leq n, 1 \leq j \leq m)$ in $\vec{P}$, since otherwise $x_i \rightsquigarrow w_1$ and $x_h \rightsquigarrow w_2$ would be adjacent controls for $\{x_i, x_h\}$ in N. Thus, there are no adjacent controls for $\vec{x}, \vec{u}$ in $\vec{P}$. Therefore by induction hypothesis on (2) we get $Q[\vec{x} := \vec{X}] \in$ PWN. From Lemma 2.2 we conclude $X_h\vec{L}[\vec{x} := \vec{X}] \in$ WN for all for all $X_1, \ldots, X_n \in$ WN. □

We can now show the "Substitution Theorem".

PROOF OF THEOREM 2.1. We show (1), being the proof of (2) almost the same. Let $\vec{x} = x_1, \ldots, x_n$ and N be the β-normal form of M. By Lemma 2.9 there are no adjacent controls for any $\{x_i, x_j\}$ $(1 \leq i, j \leq n)$ in N. Hence there are no adjacent controls for $\vec{x}$. By Lemma 2.10(1) we get $N[\vec{x} := \vec{X}] \in$ WN for all $\vec{X} \in$ WN. Since $M[\vec{x} := \vec{X}]$ reduces to $N[\vec{x} := \vec{X}]$, we have $M[\vec{x} := \vec{X}] \in$ WN for all $\vec{X} \in$ WN. □

From Theorem 2.1(2) we get the claim (2) of the introduction

Corollary 2.11 *If* $M\underbrace{X \ldots X}_{n} \in$ WN *for all* $X \in$ WN, *then* $MX_1 \ldots X_n \in$ WN *for all* $X_1, \ldots, X_n \in$ WN.

3 Strong Normalisation

We recall that a λ-term is *strongly normalising* if all reductions starting from it are finite. Let SN be the *set of strongly normalising* λ-terms.

In the proof of the "Substitution Theorem" for weak normalisation, Theorem 2.1, the β-normal forms have played a crucial role. The reason is that in studying weak normalisation we can freely substitute the β-normal form of a weakly normalising λ-term for the term itself, and look at its adjacent controls. This is not true for strong normalisation, since strong normalisation is not invariant under β-conversion. So to properly deal with strong normalisation we need to consider "non-erasing" reductions in the λ-calculus. There are many ways of formalising "non-erasing" reductions in the λ-calculus, for a survey see [12] and [8]. We consider the variant of Klop's calculus [9] proposed by Boudol in [3]. We call it λ^*-calculus.

The present section is organised as follows: first we introduce λ^*-calculus in Subsection 3.1, then we associate to each λ^*-term a set of λ-terms (called "projections") which share computational properties with the original λ^*-term (Subsection 3.2) and lastly we show the "Substitution Theorem" for strong normalisation (Subsection 3.3).

3.1 λ^*-calculus

Following [9], we extend the syntax of λ-terms with a pairing operator [,], i.e. we have the following syntax for the set Λ^* of λ^*-terms:

$$S ::= x \mid \lambda x.S \mid SS \mid [S, S].$$

We use $S, T, U, V, P, Q, R, K, X, Y$ to range over λ^*-terms. Let $[S, T_1, \ldots, T_n]$ and $[S, \vec{T}]$ be short for $[\ldots[[S, T_1], T_2], \ldots T_n]$: they become S for $n = 0$ and $\vec{T}$ empty.

On Λ^* Boudol [3] defines the following reduction rules:

$$[\lambda x.S, U_1, \ldots, U_n]T \rightarrow_\kappa [S[x := T], U_1, \ldots, U_n] \quad \text{if } x \in \mathrm{FV}(S)$$
$$[\lambda x.S, U_1, \ldots, U_n]T \rightarrow_\kappa [S, U_1, \ldots, U_n, T] \quad \text{if } x \notin \mathrm{FV}(S)$$

where FV( ) is the set of the free variables.

The relation $\rightarrow_\kappa$ is the contextual closure of these rules, and the relation $\rightarrow_\kappa^*$ is the reflexive transitive closure of $\rightarrow_\kappa$.

For example $\mathbf{BO}\Delta \rightarrow_\kappa (\lambda yz.\mathbf{O}(yz))\Delta \rightarrow_\kappa \lambda z.\mathbf{O}(\Delta z) \rightarrow_\kappa \lambda z.[\lambda t.t, \Delta z] \rightarrow_\kappa \lambda z.[\lambda t.t, zz]$, where $\mathbf{B} = \lambda xyz.x(yz)$, $\mathbf{O} = \lambda vt.t$, $\Delta = \lambda u.uu$.

A λ^*-term K is a κ-normal form if there does not exist a λ^*-term S such that $K \rightarrow_\kappa S$. We use κ-NF to denote the set of κ-normal forms.

The notions of weakly and strongly κ-normalizing λ^*-terms are defined in a similar way to the corresponding notions for λ-terms. WN* and SN* are the set of weakly and strongly κ-normalizing λ^*-terms, respectively. In [3] Boudol showed:

Theorem 3.1 *1.* SN* = WN*.

2. SN $\supseteq$ SN* $\cap\, \Lambda$.

As expected the reverse of Theorem 3.1(2) also holds, as proved in Theorem 3.3 using the following lemma.

Lemma 3.2 *$S\overrightarrow{U} \in \mathsf{SN}^*$ and $T \in \mathsf{SN}^*$ imply $[S,T]\overrightarrow{U} \in \mathsf{SN}^*$.*

PROOF. Assume ad absurd that there is an infinite reduction out of $[S,T]\overrightarrow{U}$. This implies that there is an infinite reduction out of either $S\overrightarrow{U}$ or T. □

Theorem 3.3 $\mathsf{SN} \subseteq \mathsf{SN}^*$.

PROOF. The proof is by a double induction on the longest β-reduction of M to normal form (denoted by $|M|$) and on the structure of M.

If $M = \lambda\overrightarrow{x}.x\overrightarrow{N}$, then $N \in \mathsf{SN}$ for all $N \in \overrightarrow{N}$. Since $|N| \leq |M|$, by induction hypothesis we get $N \in \mathsf{SN}^*$, so we conclude $M \in \mathsf{SN}^*$.

If $M = \lambda\overrightarrow{x}.(\lambda y.P)Q\overrightarrow{N}$, then $\lambda\overrightarrow{x}.P[y := Q]\overrightarrow{N} \in \mathsf{SN}$ and $Q \in \mathsf{SN}$. Since $|\lambda\overrightarrow{x}.P[y := Q]\overrightarrow{N}| < |M|$ and $|Q| < |M|$, by induction hypothesis we get $\lambda\overrightarrow{x}.P[y := Q]\overrightarrow{N} \in \mathsf{SN}^*$ and $Q \in \mathsf{SN}^*$. If $y \in \mathrm{FV}(P)$, we have $M \to_\kappa \lambda\overrightarrow{x}.P[y := Q]\overrightarrow{N}$, which implies $M \in \mathsf{SN}^*$ by Theorem 3.1(1). Otherwise, if $y \notin \mathrm{FV}(P)$, we have $M \to_\kappa \lambda\overrightarrow{x}.[P,Q]\overrightarrow{N}$, which implies $M \in \mathsf{SN}^*$ by Lemma 3.2. □

Analogously to the weak case, we also consider the set PSN^* of *persistently strongly normalising* λ^*-terms. A λ^*-term S is persistently strongly normalising if S preserves the strong κ-normalisation property under application to strongly κ-normalising λ^*-terms, i.e. $S \in \mathsf{PSN}^*$ if for all n and all $X_1, \ldots, X_n \in \mathsf{SN}^*$, we get $SX_1 \ldots X_n \in \mathsf{SN}^*$.

We need to show that the pairing of a λ^*-term in PSN^* with a λ^*-term in SN^* remains in PSN^* and that the application of a λ^*-term in SN^* to a λ^*-term in PSN^* remains in SN^*: these are the claims of the following lemma, respectively.

Lemma 3.4 *1. $S \in \mathsf{PSN}^*$ and $T \in \mathsf{SN}^*$ imply $[S,T] \in \mathsf{PSN}^*$.*

2. $S \in \mathsf{SN}^*$ and $T \in \mathsf{PSN}^*$ imply $ST \in \mathsf{SN}^*$.

PROOF. (1) Immediate from Lemma 3.2.

(2) First we show that $U \in \mathsf{SN}^*$ and $T \in \mathsf{PSN}^*$ imply $U[x := T] \in \mathsf{SN}^*$. By Theorem 3.1(1), we can suppose $U, T \in \kappa\text{-}\mathsf{NF}$. Using (1) and by structural induction on U we have the claim. Then (2) is immediate by letting U be Sx, where x is fresh. □

Clearly Lemma 3.4(2) is analogous to Lemma 2.2.

3.2 Projections

In this subsection we associate to each λ^*-term S a set of λ-terms (called the *projections* of S) which are built out of subterms of S in order to represent all possible κ-reductions of S by β-reductions.

In the next definition we use the following notation for sets $\mathcal{A}, \mathcal{B}$ of λ-terms:

$$\begin{array}{lcl} \lambda x.\mathcal{A} & = & \{\lambda x.M \mid M \in \mathcal{A}\}, \\ \mathcal{AB} & = & \{MN \mid M \in \mathcal{A}, N \in \mathcal{B}\}, \\ a\mathcal{A} & = & \{aM \mid M \in \mathcal{A}\}. \end{array}$$

Definition 3.5 *Fix a fresh variable a. The set of projections of S with respect to a (notation $\mathcal{P}_a(S)$) is defined by induction on S as follows:*

$$\begin{array}{lcl} \mathcal{P}_a(x) & = & \{x\} \\ \mathcal{P}_a(\lambda x.S) & = & \lambda x.\mathcal{P}_a(S) \\ \mathcal{P}_a(ST) & = & \mathcal{P}_a(S)\mathcal{P}_a(T) \\ \mathcal{P}_a([S,T]) & = & \mathcal{P}_a(S) \cup a\mathcal{P}_a(T). \end{array}$$

For example, we have $\mathcal{P}_a(\lambda x.[x,y][zx,wx]) = \{\lambda x.x(zx), \lambda x.x(a(wx)), \lambda x.ay(zx), \lambda x.ay(a(wx))\}$.

We want to prove that projections agree with substitutions and that if a κ-term S has a projection which is not strongly β-normalising, then also S is not strongly κ-normalising. These are the claims of the following lemma.

Lemma 3.6 *1. If $M \in \Lambda$, then $\mathcal{P}_a(M) = \{M\}$.*

2. If $M \in \mathcal{P}_a(S)$ and $N \in \mathcal{P}_a(T)$, then $M[x := N] \in \mathcal{P}_a(S[x := T])$.

3. If $S \in \mathsf{SN}^*$, then $\mathcal{P}_a(S) \subseteq \mathsf{SN}$.

PROOF. (1) is immediate by definition.

(2) is easily proved by induction on S.

(3) First we will show the auxiliary claim: if $M \in \mathcal{P}_a(S)$ and $M \to_\beta M'$, then there exists S' such that $S \to_\kappa S'$ and $M' \in \mathcal{P}_a(S')$. This is proved by induction on S. The interesting case is $S = S_1S_2$, $M = (\lambda x.M_3)M_2$, and $M' = M_3[x := M_2]$. Then we have $\lambda x.M_3 \in \mathcal{P}_a(S_1)$ and $M_2 \in \mathcal{P}_a(S_2)$. Hence $S_1 = [\lambda x.S_3, \overrightarrow{S_4}]$ and $M_3 \in \mathcal{P}_a(S_3)$. Case 1. If $x \in \mathrm{FV}(S_3)$, we can choose $S' = [S_3[x := S_2], \overrightarrow{S_4}]$. By (2), $M' \in \mathcal{P}_a(S_3[x := S_2]) \subseteq \mathcal{P}_a(S')$.
Case 2. If $x \notin \mathrm{FV}(S_3)$, then $x \notin \mathrm{FV}(M_3)$, because we can easily show by induction on S that $x \in \mathrm{FV}(M) \in \mathcal{P}_a(S)$ implies $x \in \mathrm{FV}(S)$. Then we have $M' = M_3$ and we can choose $S' = [S_3, \overrightarrow{S_4}, S_2]$. This concludes the proof of the auxiliary claim.

Assume $M \in \mathcal{P}_a(S)$ and $M \notin \mathsf{SN}$. We have an infinite reduction sequence $M = M_0 \to_\beta M_1 \to_\beta M_2 \to_\beta \ldots$. By the auxiliary claim, we have an infinite reduction sequence $S = S_0 \to_\kappa S_1 \to_\kappa S_2 \to_\kappa \ldots$ such that $M_i \in \mathcal{P}_a(S_i)$ for all i. Hence $S \notin \mathsf{SN}^*$. □

3.3 Substitution Theorem

Some further notational conventions are handy in the following treatment. We use $\lambda_{\overrightarrow{T}}\overrightarrow{x}.S$ as short for $[\lambda\overrightarrow{x}.S, \overrightarrow{T}]$: it becomes $[S, \overrightarrow{T}]$ for $\overrightarrow{x}$ empty. We *ambiguously* denote by $S\overrightarrow{T}$ either ST

or $[S,T]$. For example, $[\lambda_{S_1,S_2}xy.xS_3\overline{S_4}S_5,S_6]$ stands for $[[[\lambda xy.xS_3S_4S_5,S_1],S_2],S_6]$ or $[[[\lambda xy.[xS_3,S_4]S_5,S_1],S_2],S_6]$.

We can characterise the set of κ-normal forms K by

$$K ::= J \mid \lambda x.K \mid [K,K]$$
$$J ::= x \mid JK \mid [J,K]$$

One can show by induction on the definitions that these λ^*-terms are irreducible and by induction on Λ^* that all irreducible λ^*-terms have this shape. By the vector notation, we have $K ::= \overrightarrow{\lambda_{\overrightarrow{K}}\overrightarrow{x}}.J$. By the bar notation, we have $J ::= x \mid J\overline{K}$. Again by the vector notation, we have $J ::= x\overrightarrow{\overline{K}}$. Finally we get the following lemma, which characterises the shape of κ-normal forms.

Lemma 3.7 *The set* κ-NF *is defined by*

$$K ::= \overrightarrow{\lambda_{\overrightarrow{K}}\overrightarrow{x}}.x\overrightarrow{\overline{K}}.$$

For example, $\lambda x.\lambda_x y.\lambda_y z.z\overline{yx}$ represents one of the following κ-normal forms: $\lambda x.[\lambda y.[\lambda z.zyx,y],x]$, $\lambda x.[\lambda y.[\lambda z.[z,y]x,y],x]$, $\lambda x.[\lambda y.[\lambda z.[zy,x],y],x]$, and $\lambda x.[\lambda y.[\lambda z.[[z,y],x],y],x]$.

The next lemma (easily proved by structural induction) gives a clue to analyse controls in κ-NF through controls in β-NF.

Lemma 3.8 *If* $K \in \kappa$-NF, *then* $\mathcal{P}_a(K) \subseteq \beta$-NF.

We can then define the set of controls in a κ-normal form as the union of the sets of controls in its projections.

Definition 3.9 *The* adjacent controls *for* $\overrightarrow{x}$ *in* K *are the adjacent controls for* $\overrightarrow{x}$ *in* M *for some* $M \in \mathcal{P}_a(K)$.

The next lemma extends Lemma 2.9 to λ^*-calculus.

Lemma 3.10 *If* $K \in \kappa$-NF *and* $K[x := X, y = X] \in \mathsf{SN}^*$ *for all* $X \in \beta$-NF, *then there are no adjacent controls for* $\{x,y\}$ *in* K.

PROOF. Assume ad absurdum that there exists $M \in \mathcal{P}_a(K)$ such that there are adjacent controls for $\{x,y\}$ in M. By Lemma 2.9, there exists $X \in \beta$-NF such that $M[x := X, y := X] \notin \mathsf{WN}$. Then we have $M[x := X, y := X] \notin \mathsf{SN}$. By Lemma 3.6(1), we have $X \in \mathcal{P}_a(X)$. Then by Lemma 3.6(2) we get $M[x := X, y := X] \in \mathcal{P}_a(K[x := X, y := X])$. By Lemma 3.6(3) we conclude $K[x := X, y := X] \notin \mathsf{SN}^*$. □

The next lemma is the key lemma to prove the "Substitution Theorem " for strong normalisation. It is the extension of Lemma 2.10 to κ-normal forms.

Lemma 3.11 (Key Lemma) *1. If there are no adjacent controls for* $\overrightarrow{x}$ *in* $K \in \kappa$-NF, *then* $K[\overrightarrow{x} := \overrightarrow{X}] \in \mathsf{SN}^*$ *for all* $\overrightarrow{X} \in \mathsf{SN}^*$.

2. If $K = \overrightarrow{\lambda_{\overrightarrow{T}}\overrightarrow{y}}.z\overrightarrow{\overline{S}}$, *there are no adjacent controls for* $\overrightarrow{x}, \overrightarrow{y}$ *in* $\overrightarrow{\overrightarrow{T}}, z\overrightarrow{\overline{S}}$, *and* $z \notin \overrightarrow{x}, \overrightarrow{y}$, *then* $K[\overrightarrow{x} := \overrightarrow{X}] \in \mathsf{PSN}^*$ *for all* $\overrightarrow{X} \in \mathsf{SN}^*$.

PROOF. We use two mappings from the set of λ^*-terms of the shape $x\overrightarrow{\overline{S}}$ to sequences of λ^*-terms. These mappings, denoted by $^\circ$ and $^\times$, list up the arguments of variable applications and the second components of pairs, respectively. They are defined by induction as follows:

$$\begin{array}{ll} x^\circ = \epsilon & x^\times = \epsilon \\ (x\overrightarrow{\overline{S}}T)^\circ = (x\overrightarrow{\overline{S}})^\circ, T & (x\overrightarrow{\overline{S}}T)^\times = (x\overrightarrow{\overline{S}})^\times \\ ([x\overrightarrow{\overline{S}},T])^\circ = (x\overrightarrow{\overline{S}})^\circ & ([x\overrightarrow{\overline{S}},T])^\times = (x\overrightarrow{\overline{S}})^\times, T \end{array}$$

where ϵ denotes the empty sequence. For example, we have $([[xS_1S_2,S_3]S_4,S_5])^\circ = S_1,S_2,S_4$ and $([[xS_1S_2,S_3]S_4,S_5])^\times = S_3,S_5$.

We show (1) and (2) simultaneously by induction on K. Let $\overrightarrow{x} = x_1,\ldots,x_n$ and $K = \overrightarrow{\lambda_{\overrightarrow{T}}\overrightarrow{y}}.z\overrightarrow{\overline{S}}$. First let us observe that, by the definitions of projections, if $\overrightarrow{\lambda_{\overrightarrow{T}}\overrightarrow{y}}$ is $\lambda_{\overrightarrow{T}_1}\overrightarrow{y}_1\ldots\lambda_{\overrightarrow{T}_m}\overrightarrow{y}_m$, then:

$$\begin{array}{rcl} \mathcal{P}_a(K) & = & \{\lambda\overrightarrow{y}\mathcal{P}_a(z\overrightarrow{H}) \mid \overrightarrow{H} = (z\overrightarrow{\overline{S}})^\circ\} \cup \\ & & \{\lambda\overrightarrow{y_1}\ldots\overrightarrow{y_{j-1}}.a\mathcal{P}_a(J) \mid J \in \overrightarrow{T_j}\ (1 \le j \le m)\} \cup \\ & & \{\lambda\overrightarrow{y}a\mathcal{P}_a(J) \mid J \in (z\overrightarrow{\overline{S}})^\times\} \end{array}$$

Therefore, by the definitions of controls:

- if $\overrightarrow{H} = (z\overrightarrow{\overline{S}})^\circ$, then adjacent controls for $\overrightarrow{x}$ in $z\overrightarrow{H}$ are adjacent controls for $\overrightarrow{x}$ in K,
- adjacent controls for $\overrightarrow{x}$ in $\overrightarrow{\overrightarrow{T}}$ or in $(z\overrightarrow{\overline{S}})^\times$ are adjacent controls for $\overrightarrow{x}$ in K.

In the following we write U' as short for $U[\overrightarrow{x} := \overrightarrow{X}]$.

If $z \notin \overrightarrow{x}$ we have $K' = \overrightarrow{\lambda_{\overrightarrow{T'}}\overrightarrow{y}}.z\overrightarrow{\overline{S'}}$. Since there are no adjacent controls for $\overrightarrow{x}$ in $\overrightarrow{\overrightarrow{T}}$ and in $z\overrightarrow{\overline{S}}$, by induction hypothesis on (1) $\overrightarrow{\overrightarrow{T'}} \in \mathsf{SN}^*$ and $(z\overrightarrow{\overline{S'}})^\circ, (z\overrightarrow{\overline{S'}})^\times \in \mathsf{SN}^*$, so we conclude (1). Moreover, if $z \notin \overrightarrow{y}$, there are no adjacent controls for $\overrightarrow{x}, \overrightarrow{y}$ in $\overrightarrow{\overrightarrow{T}}, z\overrightarrow{\overline{S}}$, and $\mathrm{lh}(\overrightarrow{y}) = \mathrm{lh}(\overrightarrow{Y})$, then for all $\overrightarrow{Y}, \overrightarrow{Z} \in \mathsf{SN}^*$ there exists some subsequence $\overrightarrow{V}$ of $\overrightarrow{Y}$ such that $K'\overrightarrow{Y}\overrightarrow{Z}$ reduces to $[z\overrightarrow{\overline{S''}}, \overrightarrow{T''_m}, \ldots, \overrightarrow{T''_1}, \overrightarrow{V}]\overrightarrow{Z}$, where U'' stands for $U'[\overrightarrow{y} := \overrightarrow{Y}]$ for any U. By induction hypothesis on (1) $(z\overrightarrow{\overline{S''}})^\circ, (z\overrightarrow{\overline{S''}})^\times, \overrightarrow{\overrightarrow{T''}}$ are in SN^*. By using Theorem 3.1 (1), $K'\overrightarrow{Y}\overrightarrow{Z}$ is in SN^*, and therefore we conclude (2).

If $z = x_h$ $(1 \le h \le n)$ we have $K' = \overrightarrow{\lambda_{\overrightarrow{T'}}\overrightarrow{y}}.X_h\overrightarrow{\overline{S'}}$. Notice that in this case the λ^*-terms belonging to $(x_h\overrightarrow{\overline{S'}})^\circ$

are arguments of X_h. Let $J \in \overrightarrow{\overrightarrow{T}}, (x_h\overrightarrow{\overrightarrow{S}})^{\times}$: by hypothesis there are no adjacent controls for $\vec{x}$ in J, so by induction hypothesis on (1) we get $J' \in \mathsf{SN}^*$. Let $H = \overrightarrow{\lambda_{\overrightarrow{Q}}\vec{u}.v\overrightarrow{\overrightarrow{P}}} \in (x_h\overrightarrow{\overrightarrow{S}})^{\circ}$. We can observe that $v \notin \overrightarrow{x}, \overrightarrow{u}$, since otherwise $x_h \leadsto x_h$ and $v \leadsto v$ or $x_h \leadsto x_h$ and $x_h \leadsto v$ would be adjacent controls for $\overrightarrow{x}$ in K. There are no adjacent controls $u_i \leadsto w_1$ and $u_j \leadsto w_2$ for $\{u_i, u_j\}$ $(1 \leq i, j \leq m)$ in $\overrightarrow{Q}, v\overrightarrow{\overrightarrow{P}}$, since otherwise $x_h \leadsto w_1$ and $x_h \leadsto w_2$ would be adjacent controls for $\{x_h\}$ in K. Moreover, there are no adjacent controls $x_i \leadsto w_1$ and $u_j \leadsto w_2$ for $\{x_i, u_j\}$ $(1 \leq i \leq n, 1 \leq j \leq m)$ in $\overrightarrow{Q}, v\overrightarrow{\overrightarrow{P}}$, since otherwise $x_i \leadsto w_1$ and $x_h \leadsto w_2$ would be adjacent controls for $\{x_i, x_h\}$ in K. Thus there are no adjacent controls for $\overrightarrow{x}, \overrightarrow{\overrightarrow{u}}$ in $\overrightarrow{Q}, v\overrightarrow{\overrightarrow{P}}$. Therefore by induction hypothesis on (2) we get $H' \in \mathsf{PSN}^*$. By applying Lemma 3.4(1) to all J' such that $J \in \overrightarrow{\overrightarrow{T}}, (x_h\overrightarrow{\overrightarrow{S}})^{\times}$ and Lemma 3.4(2) to all H' such that $H \in (x_h\overrightarrow{\overrightarrow{S}})^{\circ}$, we conclude $K' \in \mathsf{SN}^*$. □

Theorem 3.12 (Substitution Theorem for SN) *If $M[x_i := X, x_j := X] \in \mathsf{SN}$ for all $X \in \mathsf{SN}$ and for all i, j $(1 \leq i, j \leq n)$, then $M[x_1 := X_1, \ldots, x_n := X_n] \in \mathsf{SN}$ for all $X_1, \ldots, X_n \in \mathsf{SN}$.*

PROOF. Let $\overrightarrow{x} = x_1, \ldots, x_n$. Since $M \in \mathsf{SN}$, by Theorem 3.3 we have $M \in \mathsf{SN}^*$. Then there exists $K \in \kappa\text{-NF}$ such that $M \to_{\kappa}^* K$. Since $M[x_i := X, x_j := X] \in \mathsf{SN}$ for all i, j $(1 \leq i, j \leq n)$ and all $X \in \beta\text{-NF}$, by Theorem 3.3, we have $M[x_i := X, x_j := X] \in \mathsf{SN}^*$. Then we get $K[x_i := X, x_j := X] \in \mathsf{SN}^*$. By Lemma 3.10, there are no adjacent controls for $\{x_i, x_j\}$ in K for all i, j $(1 \leq i, j \leq n)$. Hence, there are no adjacent controls for $\overrightarrow{x}$ in K. By Lemma 3.11(1), for arbitrary $\overrightarrow{X} \in \mathsf{SN}^*$, we have $K[\overrightarrow{x} := \overrightarrow{X}] \in \mathsf{SN}^*$. By Theorem 3.1(1), we have $K[\overrightarrow{x} := \overrightarrow{X}] \in \mathsf{WN}^*$, and hence we have $M[\overrightarrow{x} := \overrightarrow{X}] \in \mathsf{WN}^*$. By Theorem 3.1(1), we get $M[\overrightarrow{x} := \overrightarrow{X}] \in \mathsf{SN}^*$, and then, by Theorem 3.1(2), we conclude $M[\overrightarrow{x} := \overrightarrow{X}] \in \mathsf{SN}$. □

Claim (3) of the introduction immediately follows by letting M be $Mx_1 \ldots x_n$ in previous theorem, since substitution preserves non strong normalisation.

Corollary 3.13 *If $M\underbrace{X \ldots X}_{n} \in \mathsf{SN}$ for all $X \in \mathsf{SN}$, then $MX_1 \ldots X_n \in \mathsf{SN}$ for all $X_1, \ldots, X_n \in \mathsf{SN}$.*

4 Inductive Definitions of PSN

We define the set PSN of *persistent strongly normalising* λ-terms as the set of λ-terms which preserve the strong normalisation property under application to strongly normalising λ-terms, i.e. $M \in \mathsf{PSN}$ if for all $X_1, \ldots, X_n \in \mathsf{SN}$ we get $MX_1 \ldots X_n \in \mathsf{SN}$.

$$\frac{\lambda\overrightarrow{x}.N \in \mathsf{SN}^\sharp_n \ (\forall N \in \overrightarrow{N}) \quad \mathrm{lh}(\overrightarrow{x}) = n \quad y \notin \overrightarrow{x}}{\lambda\overrightarrow{x}.y\overrightarrow{N} \in \mathsf{PSN}^\sharp}$$

$$\frac{\lambda\overrightarrow{x}.M[y := N]\overrightarrow{L} \in \mathsf{PSN}^\sharp \quad \lambda\overrightarrow{x}.N \in \mathsf{SN}^\sharp_n \quad \mathrm{lh}(\overrightarrow{x}) = n}{\lambda\overrightarrow{x}.(\lambda y.M)N\overrightarrow{L} \in \mathsf{PSN}^\sharp}$$

$$\frac{\lambda\overrightarrow{x}.N \in \mathsf{PSN}^\sharp \ (\forall N \in \overrightarrow{N}) \quad \mathrm{lh}(\overrightarrow{x}) = n \quad x \in \overrightarrow{x}}{\lambda\overrightarrow{x}.x\overrightarrow{N} \in \mathsf{SN}^\sharp_n}$$

$$\frac{\lambda\overrightarrow{x}.N \in \mathsf{SN}^\sharp_m \ (\forall N \in \overrightarrow{N}) \quad \mathrm{lh}(\overrightarrow{x}) = m \quad y \notin \overrightarrow{x}}{\lambda\overrightarrow{x}.y\overrightarrow{N} \in \mathsf{SN}^\sharp_n}$$

$$\frac{\lambda\overrightarrow{x}.N \in \mathsf{SN}^\sharp_n \quad \mathrm{lh}(\overrightarrow{x}) = n \quad \mathrm{lh}(\overrightarrow{y}) > 0}{\lambda\overrightarrow{x}\,\overrightarrow{y}.N \in \mathsf{SN}^\sharp_n}$$

$$\frac{\lambda\overrightarrow{x}.M[y := N]\overrightarrow{L} \in \mathsf{SN}^\sharp_n \quad \lambda\overrightarrow{x}.N \in \mathsf{SN}^\sharp_m \quad \mathrm{lh}(\overrightarrow{x}) = m}{\lambda\overrightarrow{x}.(\lambda y.M)N\overrightarrow{L} \in \mathsf{SN}^\sharp_n}$$

Figure 1. Definition of $\mathsf{PSN}^\sharp$ and $\mathsf{SN}^\sharp_n$.

The inductive definition of PSN which we will discuss in this section was inspired by the following inductive definition of SN given in [11]:

$$\frac{\overrightarrow{M} \in \mathsf{SN}}{x\overrightarrow{M} \in \mathsf{SN}} \qquad \frac{M \in \mathsf{SN}}{\lambda x.M \in \mathsf{SN}} \qquad \frac{M[x := N]\overrightarrow{L} \in \mathsf{SN} \quad N \in \mathsf{SN}}{(\lambda x.M)N\overrightarrow{L} \in \mathsf{SN}}$$

It is handy to consider the class SN_n of λ-terms which preserves the strong normalisation property under application to n strongly normalising λ-terms, i.e. $M \in \mathsf{SN}_n$ if for all $X_1, \ldots, X_n \in \mathsf{SN}$ we get $MX_1 \ldots X_n \in \mathsf{SN}$. Clearly $\mathsf{SN}_0 = \mathsf{SN}$. Figure 1 defines the sets $\mathsf{PSN}^\sharp$ and $\mathsf{SN}^\sharp_n$: in the remaining of the present section we will show that $\mathsf{PSN}^\sharp = \mathsf{PSN}$ and $\mathsf{SN}^\sharp_n = \mathsf{SN}_n$.

The first lemma shows easy properties of the sets SN and PSN.

Lemma 4.1 *1. $M \in \mathsf{SN}$ and $N \in \mathsf{PSN}$ imply $MN \in \mathsf{SN}$.*

2. Let $\mathrm{lh}(\overrightarrow{x}) = \mathrm{lh}(\overrightarrow{N})$, then $M[\overrightarrow{x} := \overrightarrow{N}]\overrightarrow{L} \in \mathsf{SN}$ and $\overrightarrow{N} \in \mathsf{SN}$ imply $(\lambda\overrightarrow{x}.M)\overrightarrow{N}\overrightarrow{L} \in \mathsf{SN}$.

PROOF. (1) We can now show by induction on L that $L \in \mathsf{SN}$ and $N \in \mathsf{PSN}$ imply $L[x := N] \in \mathsf{SN}$. Then we conclude taking L as Mx, where x is fresh.

(2) Assume ad absurd that there is an infinite reduction out of $(\lambda\overrightarrow{x}.M)\overrightarrow{N}\overrightarrow{L}$. This implies that there is an infinite reduction either out of $M[\overrightarrow{x} := \overrightarrow{N}]\overrightarrow{L}$ or out of $\overrightarrow{N}$. □

The following lemma, which is the key result for proving the completeness of the given inductive definition, uses in a crucial way the " Substitution Theorem" for SN, Theorem 3.12.

Lemma 4.2 *If* $\lambda\vec{x}.x\vec{N} \in \mathsf{SN}_n$, *where* $x \in \vec{x}$ *and* $\mathrm{lh}(\vec{x}) = n$, *then* $\lambda\vec{x}.N \in \mathsf{PSN}$ *for all* $N \in \vec{N}$.

PROOF. For arbitrary $\vec{X} \in \mathsf{SN}$ with $\mathrm{lh}(\vec{X}) = n$, we have $(x\vec{N})[\vec{x} := \vec{X}] \in \mathsf{SN}$. Suppose $\mathrm{lh}(\vec{N}) = m$ and $y \notin x\vec{N}$. By Theorem 3.12, $(y\vec{N})[\vec{x} := \vec{X}, y := Y] \in \mathsf{SN}$ holds for all $\vec{X}, Y \in \mathsf{SN}$. For N_i $(1 \leq i \leq m)$, we show $(\lambda\vec{x}.N_i)\vec{X}\vec{Z} \in \mathsf{SN}$ for arbitrary $\vec{X}$, $\vec{Z} \in \mathsf{SN}$. Let Y be $\lambda\vec{z}.z_i\vec{Z}$ and $\mathrm{lh}(\vec{z}) = m$. Then we have $(y\vec{N})[\vec{x} := \vec{X}, y := Y] = (\lambda\vec{z}.z_i\vec{Z})\vec{N}[\vec{x} := \vec{X}] \to_\beta^* N_i[\vec{x} := \vec{X}]\vec{Z}$. Hence $N_i[\vec{x} := \vec{X}]\vec{Z}$ is in SN. By Lemma 4.1(2), we have $(\lambda\vec{x}.N_i)\vec{X}\vec{Z} \in \mathsf{SN}$. Therefore $\lambda\vec{x}.N_i \in \mathsf{PSN}$. □

We can show now the soundness and completeness of the given inductive characterisations.

Theorem 4.3 $\mathsf{PSN}^\sharp = \mathsf{PSN}$ *and* $\mathsf{SN}_n^\sharp = \mathsf{SN}_n$.

PROOF. We will show that *the rules generate ONLY terms which satisfy the given conditions,* that is, $\mathsf{PSN}^\sharp \subseteq \mathsf{PSN}$ and $\mathsf{SN}_n^\sharp \subseteq \mathsf{SN}_n$. This claim is proved by induction on the formation rules. It suffices to show that the premises implies the conclusion in each rule without $\sharp$. For example for the rule

$$\frac{\lambda\vec{x}.N \in \mathsf{PSN}^\sharp \ (\forall N \in \vec{N}) \quad \mathrm{lh}(\vec{x}) = n \quad x \in \vec{x}}{\lambda\vec{x}.x\vec{N} \in \mathsf{SN}_n^\sharp}$$

we will show $(\lambda\vec{x}.x\vec{N})\vec{X} \in \mathsf{SN}$ for all $\vec{X} \in \mathsf{SN}$ of length n. By induction hypothesis, we have $\lambda\vec{x}.N \in \mathsf{PSN}$. Then $N[\vec{x} := \vec{X}] \in \mathsf{PSN}$. Let $x_j = x$. By Lemma 4.1(1), we have $X_j\vec{N}[\vec{x} := \vec{X}] \in \mathsf{SN}$. By Lemma 4.1(2), we have $(\lambda\vec{x}.x\vec{N})\vec{X} \in \mathsf{SN}$.

We will show that *the rules generate ALL terms which satisfy the given conditions,* that is, $\mathsf{PSN}^\sharp \supseteq \mathsf{PSN}$ and $\mathsf{SN}_n^\sharp \supseteq \mathsf{SN}_n$. First notice that the conclusions of the given rules cover all possible shapes of λ-terms, but $\lambda\vec{x}.x\vec{N}$ with $\mathrm{lh}(\vec{x}) = n$ and $x \in \vec{x}$ for both $\mathsf{PSN}^\sharp$ and $\mathsf{SN}_m^\sharp$ with $n < m$. This is sound since if $\Delta = \lambda x.xx$, $\Delta_k = \lambda y_1 \ldots y_k.\Delta$, $k = \mathrm{lh}(\vec{N})$, $\mathrm{lh}(\vec{\Delta_k}) = n$, $\mathrm{lh}(\vec{\Delta}) = m - n$, then $(\lambda\vec{x}.x\vec{N})\vec{\Delta_k}\vec{\Delta}$ does not have normal form.

The proof is by a double induction on the length of the longest reduction to normal form and on the structure of terms. We show that if the statement holds for the conclusion then it must hold for the premises in each rule without $\sharp$.

The most interesting case is that of the rule

$$\frac{\lambda\vec{x}.N \in \mathsf{PSN} \ (\forall N \in \vec{N}) \quad \mathrm{lh}(\vec{x}) = n \quad x \in \vec{x}}{\lambda\vec{x}.x\vec{N} \in \mathsf{SN}_n}$$

We begin with $\lambda\vec{x}.x\vec{N} \in \mathsf{SN}_n$ and this implies $\lambda\vec{x}.N \in \mathsf{PSN}$ for all $N \in \vec{N}$ by Lemma 4.2.

The proofs for the other rules immediately follow by using induction hypothesis. We show the case of the rule

$$\frac{\lambda\vec{x}.M[y := N]\vec{L} \in \mathsf{SN}_n \quad \lambda\vec{x}.N \in \mathsf{SN}_m \quad \mathrm{lh}(\vec{x}) = m}{\lambda\vec{x}.(\lambda y.M)N\vec{L} \in \mathsf{SN}_n}$$

We assume $n \geq m$, the proof for $n < m$ being similar. For all $\vec{X}, \vec{Y} \in \mathsf{SN}$ of lengths m, $n - m$, respectively, we get $(\lambda\vec{x}.(\lambda y.M)N\vec{L})\vec{X}\vec{Y} \in \mathsf{SN}$. Then we have $(\lambda y.M')N'\vec{L}'\vec{Y} \in \mathsf{SN}$, where P' denotes $P[\vec{x} := \vec{X}]$ for every λ-term P. Hence we get $M'[y := N']\vec{L}'\vec{Y} \in \mathsf{SN}$ and $N' \in \mathsf{SN}$. By Lemma 4.1(2), we have $(\lambda\vec{x}.M[y := N]\vec{L})\vec{X}\vec{Y} \in \mathsf{SN}$ and $(\lambda\vec{x}.N)\vec{X} \in \mathsf{SN}$. Therefore we conclude $\lambda\vec{x}.M[y := N]\vec{L} \in \mathsf{SN}_n$ and $\lambda\vec{x}.N \in \mathsf{SN}_m$.

The induction hypothesis applies since the λ-terms in the premises can either be obtained by reducing the λ-term in the conclusion or are smaller than the λ-term in the conclusion. □

5 The Model $\mathcal{H}L_\infty$

We start by recalling the definition of the $\mathcal{D}_\infty$-model $\mathcal{H}L_\infty$ introduced in [7] to analyse perpetual strategies in λ-calculus.

Let $\mathcal{D}_0$ be the three point lattice $\bot \sqsubseteq \mathsf{s} \sqsubseteq \top$ and $\mathcal{D}_1 = [\mathcal{D}_0 \to_\bot \mathcal{D}_0]$ be the set of strict continuous functions from $\mathcal{D}_0$ to $\mathcal{D}_0$, where a continuous function f is strict if $f(\bot) = \bot$.

Moreover let $\mathtt{i}_0$ be the initial projection defined by:

$$\mathtt{i}_0(\bot) = \bot \Rightarrow \bot \quad \mathtt{i}_0(\mathsf{s}) = \top \Rightarrow \mathsf{s} \quad \mathtt{i}_0(\top) = \mathsf{s} \Rightarrow \top$$

where $\mathsf{d}_1 \Rightarrow \mathsf{d}_2$ denotes the step function defined by $(\mathsf{d}_1 \Rightarrow \mathsf{d}_2)(\mathsf{e}) =$ if $\mathsf{e} \sqsupseteq \mathsf{d}_1$ then d_2 else $\bot$.

The *inverse limit construction* $\mathcal{H}L_\infty$ obtained starting from $\mathcal{D}_0$ and $\mathtt{i}_0$ is a model of the $\lambda\mathbf{I}$-calculus and of the $\lambda\mathbf{NK}$-calculus (see Definition 11 in [7]) as shown in [7].

The interpretation of λ-terms in $\mathcal{H}L_\infty$ is defined in the standard way:

$$[\![x]\!]_\rho = \rho(x)$$
$$[\![MN]\!]_\rho = \mathtt{F}[\![M]\!]_\rho[\![N]\!]_\rho$$
$$[\![\lambda x.M]\!]_\rho = \mathtt{G}(\lambda\mathsf{d} \in \mathcal{H}L_\infty.\text{ if } \mathsf{d} \neq \bot \text{ then } [\![\mathsf{M}]\!]_{\rho[\mathsf{d}/\mathsf{x}]} \text{ else } \bot)$$

where $(\mathtt{F}, \mathtt{G})$ is the strict retraction from $[\mathcal{H}L_\infty \to_\bot \mathcal{H}L_\infty]$ to $\mathcal{H}L_\infty$ induced by $\mathtt{i}_0$. We recall that a pair of functions (f, g) is a strict retraction from $\mathcal{D}$ to $\mathcal{E}$ if they satisfy all the

$$\sigma \leq \sigma \cap \sigma \qquad \sigma \cap \tau \leq \sigma \qquad \sigma \cap \tau \leq \tau$$
$$\sigma \leq \sigma',\ \tau \leq \tau' \Rightarrow \sigma \cap \sigma' \leq \tau \cap \tau'$$
$$\sigma' \leq \sigma,\ \tau \leq \tau' \Rightarrow \sigma \to \tau \leq \sigma' \to \tau'$$
$$(\sigma \to \tau) \cap (\sigma \to \zeta) \leq \sigma \to \tau \cap \zeta$$
$$\varphi \sim \omega \to \varphi \qquad \omega \sim \varphi \to \omega \qquad \omega \leq \varphi$$
$$\sigma \leq \sigma \qquad \sigma \leq \tau,\ \tau \leq \zeta \Rightarrow \sigma \leq \zeta$$

Figure 2. Type preorder

following conditions: f and g are continuous; $f : \mathcal{E} \to \mathcal{D}$; $g : \mathcal{D} \to \mathcal{E}$; $f \circ g = \mathrm{id}_{\mathcal{D}}$; $g \circ f(\bot_{\mathcal{E}}) = \bot_{\mathcal{E}}$.

As proved in [7], we can give a finitary logical description of $\mathcal{H}L_\infty$ using intersection types. In other words we can define an intersection type theory $\mathcal{HL}$ which is the Stone dual of $\mathcal{H}L_\infty$ in the sense of [1].

The *set of types* of $\mathcal{HL}$ is built out of the constants φ and ω by the arrow and intersection constructors:

$$\tau ::= \varphi \mid \omega \mid \tau \to \tau \mid \tau \cap \tau$$

We define a preorder relation on types whose axioms and rules are justified by:

- viewing "$\to$" as the function space constructor and "$\cap$" as set intersection,
- considering the types φ and ω in correspondence with the elements $\mathtt{s}, \top$, respectively, but reversing the partial order in $\mathcal{H}L_\infty$ (this correspondence will be made explicit by the mapping $\mathtt{m}$ defined below).

Figure 2 defines the preorder $\leq$: we write $\tau \sim \sigma$ as short for $\tau \leq \sigma$ and $\sigma \leq \tau$. It is easy to check by induction on $\leq$ that ω and φ are the smallest and the biggest types, respectively.

We recall that *filters* of types are sets of types upper closed and closed under intersection. Let $\mathcal{F}$ be the set of all filters: it is easy to check that $\mathcal{F}$ is an ω-algebraic complete lattice with respect to set theoretic inclusion, whose bottom element is the empty set, and whose top element is the set of all types. Moreover, as shown in [7], $\mathcal{F}$ is isomorphic to $\mathcal{H}L_\infty$ through the mapping:

$$\hat{\mathtt{m}}(X) = \bigsqcup_{\tau \in X} \mathtt{m}(\tau)$$

where $\mathtt{m}(\varphi) = \mathtt{s}$, $\mathtt{m}(\omega) = \top$, $\mathtt{m}(\tau_1 \to \tau_2) = \mathtt{m}(\tau_1) \Rightarrow \mathtt{m}(\tau_2)$, $\mathtt{m}(\tau_1 \cap \tau_2) = \mathtt{m}(\tau_1) \sqcup \mathtt{m}(\tau_2)$.

We recall the intersection type assignment system of [7]: the typing rules are shown in Figure 3. We denote by $\vdash$ derivability in this system.

We can now formulate Stone duality for the model $\mathcal{H}L_\infty$ as follows:

$$[\![M]\!]_\rho = \bigsqcup \{\mathtt{m}(\tau) \mid \exists \Gamma \models \rho . \Gamma \vdash M : \tau\}$$

$$\frac{(x{:}\sigma) \in \Gamma}{\Gamma \vdash x{:}\sigma}\ (\mathrm{Ax}) \qquad \frac{\Gamma, x{:}\sigma \vdash M : \tau}{\Gamma \vdash \lambda x.M : \sigma \to \tau}\ (\to \mathrm{I})$$

$$\frac{\Gamma \vdash M : \sigma \to \tau \quad \Gamma \vdash N : \sigma}{\Gamma \vdash MN : \tau}\ (\to \mathrm{E})$$

$$\frac{\Gamma \vdash M : \sigma \quad \sigma \leq \tau}{\Gamma \vdash M : \tau}\ (\leq) \qquad \frac{\Gamma \vdash M : \sigma \quad \Gamma \vdash M : \tau}{\Gamma \vdash M : \sigma \cap \tau}\ (\cap \mathrm{I})$$

Figure 3. Typing rules

where $\Gamma \models \rho$ if $x : \sigma \in \Gamma$ implies $\mathtt{m}(\sigma) \sqsubseteq \rho(x)$. This statement is proved in [7].

Let $\rho_\top$ be the environment which associates $\top$ to all variables. We can characterise strongly normalising and persistently strongly normalising λ-terms in the model $\mathcal{H}L_\infty$ as the λ-terms whose interpretation in the environment $\rho_\top$ is different from $\bot$ and equal to $\top$, respectively. I.e. we have:

Theorem 5.1 (Main Theorem) *1. A λ-term M is strongly normalising iff $[\![M]\!]_{\rho_\top} \neq \bot$.*

2. A λ-term M is persistently strongly normalising iff $[\![M]\!]_{\rho_\top} = \top$.

The proof of this theorem uses the above discussed isomorphism between $\mathcal{H}L_\infty$ and $\mathcal{F}$. The theorem in fact can be reformulated as follows:

Theorem 5.2 *Let $\Gamma_\omega = \{x{:}\omega \mid x \in Var\}$.*

1. A λ-term $M \in \mathsf{SN}$ iff $\Gamma_\omega \vdash M{:}\varphi$.

2. A λ-term $M \in \mathsf{PSN}$ iff $\Gamma_\omega \vdash M{:}\omega$.

The *if parts* of Theorem 5.2(1) and (2) are shown in [7] (see Definition 35 and the following discussion) by means of the realizability interpretation of intersection types $\mathcal{V}$ defined by:

$$\begin{array}{lcl} \mathcal{V}(\varphi) & = & \mathsf{SN} \\ \mathcal{V}(\omega) & = & \mathsf{PSN} \\ \mathcal{V}(\sigma \to \tau) & = & \{M \in \Lambda \mid \forall N \in \mathcal{V}(\sigma)\ MN \in \mathcal{V}(\sigma)\} \\ \mathcal{V}(\sigma \cap \tau) & = & \mathcal{V}(\sigma) \cap \mathcal{V}(\tau). \end{array}$$

The *only if parts* of Theorem 5.2(1) and (2) can be shown using the inductive definitions of SN_n and PSN given in Section 4, and the following properties of the type assignment system which are proved in [4] and [7], respectively.

Lemma 5.3 (Generation Lemma) *1. $\Gamma \vdash x : \tau$ iff there is σ such that $x{:}\sigma \in \Gamma$ and $\sigma \leq \tau$.*

2. $\Gamma \vdash MN{:}\tau$ iff there is σ such that $\Gamma \vdash M{:}\sigma \to \tau$ and $\Gamma \vdash N{:}\sigma$.

3. $\Gamma \vdash \lambda x.M{:}\sigma \to \tau$ iff $\Gamma, x{:}\sigma \vdash M{:}\tau$.

Theorem 5.4 (Subject Expansion) *If $\Gamma \vdash M[x := N] : \tau$ and $\Gamma \vdash N{:}\varphi$, then $\Gamma \vdash (\lambda x.M)N{:}\tau$.*

More precisely the proof of the only if part easily follows from the following lemma.

Lemma 5.5 *1. If $M \in \mathsf{PSN}^\sharp$, then $\Gamma_\omega \vdash M:\omega$.*

2. If $M \in \mathsf{SN}^\sharp_n$, then $\Gamma_\omega \vdash M:\varphi^n \to \varphi$ where $\varphi^n \to \varphi = \underbrace{\varphi \to \ldots \to \varphi}_{n} \to \varphi$.

PROOF. The proof is by induction on the formation rules of $\mathsf{SN}^\sharp_n$ and $\mathsf{PSN}^\sharp$. For example for the rule

$$\frac{\lambda\overrightarrow{x}.M[y := N]\overrightarrow{L} \in \mathsf{SN}^\sharp_n \quad \lambda\overrightarrow{x}.N \in \mathsf{SN}^\sharp_m \quad \mathrm{lh}(\overrightarrow{x}) = m}{\lambda\overrightarrow{x}.(\lambda y.M)N\overrightarrow{L} \in \mathsf{SN}^\sharp_n}$$

by induction we know that $\Gamma_\omega \vdash \lambda\overrightarrow{x}.M[y := N]\overrightarrow{L} : \varphi^n \to \varphi$ and $\Gamma_\omega \vdash \lambda\overrightarrow{x}.N : \varphi^m \to \varphi$. We assume $n \geq m$, the proof for $n < m$ being similar. By Lemma 5.3(3) we get $\Gamma_\omega, \overrightarrow{x} : \overrightarrow{\varphi} \vdash M[y := N]\overrightarrow{L} : \varphi^{n-m} \to \varphi$ and $\Gamma_\omega, \overrightarrow{x} : \overrightarrow{\varphi} \vdash N : \varphi$. By Lemma 5.3(2) there exists $\overrightarrow{\tau}$ such that $\Gamma_\omega, \overrightarrow{x} : \overrightarrow{\varphi} \vdash M[y := N] : \overrightarrow{\tau} \to \varphi^{n-m} \to \varphi$ and $\Gamma_\omega, \overrightarrow{x} : \overrightarrow{\varphi} \vdash L_i : \tau_i$ for $1 \leq i \leq h$, where $h = \mathrm{lh}(\overrightarrow{L})$. This implies $\Gamma_\omega, \overrightarrow{x} : \overrightarrow{\varphi} \vdash (\lambda y.M)N : \overrightarrow{\tau} \to \varphi^{n-m} \to \varphi$ by Theorem 5.4 and so we conclude $\Gamma_\omega \vdash \lambda\overrightarrow{x}.(\lambda y.M)N\overrightarrow{L} : \varphi^n \to \varphi$ by the rules ($\to$ E) and ($\to$ I). □

6 Concluding Remarks

We have shown that the computational behaviour of λ-term application does not depend on having as arguments copies of the same λ-term or different λ-terms when we restrict to weakly or strongly normalising arguments. We call this result "Substitution Theorem". As an application of the "Substitution Theorem" for strong normalisation, we proved the completeness of the inductive definitions of persistently strongly normalising terms given in Figure 1 and shown that for a λ-term M the following four conditions are equivalent:

1. $MX_1 \ldots X_n$ is strongly normalising for all n and all strong normalising $X_1, \ldots, X_n$.
2. $M \in \mathsf{PSN}^\sharp$ as defined in Figure 1.
3. $\Gamma_\omega \vdash M : \omega$ in the intersection type assignment system induced by the type theory $\mathcal{HL}$.
4. $[\![M]\!]_{\rho_\top} = \top$ in the model $\mathcal{H}L_\infty$.

The equivalence between the third condition and the fourth one was proved in [7] and the equivalence among all of them is new. In particular, the equivalence between the first condition and the third one has solved an open problem in the conclusion of [4]. After this submission, we found we could extend the discussion in this paper to Λ^*, and we proved the above equivalencies for Λ^* in [5].

As an application of the "Substitution Theorem" for weak normalisation we get that:

$$\exists X_1, \ldots, X_n \in \mathsf{WN}.MX_1 \ldots X_n \notin \mathsf{WN} \Rightarrow$$
$$\exists X \in \mathsf{WN}.M\underbrace{X \ldots X}_{n} \notin \mathsf{WN}$$

and similarly for strong normalisation. Therefore we plan to investigate consequences of this theorem in the study of infinite reductions.

Acknowledgements. We are grateful to Henk Barendregt, Flavio Corradini, Jan Willem Klop, Yukiyoshi Kameyama, and Makoto Kanazawa for stimulating discussions on the paper subject. We strongly improved on the submitted version thanks to the precious suggestions of careful referees.

References

[1] S. Abramsky. Domain Theory in Logical Form. *Annals of Pure and Applied Logic*, 51(1-2):1–77, 1991.

[2] H. P. Barendregt. *The Lambda Calculus: its Syntax and Semantics*. North-Holland, revised edition, 1984.

[3] G. Boudol. On Strong Normalization in the Intersection Type Discipline. In M. Hofmann, editor, *TLCA'03*, volume 2701 of *Lecture Notes in Computer Science*, pages 60 –74. Springer-Verlag, 2003.

[4] M. Dezani-Ciancaglini, F. Honsell, and Y. Motohama. Compositional Characterization of λ-terms using Intersection Types. *Theoretical Computer Science*, 340(3):459–495, 2005.

[5] M. Dezani-Ciancaglini and M. Tatsuta. A Behavioural Model for Klop's Calculus. In F. Corradini and C. Toffalori, editors, *Logic, Model and Computer Science*, ENTCS. Elsevier, 2006. to appear.

[6] J. R. Hindley and J. P. Seldin. *Introduction to Combinators and Lambda Calculus*. Cambridge University Press, 1986.

[7] F. Honsell and M. Lenisa. Semantical Analysis of Perpetual Strategies in λ-calculus. *Theoretical Computer Science*, 212(1-2):183–209, 1999.

[8] F. Kamareddine. Postponement, Conservation and Preservation of Strong Normalisation for Generalised Reduction. *Logic and Computation*, 10(5):721–738, 2000.

[9] J. W. Klop. *Combinatory Reduction Systems*. PhD thesis, Utrecht University, 1980. Appeared as Mathematical Centre Tracts 127, Kruislaan 413, 1098 SJ Amsterdam.

[10] R. P. Nederpelt. *Strong Normalisation for a Typed Lambda Calculus with Lambda Structured Types*. PhD thesis, Eindhoven University, 1973.

[11] P. Severi. *Normalisation in Lambda calculus and its Relation to Type Inference*. PhD thesis, Eindhoven University of Technology, 1996.

[12] M. Sørensen. Strong Normalization from Weak Normalization in Typed λ-calculi. *Information and Computation*, 133(1):37–71, 1997.

Keynote Session

Shaken Foundations or Groundbreaking Realignment? A Centennial Assessment of Kurt Gödel's Impact on Logic, Mathematics, and Computer Science

John W. Dawson, Jr.
Penn State York
jwd7@psu.edu

Abstract

The publication of Gödel's incompleteness theorems has frequently been portrayed as a devastating event, from which mathematics has not yet recovered. Yet those same theorems have also been hailed as proving that the powers of the human mind surpass those of any computer. Both those views, however, are caricatures. Gödel's impact on modern logic has been profound, but the incompleteness theorems did not cause widespread upset at the time of their publication, and subsequent mathematical work outside logic has hardly been affected by them. Nor is mathematics any less "secure" than it was before Gödel's work.

With hindsight, Kurt Gödel's birth on April 28, 1906 — ten days after the San Francisco earthquake — might be taken as an ominous portent. For the publication of his incompleteness theorems, twenty-five years later, has often been portrayed as a similarly devastating event: one that not only undermined Hilbert's program for securing the foundations of mathematics, but that showed the axiomatic method itself — the very basis of mathematical methodology — to be fundamentally inadequate for ascertaining all truths of arithmetic. The result, in the eyes of one eminent critic, was an irredeemable "loss of certainty" within mathematics.

On the other hand, another esteemed mathematician (over the protests of logicians) has repeatedly asserted that those same theorems imply that the human mind is inherently superior to any computer. So mathematicians will not be put out of work, and we need not fear the rise of artificial intelligence.

Neither of those accounts, however, withstands critical scrutiny. Gödel's impact on modern logic, and, less directly, on computer science, has certainly been profound. But the philosophical significance of his incompleteness theorems remains a subject of debate, and mathematical practice has hardly been affected by them. As for the claim that mathematics is less "secure" now than it was before Gödel's work, his proof that the axiom of choice is consistent with the other axioms of set theory effectively resolved one of the most contentious of the foundational issues that had concerned mathematicians during the early years of the twentieth century.

It is true that Gödel himself believed that the power of the human intellect transcends that of any machine; but he stopped short of asserting that that followed from his incompleteness results. He did argue, late in his life, that Turing had erred in his analysis of the mind/ mechanism question, by overlooking that "mind, in its use, is not static, but constantly developing". Perhaps he felt the need to criticize Turing's analysis because, in the end, he came to recognize , as Judson Webb has contended [4], that "the Church-Turing thesis itself is the principal bastion protecting mechanism".

1. Logic and foundations before Gödel

Modern logic began to take form in 1847, with the publication of George Boole's *The Mathematical Analysis of Logic.* During the subsequent decades of the nineteenth century Georg Cantor created naive set theory, Augustin Cauchy and Karl Weierstrass provided a rigorous foundation for analysis, Gottlob Frege and Charles S. Peirce independently developed quantification theory, and Guiseppe Peano put forward his informal axioms for the natural numbers, together with a proof that they characterized the natural numbers up to isomorphism.

Set theory, however, led to paradoxes, and there were unsettling events in mainstream mathematics as well — most notably the construction of "pathological" functions in analysis and the recognition both that non-Euclidean geometry was consistent and that Euclid's axioms were incomplete.

In response, Hilbert gave a new axiomatization

1043-6871/06 $20.00 © 2006 IEEE

for geometry, Frege attempted to provide a logical foundation for arithmetic, and Zermelo formulated his axioms for set theory, including the axiom of choice, which he used as the basis for his proof that the reals could be well-ordered. But Frege's effort was compromised by Bertrand Russell's discovery of the antinomy that now bears his name, and the axiom of choice, though it had been employed unconsciously in many arguments in analysis, became controversial once made explicit, not only because of its non-constructive character, but because it implied such extremely unintuitive consequences as the Banach-Tarski paradox.

For all those reasons, the perception that the foundations of mathematics were in crisis took root, leading to the development of rival philosophies of mathematics. While logicists attempted to subsume mathematics within an all-embracing logic, intuitionists rejected the Law of Excluded Middle and regarded mathematical results as meaningful only if they could be established constructively. Formalists, on the other hand, hoped to justify mathematics on the basis of syntactic considerations, applied to formalized statements whose meaning was disregarded.

Before Gödel's work, and for some time afterward, semantical considerations were considered suspect. There was no clear distinction between truth and provability and no agreement on how quantifiers were to be construed. Zermelo, for example, regarded universal quantifiers as representing infinitary conjunctions. And though Peano's axioms for arithmetic and Zermelo's for set theory were landmark achievements, neither Peano nor Zermelo formulated their axioms within a syntactic framework in which the rules of inference were precisely specified.

Not until 1928, in their book *Grundzüge der theoretischen Logik* [3], did David Hilbert and Wilhelm Ackermann single out first-order logic as a subsystem worthy of scrutiny and pose the question of its semantic completeness (whether all first-order formulas that are "correct in each domain of individuals" can be formally derived by the rules of inference of first-order logic).

2. The impact of Gödel's completeness and incompleteness theorems

Two years later, in the published version of his doctoral dissertation, Gödel answered that question affirmatively. Mathematically, the details of his proof were very similar to Thoralf Skolem's proof of the Löweneheim-Skolem theorem, which Skolem had published seven years before (but which Gödel had not seen at the time he wrote his dissertation). But the Löwenheim-Skolem theorem concerns satisfiability in structures, and no one before Gödel had drawn the connection between satisfiability and formal derivability. Moreover, as a lemma in his proof Gödel also established the countable compactness theorem (that a countable set of first-order sentences has a model if every finite subset of it does), a result which lay dormant for years but was eventually recognized as a cornerstone of model theory.

Then and later, Gödel's work was marked by a clarity of vision that others lacked. In particular, his awareness of the distinction between truth and provability was crucial not only to his completeness proof, but to the *in*completeness theorems for formal number theory that he obtained soon thereafter. Far from being an iconoclast who sought to overthrow Hilbert's program, Gödel had initially set out to *advance* it. Specifically (as he explained in a letter draft, written years later in response to a graduate student's inquiry), he had hoped to reduce the consistency of analysis to that of number theory by interpreting the set membership relation in terms of arithmetic definability. But his attempt failed when (independently of Tarski) he recognized that the notion of arithmetic *truth*, unlike that of formal derivability, cannot be formally defined within arithmetic.

To convince formalists of the correctness of his result, Gödel couched his incompleteness proof in purely syntactic terms (replacing the semantic notion of truth by the syntactic one of ω-consistency) — a strategy that, contrary to popular belief, succeeded very well. For although his result came as a shock to formalists, some of whom initially found his proof difficult to understand, it quickly gained acceptance.

Gödel was not the first to believe that there were formally undecidable statements. Both Emil Post and Paul Finsler had had the idea earlier. But Finsler's attempted exhibition of such a statement was not carried out in a *formal* framework (a concept he seems never really to have understood), and Post's unpublished ideas, as he forthrightly admitted in later correspondence with Gödel, lacked "the splendid actuality" of Gödel's proof.

Gödel's incompleteness paper revealed profound truths about the extent to which metatheoretical notions can and cannot be formalized within the theory to which they pertain, and his method of *arithmetization of syntax* was a seminal insight. In addition, in that same paper he introduced the class of functions now called *primitive recursive*, and in a later presentation he gave one of the several definitions of *general recursive function* (the equivalence of which was taken by most logicians — but not by Gödel himself — as evidence for Church's Thesis). Gödel must therefore be considered one of the founders of recursive function theory. His subsequent contributions to its development, however, are not comparable to those of Post, Stephen C. Kleene or Alan Turing.

As for mathematical practice, outside of logic the incompleteness theorems have had virtually no impact. Rightly enough, most mathematicians leave foundational concerns to logicians. And though the axiomatic method has served as the ideal of mathematical methodology from Euclid's time onward, in practice it has been honored largely in the breach. Apart from Euclidean geometry, almost no mathematics has been developed within a strict axiomatic framework. Much mathematical research focuses on the study of *particular* mathematical structures (groups, manifolds, topological spaces, etc.), and so is model-theoretic, rather than axiomatic, in character. Axioms, such as those for groups, are often used to delimit the class of structures under consideration, but they generally imply very little about the properties of particular structures that satisfy them.

The incompleteness theorems forced a reassessment of Peano's proof that his axioms characterized the natural numbers. (They do so only in their second-order formulation). They also showed how careful one had to be in distinguishing object language from metalanguage, and they placed strong constraints on the means used to carry out consistency proofs. They did *not*, however, demonstrate that persuasive consistency proofs for arithmetic are *impossible* (as many still erroneously believe). As logicians are well aware, Gerhard Gentzen gave the first such proof in 1936, and Gödel himself outlined another in his last published paper, which appeared in 1958.

3. Gödel's other work in logic

The 1958 paper had an important influence on subsequent constructive foundational work, and Gödel's consistency results for the axiom of choice and the continuum hypothesis (especially the method of inner models that he employed in his proofs, and his stress on finding axioms of infinity to settle questions left undecided by the Zermelo-Fraenkel axioms) likewise gave direction to later work in set theory.

Among his less well-known publications, Gödel made significant contributions to the study of solvable cases of the decision problem, as well as to intuitionistic mathematics (including his proof that if intuitionistic arithmetic is consistent, so is its classical counterpart). One of his shortest articles contained the seed from which modal provability logic later sprouted. And the mathematical Platonism he espoused remains a subject of lively debate among philosophers of mathematics.

In the pantheon of great mathematicians, only Riemann (who died at 39) published less than Gödel. Reclusive by nature, Gödel worked largely alone, lectured relatively little, and supervised no graduate students. Yet his work permanently altered the mathematical landscape.

References

[1] J.W. Dawson, *Logical Dilemmas: The Life and Work of Kurt Gödel.* A K Peters, Wellesley, Mass., 1997

[2] Kurt Gödel, *Collected Works* (5 vols,), ed. Solomon Feferman et al. Oxford University Press, New York and Oxford, 1986–2003.

[3] D. Hilbert and W. Ackermann, *Grundzüge der theoretishcen Logik.* Julius Springer, Berlin, 1928.

[4] J.C. Webb, *Mechanism, Mentalism and Metamathematics: An Essay on Finitism.* D. Reidel, Dordrecht, 1980.

Invited Talk

Provable Implementations of Security Protocols

Andrew D. Gordon
Microsoft Research

Proving security protocols has been a challenge ever since Needham and Schroeder threw down the gauntlet in their pioneering 1978 paper:

> Protocols such as those developed here are prone to extremely subtle errors that are unlikely to be detected in normal operation. The need for techniques to verify the correctness of such protocols is great, and we encourage those interested in such problems to consider this area. [12]

This may not seem such a grand challenge, at first, as most cryptographic protocols can be written in half a dozen lines and involve even fewer players; the twist is the intruder, who actively interferes with proceedings:

> We assume that an intruder can interpose a computer on all communication paths, and thus can alter or copy parts of messages, replay messages, or emit false material. [12]

Almost all of the many papers addressing the problem of attacks on security protocols fall into two groups. They either develop informal, though empirically based, methods for designing robust protocols, or they develop formal methods for reasoning about abstract models of protocols.

The work on informal methods attempts to discern common patterns in the extensive record of flawed protocols, and to formulate positive advice for avoiding each pattern [1, 2]. For example, Anderson and Needham propose an *Explicitness Principle*, that covers many classic errors:

> Robust security is about explicitness. A cryptographic protocol should make any necessary naming, typing and freshness information explicit in its messages; designers must also be explicit about their starting assumptions and goals, as well as any algorithm properties which could be used in an attack. [2]

Much of the work on formal methods has depended on the powerful idea, introduced by Dolev and Yao [9], of idealizing cryptographic operations such as encryption and decryption as a symbolic algebra. After intense effort on symbolic reasoning, there are now several techniques [8, 7] for automatically proving properties of protocols represented within a symbolic, algebraic model. On the other hand, the formal proofs used by cryptographers tend to rely on probabilistic computational models, which make fewer unwarranted assumptions than symbolic models, but typically lack automation. Justifying symbolic models via computational models (where possible), or simply developing automation for the latter, is a growing research area.

Although either the informal design principles or the automated formal tools would catch most design errors, they clearly only work if applied. As in other areas of software, the trouble is that while practitioners are typically happy for researchers to write formal models of their natural language specifications and to apply design principles, they are reluctant to do so themselves. In practice, specifications tend to be partial and ambiguous, and the implementation code is the closest we get to a formal description of most protocols.

This motivates the subject of my talk: the relatively new enterprise of adapting formal methods for security to work on code instead of abstract models. The goal is to lower the practical cost of security protocol verification by eliminating the need to write a separate formal model.

A step in this direction is to extract formal models from the configuration and policy files that govern security processing in some implementations. For example, we built a policy analyzer [3] for web services policy files; it compiles XML policies found in actual implementations into the TulaFale modelling language [5] for analysis. We found many bugs in user written policies; a simplified version of the research tool now ships in a product [4].

A step in a different direction is to compile formal models into implementation code. Several tools have successfully demonstrated this idea [13, 14]. The difficulty is that this approach involves growing a formal model into a full programming language, building a compiler, educating developers, and so on; overall, it seems cheaper to compile from an existing programming language into a formalism.

Goubault-Larrecq and Parrennes [10] were the first to build a tool to extract a formal model from the actual implementation code (in C) of a cryptographic protocol. They apply a pointer analysis together with an analysis of the messages the intruder can send and receive to construct a

1043-6871/06 $20.00 © 2006 IEEE

logical model of the program as a set of Horn clauses; these clauses can then be analyzed by other tools.

The main technical content of my talk will be recent work with Bhargavan, Fournet, and Tse [6] on extracting π-calculus models from protocol implementation code. Our software is developed in the functional language F# [15], a dialect of ML. A central idea for structuring the code to be analyzed, is to define typed interfaces for the low-level cryptographic and communication services used by the protocol. These interfaces include operations such as performing an encryption, verifying a signature, or sending a network message. We provide dual *concrete* and *symbolic* library implementations of these interfaces, against which we can build and run our protocol code. The concrete implementation of the cryptographic interface relies on the real cryptographic operations provided by the operating system, while the symbolic implementation is a Dolev-Yao style algebraic idealization. Binaries built from the concrete libraries are for interoperability testing with production implementations, or indeed for production use. Binaries built from the symbolic libraries are for initial symbolic debugging. For verification, we stipulate protocol properties such as authentication and secrecy in terms of correspondences between events. These correspondences are to hold in the presence of an intruder, much as described by Needham and Schroeder, that is able to initiate multiple sessions, to select protocol parameters, and to compromise key material. To prove these properties, we first compile the F# protocol code and symbolic libraries to the π-calculus. The core of the translation is Milner's interpretation of λ-calculus functions as π-calculus processes [11]. Given a π-calculus model of the protocol, we apply Blanchet's ProVerif theorem prover [7] to attempt to verify or refute each correspondence property automatically. Soundness of the method relies on a proof that the compilation from F# to the π-calculus preserves attacks. Hence, if ProVerif shows there is no attack at the π-calculus level, there can be no attack at the F# level. We had to implement several optimizations of Milner's compilation strategy for the translated π-calculus to be efficiently analyzed by ProVerif. For a suite of multi-message protocols, we have both demonstrated interoperability with existing production implementations, and successfully verified expected security properties. We verify all the protocol code written against the low-level cryptographic and communications interfaces. On the other hand, we trust but do not formally verify that the symbolic libraries are correct abstractions of the concrete libraries.

In both these projects on verifying implementation code [10, 6], the verified code has been written within the research group. A challenge remaining for further work, then, is to verify independently written implementations of cryptographic protocols, such as those in common operating systems and platforms.

References

[1] M. Abadi and R. Needham. Prudent engineering practice for cryptographic protocols. *IEEE Transactions on Software Engineering*, 22(1):6–15, 1996.

[2] R. Anderson and R. Needham. Programming Satan's computer. In J. van Leeuwen, editor, *Computer Science Today: Recent Trends and Developments*, volume 1000 of *LNCS*, pages 426–440. Springer, 1995.

[3] K. Bhargavan, C. Fournet, and A. D. Gordon. Verifying policy-based security for web services. In *11th ACM Conference on Computer and Communications Security (CCS'04)*, pages 268–277, Oct. 2004.

[4] K. Bhargavan, C. Fournet, and A. D. Gordon. Policy advisor for WSE 3.0. In *Web Service Security: Scenarios, patterns, and implementation guidance for Web Services Enhancements (WSE) 3.0*. Microsoft Press, 2006.

[5] K. Bhargavan, C. Fournet, A. D. Gordon, and R. Pucella. TulaFale: A security tool for web services. In *International Symposium on Formal Methods for Components and Objects (FMCO'03)*, volume 3188 of *LNCS*, pages 197–222. Springer, 2004.

[6] K. Bhargavan, C. Fournet, A. D. Gordon, and S. Tse. Verified interoperable implementations of security protocols. In *19th IEEE Computer Security Foundations Workshop (CSFW'06)*, 2006. To appear.

[7] B. Blanchet. An efficient cryptographic protocol verifier based on Prolog rules. In *14th IEEE Computer Security Foundations Workshop (CSFW'01)*, pages 82–96, 2001.

[8] E. Cohen. TAPS: A first-order verifier for cryptographic protocols. In *13th IEEE Computer Security Foundations Workshop*, pages 144–158. IEEE Computer Society Press, 2000.

[9] D. Dolev and A. Yao. On the security of public key protocols. *IEEE Transactions on Information Theory*, IT–29(2):198–208, 1983.

[10] J. Goubault-Larrecq and F. Parrennes. Cryptographic protocol analysis on real C code. In *6th International Conference on Verification, Model Checking and Abstract Interpretation (VMCAI'05)*, volume 3385 of *LNCS*, pages 363–379. Springer, 2005.

[11] R. Milner. Functions as processes. *Mathematical Structures in Computer Science*, 2(2):119–141, 1992.

[12] R. Needham and M. Schroeder. Using encryption for authentication in large networks of computers. *Commun. ACM*, 21(12):993–999, 1978.

[13] A. Perrig, D. Song, and D. Phan. AGVI – automatic generation, verification, and implementation of security protocols. In *13th Conference on Computer Aided Verification (CAV)*, LNCS, pages 241–245. Springer, 2001.

[14] D. Pozza, R. Sisto, and L. Durante. Spi2Java: automatic cryptographic protocol Java code generation from spi calculus. In *18th International Conference on Advanced Information Networking and Applications (AINA 2004)*, volume 1, pages 400–405, 2004.

[15] D. Syme. *F#*, 2005. Project website at `http://research.microsoft.com/fsharp/`.

Session 9:
Timed and Stochastic Systems

Stochastic Games with Branching-Time Winning Objectives

Tomáš Brázdil Václav Brožek Vojtěch Forejt Antonín Kučera
Faculty of Informatics, Masaryk University,
Botanická 68a, 60200 Brno,
Czech Republic.
{brazdil,xbrozek,xforejt,kucera}@fi.muni.cz

Abstract

We consider stochastic turn-based games where the winning objectives are given by formulae of the branching-time logic PCTL. These games are generally not determined and winning strategies may require memory and/or randomization. Our main results concern history-dependent strategies. In particular, we show that the problem whether there exists a history-dependent winning strategy in $1\frac{1}{2}$-player games is highly undecidable, *even for objectives formulated in the $\mathcal{L}(F^{=5/8}, F^{=1}, F^{>0}, G^{=1})$ fragment of PCTL. On the other hand, we show that the problem becomes decidable (and in fact* **EXPTIME***-complete) for the $\mathcal{L}(F^{=1}, F^{>0}, G^{=1})$ fragment of PCTL, where winning strategies require only finite memory. This result is tight in the sense that winning strategies for $\mathcal{L}(F^{=1}, F^{>0}, G^{=1}, G^{>0})$ objectives may already require infinite memory.*

1. Introduction

In this paper we consider stochastic turn-based games where the winning objectives are given by formulae of the branching-time logic PCTL. Formally, a $2\frac{1}{2}$-player game G is a finite directed graph where the vertices are partitioned into three subsets $V_\Box$, $V_\Diamond$, $V_\bigcirc$. A *play* is initiated by putting a token on some vertex. The token is then moved from vertex to vertex by two players, $\Box$ and $\Diamond$, who are responsible for selecting outgoing transitions in the vertices of $V_\Box$ and $V_\Diamond$, respectively. In the vertices of $V_\bigcirc$, outgoing transitions are chosen randomly according to a fixed probability distribution. A *strategy* specifies how a player should play. In general, a strategy may or may not depend on the history of a play (we say that a strategy is *history-dependent (H)* or *memoryless (M)*), and the transitions may be chosen deterministically or randomly (*deterministic (D)* and *randomized (R)* strategies). In the case of randomized strategies, a player chooses a probability distribution on the set of outgoing transitions. Note that deterministic strategies can be seen as restricted randomized strategies, where one of the outgoing transitions has probability 1. Each pair of strategies (σ, π) for players $\Box$ and $\Diamond$ determines a unique Markov chain $G(\sigma, \pi)$ where the states are finite paths in G, and $wu \to wuu'$ with probability x iff (u, u') is a transition in the game and x is the probability chosen by player $\Box$ or $\Diamond$ (when $u \in V_\Box$ or $u \in V_\Diamond$, respectively), or the fixed probability of the transition (u, u') when $u \in V_\bigcirc$. A *winning objective* for player $\Box$ is some property of Markov chains that is to be achieved. A *winning strategy* for player $\Box$ is a strategy σ such that for every strategy π of player $\Diamond$ the Markov chain $G(\sigma, \pi)$ has the desired property. Usually, the aim of player $\Diamond$ is to *falsify* this property, which means that his winning objective is dual. A winning strategy for player $\Diamond$ is a strategy π such that $G(\sigma, \pi)$ does *not* have the property for any strategy σ of player $\Box$. A game is *determined* if one of the two players has a winning strategy in every vertex. $1\frac{1}{2}$-player games are "restricted" $2\frac{1}{2}$-player games where $V_\Diamond = \emptyset$. All of the above introduced notions (except for determinacy) are applicable also to $1\frac{1}{2}$-player games.

Infinite games have been studied in various fields of mathematics and computer science (recently written overviews are, e.g., [16, 6]). For example, model-checking problems for certain temporal logics (such as the modal μ-calculus) can be naturally reformulated as the questions to determine the winner in parity games, and a lot of research effort has been invested into this problem. Our work is mainly motivated by applications of games in system design, where systems are modeled as games, player $\Box$ corresponds to a "controller" which determines the system behaviour in a subset of controllable states, player $\Diamond$ models the environment, and the winning objectives for player $\Box$ correspond to the desired property of the system. The task is to find a controller (a strategy σ for player $\Box$) such that the desired property holds no matter what the environment does (i.e., the strategy σ is winning). As for stochastic games, the majority of existing results concern games with *linear time* winning objectives which are specified by some property of runs in Markov chains. Examples include quantitative reachability objectives (the probability of all runs that hit a "good" state is at least ϱ), qualitative Büchi objectives (the probability of all runs along which a "good" vertex appears infinitely often is 1), qualitative/quantitative parity objectives [7, 8], Rabin and Street objectives [5], etc. In this paper we study *branching-time* objectives that are formalized as formulae of the branching-time probabilistic logic PCTL.

Previous and related work. In [1], it is shown that winning strategies for PCTL objectives may require memory and/or randomization in general. Hence, the MD, MR, HD, and HR strategies (see above) need to be considered separately. It is also proven that the problem whether there exists a winning MD strategy in a given $1\frac{1}{2}$-player game for a given PCTL objective is **NP**-complete. MR strategies were considered in [14], where it is shown that the existence of a winning MR strategy in a given $2\frac{1}{2}$-player game for a given PCTL objective is in **EXPTIME**. The construction also yields **PSPACE** upper bound for $1\frac{1}{2}$-player games.

To prevent misunderstanding, we should say that the logic PCTL can also be interpreted directly on games (or Markov decision processes). The decidability of the model-checking problem for stochastic games and PCTL was established in [9] as a simple consequence of the results about quantitative ω-regular games. However, this is a different problem which is not directly related to the subject of this paper (as we shall, the results about stochastic games with branching-time winning objectives are quite different from the results about model-checking).

Main results. We start by observing that stochastic games with branching-time objectives are not determined, even if the objectives are formulae of the $\mathcal{L}(\mathrm{F}^{=1}, \mathrm{F}^{>0})$ fragment of PCTL (in general, $\mathcal{L}(Y_1, \cdots, Y_n)$ denotes the fragment of PCTL containing the connectives $Y_1, \cdots, Y_n$, conjunction, and disjunction (negation can be applied only to atomic propositions)). As a warm-up, we present some simple results about memoryless strategies in Section 3.1. We show that the problem whether player $\Box$ has a winning MD strategy in a given $2\frac{1}{2}$-player game for a given PCTL objective is $\Sigma_2 = \mathbf{NP}^{\mathbf{NP}}$ complete. The Σ_2 lower bound holds even for the $\mathcal{L}(\mathrm{F}^{=1}, \mathrm{F}^{>0})$ fragment of PCTL. Since the existence of a winning MD strategy for player $\Box$ in $1\frac{1}{2}$-player games with PCTL objectives is **NP**-complete [1], we yield a full complexity classification for MD strategies. The lower complexity bounds carry over to MR strategies and hold even for *qualitative* PCTL objectives for which we give the matching upper bounds—we show that the existence of a winning MR strategy for player $\Box$ in $1\frac{1}{2}$-player (or $2\frac{1}{2}$-player) games with *qualitative* PCTL objectives is **NP**-complete (or $\Sigma_2 = \mathbf{NP}^{\mathbf{NP}}$ complete, resp.). Let us note that randomized strategies are strictly more powerful than deterministic ones even for qualitative objectives (a simple example is given in Section 3.1). The existence of a winning MR strategy for player $\Box$ in $1\frac{1}{2}$-player and $2\frac{1}{2}$-player games with general PCTL objectives is known to be in **PSPACE** and **EXPTIME**, respectively [14]. We did not manage to lift the **NP** and Σ_2 lower bounds, and we also failed to improve the mentioned upper bounds. On the other hand, there is some indication that lowering the bounds below **PSPACE** would be quite difficult. We use the same argument as Etessami & Yannakakis in [11], where it is shown that the SQUARE-ROOT-SUM problem is efficiently reducible to the quantitative reachability problem for one-exit recursive Markov chains. An instance of SQUARE-ROOT-SUM is a tuple $(a_1, \cdots, a_n, b)$ of integers. The question is whether $\sum_{i=1}^{n} \sqrt{a_i} \leq b$. This problem is known to be in **PSPACE**, but its exact complexity is a long-standing open problem in computational geometry. Hence, an efficient reduction of SQUARE-ROOT-SUM to another problem $P \in$ **PSPACE** can be seen as an indication that the complexity of P is hard to improve. We show that SQUARE-ROOT-SUM is efficiently reducible to the problem whether player $\Box$ has a winning MR strategy in $1\frac{1}{2}$-player games with PCTL objectives. Let us note that the technique used in the proof is different from the one of [11].

The main results of this paper concern history-dependent strategies. First, we answer the open question formulated in [1] by showing that the existence of a winning HD (or HR) strategy in $1\frac{1}{2}$-player games is *highly undecidable* even for objectives of the $\mathcal{L}(\mathrm{F}^{=5/8}, \mathrm{F}^{=1}, \mathrm{F}^{>0}, \mathrm{G}^{=1})$ fragment of PCTL. More precisely, we show that the above problem is complete for the Σ_1^1 level of the analytical hierarchy. This is already a deep result relying on specific tricks which were developed to encode and simulate a computation of a given nondeterministic Minsky machine. A slight modification of the proof reveals that the existence of a winning HD (or HR) strategy with *finite memory* in $1\frac{1}{2}$-player games with $\mathcal{L}(\mathrm{F}^{=5/8}, \mathrm{F}^{=1}, \mathrm{F}^{>0}, \mathrm{G}^{=1})$ objectives is also undecidable (and complete for the Σ_1 level of the arithmetical hierarchy). The role of the quantitative $\mathrm{F}^{=5/8}$ operator is very important in these undecidability results[1]. In general, qualitative questions tend to be easier than quantitative ones (this also holds for PCTL and certain classes of infinite-state Markov chains [10, 4, 3]; note that the plays determined by history-dependent strategies are infinite-state Markov chains). Hence, we turn out attention to *qualitative* PCTL objectives. We start by examining the fragments with qualitative forms of reachability and safety connectives, i.e.,

1 Let us note that $5/8$ is not some kind of "magic number", it is just technically convenient. In principle, any operator of the form $\mathrm{F}^{=x}$ where $0 < x < 1$ would suffice for our purposes.

$F^{\bowtie\varrho}$ and $G^{\bowtie\varrho}$, where $\bowtie \in \{=,>,<\}$ and $\varrho \in \{0,1\}$. Even in this simplified setting, the results are not uniform and different combinations of connectives lead to quite different results. First, we show that the role of $F^{=5/8}$ operator in the aforementioned undecidability proof is *provably* crucial in the sense that the existence of a winning HD strategy in $1\frac{1}{2}$-player games with $\mathcal{L}(F^{=1}, F^{>0}, G^{=1})$ objectives is **EXPTIME** complete. Let us note that

- the **EXPTIME** upper bound is proven in two phases. First, we show that the existence of a winning HD strategy in $1\frac{1}{2}$-player games with $\mathcal{L}(F^{=1}, F^{>0}, G^{=1})$ objectives is effectively reducible to the existence of a winning HD strategy in $1\frac{1}{2}$-player games with *mixed linear-time* objectives, which are essentially conjunctions of one *qualitative-Büchi* and one *sure-Büchi* objective. This reduction is exponential. Then, we show that the existence of a winning HD strategy in $1\frac{1}{2}$-player games with mixed linear-time objectives is in **P**. Note that if we had a conjunction of two qualitative-Büchi or two sure-Büchi objectives, we could simply apply known results. To the best of our knowledge, the games where the winning objectives are "mixtures" of stochastic and non-stochastic requirements have not yet been explicitly considered (perhaps due to the lack of motivation). The solution we provide is not trivial.
- The **EXPTIME** lower bound holds even for $\mathcal{L}(F^{=1}, G^{=1})$ objectives and for both HD and HR strategies.

Our construction also reveals that a winning strategy in $1\frac{1}{2}$-player games with $\mathcal{L}(F^{=1}, F^{>0}, G^{=1})$ objectives needs only a finite memory whose size is exponential in the size of a given objective. This result does *not* hold for $\mathcal{L}(F^{=1}, F^{>0}, G^{=1}, G^{>0})$ objectives—we show that even $\mathcal{L}(F^{>0}, G^{>0})$ objectives require infinite memory in general. In this sense, the previous result is tight.

Many interesting questions remain open. For example, it is not clear whether the existence of a winning strategy in $1\frac{1}{2}$-player games with qualitative PCTL objectives is decidable or not (all we know is that these strategies may require infinite memory). Another question is whether some of our positive results can be extended to $2\frac{1}{2}$-player games and/or to *concurrent* stochastic games with branching-time winning objectives. Our knowledge about randomized strategies is also limited, we have not addressed the issue of fairness, and so on. These problems are left for future research. Due to space constrains, some proofs are sketchy or completely omitted. Full proofs can be found in [2].

2. Basic Definitions

We start by recalling basic notions of probability theory. Let A be a finite set. A *probability distribution* on A is a function $f : A \to [0,1]$ such that $\sum_{a\in A} f(a) = 1$. A distribution f is *rational* if $f(a) \in \mathbb{Q}$ for every $a \in A$, and *Dirac* if $f(a) = 1$ for some $a \in A$. The set of all distributions on A is denoted $\mathcal{D}(A)$.

A *σ-field* over a set X is a set $\mathcal{F} \subseteq 2^X$ that includes X and is closed under complement and countable union. A *measurable space* is a pair $(X, \mathcal{F})$ where X is a set called *sample space* and $\mathcal{F}$ is a σ-field over X. A *probability measure* over measurable space $(X, \mathcal{F})$ is a function $\mathcal{P} : \mathcal{F} \to \mathbb{R}^{\geq 0}$ such that, for each countable collection $\{X_i\}_{i\in I}$ of pairwise disjoint elements of $\mathcal{F}$, $\mathcal{P}(\bigcup_{i\in I} X_i) = \sum_{i\in I} \mathcal{P}(X_i)$, and moreover $\mathcal{P}(X) = 1$. A *probabilistic space* is a triple $(X, \mathcal{F}, \mathcal{P})$ where $(X, \mathcal{F})$ is a measurable space and $\mathcal{P}$ is a probability measure over $(X, \mathcal{F})$.

Markov chains. A *Markov chain* is a triple $\mathcal{T} = (S, \to, Prob)$ where S is a finite or countably infinite set of *states*, $\to \subseteq S \times S$ is a *transition relation*, and $Prob$ is a function which to each transition $s \to t$ of $\mathcal{T}$ assigns its probability $Prob(s \to t) \in (0,1]$ so that for every $s \in S$ we have $\sum_{s\to t} Prob(s \to t) = 1$.

In the rest of this paper we also write $s \stackrel{x}{\to} t$ instead of $Prob(s \to t) = x$. A *path* in $\mathcal{T}$ is a finite or infinite sequence $w = s_0, s_1, \cdots$ of states such that $s_i \to s_{i+1}$ for every i. We also use $w(i)$ to denote the state s_i of w (by writing $w(i) = s$ we implicitly impose the condition that the length of w is at least $i+1$). The prefix $s_0, s_1, \ldots, s_i$ of w is denoted by w^i. A *run* is an infinite path. The sets of all finite paths and all runs of $\mathcal{T}$ are denoted $FPath$ and Run, respectively. Similarly, the sets of all finite paths and runs that start in a given $s \in S$ are denoted $FPath(s)$ and $Run(s)$, respectively.

Each $w \in FPath$ determines a *basic cylinder* $Run(w)$ which consists of all runs that start with w. To every $s \in S$ we associate the probabilistic space $(Run(s), \mathcal{F}, \mathcal{P})$ where $\mathcal{F}$ is the σ-field generated by all basic cylinders $Run(w)$ where w starts with s, and $\mathcal{P} : \mathcal{F} \to [0,1]$ is the unique probability function such that $\mathcal{P}(Run(w)) = \Pi_{i=0}^{m-1} x_i$ where $w = s_0, \cdots, s_m$ and $s_i \stackrel{x_i}{\to} s_{i+1}$ for every $0 \leq i < m$ (if $m = 0$, we put $\mathcal{P}(Run(w)) = 1$).

The logic PCTL. The logic PCTL, the probabilistic extension of CTL, was introduced by Hansson & Jonsson in [12]. Let $Ap = \{p, q, \ldots\}$ be a countably infinite set of *atomic propositions*. The syntax of PCTL formulae is given by the following abstract syntax equation:

$$\Phi \quad ::= \quad p \mid \neg p \mid \Phi_1 \vee \Phi_2 \mid \Phi_1 \wedge \Phi_2 \mid X^{\bowtie\varrho}\,\Phi \mid \Phi_1 U^{\bowtie\varrho}\,\Phi_2$$

Here $p \in Ap$, $\varrho \in [0,1]$, and $\bowtie \in \{\leq, <, \geq, >, =, \neq\}$.

Let $\mathcal{T} = (S, \to, Prob)$ be a Markov chain, and let $\nu : Ap \to 2^S$ be a *valuation*. The semantics of PCTL is defined below.

$s \models^\nu p$	iff $s \in \nu(p)$
$s \models^\nu \neg p$	iff $s \notin \nu(p)$
$s \models^\nu \Phi_1 \vee \Phi_2$	iff $s \models^\nu \Phi_1$ or $s \models^\nu \Phi_2$

$s \models^{\nu} \Phi_1 \wedge \Phi_2$ iff $s \models^{\nu} \Phi_1$ and $s \models^{\nu} \Phi_2$
$s \models^{\nu} X^{\bowtie\varrho}\Phi$ iff $\mathcal{P}(\{w \in Run(s) \mid w(1) \models^{\nu} \Phi\}) \bowtie \varrho$
$s \models^{\nu} \Phi_1 U^{\bowtie\varrho} \Phi_2$ iff $\mathcal{P}(\{w \in Run(s) \mid \exists j \geq 0 : w(j) \models^{\nu} \Phi_2$ and $w(i) \models^{\nu} \Phi_1$ for all $0 \leq i < j\}) \bowtie \varrho$

Note that in our version of PCTL syntax, the negation can be applied only to atomic propositions. This is no restriction because the syntax is closed under dual connectives and relations: For every $\bowtie\, \in \{\leq, <, \geq, >, =, \neq\}$, let $\overline{\bowtie}$ be the complement of $\bowtie$ (for example, if $\bowtie$ is $\leq$, then $\overline{\bowtie}$ is $>$). The negation of $X^{\bowtie\varrho}\Phi$ and $\Phi_1 U^{\bowtie\varrho} \Phi_2$ then corresponds to $X^{\overline{\bowtie}\varrho}\Phi$ and $\Phi_1 U^{\overline{\bowtie}\varrho} \Phi_2$, respectively. The $F^{\bowtie\varrho}$ and $G^{\bowtie\varrho}$ operators are defined in the standard way: $F^{\bowtie\varrho}\Phi$ stands for $\mathtt{tt}\, U^{\bowtie\varrho} \Phi$, and $G^{\bowtie\varrho}\Phi$ stands for $\mathtt{tt}\, U^{\widehat{\bowtie} 1-\varrho} \neg\Phi$, where $\widehat{\bowtie}$ is $<, >, \leq, \geq, =$, or $\neq$, depending on whether $\bowtie$ is $>, <, \geq, \leq, =$, or $\neq$, respectively.

Various natural fragments of PCTL can be obtained by restricting the PCTL syntax to certain modal connectives and/or certain operator/number combinations. For example, the *qualitative* fragment of PCTL is obtained by restricting the allowed operator/number combinations to '$\bowtie 0$' and '$\bowtie 1$'. Hence, $aU^{<1}b \vee F^{>0}c$ is a qualitative PCTL formula. In this paper we also consider fragments with unary reachability and safety connectives. Formally, for each tuple $Y_1, \cdots, Y_n$, where each Y_i is of the form $X^{\bowtie\varrho}$, $F^{\bowtie\varrho}$, or $G^{\bowtie\varrho}$, we define the $\mathcal{L}(Y_1, \cdots, Y_n)$ fragment of PCTL:

$$\Phi \ ::= \ p \mid \neg p \mid \Phi_1 \vee \Phi_2 \mid \Phi_1 \wedge \Phi_2 \mid Y_1\Phi \mid \cdots \mid Y_n\Phi$$

For example, $F^{>0}(b \vee G^{\geq 0.43}(\neg c \wedge F^{<0.5}d))$ is a formula of $\mathcal{L}(F^{>0}, G^{\geq 0.43}, F^{<0.5})$. Sometimes we also use formulae of the form $p \Rightarrow \Phi$ which stand for $\neg p \vee \Phi$.

Games, strategies, and objectives. A $2\frac{1}{2}$*-player game* is a tuple $G = (V, E, (V_\Box, V_\Diamond, V_\bigcirc), Prob)$ where V is a finite set of *vertices*, $E \subseteq V \times V$ is the set of *transitions*, $(V_\Box, V_\Diamond, V_\bigcirc)$ is a partition of V, and $Prob$ is a *probability assignment* which to each $v \in V_\bigcirc$ assigns a rational probability distribution on the set of its outgoing transitions. For technical convenience, we assume that each vertex has at least one outgoing transition. The game is played by two players, $\Box$ and $\Diamond$, who move a single token from vertex to vertex along the transitions of E. Player $\Box$ selects the moves in the $V_\Box$ vertices, and player $\Diamond$ selects the moves in the $V_\Diamond$ vertices. Transitions in the $V_\bigcirc$ vertices are chosen randomly according to the corresponding probability distribution. Game graphs are drawn in the standard way; vertices of $V_\Box$, $V_\Diamond$, and $V_\bigcirc$ are depicted as squares, diamonds, and circles, respectively. Probability distributions are usually uniform, which is indicated by arcs connecting the outgoing transitions of $V_\bigcirc$ vertices. A *strategy* for player $\Box$ is a function σ which to each $wv \in V^*V_\Box$ assigns a probability distribution on the set of outgoing transitions of v. We say that a strategy σ is *memoryless (M)* if $\sigma(wv)$ depends just on the last vertex v, and *deterministic (D)* if $\sigma(wv)$ is a Dirac distribution for each $wv \in V^*V_\Box$. Consistently with [1, 14], strategies that are not necessarily memoryless are called *history-dependent (H)*, and strategies that are not necessarily deterministic are called *randomized (R)*. A special type of history-dependent strategies are strategies with *finite memory*, which are formally defined as pairs $(\mathcal{A}, f)$ where $\mathcal{A} = (Q, V, \delta, q_0)$ is a deterministic finite-state automaton over the alphabet V of vertices and f is a function which to each pair $(q, v) \in Q \times V_\Box$ assigns a probability distribution on the set of outgoing transitions of v. The pair $(\mathcal{A}, f)$ determines a unique strategy $\sigma(\mathcal{A}, f)$ such that $\sigma(\mathcal{A}, f)(wv) = f(q, v)$, where $q = \delta(q_0, wv)$. Intuitively, the states of $\mathcal{A}$ represent a finite memory of size $|Q|$ where selected properties of the history of a play are stored. Hence, we can define the following four classes of strategies: MD, MR, HD, and HR, where MD $\subseteq$ HD $\subseteq$ HR and MD $\subseteq$ MR $\subseteq$ HR, but MR and HD are incomparable. Strategies for player $\Diamond$ are defined analogously. Each pair (σ, π) of strategies for player $\Box$ and $\Diamond$ determines a unique *play* of the game G, which is a Markov chain $G(\sigma, \pi)$ where V^+ is the set of states, and $wu \xrightarrow{x} wuu'$ iff $(u, u') \in E$ and one of the following conditions holds:

- $u \in V_\bigcirc$ and $Prob(u, u') = x$;
- $u \in V_\Box$ and $\sigma(wu)$ assigns x to (u, u');
- $u \in V_\Diamond$ and $\pi(wu)$ assigns x to (u, u').

An *objective* is a pair (ν, φ), where $\nu : Ap \rightarrow 2^V$ is a valuation and φ a PCTL formula. Note that each valuation $\nu : Ap \rightarrow 2^V$ determines a valuation $\overline{\nu} : Ap \rightarrow 2^{V^+}$ defined by $\overline{\nu}(a) = \{wu \in V^+ \mid u \in \nu(a)\}$. For a given objective (ν, φ), each state of $G(\sigma, \pi)$ either does or does not satisfy φ. A (ν, φ)*-winning strategy* for player $\Box$ in a vertex $v \in V$ is a strategy σ such that for every strategy π of player $\Diamond$ we have that $v \models^{\nu} \varphi$. Similarly, a (ν, φ)-winning strategy for player $\Diamond$ in a vertex $v \in V$ is a strategy π such that for every strategy σ of player $\Box$ we have that $v \not\models^{\nu} \varphi$. The game G is (ν, φ)*-determined* if there is a (ν, φ)-winning strategy for one of the two players in every vertex v of G.

$1\frac{1}{2}$*-player games* are $2\frac{1}{2}$-player games where the set $V_\Diamond$ is empty. Formally, a $1\frac{1}{2}$-player game is a tuple $G = (V, E, (V_\Box, V_\bigcirc), Prob)$ where all elements have the expected meaning.

3. The Results

We start by observing that stochastic games with branching-time objectives are not determined, even if these objectives are taken from the $\mathcal{L}(F^{=1}, F^{>0})$ fragment of PCTL. Consider the following game:

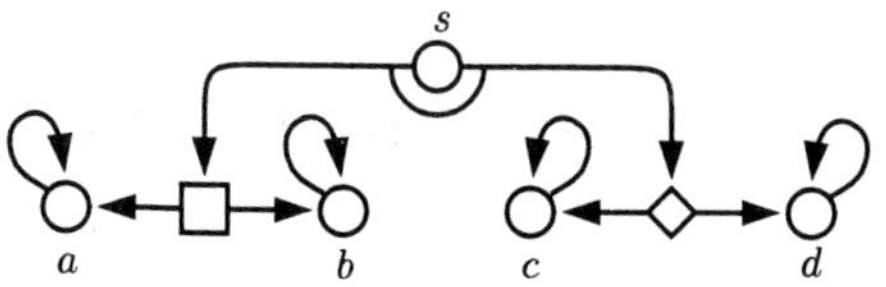

Let ν be a valuation which defines the validity of the propositions a, b, c, d as indicated in the above figure, and let $\varphi \equiv \mathrm{F}^{=1}(a \vee c) \vee \mathrm{F}^{=1}(b \vee d) \vee (\mathrm{F}^{>0}c \wedge \mathrm{F}^{>0}d)$. Now it is easy to check that none of the two players has a (ν, φ)-winning strategy in the vertex s, regardless whether we consider MD, MR, HD, or HR strategies.

3.1. Memoryless Strategies

In [1], it is shown that the problem whether there exists a winning MD strategy in a given $1\frac{1}{2}$-player game for a given PCTL objective is **NP**-complete. In fact, the **NP** lower bound holds even for the $\mathcal{L}(\mathrm{F}^{=1})$ fragment of PCTL. The following theorem gives a complexity classification for $2\frac{1}{2}$-player games.

Theorem 3.1. *The existence of a winning MD strategy for player $\Box$ in $2\frac{1}{2}$-player games with PCTL objectives is $\Sigma_2 = NP^{NP}$ complete. The Σ_2 lower bound holds even for $\mathcal{L}(\mathrm{F}^{=1}, \mathrm{F}^{>0})$ objectives and for both MD and MR strategies.*

Proof. A Σ_2 *formula* is a formula of the form

$$\exists x_1, \cdots, x_n \, \forall y_1, \cdots, y_m \, B$$

where $n, m \in \mathbb{N}$ and B is a $\wedge, \vee$-expression over the (possibly negated) variables $x_1, \cdots, x_n, y_1, \cdots, y_m$. The problem whether a given Σ_2 formula is valid is Σ_2-complete [15].

Let $\psi \equiv \exists x_1, \cdots, x_n \, \forall y_1, \cdots, y_m \, B$. We construct a $2\frac{1}{2}$-player game $G(\psi)$, a valuation ν, and a formula $\varphi \in \mathcal{L}(\mathrm{F}^{=1}, \mathrm{F}^{>0})$ such that player $\Box$ has a (ν, φ)-winning MD (or MR) strategy in a distinguished vertex v of $G(\psi)$ iff ψ is valid. Let us fix two sets $P = \{p_i, \widehat{p}_i \mid 1 \leq i \leq n\}$ and $Q = \{q_j, \widehat{q}_j \mid 1 \leq j \leq m\}$ of fresh atomic propositions, and let $P_i = P \setminus \{p_i\}$, $\widehat{P}_i = P \setminus \{\widehat{p}_i\}$, $Q_j = P \cup \{q_j\}$, $\widehat{Q}_j = P \cup \{\widehat{q}_j\}$ for all $1 \leq i \leq n$ and $1 \leq j \leq m$. The structure of $G(\psi)$ together with the valuation ν are shown in the following figure:

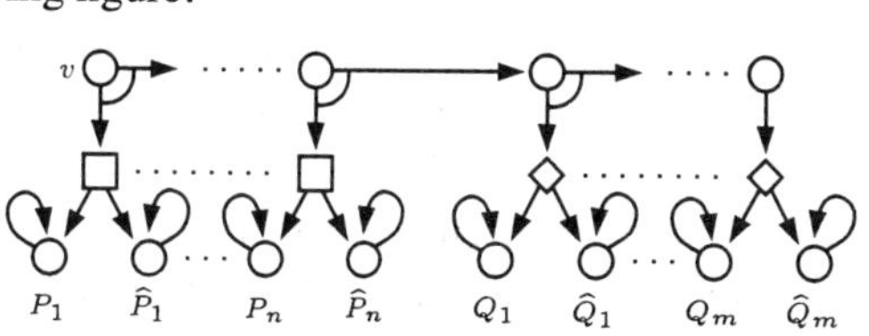

Let

$$\varphi \equiv \left(\bigvee_{j=1}^{m} (\mathrm{F}^{>0}q_j \wedge \mathrm{F}^{>0}\widehat{q}_j) \right) \vee \left(\widehat{B} \wedge \bigwedge_{i=1}^{n} (\mathrm{F}^{=1}p_i \vee \mathrm{F}^{=1}\widehat{p}_i) \right)$$

where $\widehat{B}$ is the formula obtained from B by substituting each occurrence of x_i, $\neg x_i$, y_j, and $\neg y_j$ with $\mathrm{F}^{=1}p_i$, $\mathrm{F}^{=1}\widehat{p}_i$, $\mathrm{F}^{>0}q_j$, and $\mathrm{F}^{>0}\widehat{q}_j$, respectively. Intuitively, player $\Box$ chooses an assignment for the variables $x_1, \cdots, x_n$ (x_i is set to true or false by selecting the transition to a vertex satisfying p_i or $\widehat{p}_i$, resp.). Note that player $\Box$ cannot use randomized moves because then the formula $\mathrm{F}^{=1}p_i \vee \mathrm{F}^{=1}\widehat{p}_i$ would not hold. Similarly, player $\Diamond$ chooses an assignment for $y_1, \cdots, y_m$. Observe that player $\Diamond$ cannot use randomized moves either because this would make some $\mathrm{F}^{>0}q_j \wedge \mathrm{F}^{>0}\widehat{q}_j$ true. Now it is easy to check that ψ is valid iff player $\Box$ has a (ν, φ)-winning MD (or MR) strategy in the vertex v. This establishes the Σ_2 lower bound.

The Σ_2 upper bound holds for all PCTL objectives. First, let us note that the model-checking problem for PCTL formulae and Markov chains is in **P** [12]. Hence, it suffices to "guess" a winning strategy σ for player $\Box$, and then ask the **NP** oracle whether there is a strategy π of player $\Diamond$ such that $G(\sigma, \pi)$ does *not* satisfy a given objective. The answer of the oracle is then simply negated. □

The complexity classification for MD strategies is thus established. As for MR strategies, the **NP** and Σ_2 lower bounds still hold. However, we managed to provide the matching upper bounds only for the subclass of *qualitative* PCTL objectives. Note that randomized strategies are more powerful than deterministic ones even for qualitative objectives—consider the formula $\mathrm{X}^{>0}p_u \wedge \mathrm{X}^{>0}p_v$ and a simple game G with three vertices $t, u, v \in V_\Box$ where $t \to u$, $t \to v$, $u \to u$, and $v \to v$. The propositions p_u and p_v hold only in u and v, respectively. Obviously, there is no winning (ν, φ)-winning MD strategy, but there are many (ν, φ)-winning MR strategies.

Theorem 3.2. *The existence of a winning MR strategy for player $\Box$ in $1\frac{1}{2}$-player (or $2\frac{1}{2}$-player) games with* qualitative *PCTL objectives is NP-complete (or $\Sigma_2 = NP^{NP}$ complete, resp.).*

Proof. A straightforward induction on the structure of a qualitative PCTL formula φ shows that the (in)validity of φ does not depend on the exact values of transition probabilities. It only matters which of the transition have zero/positive probability. Hence, in the case of $1\frac{1}{2}$-player games, it suffices to "guess" the subset of outgoing transitions in each vertex of $V_\Box$ which should have positive probability, and then verify that the guess was correct by a (polynomial time) PCTL model-checking algorithm [12]. The Σ_2 upper bound for $2\frac{1}{2}$-player games is established analogously (see the proof of Theorem 3.1). □

The existence of a winning MR strategy for player $\Box$ in $1\frac{1}{2}$-player and $2\frac{1}{2}$-player games with general PCTL objectives is known to be in **PSPACE** and **EXPTIME**, respectively [14]. We did not manage to lift the **NP** and Σ_2 lower bounds, and we also failed to improve the mentioned upper bounds. At least, we provide some evidence that lowering these bounds below **PSPACE** is difficult (see the discussion in Section 1). As a byproduct of this construction, we obtain an example of a $1\frac{1}{2}$-player game (where $V_\bigcirc = \emptyset$) and an objective (ν, φ) where $\varphi \in \mathcal{L}(\mathrm{X}^{>0}, \mathrm{U}^{=1/2})$ such that the only (ν, φ)-winning MR strategy assigns irrational probabilities to transitions.

Theorem 3.3. *The* SQUARE-ROOT-SUM *problem is efficiently reducible to the problem whether player $\Box$ has a winning MR strategy in $1\frac{1}{2}$-player games with PCTL objectives.*

Proof. Let $a_1, \cdots, a_n, b$ be an instance of SQUARE-ROOT-SUM (see Section 1). Let G be a game where

- the set $V = V_\Box$ contains the vertices v, u, s, $c(i)$, $d(i)$, $e(i)$, $f(i)$, $g(i)$, and $h(i)$ for all $1 \leq i \leq n$;
- the set of transitions contains $v \to u$, $u \to u$, $s \to u$, $v \to c(i)$, $c(i) \to d(i) \to f(i)$, $c(i) \to e(i) \to f(i)$, $f(i) \to g(i) \to s$, and $f(i) \to h(i) \to s$ for all $1 \leq i \leq n$.

The structure of G is shown in the following figure:

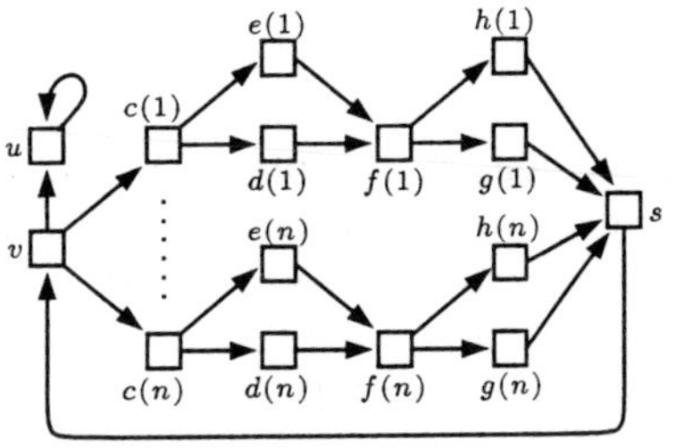

We assume that for each vertex $t \in V$ there is an atomic proposition p_t which is valid only in t (thus we obtain our valuation ν). Slightly abusing notation, we write t instead of p_t in our formulae.

Every strategy σ for player $\Box$ assigns (some) probabilities $p(c_i)$, $p(e_i)$, and $p(h_i)$ to transitions $v \to c(i)$, $c(i) \to e(i)$, and $f(i) \to h(i)$, respectively, where $1 \leq i \leq n$. Let $q = b + \sum_{i=1}^{n} a_i$. We construct a PCTL formula φ such that every (ν, φ)-winning MR strategy in v has to assign $p(c_i) = p(e_i) = p(h_i) = \sqrt{a_i}/q$ for every $1 \leq i \leq n$. Then the probability of $v \to u$ must be $1 - \sum_{i=1}^{n} \sqrt{a_i}/q$. The formula φ contains the clause $\mathrm{X}^{\geq 1-b/q} u$. Hence, player $\Box$ has a (ν, φ)-winning MR strategy in v iff $1 - \sum_{i=1}^{n} \sqrt{a_i}/q \geq 1 - b/q$, i.e., iff $\sum_{i=1}^{n} \sqrt{a_i} \leq b$.

Now we describe the formula φ in greater detail. For every $1 \leq i \leq n$, let $\Phi_i \equiv (v \vee c(i))\ \mathrm{U}^{a_i/q^2} e(i)$. Note that $v \models^\nu \Phi_i$ iff $p(c_i) \cdot p(e_i) = a_i/q^2$. Similarly, we construct the formulae Ψ_i and Ξ_i such that $v \models^\nu \Psi_i$ and $v \models^\nu \Xi_i$ iff $p(e_i) \cdot p(h_i) = a_i/q^2$ and $p(h_i) \cdot p(c_i) = a_i/q^2$, respectively:

$$\Psi_i \equiv \mathrm{X}^{>0}\big(c(i) \vee (e(i) \vee f(i))\ \mathrm{U}^{a_i/q^2} h(i)\big)$$
$$\Xi_i \equiv \mathrm{X}^{>0}\mathrm{X}^{>0}\mathrm{X}^{>0}\big((f(i) \vee h(i) \vee s \vee v)\ \mathrm{U}^{a_i/q^2} c(i)\big)$$

Observe that if $p(c_i) \cdot p(e_i) = p(e_i) \cdot p(h_i) = p(h_i) \cdot p(c_i) = a_1/q^2$, then necessarily $p(c_i) = p(e_i) = p(h_i) = \sqrt{a_i}/q$. We put $\varphi \equiv \mathrm{X}^{\geq 1-b/q} u \wedge \bigwedge_{i=1}^{n} (\Phi_i \wedge \Psi_i \wedge \Xi_i)$.

Let us consider the game obtained for $n = 1$, $a_1 = 2$, and $b = 0$. Then $\Phi_1 \wedge \Psi_1 \wedge \Xi_1 \in \mathcal{L}(X^{>0}, \mathrm{U}^{1/2})$ and the only $(\nu, \Phi_1 \wedge \Psi_1 \wedge \Xi_1)$-winning MR strategy in v assigns irrational probabilities to certain transitions. Thus, we obtain the example promised above. $\Box$

3.2. History-Dependent Strategies

The results presented in this section constitute the main contribution of our paper. We start with the negative ones.

Theorem 3.4. *The existence of a winning HD (or HR) strategy in $1\frac{1}{2}$-player games with $\mathcal{L}(\mathrm{F}^{=5/8}, \mathrm{F}^{=1}, \mathrm{F}^{>0}, \mathrm{G}^{=1})$ objectives is undecidable (and Σ_1^1-hard).*

Proof (sketch). The result is obtained by reduction of the problem whether a given nondeterministic Minsky machine with two counters initialized to zero has an infinite computation such that the initial instruction is executed infinitely often (this problem is known to be Σ_1^1-complete [13]). Formally, a nondeterministic Minsky machine with two counters c_1, c_2 is a finite sequence $\mathcal{M}$ of numbered instructions $1{:}ins_1, \cdots, n{:}ins_n$, where each ins_i is of one of the following forms (where $j \in \{1, 2\}$):

- $c_j := c_j{+}1$; *goto* k
- *if* $c_j{=}0$ *then goto* k *else* $c_j := c_j{-}1$; *goto* m
- *goto* $\{k$ *or* $m\}$

Here the indexes k, m range over $\{1, \cdots, n\}$. A *configuration* of $\mathcal{M}$ is a triple $[ins_i, v_1, v_2]$, where ins_i is the instruction to be executed, and $v_1, v_2 \in \mathbb{N}_0$ are the current values of c_1, c_2. A *computational step* $\hookrightarrow$ between configurations is defined in the expected way. A *recurrent computation* of $\mathcal{M}$ is an infinite computation initiated in $[ins_1, 0, 0]$ along which ins_1 is executed infinitely often. As we already mentioned, the problem whether a given $\mathcal{M}$ has a recurrent computation is Σ_1^1-complete.

Let $\mathcal{M} \equiv 1{:}ins_1, \cdots, n{:}ins_n$ be a nondeterministic Minsky machine. We construct a $1\frac{1}{2}$-player game $G(\mathcal{M})$ and a formula $\varphi \in \mathcal{L}(\mathrm{F}^{=5/8}, \mathrm{F}^{>0}, \mathrm{F}^{=1}, \mathrm{G}^{=1})$ such that player $\Box$ has a winning HD or HR strategy in a distinguished vertex v of $G(\mathcal{M})$ iff $\mathcal{M}$ has a recurrent computation.

Intuitively, the game $G(\mathcal{M})$ is constructed so that *every* play of $G(\mathcal{M})$ corresponds to an infinite sequence

$$[ins_1, 0, 0], \cdots, [ins_i, V_1, V_2], [ins_k, U_1, U_2], \cdots$$

of *extended* configurations of $\mathcal{M}$, where the counters can also take the ω (i.e., "infinite") value. Player $\Box$ can (to some extent) determine the sequence. In particular, he is responsible for "guessing" the counter values in each extended configuration (see below). Of course, this sequence does not necessarily correspond to a valid computation of $\mathcal{M}$. The definition of $G(\mathcal{M})$ guarantees that the above sequence *does* correspond to a recurrent computation of $\mathcal{M}$ iff the following conditions are satisfied:

(a) Counter values in all extended configurations of the sequence are finite.

(b) The sequence contains infinitely many configurations of the form $[ins_1, \cdots]$.

(c) For each pair $[ins_i, V_1, V_2], [ins_k, U_1, U_2]$ of successive configurations we have that $[ins_i, V_1, V_2] \hookrightarrow [ins_k, U_1, U_2]$.

Then we show how to express these conditions in $\mathcal{L}(\mathrm{F}^{=5/8}, \mathrm{F}^{>0}, \mathrm{F}^{=1}, \mathrm{G}^{=1})$. Conditions (a) and (b) are relatively easy. Condition (c) requires more effort, and this is the (only) place where we need the $\mathrm{F}^{=5/8}$ operator. The main problem is to verify the "compatibility" of counter values V_1, U_1 and V_2, U_2. For example, if $ins_i \equiv c_1{:=}c_1{+}1;$ *goto* k, then we must verify that $U_1 = V_1 + 1$ and $U_2 = V_2$. Here we illustrate just the basic idea of this construction (technical details can be found in [2]). We show how player $\Box$ can "guess" two numbers $I, J \in \mathbb{N}_0 \cup \{\omega\}$, and how to design a temporal formula which says that $I = J < \omega$. Let us consider the following game:

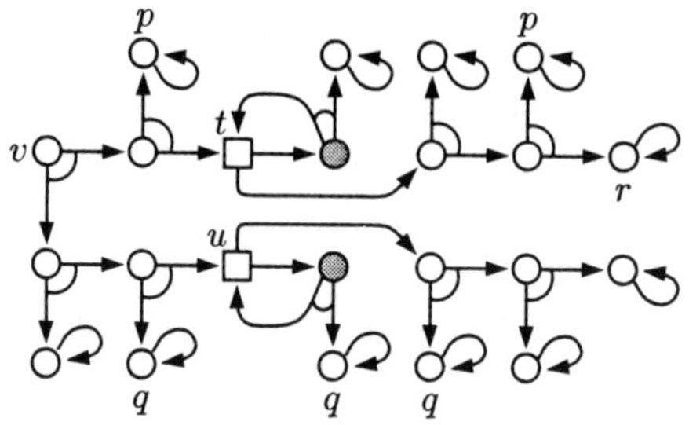

The p, q, and r are atomic propositions which are valid exactly in the indicated vertices. A play of this game (initiated in v) looks as follows:

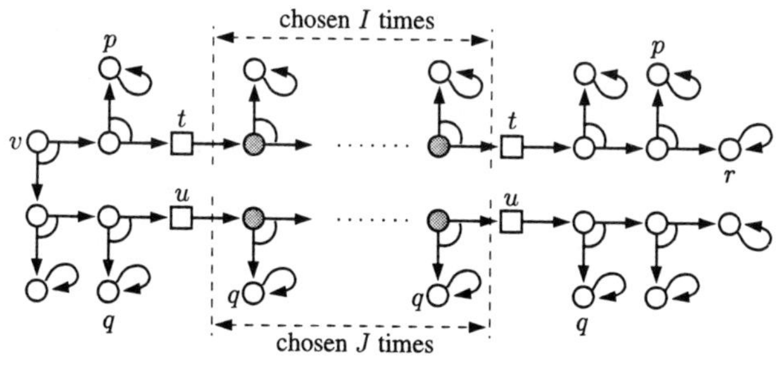

Observe that when a t vertex of the play is visited, player $\Box$ can choose between transitions leading to a "gray" or "white" vertex. If he chooses a gray vertex, then with probability $1/2$ he will make another choice after performing the next transition. Thus, player $\Box$ may decide to visit a gray vertex I-times, where I ranges from 0 to infinity, and the number of such choices represents the value of I. Similarly, the value of J is represented by the number of choices leading to a gray vertex at u vertices. The condition that $I < \omega$ is easy to express—we simply say that v satisfies $\mathrm{F}^{>0}r$. We claim that $I = J$ iff v satisfies $\mathrm{F}^{=1/2}(p \vee q)$. A closer look reveals that the probability of all $w \in \mathit{Run}(v)$ satisfying the formula $\mathrm{F}(p \vee q)$ is equal to the following sum of two binary numbers:

$$0.01\underbrace{0\cdots0}_{I}01 + 0.001\underbrace{1\cdots1}_{J}1$$

Obviously, this sum is equal to $1/2$ iff $I = J$, and we are done.

Note that in the above construction we used the $\mathrm{F}^{=1/2}$ operator, and not $\mathrm{F}^{=5/8}$. The exact value of the index does not really matter, any operator of the form $\mathrm{F}^{=x}$ where $0 < x < 1$ would suffice for our purposes. In the "full" proof, the operator $\mathrm{F}^{=5/8}$ is technically convenient, because then we can keep all transition probabilities in $G(\mathcal{M})$ equal to $1/2$. See [2] for the details. $\Box$

On the other hand, the existence of a winning HD strategy in $1\frac{1}{2}$ games with general PCTL objectives can be encoded by a Σ_1^1 formula in a straightforward way. Hence, the problem is Σ_1^1-complete.

A slight modification of the construction presented in Theorem 3.4 reveals the following:

Theorem 3.5. *The existence of a winning HD (or HR) strategy with finite memory in $1\frac{1}{2}$ games with $\mathcal{L}(\mathrm{F}^{=5/8}, \mathrm{F}^{=1}, \mathrm{F}^{>0}, \mathrm{G}^{=1})$ objectives is undecidable.*

Proof (sketch). First, let us realize that the problem is semidecidable (i.e., belongs to the Σ_1 level of the arithmetical hierarchy). Obviously, one can effectively enumerate all $(\mathcal{A}, f)$ and for each such $(\mathcal{A}, f)$ decide whether $\sigma(\mathcal{A}, f)$ is winning, because the corresponding play has only finitely many states (more precisely, the play is obtained as unfolding of an effectively constructible finite-state Markov chain). The undecidability result is obtained by a slight modification of the construction presented in Theorem 3.4. In this case, we reduce the halting problem for "ordinary" deterministic Minsky machines (i.e., there is no *goto* $\{k$ *or* $m\}$ instruction, and the last instruction is *halt*). Note that if a given Minsky machine halts, then it halts after finitely many steps and the corresponding winning strategy needs only finite memory (of course, there is no bound on its size).

If the machine does not halt, there is no winning strategy at all. □

Now we show that the previous undecidability results are tight in the sense that the existence of a winning HD strategy in $1\frac{1}{2}$-player games with $\mathcal{L}(\mathrm{F}^{=1}, \mathrm{F}^{>0}, \mathrm{G}^{=1})$ objectives is decidable, and in fact **EXPTIME**-complete.

Let G be a $1\frac{1}{2}$-player game where V is the set of vertices. A *mixed* objective is a pair (P, Q) where $P, Q \subseteq V$. A strategy σ for player $\Box$ is (P, Q)-*winning* in a vertex $v \in V$ iff all runs in $G(\sigma)$ initiated in v visit some state of P infinitely often, and the probability of all runs which visit some state of Q infinitely often is 1. Hence, a mixed objective is essentially a conjunction of a *sure-Büchi* objective specified by P and a *qualitative-Büchi* objective specified by Q. The first step towards the promised **EXPTIME** upper bound is the following:

Lemma 3.6. *Let G be a $1\frac{1}{2}$-player game, s_{in} a vertex of G, and (ν, ψ) an objective where $\psi \in \mathcal{L}(\mathrm{F}^{=1}, \mathrm{F}^{>0}, \mathrm{G}^{=1})$. Then there effectively exists a $1\frac{1}{2}$-player game G', a vertex s'_{in} of G', and a mixed objective (P, Q) such that player $\Box$ has a (ν, ψ)-winning HD strategy in the vertex s_{in} iff player $\Box$ has a (P, Q)-winning HD strategy in the vertex s'_{in}. Moreover, the G', s'_{in}, and (P, Q) are computable in time which is linear in the size of G and exponential in the size of ψ.*

Proof (sketch). For the rest of this proof, let us fix a $1\frac{1}{2}$-player game $G = (V, E, (V_\Box, V_\bigcirc), \mathit{Prob})$, a vertex $s_{in} \in V$, and an objective (ν, ψ) where $\psi \in \mathcal{L}(\mathrm{F}^{=1}, \mathrm{F}^{>0}, \mathrm{G}^{=1})$. For technical convenience, we assume that all subformulae of ψ are pairwise distinct (this can be achieved by replacing atomic propositions in φ with fresh propositions so that each proposition has a unique occurrence in ψ; the valuation ν is extended accordingly). Our aim is to define another $1\frac{1}{2}$-player game G', a vertex s'_{in} of G', and a mixed objective (P, Q) such that player $\Box$ has a (ν, ψ)-winning HD strategy in s_{in} iff player $\Box$ has a (P, Q)-winning HD strategy in s'_{in}.

Let L be the set of all *literals*, i.e., atomic propositions and their negations. Let $\mathcal{S}$ be the set of all subformulae of ψ, where negation is not considered as a connective (for example, if $\psi \equiv F^{=1}\neg q$, then $\mathcal{S} = \{\neg q, F^{=1}\neg q\}$). For each connective $\alpha \in \{\mathrm{F}^{=1}, \mathrm{F}^{>0}, \mathrm{G}^{=1}, \vee, \wedge\}$, we use $\mathcal{S}_\alpha$ to denote the subset of $\mathcal{S}$ consisting of all formulae where the topmost connective is α. We also use $\mathcal{S}_{Ap}, \mathcal{S}_{\mathrm{F}}, \mathcal{S}_{Temp}, \mathcal{S}_{Bool}$, and $\mathcal{S}_{\bar{\mathrm{F}}}$ to denote the sets $\mathcal{S} \cap L$, $\mathcal{S}_{\mathrm{F}^{=1}} \cup \mathcal{S}_{\mathrm{F}^{>0}}$, $\mathcal{S}_{\mathrm{F}^{=1}} \cup \mathcal{S}_{\mathrm{F}^{>0}} \cup \mathcal{S}_{\mathrm{G}^{=1}}$, $\mathcal{S}_\vee \cup \mathcal{S}_\wedge$, and $\{\bar{\mathrm{F}}^{\bowtie \varrho}\varphi \mid \mathrm{F}^{\bowtie \varrho}\varphi \in \mathcal{S}_{\mathrm{F}}\}$, respectively. The purpose of "barred" formulae of $\mathcal{S}_{\bar{\mathrm{F}}}$ becomes clear later.

In the following, we assume that $\mathcal{S} = \{\varphi_1, \ldots, \varphi_n\}$ where $i < j$ implies that φ_i is *not* a subformula of φ_j. The first step towards the definition of G' is the function $\Theta : 2^{\mathcal{S}} \to 2^{2^{\mathcal{S} \cup \mathcal{S}_{\bar{\mathrm{F}}}}}$ which decomposes subformulae of ψ into "subgoals". Let $A \subseteq \mathcal{S}$. If $A \subseteq \mathcal{S}_{Ap}$, then $\Theta(A) = \{A\}$. Otherwise, let i be the least index such that $\varphi_i \in A \smallsetminus \mathcal{S}_{Ap}$. We distinguish among the following possibilities:

- If $\varphi_i \equiv \varphi_k \vee \varphi_\ell$, then
$$\Theta(A) = \Theta((A \smallsetminus \{\varphi_i\}) \cup \{\varphi_k\}) \cup \Theta((A \smallsetminus \{\varphi_i\}) \cup \{\varphi_\ell\})$$
- If $\varphi_i \equiv \varphi_k \wedge \varphi_\ell$, then $\Theta(A) = \Theta((A \smallsetminus \{\varphi_i\}) \cup \{\varphi_k, \varphi_\ell\})$
- If $\varphi_i \equiv \mathrm{G}^{=1}\varphi_j$, then
$$\Theta(A) = \{D \cup \{\mathrm{G}^{=1}(\varphi_j)\} \mid D \in \Theta((A \smallsetminus \{\varphi_i\}) \cup \{\varphi_j\})\}$$
- $\varphi_i \equiv \mathrm{F}^{\bowtie \varrho}\varphi_j$, then
$$\begin{aligned}\Theta(A) \;&=\; \{D \cup \{\mathrm{F}^{\bowtie \varrho}(\varphi_j)\} \mid D \in \Theta(A \smallsetminus \{\varphi_i\})\} \\ &\cup\; \{D \cup \{\bar{\mathrm{F}}^{\bowtie \varrho}(\varphi_j)\} \mid D \in \Theta((A \smallsetminus \{\varphi_i\}) \cup \{\varphi_j\})\}\end{aligned}$$

The intuition behind the function Θ is the following: to find out whether there is a (ν, ψ)-winning HD strategy in s_{in}, we extend each vertex of G (and hence each state of an arbitrary play of G) with a set A of subformulae of ψ that should be valid when the play is in the state. Some of these formulae represent temporal "goals" which can be achieved either in the current state or in its successors. The function Θ "offers" all admissible possibilities how to distribute the goals among the current state and its successors so that all formulae in A are valid. Selecting the right alternative becomes the responsibility of player $\Box$. For example, $\Theta(\{\mathrm{F}^{=1}p\}) = \{\{\mathrm{F}^{=1}p\}, \{\bar{\mathrm{F}}^{=1}p, p\}\}$, because the "current" state satisfies $\mathrm{F}^{=1}p$ iff either all of its successors satisfy $\mathrm{F}^{=1}p$ (the goal is "postponed"), or the proposition p is satisfied in the current state (the goal is "achieved"). In the latter case, the function Θ also "marks" the current state with $\bar{\mathrm{F}}^{=1}(p)$, which means that the goal $\mathrm{F}^{=1}(p)$ has been achieved. The exact purpose of these marks will be clarified later.

The game $G' = (V', E', (V'_\Box, V'_\bigcirc), \mathit{Prob}')$ is defined as follows. The set of vertices V' consists of vertices of the following two forms (f-vertices and g-vertices):

- f-vertices are of the form $(s, A, B, C)^f$ where $s \in V$, $A \subseteq \mathcal{S}$, $B \subseteq \mathcal{S}_{\mathrm{F}^{=1}} \cup \{\bullet\}$, and $C \subseteq \mathcal{S}_{\mathrm{F}^{>0}}$. Intuitively, the set A consists of formulas that should be satisfied in the current state (see the intuitive description of Θ above). The sets B and C assure that all subgoals of the form $F^{=1}\varphi$ and $F^{>0}\varphi$ are eventually fullfilled (see the mixed winning objective defined below).
- g-vertices are of the form $(s, A, B, C, \vec{D})^g$ where $s \in V$, $A \subseteq \mathcal{S} \cup \mathcal{S}_{\bar{\mathrm{F}}}$, $B \subseteq \mathcal{S}_{\mathrm{F}^{=1}} \cup \{\bullet\}$, $C \subseteq \mathcal{S}_{\mathrm{F}^{>0}}$, and $\vec{D} \in \prod_{t \in V} 2^{\mathcal{S}_{\mathrm{F}^{>0}}}$. The purpose of B and C is similar as in the case of f-vertices. The set A consists of subgoals that should be satisfied in successors of the current state. The vector $\vec{D}$ is used to distribute the subgoals of the form $\mathrm{F}^{>0}\varphi$ to the successors of the current state.

The set $V'_\Box$ consists of all f-vertices and of all g-vertices of the form $(s, A, B, C, \vec{D})^g$ where $s \in V_\Box$. The set $V'_\bigcirc$ consists of all g-vertices of the form $(s, A, B, C, \vec{D})^g$ where

$s \in V_{\bigcirc}$. The set E' of transitions of G' is defined as follows:

1. $(s, A, B, C)^f \to (s, A', B', C', \vec{D})^g$ iff the following conditions are satisfied:
   - $A' \in \Theta(A)$
   - B' is equal to
     - $\{\bullet\}$, if $A' \cap Ap \not\subseteq \nu(s)$ or there is $\neg p \in A'$ such that $p \in \nu(s)$;
     - $A' \cap \mathcal{S}_{\mathrm{F}^{=1}}$, if $B = \emptyset$;
     - $B \setminus \{\mathrm{F}^{=1}\xi \mid \bar{\mathrm{F}}^{=1}\xi \in A'\}$ otherwise.
   - if $C = \emptyset$ then $C' = A' \cap \mathcal{S}_{\mathrm{F}^{>0}}$; otherwise $C' = C \setminus \{\mathrm{F}^{>0}\xi \mid \bar{\mathrm{F}}^{>0}\xi \in A'\}$.
   - $\bigcup_{(s,t)\in E} \vec{D}_t = A' \cap \mathcal{S}_{\mathrm{F}^{>0}}$
   - if $s \in V_{\Box}$ then for each $t \in V$ such that $(s, t) \in E$ we have that $D_t = A' \cap \mathcal{S}_{\mathrm{F}^{>0}}$.

   Intuitively, the f-vertices are controlled by player $\Box$ who chooses a set of subgoals $A' \in \Theta(A)$. The atomic propositions in A' are immediately verified (if there is some inconsistency then $\bullet$ is put into B') while the other formulae in A' are passed to successors. The sets B' and C' are updated depending on which subgoals (subformulae) are chosen by player $\Box$ as "achieved" in the current state (cf. the intuitive description of Θ above). Note that the vertex s is not changed in the successors of f-vertices. The transitions of G are simulated in g-vertices (see below).

2. $(s, A, B, C, \vec{D})^g \to (t, A', B', C')^f$ if $(s,t) \in E$, $A' = (A \setminus (\mathcal{S}_{\mathrm{F}^{>0}} \cup \mathcal{S}_{\bar{\mathrm{F}}} \cup \mathcal{S}_{Ap})) \cup \vec{D}_t$, $B' = B$, and $C' = C \cap \vec{D}_t$

3. There are no other transitions in E' than those given by the rules 1. and 2.

Prob' is defined as follows: For all $s \in V_{\bigcirc}$, the probability of $(s, A, B, C, \vec{D})^g \to (t, A', B', C')^f$ is the same as the probability of $s \to t$ in G. We put $s'_{in} = (s_{in}, \{\psi\}, \emptyset, \emptyset)^f$. Finally, we define the mixed (P, Q) objective as follows:

- the set P consists of all vertices of the form $(s, A, B, \emptyset, \vec{D})^g$;
- the set Q consists of all vertices of the form $(s, A, \emptyset, C, \vec{D})^g$.

It remains to show that player $\Box$ has a (ν, ψ)-winning HD strategy in s_{in} iff player $\Box$ has a (P, Q)-winning HD strategy in s'_{in}. A full proof of this assertion can be found in [2]. □

Hence, the problem of our interest is reducible to another game-theoretic problem, whose complexity is analyzed in our next lemma.

Lemma 3.7. *The existence of a winning strategy in $1\frac{1}{2}$-player games with mixed objectives is decidable in polynomial time.*

A direct consequence of Lemma 3.6 and Lemma 3.7 is that the existence of a winning HD strategy in $1\frac{1}{2}$-player games with $\mathcal{L}(\mathrm{F}^{=1}, \mathrm{F}^{>0}, \mathrm{G}^{=1})$ objectives is in **EXPTIME**. It remains to establish the matching lower bound.

Lemma 3.8. *The existence of a winning HD (or HR) strategy in $1\frac{1}{2}$-player games with $\mathcal{L}(\mathrm{F}^{=1}, \mathrm{G}^{=1})$ objectives is **EXPTIME**-hard.*

A simple corollary of Lemma 3.6, Lemma 3.7, and Lemma 3.8 is the following:

Theorem 3.9. *The existence of a winning HD strategy in $1\frac{1}{2}$-player games with $\mathcal{L}(\mathrm{F}^{=1}, \mathrm{F}^{>0}, \mathrm{G}^{=1})$ objectives is **EXPTIME**-complete. The **EXPTIME** lower bound holds even for $\mathcal{L}(\mathrm{F}^{=1}, \mathrm{G}^{=1})$ objectives.*

It follows from the proofs of Lemma 3.6 and Lemma 3.7 that a winning HD strategy in $1\frac{1}{2}$-player games with $\mathcal{L}(\mathrm{F}^{=1}, \mathrm{F}^{>0}, \mathrm{G}^{=1})$ objectives actually requires only *finite memory* whose size is linear in the size of a given game and exponential in the size of a given objective. A natural question is whether Theorem 3.9 can be generalized to a larger class of qualitative PCTL objectives. One natural possibility is to add the $\mathrm{G}^{>0}$ operator, which yields the $\mathcal{L}(\mathrm{F}^{=1}, \mathrm{F}^{>0}, \mathrm{G}^{=1}, \mathrm{G}^{>0})$ fragment. However, there is a strong evidence that the method of Lemma 3.6 cannot be generalized to this class of objectives. This is because these objectives may already require *infinite memory*, which is demonstrated in our last theorem:

Theorem 3.10. *A winning HD strategy in $1\frac{1}{2}$ games with $\mathcal{L}(\mathrm{F}^{>0}, \mathrm{G}^{>0})$ objectives may require infinite memory.*

Proof. Let $\varphi \equiv \mathrm{G}^{>0}(\neg stop \wedge \mathrm{F}^{>0} stop)$ and let G be the following game (the valuation ν for atomic propositions *stop*, *left*, and *right* is also indicated in the figure):

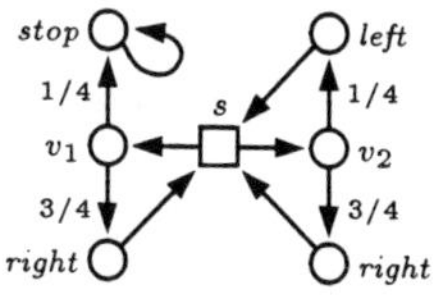

First we show that there is a (ν, φ)-winning HD strategy σ for player $\Box$ in the vertex v_1. We define $\sigma(ws)$ to be the Dirac distribution which assigns 1 to the transition leading to v_1 or v_2, depending on whether $\#_{right}(w) - \#_{left}(w) \leq 0$ or $\#_{right}(w) - \#_{left}(w) > 0$, respectively. Here $\#_{right}(w)$ denotes the number of occurrences of a state satisfying the proposition *right* in w. We claim that the state v_1 in the play $G(\sigma)$ satisfies the formula $\mathrm{G}^{=2/3}(\neg stop \wedge \mathrm{F}^{>0} stop)$ and hence also the formula φ. To see this, realize that the play $G(\sigma)$ corresponds to the unfolding of the following infinite Markov chain:

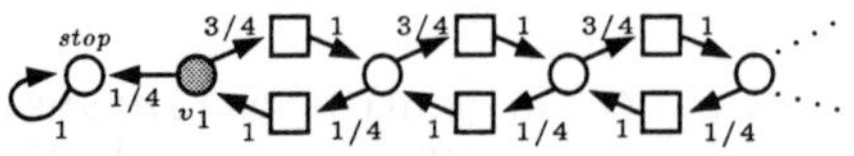

A standard calculation reveals that the probability of hitting the *stop* state from v_1 is equal to $1/3$. Hence, the probability of all runs initiated in v_1 which do *not* hit the *stop* state is $2/3$. All states in all these runs can reach the *stop* state with positive probability. Hence, v_1 satisfies the formula $G^{=2/3}(\neg stop \wedge F^{>0} stop)$.

Now we show that there is no (ν, φ)-winning HD strategy with finite memory. Suppose the converse. Let $(\mathcal{A}, f)$ be such a strategy where the automaton $\mathcal{A} = (Q, V, \delta, q_0)$ has n states. We show that the state v_1 in the corresponding play satisfies the formula $G^{=0}(\neg stop \wedge F^{>0} stop)$, which means that v_1 does not satisfy φ. We say that a state w in the play $G(\sigma(\mathcal{A}, f))$ is *live* if there is a state $ww's$ such that $w \to^* ww's$ and $f(\delta(q_0, ww's), s)$ assigns 1 to the transition leading to v_1. A state which is not live is *dead*. We claim that there is a fixed $\varepsilon > 0$ such that the probability of hitting a *stop* state from a given live state w is at least ε. To see this, it suffices to observe that whenever w is a live state, then there is a path from w to a *stop* state of length at most $3n+1$. Note that a state w is dead iff w is a *stop* state or w cannot reach a *stop* state at all. By applying standard arguments of Markov chain theory, we can now conclude that the probability of hitting a dead state from v_1 is equal to one. Since a dead state does not satisfy $\neg stop \wedge F^{>0} stop$, we obtain that v_1 satisfies $G^{=0}(\neg stop \wedge F^{>0} stop)$ and we are done. □

References

[1] C. Baier, M. Größer, M. Leucker, B. Bollig, and F. Ciesinski. Controller synthesis for probabilistic systems. In *Proceedings of IFIP TCS'2004*. Kluwer, 2004.

[2] T. Brázdil, V. Brožek, V. Forejt, and A. Kučera. Stochastic games with branching-time winning objectives. Technical report FIMU-RS-2006-02, Faculty of Informatics, Masaryk University, 2006.

[3] T. Brázdil, J. Esparza, and A. Kučera. Analysis and prediction of the long-run behavior of probabilistic sequential programs with recursion. In *Proceedings of FOCS 2005*, pp. 521–530. IEEE, 2005.

[4] T. Brázdil, A. Kučera, and O. Stražovský. On the decidability of temporal properties of probabilistic pushdown automata. In *Proceedings of STACS'2005*, vol. 3404 of *LNCS*, pp. 145–157. Springer, 2005.

[5] K. Chatterjee, L. de Alfaro, and T. Henzinger. The complexity of stochastic Rabin and Streett games. In *Proceedings of ICALP 2005*, vol. 3580 of *LNCS*, pp. 878–890. Springer, 2005.

[6] K. Chatterjee and T. Henzinger. Semiperfect-information games. In *Proceedings of FST&TCS 2005*, vol. 3821 of *LNCS*, pp. 1–18. Springer, 2005.

[7] K. Chatterjee, M. Jurdzinski, and T. Henzinger. Simple stochastic parity games. In *Proceedings of CSL'93*, vol. 832 of *LNCS*, pp. 100–113. Springer, 1994.

[8] K. Chatterjee, M. Jurdzinski, and T. Henzinger. Quantitative stochastic parity games. In *Proceedings of SODA 2004*, pp. 121–130. SIAM, 2004.

[9] L. de Alfaro and R. Majumdar. Quantitative solution of omega-regular games. *JCSS*, 68:374–397, 2004.

[10] J. Esparza, A. Kučera, and R. Mayr. Model-checking probabilistic pushdown automata. In *Proceedings of LICS 2004*, pp. 12–21. IEEE, 2004.

[11] K. Etessami and M. Yannakakis. Recursive Markov chains, stochastic grammars, and monotone systems of non-linear equations. In *Proceedings of STACS'2005*, vol. 3404 of *LNCS*, pp. 340–352. Springer, 2005.

[12] H. Hansson and B. Jonsson. A logic for reasoning about time and reliability. *Formal Aspects of Computing*, 6:512–535, 1994.

[13] David Harel. Effective transformations on infinite trees, with applications to high undecidability, dominoes, and fairness. *J. ACM*, 33(1):224–248, 1986.

[14] A. Kučera and O. Stražovský. On the controller synthesis for finite-state Markov decision processes. In *Proceedings of FST&TCS 2005*, vol. 3821 of *LNCS*, pp. 541–552. Springer, 2005.

[15] Ch. Papadimitriou. *Computational Complexity*. Addison-Wesley, 1994.

[16] W. Thomas. Infinite games and verification. In *Proceedings of CAV 2003*, vol. 2725 of *LNCS*, pp. 58–64. Springer, 2003.

Coinductive Proof Principles for Stochastic Processes

Dexter Kozen
Department of Computer Science
Cornell University
Ithaca, New York 14853-7501, USA
kozen@cs.cornell.edu

Abstract

We give an explicit coinduction principle for recursively-defined stochastic processes. The principle applies to any closed property, not just equality, and works even when solutions are not unique. The rule encapsulates low-level analytic arguments, allowing reasoning about such processes at a higher algebraic level. We illustrate the use of the rule in deriving properties of a simple coin-flip process.

1 Introduction

Coinduction has been shown to be a useful tool in functional programming. Streams, automata, concurrent and stochastic processes, and recursive types have been successfully analyzed using coinductive methods; see [1, 8, 3, 11, 6] and references therein.

Most approaches emphasize the relationship between coinduction and bisimulation. In Rutten's treatment [11] (see also [6, 1]), the coinduction principle states that under certain conditions, two bisimilar processes must be equal. For example, to prove the equality of infinite streams $\sigma = \mathtt{merge}(\mathtt{split}(\sigma))$, where merge and split satisfy the familiar coinductive definitions

$$\begin{aligned}\mathtt{merge}(a :: \sigma, \tau) &= a :: \mathtt{merge}(\tau, \sigma)\\ \#1(\mathtt{split}(a :: b :: \rho)) &= a :: \#1(\mathtt{split}(\rho))\\ \#2(\mathtt{split}(a :: b :: \rho)) &= b :: \#2(\mathtt{split}(\rho)),\end{aligned}$$

it suffices to show that the two streams are bisimilar. An alternative view is that certain systems of recursive equations over a certain algebraic structure have unique solutions. Desharnais et al. [3, 8] study bisimulation in a probabilistic context. They are primarily interested in the approximation of one process with another. Again, they focus on bisimulation, but do not formulate an explicit coinduction rule.

In this paper we introduce a generalization of the coinduction principle that applies to other properties besides equations and to situations in which solutions are not unique. We illustrate its use with an extended example that demonstrates how the rule encapsulates low-level analytic arguments involving convergent sequences in its proof of soundness, thereby allowing reasoning about such processes at a higher algebraic level.

2 An Example

Consider the following procedure for simulating a coin of arbitrary real bias q, $0 \leq q \leq 1$, with a coin of arbitrary real bias p, $0 < p < 1$. We assume unit-time exact arithmetic on real numbers.

```
boolean qflip(q) {
   if (p < q) {
      if (pflip()) return true;
      else return qflip(1-(1-q)/(1-p));
   } else {
      if (pflip()) return qflip(q/p);
      else return false;
   }
}
```

Intuitively, if $p < q$ and the bias-p coin flip returns heads (true), then we halt and output heads; this gives a fraction p/q of the desired probability q of heads of the simulated bias-q coin. If the bias-p coin returns tails, we rescale the problem appropriately and call qflip tail-recursively. Similarly, if $p \geq q$ and the bias-p coin returns tails, then we halt and output tails, and if not, we rescale appropriately and call qflip tail-recursively.

On any input $0 \leq q \leq 1$, the probability of halting is 1, since the procedure halts with probability at least $\min(p, 1-p)$ in each iteration. The probability that qflip halts and returns heads on input q exists and satisfies the recurrence

$$H(q) = \begin{cases} p \cdot H(\frac{q}{p}), & \text{if } q \leq p,\\ p + (1-p) \cdot H(1 - \frac{1-q}{1-p}), & \text{if } q > p.\end{cases} \qquad (1)$$

Now $H^*(q) = q$ is a solution to this recurrence, as can be seen by direct substitution. There are uncountably many other solutions as well, but these are all unbounded (see Section 4). Since H^* is the unique bounded solution, it must give the probability of heads.

We can do the same for the expected running time. Let us measure the expected number of calls to `pflip` on input q. The expectation exists and is uniformly bounded on the unit interval by $1/\min(p, 1-p)$, the expected running time of a Bernoulli (coin-flip) process with success probability $\min(p, 1-p)$. From the program, we obtain the recurrence

$$\begin{aligned} &E_0(q) \\ &= \begin{cases} (1-p)\cdot 1 \;+\; p\cdot(1+E_0(\frac{q}{p})), & \text{if } q \le p, \\ p\cdot 1 \;+\; (1-p)\cdot(1+E_0(1-\frac{1-q}{1-p})), & \text{if } q > p \end{cases} \\ &= \begin{cases} 1 \;+\; p\cdot E_0(\frac{q}{p}), & \text{if } q \le p, \\ 1 \;+\; (1-p)\cdot E_0(1-\frac{1-q}{1-p}), & \text{if } q > p. \end{cases} \end{aligned}$$

The unique bounded solution to this recurrence is

$$E_0^*(q) \;=\; \frac{q}{p} + \frac{1-q}{1-p}. \qquad (2)$$

That it is a solution can be ascertained by direct substitution; uniqueness requires a further argument. As above, there are uncountably many unbounded solutions, but since E_0^* is the unique bounded solution, it must give the expected running times.

So far there is nothing that cannot be handled with Rutten or Desharnais et al. approach. However, the situation gets more interesting when we observe that slight modifications of the algorithm lead to noncontinuous fractal solutions with no simple characterizations like (2). The fractal behavior of stochastic processes has been previously observed in [7].

Assume $p \le 1-p$. Say we want to save time by taking off a larger fraction $1-p$ of the remaining "heads" weight when $q > 1-p$. In that case, we will halt and report heads if `pflip` gives tails. The new code is set in boldface.

```
boolean qflip(q) {
  if (1-p < q) {
    if (pflip()) return qflip(1-(1-q)/p);
    else return true;
  } else if (p < q) {
    if (pflip()) return true;
    else return qflip(1-(1-q)/(1-p));
  } else {
    if (pflip()) return qflip(q/p);
    else return false;
  }
}
```

The recurrence for the expected running time is

$$E_1(q) \;=\; 1 + r(q)E_1(f_1(q)), \qquad (3)$$

where

$$f_1(q) \;=\; \begin{cases} \frac{q}{p}, & \text{if } q \le p \\ 1-\frac{1-q}{1-p}, & \text{if } p < q \le 1-p \\ 1-\frac{1-q}{p}, & \text{if } 1-p < q \end{cases}$$

$$r(q) \;=\; \begin{cases} 1-p, & \text{if } p < q \le 1-p \\ p, & \text{otherwise.} \end{cases}$$

Again, there is a unique bounded solution E_1^*, but there is no longer a nice algebraic characterization like (2). The solution for $p = 1/4$ is the noncontinuous fractal shown in Fig. 1, shown compared to the straight line E_0^* running from 4/3 to 4. The large discontinuity at $q = 1-p = 3/4$ is due to the modification of the algorithm for $q > 1-p$, and this discontinuity is propagated everywhere by the recurrence.

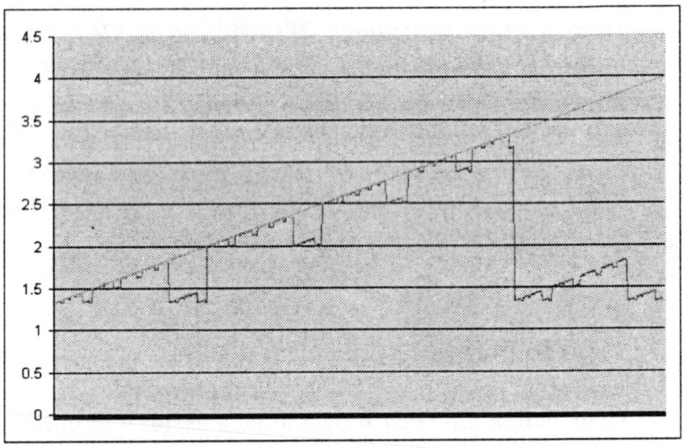

Figure 1. Fractal solution of (3)

Fig. 1 and intuition dictate that $E_1^* \le E_0^*$, but how do we prove this? Not by induction, because there is no basis. An analytic argument involving convergence of sequences would be one possibility. However, there is a simpler alternative. It will follow from our coinductive proof principle that to conclude $E_1^* \le E_0^*$, it suffices to show that $\tau(E)(q) \le E_0^*(q)$ whenever $E(f_1(q)) \le E_0^*(f_1(q))$, where τ is a suitably defined operator representing the unwinding of the recurrence once. This property is easily checked algebraically, and no analysis is necessary.

We can modify the algorithm further to achieve more savings. If $1/2 < q \le 1-p$, it would seem to our advantage to remove p from the tail probability of q rather than from the head probability. Although the weight removed in both cases is the same, savings for q in this region are realized in the next step. The new code is again set in boldface.

```
boolean qflip(q) {
  if (1-p < q) {
    if (pflip()) return qflip(1-(1-q)/p);
    else return true;
  } else if (.5 < q) {
    if (pflip()) return false;
    else return qflip(q/(1-p));
  } else if (p < q) {
    if (pflip()) return true;
    else return qflip(1-(1-q)/(1-p));
  } else {
    if (pflip()) return qflip(q/p);
    else return false;
  }
}
```

The recurrence is

$$E_2(q) = 1 + r(q)E_2(f_2(q)) \tag{4}$$

with

$$f_2(q) = \begin{cases} \frac{q}{p}, & \text{if } q \le p, \\ 1 - \frac{1-q}{1-p} & \text{if } p < q \le 1/2, \\ \frac{q}{1-p} & \text{if } 1/2 < q \le 1-p, \\ 1 - \frac{1-q}{p} & \text{if } 1-p < q, \end{cases}$$

and $r(q)$ as above. The symmetric fractal solution E_2^* is shown in Fig. 2. Intuition seems to say that this solution

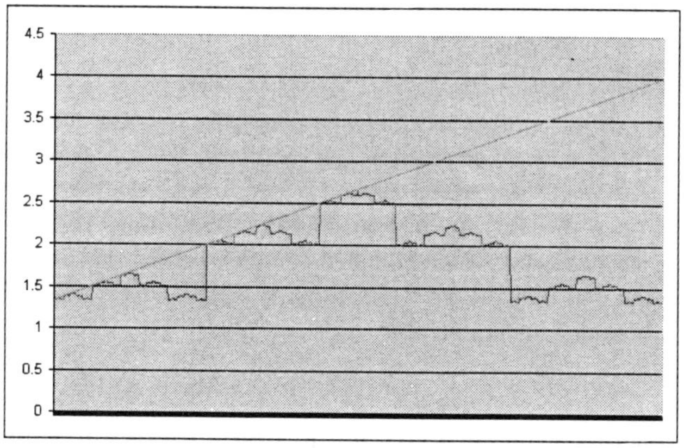

Figure 2. Fractal solution of (4)

should be better, but it turns out that this is not always the case: for $p = 1/4$, there are countably many minute intervals on which $E_2^*(q) > E_1^*(q)$.

One might ask whether there is a slight modification of E_2^* that is everywhere better than E_1^*. The answer is yes: take the breakpoint not at 1/2, but at $c = \max((1-p)^2, 1-(1-p)^2)$, provided $p \le (1-p)^2$. For $p = 1/4$, this would give $c = 9/16$. Now the recurrence is $E_3(q) = 1 + r(q)E_3(f_3(q))$ with

$$f_3(q) = \begin{cases} \frac{q}{p}, & \text{if } q \le p, \\ 1 - \frac{1-q}{1-p} & \text{if } p < q \le c, \\ \frac{q}{1-p} & \text{if } c < q \le 1-p, \\ 1 - \frac{1-q}{p} & \text{if } 1-p < q. \end{cases} \tag{5}$$

Now we wish to show that $E_3^* \le E_1^*$ on the whole unit interval. Note that we are comparing two nowhere-differentiable functions[1]; we have no nice algebraic description of them save as solutions of the recurrences $E_i(q) = 1 + r(q)E_i(f_i(q))$. However, we can prove the desired inequality purely algebraically using the coinductive principle below, without recourse to analysis. We outline a proof below, after we have stated and proved the validity of the principle.

3 Statement and Proof of the Coinduction Principle

Here is a statement and proof of the coinduction principle. See [4] for the necessary background. Let B be a Banach space (complete normed linear space) over $\mathbb{C}$ and let R be a bounded linear operator on B (*bounded* is synonymous with *continuous* for linear operators on B). Suppose that $I - R$ is invertible; that is, $1 \notin \sigma(R)$, where $\sigma(R)$ is the *spectrum* of R, or the set of $\lambda \in \mathbb{C}$ such that $\lambda I - R$ is invertible. Let $a \in B$. Since $I - R$ is invertible, there is a unique solution e^* to $e = a + Re$ given by $e^* = (I-R)^{-1}a$.

Theorem 3.1 *Consider the affine operator $\tau(e) = a + Re$, where R has spectral radius < 1. Let $\phi \subseteq B$ be a closed nonempty region preserved by τ. Then $e^* \in \phi$.*

Proof. The spectral radius of R is

$$\sup_{\lambda \in \sigma(R)} |\lambda| = \inf_n \sqrt[n]{|R^n|}.$$

If this quantity is < 1, then there exists n such that $|R^n| < 1$, thus $\sum_n R^n$ converges and equals $(I - R)^{-1}$. One can show by elementary arguments that

$$|\tau^{m+k}(e_0) - \tau^m(e_0)| \le |R^m| \cdot |\sum_{r=0}^{k-1} R^r| \cdot |\tau(e_0) - e_0|,$$

thus the sequence $\tau^n(e_0)$ is a Cauchy sequence. Since B is a complete metric space, the sequence converges, and from

[1] Hermite and Poincaré eschewed such functions, calling them a "dreadful plague". Poincaré wrote: "Yesterday, if a new function was invented, it was to serve some purpose; today, they are invented only to debunk the arguments of our predecessors, and they will never have any other use."

the continuity of τ it follows that its limit is a fixpoint of τ, therefore must be e^*, the unique bounded solution of $e = a + Re$. If $e_0 \in \phi$, then $\tau^n(e_0) \in \phi$ for all n since τ preserves ϕ, and $e^* \in \phi$ since ϕ is closed. □

This translates to the following coinduction principle.

Theorem 3.2 *Let τ be as in Theorem 3.1. Let ϕ be a closed property. The following proof rule is valid:*

$$\frac{\exists e\ \phi(e) \qquad \forall e\ \phi(e) \Rightarrow \phi(\tau(e))}{\phi(e^*)}. \tag{6}$$

More generally, for any $n \geq 1$,

$$\frac{\exists e\ \phi(e) \qquad \forall e\ \phi(e) \Rightarrow \phi(\tau^n(e))}{\phi(e^*)}. \tag{7}$$

Proof. The rule (6) is just a restatement of Theorem 3.1. The rule (7) follows by applying (6) to the closed property $\psi(e) = \bigvee_{i=0}^{n-1} \phi(\tau^i(e))$. This is a closed property because τ is continuous on B. □

For example, to show that $E_1^* \leq E_0^*$ using the rule (6), we take B to be the space of bounded complex-valued functions on the unit interval, $a = \lambda x.1$, $R : B \to B$ the bounded linear operator $RE = \lambda q.r(q)E(f_1(q))$ with spectral radius $1-p$, $\phi(E)$ the closed property

$$\forall q\ E(q) \ \leq\ \frac{q}{p} + \frac{1-q}{1-p},$$

and

$$\tau(E) \ =\ \lambda q.(1 + r(q)E(f_1(q))), \tag{8}$$

where

$$f_1(q) \ =\ \begin{cases} \frac{q}{p}, & \text{if } q \leq p \\ 1 - \frac{1-q}{1-p}, & \text{if } p < q \leq 1-p \\ 1 - \frac{1-q}{p}, & \text{if } 1-p < q \end{cases}$$

$$r(q) \ =\ \begin{cases} 1-p, & \text{if } p < q \leq 1-p \\ p, & \text{otherwise.} \end{cases}$$

In this special case, the desired conclusion is

$$\forall q\ E_1^*(q) \ \leq\ \frac{q}{p} + \frac{1-q}{1-p}, \tag{9}$$

and the two premises we must establish are

$$\exists E\ \forall q\ E(q) \ \leq\ \frac{q}{p} + \frac{1-q}{1-p}, \tag{10}$$

$$\forall E\ (\forall q\ E(q) \leq \frac{q}{p} + \frac{1-q}{1-p} \Rightarrow \forall q\ \tau(E)(q) \leq \frac{q}{p} + \frac{1-q}{1-p}). \tag{11}$$

The premise (10) is trivial; for example, take $E = \lambda q.0$. For (11), let E be arbitrary. We wish to show that

$$\forall q\ E(q) \leq \frac{q}{p} + \frac{1-q}{1-p} \Rightarrow \forall q\ \tau(E)(q) \leq \frac{q}{p} + \frac{1-q}{1-p}. \tag{12}$$

Picking q arbitrarily on the right-hand side and then specializing the left-hand side at $f_1(q)$, it suffices to show

$$E(f_1(q)) \leq \frac{f_1(q)}{p} + \frac{1-f_1(q)}{1-p} \Rightarrow \tau(E)(q) \leq \frac{q}{p} + \frac{1-q}{1-p}. \tag{13}$$

Substituting the definition of τ, we need to show

$$E(f_1(q)) \leq \frac{f_1(q)}{p} + \frac{1-f_1(q)}{1-p} \Rightarrow 1 + r(q)E(f_1(q)) \leq \frac{q}{p} + \frac{1-q}{1-p}. \tag{14}$$

The proof breaks into three cases, depending on whether $q \leq p$, $p < q \leq 1-p$, or $q > 1-p$. In the first case, $f_1(q) = q/p$ and $r(q) = p$. Then (14) becomes

$$E(\frac{q}{p}) \leq \frac{q}{p^2} + \frac{1-\frac{q}{p}}{1-p} \quad \Rightarrow \quad 1 + pE(\frac{q}{p}) \leq \frac{q}{p} + \frac{1-q}{1-p}.$$

But

$$1 + pE(\frac{q}{p}) \ \leq\ 1 + p(\frac{q}{p^2} + \frac{1-\frac{q}{p}}{1-p}) \ =\ \frac{q}{p} + \frac{1-q}{1-p}.$$

The remaining two cases are equally straightforward. The last case, $q > 1-p$, uses the fact that $p \leq 1/2$.

One can also prove closed properties of more than one function E. For example, as promised, we can show that $E_3^* \leq E_1^*$ whenever $\max((1-p)^2, 1-(1-p)^2) \leq c \leq 1-p$. For this application, B is the space of pairs (E, E'), where E and E' are bounded complex-valued functions on the unit interval, $a = (\lambda x.1, \lambda x.1)$, and $R : B \to B$ is the bounded linear operator

$$R(E, E') \ =\ (\lambda q.r(q)E(f_3(q)), \lambda q.r(q)E'(f_1(q)))$$

with spectral radius $1-p$. The closed property of interest is $E \leq E'$, but we need the stronger induction hypothesis

$$\begin{aligned} &\phi(E, E') \\ &= \forall q\ E(q) \leq E'(q) && (15) \\ &\quad \wedge\ E'(q) \geq \frac{1}{1-p} && (16) \\ &\quad \wedge\ p < q \leq 1-p \ \Rightarrow\ E'(q) \geq 2 && (17) \\ &\quad \wedge\ E(q) \leq \frac{q}{p} + \frac{1-q}{1-p} && (18) \\ &\quad \wedge\ 0 < q \leq p \ \Rightarrow\ E(q) = E(q+1-p). && (19) \end{aligned}$$

There certainly exist (E, E') satisfying ϕ. We have also already argued that induction hypothesis (18) is preserved by τ. The argument for (16) is similar. For (19), if $0 < q \leq p$, then

$$1-p \;<\; q+1-p \;\leq\; 1,$$

therefore

$$\begin{aligned} r(q) &= r(q+1-p) \;=\; p \\ f_3(q) &= q/p \\ f_3(q+1-p) &= 1-(1-(q+1-p))/p \\ &= q/p. \end{aligned}$$

It follows that

$$\begin{aligned} &1+r(q)E(f_3(q)) \\ &\quad= 1+r(q+1-p)E(f_3(q+1-p)) \\ &\quad= 1+pE(q/p). \end{aligned}$$

For (17), if $p < q \leq 1-p$, then

$$\begin{aligned} r(q) &= 1-p \\ E'(f_1(q)) &\geq \frac{1}{1-p} \end{aligned}$$

by the induction hypothesis (16), thus

$$\begin{aligned} 1+r(q)E'(f_1(q)) &\geq 1+(1-p)\frac{1}{1-p} \\ &= 2. \end{aligned}$$

Finally, for (15), we wish to show

$$1+r(q)E(f_3(q)) \;\leq\; 1+r(q)E'(f_1(q)),$$

or equivalently,

$$E(f_3(q)) \;\leq\; E'(f_1(q)). \tag{20}$$

Since f_1 and f_3 coincide except in the range $c < q \leq 1-p$, we need only show (20) for q in this range.

It follows from the assumptions in effect that

$$\begin{aligned} p \;<\; f_1(q) \;&=\; 1-\frac{1-q}{1-p} \\ \leq\; 1-p \;<\; f_3(q) \;&=\; \frac{q}{1-p}, \end{aligned}$$

thus

$$\begin{aligned} &E(f_3(q)) \\ &= E(\frac{q}{1-p}-(1-p)) && \text{by (19)} \\ &\leq \frac{\frac{q}{1-p}-(1-p)}{p}+\frac{1-(\frac{q}{1-p}-(1-p))}{1-p} && \text{by (18)} \\ &= (\frac{q}{1-p}-1)\frac{1-2p}{p(1-p)}+2 \\ &\leq 2 && \text{since } p, q \leq 1-p \\ &\leq E'(f_1(q)) && \text{by (17).} \end{aligned}$$

Note that nowhere in this proof did we use any analytic arguments. All the necessary analysis is encapsulated in the proof of Theorem 3.1.

As a final application, we show how to use the coinductive proof rule (6) of Theorem 3.2 to argue that for $p < 1/2$, the function E_1^* is nowhere differentiable. We do this by showing that E_1^* has a dense set of discontinuities on the unit interval.

Consider the closed property

$$\forall q\; E(q) \geq 1/(1-p). \tag{21}$$

We would like to show that E_1^* satisfies this property. There exists an E satisfying this property, namely $\lambda q.1/(1-p)$, thus the first premise of (6) is satisfied. For the second premise, we show that (21) is preserved under the map τ defined by (8); that is,

$$\forall q\; E(q) \;\geq\; \frac{1}{1-p} \quad\Rightarrow\quad \forall q\; \tau(E)(q) \;\geq\; \frac{1}{1-p}.$$

Choosing q on the right-hand side arbitrarily, then specializing the left-hand side at $f_1(q)$, it suffices to show

$$E(f_1(q)) \;\geq\; \frac{1}{1-p} \quad\Rightarrow\quad 1+r(q)E(f_1(q)) \;\geq\; \frac{1}{1-p}.$$

But

$$\begin{aligned} 1+r(q)E(f_1(q)) &\geq 1+\frac{r(q)}{1-p} \;\geq\; 1+\frac{p}{1-p} \\ &= \frac{1}{1-p}. \end{aligned}$$

By the rule (6), we can conclude that

$$\forall q\;\; E_1^*(q) \;\;\geq\;\; \frac{1}{1-p}. \tag{22}$$

Now we show that E_1^* has discontinuities at p and $1-p$. It follows from (22) that for all q in the range $p < q \leq 1-p$,

$$\begin{aligned} E_1^*(q) &= 1+r(q)E_1^*(f_1(q)) \\ &\geq 1+(1-p)\frac{1}{1-p} \;=\; 2. \end{aligned} \tag{23}$$

Also, for all q in the range $0 < q < p$,

$$\begin{aligned} E_1^*(1-p+q) &= 1+pE_1^*(1-\frac{1-(1-p+q)}{p}) \\ &= 1+pE_1^*(\frac{q}{p}) \;=\; E_1^*(q). \end{aligned} \tag{24}$$

Moreover, by (9) we have that $E_1^*(q) \leq 1/p$ for all q. Then for $\varepsilon < p^2$,

$$\begin{aligned}
E_1^*(\varepsilon) &= 1 + pE_1^*(\frac{\varepsilon}{p}) \\
&= 1 + p(1 + pE_1^*(\frac{\varepsilon}{p^2})) \;\leq\; 1 + 2p \\
E_1^*(1-\varepsilon) &= 1 + pE_1^*(1 - \frac{\varepsilon}{p}) \\
&= 1 + p(1 + pE_1^*(1 - \frac{\varepsilon}{p^2})) \;\leq\; 1 + 2p.
\end{aligned}$$

From these facts and (24) it follows that

$$E_1^*(1-p+\varepsilon) = E_1^*(\varepsilon) \leq 1+2p \quad (25)$$

$$E_1^*(p-\varepsilon) = E_1^*(1-\varepsilon) \leq 1+2p. \quad (26)$$

Since $1 + 2p < 2$, (23), (25), and (26) imply that E_1^* has discontinuities at p and $1 - p$.

Finally, we show that every nonempty open interval contains a discontinuity. Suppose for a contradiction that E_1^* is continuous on a nonempty open interval (a, b). The interval (a, b) can contain neither p nor $1 - p$, so the entire interval must be contained in one of the three regions $(0, p)$, $(p, 1 - p)$, or $(1 - p, 1)$.

Suppose it is contained in $(0, p)$. Then

$$E_1^*(q) = 1 + pE_1^*(q/p)$$

for $a < q < b$, thus

$$E_1^*(q/p) = (E_1^*(q) - 1)/p$$

for $a/p < q/p < b/p$, so E_1^* is also continuous on the interval $(a/p, b/p)$. But the length of this interval is $(b - a)/p$, thus we have produced a longer interval on which E_1^* is continuous.

A similar argument holds if (a, b) is contained in one of the intervals $(p, 1-p)$ or $(1-p, 1)$. In the former case, E_1^* must also be continuous on the interval

$$(1 - (1-a)/(1-p),\; 1 - (1-b)/(1-p))$$

of length $(b - a)/(1 - p)$, and in the latter case, E_1^* must also be continuous on the interval

$$(1 - (1-a)/p,\; 1 - (1-b)/p)$$

of length $(b - a)/p$.

In each of these three cases, we have produced an interval of continuity that is longer than (a, b) by a factor of at least $1/(1 - p)$. This process can be repeated at most $\log(b-a)/\log(1-p)$ steps before the interval must contain one of the discontinuities p or $1-p$. This is a contradiction.

4 Unbounded Solutions

That these coinductive proofs have no basis is reflected in the fact that there exist unbounded solutions in addition to the unique bounded solutions. All unbounded solutions are necessarily noncontinuous, because any continuous solution on a closed interval is bounded.

Theorem 3.1 does not mention these unbounded solutions, because they live outside the Banach space B. Nevertheless, it is possible to construct unbounded solutions to any of the above recurrences. Let G be the graph with vertices $q \in [0, 1]$ and edges $(q, f(q))$. Note that every vertex in G has outdegree 1. Let C be an undirected connected component of G. One can show easily that the following are equivalent:

(i) C contains an undirected cycle;

(ii) C contains a directed cycle;

(iii) for some $q \in C$ and $k \geq 0$, $f^k(q) = q$.

Call C *rational* if these conditions hold of C, *irrational* otherwise. For example, the connected components of 0 and 1 are rational, since $f(0) = 0$ and $f(1) = 1$. There are other rational components besides these; for example, if $p = 1/2$, the component of $q = 2/3$ is rational, since $f^2(2/3) = 2/3$.

Now any solution E must agree with the unique bounded solution E^* on the rational components. This is because if $f^k(q) = q$, then the set $\{f^k(q) \mid k \geq 0\}$ is finite, hence E is bounded on this set, and one can show by an extension of the uniqueness argument above that E and E^* must agree on this set. But the values of E on an entire connected component are uniquely determined by its value on a single element of the component, since $E(q)$ uniquely determines $E(f(q))$ and vice-versa. Thus E and E^* must agree on the entire component.

For an irrational component, since there are no cycles, it is connected as a tree. We can freely assign an arbitrary value to an arbitrarily chosen element q of the component, then extend the function to the entire component uniquely and without conflict.

It therefore remains to show that there exists an irrational component. This follows from the fact that if $f^k(q) = q$, then q is a rational function of p. To see this, note that any $f^k(q)$ is of the form

$$\frac{q}{p^m(1-p)^{k-m}} - r$$

for some $0 \leq m \leq k$ and $r \in \mathbb{Q}(p)$, the field of rational function of p. This can be shown by induction on k. Solving $f^k(q) = q$ for q gives

$$q = \frac{rp^m(1-p)^{k-m}}{1 - p^m(1-p)^{k-m}} \in \mathbb{Q}(p).$$

Thus the component of any real $q \notin \mathbb{Q}(p)$ is an irrational component. There exist uncountably many such q, since $\mathbb{Q}(p)$ is countable. In fact, there are uncountably many irrational components, since each component is countable, and a countable union of countable sets is countable. Moreover, it can be shown that if q_1 and q_2 are in the same component, then $\mathbb{Q}(p, q_1) = \mathbb{Q}(p, q_2)$. This is because if q_1 and q_2 are in the same component, then $f^{k_1}(q_1) = f^{k_2}(q_2)$ for some $k_1, k_2 \in \mathbb{N}$, so

$$\frac{q_1}{p^{m_1}(1-p)^{k_1-m_1}} - r_1 \quad = \quad \frac{q_2}{p^{m_2}(1-p)^{k_2-m_2}} - r_2,$$

therefore $q_1 \in \mathbb{Q}(p, q_2)$ and $q_2 \in \mathbb{Q}(p, q_1)$.

We have thus characterized all the possible solutions.

5 Why Is This Coinduction?

The reader may be curious why we have called the rule (6) a coinduction rule, since it may seem different from the usual forms of coinduction found in the literature. The form of the rule and its use in applications certainly bears a resemblance to other versions in the literature, but to justify the terminology on formal grounds requires a more lengthy discussion.

One common formulation of induction and coinduction (see e.g. [5]) is as follows. Let U be a universal set, and let 2^U denote the powerset of U. This is a complete lattice under set inclusion. A function $F : 2^U \to 2^U$ is *monotone* if $X \subseteq Y$ implies $FX \subseteq FY$. By the Knaster–Tarski theorem, F has a unique $\subseteq$-least fixpoint

$$\mu F \quad = \quad \sup_\alpha F^\alpha \emptyset \quad = \quad \bigcap\{X \mid FX \subseteq X\}$$

and a unique $\subseteq$-greatest fixpoint $\nu F = {\sim}\mu({\sim}F{\sim})$, where $\sim$ denotes set complementation in U. One can think of F as a closure condition specifying some inductively defined set of individuals, and μF as the set so defined. In this approach, the induction rule says that for any X, if $FX \subseteq X$ then $\mu F \subseteq X$. That is, any set that is closed under F contains the least such set.

In this framework, the coinduction rule says that if $X \subseteq FX$, then $X \subseteq \nu X$. That is, any set that is *F-consistent* is contained in the largest such set. Here we think of F as specifying a consistency condition. To say that an element is *consistent* just means that is not inconsistent, where inconsistency is inductively defined by the dual operator ${\sim}F{\sim}$. Intuitively, the difference is that we take an element in μF if there is good reason to take it, whereas we take an element in νF if there is no good reason not to take it. Here we have formulated these rules in terms of a lattice of sets, but one can easily generalize to any complete lattice.

There is a somewhat more general formulation (see e.g. [10]) in terms of algebras and coalgebras. Let C be a category and $F : C \to C$ a covariant endofunctor. An *F-algebra* is a pair (X, β), where X is an object of C and β is an arrow $\beta : FX \to X$, the *evaluation morphism.* The F-algebras are the objects of a category F-Alg with arrows consisting of all arrows h of C that commute with the evaluation morphisms. Similarly, an *F-coalgebra* is a pair (Y, γ), where Y is an object of C and γ is an arrow $\gamma : X \to FX$. The F-coalgebras form a category F-Coalg with arrows consisting of all those arrows of C that commute with the evaluation morphisms.

This formulation is most useful for dealing with inductively defined data structures such as finite lists and trees and coinductively defined data structures such as streams and recursive types. In such applications, the underlying category C is Set, and the functor F typically specifies an algebraic signature consisting of a set of *constructors* or a coalgebraic signature consisting of a set of *destructors*.

The induction and coinduction principles in this setting come in weak and strong forms. The strong form of the induction principle declares a certain F-algebra—usually some inductively-defined data structure like finite lists or finite binary trees—to be *initial* in the category F-Alg, which says that there is a unique morphism from that algebra to any other F-algebra. The weak form says that that algebra has no proper subalgebras (monomorphisms in). Over Set this means that any subalgebra (subset closed under the constructors) is the whole algebra. The strong form implies the weak form.

Dually, the strong form of the coinduction principle declares a certain F-coalgebra—usually something like streams or recursive types—to be *final* in the category F-Coalg, which says that there is a unique morphism from any other F-coalgebra to that F-coalgebra. The weak form says that that coalgebra has no proper homomorphic images (epimorphisms out). For example, the coalgebra $(\Sigma^\omega, \mathsf{head}, \mathsf{tail})$ of streams over Σ is final in the category of Σ-simple transition systems (Σ-STS) whose objects are $(X, \mathsf{obs}, \mathsf{cont})$, where $\mathsf{obs} : X \to \Sigma$ gives an *observation* at each state and $\mathsf{cont} : X \to X$ gives a *continuation* (next state) for each state. The unique morphism $(X, \mathsf{obs}, \mathsf{cont}) \to (\Sigma^\omega, \mathsf{head}, \mathsf{tail})$ maps a state $s \in X$ to the stream $(\mathsf{obs}(s), \mathsf{obs}(\mathsf{cont}(s)), \mathsf{obs}(\mathsf{cont}^2(s)), \ldots) \in \Sigma^\omega$. Here obs and cont are destructors rather than constructors. The functor F is of the form $FX = \Sigma \times X$ and $Fh = (\mathsf{Id}_\Sigma, h)$ with evaluation morphisms $\beta = (\mathsf{obs}, \mathsf{cont})$.

Coinductive proofs in this framework often take the following form. If (X, β) is an F-coalgebra over $C =$ Set, and if h is the unique morphism to the final F-coalgebra, then for $s, t \in X$, one can prove that $h(s) = h(t)$ by exhibiting an F-coalgebra congruence R (kernel of an F-coalgebra morphism) containing the pair (s, t). For example, in a Σ-STS, an F-coalgebra congruence is just a *bisimulation*, or a relation R such that

$$\forall u \forall v \;\; u \, R \, v \;\; \Rightarrow \;\; \mathsf{obs}(u) = \mathsf{obs}(v) \wedge \mathsf{cont}(u) \, R \, \mathsf{cont}(v).$$

This version of the coinduction rule just states that R refines the unique maximal F-coalgebra congruence, which is the kernel of the unique morphism to the final coalgebra.

The set-theoretic formulation is a special case of the category-theoretic formulation. In the set-theoretic formulation, the objects of the underlying category C are the subsets of U and the arrows are the set inclusions. To say that F is monotone says just that F is an endofunctor on C. The induction rule $FX \subseteq X \Rightarrow \mu F \subseteq X$ says just that μX is an initial F-algebra, and the coinduction rule $X \subseteq FX \Rightarrow X \subseteq \nu F$ says just that νX is a final F-coalgebra.

In the present case, we also have a category of coalgebras with a final object. Say we have a contractive map τ on a metric space B and a nonempty closed subset $\phi \subseteq B$ preserved by τ. Define $\tau(\phi) = \{\tau(s) \mid s \in \phi\}$. Consider the category C whose objects are the nonempty closed subsets of B and whose arrows are the reverse set inclusions; thus there is a unique arrow $\phi_1 \to \phi_2$ iff $\phi_1 \supseteq \phi_2$. The map $\bar{\tau}$ defined by $\bar{\tau}(\phi) = \mathsf{cl}(\tau(\phi))$, where cl denotes closure in the metric topology, is an endofunctor on C, since $\bar{\tau}(\phi)$ is a nonempty closed set, and $\phi_1 \supseteq \phi_2$ implies $\bar{\tau}(\phi_1) \supseteq \bar{\tau}(\phi_2)$. A $\bar{\tau}$-coalgebra is then a nonempty closed set ϕ such that $\phi \supseteq \bar{\tau}(\phi)$; equivalently, such that $\phi \supseteq \tau(\phi)$. The final coalgebra is $\{e^*\}$, where e^* is the unique fixpoint of τ. The coinduction rule (6) says that $\phi \supseteq \tau(\phi) \Rightarrow \phi \supseteq \{e^*\}$, which is equivalent to the statement that $\{e^*\}$ is final in the category of $\bar{\tau}$-coalgebras.

6 Future Work

There is great potential in the use of proof principles similar to those of Theorem 3.2 for simplifying arguments involving probabilistic programs, stochastic processes, and dynamical systems. Such rules encapsulate low-level analytic arguments, thereby allowing reasoning about such processes at a higher algebraic or logical level. Applications might be found in complex and functional analysis, the theory of linear operators, Markov decision processes, non-well-founded set theory, measure theory and integration, random walks, fractal analysis, functional programming, and probabilistic logic and semantics.

In particular, probabilistic programs can be modeled as measurable kernels $R(x, A)$, which can be interpreted as forward-moving measure transformers or backward-moving measurable function transformers [2, 9]. The expectation functions considered in this paper were uniformly bounded, but there are examples of probabilistic programs for which this is not true. It would be nice to find rules to handle these cases.

Acknowledgements

Thanks to Terese Damhøj Andersen, Lars Backstrom, Juris Hartmanis, Geoff Kozen, Prakash Panangaden, and the anonymous referees. This work was supported in part by ONR Grant N00014-01-1-0968. The views and conclusions contained herein are those of the author and should not be interpreted as necessarily representing the official policies or endorsements, either expressed or implied, of these organizations or the US Government.

References

[1] J. Barwise and L. Moss. *Vicious Circles: On the Mathematics of Non-Wellfounded Phenomena*, volume 60 of *CSLI Lecture Notes*. Center for the Study of Language and Information (CSLI), Stanford University, 1996.

[2] J. Desharnais, V. Gupta, R. Jagadeesan, and P. Panangaden. Metrics for labeled Markov processes. In *Proc. Int. Conf. Concurrency Theory (CONCUR'99)*. Springer-Verlag, 1999.

[3] J. Desharnais, V. Gupta, R. Jagadeesan, and P. Panangaden. The metric analogue of weak bisimulation for probabilistic processes. In *Proc. Conf. Logic in Computer Science (LICS'02)*. IEEE, 2002.

[4] N. Dunford and J. T. Schwartz. *Linear Operators: Part I: General Theory*. John Wiley, 1957.

[5] V. Gapeyev, M. Y. Levin, and B. C. Pierce. Recursive subtyping revealed: (functional pearl). In *Proc. 5th ACM SIGPLAN Int. Conf. Functional Programming (ICFP'00)*, pages 221–231, New York, 2000. ACM Press.

[6] A. D. Gordon. A tutorial on co-induction and functional programming. In *Proc. 1994 Glasgow Workshop on Functional Programming*. Springer Workshops in Computing, September 1994.

[7] V. Gupta, R. Jagadeesan, and P. Panangaden. Stochastic processes as concurrent constraint programs. In *Proc. Conf. Principles of Programming Languages (POPL'99)*, pages 189–202, January 1999.

[8] V. Gupta, R. Jagadeesan, and P. Panangaden. Approximate reasoning for real-time probabilistic processes. In *Proc. 1st Conf. Quantitative Evaluation of Systems (QEST'04)*. IEEE Press, 2004.

[9] D. Kozen. Semantics of probabilistic programs. *J. Comput. Syst. Sci.*, 22:328–350, 1981.

[10] J. Rutten. Universal coalgebra: A theory of systems. *Theor. Comput. Sci.*, 249:3–80, 2000.

[11] J. Rutten. Behavioural differential equations: a coinductive calculus of streams, automata, and power series. *Theoretical Computer Science*, 308:1–53, 2003.

Control in o-minimal hybrid systems

Patricia Bouyer*[1], Thomas Brihaye**[2], Fabrice Chevalier*[1]

* LSV - CNRS & ENS de Cachan
61, avenue du Président Wilson, 94230 Cachan, France
e-mails: {bouyer,chevalie}@lsv.ens-cachan.fr

** Université de Mons-Hainaut, Institut de Mathématique
6, avenue du Champ de Mars, 7000 Mons, Belgium
e-mail: thomas.brihaye@umh.ac.be

Abstract

In this paper, we consider the control of general hybrid systems. In this context we show that time-abstract bisimulation is not adequate for solving such a problem. That is why we consider an other equivalence, namely the suffix equivalence based on the encoding of trajectories through words. We show that this suffix equivalence is in general a correct abstraction for control problems. We apply this result to o-minimal hybrid systems, and get decidability and computability results in this framework.

1 Introduction

Control of hybrid systems. Hybrid systems are finite-state machines equipped with a continuous dynamics. In the last thirty years, formal verification of such systems has become a very active field of research in computer science, with numerous success stories. In this context, hybrid automata, an extension of timed automata [1], have been intensively studied [12, 13], and decidable subclasses of hybrid systems have been drawn like initialized rectangular hybrid automata [13]. More recently, the control of hybrid systems has appeared as a new interesting and active field of research, and many results have already been obtained, like the (un)decidability of control problems for hybrid automata [14], or (semi-)algorithms for solving such problems [10]. Given a system S (with controllable and uncontrollable actions) and a property φ, controlling the system means building another system C (which can only enforce controllable actions), called the controller, such that $S \parallel C$ (the system S guided by the controller C) satisfies the property φ. In our context, the property is a reachability property and our aim is to build a controller enforcing a given location of the system, whatever the environment does (which plays with the uncontrollable actions).

O-minimal hybrid systems. O-minimal hybrid systems have been first proposed in [18] as an interesting class of systems (see [21] for an overview of properties of o-minimal structures). They have very rich continuous dynamics, but limited discrete steps (at each discrete step, all variables have to be reset, independently from their initial values). This allows to decouple the continuous and discrete components of the hybrid system (see [18]). Thus, properties of a global o-minimal system can be deduced directly from properties of the continuous parts of the system. Since the introductory paper [18], several works have considered o-minimal hybrid systems [9, 8, 7, 17], mostly focusing on abstractions of such systems, on reachability properties, and on bisimulation properties.

Word encoding. In [8], an encoding of trajectories with words has been proposed in order to prove the existence of finite bisimulations for o-minimal hybrid systems (see also [7]). Let us mention that this technique has been used in [17] in order to provide an exponential bound on the size of the finite bisimulation in the case of pfaffian hybrid systems. Let us also notice that similar techniques already appeared in the literature, see for instance the notion of *signature* in [4]. Different word encoding techniques have been studied in a wider context in [6]. In this paper we use the so-called suffix encoding, which was shown to be in general too fine to provide the coarsest time-abstract bisimulation.

[1]Work partly supported by ACI Cortos, a program of the French ministry of research.

[2]This author is supported by the following research programs: FRFC 2.4.530.02., FRFC 2.4.564.02, Modnet MRTN-CT-2004-512234 and by a grant from the National Bank of Belgium.

1043-6871/06 $20.00 © 2006 IEEE

However, based on this encoding, a semi-algorithm has been proposed in [6] for computing a time-abstract bisimulation, and it terminates in the case of o-minimal hybrid systems (under some word uniqueness hypothesis).

Contributions of this paper. In this paper, we focus on the control of hybrid systems, and use the above-mentioned suffix word encoding of trajectories for giving sufficient computability conditions for the winning states of a game. Time-abstract bisimulation is an equivalence relation which is correct with respect to reachability properties [2]. Game bisimulation is correct for discrete infinite-state games [10]. Here, we show that the time-abstract bisimulation is not correct for solving control problems: we exhibit a system in which two states are time-abstract bisimilar, but one of the states is winning and the other is not winning. Using the word encoding of trajectories of [6], we prove that two states having the same suffixes in this encoding are equivalently winning or losing (this is a stronger condition than the one for the time-abstract bisimulation). We finally focus on o-minimal hybrid games and prove that, under the assumption that the theory of the underlying o-minimal structure is decidable, the control problem can be solved and that winning states and winning strategies can be computed.

Related work. The most relevant related works are those on hybrid games [14, 10]. However the framework of these papers is pretty different from ours:

1) In their framework, time is considered as a discrete action, and once action "let time elapse" has been chosen, it is not possible to bound the time elapsing, which is quite restrictive. For instance, the timed game of Figure 1 is winning from $(\ell_0, x = 0)$ in our framework (the strategy is to wait some amount of time $t \in [2, 5]$ and to take the controllable action c), whereas it is not winning in their framework (once x is above 5, it is no more possible to take the transition and reach the winning location ℓ_1, and there is no way to impose a delay within $[2, 5]$). This yields significant differences in the properties: in their framework, game bisimulation is one of the tools for solving the games, and as stated by [14, Prop. 1], the classical bisimulation tool is then sufficient to solve games. On the contrary, in our framework, the notion of bisimulation relevant to our model (time-abstract bisimulation) is not correct for solving games, as will be explored in this paper.

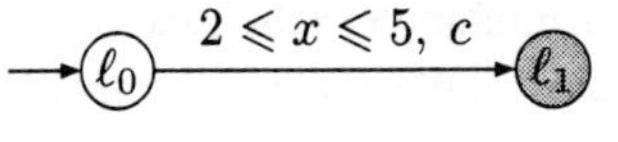

Figure 1. A simple game

2) Our games are control games, they are thus asymmetric, which is not the case of the games in the above-mentioned works; in our framework, the environment is more powerful than the controller in that it can outstrip the controller and do an action right before the controller decides to do a controllable action.

Let us also mention the paper [22] on control of Linear Hybrid Automata. In [22] the author proposes a semidecision procedure for synthesizing controllers for such automata. No general decidability result is given in this paper.

Plan of the paper. In Section 2, we define the games over dynamical systems we consider, and we show that time-abstract bisimulation is not correct for solving them. The word encoding technique is presented in Section 3 and used in Section 4 to present a general framework for solving games over dynamical systems. We apply and extend these results in Section 5 for computing winning states and winning strategies in o-minimal games.

2 Games over dynamical systems

2.1 Dynamical systems

Let $\mathcal{M}$ be a structure. In this paper when we say that some relation, subset or function is *definable*, we mean it is first-order definable in the sense of the structure $\mathcal{M}$. A general reference for first-order logic is [16]. We denote by $\mathsf{Th}(\mathcal{M})$ the theory of $\mathcal{M}$. In this paper we only consider structures $\mathcal{M}$ that are expansions of ordered groups, we also assume that the structure $\mathcal{M}$ contains two symbols of constants, *i.e.* $\mathcal{M} = \langle M, +, 0, 1, <, \ldots \rangle$ and w.l.o.g. we assume that $0 < 1$.

Definition 2.1 *A* dynamical system *is a pair* $(\mathcal{M}, \gamma)$ *where:*

- $\mathcal{M} = \langle M, +, 0, 1, <, \ldots \rangle$ *is an expansion of an ordered group,*
- $\gamma : V_1 \times M^+ \to V_2$ *is a function definable in* $\mathcal{M}$ *(where* $M^+ = \{m \in M \mid m \geqslant 0\}$*,* $V_1 \subseteq M^{k_1}$*, and* $V_2 \subseteq M^{k_2}$*).*[3]

The function γ *is called the dynamics of the system.*

Classically, when M is the field of the reals, we see M^+ as the time, $V_1 \times M^+$ as the space-time, V_2 as the (output) space and V_1 as the input space. We keep this terminology in the more general context of a structure $\mathcal{M}$.

The definition of *dynamical systems* encompasses a lot of different behaviors. Let us first give a simple example, several others will be presented later.

[3]We use these notations in the rest of the paper.

Example 2.2 We can recover the continuous dynamics of *timed automata* (see [1]). In this case, we have that $\mathcal{M} = \langle \mathbb{R}, <, +, 0, 1\rangle$ and the dynamics $\gamma : \mathbb{R}^n \times [0, +\infty[\to \mathbb{R}^n$ is defined by $\gamma(x_1, \dots, x_n, t) = (x_1 + t, \dots, x_n + t)$.

Definition 2.3 *If we fix a point $x \in V_1$, the set $\Gamma_x = \{\gamma(x, t) \mid t \in M^+\} \subseteq V_2$ is called the* trajectory *determined by x.*

We define a transition system associated with the dynamical system, this definition is an adaptation to our context of the classical *continuous transition system* in the case of hybrid systems (see [18] for example).

Definition 2.4 *Given $(\mathcal{M}, \gamma)$ a dynamical system, we define a* transition system $T_\gamma = (Q, \Sigma, \to_\gamma)$ associated with the dynamical system *by:*

- *the set Q of states is V_2;*
- *the set Σ of events is $M^+ = \{m \in M \mid m \geqslant 0\}$;*
- *the transition relation $y_1 \xrightarrow{t}_\gamma y_2$ is defined by: $\exists x \in V_1$, $\exists t_1, t_2 \in M^+$ such that $t_1 \leqslant t_2$, $\gamma(x, t_1) = y_1$, $\gamma(x, t_2) = y_2$ and $t = t_2 - t_1$*

2.2 $\mathcal{M}$-games

In this subsection, we define $\mathcal{M}$-automata, which are automata with guards, resets and continuous dynamics definable in the $\mathcal{M}$-structure. We then introduce our model of dynamical game which is an $\mathcal{M}$-automaton with two sets of actions, one for each player; we finally express in terms of winning strategy the main problem we will be interested in, the control problem in a class $\mathcal{C}$ of $\mathcal{M}$-automata.

Definition 2.5 ($\mathcal{M}$-automaton) *An* $\mathcal{M}$-automaton $\mathcal{A}$ *is a tuple $(\mathcal{M}, Q, \mathsf{Goal}, \Sigma, \delta, \gamma)$ where $\mathcal{M} = \langle M, +, 0, 1, <, \dots\rangle$ is an expansion of an ordered group, Q is a finite set of locations, $\mathsf{Goal} \subseteq Q$ is a subset of winning locations, Σ is a finite set of actions, δ consists in a finite number of transitions $(q, g, a, R, q') \in Q \times 2^{V_2} \times \Sigma \times (V_2 \to 2^{V_2}) \times Q$ where g and R are definable in $\mathcal{M}$, and γ maps every location $q \in Q$ to a dynamic $\gamma_q : V_1 \times M^+ \to V_2$.*

We use a general definition for resets: a reset R is indeed a general function from V_2 to 2^{V_2}, which may correspond to a non-deterministic update. If the current state is (q, y) the system will jump to some (q', y') with $y' \in R(y)$.

An $\mathcal{M}$-automaton $\mathcal{A} = (\mathcal{M}, Q, \mathsf{Goal}, \Sigma, \delta, \gamma)$ defines a *mixed transition system* $T_{\mathcal{A}} = (S, \Gamma, \to)$ where:

- the set S of states is $Q \times V_2$;
- the set Γ of labels is $M^+ \cup \Sigma$;
- the transition relation $(q, y) \xrightarrow{e} (q', y')$ is defined when:
  - $e \in \Sigma$ and there exists $(q, g, e, R, q') \in \delta$ with $y \in g$ and $y' \in R(y)$, or
  - $e \in M^+$, $q = q'$, and $y \xrightarrow{e}_{\gamma_q} y'$ where γ_q is the dynamic in location q.

In the sequel, we will focus on behaviors of $\mathcal{M}$-automata which alternate between continuous transitions and discrete transitions.

We will also need more precise notions of transitions. When $(q, y) \xrightarrow{t'} (q, y')$ with $t' \in M^+$, this is due to some choice of $(x, t) \in V_1 \times M^+$ such that $\gamma_q(x, t) = y$. We say that $(q, y) \xrightarrow{t'}_{x,t} (q, y')$ if $\gamma_q(x, t) = y$ and $\gamma_q(x, t + t') = y'$. To ease the reading of the paper, we will sometimes write $(q, x, t, y) \xrightarrow{t'} (q, x, t + t', y')$ for $(q, y) \xrightarrow{t'}_{x,t} (q, y')$. We say that an action $(d, a) \in M^+ \times \Sigma$ is enabled in a state (q, x, t, y) if there exists (q', x', t', y') and (q'', x'', t'', y'') such that $(q, x, t, y) \xrightarrow{d} (q', x', t', y') \xrightarrow{a} (q'', x'', t'', y'')$. We then write $(q, x, t, y) \xrightarrow{d,a} (q'', x'', t'', y'')$.

A *run* of $\mathcal{A}$ is a finite or infinite sequence $(q_0, x_0, t'_0, y_0) \xrightarrow{t_1, a_1} (q_1, x_1, t'_1, y_1) \dots$ where for every i, $(q_i, y_i) \xrightarrow{t_i}_{x_i, t'_i} (q_i, y'_i) \xrightarrow{a} (q_{i+1}, y_{i+1})$. Such a run is said *winning* if $q_i \in \mathsf{Goal}$ for some i.

We note $\mathsf{Runs}_f(\mathcal{A})$ the set of finite runs in $\mathcal{A}$. If ρ is a finite run $(q_0, x_0, t'_0, y_0) \xrightarrow{t_1, a_1} \dots \xrightarrow{t_n, a_n} (q_n, x_n, t'_n, y_n)$ we define $last(\rho) = (q_n, x_n, t'_n, y_n)$.

Definition 2.6 ($\mathcal{M}$-game) *An* $\mathcal{M}$-game *is an $\mathcal{M}$-automaton $(\mathcal{M}, Q, \mathsf{Goal}, \Sigma, \delta, \gamma)$ where Σ is partitioned into two subsets Σ_c and Σ_u corresponding to controllable and uncontrollable actions.*

Without loss of generality, we assume that there is a loop labeled by a controllable action on every state of Goal.

Definition 2.7 (Strategy) *A* strategy[4] *is a partial function λ from $\mathsf{Runs}_f(\mathcal{A})$ to $M^+ \times \Sigma_c$ such that for all runs ρ in $\mathsf{Runs}_f(\mathcal{A})$, $\lambda(\rho)$ is enabled in $last(\rho)$.*

The strategy tells what needs to be done for controlling the system: at each instant it tells what delay we need to wait and which controllable action needs to be done after this delay. Note that the environment may have to choose between several edges, each labeled by the action given by the strategy (because the original game is not deterministic).

A strategy λ is said *memoryless* if for all finite runs ρ_1 and ρ_2, $last(\rho_1) = last(\rho_2)$ implies $\lambda(\rho_1) = \lambda(\rho_2)$. Let $\rho = (q_0, x_0, t'_0, y_0) \xrightarrow{t_1, a_1} \dots$ be a run, and set for every i,

[4] In the context of control problems, a strategy is also called a *controller*.

ρ_i the prefix of length i of ρ. The run ρ is said *consistent with a strategy* λ when for all i, if $\lambda(\rho_i) = (t, a)$ then either $t_{i+1} = t$ and $a_{i+1} = a$, or $t_{i+1} \leqslant t$ and $a_{i+1} \in \Sigma_u$. A run ρ is said *maximal* if it is infinite or if it is finite ending in (q, x, t, y) and satisfies that for all $t' \geqslant 0$, for all $a \in \Sigma$, "$(q, x, t, y) \xrightarrow{t',a}$" implies $a \in \Sigma_u$. A strategy λ is *winning from a state (q,y)* if for all (x, t) such that $\gamma(x, t) = y$, all maximal runs starting in (q, x, t, y) compatible with λ are winning. The *set of winning states* is the set of states from which there is a winning strategy.

We can now define the control problem we will study.

Problem (Control problem in a class $\mathcal{C}$ of $\mathcal{M}$-automata). Given an $\mathcal{M}$-game $\mathcal{A} \in \mathcal{C}$, and a definable initial state (q, y), determine whether there exists a winning strategy in $\mathcal{A}$ from (q, y).

2.3 $\mathcal{M}$-game and bisimulation

Time-abstract bisimulation [9, 2, 12] is a sufficient behavioral relation to check reachability properties of timed systems, and in particular of $\mathcal{M}$-automata [6]. When considering control problems, we will see that this tool is not sufficient for solving control problems.

Definition 2.8 *Given a mixed transition system* $T = (S, \Gamma, \to)$*, a* time-abstract bisimulation *for* T *is an equivalence relation* $\sim \subseteq S \times S$ *such that* $\forall q_1, q_1', q_2 \in S$*, the two following conditions are satisfied:*

$$\forall a \in \Sigma, \left(q_1 \sim q_1' \text{ and } q_1 \xrightarrow{a} q_2\right) \Rightarrow \left(\exists q_2' \in S \text{ s.t. } q_2 \sim q_2' \text{ and } q_1' \xrightarrow{a} q_2'\right)$$

$$\forall t \in M^+, \left(q_1 \sim q_1' \text{ and } q_1 \xrightarrow{t} q_2\right) \Rightarrow \left(\exists t' \in M^+, \exists q_2' \in S \text{ s.t. } q_2 \sim q_2' \text{ and } q_1' \xrightarrow{t'} q_2'\right)$$

Example 2.9 Let us consider the $\mathcal{M}$-game $\mathcal{A} = (\mathcal{M}, Q, \mathsf{Goal}, \Sigma, \delta, \gamma)$ where $\mathcal{M} = \langle \mathbb{R}, <, +, 0, 1, \equiv_2 \rangle$ ($\equiv_2$ denotes the "modulo 2" relation), $Q = \{q_1, q_2, q_3\}$, $\mathsf{Goal} = \{q_2\}$, $\Sigma = \Sigma_c \cup \Sigma_u = \{c, u\}$ where $\Sigma_c = \{c\}$ (resp. $\Sigma_u = \{u\}$) is the set of controllable (resp. uncontrollable) actions. The dynamic in q_1, $\gamma_{q_1} : \mathbb{R}^+ \times \{0, 1\} \times \mathbb{R}^+ \to \mathbb{R}^+ \times \{0, 1\}$ is defined as $\gamma_{q_1}(x_1, x_2, t) = (x_1 + t, x_2)$.

We consider the partition depicted on Figure 2(b). The guard g_C is satisfied on C-states and the guard g_B is satisfied on B-states. Note that this partition is compatible with Goal and w.r.t. discrete transitions.

In this game, the controller can win when it enters a C-state by performing action c and it loses when entering a B-state because it cannot prevent the environment from performing a u and going in the losing state q_3.

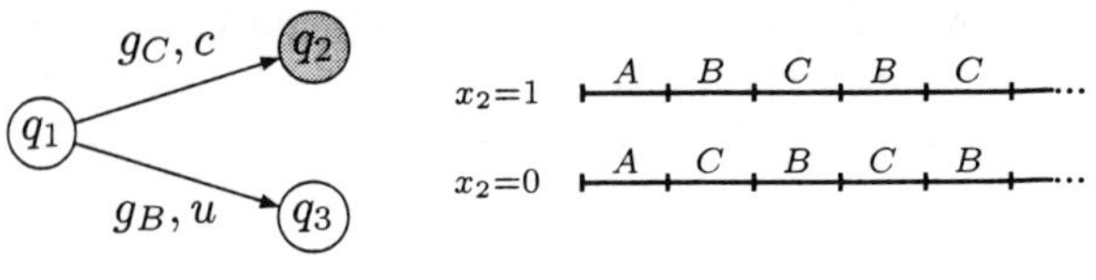

(a) The $\mathcal{M}$-game $\mathcal{A}$ (b) Dynamics in q_1

Figure 2. Time-abstract bisimulation does not preserve winning states

It follows that the state $s_1 = (q_1, (0, 1))$ is losing, whereas the state $s_2 = (q_1, (0, 0))$ is winning. However the equivalence relation induced by the partition $\{A, B, C\}$ is a time-abstract bisimulation: the two states s_1 and s_2 are thus time-abstract bisimilar, but not equivalent for the game. It follows that time-abstract bisimulation is not correct for solving control problems, in the sense that a time-abstract bisimulation cannot always distinguish between winning and losing states.

Proposition 2.10 *Let* $\mathcal{M}$ *be a structure and* $\mathcal{A}$ *an* $\mathcal{M}$*-game. A partition respecting* Goal *and inducing a time-abstract bisimulation on* $Q \times V_2$ *does not necessarily respect the set of winning states of* $\mathcal{A}$*.*

3 Suffix and dynamical type

In this section we explain how to encode trajectories of dynamical systems with words. This technique was introduced in [8, 7] in order to study o-minimal hybrid systems. We focus on the *suffix partition* introduced in [6].

We first explain how to build words associated with trajectories. Given $(\mathcal{M}, \gamma)$ a dynamical system and $\mathcal{P}$ a finite partition of V_2, given $x \in V_1$ we associate a word with the trajectory $\Gamma_x = \{\gamma(x, t) \mid t \in M^+\}$ in the following way. We consider the sets $\{t \in M^+ \mid \gamma(x, t) \in P\}$ for $P \in \mathcal{P}$. This gives a partition of the time M^+. In order to define a word on $\mathcal{P}$ associated with the trajectory determined by x, we need to define the set of intervals $\mathcal{F}_x = \{I \mid I$ is a time interval or a point and is maximal for the property $\exists P \in \mathcal{P}, \forall t \in I, \gamma(x, t) \in P\}$. For each x, the set $\mathcal{F}_x$ is totally ordered by the order induced from M. This allows us to define *the word on* $\mathcal{P}$ *associated with* Γ_x denoted ω_x.

Definition 3.1 *Given* $x \in V_1$, the word associated with Γ_x *is given by the function* $\omega_x : \mathcal{F}_x \to \mathcal{P}$ *defined by* $\omega_x(I) = P$*, where* $I \in \mathcal{F}_x$ *is such that* $\forall t \in I, \gamma(x, t) \in P$*.*

The set of words associated with $(\mathcal{M}, \gamma)$ over $\mathcal{P}$ gives in some sense a complete *static* description of the dynamical system $(\mathcal{M}, \gamma)$ through the partition $\mathcal{P}$. In order to recover the *dynamics*, we need further information.

Given a point x of the input space V_1, we have associated with x a trajectory Γ_x and a word ω_x. If we consider (x, t) a point of the space-time $V_1 \times M^+$, it corresponds to a point $\gamma(x, t)$ lying on Γ_x. To recover in some sense the position of $\gamma(x, t)$ on Γ_x from ω_x, we associate with (x, t) a suffix of the word ω_x denoted $\omega_{(x,t)}$. The construction of $\omega_{(x,t)}$ is similar to the construction of ω_x, we only need to consider the sets of intervals $\mathcal{F}_{(x,t)} = \{I \cap \{t' \in M^+ \mid t' \geqslant t\} \mid I \in \mathcal{F}_x\}$.

Let us notice that given (x, t) a point of the space-time $V_1 \times M^+$ there is a unique suffix $\omega_{(x,t)}$ of ω_x associated with (x, t). Given a point $y \in V_2$ it may have several (x, t) such that $\gamma(x, t) = y$ and so several suffixes are associated with y. In other words, given $y \in V_2$, the *future* of y is non-deterministic, and a single suffix $\omega_{(x,t)}$ is thus not sufficient to recover the dynamics of the transition system through the partition $\mathcal{P}$. To encode the dynamical behavior of a point y of the output space V_2 through the partition $\mathcal{P}$, we introduce the notion of *suffix dynamical type* of a point y w.r.t. $\mathcal{P}$.

Definition 3.2 *Given a dynamical system $(\mathcal{M}, \gamma)$, a finite partition $\mathcal{P}$ of V_2, a point $y \in V_2$, the* suffix dynamical type of y w.r.t. $\mathcal{P}$ *is denoted* $\mathsf{Suf}_{\mathcal{P}}(y)$ *and defined by* $\mathsf{Suf}_{\mathcal{P}}(y) = \{\omega_{(x,t)} \mid \gamma(x, t) = y\}$.

This allows us to define an equivalence relation on V_2. Given $y_1, y_2 \in V_2$, we say that they are *suffix-equivalent* if and only if $\mathsf{Suf}_{\mathcal{P}}(y_1) = \mathsf{Suf}_{\mathcal{P}}(y_2)$.

We denote by $\mathsf{Suf}(\mathcal{P})$ the partition induced by this equivalence. We say that a partition $\mathcal{P}$ is *suffix-stable* if $\mathsf{Suf}(\mathcal{P}) = \mathcal{P}$ (it implies that if y_1 and y_2 belong to the same piece of $\mathcal{P}$ then $\mathsf{Suf}_{\mathcal{P}}(y_1) = \mathsf{Suf}_{\mathcal{P}}(y_2)$).

To understand the word encoding technique, we provide several examples.

Example 3.3 We first consider a two dimensional timed automata dynamics (see Example 2.2). In this case we have that $\gamma(x_1, x_2, t) = (x_1 + t, x_2 + t)$. We associate with this dynamics the partition $\mathcal{P} = \{A, B\}$ where $B = [1, 2]^2$ and $A = \mathbb{R}^2 \setminus B$. In this example the suffix partition is made of three pieces, which are depicted in Figure 3.

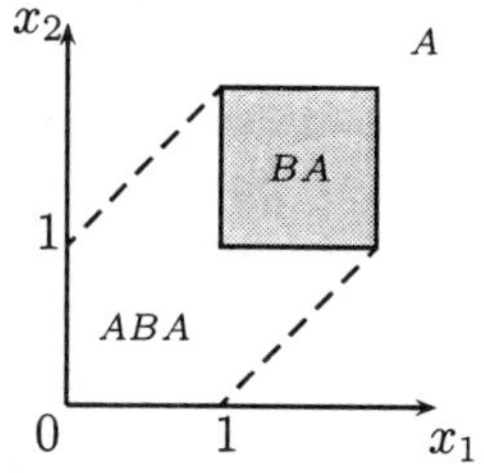

Figure 3. Suffixes for the timed automata dynamics

Example 3.4 We consider the dynamical system $(\mathcal{M}, \gamma)$ where $\mathcal{M} = \langle \mathbb{R}, +, \cdot, 0, 1, <, \sin_{|[0,2\pi]}, \cos_{|[0,2\pi]} \rangle$ [5] and $\gamma : \mathbb{R}^2 \times [0, 2\pi] \times \mathbb{R} \to \mathbb{R}^2$ is defined as follows.

$$\gamma(x_1, x_2, \theta, t) = \begin{cases} (t.\cos(\theta), t.\sin(\theta)) & \text{if } (x_1, x_2) = (0, 0) \\ (x_1 + t.x_1, x_2 + t.x_2) & \text{if } (x_1, x_2) \neq (0, 0) \end{cases}$$

We associate with this dynamical system the partition $\mathcal{P} = \{A, B, C\}$ where $A = \{(0, 0)\}$, $B = \{(\theta\cos(\theta), \theta\sin(\theta)) \mid 0 < \theta \leqslant 2\pi\}$ and $C = \mathbb{R}^2 \setminus (A \cup C)$. Let us call piece B *the spiral* (see Figure 4). There are four dynamical types for this system: $\{ACBC\}$ for the central point $(0, 0)$, $\{CBC\}$ for the "interior" of the spiral, $\{BC\}$ for the spiral, and $\{C\}$ for the "exterior" of the spiral. Let us notice that though the dynamical system is infinitely branching in $(0, 0)$, there is a unique suffix associated with each point y of the output space.

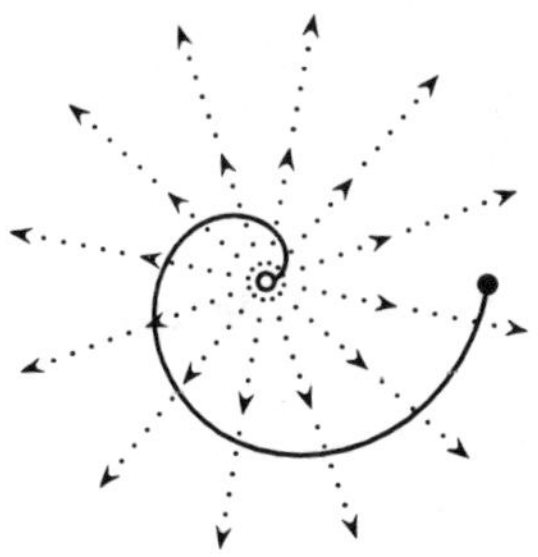

Figure 4. The dynamical system of the spiral

Dynamical systems and suffix dynamical type allow also to encode more sophisticated continuous dynamics. In the next example we recover in some sense the continuous dynamics of *rectangular automata* [15], which requires to use the suffix dynamical types (some of the points do not have a unique suffix).

Example 3.5 We consider the dynamical system $(\mathcal{M}, \gamma)$ where $\mathcal{M} = \langle \mathbb{R}, +, \cdot, 0, 1, < \rangle$ and $\gamma : \mathbb{R}^2 \times [0, 2] \times \mathbb{R}^+ \to \mathbb{R}^2$ is defined by $\gamma(x_1, x_2, p, t) = (x_1 + t, x_2 + p \cdot t)$. We associate with this dynamical system the partition $\mathcal{P} = \{A, B, C\}$ where $B = [2, 5] \times [3, 4]$, $C = [3, 5] \times [1, 2]$ and $A = \mathbb{R}^2 \setminus (B \cup C)$ (see Figure 5(a)). Let us focus on the suffix dynamical types of the two points $y_1 = (1, 2.5)$ and $y_2 = (2, 0.5)$. We have that $\mathsf{Suf}_{\mathcal{P}}(y_1) = \{A, ABA\}$ and $\mathsf{Suf}_{\mathcal{P}}(y_2) = \{ABA, ACABA\}$. Though several points have several possible suffixes, the partition induced by the suffix dynamical type is finite and illustrated in Figure 5(b).

[5] $\sin_{|[0,2\pi]}$ and $\cos_{|[0,2\pi]}$ correspond to the sinus and cosinus functions restricted to the segments $[0, 2\pi]$.

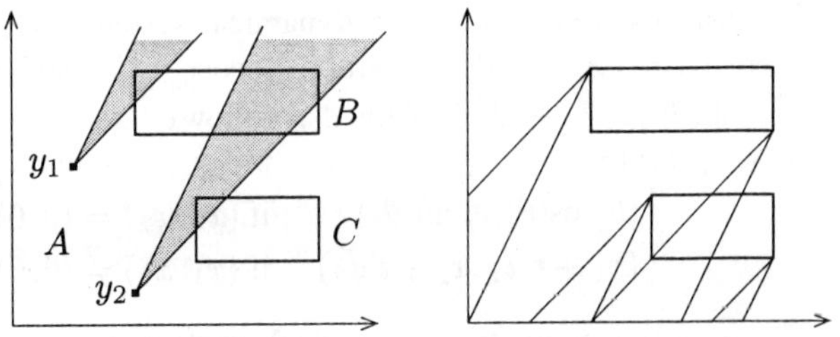

(a) The dynamics (b) The suffix partition

Figure 5. A rectangular dynamics

4 Solving an $\mathcal{M}$-game

In this section we present a general procedure to compute the set of winning states for an $\mathcal{M}$-game. We then show that if a partition is *suffix-stable*, the procedure can be performed symbolically on pieces of the partition. The procedure described is not always effective [6] and we will point out specific $\mathcal{M}$-structures for which each step of the procedure is computable.

4.1 Controllable predecessors

As for classical reachability games [11], one way of computing winning states is to compute the *attractor* of goal states by iterating a *controllable predecessor* operator.

Let $\mathcal{A} = (\mathcal{M}, Q, \mathsf{Goal}, \Sigma, \delta, \gamma)$ be an $\mathcal{M}$-game. For $A \subseteq Q \times V_2$ and $a \in \Sigma$ we define the controllable and uncontrollable discrete predecessors as follows:
$\mathsf{cPred}(A) =$

$$\left\{ (q,y) \in Q \times V_2 \,\middle|\, \begin{array}{l} \exists c \in \Sigma_c,\ \text{c is enabled in } (q,y), \\ \text{and } \forall (q',y') \in Q \times V_2, \\ (q,y) \xrightarrow{c} (q',y') \Rightarrow (q',y') \in A \end{array} \right\}$$

$\mathsf{uPred}(A) =$

$$\left\{ (q,y) \in Q \times V_2 \,\middle|\, \begin{array}{l} \exists u \in \Sigma_u,\ \exists (q',y') \in Q \times V_2 \text{ s.t.} \\ (q,y) \xrightarrow{u} (q',y') \text{ and } (q',y') \in A \end{array} \right\}$$

As for timed and hybrid games [3, 14], we also define a *safe* time predecessor of a set A w.r.t. a set B: a state (q,y) is in $\mathsf{Pred}_t(A,B)$ if, by letting time elapse, one reaches $(q',y') \in A$, avoiding B. Formally the operator Pred_t is defined as follows:
$\mathsf{Pred}_t(A,B) =$

$$\left\{ (q,y) \in Q \times V_2 \,\middle|\, \begin{array}{l} \forall (x,t) \text{ s.t. } \gamma_q(x,t) = y,\ \exists t' \in M^+ \\ (q,y) \xrightarrow{t'}_{x,t} (q',y'),\ (q',y') \in A, \\ \text{and } \mathsf{Post}^{q,x}_{[t,t+t']} \subseteq \overline{B} \end{array} \right\}$$

[6] The effectivity of the computation will be discussed later.

where $\mathsf{Post}^{q,x}_{[t,t+t']} = \{\gamma_q(x,t'') \mid t \leqslant t'' \leqslant t+t'\}$.

The *controllable predecessor* operator is then defined as:

$$\pi(A) = A \cup \mathsf{Pred}_t(\mathsf{cPred}(A), \mathsf{uPred}(\overline{A}))$$

Intuitively, a state (q,y) is in $\pi(A)$ whenever either it is already in A or there is a way of waiting some amount of time, and of performing a controllable action to enter A, and no uncontrollable action leads outside A.

We say that a partition $\mathcal{P}$ is *stable under* π if for every piece $A \in \mathcal{P}$, $\pi(A)$ is a union of pieces of $\mathcal{P}$.

Remark 4.1 Note that the operator π is definable in any expansion of an ordered group. Hence, if A is definable, so is $\pi(A)$.

We will compute the set of winning states by iterating the operator π. Denoting $\pi^*(\mathsf{Goal}) = \bigcup_{k \geqslant 0} \pi^k(\mathsf{Goal})$, we will show that if the iterative computation of $\pi^k(\mathsf{Goal})$ stabilizes, the set of winning states for the game is precisely $\pi^*(\mathsf{Goal})$. This will help getting further effective definability and computability results of winning states and winning strategies under some assumption on the underlying structure.

Proposition 4.2 *Let $\mathcal{A} = (\mathcal{M}, Q, \mathsf{Goal}, \Sigma, \delta, \gamma)$ be an $\mathcal{M}$-game, and $(q,y) \in Q \times V_2$. If there exists $n \in \mathbb{N}$ s.t. $\pi^n(\mathsf{Goal}) = \pi^{n+1}(\mathsf{Goal})$ then $\pi^*(\mathsf{Goal}) = \pi^n(\mathsf{Goal})$ is the set of winning states of $\mathcal{A}$.*

This property is quite classical in the framework of hybrid games, see for example [5]. Note that the hypothesis that π stabilizes is really needed.

We now deduce an algorithmic result from proposition 4.2. The set of winning states is $\pi^*(\mathsf{Goal})$ but this does not imply that we can compute this set as many $\mathcal{M}$-structures are already intrinsically undecidable. The following corollary states that if some conditions on the structure and on π are satisfied, then this procedure provides an algorithmic solution to the control problem.

Corollary 4.3 *Let $\mathcal{M}$ be a structure such that* $\mathsf{Th}(\mathcal{M})$ *is decidable.*[7] *Let $\mathcal{C}$ be a class of $\mathcal{M}$-games such that for every $\mathcal{A}$ in $\mathcal{C}$, there exists a finite partition $\mathcal{P}$ of $Q \times V_2$ definable in $\mathcal{M}$, respecting* Goal[8]*, and stable under π. Then the control problem in the class $\mathcal{C}$ is decidable. Moreover if $\mathcal{A} \in \mathcal{C}$, the set of winning states of $\mathcal{A}$ is computable.*

[7] We recall that a theory $\mathsf{Th}(\mathcal{M})$ is decidable iff there is an algorithm which can determine whether or not any sentence (*i.e.* a formula with no free variable.) is a member of the theory (*i.e.* is true). We suggest to readers interested in general decidability issues on o-minimal hybrid systems to refer to Section 5 of [7].

[8] *i.e.* Goal is a union of pieces of $\mathcal{P}$.

4.2 Stability of $\mathsf{Suf}(\mathcal{P})$ under π

In section 2.3, we have presented a counter-example which showed that time-abstract bisimulation is not always correct to solve control problems. The main reason is that the partition induced by time-abstract bisimilarity is not stable under the operator π.

We now present a sufficient condition for a partition to be stable under the operator π: we require that the partition is stable under cPred and uPred to handle the discrete part of the automaton and we show that the stability by suffix is fine enough to be correct for solving control problems.

Proposition 4.4 *Let $\mathcal{A}$ be an $\mathcal{M}$-game, $\mathcal{P}$ be a partition of $Q \times V_2$ and π be the controllable predecessor operator. If $\mathcal{P}$ respects* Goal, *is stable under* cPred, uPred *and suffix-stable, then $\mathcal{P}$ is stable under the operator π.*

Proof. The idea of the proof of Proposition 4.4 is the following. Given X a piece of $\mathcal{P}$ and $y \in \pi(X)$. The fact that $y \in \pi(X)$ can be translated as follows in term of words. There exists a word $\omega \in \mathrm{Suf}_{\mathcal{P}}(y)$ with prefix ω_s such that the last letter of ω_s belongs to $\mathsf{cPred}(X)$ and ω_s contains no occurence of letters included in $\mathsf{uPred}(\overline{X})$. By *suffix-stability hypothesis* we know that any y' belonging to the same piece of $\mathcal{P}$ as y has the same suffix as y. This allows to conclude that $y' \in \pi(X)$. □

As a corollary of this proposition and of Corollary 4.3, we get the following general decidability result.

Corollary 4.5 *Let $\mathcal{M}$ be a structure such that $\mathsf{Th}(\mathcal{M})$ is decidable. Let $\mathcal{C}$ be a class of $\mathcal{M}$-games such that for every $\mathcal{A}$ in $\mathcal{C}$, there exists a finite partition $\mathcal{P}$ of $Q \times V_2$ definable in $\mathcal{M}$, respecting* Goal, *and suffix-stable. Then the control problem in the class $\mathcal{C}$ is decidable, and if $\mathcal{A} \in \mathcal{C}$, the set of winning states of $\mathcal{A}$ is computable.*

Note that being suffix-stable is a stronger condition than being a time-abstract bisimulation [6], and we see here that this is one of the right tools to solve control problems. For instance in Example 2.9 the partition $\mathcal{P}$ is a time-abstract bisimulation but is not suffix-stable. Indeed $s_1, s_2 \in A$ but $\mathrm{Suf}_{\mathcal{P}}(s_1) \neq \mathrm{Suf}_{\mathcal{P}}(s_2)$.

Remark 4.6 The results of this section permit to recover the results of [3] about control of timed automata. Indeed we consider the classical finite partition of timed automata that induces the region graph (see [1]). Let us call $\mathcal{P}_R$ this partition, and notice that $\mathcal{P}_R$ is definable in $\langle \mathbb{R}, <, +, 0, 1 \rangle$. $\mathcal{P}_R$ is stable under the action of cPred and uPred. By Example 2.2 the continuous dynamics of timed automata is definable in $\langle \mathbb{R}, <, +, 0, 1 \rangle$. Hence it makes sense to encode continuous trajectories of timed automata as words. Then one can easily be convinced that $\mathsf{Suf}(\mathcal{P}_R) = \mathcal{P}_R$. By Corollary 4.5 we get the decidability and computability of winning states in timed games [3] as a side result.

Corollary 4.7 *The control problem in the class of timed automata is decidable. Moreover the set of winning states $\pi^*(\mathsf{Goal})$ is computable.*

5 O-minimal games

In this section, we focus on the particular case of o-minimal games (*i.e.* $\mathcal{M}$-games where $\mathcal{M}$ is an o-minimal structure and in which extra assumptions are made on the resets) [18].

We first briefly recall definitions and results related to o-minimality [19]. The reader interested in o-minimality should refer to [21] for further results and an extensive bibliography on this subject. Then we focus on o-minimal structures with a decidable theory in order to obtain decidability and computability results.

Definition 5.1 *An extension of an ordered structure $\mathcal{M} = \langle M, <, \ldots \rangle$ is* o-minimal *if every definable subset of M is a finite union of points and open intervals (possibly unbounded).*

In other words the definable subsets of M are the simplest possible: the ones which are definable in $\langle M, < \rangle$. The following are examples of o-minimal structures.

Example 5.2 There are many examples of o-minimal structures: the ordered group of rationals $\langle \mathbb{Q}, <, +, 0, 1 \rangle$, the ordered field of reals $\langle \mathbb{R}, <, +, \cdot, 0, 1 \rangle$, the field of reals with exponential function, the field of reals expanded by restricted pfaffian functions and the exponential function, and many more interesting structures.

5.1 Generalities on o-minimal games

Definition 5.3 *Given $\mathcal{A}$ an $\mathcal{M}$-game, we say that $\mathcal{A}$ is an* o-minimal game *if the structure $\mathcal{M}$ is o-minimal and if all transitions (q, g, a, R, q') of $\mathcal{A}$ belong to*[9] $Q \times 2^{V_2} \times \Sigma \times 2^{V_2} \times Q$.

Let us notice that the previous definition implies that given $\mathcal{A}$ an o-minimal game, the guards, the resets and the dynamics are definable in the underlying o-minimal structure. We denote by $\mathcal{P}_{\mathcal{A}}$ the partition of the state space $S = Q \times V_2$ which respects Goal, and all guards and resets in $\mathcal{A}$. Note that $\mathcal{P}_{\mathcal{A}}$ is a finite definable partition of S.

Due to the strong reset condition we have that $\mathcal{P}_{\mathcal{A}}$ is stable under the action of cPred and uPred. This holds by the

[9] This is a particular case of reset for $\mathcal{M}$-game where we consider only constant functions for resets.

same argument that allows to decouple the continuous and discrete components of the hybrid system in [18]. Let us also notice that, in the framework of o-minimal games, any refinement of $\mathcal{P}_{\mathcal{A}}$ is stable under the action of cPred and uPred.

O-minimal games are *o-minimal hybrid systems* (as defined in [7]). With slight adaptations of Lemma 4.13 and Theorem 4.18 of [7], we can easily deduce the following result.

Theorem 5.4 ([7]) *Let $\mathcal{A}$ be an o-minimal game.*

- *Given $y \in V_2$ we have that $\mathsf{Suf}_{\mathcal{P}_{\mathcal{A}}}(y)$ consists of finitely many finite words on $\mathcal{P}_{\mathcal{A}}$,*
- *the partition $\mathsf{Suf}(\mathcal{P}_{\mathcal{A}})$ is finite and definable,*
- *if there exists a unique suffix on $\mathcal{P}_{\mathcal{A}}$ associated with each $y \in V_2$ we have that $\mathsf{Suf}(\mathcal{P}_{\mathcal{A}})$ is a time-abstract bisimulation.*

5.2 O-minimal games with unique suffixes

In this subsection, we apply the general results obtained in Section 4 to the particular case of o-minimal games, and we get partial results when we assume that the game satisfies a suffix uniqueness hypothesis.

Proposition 5.5 *Let $\mathcal{A}$ be an o-minimal game, $\mathcal{P}$ a partition inducing a time-abstract bisimulation and respecting* Goal, *guards and resets of $\mathcal{A}$. If there exists a unique suffix on $\mathcal{P}$ associated with each $(q, y) \in Q \times V_2$ then $\mathcal{P}$ is stable under the action of π.*

Proof. This proposition holds because:

- if $\mathcal{P}$ is a partition inducing a time-abstract bisimulation, and if there is a unique suffix on $\mathcal{P}$, then $\mathsf{Suf}(\mathcal{P}) = \mathcal{P}$
- we can then apply Proposition 4.4 with partition $\mathcal{P}$.

□

Note that thanks to Theorem 5.4 the *suffix partition* $\mathsf{Suf}(\mathcal{P}_{\mathcal{A}})$ is a partition which satisfies the hypotheses of the above proposition under the suffix uniqueness hypothesis.

This result does however not contradict Proposition 2.10 which stated that time-abstract bisimulation is in general not a correct tool to solve control problems. Indeed, the example of Figure 2(b) satisfies the suffix uniqueness hypothesis but is not o-minimal. It is also possible to construct another example which is o-minimal but does not satisfy the suffix uniqueness hypothesis. The above proposition thus really requires both hypotheses "o-minimal" and "unique suffix".

In the next subsection, we will describe another partition, which satisfies a stronger property than time-abstract bisimulation, and which will also be a correct tool for analyzing all o-minimal games, even the ones which don't satisfy the suffix uniqueness hypothesis.

Remark 5.6 Let us notice that the "unique suffix" assumption of Proposition 5.5 already encompasses the continuous behavior allowed in [18] (where the dynamics γ is the flow of a vector field that does not depend on the time, and is thus time-deterministic). More general systems can also be handled, for example the spiral dynamics (Example 5.9) which is an infinitely branching system with unique suffix.

5.3 Relaxing the suffix uniqueness hypothesis

In the previous subsection, under a suffix uniqueness assumption, applying Proposition 4.4, we have shown that $\mathsf{Suf}(\mathcal{P}_{\mathcal{A}})$ is stable under the action of π. We will now prove that we can remove this suffix uniqueness assumption and keep the stability of $\mathsf{Suf}(\mathcal{P}_{\mathcal{A}})$ under the action of π. From now and for the rest of the paper, we ignore the suffix uniqueness hypothesis. Of course in this more general framework we can not apply Proposition 4.4 anymore as in general the partition $\mathsf{Suf}(\mathcal{P}_{\mathcal{A}})$ is not suffix-stable (even in the restricted framework of o-minimal systems); this is for instance the case for the rectangular semantics described in Figure 5(a)).

The goal of this subsection is to provide a new tool, namely the suffix partition $\mathsf{Suf}(\mathcal{P}_{\mathcal{A}})$, for analyzing o-minimal games (even when the suffix uniqueness assumption is removed). Theorem 5.4 then ensures finiteness of $\mathsf{Suf}(\mathcal{P}_{\mathcal{A}})$. Even though $\mathsf{Suf}(\mathcal{P}_{\mathcal{A}})$ is not always a time-abstract bisimulation (as on Figure 5(b)), we will show that it is stable under the action of π.

Proposition 5.7 *Let $\mathcal{A}$ be an o-minimal game. The suffix partition $\mathsf{Suf}(\mathcal{P}_{\mathcal{A}})$ is finite and stable under the action of π.*

Proof. The proof of this proposition uses same kinds of ideas as the proof of Proposition 4.4. The difficult point is the translation of "the belonging to $\pi(X)$" in term of words. However we can not rely anymore on the suffix stability of the partition we are working with, namely $\mathsf{Suf}(\mathcal{P}_{\mathcal{A}})$, (see Figure 6). That is why we need to consider the strong reset conditions of o-minimal games in order to conclude. □

5.4 Synthesis of winning strategies

We now prove that given $\mathcal{A}$ an o-minimal game definable in $\mathcal{M}$, we can construct a *definable* strategy (in the same structure $\mathcal{M}$) for the winning states. The effectiveness of this construction will be discussed in subsection 5.5.

Theorem 5.8 *Given $\mathcal{A}$ an o-minimal game, there exists a definable memoryless winning strategy for each $(q, y) \in \pi^*(\mathsf{Goal})$.*

Proof. The key point in the proof of Theorem 5.8 is to be able to definably pick a delay $d \in M^+$ making the strategy $\lambda(q, x, t, y) = (d, a)$ winning, for some $a \in \Sigma_c$. This is possible by using the *curve selection* for o-minimal expansions of ordered groups (see [21, chap.6]). This allows for example to definably pick the middle point of a open interval of the form (m, m'). □

Let us now illustrate Theorem 5.8 on two examples.

Example 5.9 Let us consider again the automaton shape of Example 2.9. We now define from $\mathcal{A}$ an o-minimal game $\mathcal{A}_s$ related to the spiral example (Example 3.4). The underlying o-minimal structure[10] $\mathcal{M}$ is $\langle \mathbb{R}, +, \cdot, 0, 1, <, \sin_{|[0,2\pi]}, \cos_{|[0,2\pi]} \rangle$. The o-minimal game $\mathcal{A}_s$ has the same set of locations, same Goal, same set of actions and same underlying finite automaton as $\mathcal{A}$ (*i.e.* Figure 2(a) represents also $\mathcal{A}_s$). The two differences between $\mathcal{A}$ and $\mathcal{A}_s$ are the guards and the continuous dynamics. Let us first define the guards. We have that g_B can be taken on B-states (*i.e.* points on the spiral) and g_C on C-states (points not on the spiral and different from the origin). The continuous dynamics in q_1 are the one described by the dynamical system of Example 3.4 (the continuous dynamics in q_2 and q_3 do not play any role). Clearly g_B, g_C and γ_{q_1} are definable in $\mathcal{M}$.

The winning strategy in point $(0, 0)$ given by Theorem 5.8 is $\lambda(0, 0, \theta, t) = (\frac{\theta}{2}, c)$ where c consists in taking the transition leading to state q_2 (which is winning).

Example 5.10 Let us notice that in the case of timed automata dynamics (described in Example 2.2), our definable strategies correspond in some sense to the realizable strategies obtained in [5].

5.5 Decidability result

Theorem 5.8 is an existential result. It claims that given an o-minimal game, there exists a definable memoryless strategy for each $y \in \pi^*(\mathsf{Goal})$, and by Theorem 5.4 we know that $\mathsf{Suf}(\mathcal{P})$ is finite. The conclusion of the previous subsection is that given an o-minimal game there exists a definable memoryless winning strategy for each $y \in \pi^*(\mathsf{Goal})$.

In general, Theorem 5.8 does not allow to conclude that the control problem in an $\mathcal{M}$-structure is decidable. Indeed it depends on the decidability of $\mathsf{Th}(\mathcal{M})$. We can state the following theorem:

[10]This structure is o-minimal (see [20]).

Theorem 5.11 *Let $\mathcal{M}$ be an o-minimal structure such that $\mathsf{Th}(\mathcal{M})$ is decidable and $\mathcal{C}$ a class of $\mathcal{M}$-automata. Then the control problem in class $\mathcal{C}$ is decidable. Moreover if $\mathcal{A} \in \mathcal{C}$, the set of winning states $\pi^*(\mathsf{Goal})$ is computable and a memoryless strategy can be effectively computed for each $(q, y) \in \pi^*(\mathsf{Goal})$.*

Proof. By Theorem 5.4, for each $\mathcal{A} \in \mathcal{C}$, $\mathsf{Suf}(\mathcal{P}_\mathcal{A})$ is a definable finite partition respecting Goal; Proposition 5.7 ensures that this partition is stable under π. Hypothesis of Corollary 4.3 are thus satisfied and we get that the control problem in class $\mathcal{C}$ is decidable and that the winning states of a game $\mathcal{A} \in \mathcal{C}$ are computable. □

Remark 5.12 Let us notice that $\langle \mathbb{R}, <, +, 0, 1 \rangle$ and $\langle \mathbb{R}, <, +, \cdot, 0, 1 \rangle$ are examples of o-minimal structures with decidable theory.

Remark 5.13 In fact, Theorem 5.11 can be proved for a wider class than o-minimal systems, the condition that every variable is reset on every transition is not mandatory: it is sufficient to have a suffix-stable partition which is stable under the action of cPred and uPred; if this condition is satisfied (and the dynamic in every state is o-minimal) the resets can be arbitrary.

Timed automata can be treated in this framework. Theorem 5.11 thus provides in particular a way to compute winning strategies for timed games.

6 Conclusion

In this paper we have studied the control problem of dynamical systems with general dynamics. We have shown that time-abstract bisimulation is not fine enough to solve them, which is a major difference with the discrete case. Using an encoding of trajectories by words [6], we have proved that the so-called suffix partition is a good abstraction for control problems (with reachability winning conditions, but it applies also to basic safety winning conditions). We have finally provided decidability and computability results for o-minimal games. Our technique applies to timed automata, and we get the decidability of timed games [3], as well as the construction of winning strategies [5] as side results.

There are several interesting further research directions: we could try to assume only partial observability of the system, or we could try to apply similar techniques to systems where there is not such a strong reset condition when a discrete action is done.

References

[1] R. Alur and D. Dill. A theory of timed automata. *Theoretical Computer Science*, 126(2):183–235, 1994.

[2] R. Alur, Th. A. Henzinger, G. Lafferriere, and G. J. Pappas. Discrete abstractions of hybrid systems. *Proc. of the IEEE*, 88:971–984, 2000.

[3] E. Asarin, O. Maler, A. Pnueli, and J. Sifakis. Controller synthesis for timed automata. In *Proc. IFAC Symposium on System Structure and Control*, pages 469–474. Elsevier Science, 1998.

[4] E. Asarin, G. Schneider, and S. Yovine. On the decidability of the reachability problem for planar differential inclusions. In *Proc. 4th International Workshop on Hybrid Systems: Computation and Control (HSCC'01)*, volume 2034 of *Lecture Notes in Computer Science*, pages 89–104. Springer, 2001.

[5] P. Bouyer, F. Cassez, E. Fleury, and K. G. Larsen. Optimal strategies in priced timed game automata. In *Proc. 24th Conference on Foundations of Software Technology and Theoretical Computer Science (FST&TCS'04)*, volume 3328 of *Lecture Notes in Computer Science*, pages 148–160. Springer, 2004.

[6] Th. Brihaye. Words and bisimulation of dynamical systems. *Journal of Automata, Languages and Combinatorics*, 2006. To appear.

[7] Th. Brihaye and Ch. Michaux. On the expressiveness and decidability of o-minimal hybrid systems. *Journal of Complexity*, 21(4):447–478, 2005.

[8] Th. Brihaye, Ch. Michaux, C. Rivière, and C. Troestler. On o-minimal hybrid systems. In *Proc. 7th International Workshop on Hybrid Systems: Computation and Control (HSCC'04)*, volume 2993 of *Lecture Notes in Computer Science*, pages 219–233. Springer, 2004.

[9] J. M. Davoren. Topologies, continuity and bisimulations. *Informatique Théorique et Applications*, 33(4-5):357–382, 1999.

[10] L. de Alfaro, Th. A. Henzinger, and R. Majumdar. Symbolic algorithms for infinite-state games. In *Proc. 12th International Conference on Concurrency Theory (CONCUR'01)*, volume 2154 of *Lecture Notes in Computer Science*, pages 536–550. Springer, 2001.

[11] E. Grädel, W. Thomas, and Th. Wilke, editors. *Automata, Logics, and Infinite Games: A Guide to Current Research*, volume 2500 of *Lecture Notes in Computer Science*. Springer, 2002.

[12] Th. A. Henzinger. Hybrid automata with finite bisimulations. In *Proc. 22nd International Colloquium on Automata, Languages and Programming (ICALP'95)*, volume 944 of *Lecture Notes in Computer Science*, pages 324–335. Springer, 1995.

[13] Th. A. Henzinger. The theory of hybrid automata. In *Proc. 11th Annual Symposim on Logic in Computer Science (LICS'96)*, pages 278–292. IEEE Computer Society Press, 1996.

[14] Th. A. Henzinger, B. Horowitz, and R. Majumdar. Rectangular hybrid games. In *Proc. 10th International Conference on Concurrency Theory (CONCUR'99)*, volume 1664 of *Lecture Notes in Computer Science*, pages 320–335. Springer, 1999.

[15] Th. A. Henzinger, P. W. Kopke, A. Puri, and P. Varaiya. What's decidable about hybrid automata? *Journal of Computer and System Sciences*, 57(1):94–124, 1998.

[16] W. Hodges. *A Shorter Model Theory*. Cambridge University Press, 1997.

[17] M. V. Korovina and N. Vorobjov. Pfaffian hybrid systems. In *Proc. 18th International Workshop on Computer Science Logic (CSL'04)*, volume 3210 of *Lecture Notes in Computer Science*, pages 430–441. Springer, 2004.

[18] G. Lafferriere, G. J. Pappas, and S. Sastry. O-minimal hybrid systems. *Mathematics of Control, Signals, and Systems*, 13(1):1–21, 2000.

[19] A. Pillay and C. Steinhorn. Definable sets in ordered structures. *Transactions of the American Mathematical Society*, 295(2):565–592, 1986.

[20] L. Van den Dries. O-minimal structures. In *Logic: From Foundations to Applications*, Oxford Science Publications, pages 137–185. Oxford University Press, 1996.

[21] L. van den Dries. *Tame Topology and O-Minimal Structures*, volume 248 of *London Mathematical Society Lecture Note Series*. Cambridge University Press, 1998.

[22] H. Wong-Toi. The synthesis of controllers for linear hybrid automata. *Proceedings of IEEE Conference on Decision and Control*, pages 4607–4612, 1997.

Session 10: Verification

An Abstraction-Refinement Framework for Multi-Agent Systems

Thomas Ball
Microsoft Research*

Orna Kupferman
Hebrew University†

Abstract

Abstraction is a key technique for reasoning about systems with very large or even infinite state spaces. When a system is composed of reactive components, the interaction between the components is modeled by a multi-player game and verification corresponds to finding winners in the game. We describe an abstraction-refinement framework for multi-player games, with respect to specifications in the alternating μ-calculus (AMC). Our framework is based on abstract alternating transition systems (AATSs). Each agent in an AATS has transitions that over-approximate its power and transitions that under-approximate its power. We define the framework, define a 3-valued semantics for AMC formulas in an AATS, study the model-checking problem, define an abstraction preorder between AATSs, suggest a refinement procedure (in case model checking returns an indefinite answer), and study the completeness of the framework. For the case of predicate abstraction, we show how reasoning can be automated with a theorem prover.

Abstractions of multi-player games have been studied in the past. Our main contribution with respect to earlier work is that we study general (rather than only turn-based) ATSs, we add a refinement procedure on top of the model checking procedure, and our abstraction preorder is parameterized by a set of agents.

1 Introduction

We consider how to verify systems composed from *reactive* components. Each component is an *open system*, which interacts with its environment and whose behavior depends on the state of the system as well as the behavior of the environment. Modeling languages for open systems, such as CSP [16] and I/O Automata [22], distinguish between *internal* nondeterminism — choices made by the system, and *external* nondeterminism — choices made by the environment. Such a distinction exists naturally also in software, where processes have internal and external variables.

A game-theoretic property arises naturally: can the system resolve its internal choices so that the satisfaction of a property is guaranteed no matter how the environment resolves the external choices? For example, if P_1 and P_2 are processes that assign values to the variables x and y, we wish to verify properties like "it is possible for P_1 to make x always bigger than y, no matter how P_2 behaves" or "it is possible for P_1 to eventually prevent P_2 from making y positive". Such an *alternating* satisfaction can be viewed as a winning condition in a two-player game between the system and the environment [24].

Alternating transition systems (ATSs) model reactive components and their interactions, providing a general framework for verification of systems composed from reactive components [1]. *Alternating temporal logics* (ATLs) logically characterize ATSs and have, in addition to the usual universal and existential path quantifiers, a path quantifier that is parameterized by a set Ω of agents[1]. The path quantifier ranges over those paths that the agents in Ω can force the system into no matter how the other agents behave. For example, the ATL formula $\langle\langle\Omega\rangle\rangle\bigcirc(x = y)$ means that the agents in Ω can cooperate to make x and y equal in the next state. Dually, $[\![\Omega]\!]\bigcirc(x = y)$ means that the agents in Ω cannot prevent the next values of x and y from being equal.

The game theoretic-approach, which is the essence of ATS and ATL, has turned out to be very useful. In particular, games are used in compositional verification [9], reasoning about security protocols [19], multi-agent planning [28, 29], control and synthesis [24], and more. The complexity of game solving, however, is higher than that of model checking [1]. Thus, methods for coping with large state spaces are even more crucial than in verification of closed systems.

A key technique for coping with very large or even infinite state spaces is *abstraction*. Abstraction frameworks in the 3-valued semantics [3] are typically based on *modal transition systems* (MTS). Such systems have two types of transitions: *may* transitions, which over-approximate the transitions of the concrete system, and *must* transitions,

*Address: One Microsoft way, Redmond, WA 98052, USA, Email: tball@microsoft.com

†Address: School of Computer Science and Engineering, Jerusalem 91904, Israel. Email: orna@cs.huji.ac.il

[1]We adopt the terminology of game theory and refer to the underlying components as *agents*.

1043-6871/06 $20.00

which under-approximate the transitions of the concrete system. Accordingly, verification of universal and existential properties is done with respect to may and must transitions, respectively. One can extend the abstraction framework to an *abstraction-refinement* framework, in which an indefinite answer carries with it information that enables the refinement of the abstract system. In the case of 3-valued semantics, the information comes from analyzing the source of the answer being unknown [25, 26].

We describe an abstraction-refinement framework for games, based on ATSs and ATL. Our abstraction framework for games is based on lifting the notions of may and must transitions to *abstract alternating transition systems* (AATSs), where the may transitions over-approximate the power of the agents, and the must transitions under-approximate them. Accordingly, must transitions are helpful for the verification of properties referring to the ability of the agents to achieve a goal ($\langle\langle\ \rangle\rangle$ properties), and may transitions are helpful for the verification of properties referring to their disability ($[\![\ ]\!]$ properties).

Two earlier works in this direction are [15] and [8]. In [15], the authors describe an abstract interpretation of game properties: the basic modalities $\langle\langle\Omega\rangle\rangle\bigcirc$ and $[\![\Omega]\!]\bigcirc$ of ATL correspond to the predicate transformers $CPre_\Omega$ and $UPre_\Omega$, which take as an argument a set of agents and return the controllable and uncontrollable predecessors of it. These predicates are extended in [15] to predicates that operate on sets of abstract states, and are used in an abstract model-checking procedure for the *alternating μ-calculus*. In [8], the authors suggest an abstraction framework for turn-based games. In a turn-based game, a single agent proceeds in each position. Thus, turn-based games can model systems with a limited type of concurrency – one in which a single component proceeds in each transition. As noted in [8], the extension of the turn-based setting described there to general concurrent games is technically difficult. As we explain below, the extension carries with it interesting theoretical observations and significantly extends the type of systems for which abstraction can be applied[2].

In addition to defining AATSs, a 3-valued semantics for the alternating μ-calculus with respect to them, and a corresponding model-checking procedure, we make the following contributions. In case the model-checking procedure returns an indefinite answer, we accompany the answer by a suggestion for a *refinement*. Such an automatic refinement procedure does not exist in previous works on abstract games. As in the case of MTS, our procedure analyzes the sources to the "unknown" answer [25, 26][3].

We define an abstraction preorder between AATSs. An *alternating-simulation* preorder between ATSs is defined in [2]. The preorder there is parameterized by a set Ω of agents and $\mathcal{S} \leq_\Omega \mathcal{S}'$ reflects the fact that the agents in Ω are more powerful in $\mathcal{S}$ than in $\mathcal{S}'$. That is, if an alternating μ-calculus formula ψ that expresses the ability of the agents in Ω to achieve some goal is satisfied in $\mathcal{S}'$, it also is satisfied in $\mathcal{S}$. In contrast, our order reflects the abstraction level of the agents in Ω. Thus, if ψ has a definite value in $\mathcal{S}'$, and this value may be either "true" or "false", then it would have a definite value also in $\mathcal{S}$. Our order also is different from the one in [8], which does not take a set of agents as a parameter.

We argue that our definition is the appropriate one in the context of abstraction. In particular, we show that our order, when parameterized with a set Ω of agents, is logically characterized by the fragment of the alternating μ-calculus in which all $\langle\langle\ \rangle\rangle$ and $[\![\ ]\!]$ quantifiers are parameterized by sets $\Omega' \subseteq \Omega$ of agents[4].

Finally, for the special case of predicate abstraction of software, we show how a theorem prover can be used in order to automatically generate the may and must transitions of the AATS. This involves an extension of the traditional notions of *weakest precondition* to programs with internal nondeterminism and expressing the existence of may and must transitions by means of first order logic formulas that use the extended notions. We demonstrate our approach by verifying properties of a program composed of two processes that concurrently assign variables to integers.

A nice theoretical contribution of our framework is that it unifies three games: the model-checking game (cf. [27]), the abstraction game (cf. [7]), and the game between the different agents. In particular, though the may and must transitions of an AATS have the same structure, which is similar to the one of an ATS, the special case of an AATS with a single agent corresponds to an MTS with hyper-must transitions. Thus, AATSs provide a good explanation, based on the game nature of model checking and abstraction, of the asymmetry between must and may transitions. The appropriateness of the model is also reflected in the fact that AATSs enjoy monotonicity [26] and completeness [6]. From a practical point of view, handling general ATSs broadens the scope of abstraction to systems with full concurrency. In particular, the success of the game-theoretic approach in the verification of security protocols and multi-agent planning is in systems with full concurrency [19, 29], thus the richer setting is the interesting one.

Due to the lack of space, some details are omitted. A full version can be found in the authors' URLs.

---

[2]In addition, the abstraction in the turn-based setting are limited to *agent-preserving* abstractions, where concrete states that correspond to the same abstract state agree on the agent that proceeds in them. Such a limitation does not exist in our general case.

[3]Note that the standard method of counterexample-based refinement cannot be applied in the 3-valued semantics.

[4]Note that we allow the formulas to refer to both the abilities and disabilities of the agents of Ω. This is in contrast to the "Ω-universal" fragment of [2], where the simulation relation refers to the truth-value lattice (rather than the information lattice), and only the $\langle\langle\ \rangle\rangle$ quantifier is allowed.

2 The Model

2.1 Alternating transition systems

In ordinary transition systems, each transition corresponds to a possible step of the system. In *alternating transition systems* (ATSs, for short) [1], each transition corresponds to a possible move in a game between the underlying components of the system. We refer to the components as *agents*. In each move of the game, every agent chooses a set of successor states. The game then proceeds to the state in the intersection of the sets chosen by all agents. Equivalently, each agent puts a constraint on the choice of the successor state, and the game proceeds to a state that satisfies the constraints imposed by all the agents.

Formally, an ATS is a 6-tuple $S = \langle \Pi, \Sigma, S, s_{in}, \pi, \delta \rangle$, where Π is a set of propositions, Σ is a finite set of agents, S is a set of states, s_{in} is an initial state, $\pi : S \times \Pi \rightarrow \{\mathbf{T}, \mathbf{F}\}$ maps each state and proposition to the truth value of the proposition in the state, and $\delta : S \times \Sigma \rightarrow 2^{2^S}$ is a transition function that maps a state and an agent to a nonempty set of moves, where each move is a set of possible next states. Whenever the system is in state s, each agent σ chooses a set $S_\sigma \in \delta(s, \sigma)$. In this way, an agent σ ensures that the next state of the system will be in its move S_σ. However, which state in S_σ will be next depends on the moves made by the other agents, because the successor of s must lie in the intersection $\bigcap_{\sigma \in \Sigma} S_\sigma$ of the moves made by all the agents. We require that the transition function is nonblocking and that the agents together choose a unique next state: assuming $\Sigma = \{\sigma_1, \ldots, \sigma_n\}$, for every state $s \in S$ and every set $S_1, \ldots, S_n$ of moves $S_i \in \delta(s, \sigma_i)$, the intersection $S_1 \cap \ldots \cap S_n$ is a singleton.

For two states s and s', we say that s' is a *successor* of s if whenever the system S is in state s, the agents in Σ can cooperate so that s' will be the next state. Thus, for each $\sigma \in \Sigma$, there is $S_\sigma \in \delta(s, \sigma)$ such that $\{s'\} = \bigcap_{\sigma \in \Sigma} S_\sigma$. Consider a state $s \in S$, an agent $\sigma \in \Sigma$, and a set $A \in \delta(s, \sigma)$. If A contains a state s' such that the transition to s' is disabled no matter how the other agents proceed, we can remove s' from A. Accordingly, we assume that the transitions of the ATS contains no redundancy, in the sense that all the states in A are successors of s.

Example 2.1 Consider two variables x and y ranging over the integers $\mathcal{Z}$. We use the predicate s to indicate whether x and y agree on their sign (that is, they are both positive or both negative) and the predicate p to indicate whether x and y agree on their parity (that is, they are both odd or both even). Figure 1 describes a program that assigns values to x and y. For clarity, the next values of x and y are termed x' and y', respectively. The program is a synchronous composition of two processes P_1 and P_2. The processes have internal nondeterministic choices. For example, when P_1 executes $x' := x - 1 \mid x \mid x + 1$, it can resolve the nondeterministic choice in three possible ways and it can make x' either $x - 1$, x, or $x + 1$.

```
P1:
  while true do
    if s ∧ p then x' := x − 1 | x ; y' := y − 1 | y;
    if ¬s ∧ p then x' := x − 1 | x | x + 1;
    if s ∧ ¬p then x' := x − 1 | x | x + 1

P2:
  while true do
    if ¬s ∧ p then y' := y | y + 1;
    if ¬s ∧ ¬p then x' := x | x + 1 ; y' := y | y + 1
```

Figure 1. The processes P_1 and P_2.

Note that in some cases both P_1 and P_2 assign values to the variables (for example, when $\neg s \wedge p$ then P_1 assigns a value to x and P_2 assigns a value to y) and in some cases only P_1 or P_2 assigns value (for example, when $s \wedge \neg p$, only P_1 assigns a value to x, and the value of y is unchanged).

The ATS that corresponds to the composition of P_1 with P_2 has state space $\mathcal{Z} \times \mathcal{Z}$ and has the following transitions:

- If $s \wedge p$, then
  - $\delta((x, y), P_1) = \{\{(x - 1, y - 1)\}, \{(x - 1, y)\}, \{(x, y - 1)\}, \{(x, y)\}\}$.
  - $\delta((x, y), P_2) = \{\{(x - 1, y - 1), (x - 1, y), (x, y - 1), (x, y)\}\}$.
- If $\neg s \wedge p$, then
  - $\delta((x, y), P_1) = \{\{(x - 1, y), (x - 1, y + 1)\}, \{(x, y), (x, y + 1)\}, \{(x + 1, y), (x + 1, y + 1)\}\}$.
  - $\delta((x, y), P_2) = \{\{(x - 1, y), (x, y), (x + 1, y)\}, \{(x - 1, y + 1), (x, y + 1), (x + 1, y + 1)\}\}$.
- If $s \wedge \neg p$, then
  - $\delta((x, y), P_1) = \{\{(x - 1, y)\}, \{(x, y)\}, \{(x + 1, y)\}\}$.
  - $\delta((x, y), P_2) = \{\{(x - 1, y), (x, y), (x + 1, y)\}\}$.
- If $\neg s \wedge \neg p$, then
  - $\delta((x, y), P_1) = \{\{(x, y), (x, y + 1), (x + 1, y), (x + 1, y + 1)\}\}$.
  - $\delta((x, y), P_2) = \{\{(x, y)\}, \{(x, y + 1)\}, \{(x + 1, y)\}, \{(x + 1, y + 1)\}\}$.

For example, if the current values of x and y are $(-6, 2)$, thus $\neg s$ and p, then P_1 can either decrease x by 1 and force (x', y') to be in $\{(-7, 2), (-7, 3)\}$, leave x unchanged and force (x', y') to be in $\{(-6, 2), (-6, 3)\}$, or increase x by 1 and force (x', y') to be in $\{(-5, 2), (-5, 3)\}$. Process P_1, however, cannot influence the next value of y and it therefore cannot influence which values inside the sets would be the next ones. Process P_2 can either leave y unchanged and force (x', y') to be in $\{(-7, 2), (-6, 2), (-5, 2)\}$, or increase y by 1 and force (x', y') to be in $\{(-7, 3), (-6, 3), (-5, 3)\}$. As with P_1, process P_2 cannot influence the next value of x and it therefore cannot influence which values inside these sets would be the next ones. Once P_1 and P_2 have made their choices, (x', y') is fixed. □

An ordinary *labeled transition system*, or Kripke structure, is the special case of an ATS where the set $\Sigma = \{sys\}$ of agents is a singleton set. In this special case, the sole agent sys can always determine the successor state: for all states $q \in S$, the transition $\delta(q, sys)$ must contain a nonempty set of moves, each of which is a singleton set.

Often, we are interested in the cooperation of a subset $\Omega \subseteq \Sigma$ of the agents. Given Ω, we define $\delta(q, \Omega) = \{T : \text{for each } \sigma \in \Omega \text{ there exists } S_\sigma \in \delta(q, \sigma) \text{ and } T = \bigcap_{\sigma \in \Omega} S_\sigma\}$. For example, if $\Sigma = \{a, b, c\}$, $\delta(q, a) = \{\{q_1, q_2, q_5\}, \{q_3, q_4\}\}$ and $\delta(q, b) = \{\{q_1, q_4, q_5\}, \{q_2, q_3\}\}$, then $\delta(q, \{a, b\}) = \{\{q_1, q_5\}, \{q_2\}, \{q_4\}, \{q_3\}\}$. Intuitively, whenever the system is in state q, the agents in Ω can choose a set $T \in \delta(q, \Omega)$ such that, no matter what the other agents do, the next state of the system is in T. In particular, when all agents cooperate, they can decide the next state, thus, $\delta(q, \Sigma)$ is a set of singletons. Likewise, $\delta(q, \emptyset)$ contains the single set of all successors of q.

2.2 Alternating μ-calculus

The temporal logic AMC (*Alternating μ-calculus*) is the alternating extension of the μ-calculus [18]. Formulas of AMC are defined with respect to a finite set Π of *propositions* and a finite set Σ of *agents*. Formulas of AMC are interpreted over states of an ATS. The $\forall\bigcirc$ and $\exists\bigcirc$ modalities of the μ-calculus are replaced in AMC by the modality $\langle\langle\Omega\rangle\rangle\bigcirc$, for a set Ω of agents. The path quantifier $\langle\langle\Omega\rangle\rangle$ ranges over computations that the agents in Ω can force the system into. Thus, the AMC formula $\langle\langle\Omega\rangle\rangle\bigcirc\theta$ intuitively means that the agents in Ω can cooperate to make θ true in the next state (they can "enforce" the next state to satisfy θ). Formally, $q \models \langle\langle\Omega\rangle\rangle\bigcirc\theta$ iff there is $T \in \delta(q, \Omega)$ such that $q' \models \theta$ for all $q' \in T$. It is often useful to express an AMC formula in a dual form. For this purpose, we use the path quantifier $[\![\Omega]\!]$, for a set Ω of agents. Then, $[\![\Omega]\!]\bigcirc\theta$ means that the agents in Ω cannot cooperate to make θ false in the next state (they cannot avoid θ). Note that[5] $[\![\Omega]\!]\bigcirc\theta = \neg\langle\langle\Omega\rangle\rangle\bigcirc\neg\theta$. The least and greatest fixed-point operators $\mu z.\theta(z)$ and $\nu z.\theta(z)$ can be applied to monotonic AMC formulas and enable the specification of global properties. For a full definition of the syntax and semantics of AMC see [1].

Example 2.2 Consider the ATS from Example 2.1. The state $(1, -1)$ satisfies $\langle\langle P_1\rangle\rangle\bigcirc(x \neq y)$. Indeed, by increasing x by 1 (or leaving it unchanged), the process P_1 can guarantee that, no matter how P_2 modifies the value of y, the next values of x and y would be different. The state $(1, -1)$ also satisfies $\langle\langle P_2\rangle\rangle\bigcirc(x \neq y)$. Indeed, by decreasing y by 1 (or leaving it unchanged), the process P_2 can guarantee that, no matter how P_1 modifies the value of x, the next values of x and y would be different. Finally, $(1, -1)$ also satisfies $\langle\langle\{P_1, P_2\}\rangle\rangle\bigcirc\nu z.(x = y) \wedge \langle\langle\{P_1\}\rangle\rangle\bigcirc z$. Indeed, by decreasing x by 1 and increasing y by 1, the two processes can collaborate and make $x = y = 0$, and then P_1 can keep $x = y = 0$ forever.

We would like to be able to answer questions like "can P_1 make sure that x and y eventually always agree on their parity?", "Can P_2 make y eventually negative?", "can P_1 and P_2 collaborate so that eventually x and y never have the same sign?", and so on. The way we do it is by reasoning about a finite state AATS that abstracts the interaction between the two processes. □

3 Abstraction

For finite state systems, abstraction frameworks often are based on *modal transition systems* (MTS) [20]. Traditional MTS have two types of transitions: *must* (under-approximating transitions) and *may* (over-approximating transitions). The idea is that universal properties of a concrete system can be proven by referring to the may transitions of the abstract systems whereas existential properties can be proven by referring to the must transitions. In the case of multi-agent systems, we do not consider universal and existential properties. Instead, we refer to properties that the agents can force the system to satisfy and properties they cannot avoid. Accordingly, rather than using may and must transitions in order to under- and over- approximate the transitions, we are going to use them in order to under- and over- approximate the power of the agents.

[5] On the other hand, note that the path quantifiers $\langle\langle\ \rangle\rangle$ and $[\![\ ]\!]$ are not semantically dual with respect to the set of agents: if the agents in Ω can enforce a set τ of successor states, then the agents in $\Sigma \setminus \Omega$ cannot avoid τ. Therefore, $q \models \langle\langle\Omega\rangle\rangle\bigcirc\psi$ implies $q \models [\![\Sigma \setminus \Omega]\!]\bigcirc\psi$. The converse of this statement, however, is not necessarily true.

3.1 Abstract ATS

An AATS is an ATS $S' = \langle \Pi, \Sigma, S_A, s_{in}, \pi, \delta_{must}, \delta_{may} \rangle$ in which the labeling function $\pi : S_A \times \Pi \to \{\mathbf{T}, \mathbf{F}, \bot\}$ is three-valued, and there are two types of transitions, $\delta_{must} : S_A \times \Sigma \to 2^{2^{S_A}}$ and $\delta_{may} : S_A \times \Sigma \to 2^{2^{S_A}}$.

The elements of $\{\mathbf{T}, \mathbf{F}, \bot\}$ can be arranged in an "information lattice" [17] in which $\bot \sqsubseteq \mathbf{T}$ and $\bot \sqsubseteq \mathbf{F}$. Note that for two values $v_1, v_2 \in \{\mathbf{T}, \mathbf{F}, \bot\}$, we have $v_1 \sqsubseteq v_2$ iff $v_1 \neq \bot$ implies $v_1 = v_2$.

Consider an ATS $S = \langle \Pi, \Sigma, S_C, c_{in}, \pi, \delta \rangle$. Let S_A be a set of abstract states and let $\rho : S_C \to S_A$ be an abstraction function[6]. We extend ρ to subsets of S_C in the expected way, thus $\rho(C) = \bigcup_{c \in C} \rho(c)$. We also use $c \in a$ to indicate that $\rho(c) = a$.

An AATS $S' = \langle \Pi, \Sigma, S_A, a_{in}, \pi', \delta_{must}, \delta_{may} \rangle$ is an abstraction of S if for all concrete states $c \in S_c$, we have $\pi'(\rho(c)) \sqsubseteq \pi(c)$, and for all abstract states $a \in S_A$ and agents $\sigma \in \Sigma$, the following hold:

- $\delta_{must}(a, \sigma) = \{A \subseteq S_A :$ for all $c \in a$ there is $C_c \in \delta(c, \sigma)$, and $A = \bigcup_{c \in a} \rho(C_c)\}$.
- $\delta_{may}(a, \sigma) = \{A \subseteq S_A :$ there is $c \in a$ and $C_c \in \delta(c, \sigma)$ and $A = \rho(C_c)\}$.

Intuitively, $A \in \delta_{must}(a, \sigma)$ if for each $c \in a$, the agent σ can force the successor of c to correspond to a state in A. Likewise, $A \in \delta_{may}(a, \sigma)$ if for some $c \in a$, the agent σ can force the successor of c to correspond to a state in A. Recall that in MTS, must transitions are used in order to prove existential properties or refute universal properties, whereas may transitions are used in order to prove universal properties or refute existential ones. In AATSs, must transitions are used in order to prove $\langle\!\langle\ \rangle\!\rangle$ properties and refute $[\![\ ]\!]$ properties, whereas may transitions are used in order to prove $[\![\ ]\!]$ properties and refute $\langle\!\langle\ \rangle\!\rangle$ properties.

As with the usual transitions of an ATS, we can refer to the *must* and *may* transitions of a set of agents in an AATS. Thus, $\delta_{must}(q, \Omega)$ underapproximates the power of the agents in Ω when they cooperate, and $\delta_{may}(q, \Omega)$ overapproximates their power.

Remark 3.1 An MTS can be viewed as a special case of an AATS – one with a single agent *sys*. Recall that then, the ATS S is such that $\delta(c, sys)$ is a set of singletons. Accordingly, in an abstraction of S, we have $A \in \delta_{must}(a, sys)$ iff for every $c \in a$, there exists $\{c'_c\} \in \delta(c, sys)$ and $A = \bigcup_{c \in a} \rho(c'_c)$. Also, $\{a'\} \in \delta_{may}(a, sys)$ iff there is $c \in a$ and $\{c'\} \in \delta(c, sys)$ such that $a' = \rho(c')$. Thus, the definition coincides with the standard definition for hyper-must and may transitions [21]. The fact that we get hyper-must highlights that AATSs naturally have the game nature of model checking and abstraction "built in": each of the sets $A \in \delta_{must}(a, sys)$ corresponds to a choice the system is making from each of the concrete states that correspond to a. In order for an existential property to hold in a, each of the concrete states should have a successor that satisfies the existential property, and thus $\delta_{must}(a, sys)$ should have a set A all of whose states satisfy the property. □

[6]Note that since S is a general ATS, we do not have to limit ρ to an agent preserving function, as is the case with the restricted case of turn-based ATSs [8].

We define a 3-*valued semantics* of AMC formulas with respect to AATSs. The value of a formula θ in a state a of an AATS $\mathcal{A} = \langle \Pi, \Sigma, S_A, a_{in}, \pi', \delta_{must}, \delta_{may} \rangle$, denoted $[(\mathcal{A}, a) \models \theta]$, is defined as follows. Due to the lack of space, we do not include the semantics of fixed-point operators[7]. The latter is similar to the one described for 3-valued μ-calculus in [4], where the semantics we give below to the $\langle\!\langle\ \rangle\!\rangle$ operator, replaces the one described there for the usual modal operators of μ-calculus.

$$[(\mathcal{A}, a) \models p] = \pi(a, p).$$

$$[(\mathcal{A}, a) \models \neg\theta] = \begin{cases} \mathbf{T} & \text{if } [(\mathcal{A}, a) \models \theta] = \mathbf{F}. \\ \mathbf{F} & \text{if } [(\mathcal{A}, a) \models \theta] = \mathbf{T}. \\ \bot & \text{otherwise.} \end{cases}$$

$$[(\mathcal{A}, a) \models \theta_1 \wedge \theta_2] = \begin{cases} \mathbf{T} & \text{if } [(\mathcal{A}, a) \models \theta_1] = \mathbf{T} \text{ and } \\ & [(\mathcal{A}, a) \models \theta_2] = \mathbf{T}. \\ \mathbf{F} & \text{if } [(\mathcal{A}, a) \models \theta_1] = \mathbf{F} \text{ or } \\ & [(\mathcal{A}, a) \models \theta_2] = \mathbf{F}. \\ \bot & \text{otherwise.} \end{cases}$$

$$[(\mathcal{A}, a) \models \langle\!\langle \Omega \rangle\!\rangle \bigcirc \theta] = \begin{cases} \mathbf{T} & \text{if there is } A \in \delta_{must}(a, \Omega) \\ & \text{such that } [(\mathcal{A}, a') \models \theta] = \mathbf{T} \\ & \text{for all } a' \in A. \\ \mathbf{F} & \text{if for all } A \in \delta_{may}(a, \Omega), \\ & \text{we have} [(\mathcal{A}, a') \models \theta] = \mathbf{F} \\ & \text{for some } a' \in A. \\ \bot & \text{otherwise.} \end{cases}$$

Abstracting an ATS may cause the truth value of some formulas to become indefinite, but definite values are consistent with the values in the concrete ATS. Formally, we have the following:

Theorem 3.2 *Consider an ATS S, an AATS $\mathcal{A}$ that is an abstraction of S, a state a of $\mathcal{A}$, and an AMC formula θ. For all $c \in a$, we have $[(S, c) \models \theta] \sqsupseteq [(\mathcal{A}, a) \models \theta]$.*

Remark 3.3 The semantics of the $\langle\!\langle \Omega \rangle\!\rangle \bigcirc$ operator corresponds to our intuition, where in order to prove that the agents in Ω can force the concrete system to a set of states that satisfy θ, one should check that they can achieve this task in the abstraction even if we under-approximate their power and over-approximate the power of the complementary set of agents. Indeed, the semantics of the $\langle\!\langle \Omega \rangle\!\rangle \bigcirc$ operator is equivalent to one in which the agents in Ω proceed with their must transitions and the agents in $\Sigma \setminus \Omega$

[7]Note that this makes the description of the semantics much cleaner as we do not have to view a formula as a mapping from environments (3-valued assignments to the free variables) to mappings of S_A to $\{\mathbf{T}, \mathbf{F}, \bot\}$.

proceed with their may transitions. Formally, $[(\mathcal{A}, a) \models \langle\langle\Omega\rangle\rangle\bigcirc\varphi] = \mathbf{T}$ iff there is $A \in \delta_{must}(a, \Omega)$ such that for all $A' \in \delta_{may}(a, \Sigma \setminus \Omega)$, we have that $[(\mathcal{A}, a') \models \theta] = \mathbf{T}$ for all $a' \in A \cap A'$. □

Example 3.4 Consider the Processes P_1 and P_2 described in Example 2.1. We define an AATS $\mathcal{S}_s$ according to the predicate s. Thus, $\mathcal{S}_s$ has two states, which we denote by s and $-$. Formally $\mathcal{S}_s = \{\{s\}, \{P_1, P_2\}, \{s, -\}, s, \pi', \delta_{must}, \delta_{may}\}$, where $\pi'(s, s) = \mathbf{T}$, $\pi'(-, s) = \mathbf{F}$, and the transitions are as follows.

$\bullet\delta_{must}(s, P_1) = \{\{s\}\}$	$\bullet\delta_{must}(s, P_2) = \{\{s, -\}\}$
$\bullet\delta_{may}(s, P_1) = \{\{s\}, \{-\}\}$	$\bullet\delta_{may}(s, P_2) = \{\{s\}\}$
$\bullet\delta_{must}(-, P_1) = \{\{s, -\}\}$	$\bullet\delta_{must}(-, P_2) = \{\{s, -\}\}$
$\bullet\delta_{may}(-, P_1) = \{\{s\}, \{-\}\}$	$\bullet\delta_{may}(-, P_2) = \{\{s\}, \{-\}\}$

Let us explain the δ_{must} transition of P_1 from s. By the definition of δ_{must}, we have that $\{s\} \in \delta_{must}(s, P_1)$ iff for all (x, y) that satisfy s, the process P_1 can force (x', y') to satisfy s. This is true, as for all x and y that satisfy s, the set $\delta_{must}((x, y), P_1)$ contains the set $\{(x, y)\}$.

Note that the must transitions underapproximate the power of the processes and the may transitions overapproximate their power. For example, while the only must transition of P_1 from s is to $\{s\}$, it is possible for P_1 to resolve the nondeterminism in the state $(0, 0)$, which satisfies s, so that the next state will be $(-1, 0)$, which does not satisfy s. This is reflected in the may transitions, which overapproximate the power of the processes, and also contains the set $\{-\}$. Likewise, while the only must transition of P_2 from s is to $\{s, -\}$, indicating P_2 cannot influence the next values, there are states (in fact, all states except for those in which $x = 0$ or $y = 0$) that satisfy s for which s is guaranteed to stay true in the next state no matter how P_1 resolves its internal nondeterminism, thus $\{s\} \in \delta_{may}(s, P_2)$.

Even though our abstraction is based on a single predicate, we can verify some properties. For example, since $[(\mathcal{S}_s, s) \models \langle\langle P_1\rangle\rangle\bigcirc s] = \mathbf{T}$, Theorem 3.2, implies that $c \models \langle\langle P_1\rangle\rangle\bigcirc s$ for all concrete states c that satisfy s. In fact, $[(\mathcal{S}_s, s) \models \nu z.s \wedge \langle\langle P_1\rangle\rangle z] = \mathbf{T}$; thus once in a s state, P_1 can force s forever. □

3.2 AMC model checking

The standard symbolic μ-calculus model-checking algorithm of [11] can be extended to a symbolic model-checking algorithm for AMC formulas with respect to ATSs. As we show now, this can be done also with respect to AATSs, yielding a symbolic model-checking algorithm with respect to the abstraction. In more details, the algorithm starts with the innermost subformulas of the specification and computes, for each subformula θ, the sets $|\theta|_{\mathbf{T}}$ and $|\theta|_{\mathbf{F}}$ of abstract states a such that $[(\mathcal{A}, a) \models \theta] = \mathbf{T}$ and $[(\mathcal{A}, a) \models \theta] = \mathbf{F}$, respectively. For Boolean and fixed-point operators, the algorithm proceeds as known symbolic multi-valued model-checking algorithms (c.f., [5]). For the symbolic operator $\langle\langle\Omega\rangle\rangle$, the algorithm proceeds according to the following characterization:

- $|\langle\langle\Omega\rangle\rangle\bigcirc\theta|_{\mathbf{T}} = \{a : \exists A \in \delta_{must}(a, \Omega) \text{ s.t. } A \subseteq |\theta|_{\mathbf{T}}\}$,
- $|\langle\langle\Omega\rangle\rangle\bigcirc\theta|_{\mathbf{F}} = \{a : \forall A \in \delta_{may}(a, \Omega), A \cap |\theta|_{\mathbf{F}} \neq \emptyset\}$.

As discussed in [8], an alternative algorithm reduces the model checking of an AMC formula θ in an AATS $\mathcal{A}$ to model checking of an AMC formula θ' in an ATS $\mathcal{S}$ such that the transition from θ and $\mathcal{A}$ to θ' and $\mathcal{S}$ involves only a linear blow up. Such a reduction is possible also in our case (and is in fact simpler than the one described in [8], as our reduction does not have to end up in a turn-based ATS and does not need the technicality that the latter involves).

3.3 Completeness of abstraction

We now show that our abstraction framework is complete in the sense discussed in [6, 7]. Thus, we can model check a specification θ in an infinite ATS, by reasoning about finite abstractions of it. It is shown in [2] that two states of an ATS satisfy the same AMC formulas iff they are *alternating bisimilar*. An infinite ATS can, in general, have an infinite number of alternating-bisimulation equivalence classes. When, however, we are concerned with the ability of a finite number of AMC formulas to distinguish between states of an ATS, the number of equivalence classes is finite. This finiteness is the key to our completeness result.

In case θ is a safety property (in particular, if θ is in *safe-AMC* — the syntactic fragment of AMC in which formulas are in positive normal form and only the greatest fixed-point operator is allowed), things are simple, as θ induces a finite set of equivalence classes, each consisting of concrete states that are indistinguishable by the subformulas of θ. Formally, we have the following:

Theorem 3.5 *Consider an ATS $\mathcal{S}$, a state c of $\mathcal{S}$, and a safe-AMC formula θ. There is a finite AATS $\mathcal{A}$ such that $\mathcal{A}$ is an abstraction of $\mathcal{S}$ and $[(\mathcal{A}, \rho(c)) \models \theta] \in \{\mathbf{T}, \mathbf{F}\}$.*

Once we allow θ to include least fixed-points, things are more complicated, as the alternating-bisimulation equivalence classes described above are with respect to an AATS augmented with a fairness condition [1]. Thus, completeness is achievable, but goes beyond the model we study here.

4 Abstraction preorder

An *alternating simulation* preorder between two AATSs is defined in [2]. The order is parameterized by a set Ω of agents and corresponds to the ability of the agents in Ω to restrict the ATS to a smaller set of behaviors in the simulated ATS. In this section we define an abstraction preorder that also is parameterized by a set of agents. Our order, however, corresponds to the agents in Ω being less abstract in the simulated ATS.

For a set S, consider two sets Δ and Δ' in 2^{2^S}. We say that Δ is *more refined than* Δ' if for every set $A' \in \Delta'$, there is $A \in \Delta$ such that $A \subseteq A'$. Thus, each of the sets in Δ' can be restricted to a set in Δ. For example, if $S = \{q_1, q_2, q_3, q_4\}$ then $\{\{q_1\}, \{q_2\}, \{q_3\}\}$ is more refined than $\{\{q_1, q_2\}, \{q_2, q_3\}\}$. Intuitively, if both Δ and Δ' describe the transitions of some agent σ from state q, then σ is more refined with the transitions in Δ than with these in Δ', as it can force the ATS into smaller sets (and possibly more sets) of next successors.

Every must transition is a may transition in the sense that if the agent can force a set in a must transition, it can force a subset of it in a corresponding may transition. Formally, we have the following:

Lemma 4.1 *For every state a and agent σ, we have that $\delta_{may}(a, \sigma)$ is more refined than $\delta_{must}(a, \sigma)$.*

We can now define a preorder $\preceq_\Omega$ between AATSs. The preorder is parameterized by a set Ω of agents. Intuitively, $\mathcal{S} \preceq_\Omega \mathcal{S}'$ if the behavior of each of the agents in Ω is less abstract in $\mathcal{S}$ than in $\mathcal{S}'$.

We first extend the definition of "more refined" to sets over different, but related, domains. Consider two sets S and S', and a relation $H \subseteq S \times S'$. For a set $\Delta \in 2^{2^S}$, we use $H(\Delta)$ to denote the set of sets obtained by replacing each member s of a set in Δ by all elements $s' \in S'$ with $H(s, s')$. Thus, $A' \in H(\Delta)$ if there is $A \in \Delta$ and $A' = \bigcup_{s \in A}\{s' : H(s, s')\}$. Now, we say that Δ is *more refined than Δ' with respect to H* (more H-refined, for short) iff $H(\Delta)$ is more refined than Δ'. Thus, each of the sets in Δ' has a set in Δ that corresponds to it. Likewise, Δ' is *more H-refined than* Δ iff Δ' is more refined than $H(\Delta)$. Thus, each of the sets in Δ has a set in Δ' that corresponds to it. For example, if $S = \{q_1, q_2, q_3, q_4, q_5\}$, $S' = \{a_1, a_2, a_3\}$, and $H = \{(q_1, a_1), (q_2, a_1), (q_3, a_2), (q_4, a_3), (q_5, a_3)\}$, then $\{\{q_1, q_2\}, \{q_4\}\}$ is more H-refined than $\{\{a_1, a_2\}\}$ and $\{\{a_1\}, \{a_2\}\}$ is more H-refined than $\{\{q_1, q_2, q_3\}, \{q_3, q_4\}\}$.

Lemma 4.2 *Consider two sets S and S', and a relation $H \subseteq S \times S'$. Consider four sets $\Delta_1, \Delta_2 \in 2^{2^S}$ and $\Delta'_1, \Delta'_2 \in 2^{2^{S'}}$. If Δ_1 is more H-refined than Δ'_1 and Δ_2 is more H-refined than Δ'_2, then $\{A_1 \cap A_2 : A_1 \in \Delta_1$ and $A_2 \in \Delta_2\}$ is more H-refined than $\{A'_1 \cap A'_2 : A'_1 \in \Delta'_1$ and $A'_2 \in \Delta'_2\}$.*

Consider two AATSs $\mathcal{S} = \langle \Pi, \Sigma, S, s_{in}, \pi, \delta_{must}, \delta_{may} \rangle$ and $\mathcal{S}' = \langle \Pi', \Sigma, S', s'_{in}, \pi', \delta'_{must}, \delta'_{may} \rangle$. For a subset $\Omega \subseteq \Sigma$ of agents, a relation $H \subseteq S \times S'$ is an *Ω-abstraction relation from $\mathcal{S}$ to $\mathcal{S}'$* if for all pairs $\langle s, s' \rangle \in H$, the following conditions hold:

(1) $\pi(s) \sqsupseteq \pi'(s')$.

(2) For all $\sigma \in \Omega$, we have that $\delta_{must}(s, \sigma)$ is more H-refined than $\delta'_{must}(s', \sigma)$.

(3) For all $\sigma \in \Omega$, we have that $\delta'_{may}(s', \sigma)$ is more H-refined than $\delta_{may}(s, \sigma)$.

If H is an Ω-abstraction from $\mathcal{S}$ to $\mathcal{S}'$ and $\langle s, s' \rangle \in H$, we write $(\mathcal{S}, s) \preceq_\Omega (\mathcal{S}', s')$, which indicates that the agents in Ω are less abstract in $(\mathcal{S}, s)$ than in $(\mathcal{S}', s')$. That is, the must transitions, which under-approximate the agents' power, are more refined in $\mathcal{S}$ than in $\mathcal{S}'$ (so in $\mathcal{S}$, the under-approximation is "less under"). Dually, the may transitions, which over-approximate their power, are more refined in $\mathcal{S}'$ than in $\mathcal{S}$ (so in $\mathcal{S}$, the over-approximation is "less over").

When $(\mathcal{S}, s_{in}) \preceq_\Omega (\mathcal{S}', s'_{in})$, we write $\mathcal{S} \preceq_\Omega \mathcal{S}'$. Note that the definition of $\preceq_\Omega$ refers to the individual agents in Ω. Thus, by Lemma 4.2, we have the following:

Lemma 4.3 *Let H be an Ω-abstraction from $\mathcal{S}$ to $\mathcal{S}'$. For all $\langle s, s' \rangle \in H$ and $\Omega' \subseteq \Omega$, the following holds:*

(2) *$\delta_{must}(s, \Omega')$ is more H-refined than $\delta'_{must}(s', \Omega')$.*

(3) *$\delta'_{may}(s', \Omega')$ is more H-refined than $\delta_{may}(s, \Omega')$.*

When $\mathcal{S} \preceq_\sigma \mathcal{S}'$ for all agents σ, we say that $\mathcal{S}$ is less abstract than $\mathcal{S}'$, denoted $\mathcal{S} \preceq \mathcal{S}'$.

Remark 4.4 It may be that $\mathcal{S} \preceq_{\Omega_1} \mathcal{S}'$, $\mathcal{S} \not\preceq_{\Omega_2} \mathcal{S}'$, $\mathcal{S}' \preceq_{\Omega_2} \mathcal{S}$, and $\mathcal{S}' \not\preceq_{\Omega_1} \mathcal{S}$. For example, suppose that P_x assigns values to x, P_y assigns values to y, in $\mathcal{S}$ we maintain the concrete value of x and the parity of y, and in $\mathcal{S}'$ we maintain the parity of x and the concrete value of y. Then, $\mathcal{S} \preceq_{P_x} \mathcal{S}'$, $\mathcal{S} \not\preceq_{P_y} \mathcal{S}'$, $\mathcal{S}' \preceq_{P_y} \mathcal{S}$, and $\mathcal{S}' \not\preceq_{P_x} \mathcal{S}$. □

Remark 4.5 Recall that our definition refers to the abstraction level of the agents, and not the power of the agents with respect to each other. To emphasize this fact further, consider two programs, each being a composition of two processes P_1 and P_2. In the first program, P_1 can increase or decrease by 1 the value of both x and y, and P_2 does nothing. In the second program, P_1 can increase or decrease by 1 the value of x, and P_2 can increase or decrease by 1 the value of y. Clearly, P_1 is more powerful in the first program, and the simulation order of [2] would show that. On the other hand, the first program is not less abstract, with respect to either P_1 or P_2, than the second program. Accordingly, if we examine two AATSs, abstracted, say, according to a predicate referring to the parity of x and y, then there is no abstraction relation between the two AATSs. □

By viewing a concrete ATS as an AATS whose may and $must$ transition relations are equivalent to the transition relation of the ATS, we can use the abstraction preorder to relate a concrete system and its abstraction, with respect to all subsets of agents. Formally, we have the following:

Theorem 4.6 *Consider an ATS $\mathcal{S} = \langle \Pi, \Sigma, S_C, c_{in}, \pi, \delta \rangle$, a set of abstract states S_A, and a function $\rho : S_C \to S_A$. Let the AATS $\mathcal{S}' = \langle \Pi', \Sigma, S_A, a_{in}, \pi', \delta_{must}, \delta_{may} \rangle$ be the abstraction of $\mathcal{S}$ according to ρ, and let $H \subseteq S_C \times S_A$ be such that $H(c, a)$ iff $\rho(c) = a$. For all sets Ω of agents, H is an Ω-abstraction relation from $\mathcal{S}$ to $\mathcal{S}'$.*

While the μ-calculus logically characterizes the abstraction preorder on MTSs [13], AMC characterizes the abstraction preorder on AATSs. Formally, for a set Ω of agents, let AMC$^\Omega$ be the fragment of AMC in which all $\langle\langle\ \rangle\rangle$ and $[\![\ ]\!]$ quantifiers are parameterized by a set $\Omega' \subseteq \Omega$ of agents. Note that we do not require the formulas to be in a positive normal form. Thus, AMC$^\Omega$ formulas refer both to the strength and weakness of the agents of Ω. This is in contrast to the fragment Ω-AMC of [2], where the simulation relation refers to the truth-value lattice rather than the information lattice, and accordingly Ω-AMC formula are in positive normal form and can refer only to the power of the agents of Ω.

Theorem 4.7 *Let $\mathcal{S} = \langle \Pi, \Sigma, S, s_{in}, \pi, \delta_{must}, \delta_{may} \rangle$ and $\mathcal{S}' = \langle \Pi', \Sigma, S', s'_{in}, \pi', \delta'_{must}, \delta'_{may} \rangle$ be two AATSs. Consider a set Ω of agents. For every two states $a \in S$ and $a' \in S'$, we have that $(\mathcal{S}, a) \preceq_\Omega (\mathcal{S}', a')$ iff $[(\mathcal{S}, a) \models \theta] \sqsupseteq [(\mathcal{S}', a')) \models \theta]$ for all AML$^\Omega$ formulas θ.*

Note that, by Theorem 4.6, we have that Theorem 3.2 is a special case of Theorem 4.7.

As with usual simulation relations and alternating-simulation relations [23, 2], a maximal Ω-abstraction relation H between two AATSs can be calculated as a fixed-point of intermediate relations (the sequence $H_0, H_1, \ldots$ used in the proof of Theorem 4.7). Accordingly, we have the following:

Theorem 4.8 *Given two AATSs $\mathcal{S}$ and $\mathcal{S}'$ and a set Ω of agents, deciding whether $\mathcal{S} \preceq_\Omega \mathcal{S}'$ can be done in polynomial time.*

5 Refinement

In case the model-checking procedure returns an indefinite answer, we accompany the answer by a suggestion for a *refinement*. As in the case of MTS, our procedure analyzes the sources to the "unknown" answer. Technically, as in [25, 26], the refinement procedure first finds a *failure state* – a state in which the evaluation of the specification became indefinite (with respect to some subformula), and then refines the AATS in a way that makes the satisfaction of this subformula definite. We first show that our model of AATSs enjoys monotonicity, thus the refined AATS gives a definite truth value to at least all formulas that have a definite truth value in the AATS before the refinement.

5.1 Monotonicity

As argued in [26], refining an MTS by splitting a state into two states may result in an MTS with fewer must transitions. As a result, formulas that have a definite value in the original MTS may have an indefinite value in the refined MTS. The solution to this annoying fact is to have hyper-must transitions. As we now show, splitting states of an AATS $\mathcal{S}_1$ that abstracts a concrete ATS results in an AATS $\mathcal{S}_2$ such that $\mathcal{S}_2 \preceq \mathcal{S}_1$. Thus, by Theorem 4.7, monotonicity holds in our framework.

Theorem 5.1 *Consider an ATS $\mathcal{S} = \langle \Pi, \Sigma, S, c_{in}, \pi, \delta \rangle$. Let S_1 and S_2 be sets of abstract states and let $\rho_1 : S \to S_1$ and $\rho_2 : S \to S_2$ be such that for all $c, c' \in S$, if $\rho_2(c) = \rho_2(c')$, then $\rho_1(c) = \rho_1(c')$. Let $\mathcal{S}_1$ and $\mathcal{S}_2$ be the AATSs induced by ρ_1 and ρ_2, respectively. Then, $\mathcal{S}_2 \preceq \mathcal{S}_1$.*

5.2 Refinement based on failure states

We can now turn to the problem of finding failure states and using them for refining the AATS. For simplicity, we first handle *alternating modal logic* (AML), that is, AMC without the fixed-point operator. We then discuss, in Section 5.3, the treatment of fixed points.

For an abstract state a and a formula φ, we say that a is a *failure state with respect to* φ if $[(\mathcal{A}, a) \models \varphi] = \bot$ even though $\mathcal{A}$ has definite value for subformulas of φ in the relevant states. Formally, a is a failure state with respect to φ if $[(\mathcal{A}, a) \models \varphi] = \bot$, and in addition, either $\varphi = p \in \Pi$ or $\varphi = \langle\langle\Omega\rangle\rangle\bigcirc\theta$ and $[(\mathcal{A}, a') \models \theta] \in \{\mathbf{T}, \mathbf{F}\}$, for all the successors a' of a.

Note that if a is a failure state with respect to $\langle\langle\Omega\rangle\rangle\bigcirc\theta$, then for all $A \in \delta_{must}(a, \Omega)$, there is $a' \in A$ with $[(\mathcal{A}, a') \models \theta] = \mathbf{F}$, and there is $A \in \delta_{may}(a, \Omega)$ such that for all $a' \in A$, we have that $[(\mathcal{A}, a') \models \theta] = \mathbf{T}$.

The drawback of the above definition is that it defines a to be a failure state with respect to θ even if the indefinite value of θ in a is irrelevant to the indefinite value of the specification in the initial state of the AATS. In order to restrict attention to *relevant* failure states, the procedure that searches for failure states proceeds in a top-down manner. The procedure FRFS (find relevant failure states) we describe is similar to the one in [26], only that the treatment of the $\forall\bigcirc$ modality there is generalized to our $\langle\langle\Omega\rangle\rangle\bigcirc$ modality.

The procedure $\texttt{FRFS}(a, \psi)$ gets as input an abstract state a and a formula ψ such that $[(\mathcal{A}, a) \models \theta] = \bot$ and return an abstract state a' and a subformula ψ' of ψ such that a' is a failure state with respect to ψ', and the indefinite value of ψ' in a' is relevant to the value of ψ in a being indefinite.

Formally, $\texttt{FRFS}(a, \psi)$ proceeds as follows.

- If $\psi = p$, then return $\langle a, \psi \rangle$.
- If $\psi = \neg\theta$, then return $\texttt{FRFS}(a, \theta)$.
- If $\psi = \theta_1 \vee \theta_2$, then let i be $\min\{1, 2\}$ such that $[(\mathcal{A}, a) \models \theta_i] = \bot$; return $\texttt{FRFS}(a, \theta_i)$.
- If $\psi = \langle\!\langle \Omega \rangle\!\rangle \bigcirc \theta$, then if for all the successors a' of a, we have $[(\mathcal{A}, a) \models \theta] \in \{\mathbf{T}, \mathbf{F}\}$, return $\langle a, \psi \rangle$. Otherwise, let a' be a successor of a for which $[(\mathcal{A}, a) \models \theta] = \bot$; return $\texttt{FRFS}(a', \theta)$.

It is not hard to see that since the initial call to $\texttt{FRFS}$ is with a pair $\langle a, \psi \rangle$ for which $[(\mathcal{A}, a) \models \psi] = \bot$, the "let" statements in the procedure are guaranteed to be satisfied, and it eventually returns a relevant failure state.

Let a be a relevant failure state with respect to φ. We describe a separation of a into two abstract states a_T and a_F such that the value of φ in both states is definite. Intuitively, a_T abstracts the set of concrete states in a that satisfy φ, and a_F abstracts those states that do not satisfy φ. Formally, we have the following:

- If $\varphi = p$, then $conc_T(a) = \{c \in a : p \in L(c)\}$ and $conc_F(a) = \{c \in a : p \notin L(c)\}$.
- If $\varphi = \langle\!\langle \Omega \rangle\!\rangle \bigcirc \theta$, we define
  - $conc_T(a) = \{c \in a :$ there is $C_c \in \delta(c, \Omega)$ such that $[(\mathcal{A}, a') \models \theta] = \mathbf{T}]$ for all $a' \in \rho(C_c)\}$.
  - $conc_F(a) = \{c \in a :$ for all $C_c \in \delta(c, \Omega)$, there is $a' \in \rho(C_c)$ with $[(\mathcal{A}, a') \models \theta] = \mathbf{F}]\}$.

Note that $conc_T$ and $conc_F$ form a partition of the concrete states in a. We refine ρ to map the states in $conc_T(a)$ to a_T and map states in $conc_F(a)$ to a_F.

Theorem 5.2 *Iterating the abstraction-refinement process with respect to an abstraction of a finite ATS is guaranteed to terminate with a definite answer.*

The proof, detailed in the full version, shows that in each of the cases, the suggested separation of a causes the value of φ in a_T and a_F to become definite. In addition, the monotonicity of our framework implies that no truth value of other formulas with respect to other states becomes indefinite.

5.3 Handling fixed-points

Consider a fixed-point formula $\psi = \mu z.\theta(z)$. The model-checking algorithm in Section 3.2 calculates the set $|\psi|_{\mathbf{T}}$ as the fixed point of the sequence $|\psi|^0_{\mathbf{T}} = \emptyset$, $|\psi|^1_{\mathbf{T}} = \theta(|\psi|^0_{\mathbf{T}})$, ..., $|\psi|^{i+1}_{\mathbf{T}} = \theta(|\psi|^i_{\mathbf{T}})$, and it calculates $|\psi|_{\mathbf{F}}$ as the fixed point of the sequence $|\psi|^0_{\mathbf{F}} = S_A$, $|\psi|^1_{\mathbf{F}} = \neg\theta(|\psi|^1_{\mathbf{F}})$, ..., $|\psi|^{i+1}_{\mathbf{F}} = \neg\theta(|\psi|^i_{\mathbf{F}})$. If $|\psi|_{\mathbf{T}} \cup |\psi|_{\mathbf{F}} \neq S_A$, then there is a minimal index i such that $|\psi|^i_{\mathbf{T}} \cup |\psi|^i_{\mathbf{F}} \neq S_A$. Accordingly, when we define a to be a failure state with respect to a fixed-point formula ψ with variable z, we parameterize the definition also with an integer i – the iteration in which the value of the variable z becomes indefinite. The reasoning then is along the same lines described for AML formulas.

In fact, every refinement algorithm of MTSs that is based on a symbolic model-checking procedure can be adjusted to AATSs. Indeed, as demonstrated above, such an adjustment replaces the treatment of the modal operator $\forall\bigcirc$ with the one described in Section 5.2 for $\langle\!\langle \Omega \rangle\!\rangle \bigcirc$. We note, however, that while such a refinement procedure exists for the temporal logic CTL [26], the refinement procedure for the μ-calculus is based on Zielonka's enumerative algorithm for solving parity games, and thus it is not symbolic [14].

6 Predicate Abstraction

In this section we focus on the special case where the ATS models several concurrent processes, each given as a program. Each program location is associated with a statement $s = s_1 \mid s_2 \mid \cdots \mid s_n$, which denotes an internal nondeterminism: when the process executes s, it chooses $1 \leq i \leq n$ and executes s_i.

When each abstract state is associated with a program location, and thus it also is associated with a statement, we can calculate the may and must transitions by a theorem prover. For a statement s and a predicate e over the state space, the *weakest precondition* $\mathrm{WP}(s, e)$ is such that the execution of s from every state that satisfies $\mathrm{WP}(s, e)$ results in a state that satisfies e, and $\mathrm{WP}(s, e)$ is the weakest predicate for which the above holds [10]. For example, for an assignment statement $x := v$, we have that $\mathrm{WP}(x := v, e) = e[x/v]$ (that is, e with all occurrences of x replaced by v). In the case of MTSs, weakest preconditions can be used in order to automate the generation of must and may transitions [12]. As we show now, the same can be done in AATSs, given a definition of weakest precondition that takes internal nondeterminism into an account.

For a statement $s = s_1 \mid s_2 \mid \cdots \mid s_n$ with internal nondeterminism, we have that $\mathrm{WP}(s, e) = \bigvee_{1 \leq i \leq n} \mathrm{WP}(s_i, e)$. Note that since the nondeterminism is internal, taking the disjunctions of the different weakest preconditions reflects the fact that satisfying one of them is sufficient in order to guarantee that the process can resolve the nondeterministic choices and reach a state satisfying e. For example, $\mathrm{WP}(x := x + 2 \mid x := x - 4, x = 5)$ is $x = 3 \vee x = 9$. In other words, if the agent can choose between increasing x by 2 or decreasing x by 4, the weakest condition with which it can force the system into a state satisfying $x = 5$ is that $x = 3$ or $x = 9$.

For a concrete state c, let $s = s_1^c \mid s_2^c \mid \cdots \mid s_{n^c}^c$ be the statement that agent σ can choose at c. For a set τ of abstract states, $\tau \in \delta_{must}(a, \sigma)$ iff for all $c \in a$, we have that c implies $\bigvee_{1 \leq i \leq n^c} \mathrm{WP}(s, \tau)$. Also, $\tau \in \delta_{may}(a, \sigma)$ iff there is $c \in a$ for which c implies $\bigvee_{1 \leq i \leq n^c} \mathrm{WP}(s, \tau)$.

Example 6.1 Consider again the ATS from Example 2.1. We define an AATS $\mathcal{S}_{s,p}$ according to the predicates s and p. Thus, the AATS has four states, which we denote by sp, s, p, and $-$. In the full version, we describe the $\mathcal{S}_{s,p}$ in detail. Finding the transitions of $\mathcal{S}_{s,p}$ is not an easy task, and we used a theorem prover to generate them. For example, the fact that $\{-\}$ does not belong to $\delta_{may}(s, P_1)$ follows from the validity of the FOL formula $\neg\exists x, y.s(x, y) \wedge \neg p(x, y) \wedge [(\neg s(x - 1, y) \wedge \neg p(x - 1, y)) \vee (\neg s(x, y) \wedge \neg p(x, y)) \vee (\neg s(x + 1, y) \wedge \neg p(x + 1, y))]$. □

In the full version, we show how useful properties of the program from Example 2.1 can be proven by reasoning about $\mathcal{S}_{s,p}$. We also relate the AATS $\mathcal{S}_{s,p}$ with the AATS $\mathcal{S}_s$ described in Example 3.4, and show that $\mathcal{S}_{s,p} \preceq \mathcal{S}_s$.

References

[1] R. Alur, T.A. Henzinger, and O. Kupferman. Alternating-time temporal logic. *JACM*, 49(5):672–713, 2002.

[2] R. Alur, T.A. Henzinger, O. Kupferman, and M.Y. Vardi. Alternating refinement relations. In *Proc. 9th CONCUR*, LNCS 1466, pages 163–178, 1998.

[3] G. Bruns and P. Godefroid. Model checking partial state spaces with 3-valued temporal logics. In *Proc 11th CAV*, pages 274–287, 1999.

[4] G. Bruns and P. Godefroid. Model checking with 3-valued temporal logics. In *Proc 31st ICALP*, LNCS 3142, pages 281–293, 2004.

[5] M. Chechik, B. Devereux, and S. Easterbrook. Implementing a multi-valued symbolic model checker. In *Proc. 7th TACAS*, LNCS 2031, pages 404–419, 2001.

[6] D. Dams and K.S. Namjoshi. The existence of finite abstractions for branching time model checking. In *Proc. 19th LICS*, pages 335–344, 2004.

[7] D. Dams and K.S. Namjoshi. Automata as abstractions. In *Proc. 6th VMCAI*, LNCS 3385, pages 216–232, 2005.

[8] L. de Alfaro, P. Godefroid, and R. Jagadeesan. Three-valued abstractions of games: Uncertainty, but with precision. In *Proc. 19th LICS*, pages 170–179, 2004.

[9] L. de Alfaro, T.A. Henzinger, and F.Y.C. Mang. Detecting errors before reaching them. In *Proc. 12th CAV*, LNCS 1855, pages 186–201, 2000.

[10] E.W. Dijksta. *A Discipline of Programming*. Prentice-Hall, 1976.

[11] E.A. Emerson and C.-L. Lei. Efficient model checking in fragments of the propositional μ-calculus. In *Proc. 1st LICS*, pages 267–278, 1986.

[12] P. Godefroid, M. Huth, and R. Jagadeesan. Abstraction-based model checking using modal transition systems. In *Proc. 12th CONCUR*, LNCS 2154, pages 426–440, 2001.

[13] P. Godefroid and R. Jagadeesan. Automatic abstraction using generalized model checking. In *Proc. 14th CAV*, LNCS 2404, pages 137–150, 2002.

[14] O. Grumberg, M. Lange, M. Leucker, and S. Shoham. Don't know in the μ-calculus. In *Proc. 6th CVMAI*, LNCS 3385, pages 233–249, 2005.

[15] T.A. Henzinger, R. Majumdar, F.Y.C. Mang, and J-F Raskin. Abstract interpretation of game properties. In *Proc. 7th SAS*, LNCS 1824, pages 245–252, 2000.

[16] C.A.R. Hoare. *Communicating Sequential Processes*. Prentice-Hall, 1985.

[17] S.C. Kleene. *Introduction to Metamathematics*. North Holland, 1987.

[18] D. Kozen. Results on the propositional μ-calculus. *Theoretical Computer Science*, 27:333–354, 1983.

[19] S. Kremer and J.-F. Raskin. A game-based verification of non-repudiation and fair exchange protocols. In *Proc. 12th CONCUR*, LNCS 2154, pages 551–565, 2001.

[20] K.G. Larsen and G.B. Thomsen. A modal process logic. In *Proc. 3rd LICS*, Edinburgh, 1988.

[21] K.G. Larsen and L. XinXin. Equation solving using modal transition systems. In *Proc. 5th LICS*, pages 108–117, 1990.

[22] N.A. Lynch. *Distributed Algorithms*. Morgan Kaufmann, 1996.

[23] R. Milner. *A Calculus of Communicating Systems*, LNCS 92, Springer Verlag, 1980.

[24] A. Pnueli and R. Rosner. On the synthesis of a reactive module. In *Proc. 16th POPL*, pages 179–190, 1989.

[25] S. Shoham and O. Grumberg. A game-based framework for CTL counterexamples and 3-valued abstraction-refinement. In *Proc. 15th CAV*, LNCS 2725, pages 275–287, 2003.

[26] S. Shoham and O. Grumberg. Monotonic abstraction-refinement for CTL. In *Proc. TACAS*, LNCS 2988, pages 546–560, 2004.

[27] C. Stirling. Games and modal μ-calculus. In *Proc. 13th STACS*, LNCS 1055, pages 298–312, 1996.

[28] W. van der Hoek and M. Wooldridge. Tractable multi agent planning for epistemic goals. In *Proc. 1st International Conference on Autonomous Agents and Multiagent Systems*, pages 1167 – 1174. ACM Press, 2002.

[29] W. van der Hoek and M. Wooldridge. Cooperation, knowledge, and time: Alternating-time temporal epistemic logic and its applications. *Studia Logica*, 75(1):125– 157, 2003.

Temporal logics and model checking for fairly correct systems

Daniele Varacca*
Imperial College London, UK

Hagen Völzer
Universität zu Lübeck, Germany

Abstract

We motivate and study a generic relaxation of correctness of reactive and concurrent systems with respect to a temporal specification. We define a system to be fairly correct *if there exists a fairness assumption under which it satisfies its specification. Equivalently, a system is fairly correct if the set of runs satisfying the specification is large from a topological point of view, i.e., it is a* co-meager *set.*

We compare topological largeness with its more popular sibling, probabilistic largeness, where a specification is probabilistically large *if the set of runs satisfying the specification has probability 1. We show that topological and probabilistic largeness of ω-regular specifications coincide for bounded Borel measures on finite-state systems. As a corollary, we show that, for specifications expressed in LTL or by Büchi automata, checking that a finite-state system is fairly correct has the same complexity as checking that it is correct.*

Finally we study variants of the logics CTL and CTL, where the 'for all runs' quantifier is replaced by a 'for a large set of runs' quantifier. We show that the model checking complexity for these variants is the same as for the original logics.*

1 Introduction

Sometimes, a model of a concurrent or reactive system does not satisfy a desired linear-time temporal specification but the runs violating the specification seem to be artificial and rare. For example, in Dijkstra's dining philosophers, a philosopher may starve because his two neighbours 'conspire' against him by alternately eating in such a way that the philosopher's two forks are never available at the same time. If a specification prescribed starvation-freedom, such a run would obviously violate it. Although such runs exist, they require special conditions that in practice may not arise.

For this particular example, there are also starvation-free solutions, but for many problems, a system satisfying the actual specification is impossible, too difficult, or too expensive to obtain [13]. In such cases, we could be content with a system where the specification is almost satisfied, i.e., the set of runs satisfying the specification is 'large'.

One natural way to formalise 'large set' is to mean *probabilistically large*, i.e., a set of measure 1 for a given probability measure. This notion however needs a concrete probability measure, which may be hard to justify for a given system. Alternatively, one can define a *fairness assumption* under which the specification is satisfied, with the intuition that 'most' runs are fair. This intuition has a formal counterpart: Ben-Eliyahu and Magidor [7] observe that for many fairness notions from the literature, the set of fair runs is *topologically large*, i.e., a *co-meager* set in the natural topology of runs of a given system. Völzer *et al.* [28] show that this is in fact true for most of the existing fairness notions and they also give more arguments why fairness should be *defined* as co-meagerness in the natural topology. An important consequence of this definition is the following: A linear-time property X is topologically large in a system iff there exists a fairness assumption F such that $(F \Rightarrow X)$ is satisfied in that system.

The notions of probabilistic and topological largeness share many properties. A classic mathematical text book [23] is devoted to study their similarities and differences. Although similar, these notions do not coincide in general—in fact, even for the most straightforward probability measure on the set of runs, there are topologically large sets that have probability 0.

In this paper we propose to call a system *fairly correct* if the set of its runs that satisfy the specification is co-meager or, equivalently, if it is correct under some fairness assumption. We study the problem of verifying when a finite system is fairly correct for a specification expressed in some temporal logic, or via Büchi automata.

We prove that probabilistic and topological largeness of ω-regular specifications coincide for bounded Borel measures on finite-state systems. This allows us to decide fair correctness by using known algorithms for finite Markov chains.

In particular, we show that fair correctness of a finite system is decidable and can be checked with the same com-

*Funded by EPSRC grant GR/T04724/01

plexity as correctness for LTL and Büchi automata specifications (but without the necessity to specify any fairness assumption explicitly). We also show that fair correctness of a system with respect to an LTL+past specification is expressible in CTL+past, strengthening a result of Berwanger *et al.* [8].

Then, we consider variants of the logics CTL and CTL*, where the quantifier 'for all runs' is replaced by 'for a large set of runs'. We show that also for these logics, the model checking complexity is the same as in the standard case: PSPACE-complete for CTL* and linear for CTL.

The path quantifier 'for a large set of runs' also occurs (under a different point of view) in a logic introduced by Pistore and Vardi [24]. We reinterpret their work from a topological point of view, which allows us to derive some basic properties of their logic.

2 Preliminary notions

2.1 Systems and temporal properties

Let Σ be a countable set of *states*. Σ^*, Σ^+ and Σ^ω denote the set of finite, nonempty finite, and infinite sequences over Σ respectively. Finite sequences are denoted α, β and infinite ones by x, y. We set $\alpha\uparrow = \{x \mid \alpha \text{ is a prefix of } x\}$ and $x\downarrow = \{\alpha \mid \alpha \text{ is a prefix of } x\}$. A set $X \subseteq \Sigma^\omega$ is called a *(linear-time temporal) property* and a set $Q \subseteq \Sigma^+$ a *finitary (temporal) property*.

Let AP be a nonempty set of *atomic propositions*. A *temporal structure* $M = (\Sigma, R, L)$ over AP consists of a set Σ of *states*, a total binary relation $R \subseteq \Sigma \times \Sigma$, and a mapping $L : \Sigma \to 2^{AP}$. A pair $(M, s\ )$ of a temporal structure M and a state s of M will be called a *system*. A *path* (*path fragment*) of $(M, s\ )$ is an infinite (finite) sequence $s\ , s\ , \ldots$ that starts in s such that $(s_i, s_{i+}\ ) \in R$ for all $i \geq 0$. The set of all paths of $(M, s\ )$ is denoted by $M(s\ )$.

2.2 Temporal-logical properties

We consider various temporal logics here. The most expressive one is CTL*+past [16], which is defined by the following syntax rules (S1)-(P1), where a ranges over atomic propositions, p over *state formulas*, h over *history formulas*, and ϕ over *path formulas*:

$$p := a \mid \neg p \mid p \wedge p \tag{S1}$$
$$p := \mathsf{A}\,\phi \mid \mathsf{E}\,\phi \tag{S2}$$
$$h := p \mid \neg h \mid h \wedge h \mid \mathsf{Y}\,h \mid h\,\mathsf{S}\,h \tag{H1}$$
$$h := \phi \tag{H2}$$
$$\phi := h \mid \neg\phi \mid \phi \wedge \phi \mid \mathsf{X}\,\phi \mid \phi\,\mathsf{U}\,\phi \tag{P1}$$

LTL+past is the sublanguage where rule (S2) is removed. CTL+past [16] is the sublanguage where (H2) is removed and (P1) is replaced by (P3) below. Finally, versions without past are defined by replacing (H1) by (H3) below.

$$\phi := \mathsf{X}\,h \mid h\,\mathsf{U}\,h \tag{P3}$$
$$h := p \tag{H3}$$

Satisfaction is defined as usual [10, 16]. In particular, we follow the *Ockhamist* interpretation of the past, where each state has a unique past. The semantics of history formulas is as follows:

- $M, x, i \models \mathsf{Y}\,h$ iff $(i > 0)$ and $M, x, i-1 \models h$
- $M, x, i \models h\,\mathsf{S}\,g$ iff $\exists j \leq i : M, x, j \models g$ and $\forall k : j < k \leq i : M, x, k \models h$

Additional operators, such as $\bot$, $\top$, $\mathsf{F}\,\phi$, $\mathsf{G}\,\phi$, $\mathsf{F}^-\ \phi$, $(\phi\ \mathsf{W}\ \psi)$, etc. are also defined as usual. In particular, $(\phi\ \mathsf{W}\ \psi)$ stands for $(\phi\ \mathsf{U}\ \psi) \vee \mathsf{G}\,\phi$ and $\mathsf{F}^-\ \phi$ for $\top\ \mathsf{S}\ \phi$. For an LTL(+past) formula ϕ, we will also use ϕ to denote the set of paths that satisfy ϕ when no confusion arises.

An *ω-regular property* is a property that is accepted by some *Büchi automaton* (see e.g. [26]).

2.3 Path games and the Pistore-Vardi logic

The path quantifiers A ('for all paths') and E ('there exists a path') of CTL* are two extreme notions of satisfaction of a path formula in a system. We can think of them as a hostile player (A) and a friendly player (E) that resolve the nondeterminism in the system. Player A tries to violate the formula and E tries to satisfy the formula. Intermediate notions of satisfaction can be derived through a *path game* [8, 24] where hostile and friendly player alternately resolve the nondeterminism for some time.

Let $\kappa \in \{\mathsf{A}, \mathsf{E}\}^\omega$, $X \subseteq \Sigma^\omega$ a linear-time property, and $(M, s\ )$ be a system. The game $G(\kappa, X, M, s\ )$ is played by the two players A (Alter) and E (Ego) and the state of a play is a path fragment of $(M, s\ )$. A play starts in s and in the i-th move ($i \geq 0$), player $\kappa(i)$ extends by a finite, possibly empty sequence α_i yielding the path fragment $s\ \alpha\ \ldots\alpha_i$. The play goes on forever converging either to a path x or a path fragment α of the system. Ego wins if $x \in X$ (resp. $\alpha\uparrow \subseteq X$), otherwise Alter wins.

A *strategy* is a mapping $f : \Sigma^+ \to \Sigma^*$ such that for each path fragment α of (M, s), $\alpha f(\alpha)$ is a path fragment of (M, s). A strategy f is *winning* for player $P \in \{\mathsf{A}, \mathsf{E}\}$ if for each strategy g of the other player, P wins the play that results from P playing f and the other player playing g.

It can be shown [24, 8] that each game $G(\kappa, X, M, s\ )$ is equivalent to a game $G(\kappa', X, M, s\ )$ where κ' is one of the

[1]This version of the game is essentially equivalent with those described in [8, 24].

[2]More general strategies that depend on what moves produced the current path fragment are not more powerful in the game considered here.

following: $\mathsf{A}^\omega, \mathsf{AEA}^\omega, (\mathsf{AE})^\omega, \mathsf{AE}^\omega, \mathsf{EA}^\omega, (\mathsf{EA})^\omega, \mathsf{EAE}^\omega, \mathsf{E}^\omega$, abbreviated A, AEA, $\overline{\mathsf{AE}}$, AE, EA, $\overline{\mathsf{EA}}$, EAE, E respectively.

Pistore and Vardi [24] proposed the following extension of LTL. A formula in the Pistore-Vardi logic is of the form $\kappa.\phi$ where $\kappa \in \{\mathsf{A}, \mathsf{E}\}^\omega$ is a *path quantifier* and ϕ is an LTL formula. Satisfaction is defined by

- $M, s \models \kappa.\phi$ iff Ego has a winning strategy in the game $G(\kappa, \phi, M, s)$.

More general, we write $M, s \models \kappa.X$ for any $X \subseteq \Sigma^\omega$ iff Ego has a winning strategy in the game $G(\kappa, X, M, s)$. It is known [8] that $G(\kappa, X, M, s)$ is *determined*, i.e., either Ego or Alter has a winning strategy if X is ω-regular.

To exemplify the properties that can be expressed in the Pistore-Vardi logic, consider the temporal structure $M = (\Sigma, R, L)$, where $\Sigma = \{a, b\}, R = \Sigma \times \Sigma, AP = \Sigma$, and $L(a) = \{a\}, L(b) = \{b\}$. The system (M, a) generates all infinite sequences on $\{a, b\}$ starting with a. We therefore have: $M, a \models \mathsf{A}.a$, $M, a \models \mathsf{AEA}.\mathsf{F}\,b$, $M, a \models \overline{\mathsf{AE}}.\mathsf{G}\,\mathsf{F}\,b$, $M, a \models \mathsf{AE}.\mathsf{F}\,\mathsf{G}\,b$, $M, a \models \mathsf{E}.\mathsf{G}\,a$.

3 Topological classifications

Different topological classifications of linear-time properties have improved our understanding of the verification problem. In this section, we recall those topological classifications.

3.1 Some topological notions

The natural, i.e., Cantor topology on Σ^ω is defined by the sets of the form $\alpha\!\uparrow$ for $\alpha \in \Sigma^*$. Such a set is a *basic open set* of that topology. As usual, an *open set* is an arbitrary union of basic open sets, a *closed set* is the complement of some open set, and a *dense set* is a set that has a nonempty intersection with every open set.

The family G of open sets is closed under arbitrary union and finite intersection. By duality, the family F of closed sets is closed under arbitrary intersection and finite union. Given a family $\mathscr{F} \subseteq 2^{\Sigma^\omega}$, the family $\mathscr{F}_\delta$ ($\mathscr{F}_\sigma$) is the family of countable intersections (unions) of members of $\mathscr{F}$. Thus, G_δ is the family of sets that can be represented as the intersection of countably many open sets. The family of *Borel sets* is the smallest family $\mathscr{F} \subseteq 2^{\Sigma^\omega}$ that contains all open and closed sets and is closed under countable union and intersection.

Each nonempty set $X \subseteq \Sigma^\omega$ is equipped with the Cantor topology *relative to* X, which is defined by the basic open sets of the form $\alpha\!\uparrow \cap X$ for each $\alpha \in \Sigma^*$. In particular, a system (M, s) defines the Cantor topology relative to $M(s)$. A set is *dense in* X if it is dense in the topology relative to X.

A set X is *somewhere dense* if it is dense in some open set. X is *nowhere dense* if it is not somewhere dense (or equivalently, if its complement contains a dense open set). A set is *meager* if it is the countable union of nowhere dense sets. A complement of a meager set is called *co-meager*. In this paper, we also say that a co-meager set is *topologically large* or *T-large*.

3.2 The safety-liveness classification

We say that a property $X \subseteq \Sigma^\omega$ is *live in* $\alpha \in \Sigma^*$ if $\alpha\!\uparrow \cap X \neq \emptyset$. Following Alpern and Schneider [1], a *safety property* is a property X such that $x \notin X$ implies that x has a finite prefix α where X is not live. X is *live* in a safety property S (also: (S, X) is *machine-closed*) if X is live in every $\alpha \in S\!\downarrow$, where $S\!\downarrow := \bigcup_{x \in S} x\!\downarrow$. X is a *liveness property* if X is live in every $\alpha \in \Sigma^*$.

It is easy to see that safety properties are exactly the closed sets and that liveness properties are exactly the dense sets of the Cantor topology [1]. Moreover, X is live in S iff X is dense in S. Every set in a topological space can be obtained as the intersection of a closed and a dense set, therefore every property is the intersection of a safety and a liveness property [1].

3.3 The safety-progress classification

As an alternative to the safety-liveness classification, Manna and Pnueli [22] propose the safety-progress classification. Let $X \subseteq \Sigma^\omega$.

- X is a safety property iff there exists a finitary property Q such that for each $x \in X$, all finite prefixes of x are in Q,
- X is a *guarantee property* iff there exists a finitary property Q such that for each $x \in X$, there exists a finite prefix of x that is in Q,
- X is an *obligation property* if X is expressible as a positive boolean combination of safety and guarantee properties,
- X is a *recurrence property* if there is a finitary property Q such that for each $x \in X$, there are infinitely many prefixes of x in Q,
- X is a *persistence property* if there is a finitary property Q such that for each $x \in X$, all but finitely many finite prefixes of x are in Q,
- X is a *reactivity property* if X is expressible as a positive boolean combination of recurrence and persistence properties.

Simple examples are: guarantee: $\mathsf{F}\,a$, obligation: $\mathsf{F}\,a \rightarrow \mathsf{F}\,b$, recurrence: $\mathsf{G}\,\mathsf{F}\,a$, persistence: $\mathsf{F}\,\mathsf{G}\,a$, and reactivity: $\mathsf{G}\,\mathsf{F}\,a \rightarrow \mathsf{G}\,\mathsf{F}\,b$. It can be shown [22] that safety, guarantee, recurrence, persistence are exactly closed, open, G_δ, and F_σ sets, respectively. Obligation is exactly $G_\delta \cap F_\sigma$ and reactivity is exactly $F_{\sigma\delta} \cap G_{\delta\sigma}$. Furthermore, each ω-regular property and hence each property expressible in LTL+past is a reactivity property [26, 22]. The classes of the safety-progress classification also have natural characterisations in temporal-logical and automata-theoretical terms [22, 9].

3.4 Fairness

Fairness is defined with respect to a given system (M, s) or, more general, with respect to a safety property S. (Note that $M(s)$ is a safety property.) It has been pointed out by Apt, Francez, and Katz [5] and by Lamport [18] that a fairness property for S should be live (i.e., dense) in S. This requirement alone, however, does not rule out some properties that are intuitively not fairness properties, and it implies that fairness is not closed under (finite) intersection [28]. We propose elsewhere [28] to call a property X a *fairness property for S* iff X is co-meager in S, that is a co-meager set in the topology relative to S. The following statements are equivalent with X being a fairness property for $M(s)$:

- X contains a dense G_δ set (relative to $M(s)$), i.e., a recurrence property that is live in $M(s)$,
- Ego has a winning strategy in the game $G(\overline{\mathsf{AE}}, X, M, s)$.

The first statement intuitively says that fairness requires, possibly under some condition, that some live finitary property is satisfied infinitely often. The latter statement is a classical result by Banach and Mazur. That game is also called *Banach-Mazur game*. We can view Ego here as a scheduler that wants to guarantee that all paths are fair.

It follows that:

- each fairness property for S is dense relative to S,
- fairness for S is closed under countable intersection, and
- fairness for S includes some basic intuitive fairness properties, viz. all recurrence properties that are live in S.

It can be shown [28] that this is, in a strong sense, the most liberal definition of fairness that has all three properties above. Furthermore, most fairness notions from the literature fall into this class, i.e., the usual *fairness notions* such as *strong fairness* map each system (safety property) S to a fairness property for S.

For examples of fairness properties, consider the system (M, a) described in Sect. 2. The property $\mathsf{G}\,\mathsf{F}\,b$ is a fairness property for $M(a)$. Another fairness property is $\mathsf{G}\,\mathsf{F}\,a \rightarrow \mathsf{G}\,\mathsf{F}(a \wedge \mathsf{X}\,b)$. These formulas do not represent fairness *notions*, as for some systems, the set of paths satisfying them may not be large. Note that $\mathsf{F}\,\mathsf{G}\,b$ is live but not a fairness property in $M(a)$.

We say that a system (M, s) is *fairly correct* with respect to a linear time specification X if X is large in (M, s). Equivalently, (M, s) is fairly correct wrt X if there exists a fairness assumption F for $M(s)$ such that $F \cap M(s) \subseteq X$.

4 T- versus P-largeness

In this section, we compare topological and probabilistic largeness and prove that they coincide for ω-regular properties in finite-state systems with bounded Borel measures.

4.1 Probabilistic largeness

Given a system (M, s), a probability measure μ on $\Omega = M(s)$ over the family of Borel sets of the Cantor topology relative to Ω is called a *Borel measure* over Ω. A Borel measure μ is a *Markov measure* when $\mu(\alpha s s'\!\uparrow \mid \alpha s\!\uparrow) = \mu(\beta s s'\!\uparrow \mid \beta s\!\uparrow)$ for all $\alpha, \beta \in \Sigma^*$ and $s, s' \in \Sigma$ such that $\alpha s s'$ and $\beta s s'$ are path fragments of (M, s). A Borel measure μ is *positive* if $\mu(\alpha\!\uparrow) > 0$ for each path fragment α of (M, s), μ is said to be *bounded* if there exists a $c > 0$ such that $\mu(\alpha s\!\uparrow \mid \alpha\!\uparrow) > c$ for each path fragment αs of (M, s). A Borel set $X \subseteq M(s)$ is *μ-large* (or *probabilistically large* or *P-large* when μ is understood from the context) if $\mu(X) = 1$.

4.2 Similarities

Topological and probabilistic largeness are very similar notions. Oxtoby's classic book [23] is devoted to study this similarity. The following observations, taken from there, are true for both T-largeness and P-largeness and confirm our intuition of largeness.

- If a set is large, its complement is not. (Note that this is not true for density.) Call a set *small* if its complement is large.
- Largeness is closed under superset and countable intersection (, i.e., the family of large sets is a *σ-filter*).
- If A is large and B is not small, then $A \cap B$ is not small.
- Every large set is nonempty. Since we restrict to positive Borel measures, every large set is also dense.
- Every countable set is small, but there are uncountable sets that are small.

Furthermore, there is also a strong duality between the two notions [23, Ch.19].

4.3 Separation

Although similar, the two notions do not coincide in general: there are sets that are T-large but not P-large as well as sets where it is the other way around.

Consider an (unrestricted asymmetric) random walk on the integer line starting at 0 going right with probability $p \neq 1/2$ and going left with probability $1 - p$. The property X = 'The walk returns to 0 infinitely often' has probability 0 but is T-large. (One easily displays a winning strategy for Ego in the Banach-Mazur game.) The complement of X has probability 1 but is not T-large.

A similar set can be displayed in a finite system: Consider an initial state from which one can go to a state a with probability $p \neq 1/2$ and to a state b with probability $1 - p$. From a and b we always go back to the initial state. The set X = 'The number of previous a's equals the number of previous b's infinitely often' has probability 0 but is clearly T-large. Note however that a winning strategy for Ego is unbounded, i.e., the length of the sequences Ego adds is unbounded because it has to be able to compensate for unbounded moves by Alter.

The following proposition says that, under mild assumptions, a set can always be found that is large in one sense but small in the other.

Proposition 1 *Let $(M, s\ )$ be a finite system such that every path $x = s\ ,\ldots$ has infinitely many* choices, *i.e., positions i such that s_i has more than one R-successor in M. Let μ be a positive Markov measure on $M(s\ )$. Then $M(s\ )$ can be partitioned into a T-large and a μ-large set.*

4.4 Coincidence

We now prove that for bounded Borel measures on finite systems and ω-regular properties, the two notions of largeness coincide. Note that the property X described in the counterexample in Sect. 4.3. is not accepted by any finite-state automaton.

Proposition 2 *Let $(M, s\ )$ be a finite system, μ a bounded Borel measure on $M(s\ )$, and X an ω-regular property. If X is T-large, then it is also μ-large.*

Proof: If X is T-large, Ego has a winning strategy for X in the Banach-Mazur game. Berwanger, Grädel, and Kreutzer [8] have shown that Ego has then also a *positional* winning strategy, i.e., a strategy f such that $f(\alpha s) = f(\beta s)$ for all $\alpha,\beta \in \Sigma^*$ and $s \in \Sigma$. Since there are only finitely many states, the positional strategy is also *bounded*, i.e., there exists a k such that $|f(\alpha)| < k$ for all α. It follows that, in each path fragment, playing f has a positive probability bounded away from zero and therefore the property $\{x \mid x$ has infinitely many positions where the extension is according to $f\}$ has probability 1 (by application of Borel-Cantelli Lemmas). Hence $\{x \mid x$ is the result of some play of the Banach-Mazur game where Ego plays $f\}$ has probability 1. Because f is winning for X, X is μ-large. □

The converse also holds.

Proposition 3 *Let $(M, s\ )$ be a finite system, μ a bounded Borel measure on $M(s\ )$, and X an ω-regular property. If X is μ-large, then it is also T-large.*

Proof: If X is not T-large, then Alter has, due to determinacy, a winning strategy f in the Banach-Mazur game. Let α be the first move of Alter in that strategy. We have $\mu(\alpha\uparrow) > 0$. Since f is a winning strategy for Alter, f is also a winning strategy for Ego in the Banach-Mazur game that starts in α and in which Ego plays for $\Omega \setminus X$. From Prop. 2 now follows that $\mu(\Omega \setminus X \mid \alpha\uparrow) = 1$. Hence we conclude $\mu(X) < 1$. □

We obtain:

Theorem 1 *T-largeness and P-largeness of ω-regular properties coincide for bounded Borel measures on finite systems.*

In particular they also coincide for properties expressible in LTL(+past).

4.5 Complete fairness

To prove T-largeness of a property X in a system (M, s), it suffices to show $F \cap M(s) \subseteq X$ for some fairness property F for (M, s). We now ask whether there is a *complete* fairness notion to prove T-largeness.

Definition 1 *Let (M, s) be a system and $\mathscr{F}$ a family of linear-time properties. A fairness property F for (M, s) is $\mathscr{F}$-*complete *with respect to (M, s) if for each property $X \in \mathscr{F}$ that is T-large in (M, s), we have $F \cap M(s) \subseteq X$.*

Note that if F is complete for a family $\mathscr{F}$ then it is also complete for every subfamily of $\mathscr{F}$. Lichtenstein *et al.* [21] introduced *α-fairness* and showed that it is complete for showing P-largeness of ω-regular properties of finite-state systems. Zuck, Pnueli, and Kesten [29] point out that *state fairness* is complete for showing P-largeness of properties that are expressible in LTL without the next- and until-operators.

We show now that completeness w.r.t. ω-regular and LTL expressible properties can be characterised through *word fairness*. Say that a word $\beta \in \Sigma^+$ is *enabled* in a state s of a M if $s\beta$ is a path fragment of (M, s) and say that β is *taken* in a position i of a path $x = s\ ,\ldots$ if there exists a position j such that $\beta = s_i, s_{i+}\ ,\ldots, s_j$. Call a path x of a system (M, s) *fair* w.r.t. β if β is enabled only finitely many times in x or β is taken infinitely many times in x; x is *word fair* if it is fair w.r.t. all $\beta \in \Sigma^+$.

Proposition 4 *A fairness property F is $\mathcal{F}$-complete w.r.t. a system (M, s) if and only if each run in $F \cap M(s)$ is word fair, where $\mathcal{F}$ denotes the family of ω-regular or LTL expressible properties. In particular, word fairness is complete for ω-regular properties.*

Proof: ($\Leftarrow$) If X is an ω-regular property that is large in $M(s)$, then it follows as in the proof of Prop. 2 that Ego has a positional winning strategy f. However, that means that every word-fair path $x \in M(s)$ is the result of some play where Ego plays f. Therefore x is in X and hence word fairness is complete. ($\Rightarrow$) Follows from the fact that word fairness w.r.t. a particular word can be expressed in LTL. □

Note that Prop. 4 does not assume the system to be finite. However, to use Prop. 4 for P-largeness we need to restrict to finite systems.

Clearly, there is a complete fairness property for every countable family $\mathcal{F}$ that contains at least one fairness property. It is obtained by intersecting all fairness properties for (M, s) in $\mathcal{F}$. However, that intersection is not necessarily a member of $\mathcal{F}$. (Note that in Def. 1, F is not required to be a member of $\mathcal{F}$.) It can be shown that this is in fact the case for ω-regular and LTL-expressible properties:

Proposition 5 *There are finite systems (M, s) such that there is no ω-regular fairness property that is complete for the family of LTL expressible properties w.r.t. (M, s).*

For the proof, we consider a completely connected graph and show that Ego has no positional strategy for word fairness. Prop. 5 shows that largeness of an LTL formula ϕ can in general not be checked by expressing a complete fairness property as LTL formula ψ and then checking the formula $(\psi \to \phi)$.

5 Checking largeness

Berwanger *et al.* [8] showed that checking largeness of an LTL specification for a finite system is decidable by showing that largeness of an LTL formula can be expressed as satisfaction of a CTL* formula. Their translation however is of non-elementary complexity and hence not suitable for complexity analysis. Pistore and Vardi [24] provide an efficient translation into the logic EGCTL* of Kupferman [15], whose model checking complexity is double exponential time [15]. Kupferman and Vardi [17] show that model checking the Pistore-Vardi logic without $\overline{\mathsf{AE}}$ and $\overline{\mathsf{EA}}$ is EXPSPACE-complete leaving the complexity of checking largeness open.

From Thm. 1, we can immediately conclude that checking largeness is PSPACE-complete for LTL or Büchi automata specifications.

5.1 Büchi automata and LTL specifications

Vardi [27] has shown that checking P-largeness of an ω-regular property given by a Büchi automaton is PSPACE-complete in the size of the automaton. Hence we obtain:

Theorem 2 *The problem of checking T-largeness of a Büchi automata specification against a finite system is PSPACE-complete in the size of the automaton.*

Courcoubetis and Yannakakis [11] have shown that checking P-largeness of an LTL formula is PSPACE-complete in the size of the formula. Therefore:

Theorem 3 *The problem of checking T-largeness of an LTL formula in a finite system is PSPACE-complete in the size of the formula.*

Note that the corresponding algorithms for Thms. 2 and 3 use time linear in the size of the temporal structure.

5.2 Reactivity formulas and Streett constraints

It is interesting to provide an independent algorithm for LTL(+past) formulas which, although less efficient in general, can be efficiently applied to an important class of formulas.

A *reactivity formula* [22] is a formula of the form

$$\phi = \bigwedge_{i=}^{n} (\mathsf{G}\,\mathsf{F}\,h_i \vee \mathsf{F}\,\mathsf{G}\,g_i)$$

where h_i and g_i are *past formulas*, that is, history formulas that do not contain the future operators X, U, and their derivatives. In case all p_i and q_i are state formulas we call ϕ a *state reactivity formula*. A formula of the form $(\mathsf{G}\,\mathsf{F}\,p \vee \mathsf{F}\,\mathsf{G}\,q)$ is called a *Streett constraint* [3].

Consider the following translation of a reactivity formula into a CTL+past formula:

- $[\![\mathsf{F}\,\mathsf{G}\,h]\!] = \mathsf{AG}\,\mathsf{EF}\,\mathsf{AG}\,h$
- $[\![\mathsf{G}\,\mathsf{F}\,h]\!] = \mathsf{AG}\,\mathsf{EF}\,h$
- $[\![\mathsf{G}\,\mathsf{F}\,h \vee \mathsf{F}\,\mathsf{G}\,g]\!] = \mathsf{AG}(\neg[\![\mathsf{F}\,\mathsf{G}\,\neg h]\!] \vee \neg[\![\mathsf{G}\,\mathsf{F}\,\neg g]\!])$
- $[\![\phi \wedge \psi]\!] = [\![\phi]\!] \wedge [\![\psi]\!]$

Proposition 6 *For every system (M, s), we have that a reactivity formula ϕ is large in (M, s) if and only if $M, s \models [\![\phi]\!]$.*

For the first two clauses, the CTL+past formula essentially describes the winning strategy for Ego. (They can also be seen as applications of Proposition 10.3 and 10.4 below, respectively.) For the last clause, we observe that the intersection of two sets is large if and only if both sets are large. In the third clause, the union of two sets could be large even if neither of them is. The proof instead uses determinacy. We know that all sets involved are determinate [8]. The translated formula says that in every state, Ego does not have a winning strategy for the negation of one of the disjuncts. By determinacy, this happens if and only if Alter has a winning strategy for one of the disjuncts. But this means that after the first move of Alter, Ego (who has now the first move) has a winning strategy for one of the disjuncts.

To check the largeness of a reactivity formula we check the satisfaction of the corresponding CTL+past formula. The model checking problem for CTL+past is PSPACE-complete [19, 25].

Reactivity formulas encompass many interesting formulas, e.g. safety formulas such as $\mathsf{G}\,p$ or $\mathsf{G}(p \rightarrow \mathsf{F}^{-}\,q)$, persistence formulas such as $\mathsf{F}\,\mathsf{G}\,p$ and recurrence formulas such as $\mathsf{G}\,\mathsf{F}\,p$, also forms of response such as $\mathsf{F}\,\mathsf{G}\,p \rightarrow \mathsf{G}\,\mathsf{F}\,q$ and $\mathsf{G}\,\mathsf{F}\,p \rightarrow \mathsf{G}\,\mathsf{F}\,q$.

In fact, every LTL formula can be expressed as a reactivity formula [22]. However, the translation can produce an exponential blowup. Therefore we do not obtain the optimal upper bound of Thm. 3 for the above procedure applied to general LTL formulas.

The translation is also interesting in that it shows that largeness of an LTL+past formula can be expressed in CTL+past, a temporal logic strictly less expressive than CTL* [16], thus strengthening the result of Berwanger *et al.* [8], who showed that largeness of an LTL+past formula can be translated into satisfaction of a CTL* formula.

Checking whether a state reactivity formula is dense in a structure requires time quadratic in the size of the formula [12]. On the other hand, Alur and Henzinger [3] claim that checking whether a state reactivity is large requires linear time. We provide an alternative proof of their result.

For a state reactivity formula, the translation produces a CTL formula without past, whose model checking problem is linear. Thus we have:

Proposition 7 *The problem of checking T-largeness of a state reactivity formula in a finite system can be solved in time linear in the size of the formula.*

In the light of Thm. 1, also checking P-largeness of a state reactivity formula can be done in linear time. We are not aware of any analogous result in the literature.

6 Branching-time largeness

We now study the problem of expressing largeness in a branching time context. We consider logics that are obtained from CTL* and CTL by replacing the universal and existential path quantifiers by path quantifiers expressing largeness and non-smallness respectively.

6.1 The Lehmann-Shelah logic

First consider the logic *T-large CTL**, which is defined as CTL* but where instead of the path quantifiers A and E we have the path quantifiers $\overline{\mathsf{AE}}$ and $\overline{\mathsf{EA}}$ with their meaning defined above. This is essentially the logic studied by Ben-Eliyahu and Magidor [7]. By *P-large CTL** we refer to the logic that is defined as CTL* but where instead of the path quantifiers A and E we have the path quantifiers ∇ and Δ, where $\nabla.\phi$ means ϕ is satisfied with probability 1 and $\Delta.\phi$ means ϕ is satisfied with probability > 0. This is essentially the logic studied by Lehmann and Shelah [20]. Call τ the bijection between T-large CTL* and P-large CTL* where $\overline{\mathsf{AE}}$ is replaced by ∇ and $\overline{\mathsf{EA}}$ by Δ. Using structural induction and Thm. 1 it is easy to prove that:

Theorem 4 *For any T-large-CTL* formula ϕ and finite probabilistic system (M, s), we have $M, s \models \phi$ if and only if $M, s \models \tau(\phi)$.*

Lehmann and Shelah [20] provide sound and complete axiomatic systems for P-large CTL* and different classes of probabilistic systems. Ben-Eliyahu and Magidor [7] show that the axiomatic system for finite systems is sound and complete for T-large CTL* and systems of arbitrary size. This is now a corollary of Lehmann and Shelah's work, Thm. 4, and the finite model property of T-large CTL*, where the latter is shown by Ben-Eliyahu and Magidor [7].

It is straightforward to adapt the model checking algorithm for CTL* [10] to our case, thus obtaining:

Theorem 5 *The model-checking problem for T-large CTL* and P-large CTL* is PSPACE-complete in the size of the formula.*

The procedure is precisely the same as in [10]. For every subformula of the form $\overline{\mathsf{AE}}\,\phi$, where ϕ is a formula without quantifiers, we label the states of the system with a new proposition p, depending on whether $\overline{\mathsf{AE}}\,\phi$ is true or not. This requires polynomial space, as it amounts to check largeness of ϕ for every state. We substitute p for $\overline{\mathsf{AE}}\,\phi$ and we repeat the procedure until there are no more nested quantifiers. Hardness follows from the fact that checking largeness of LTL is PSPACE-hard.

The logic P-large CTL* can be also seen as a restricted version of more expressive probabilistic logics, such as pCTL* [6], which can express all probabilities between 0 and 1. The model checking of pCTL* is also in PSPACE.

One can consider a logic that combines the universal/existential and largeness/non-smallness quantifiers. Again, this does not change the model checking complexity. One could also consider a version of CTL* containing all eight quantifiers of the Pistore-Vardi logics. In the light of the EXPSPACE-completeness of the model checking of the Pistore-Vardi logic [17], the model checking problem for this version would also be EXPSPACE-complete.

6.2 Large CTL

The logic *T-Large CTL* is obtained by restricting T-large CTL* just like CTL is obtained as restriction of CTL*. We now prove that model checking T-large CTL can be done by a simple algorithm in linear time. To this end, we use the following translation into standard CTL :

$$\begin{aligned}
[\![a]\!] &= a \\
[\![\neg p]\!] &= \neg [\![p]\!] \\
[\![p \ \wedge p \ ]\!] &= [\![p \ ]\!] \wedge [\![p \ ]\!] \\
[\![\overline{\mathsf{AE}}\, \mathsf{X}\, p]\!] &= \mathsf{A}\,\mathsf{X}[\![p]\!] \\
[\![\overline{\mathsf{EA}}\, \mathsf{X}\, p]\!] &= \mathsf{E}\,\mathsf{X}[\![p]\!] \\
[\![\overline{\mathsf{EA}}(p \ \ \mathsf{U}\, p \ )]\!] &= \mathsf{E}\,([\![p \ ]\!]\, \mathsf{U}\, [\![p \ ]\!]) \\
[\![\overline{\mathsf{AE}}(p \ \ \mathsf{U}\, p \ )]\!] &=
\end{aligned}$$

$$\mathsf{A}\,([\![p \ ]\!]\, \mathsf{W}\, [\![p \ ]\!]) \wedge \neg\, \mathsf{E}\,([\![p \ ]\!]\, \mathsf{U}\, \mathsf{AG}\neg[\![p \ ]\!])$$

Proposition 8 *For a T-large CTL formula p we have*

$$M, s \models p \Leftrightarrow M, s \models [\![p]\!]\,.$$

The translation is homomorphic, except for the formula $p = p \ \ \mathsf{U}\, p$. For this case suppose that the translation of p is true. We prove that there is a winning strategy for p. It is easy to see that such strategy is winning in only one move. Indeed if Alter has already produced a run which satisfies p, Ego does nothing. If Alter has produced a run in which p is always true, Ego just needs to produce a continuation where p is always true until p is true.

The first part of the translation makes sure that Alter cannot produce a path that violates p. The second part makes sure that if Alter has not yet validated p, Ego can always get to a place where p is true. In order for p to be validated by such a play, Ego must not have touched a state where p and p are both false. This is again ensured by the first part.

Conversely, suppose the translated formula is false. If the first part is false, then Alter can produce a path that violates p. If the second part is false, then Alter can force the play to a place where Ego can never validate p, as he can never make p true.

In all the other cases it is easy to verify that the homomorphic translation is enough. For instance, since for every state there are only finitely many 'next' states, we have that a large set of runs satisfies $\mathsf{X}\, p$ if and only if all runs satisfy $\mathsf{X}\, p$.

Theorem 6 *The model checking problem for T-large CTL can be solved in linear time.*

[3] A similar translation can be found in [4], where it is used for model checking CTL under *transition fairness*.

The translation produces an exponential blow up, but the model checking algorithm can by-pass this, by a form of dynamic programming. The algorithm proceeds as for CTL, labelling each state with the subformulas that are satisfied in that state. In checking the subformulas, every time we check for a subformula p that appears as second formula within and until operator, we also check for the formula $\mathsf{AG}\neg p$. When checking $\mathsf{A}(p \ \ \mathsf{U}\ p \ )$, we have to run two procedures, one for each part of the translation. This at most doubles the time of the checking, but does not change the asymptotic complexity.

Note that, by Thm. 4, this algorithm can also be used for checking P-large CTL formulas on a finite Markov chain. This provides an alternative to the known linear time algorithm for P-large CTL [2]. Other polynomial model checking algorithms could be derived by viewing P-large CTL as a restricted version of pCTL [6] and PCTL [14].

7 Pistore-Vardi revisited

As indicated in Sect. 2.3, besides $\overline{\mathsf{AE}}$, also the other path quantifiers of the Pistore-Vardi logic could be considered as relaxations of correctness. In this section, we observe that also those other path quantifiers have a perfect topological meaning. We use this to derive some basic properties of the path quantifiers.

Proposition and Definition 9 *Let X be a linear-time property and (M, s) a system.*

- *$M, s \models \mathsf{A}.X$ iff X contains M(s). We say that X is* satisfied *in (M, s) or that X holds in* all paths.
- *$M, s \models \mathsf{AEA}.X$ iff X contains a dense open set in M(s) (or equivalently, it is the complement of a nowhere dense set in M(s)). We say that X is* observably large *in M(s).*
- *$M, s \models \overline{\mathsf{AE}}.X$ iff X is co-meager in M(s). We say that X is* large *or* fairly satisfied *in (M, s) or that X holds for* almost all *paths.*
- *$M, s \models \mathsf{AE}.X$ iff X is dense in M(s). We say that X is* live *or* everywhere satisfiable *in (M, s) or that X holds* everywhere for some *path.*
- *$M, s \models \mathsf{EA}.X$ iff X contains a nonempty open subset of M(s) (or equivalently its complement is not dense in M(s)). We say that X is* somewhere satisfied *in (M, s) or that X holds* somewhere for all *paths.*
- *$M, s \models \overline{\mathsf{EA}}.X$ iff X is co-meager in some open subset of M(s). We say that X is* somewhere large *in (M, s) or* somewhere fairly satisfied.

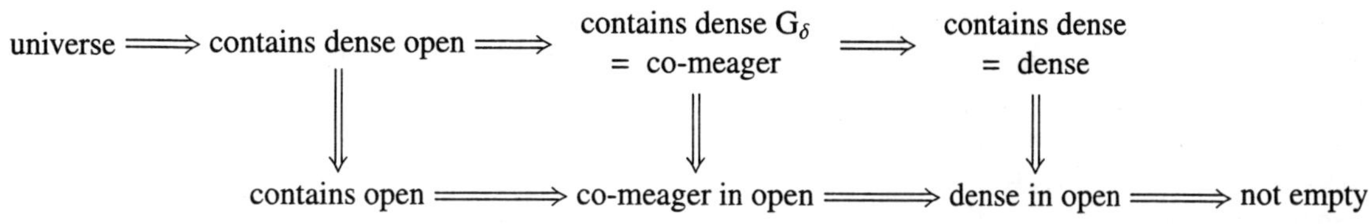

Figure 1. A schema of implications

- $M, s \models \mathsf{EAE}.X$ *iff X is dense in some open subset of M(s). We say that X is* somewhere dense *or* somewhere live *in* (M, s).

- $M, s \models \mathsf{E}.X$ *iff X is a nonempty subset of M(s). We say X is* satisfiable *in* (M, s) *or X holds for* some *path.*

Note that density is not a good notion of largeness because, for instance, there are dense sets whose complement is also dense. Nevertheless density is interesting because it formalises that at least the safety property implied by the specification is not violated, i.e., a property is dense in (M, s) iff $\overline{X}$ is satisfied in (M, s), where $\overline{X}$ denotes the smallest safety property that contains X.

Note that all the above classes of properties are upward closed, that is, $M, s \models \kappa.X$ and $X \subseteq Y$ implies $M, s \models \kappa.Y$. The following implications, taken from [24, 8],

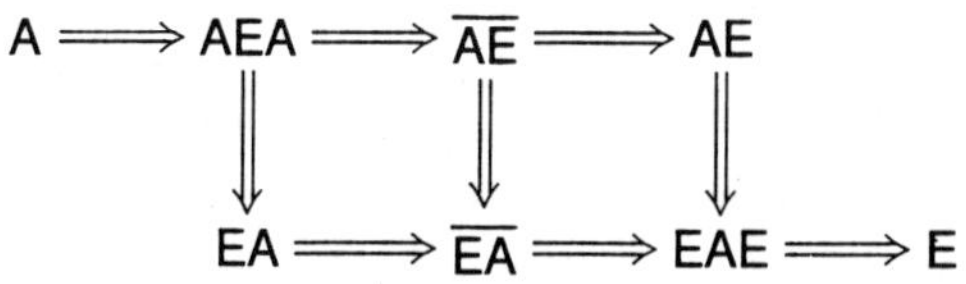

can be seen topologically (see Fig. 1). All the implications are trivial there.

Furthermore we observe that for LTL formulas ϕ, the latter four path quantifiers are duals of the former four, that is

$$M, s \models \mathsf{A}.\phi \text{ iff } M, s \not\models \mathsf{E}.\neg\phi$$
$$M, s \models \mathsf{AEA}.\phi \text{ iff } M, s \not\models \mathsf{EAE}.\neg\phi$$
$$M, s \models \overline{\mathsf{AE}}.\phi \text{ iff } M, s \not\models \overline{\mathsf{EA}}.\neg\phi$$
$$M, s \models \mathsf{AE}.\phi \text{ iff } M, s \not\models \mathsf{EA}.\neg\phi$$

Only the proof for $\overline{\mathsf{AE}}$ is not straightforward. There, we must use the fact that ϕ is *determinate* in the Banach-Mazur game.

Recall that checking the quantifiers A and $\overline{\mathsf{AE}}$ and their duals is PSPACE-complete. Checking AE and its dual is EXPSPACE-complete [17]. The complexity of checking AEA and its dual remains open.

Finally, the topological interpretation allows us to prove that in particular situations, different classes collapse.

Proposition 10 *Consider a property* $X \subseteq \Sigma^\omega$. *All the following statements are true relative to any fixed system* (M, s)*:*

1. *If X is a safety property, then X is satisfied iff X is live and X is somewhere satisfied iff it is somewhere live.*

2. *If X is a guarantee property then X is observably large iff X is live and X is somewhere satisfied iff it is satisfiable.*

3. *If X is a persistence property then X is observably large iff it is fairly satisfied and X is somewhere satisfied iff somewhere fairly satisfied.*

4. *If X is a recurrence property then X is fairly satisfied iff it is live in M and X is somewhere satisfied iff X is somewhere live.*

5. *If X is a obligation property then X is observably large iff it is live and X is somewhere satisfied iff it is somewhere live.*

8 Conclusions

We argued that topological largeness is an interesting notion as it can serve as a natural relaxation of correctness of a system: It has similar properties as probabilistic largeness that confirm our intuitive understanding of largeness, it formalises the intuitive notion of fairness. It is pleasing that topological largeness has various independent characterisations in terms of game-theory, language-theory, automata-theory, and temporal logic.

By showing coincidence of topological and probabilistic largeness, we solved the model checking problem for topological largeness of LTL and ω-regular specifications. Coincidently, this settles the complexity of model checking of the full Pistore-Vardi logic [24] and the complexity of deciding Banach-Mazur games for ω-regular goals [8]. As a side effect,

1. we obtain new characterisations of probabilistic largeness in finite Markov chains, and

2. this shows that any ω-regular fairness property has probability 1 under randomised scheduling.

Checking largeness of a specification maybe useful whenever the specifications is satisfied only under some, possibly strong, fairness assumption and the fairness assumption is either unknown, expensive to specify, or impossible to specify in the temporal logic.

We have shown that the complexity of checking largeness is the same as the complexity of checking satisfaction for the most popular specification formalisms. We have explicitly mentioned only the complexity with respect to the formula, however, as for standard satisfaction algorithms, all algorithms described use time linear in the size of the system.

Our work could be generalised to a situation where fairness is not required for all choices. Some choices would be fair, and some would be completely nondeterministic. This leads us to a model analogous to the concurrent Markov chains of [27], with fair states substituted for probabilistic states. In terms of the Banach-Mazur game, this amounts to not giving Ego access to all transitions. Again we can use Theorem 1 and the results in [11] to get the complexity of model checking for these systems.

References

[1] B. Alpern and F. B. Schneider. Defining liveness. *Inf. Proc. Letters*, 21:181–185, Oct. 1985.

[2] R. Alur, C. Courcoubetis, and D. L. Dill. Model-checking for probabilistic real-time systems (extended abstract). Proc. *ICALP*, *LNCS* 510, pp. 115–126. Springer, 1991.

[3] R. Alur and T. A. Henzinger. Local liveness for compositional modeling of fair reactive systems. In *Proc. CAV*, *LNCS* 939, pp. 166–179. Springer, 1995.

[4] B. Aminof, T. Ball, and O. Kupferman. Reasoning about systems with transition fairness. In *Proc. LPAR*, *LNCS* 3452, pp. 194–208. Springer, 2004.

[5] K. R. Apt, N. Francez, and S. Katz. Appraising fairness in languages for distributed programming. *Distr. Comput.*, 2:226–241, 1988.

[6] A. Aziz, V. Singhal, F. Balarin, R. K. Brayton, and A. L. Sangiovanni-Vincentelli. It usually works: The temporal logic of stochastic systems. In *Proc. CAV*, *LNCS* 939, pp. 155–165. Springer, 1995.

[7] R. Ben-Eliyahu and M. Magidor. A temporal logic for proving properties of topologically general executions. *Inf. and Comp.*, 124(2):127–144, 1996.

[8] D. Berwanger, E. Grädel, and S. Kreutzer. Once upon a time in the west - determinacy, definability, and complexity of path games. In *Proc. LPAR*, *LNAI* 2850, pp. 229–243, 2003.

[9] E. Y. Chang, Z. Manna, and A. Pnueli. Characterization of temporal property classes. In *Proc. ICALP*, *LNCS* 623, pp. 474–486. Springer, 1992.

[10] E. M. Clarke, E. A. Emerson, and A. P. Sistla. Automatic verification of finite-state concurrent systems using temporal logic specifications. *ACM Trans. Program. Lang. Syst.*, 8(2):244–263, 1986.

[11] C. Courcoubetis and M. Yannakakis. The complexity of probabilistic verification. *J. ACM*, 42(4):857–907, 1995.

[12] E. A. Emerson and C.-L. Lei. Modalities for model checking: Branching time strikes back. In *Proc. POPL*, pp. 84–96, 1985.

[13] F. E. Fich and E. Ruppert. Hundreds of impossibility results for distributed computing. *Distr. Comput.*, 16(2-3):121–163, 2003.

[14] H. Hansson and B. Jonsson. A logic for reasoning about time and reliability. *Formal Asp. Comput.*, 6(5):512–535, 1994.

[15] O. Kupferman. Augmenting branching temporal logics with existential quantification over atomic propositions. *J. Log. Comput.*, 9(2):135–147, 1999.

[16] O. Kupferman and A. Pnueli. Once and for all. In *Proc. LICS*, pp. 25–35. IEEE Computer Society, 1995.

[17] O. Kupferman and M. Y. Vardi. Memoryful branching-time logic. This volume.

[18] L. Lamport. Fairness and hyperfairness. *Distr. Comput.*, 13(4):239–245, 2000.

[19] F. Laroussinie and P. Schnoebelen. Specification in CTL+past for verification in CTL. *Inf. and Comput.*, 156(1-2):236–263, 2000.

[20] D. Lehmann and S. Shelah. Reasoning with time and chance. *Inf. and Contr.*, 53(3):165–198, 1982.

[21] O. Lichtenstein, A. Pnueli, and L. D. Zuck. The glory of the past. In *Proc. of Logic of Programs*, *LNCS* 193, pp. 196–218. Springer, 1985.

[22] Z. Manna and A. Pnueli. A hierarchy of temporal properties. In *Proc. PODC*, pp. 377–408. ACM, 1990.

[23] J. C. Oxtoby. *Measure and Category. A Survey of the Analogies between Topological and Measure Spaces.* Springer-Verlag, 1971.

[24] M. Pistore and M. Y. Vardi. The planning spectrum - one, two, three, infinity. In *Proc. LICS*, pp. 234–243, 2003.

[25] P. Schnoebelen. The complexity of temporal logic model checking. In *Selected Papers from the 4th Workshop on Advances in Modal Logics (AiML'02)*, pp. 393–436, 2003.

[26] W. Thomas. Automata on infinite objects. In J. van Leeuwen, editor, *Handbook of Theoretical Computer Science*, volume B: Formal Models and Semantics. Elsevier, 1990.

[27] M. Y. Vardi. Automatic verification of probabilistic concurrent finite-state programs. In *Proc. FOCS*, pp. 327–338, 1985.

[28] H. Völzer, D. Varacca, and E. Kindler. Defining fairness. In *Proc. CONCUR*, *LNCS* 3653, pp. 458–472. Springer, 2005.

[29] L. D. Zuck, A. Pnueli, and Y. Kesten. Automatic verification of probabilistic free choice. In *Proc. VMCAI*, *LNCS* 2294, pp. 208–224. Springer, 2002.

3-Valued Abstraction: More Precision at Less Cost

Sharon Shoham Orna Grumberg
Computer Science Department, Technion, Haifa, Israel
E-mail: {sharonsh,orna}@cs.technion.ac.il

Abstract

This paper investigates both the precision *and the model checking* efficiency *of abstract models designed to preserve branching time logics w.r.t. a 3-valued semantics. Current abstract models use ordinary transitions to over approximate the concrete transitions, while they use* hyper transitions *to under approximate the concrete transitions. In this work we refer to precision measured w.r.t. the choice of abstract states, independently of the formalism used to describe abstract models. We show that current abstract models do not allow maximal precision. We suggest a new class of models and a construction of an abstract model which is* most precise *w.r.t.* any *choice of abstract states. As before, the construction of such models might involve an exponential blowup, which is inherent by the use of hyper transitions. We therefore suggest an efficient algorithm in which the abstract model is constructed* during *model checking, by need. Our algorithm achieves maximal precision w.r.t. the given property while remaining quadratic in the number of abstract states. To complete the picture, we incorporate it into an abstraction-refinement framework.*

1. Introduction

Abstraction is one of the most successful techniques for fighting the state explosion problem in model checking [3]. Abstractions hide some of the details of the verified system, thus result in smaller models. Most commonly used are state abstractions that collapse (possibly non disjoint) sets of concrete states into abstract states. As such, an abstraction consists of a set of abstract states S_A and a mapping (or concretization function) γ that defines the relation between abstract states and the concrete states that they represent. The rest of the components of the concrete model then also need to be lifted into the abstract world, in order to result in an abstract model. This can be done in various ways.

When using a 2-valued semantics, abstract models are usually designed to be *conservative* for *true*, meaning that truth of a formula is preserved from the abstract model to the concrete model. A greater advantage is obtained if the formula is interpreted w.r.t. a 3-valued semantics [1]. This semantics evaluates a formula to either *true*, *false* or *indefinite*. Abstract models can then be designed to be conservative for both *true* and *false*. Only if the value of a formula in the abstract model is indefinite, its value in the concrete model is unknown. We follow this approach.

The logic specifications we consider in this paper are formulas of the modal *μ-calculus* [15]. The modal μ-calculus is a powerful formalism for expressing properties of transition systems using fixpoint operators. In particular, it combines both existential and universal properties. As such, two transition relations are needed in an abstract model for it to be conservative w.r.t. the full μ-calculus (be it over a 2-valued or a 3-valued semantics). Examples of such abstract models are *modal transition systems* [18, 16] or *mixed transition systems* [7] that contain *may* transitions which over-approximate transitions of the concrete model, and *must* transitions, which under-approximate the concrete transitions. To ensure logic preservation, truth of universal formulas is then examined over may transitions, whereas truth of existential formulas is examined over must transitions. Dually for falsity when a 3-valued semantics is considered.

It was shown in [19, 8, 9] that must transitions are a source of incompleteness, in the sense that when limited to the use of must transitions, it is not always possible to construct a finite abstract model in which a property holds, even if it holds on the concrete model. Must transitions were also shown to behave badly in refinement in the sense of causing a loss of precision [23]. It was therefore suggested to model the must transitions of an abstract model as *hyper transitions*, which connect a single state to a *set* of state. Hyper transitions, first introduced in [17], were shown in [23] to prevent the loss of precision during refinement. They were also shown in [8, 9] to result in a *complete* abstraction framework for the fragment of the μ-calculus defined with greatest fixpoints only ([8] also introduces fairness and hence achieves completeness for the full μ-calculus). Following [23], we refer to such models, defined with may transitions and must hyper transitions, as *generalized kripke modal transition systems* (GTSs).

In this paper we investigate both the *precision* of ab-

1043-6871/06 $20.00 © 2006 IEEE

stract models, and the *efficiency* of their model checking. We show that GTSs are not yet satisfactory in terms of precision. We suggest how to overcome their imprecision by using may hyper transitions. We then suggest an efficient abstract model checking algorithm that achieves the newly obtained maximal precision while avoiding the exponential blowup inherent by the use of hyper transitions.

Precision of an abstract model is measured by the extent to which it enables to verify or falsify formulas. Specifically, given an abstraction (S_A, γ), it is desirable to construct an abstract model over the states S_A in which as many formulas as possible have a definite value (true or false). With this purpose in mind, we address the allegedly non-problematic *may* transitions. We show that while being good enough for completeness purposes [8, 9], they are in fact a source of *imprecision*. This might sound surprising, yet the explanation is simple: when completeness is investigated, the choice of the abstraction (S_A, γ) is left open. On the other hand, when precision is investigated, one is interested in how precise the model is for a *given* abstraction.

In order to elaborate further on the imprecision problem we need a more detailed description of abstract models. Typically, to ensure logic preservation, may transitions in an abstract model have to be such that whenever there is a concrete transition from a concrete state s_c to a concrete state s_c', then every abstract state that represents s_c has to have a may transition to some abstract state that represents s_c'. Now, consider the following example.

Example 1.1 Suppose that we are interested in verifying the formulas $\Box p$ ("all the successors satisfy p") and $\Box q$ ("all the successors satisfy q") in a concrete state s_c that has exactly one successor s_c' satisfying both p and q. Suppose further that we are given an abstraction in which s_c is represented by s_a, and no other concrete state is represented by s_a. Moreover suppose that s_c' is represented by two abstract states: s_{1a} that satisfies p but has an indefinite value on q, and s_{2a} that satisfies q but has an indefinite value on p. Fig. 1 illustrates this setting. Then at least one of the transitions (s_a, s_{1a}) or (s_a, s_{2a}) has to be included as a may transition in the abstract model to ensure logic preservation. However, choosing the first will enable verification of $\Box p$, but not $\Box q$, choosing the second will enable the opposite, and including both transitions will prevent verification of both properties. In other words, no choice of a may transition relation will enable verification of both $\Box p$ and $\Box q$. In particular, none of them will enable to verify $\Box p \wedge \Box q$.

Intuitively, in order to achieve the desired precision in the above example one has to consider both may transitions, but each of them has to be considered separately. We therefore suggest a new class of models, called *hyper kripke modal transition systems* (HTSs), in which may transitions are also replaced by hyper transitions, with the meaning that each

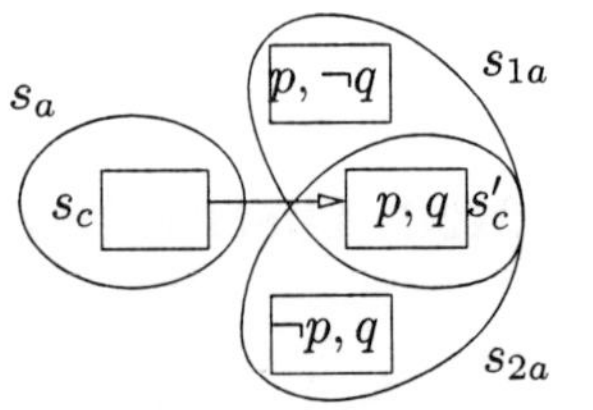

Rectangles depict concrete states circled by the abstract states representing them.

Figure 1. Illustration of Example 1.1

outgoing may hyper transition of an abstract state s_a over approximates *all* the concrete transitions of the states represented by s_a, but several different approximations (may hyper transitions) can be used. Other possible solutions involve changing the abstract state space, for example by some kind of completion that improves the states precision (e.g. [6]). However, we wish to "make the most" of the *given* abstract states.

Using HTSs as abstract models solves the problem demonstrated by Example 1.1, but one may wonder if there are other imprecision sources that HTSs do not address. To answer this question and justify the use of HTSs as abstract models we show how to construct, given *any* abstraction, an HTS which is as *precise* as the abstraction allows. We formalize this by introducing a new notion of precision which only depends on the abstraction (S_A, γ) itself and not on the class of abstract models. This enables us to claim that the constructed HTS is as precise as possible, among all possible abstract models with a standard 3-valued semantics.

HTSs therefore settle the issue of precision, as they allow maximal precision. Yet, in terms of efficiency, their use only increases the problem which already exists in GTSs due to the must hyper transitions: In general, the number of hyper-transitions might be exponential in the number of states in the abstract model. Thus, the need to handle hyper transitions makes both the construction of an abstract model and its model checking computationally expensive.

This problem was already addressed in [23] with respect to must hyper transitions. They suggested an automatic construction of abstract GTSs within an abstraction-refinement framework for CTL. Their algorithm starts with some initial model which consists of (mostly) ordinary transitions. Then, during refinement, when the abstract states are split, instead of computing all must hyper transitions, they "learn" must hyper transitions from must transitions (and hyper transitions) that existed in the previous iteration. Thus, in many cases they avoid the exponential blowup.

This approach suffers from several disadvantages. First, it only works as part of an abstraction-refinement loop. More importantly, the produced must hyper transitions are not necessarily the ones that are needed in practice for a specific proof. Some of them might be redundant, as they are irrelevant for proving the desired property, whereas others which are needed to verify the desired property might not be produced, making the model not precise enough.

We wish to obtain efficiency without compromising the precision that an HTS enables to get. We achieve this goal for the alternation free fragment of the μ-calculus. The ability to do this results from the fact that the precise HTS is precise w.r.t. *every* μ-calculus formula, whereas we are only interested in *one* particular (alternation-free) formula. This can be exploited to save unnecessary efforts.

Suppose, for example, that we wish to check the formula $\Diamond p$ ("there is a successor that satisfies p") in an abstract state s_a, for which the number of outgoing must hyper-transitions in the precise HTS is exponential in the number of states. If we want the abstract model to be as precise as possible w.r.t every μ-calculus formula, we might need to consider all of the hyper transitions (or at least the minimal ones). However, for the verification of $\Diamond p$ in s_a it suffices to consider a single must hyper transition (under approximation), in which all the target states satisfy p. In other words, w.r.t. the particular formula, a HTS that contains only the relevant must hyper transition is as precise as the precise HTS. Similar reasoning applies to may hyper transitions. The question is how to find these designated hyper transitions and avoid the computation of the rest.

The key idea is to construct the HTS *during* the model checking, and thus avoid the (exponential) construction of the precise HTS. We use the model checking to guide the computation of hyper transitions, by checking for the existence of hyper transitions only when needed.

We obtain an automatic construction of an abstract model which is as precise as the precise HTS w.r.t. the property of interest, along with a model checking algorithm with complexity $O(|S_A|^2 \times |\varphi|)$. This is comparable to the model checking complexity of the alternation free μ-calculus over models limited to ordinary transitions (recall that the number of ordinary transitions over $|S_A|$ states is $O(|S_A|^2)$), except that our algorithm also ensures maximal precision. We believe that similar techniques can be used to develop precise abstract model checking algorithms for the full μ-calculus, with complexity comparable to model checking of ordinary transition systems.

We emphasize that while may hyper transitions are not always necessary for maximal precision, must hyper transitions are in fact mandatory for completeness. This demonstrates the importance of such an algorithm, which handles hyper transitions efficiently. Moreover, our approach can be beneficial even in cases where ordinary transitions suffice for the construction of a precise abstract model for a formula. This is because such constructions are usually expensive as they require finding best approximations of the concrete transitions (e.g. [7]). In our approach, instead of computing best approximations, the model checking algorithm wisely chooses candidates for which we perform the simpler task of checking if the *given* candidate is a correct approximation – not necessarily the best one.

To complete the discussion, we show how to use our abstract model checking within an abstraction-refinement framework, and show that the refinement has the desirable property of monotonicity, meaning that the precision of an abstract model never decreases as a result of refinement.

To sum up, the main contributions of this paper are:

- New simple definition of precision of abstract models, which measures the precision w.r.t. the abstraction (S_A, γ), independently of the class of models used.
- New class of abstract models and a construction of an abstract model of this class which is precise w.r.t. any given abstraction.
- New abstract model checking algorithm for the alternation free μ-calculus that achieves maximal precision for a given formula, while remaining quadratic in the number of abstract states. This algorithm results in a more precise abstraction-refinement framework.

Related Work. Precision of modal (or mixed) transition systems, with ordinary may and must transitions, is studied in [4, 7, 21]. They suggest constructions of such abstract models which are most precise among all models from this *specific* class. In [23] GTSs are considered. They suggest a construction of an abstract GTS (with must hyper transitions) and show that it is most precise among all models produced by a *specific* construction method. In contrast to the above, we define a general notion of precision, which is independent not only of the construction method, but also of the class of abstract models.

A similar approach is taken in [13]. They refer to multi-valued concrete models and use an abstract semantics which is more general than the 3-valued semantics. They also define precision w.r.t. the abstraction itself, but then use (multi-valued) transition systems as abstract models, which causes a loss of precision. Our work, on the other hand, suggests a class of models that achieves maximal precision for the case of 2-valued concrete models. Moreover, [13] defines precision within the framework of abstract interpretation [5] and assumes that every set of concrete states has a unique most precise abstract state that describes it. We do not impose any restrictions on the abstraction and provide a simple, "stand alone", definition of precision.

The work of [9] also measures the precision of an abstract model by comparison to the precision of the abstraction. They define the precision of an abstraction (S_A, γ) in terms of a game over the concrete model. Their definition considers abstract states as precise in less cases than our definition. In particular, the abstract state s_a from Example 1.1 is not considered precise for $\Box p$ by their definition (when translating it to logic terms), although as demonstrated by Example 1.1, it *does* carry enough information to verify $\Box p$ in the (only) concrete state it represents. Using this stronger definition they show that the construction of an abstract GTS, which is also suggested in [23], results in a precise abstract model. This is in contrast to our result that shows that GTSs do not allow maximal precision, since we measure the precision of a model compared to a more general definition of precision of an abstraction. As a consequence, when pursuing precision w.r.t. our definition, we get abstract models which are strictly more precise.

[10] refers to precision with a different motivation. They suggest how to define the abstraction (S_A, γ) after refinement in order to maintain precision of an abstract model after refinement. Thus, they measure precision only w.r.t. the precision before refinement and not independently.

A different approach to precision pursued in [2, 11] uses a more precise 3-valued semantics, referred to as the *thorough semantics*. This semantics gives more definite answers than the standard 3-valued semantics, at the expense of increasing the complexity of model checking. Namely, the resulting model checking problem has the same complexity as satisfiability. We are interested in an effective framework, thus we use the standard 3-valued semantics, which is less precise, but enjoys a better model checking complexity. We note that the imprecision problem described in this paper still exists even if the thorough semantics is used.

May hyper transitions resemble the de-focus operations of [8]. We give them a new motivation and use.

In terms of model checking in the presence of hyper transitions, [9] shows that the model checking problem for GTSs is reducible to concrete model checking in linear time (and logarithmic space) in the size of the GTS. Yet, the GTS itself might be of size exponential in the size of the abstract state space S_A (due to the existence of hyper transitions). Thus the overall complexity is exponential.

Our approach in which we construct the abstract model during the model checking has some resemblance to the work of [20]. They perform reachability analysis, where they execute the concrete transitions, while storing abstract versions of the concrete states that are visited. Their approach is limited to falsification of safety properties, as they consider only an under approximation of the concrete model. Our work, on the other hand, is suitable for any property expressed in the alternation free μ-calculus, and is based on a 3-valued setting which enables both verification and falsification.

2. Preliminaries

μ-calculus. [15] Let AP be a finite set of atomic propositions and $\mathcal{V}$ a set of propositional variables. We define the set Lit of literals over AP to be the set $AP \cup \{\neg p : p \in AP\}$. We identify $\neg\neg p$ with p. The logic *μ-calculus* in *negation normal form* is defined as follows:

$$\varphi ::= l \mid Z \mid \varphi \wedge \varphi \mid \varphi \vee \varphi \mid \Box \varphi \mid \Diamond \varphi \mid \mu Z.\varphi \mid \nu Z.\varphi$$

where $l \in Lit$ and $Z \in \mathcal{V}$. μ denotes a least fixpoint, whereas ν denotes greatest fixpoint. Let $\mathcal{L}_\mu$ denote the set of *closed* formulas generated by the above grammar, where the fixpoint quantifiers μ and ν are variable binders. We will also write η for either μ or ν. Furthermore we assume that formulas are well-named, i.e. no variable is bound more than once in any formula. Thus, every variable Z *identifies* a unique subformula $fp(Z) = \eta Z.\psi$ of φ, where the set $Sub(\varphi)$ of *subformulas* of φ is defined in the usual way.

We also consider the *alternation-free* fragment of the μ-calculus, denoted $\mathcal{L}^0_\mu$, where no nesting of fixpoints is allowed. Namely, $\varphi \in \mathcal{L}^0_\mu$ if for every subformula $\eta Z.\psi \in Sub(\varphi)$, no variable other than Z occurs freely in ψ.

Concrete Semantics. Concrete systems are typically modelled as *Kripke structures*. A Kripke structure [3] is a tuple $M = (S, R, L)$, where S is a (possibly infinite) set of states, $R \subseteq S \times S$ is a transition relation, which must be *total*, and $L : S \rightarrow 2^{Lit}$ is a labeling function, such that for every state s and every $p \in AP$, exactly one of p and $\neg p$ is in $L(s)$.

The *concrete semantics* $[\![\varphi]\!]^M$ of a formula $\varphi \in \mathcal{L}_\mu$ w.r.t. a Kripke structure $M = (S, R, L)$ is a mapping from S to $\{\text{tt}, \text{ff}\}$. $[\![\varphi]\!]^M(s) = \text{tt}$ ($= \text{ff}$) means that the formula φ is true (false) in the state s of the Kripke structure M. Intuitively, in this context $\Box$ stands for "all successors", whereas $\Diamond$ stands for "exists a successor".

2.1. Abstraction Framework

Let M_C be a concrete Kripke structure with a set of concrete states S_C. An *abstraction* (S_A, γ) for S_C consists of a finite set of *abstract states* S_A and a total *concretization function* $\gamma : S_A \rightarrow 2^{S_C}$ that maps each abstract state to the (nonempty) set of concrete states it represents. Every $s_c \in S_C$ is represented by some $s_a \in S_A$.

The abstract states provide descriptions of the concrete states. The other components of the model M_C then also need to be lifted into the abstract world. Several classes of abstract models have been suggested for this purpose.

A *class of models* consists of some form of a transition system. It is accompanied with a *semantics* for the logic of interest, in our case the μ-calculus, over models from the class, and some *preservation relation* $\preceq$ between states that ensures preservation of the logic. An *abstract model* for M_C is then a model M_A from the class, over S_A, in which $(M_C, s_c) \preceq (M_A, s_a)$ whenever $s_c \in \gamma(s_a)$.

We are particularly interested in classes of abstract models that use a 3-valued semantics. The *3-valued semantics* [1] of a formula in a model M enables preservation of both satisfaction (tt) and refutation (ff) from an abstract model to the concrete one. In addition, a new truth value, $\perp$, is introduced, meaning that the truth value over the concrete model is unknown and can be either tt or ff. Such a 3-valued semantics was suggested for various classes of abstract models (e.g. [14, 12, 23]). We define a *generic 3-valued semantics* that generalizes these definitions. We refer to classes of models defined with such a 3-valued semantics, where the preservation relation ensures preservation of both tt and ff, as *3-valued classes*.

A 3-valued class defines, for each model M from the class, sets $l^M \in 2^S$, for every $l \in Lit$, and operators $\Box^M, \Diamond^M : 2^S \rightarrow 2^S$. These definitions are given in terms of the components of M, with the requirements that l^M and $(\neg l)^M$ are disjoint and the operators $\Box^M$ and $\Diamond^M$ are monotone w.r.t. set inclusion. The 3-valued semantics for the class is then defined by the following definition.

Definition 2.1 (Generic 3-Valued Semantics) *Let M be a model from a 3-valued class. The* tt*-set $[\![\varphi]\!]^M_{tt} \subseteq S$ and* ff*-set $[\![\varphi]\!]^M_{ff} \subseteq S$ of $\varphi \in \mathcal{L}_\mu$ over M are defined inductively in the style of [1] (based on Kleene's 3-valued logic for $\wedge$ and $\vee$, and with the standard definition for fixpoints [1]), except that the definition for formulas of the form $l \in Lit$, $\Box\psi$, or $\Diamond\psi$ depends on the particular class of M, as follows.*

$$[\![l]\!]^M_{tt} = l^M, \qquad [\![l]\!]^M_{ff} = (\neg l)^M$$
$$[\![\Box\psi]\!]^M_{tt} = \Box^M([\![\psi]\!]^M_{tt}), \qquad [\![\Box\psi]\!]^M_{ff} = \Diamond^M([\![\psi]\!]^M_{ff})$$

and dually for $\Diamond\psi$ when exchanging $\Box$ and $\Diamond$.

If for every $\varphi \in \mathcal{L}_\mu$, $[\![\varphi]\!]^M_{tt} \cap [\![\varphi]\!]^M_{ff} = \emptyset$, then M is consistent*. The 3-valued semantics of $\varphi \in \mathcal{L}_\mu$ over M, denoted $[\![\varphi]\!]^M_3$, is then defined to be a mapping $S \rightarrow \{\text{tt}, \text{ff}, \perp\}$:*

$$[\![\varphi]\!]^M_3(s) = \begin{cases} \text{tt}, & \text{if } s \in [\![\varphi]\!]^M_{tt} \\ \text{ff}, & \text{if } s \in [\![\varphi]\!]^M_{ff} \\ \perp, & \text{otherwise} \end{cases}$$

Note that if M is an abstract model, preservation of both tt and ff of the $\mathcal{L}_\mu$ from M to the concrete model guarantees that M is consistent.

An example of a 3-valued class of models is the class of Generalized Kripke Modal Transition Systems described below with generalized mixed simulation as a relation that ensures logic preservation.

Generalized Kripke Modal Transition Systems.

Definition 2.2 *Given a set of states S, a* hyper-transition *is a pair (s, A) where $s \in S$ and $A \subseteq S$ is a nonempty set.*

Definition 2.3 *[23] A* Generalized Kripke Modal Transition System *(**GTS**) is a tuple $M = (S, R^+, R^-, L)$, where S is defined as before, R^-, R^+ are may and must transition relations s.t. $R^- \subseteq S \times S$ is total and $R^+ \subseteq S \times 2^S$. $L : S \rightarrow 2^{Lit}$ is a labeling function s.t. for every state s and $p \in AP$,* at most *one of p and $\neg p$ is in $L(s)$.*

3-Valued Semantics for GTSs. For a GTS $M = (S, R^+, R^-, L)$, we define $l^M, \Box^M, \Diamond^M$ as follows. For every $l \in Lit$, $l^M = \{s \mid l \in L(s)\}$. For every $U \subseteq S$: $\Box^M(U) = \{s \mid \forall t \in S, \text{ if } sR^-t \text{ then } t \in U\}$, and $\Diamond^M(U) = \{s \mid \exists A \subseteq S \text{ s.t. } sR^+A \text{ and } A \subseteq U\}$. When integrated into Definition 2.1 this results in a 3-valued semantics. In particular, for a consistent GTS the definition for formulas of the form $l \in Lit$, $\Box\psi$ or $\Diamond\psi$ results in

$$[\![l]\!]^M_3(s) = \text{tt if } l \in L(s), \text{ff if } \neg l \in L(s), \text{ and } \perp \text{ otherwise.}$$

$$[\![\Box\psi]\!]^M_3(s) = \begin{cases} \text{tt}, & \text{if } \forall t \in S, \text{ if } sR^-t \text{ then } [\![\psi]\!]^M_3(t) = \text{tt} \\ \text{ff}, & \text{if } \exists A \subseteq S \text{ s.t. } sR^+A \text{ and} \\ & \quad \forall t \in A : [\![\psi]\!]^M_3(t) = \text{ff} \\ \perp, & \text{otherwise} \end{cases}$$

$[\![\Diamond\psi]\!]^M_3(s)$ is defined dually when exchanging tt with ff.

Definition 2.4 (Generalized Mixed Simulation) *[23] Let $M_1 = (S_1, R_1^+, R_1^-, L_1)$ and $M_2 = (S_2, R_2^+, R_2^-, L_2)$ be two GTSs. We say that $H \subseteq S_1 \times S_2$ is a* generalized mixed simulation *from M_1 to M_2 if $(s_1, s_2) \in H$ implies:*

1. *$L_2(s_2) \subseteq L_1(s_1)$.*
2. *if $s_1 R_1^- s_1'$, then there is some $s_2' \in S_2$ s.t. $s_2 R_2^- s_2'$ and $(s_1', s_2') \in H$.*
3. *if $s_2 R_2^+ A_2$, then there is some $A_1 \subseteq S_1$ s.t. $s_1 R_1^+ A_1$ and $(A_1, A_2) \in H^{\forall\exists}$, where $(A_1, A_2) \in H^{\forall\exists} \Leftrightarrow \forall s_1' \in A_1\, \exists s_2' \in A_2 : (s_1', s_2') \in H$.*

If there is a generalized mixed simulation H such that $(s_1, s_2) \in H$, we write $(M_1, s_1) \preceq (M_2, s_2)$.

In particular, Definition 2.4 can be applied to a (concrete) Kripke structure M_C and an (abstract) GTS M_A, by viewing the Kripke structure as a GTS where $R^- = R$, $R^+ = \{(s, \{s'\}) \mid (s, s') \in R\}$. For a Kripke structure the 3-valued semantics agrees with the concrete semantics. Thus, preservation of $\mathcal{L}_\mu$ formulas is guaranteed by the following theorem, which is adapted from [23] to $\mathcal{L}_\mu$.

Theorem 2.5 *For GTSs M_1 and M_2 with states s_1 and s_2 resp., if $(M_1, s_1) \preceq (M_2, s_2)$ then for every $\varphi \in \mathcal{L}_\mu$: $s_2 \in [\![\varphi]\!]^{M_2}_{tt} \Rightarrow s_1 \in [\![\varphi]\!]^{M_1}_{tt}$, and $s_2 \in [\![\varphi]\!]^{M_2}_{ff} \Rightarrow s_1 \in [\![\varphi]\!]^{M_1}_{ff}$.*

Construction of an Abstract GTS. Let $M_C = (S_C, R, L_C)$ be a (concrete) Kripke structure and (S_A, γ) an abstraction for S_C. An abstract GTS $M_A = (S_A, R^+, R^-, L_A)$ can be constructed as follows [23].

The labeling of an abstract state is defined in accord with the labeling of all the concrete states it represents. For $l \in Lit$, $l \in L_A(s_a)$ only if $\forall s_c$ if $s_c \in \gamma(s_a)$ then $l \in L_C(s_c)$. It is thus possible that neither p nor $\neg p$ are in $L_A(s_a)$.

The *may* transitions are computed by an [$\exists\exists$] rule such that every concrete transition is represented by them:

$$\exists s_c \in \gamma(s_a)\, \exists s_c' \in \gamma(s_a') \text{ s.t. } s_c R s_c' \Longrightarrow s_a R^- s_a'$$

The *must* hyper transitions, on the other hand, represent concrete transitions that are common to all the concrete states represented by the source abstract state. They are computed by an [$\forall\exists\exists$] rule:

$$\forall s_c \in \gamma(s_a)\, \exists s_a' \in A_a\, \exists s_c' \in \gamma(s_a') \text{ s.t. } s_c R s_c' \Longleftarrow s_a R^+ A_a$$

[1] We omit the use of an environment for simplicity of the presentation.

Exact GTS. If the three implications above are replaced by "iff", then the labeling, may transitions and must hyper transitions are *exact*, resulting in the *exact GTS*.

Other constructions of abstract GTSs can also be suggested. For example, the construction of a mixed transition system from [7] within the framework of abstract interpretation can be extended to GTSs as well.

All the above constructions assure us that whenever $s_c \in \gamma(s_a)$, then $(M_C, s_c) \preceq (M_A, s_a)$. The generalized mixed simulation $H \subseteq S_C \times S_A$ is induced by γ as follows: $(s_c, s_a) \in H$ iff $s_c \in \gamma(s_a)$. Therefore, Theorem 2.5 guarantees preservation of $\mathcal{L}_\mu$ from M_A to M_C.

3. Increasing Precision

Let M_C be a concrete Kripke structure. In this section we are interested in the *precision* of the abstract model constructed for M_C with a given abstraction (S_A, γ).

Specifically, in Section 2 we described GTSs as a class of abstract models, along with constructions of abstract models from this class. We now ask the following questions: (1) Do the constructions of GTSs from Section 2 produce the most precise abstract model that we can hope for, given an abstraction? and more fundamentally: (2) Does the use of GTSs *enable* to express the most precise abstract model?

Of course, to answer these questions we first need to define what the most precise abstract model that we can hope for is, given an abstraction. We measure precision with respect to a 3-valued semantics. We therefore restrict the discussion to abstract models from 3-valued classes.

3.1. Precision of Abstract Models

We wish to capture maximal precision within the boundaries of the inductive 3-valued semantics as defined in Definition 2.1. When using this semantics, the verification or refutation of any $\mathcal{L}_\mu$ formula over an abstract model M_A boils down to manipulations of l^{M_A}, $\Box^{M_A}(U_A)$, and $\Diamond^{M_A}(U_A)$ for various $l \in Lit$ and $U_A \subseteq S_A$. We therefore view a set $U_A \subseteq S_A$ as a new formula with the following semantics. Let $\gamma(U_A)$ stand for $\bigcup_{s_a \in U_A} \gamma(s_a)$. Then in a concrete model M_C, $[\![U_A]\!]^{M_C}_{\text{tt}} = \{s_c \mid s_c \in \gamma(U_A)\}$. In an abstract model M_A (from a 3-valued class), $[\![U_A]\!]^{M_A}_{\text{tt}} = U_A$. This makes the tt-sets of formulas of the form l, $\Box U_A$, and $\Diamond U_A$ over M_A the building blocks of any model checking problem over M_A. As such, the precision of M_A is determined by its precision w.r.t. truth of such formulas.

In the spirit of [9] we first define the precision of an *abstraction* w.r.t. such formulas. This is the precision that a precise abstract *model* will then be expected to match.

Definition 3.1 (Precision of Abstractions) *Given an abstraction (S_A, γ) for M_C and a state $s_a \in S_A$, we say that s_a fulfills $\varphi = l$, $\Box U_A$ or $\Diamond U_A$, for $l \in Lit$ and $U_A \subseteq S_A$, if $\forall s_c \in \gamma(s_a) : [\![\varphi]\!]^{M_C}(s_c) = \text{tt}$.*

Note that this definition is independent of the class of abstract models, as it is meant to capture the precision of the abstraction itself, in terms of the information carried within the abstract states. For example, for the abstraction to reflect the fact that $\Box U_A$ holds in an abstract state s_a (meaning it holds in all the concrete states it represents), it has to be the case that *all* the concrete states in $\gamma(s_a)$ share the property that all of their outgoing (concrete) transitions are to $\gamma(U_A)$, which is the "description" of U_A in the concrete world.

Definition 3.2 (Precision of Models) *An abstract model M_A for M_C (from some 3-valued class) is* precise *w.r.t. (S_A, γ) if for all $s_a \in S_A$, $l \in Lit$ and $U_A \subseteq S_A$: whenever s_a fulfills $\varphi = l$, $\Box U_A$ or $\Diamond U_A$, then $s_a \in [\![\varphi]\!]^{M_A}_{\text{tt}}$.*

Thus whenever the information about l, $\Box U_A$, or $\Diamond U_A$ exists in the abstract states, a precise abstract model enables to see that. To formalize the generality of Definition 3.2, we extend Definition 3.1 to more complicated formulas and to falsification, following the 3-valued semantics. We then show that whenever an abstract model is precise w.r.t. truth of $l, \Box U_A, \Diamond U_A$, it is also precise w.r.t. any other formula.

Definition 3.3 *Let $\mathcal{A} = (S_A, \gamma)$ be an abstraction. We define an* abstract semantics *$[\![\varphi]\!]^{\mathcal{A}}_3$ by using the generic 3-valued semantics (see Definition 2.1) with the following definitions of $l^{\mathcal{A}} \in 2^{S_A}$, and $\Box^{\mathcal{A}}, \Diamond^{\mathcal{A}} : 2^{S_A} \rightarrow 2^{S_A}$. For $l \in Lit$: $l^{\mathcal{A}} = \{s_a \mid s_a \text{ fulfills } l\}$. For $U_A \subseteq S_A$: $\Box^{\mathcal{A}}(U_A) = \{s_a \mid s_a \text{ fulfills } \Box U_A\}$, and $\Diamond^{\mathcal{A}}(U_A) = \{s_a \mid s_a \text{ fulfills } \Diamond U_A\}$. We say that $s_a \in S_A$* enables verification (falsification) *of $\varphi \in \mathcal{L}_\mu$ if $[\![\varphi]\!]^{\mathcal{A}}_3(s_a) = \text{tt (ff)}$.*

The abstract semantics is well defined since whenever $s_a \in [\![\varphi]\!]^{\mathcal{A}}_{\text{tt}}$ (resp. $[\![\varphi]\!]^{\mathcal{A}}_{\text{ff}}$), then $\forall s_c \in \gamma(s_a) : [\![\varphi]\!]^{M_C}(s_c) = \text{tt}$ (resp. ff). This ensures that $[\![\varphi]\!]^{\mathcal{A}}_{\text{tt}} \cap [\![\varphi]\!]^{\mathcal{A}}_{\text{ff}} = \emptyset$.

For example, by this definition s_a enables verification of $\varphi = \Box\psi$ iff s_a fulfills $\Box U_A$ for some $U_A \subseteq S_A$ such that every $s'_a \in U_A$ enables verification of ψ.

Theorem 3.4 *Let M_A be an abstract model for M_C (from some 3-valued class) which is* precise *w.r.t. (S_A, γ). Then whenever $s_a \in S_A$ enables verification (falsification) of $\varphi \in \mathcal{L}_\mu$, then $[\![\varphi]\!]^{M_A}_3(s_a) = \text{tt (ff)}$.*

The following theorem ensures that an abstract model which is precise w.r.t. the abstraction is also most precise when compared to other abstract models, provided that their class has the following property. A 3-valued class of models is *structural* if its definitions of $\Box^M, \Diamond^M : 2^{S_A} \rightarrow 2^{S_A}$ ensure that for every $U_A \subseteq S_A$, whenever $s_a \in \Box^M(U_A)$, then for every $s_c \in \gamma(s_a)$ all the concrete successors of s_c

are in $\gamma(U_A)$. Similarly, whenever $s_a \in \Diamond^M(U_A)$, then every $s_c \in \gamma(s_a)$ has a successor in $\gamma(U_A)$. Intuitively, for $\Box^M$ and $\Diamond^M$ to maintain such consistency with the concrete world, they have to be based on some (structural) abstract description of the concrete transitions in the abstract model. For example, GTSs and their variants are such classes.

Theorem 3.5 *Let M_A, M'_A be two abstract models for M_C (from possibly different 3-valued classes) based on an abstraction (S_A, γ). If M_A is* precise *w.r.t. (S_A, γ) and the class of M'_A is structural, then for every $s_a \in S_A$ and every $\varphi \in \mathcal{L}_\mu$: $[\![\varphi]\!]_3^{M'_A}(s_a) \neq \perp \Rightarrow [\![\varphi]\!]_3^{M_A}(s_a) = [\![\varphi]\!]_3^{M'_A}(s_a)$.*

Now, equipped with formal definitions of precision, we go back to our questions about the precision of GTSs.

Theorem 3.6 *If the abstraction (S_A, γ) partitions the concrete states, i.e. for each $s_a, s'_a \in S_A : \gamma(s_a) \cap \gamma(s'_a) = \emptyset$, then the exact GTS from section 2 is precise w.r.t. (S_A, γ).*

However, in many cases it might be desirable to gather the concrete states into non-disjoint sets, as this can reduce the size of the abstract state space that enables verification or falsification of the desired property. We show that in this general setting, the answer to both questions is "no".

3.2. May Transitions as a Source of Imprecision

As demonstrated by Example 1.1, when the given abstract states do not represent disjoint sets of concrete states, the may transitions can become a source of imprecision. In this example there is *no* abstract GTS for M_C over S_A that will enable verification of both $\Box p$ and $\Box q$ in s_a. This is while the abstraction *does* enable verification of both $\Box p$ and $\Box q$ in s_a (see Definition 3.3). Thus, none of the possible GTSs is precise w.r.t. the given abstraction.

Theorem 3.7 *GTSs do not always suffice for the construction of a precise abstract model w.r.t. a given abstraction.*

We emphasize that this imprecision is not limited to a certain construction. Indeed, the construction of the exact GTS from Section 2 is simplistic, as it might introduce redundancy in the may transitions (for example, in Example 1.1 both may transitions would be included). Yet, Theorem 3.7 holds even for optimized constructions that avoid redundant may transitions (e.g. in the style of [7]).

It can be shown that the imprecision results from the may transitions and not from the other components of the GTS. This is because whenever the abstraction enables verification of $l \in Lit$ or $\Diamond U_A$, so does the exact GTS, which implies that the labeling and the must hyper transitions (used for verification of such formulas) are precise enough.

More than that, analyzing Example 1.1 shows that the imprecision arises when there is no "best" choice of may transitions, in which case one needs to consider *all* of their (incomparable) possibilities to achieve maximal precision. Unfortunately, a GTS does not enable to do that. We therefore suggest to model the may transitions as hyper transitions as well, with the meaning that each may hyper transition $(s_a, A_a) \in S_A \times 2^{S_A}$ provides *some* over approximation of *all* the outgoing transitions of the concrete states represented by s_a.

3.3. Hyper Kripke Modal Transition Systems

This brings us to the new class of abstract models that we suggest to be used in order to obtain maximal precision.

Definition 3.8 *A* Hyper Kripke Modal Transition System *(**HTS**) is a tuple $M = (S, R^+, R^-, L)$, where S, L, R^+ are defined as before, and $R^- \subseteq S \times 2^S$ (not necessarily total).*

3-Valued Semantics for HTSs. To adapt the 3-valued semantics of $\mathcal{L}_\mu$ for HTSs we redefine $\Box^M$. For every $U \subseteq S$: $\Box^M(U) = \{s \mid \exists A \subseteq S \text{ s.t. } sR^-A \text{ and } \forall t \in A : t \in U\}$. This changes the definition for $\Box\psi$ in a consistent HTS to:

$$[\![\Box\psi]\!]_3^M(s) = \begin{cases} \text{tt}, & \text{if } \exists A \subseteq S \text{ s.t. } sR^-A \text{ and} \\ & \quad \forall t \in A : [\![\psi]\!]_3^M(t) = \text{tt} \\ \text{ff}, & \text{if } \exists A \subseteq S \text{ s.t. } sR^+A \text{ and} \\ & \quad \forall t \in A : [\![\psi]\!]_3^M(t) = \text{ff} \\ \perp, & \text{otherwise} \end{cases}$$

and dually for $[\![\Diamond\psi]\!]_3^M(s)$ when exchanging tt with ff.

Thus, in order to evaluate a $\Box\psi$ formula to tt, instead of requiring that *all* the may transitions are to states that satisfy ψ, we now require that there *exists* a may hyper transition such that *all* the states within the target set satisfy ψ.

A GTS, and thus also a Kripke structure, can be viewed as a HTS, where every state has exactly *one* outgoing may hyper transition, whose target set consists of the target states of *all* of its (ordinary) may transitions. Preservation of $\mathcal{L}_\mu$ between HTSs (and in particular between an HTS and a Kripke structure) is guaranteed by the following relation.

Definition 3.9 (Hyper Mixed Simulation) *Let $M_1 = (S_1, R_1^+, R_1^-, L_1)$ and $M_2 = (S_2, R_2^+, R_2^-, L_2)$ be two HTSs. $H \subseteq S_1 \times S_2$ is a* hyper mixed simulation *from M_1 to M_2 if $(s_1, s_2) \in H$ implies the requirements of Definition 2.4, except that requirement 2 is replaced by:*

2. *if $s_2 R_2^- A_2$, then there is some $A_1 \subseteq S_1$ s.t. $s_1 R_1^- A_1$ and $(A_1, A_2) \in H^{\forall\exists}$, where as before: $(A_1, A_2) \in H^{\forall\exists} \Leftrightarrow \forall s'_1 \in A_1 \, \exists s'_2 \in A_2 : (s'_1, s'_2) \in H$.*

If there is a hyper mixed simulation H such that $(s_1, s_2) \in H$, we write $(M_1, s_1) \preceq (M_2, s_2)$.

Intuitively, there can be less may hyper transitions in M_2 but each one has to over approximate *some* hyper transition in M_1. Thus, if some may hyper transition was used to verify $\Box\psi$ in M_2, then the may hyper transition that it over approximates can be used to verify it in M_1. Note that a may hyper transition of M_1 that has no representation in M_2 can only cause formulas with a definite value in M_1 to be indefinite in M_2 and not vice versa.

Theorem 3.10 *For HTSs M_1 and M_2 with states s_1 and s_2 resp., if $(M_1, s_1) \preceq (M_2, s_2)$ then for every $\varphi \in \mathcal{L}_\mu$: $s_2 \in [\![\varphi]\!]^{M_2}_{tt} \Rightarrow s_1 \in [\![\varphi]\!]^{M_1}_{tt}$, and $s_2 \in [\![\varphi]\!]^{M_2}_{ff} \Rightarrow s_1 \in [\![\varphi]\!]^{M_1}_{ff}$.*

Construction of an Abstract HTS. Let $M_C = (S_C, R, L_C)$ be a (concrete) Kripke structure. Given an abstraction (S_A, γ) for it, an abstract model in the form of a HTS $M_A = (S_A, R^+, R^-, L_A)$, can be constructed as before with the exception that R^- now consists of hyper transitions, constructed as follows. A may hyper transition $s_a R^- A_a$ exists only if an [∀∀∃] condition holds:

$$\forall s_c \in \gamma(s_a)\, \forall s'_c\, [\, s_c R s'_c \Rightarrow \exists s'_a \in A_a \text{ s.t. } s'_c \in \gamma(s'_a)\,]$$

That is, every outgoing may hyper transition of s_a over approximates *all* the concrete transitions of the states represented by s_a. An example of a "legal" may hyper transition is (s_a, A_a) for $A_a = \{s'_a \mid \exists s_c \in \gamma(s_a)\ \exists s'_c \in \gamma(s'_a) \text{ s.t. } s_c R s'_c\}$. Note that the "only if" allows to include less hyper transitions than allowed by the rule. The following theorem formalizes the correctness of the construction.

Theorem 3.11 *Let M_C be a concrete Kripke structure over S_C, and let M_A be an HTS computed as described above based on an abstraction (S_A, γ) for S_C. Then whenever $s_c \in \gamma(s_a)$ then $(M_C, s_c) \preceq (M_A, s_a)$.*

For example, to verify $\Box p$ and $\Box q$ in Example 1.1, we include $(s_a, \{s_{1a}\})$ and $(s_a, \{s_{2a}\})$ as may hyper transitions.

Exact HTS. If the "only if" in the definition of may hyper transitions is replaced by "iff", the may hyper transitions are *exact*. If all components are exact, we get the *exact HTS*.

Theorem 3.12 *Let M_C be a Kripke structure and M^E_A the* exact HTS *computed as described above based on an abstraction (S_A, γ). Then M^E_A is precise w.r.t. (S_A, γ).*

4. Decreasing the Model Checking Cost

Using the exact HTS as an abstract model ensures maximal precision. Yet, it involves an exponential blowup. In this section we suggest an efficient model checking, which remains quadratic in the number of abstract states, and yet produces a result which is *as precise as possible* with respect to a specific property.

From now on, we restrict the discussion to the alternation free fragment of the μ-calculus. Let M_C be a concrete Kripke structure and $\varphi \in \mathcal{L}^0_\mu$ a formula that we wish to check in some state s_c of M_C. Moreover, suppose that we are given a (finite) abstraction (S_A, γ). All the abstract states that represent s_c are candidates to enable verification or falsification of φ in s_c. We therefore refer to them as *designated* states. Our purpose is to evaluate φ in all these designated abstract states in the exact HTS M^E_A.

Our algorithm is based on a generalization of the game-based model checking suggested in [22] for CTL over abstract models with ordinary may and must transitions. We omit the details of the game, but continue with the game-graph, to which we refer as the *product graph.*

$\dfrac{s \vdash \psi_0 \vee \psi_1}{s \vdash \psi_i} : i \in \{0,1\}$	$\dfrac{s \vdash \psi_0 \wedge \psi_1}{s \vdash \psi_i} : i \in \{0,1\}$
$\dfrac{s \vdash \eta Z.\psi}{s \vdash Z}$	$\dfrac{s \vdash Z}{s \vdash \psi} : \text{if } fp(Z) = \eta Z.\psi$
$\dfrac{s \vdash \Diamond\psi}{t \vdash \psi} : s\widetilde{R}t$	$\dfrac{s \vdash \Box\psi}{t \vdash \psi} : s\widetilde{R}t$

Figure 2. Rules for product graph construction

Product Graph. The product graph presents all the information "relevant" for the model checking: Every node in the graph is labeled by $s_a \vdash \psi$, where s_a is an abstract state and ψ is a subformula of φ, indicating that the value of ψ in s_a is relevant for determining the model checking result. The outgoing edges of a node $s_a \vdash \psi$ can be seen as defining "subgoals" for the goal of checking ψ in s_a.

Formally, let $\varphi \in \mathcal{L}^0_\mu$ be a formula, S_A a set of states, $S_d \subseteq S_A$ a set of designated states in which we want to evaluate φ, and $\widetilde{R} \subseteq S_A \times S_A$ a total transition relation. $\widetilde{R}$ is meant to provide a basic description of the possible transitions between states (we will soon see how it is obtained). The *product graph* $G_{S_d,\widetilde{R},\varphi}$, or in short G, is a graph (N, E) with a set of nodes $N \subseteq S_A \times Sub(\varphi)$ and a set of edges $E \subseteq N \times N$, defined as follows. The *initial nodes* $N_0 \subseteq N$ consist of $S_d \times \{\varphi\}$. The (rest of the) nodes and the edges are defined by the rules of Fig. 2, with the meaning that whenever $n \in N$ is of the form of the upper part of the rule, then the result in the lower part of the rule is also a node $n' \in N$ and $(n, n') \in E$.

The nodes of G are classified as $\wedge$, $\vee$, $\Box$, $\Diamond$ nodes, based on their subformuals. Nodes whose subformula is a literal are *terminal nodes* (they have no outgoing edges). Nodes whose subformulas are of the form Z or $\eta Z.\psi$ are *deterministic* – they have exactly one son.

Each strongly connected component (SCC) in G which is non-trivial, i.e. has at least one edge, contains exactly one free fixpoint variable $Z \in \mathcal{V}$, called a *witness.* If $fp(Z) = \mu Z.\psi$, then Z is a μ-witness. Otherwise it is a ν-witness.

Coloring Algorithm. To determine the model checking result, a coloring algorithm is applied on the product graph with the purpose of labeling each node $n = s_a \vdash \psi$ in it by T, F, ? depending on the value of ψ in the state s_a in M^E_A.

The coloring algorithm of [22] processes the product

graph bottom-up by iterating two phases: In the sons-coloring phase, a node is colored based on the colors of its sons by rules which reflect the 3-valued semantics of the logic. In the witness-coloring phase a special procedure is applied to handle cycles (non trivial SCCs) in the graph.

As for our algorithm, for the sake of the explanation, suppose first that we construct the product graph based on M_A^E (of course, eventually the point will be to avoid the construction of M_A^E). $\widetilde{R}$ will then simply be the set $\widetilde{R}^E = \{(s_a, s'_a) \mid s'_a \in A_a \text{ and } (s_a R^- A_a \text{ or } s_a R^+ A_a)\}$, where R^- and R^+ are the transition relations of M_A^E. In this case we also define may and must hyper-sons in G: If $n = s \vdash \heartsuit\psi \in N$ for $\heartsuit \in \{\Box, \Diamond\}$ and $sR^- A$ ($sR^+ A$), then $B = A \times \{\psi\} \subseteq N$ is a *may (must) hyper-son* of n.

The coloring can be extended to handle hyper sons in the same way that the 3-valued semantics is extended to handle hyper transitions. For example, a $\Box$-node will be colored by F iff it has a must hyper-son whose nodes are all colored by F. It will be colored by T iff it has a may hyper-son whose nodes are all colored by T. Otherwise it will be colored ?. Dually for a $\Diamond$-node. Yet, instead of considering *all* the hyper sons and checking if any of them justifies coloring the node, we suggest to use the information gathered so far in the bottom-up coloring to perform this check wisely.

For example, to color a $\Box$-node n by F, it suffices to check, whenever some son of n gets colored by F, if all of n's currently F-colored sons comprise a must hyper-son (i.e., their underlying states fulfill the $\forall\exists\exists$ rule). Similarly, to conclude that n should not be colored F, it suffices to check that n's currently F-colored sons along with the uncolored sons (if exist) do not form a must hyper-son. Thus, checking these candidates is as informative as checking *all* of the possible must hyper sons. Similar reasoning applies to may hyper sons. This leads us to the following algorithm, where M_A^E is *not* constructed in advance.

4.1. Optimized Abstract Model Checking

Let M_C be a concrete model, $s_c \in S_C$ a concrete state, $\varphi \in \mathcal{L}_\mu^0$ a formula that we wish to check in s_c, and (S_A, γ) an abstraction. The algorithm is as follows.

Product Graph Construction. Construct a *partial* HTS $\widetilde{M}_A = (S_A, \widetilde{R}, L_A)$, where L_A is defined as in the exact HTS, and $\widetilde{R} \subseteq S_A \times S_A$ is defined by $\widetilde{R} = \{(s_a, s'_a) \mid \exists s_c \in \gamma(s_a)\, \exists s'_c \in \gamma(s'_a) \text{ s.t. } s_c R s'_c\}$. This ensures that $\widetilde{R} \supseteq \widetilde{R}^E$. Construct the product graph $G_{S_d, \widetilde{R}, \varphi}$ based on φ, S_A, $\widetilde{R}$ as above, and $S_d = \{s_a \mid s_c \in \gamma(s_a)\}$.

Partition. $G_{S_d, \widetilde{R}, \varphi}$ is partitioned into Maximal Strongly Connected Components (MSCCs), denoted Q_i's, and a (total) order $\leq$ is determined on them, s.t. for every $n \in Q_i$ and $n' \in Q_j$, $(n, n') \in E$ only if $Q_j \leq Q_i$. Such an order exists because the MSCCs form a directed acyclic graph.

Coloring. The following two phases are performed repeatedly until all nodes are colored.

1. *Sons-coloring phase.* Apply the following rules until none is applicable.
   - A terminal node $s_a \vdash l$ is colored T if $l \in L_A(s_a)$, F if $\neg l \in L_A(s_a)$, and ? otherwise.
   - An $\wedge$-node ($\vee$-node) is colored by:
     - $T(F)$ if both its sons are colored $T(F)$.
     - $F(T)$ if it has a son that is colored $F(T)$.
     - ? if it has a son that is colored ? and the other is colored $\neq F(T)$.
   - A deterministic node is colored as its (only) son.
   - A $\Box$-node ($\Diamond$-node) is colored by:
     - $T(F)$ if its currently $T(F)$-colored sons form a may hyper son.
     - $F(T)$ if its currently $F(T)$-colored sons form a must hyper son.
     - ? if all of its sons are colored, yet none of the above holds.
2. *Witness-coloring phase.* If there are still uncolored nodes, let Q_i be the smallest MSCC w.r.t. $\leq$ that is not yet fully colored. Q_i is necessarily a non-trivial MSCC that has exactly one witness. Its uncolored nodes are colored according to the witness. For a μ-witness:
   (a) Repeatedly color ? each node in Q_i satisfying one of the following.
     - An $\wedge$-node ($\vee$-node) that both (at least one) of its sons are colored $\neq F$.
     - A deterministic node whose son is colored ?.
     - A $\Box$-node ($\Diamond$-node) whose F-colored sons along with its remaining uncolored sons do not form a must (may) hyper-son.

   (b) Color the remaining nodes in Q_i by F.

   The case where the witness is of type ν is dual, when exchanging F with T, $\wedge$ with $\vee$, and $\Box$ with $\Diamond$.

In each phase of the coloring, the rules will initially be checked once for every uncolored node, and later will only be checked when one of the sons of the node gets colored by an appropriate color. Several optimizations can be used.

Remark 4.1 *Checking if a set B of nodes forms a may or must hyper son of a $\Box$-node or a $\Diamond$-node n is performed by checking the $\forall\exists\exists$ or the $\forall\forall\exists$ condition (resp.) between the underlying states of the node n and the set of nodes B.*

Theorem 4.2 *Let M_A^E denote the exact HTS for M_C w.r.t. (S_A, γ). Let $G = G_{S_d, \widetilde{R}, \varphi}$ be the product graph produced by the algorithm. Then for every $n = s_a \vdash \varphi_1 \in G$ such that φ_1 is closed the following holds:*

1. $[\![\varphi_1]\!]_3^{M_A^E}(s_a) = \mathrm{tt}$ *iff $n = s_a \vdash \varphi_1$ is colored by T.*

2. $[\![\varphi_1]\!]_3^{M_A^E}(s_a) = \text{ff}$ *iff* $n = s_a \vdash \varphi_1$ *is colored by* F.

3. $[\![\varphi_1]\!]_3^{M_A^E}(s_a) = \perp$ *iff* $n = s_a \vdash \varphi_1$ *is colored by* ?.

Thus, for all nodes with closed formulas in the product graph, the coloring is as precise as model checking with M_A^E, even though M_A^E is *not* constructed by the algorithm. In particular, this is true for $N_0 = S_d \times \{\varphi\}$, and by the choice of S_d, we are guaranteed that whenever the abstraction is precise enough, at least one initial node will be colored by a definite color T or F, in which case by Theorems 4.2 and 3.10, $[\![\varphi]\!]^{M_C}(s_c) = \text{tt}$ or ff respectively. Note, that it is impossible that some initial node will be colored T and another will be colored F. If all the initial nodes in the product graph are colored ?, then the result is indefinite.

Remark 4.3 *By considering the underlying hyper transitions of hyper sons computed by the algorithm, the final product graph induces an abstract HTS for* M_C *which is as precise as the exact HTS w.r.t.* φ.

Complexity. During all applications of the sons-coloring phase, the $\forall\exists\exists$ and the $\forall\forall\exists$ conditions are checked at most $|S_A|$ times for each node, as each node has at most $|S_A|$ sons, and between checks the set of candidates to comprise a hyper son is monotonically increasing. Similar analysis holds for phase 2a, with the difference that the sets of candidates to comprise a hyper son are monotonically decreasing. As the number of nodes in the product graph is $O(|S_A| \times |\varphi|)$, the total number of checks of the $\forall\exists\exists$ and the $\forall\forall\exists$ conditions is $O(|S_A|^2 \times |\varphi|)$. This is the dominant part which determines the model checking complexity.

5. Abstraction-Refinement

Our abstract model checking ensures maximal precision. Still, its result might be indefinite if the abstraction is not precise enough. In this case, refinement can be applied by splitting the abstract states, similarly to the refinement of [22] for models with ordinary transitions (with various optimizations that exploit the use of hyper transitions).

When refinement is introduced, monotonicity in the precision of the abstract models before and after the refinement is desirable, meaning that formulas that had a definite value before the refinement will not become indefinite after refinement [23]. This is guaranteed by the following theorem.

Theorem 5.1 (Monotonicity of HTSs) *Let* M'_A *and* M_A *be exact HTSs defined based on abstractions* (S'_A, γ') *and* (S_A, γ) *resp., where* (S'_A, γ') *is the result of splitting the states of* (S_A, γ). *Then whenever* $s'_a \in S'_A$ *is a substate of* $s_a \in S_A$ *then* $(M'_A, s'_a) \preceq (M_A, s_a)$.

Monotonicity implies that refinement of an exact HTS will never take us further from the (definite) result. In particular, we will not "miss" the opportunity to get a definite result only due to excess refinement. Thus, our approach, which is as precise as using the exact HTS w.r.t. the desired property, will ensure the same. Recall that the same is not guaranteed when using ordinary must transitions [23].

If the concrete model is finite, an iterative abstraction-refinement is guaranteed to terminate with a definite answer.

References

[1] G. Bruns and P. Godefroid. Model checking partial state spaces with 3-valued temporal logics. In *CAV*, 1999.

[2] G. Bruns and P. Godefroid. Generalized model checking: Reasoning about partial state spaces. In *CONCUR*, 2000.

[3] E. Clarke, O. Grumberg, and D. Peled. *Model Checking*. MIT press, 1999.

[4] R. Cleaveland, P. Iyer, and D. Yankelevich. Optimality in abstraction of model checking. In *SAS*, 1995.

[5] P. Cousot and R. Cousot. Abstract interpretation: A unified lattice model for static analysis of programs by construction or approximation of fixpoints. In *POPL*, 1977.

[6] P. Cousot and R. Cousot. Abstract interpretation frameworks. *J. Log. Comput.*, 2(4), 1992.

[7] D. Dams, R. Gerth, and O. Grumberg. Abstract interpretation of reactive systems. *TOPLAS*, 19(2), 1997.

[8] D. Dams and K. Namjoshi. The existence of finite abstractions for branching time model checking. In *LICS*, 2004.

[9] L. de Alfaro, P. Godefroid, and R. Jagadeesan. Three-valued abstractions of games: Uncertainty, but with precision. In *LICS*, 2004.

[10] P. Godefroid, M. Huth, and R. Jagadeesan. Abstraction-based model checking using modal transition systems. In *CONCUR*, 2001.

[11] P. Godefroid and R. Jagadeesan. Automatic abstraction using generalized model checking. In *CAV*, 2002.

[12] P. Godefroid and R. Jagadeesan. On the expressiveness of 3-valued models. In *VMCAI*, 2003.

[13] A. Gurfinkel, O. Wei, and M. Chechik. Systematic construction of abstractions for model-checking. In *VMCAI*, 2006.

[14] M. Huth, R. Jagadeesan, and D. Schmidt. Modal transition systems: A foundation for three-valued program analysis. In *ESOP*, 2001.

[15] D. Kozen. Results on the propositional μ-calculus. *TCS*, 27, 1983.

[16] K. Larsen and B. Thomsen. A modal process logic. In *LICS*, 1988.

[17] K. Larsen and L. Xinxin. Equation solving using modal transition systems. In *LICS*, 1990.

[18] K. G. Larsen. Modal specifications. In *Automatic Verification Methods for Finite State Systems, Grenoble*, 1989.

[19] K. Namjoshi. Abstraction for branching time properties. In *CAV*, 2003.

[20] C. S. Pasareanu, R. Pelánek, and W. Visser. Concrete model checking with abstract matching and refinement. In *CAV'05*.

[21] D. A. Schmidt. Closed and logical relations for over- and under-approximation of powersets. In *SAS*, 2004.

[22] S. Shoham and O. Grumberg. A game-based framework for CTL counterexamples and 3-valued abstraction-refinement. In *CAV*, 2003. To appear in TOCL.

[23] S. Shoham and O. Grumberg. Monotonic abstraction-refinement for CTL. In *TACAS*, 2004.

Session 11: Approximations

Approximation Schemes for First-Order Definable Optimisation Problems

Anuj Dawar* Martin Grohe** Stephan Kreutzer** Nicole Schweikardt**

* University of Cambridge, U.K., Email: anuj.dawar@cl.cam.ac.uk
** Humboldt-Universität zu Berlin, Germany, Email: {grohe | kreutzer | schweika}@informatik.hu-berlin.de

Abstract

Let $\varphi(X)$ be a first-order formula in the language of graphs that has a free set variable X, and assume that X only occurs positively in $\varphi(X)$. Then a natural minimisation problem associated with $\varphi(X)$ is to find, in a given graph G, a vertex set S of minimum size such that G satisfies $\varphi(S)$. Similarly, if X only occurs negatively in $\varphi(X)$, then $\varphi(X)$ defines a maximisation problem. Many well-known optimisation problems are first-order definable in this sense, for example, MINIMUM DOMINATING SET *or* MAXIMUM INDEPENDENT SET.

We prove that for each class $\mathscr{C}$ of graphs with excluded minors, in particular for each class of planar graphs, the restriction of a first-order definable optimisation problem to the class $\mathscr{C}$ has a polynomial time approximation scheme.

A crucial building block of the proof of this approximability result is a version of Gaifman's locality theorem for formulas positive in a set variable. This result may be of independent interest.

1. Introduction

It has long been known that many combinatorial optimisation problems that are hard to approximate in general have polynomial time approximation schemes (PTASs) on planar graphs, that is, they can be approximated to any given ratio in polynomial time. Among these problems are MINIMUM DOMINATING SET, MINIMUM VERTEX COVER, and MAXIMUM INDEPENDENT SET. The two main techniques for proving such approximation results on planar graphs are Lipton and Tarjan's planar separator theorem [20] and Baker's layerwise decomposition technique [4]. Both techniques have been generalised from planar graphs to more general graph classes such as graphs of bounded genus and ultimately to arbitrary classes of graphs with excluded minors [1, 10, 14, 7]. Recall that a *minor* of a graph G is a graph that can be obtained from a subgraph of G by contracting edges. We say that a class $\mathscr{C}$ of graphs *has an excluded minor* if there is some graph H such that H is not a minor of any graph in G. For example, the complete graph on five vertices, K_5, is an excluded minor of the class of all planar graphs. Most approximation results on general classes of graphs with excluded minors make heavy use of Robertson and Seymour's structure theory for graphs with excluded minors [23]. In a recent paper, Demaine, Hajiaghayi, and Kawarabayashi [7] have proved algorithmic versions of some of the central parts of this theory and use these to obtain several new approximability results.

What kind of problems are approximable on graphs with excluded minors? Demaine et al. [7] gave a general criterion that is met by most problems known to be approximable, but is somewhat unsatisfactory because it describes when a certain proof technique works rather than describing a "natural" class of problems. On planar graphs, Khanna and Motwani [17] tried a more systematic "syntactic" approach: They defined three "generic" problems based on propositional logic and showed that the planar versions of these problems have PTASs. Then they showed that most problems which at that time were known to have PTASs can easily be reduced to one of these three problems. In this paper, we carry out a different logic based approach towards identifying a large class of problems that have PTASs on classes of graphs with excluded minors. Our approach, in contrast to that of Khanna and Motwani, is based on first-order logic: Let $\varphi(X)$ be a first-order formula in the language of graphs that has a free set variable X, and assume that X only occurs positively in $\varphi(X)$. Then a natural minimisation problem $\text{MIN}_{\varphi(X)}$ associated with $\varphi(X)$ is to find, in a given graph G, a vertex set S of minimum size such that G satisfies $\varphi(S)$. Many natural minimisation problems can be described as problems $\text{MIN}_{\varphi(X)}$ for a suitable formula $\varphi(X)$. For example, the MINIMUM DOMINATING SET problem is $\text{MIN}_{\varphi(X)}$ for the formula $\varphi(X) = \forall x(Xx \vee \exists y(Xy \wedge Exy))$. The condition that $\varphi(X)$ be positive in X is imposed to guarantee monotonicity, which is necessary to exclude pathological examples (see Example 11). Similarly, if X only occurs negatively in a formula $\psi(X)$ then this formula defines a natural maximisation problem $\text{MAX}_{\psi(X)}$. For example, MAX-

IMUM INDEPENDENT SET is $\text{MAX}_{\psi(X)}$ for the formula $\psi(X) = \forall x \forall y(\neg Xx \vee \neg Xy \vee \neg Exy)$. Papadimitriou and Yannakakis [22] considered similar syntactically defined optimisation problems to introduce their well-known class MAXSNP; a more detailed analysis of such problems was later carried out by Kolaitis and Thakur [18, 19]. The syntactical problems studied by these authors can be directly translated to problems of the form $\text{MAX}_{\varphi(X)}$ or $\text{MIN}_{\varphi(X)}$, where φ is a formula of first-order or existential second-order logic and X a (not necessarily unary) relation variable.

We call problems of the form $\text{MIN}_{\varphi(X)}$ or $\text{MAX}_{\varphi(X)}$ *first-order definable optimisation problems*. For a class $\mathscr{C}$ of graphs, we write $\text{MIN}_{\varphi(X)}(\mathscr{C})$ and $\text{MAX}_{\varphi(X)}(\mathscr{C})$ to denote the restriction of $\text{MIN}_{\varphi(X)}$ ($\text{MAX}_{\varphi(X)}$, respectively) to instances from $\mathscr{C}$. Our main result states that the restrictions of first-order definable optimisation problems to graphs with excluded minors have PTASs. More precisely:

Theorem 1. *Let $\varphi(X)$ be a first-order formula in the language of graphs that is positive in a set variable X, and let $\mathscr{C}$ be a class of graphs with an excluded minor. Then $\text{MIN}_{\varphi(X)}(\mathscr{C})$ has a PTAS.*

Similarly, if $\varphi(X)$ is negative in X, then $\text{MAX}_{\varphi(X)}(\mathscr{C})$ has a PTAS.

In fact, we prove a stronger result; we actually get an *EPTAS* (*efficient polynomial time approximation scheme*, cf. [11, 21]). This means that the running time of the ε-approximation algorithm is $f(\varepsilon) \cdot n^{O(1)}$ for some function f. Let us remark that the statement of Theorem 1 does not extend, for example, to monadic second-order logic (cf. Example 11).

We see our result as an algorithmic meta theorem in the style of Courcelle's theorem [6]. It gives a uniform and natural explanation for a large family of algorithmic results, and for many problems it gives a quick way of proving that they have a PTAS on graphs with excluded minors. Consider, for example, the MINIMUM DISTANCE d DOMINATING SET problem (for a constant $d \geq 1$), which asks for a minimum set S of vertices of a graph such that each vertex is within distance d of the set S. It is easy to find a first-order formula $\varphi(X)$ such that this problem is $\text{MIN}_{\varphi(X)}$. Thus it has a PTAS on all classes with excluded minors. This was not known before, and the problem also does not meet Demaine et al.'s general approximability criterion mentioned above. Our theorem can easily be extended from graphs to arbitrary relational structures and also to weighted versions of the problems, but we defer the details of these generalisations to the full version of this paper. Even with these generalisations, we do not claim that our theorem captures all problems that have PTASs on classes of graphs with excluded minors. Indeed, it is easy to find problems that meet Demaine et al.'s approximability criterion, but are not first-order definable in our sense. Even on planar graphs, our approach seems incomparable with Khanna and Motwani's in that there is no obvious translation of our syntactically defined problems into theirs or vice versa. An important difference between our result and those of Demaine et al. and Khanna and Motwani is that we obtain an EPTAS. For the problem PLANAR TMIN, for which Khanna and Motwani obtained a PTAS, it can actually be proved that, under reasonable complexity theoretic assumptions, it does not have an EPTAS [5, 21].

The proof of Theorem 1 has two parts: the second, algorithmic, part builds on techniques that were first applied in [14] to classes of graphs with excluded minors and generalise Baker's layerwise decomposition technique [4]. However, the techniques have to be generalised considerably to handle the very general class of problems we consider here. The crucial property of first-order definable optimisation problems that our algorithms exploit is the locality of first-order logic. In the first part of the proof of Theorem 1, we prove a "positive version" of Gaifman's locality theorem, a result which may be of independent interest:

Theorem 2. *Let $\varphi(X)$ be a first-order sentence that is positive in the set variable X. Then there is a Boolean combination $\psi(X)$ of basic local sentences so that $\psi(X)$ is positive in X and equivalent to $\varphi(X)$.*

The necessary definitions will be given later. Rather unexpectedly, the proof of this theorem proved to be fairly difficult, as we were unable to adapt the known proofs of Gaifman's theorem [12] (see [9, 16] for alternative proofs) or of its existential version [15]. Our proof of the positive version uses ideas from [3] to analyse the spatial distribution of the types occurring in a structure, and it uses a lemma from [15] to get from a nonuniform to a uniform version of the theorem, but the core combinatorial argument is new.

2. Preliminaries

A *vocabulary* is a finite set of relation symbols and constant symbols. Associated with every relation symbol R is a positive integer called the *arity* of R. In the following, τ always denotes a vocabulary. τ is called *relational* if it does not contain any constant symbol.

A τ-structure $\mathscr{A}$ consists of a non-empty set A, called the *universe* of $\mathscr{A}$, an element $c^{\mathscr{A}} \in A$ for each constant symbol $c \in \tau$, and a relation $R^{\mathscr{A}} \subseteq A^r$ for each r-ary relation symbol $R \in \tau$.

The *Gaifman graph* of a τ-structure $\mathscr{A}$ is the (undirected, loop-free) graph $\mathscr{G}_{\mathscr{A}}$ with vertex set A and an edge between two vertices $a, b \in A$ iff there exists an $R \in \tau$ and a tuple $(a_1, \ldots, a_r) \in R^{\mathscr{A}}$ such that $a, b \in \{a_1, \ldots, a_r\}$.

The *distance* between two elements $a, b \in A$ in $\mathscr{A}$, denoted by $\text{dist}^{\mathscr{A}}(a, b)$, is defined to be the length (that is, number of edges) of the shortest path from a to b in the Gaifman graph of $\mathscr{A}$. For $r \geq 0$ and $a \in A$, the r-neighbourhood of a in $\mathscr{A}$ is the set $N_r^{\mathscr{A}}(a) = \{b \in A : \text{dist}^{\mathscr{A}}(a,b) \leq r\}$.

The induced substructure of $\mathscr{A}$ with universe $N_r^{\mathscr{A}}(a)$ is denoted by $\mathscr{N}_r^{\mathscr{A}}(a)$. We omit superscripts $^{\mathscr{A}}$ if $\mathscr{A}$ is clear from the context.

We write FO(τ) to denote the class of all formulae in first-order logic over the vocabulary τ, and we write qr(φ) to denote the *quantifier rank* of an FO(τ)-formula φ. If X is a unary relation symbol not in τ, then an occurrence of X in an FO($\tau \cup \{X\}$)-formula φ is said to be *positive* if it is within the scope of an *even* number of negations and it is said to be *negative* otherwise. We say that the formula φ is *positive in* X (or X*-positive*) if all occurrences of X in φ are positive. Similarly, we say that φ is *negative in* X (or X*-negative*) if all occurrences of X in φ are negative.

For every $r \geq 0$, we let $\text{dist}_{\leq r}(x,y)$ be an FO(τ)-formula expressing that the distance between x and y is at most r. We often write $\text{dist}(x,y) \leq r$ instead of $\text{dist}_{\leq r}(x,y)$ and $\text{dist}(x,y) > r$ or $\text{dist}_{>r}(x,y)$ instead of $\neg\text{dist}_{\leq r}(x,y)$.

The *r-relativisation* of a formula $\varphi(x)$ is the formula $\varphi^r(x)$ obtained from φ by first renaming all bound variables so that they are different from x and then replacing each subformula of the form $\exists y \psi$ by $\exists y(\text{dist}(x,y) \leq r \wedge \psi)$ and each subformula of the form $\forall y \psi$ by $\forall y(\text{dist}(x,y) \leq r \rightarrow \psi)$. Clearly, the r-relativisation of every formula $\varphi(x)$ is *r-local*, that is, for every τ-structure $\mathscr{A}$ and every $a \in A$ we have $\mathscr{A} \models \varphi^r(a) \iff \mathscr{N}_r(a) \models \varphi^r(a)$. Note that we also have $\mathscr{A} \models \varphi^r(a) \iff \mathscr{N}_r(a) \models \varphi(a)$.

A (symmetric) *basic local sentence* (with parameters k,r,q) is a sentence of the form

$$\exists x_1 \cdots \exists x_k \Big(\bigwedge_{1 \leq i < j \leq k} \text{dist}(x_i,x_j) > 2r \wedge \bigwedge_{1 \leq i \leq k} \psi(x_i) \Big),$$

where $k,r \geq 1$ and $\psi(x)$ is r-local and of quantifier rank q (here, the adjective "symmetric" emphasises that the same formula ψ is used for each of the variables x_i).

Theorem 3 (Gaifman [12]). *Every first-order sentence over a relational vocabulary is equivalent to a Boolean combination of basic local sentences.*

3. A positive locality theorem

In this section we present a proof of the version of Gaifman's theorem for formulae *positive* in a unary relation symbol, stated in Theorem 2. From now on, fix a relational vocabulary τ and a unary relation symbol $X \notin \tau$. For proving Theorem 2 we adopt the approach of [15] of using *asymmetric* basic local formulae in an intermediate step.

An *asymmetric basic local sentence with parameters* k, κ, r, q is a sentence of the form

$$\exists x_1 \ldots \exists x_k \Big(\bigwedge_{1 \leq i < j \leq k} \text{dist}(x_i,x_j) > \kappa{\cdot}2r \wedge \bigwedge_{i=1}^{k} \psi_i(x_i) \Big),$$

where $\psi_i(x_i)$ is r-local and of quantifier rank at most q. We denote the set of all asymmetric basic local sentences with parameters $k' \leq k$, κ, $r' \leq r$, and $q' \leq q$ by ABL(k,κ,r,q). By ABL$^+(k,\kappa,r,q)$ (respectively, ABL$^-(k,\kappa,r,q)$) we denote the set of all sentences in ABL(k,κ,r,q) that are *positive* (respectively, *negative*) in X.

Similarly, we write BL(k,r,q), BL$^+(k,r,q)$, and BL$^-(k,r,q)$ for, respectively, the set of all, all X-positive, and all X-negative symmetric basic local sentences with parameters $k' \leq k$, $r' \leq r$, and $q' \leq q$.

For a sentence $\varphi \in$ ABL(k,κ,r,q) of the form

$$\exists x_1 \ldots \exists x_k \Big(\bigwedge_{1 \leq i < j \leq k} \text{dist}(x_i,x_j) > \kappa{\cdot}2r \wedge \bigwedge_{i=1}^{k} \psi_i(x_i) \Big)$$

we write $\varphi_{[1/\kappa]}$ to denote the sentence

$$\exists x_1 \ldots \exists x_k \Big(\bigwedge_{1 \leq i < j \leq k} \text{dist}(x_i,x_j) > 2r \wedge \bigwedge_{i=1}^{k} \psi_i(x_i) \Big)$$

(in particular, $\varphi_{[1/\kappa]} \in$ ABL$(k,1,r,q)$).

The two major steps in proving Theorem 2 consist of showing the following two technical lemmas:

Lemma 4. *Let $K,Q,R \geq 2$ and let $\kappa := 2^{K^2-1}$. Suppose $\mathscr{A}$ and $\mathscr{B}$ are $\tau \cup \{X\}$-structures such that every X-positive (resp. X-negative) basic local sentence in* BL$(K,\kappa{\cdot}2R,Q)$ *that holds in $\mathscr{A}$ also holds in $\mathscr{B}$. Then we have for every X-positive (resp. X-negative) sentence $\varphi \in$* ABL(K,κ,R,Q) *that $\mathscr{A} \models \varphi$ implies $\mathscr{B} \models \varphi_{[1/\kappa]}$.*

We omit the proof of Lemma 4 since it is virtually identical to the proof of Lemma 4 in [15]. We will use Lemma 4 as an intermediate step in proving the following:

Lemma 5. *For every $q \geq 0$ there exist $K,R,Q \geq 2$ such that for all $\tau \cup \{X\}$-structures $\mathscr{A},\mathscr{B}$ the following holds: If for every $\varphi \in$* BL$^+(K,R,Q)$, *$\mathscr{A} \models \varphi$ implies $\mathscr{B} \models \varphi$, and for every $\varphi \in$* BL$^-(K,R,Q)$, *$\mathscr{B} \models \varphi$ implies $\mathscr{A} \models \varphi$, then we have for every X-positive* FO$(\tau \cup \{X\})$*-sentence ζ of quantifier rank at most q that $\mathscr{A} \models \zeta$ implies $\mathscr{B} \models \zeta$.*

Note that by using Lemma 5 one easily obtains a proof of Theorem 2 (details of this will be given in the full version of the paper).

The remainder of Section 3 is devoted to the proof of Lemma 5. To prove Lemma 5, we use the following "X-positive" variant of the classical *Ehrenfeucht-Fraïssé game* (EF-game, for short) for first-order logic.

3.1. The X-positive EF-game.

The rules of this game are the same as for the "classical" EF-game for first-order logic (cf., e.g. [9]), the winning condition, however, is slightly different. To be precise, the "X-positive" EF-game is defined as follows:

Let q be a positive integer. The *q-round X-positive EF-game* is played by two players, *the spoiler* and *the duplicator*, on two $\tau \cup \{X\}$-structures $\mathscr{A}$ and $\mathscr{B}$. The spoiler's intention is to show a difference between the two structures, while the duplicator tries to make them look alike. There is a fixed number q of rounds. Each round $i \in \{1,..,q\}$ is played as follows: First, the spoiler chooses either an element a_i in A or an element b_i in B. Next, the duplicator chooses an element in the other structure. I.e., she chooses an element b_i in B if the spoiler's move was in A, or an element a_i in A if the spoiler's move was in B. After q rounds the game ends with elements $a_1,..,a_q$ chosen in A and $b_1,..,b_q$ chosen in B. The *duplicator has won the game* iff the mapping f defined via $(a_j \mapsto b_j)_{j=1,..,q}$ is an *X-positive partial isomorphism from $\mathscr{A}$ to $\mathscr{B}$*, i.e.,

(i) for any tuple of elements $(v_1,..,v_s)$ within the domain of f and any relation symbol $R \in \tau$ of arity s, we have $(v_1,..,v_s) \in R^{\mathscr{A}} \iff (f(v_1),..,f(v_s)) \in R^{\mathscr{B}}$, and

(ii) for any element v within the domain of f and for the particular unary relation symbol X, we have $v \in X^{\mathscr{A}} \implies f(v) \in X^{\mathscr{B}}$.

Otherwise, the spoiler has won the game. Since the game is finite, one of the two players must have a *winning strategy*, i.e., he or she can always win the game, no matter how the other player plays. We write $\mathscr{A} \Rrightarrow_q^{X\text{-pos}} \mathscr{B}$ to denote that the duplicator has a winning strategy in the q-round X-positive EF-game on $\mathscr{A}$ and $\mathscr{B}$. Note that the relation defined by $\Rrightarrow^{X\text{-pos}}$ on the class of all $\tau \cup \{X\}$-structures is reflexive and transitive, but not symmetric.

The fundamental use of the q-round X-positive EF-game comes from the fact that it characterises definability by X-positive first-order sentences in the following sense:

Proposition 6. *Let $\mathscr{A}$ and $\mathscr{B}$ be $\tau \cup \{X\}$-structures and let q be a positive integer. If $\mathscr{A} \Rrightarrow_q^{X\text{-pos}} \mathscr{B}$, then we have for every X-positive* FO$(\tau \cup \{X\})$*-sentence ζ of quantifier rank at most q, that $\mathscr{A} \models \zeta$ implies $\mathscr{B} \models \zeta$.*

The proof is straightforward.

Now, note that Lemma 5 is an immediate consequence of Proposition 6 and the following lemma.

Lemma 7. *For every $q \geq 0$ there exist $K,R,Q \geq 2$ such that for all $\tau \cup \{X\}$-structures $\mathscr{A},\mathscr{B}$: If for every $\varphi \in$ BL$^+(K,R,Q)$, $\mathscr{A} \models \varphi$ implies $\mathscr{B} \models \varphi$, and for every $\varphi \in$ BL$^-(K,R,Q)$, $\mathscr{B} \models \varphi$ implies $\mathscr{A} \models \varphi$, then $\mathscr{A} \Rrightarrow_q^{X\text{-pos}} \mathscr{B}$.*

Subsection 3.2 below is devoted to the proof of Lemma 7.

3.2. Proof of Lemma 7.

Before describing the duplicator's winning strategy we need some preparation.

Let $r,q \geq 0$, $\mathscr{A}$ a $\tau \cup \{X\}$-structure and $a \in A$. The *full (r,q)-type* of a in $\mathscr{A}$ is the set *full-(r,q)-type*$^{\mathscr{A}}(a)$:=

$$\{\varphi^r(x) \mid \varphi \in \text{FO}(\tau \cup \{X\}),\ \text{qr}(\varphi) \leq q,\ \mathscr{A} \models \varphi^r(a)\}.$$

Note that there is a formula

$$\theta_{(r,q,\mathscr{A},a)}(x) \quad := \quad \bigwedge_{\varphi \in \textit{full-}(r,q)\textit{-type}^{\mathscr{A}}(a)} \varphi(x),$$

defining an element's full (r,q)-type and for all $\tau \cup \{X\}$-structures $\mathscr{B}$ and all $b \in B$ we have $\mathscr{B} \models \theta_{(r,q,\mathscr{A},a)}(b) \iff$ *full-(r,q)-type*$^{\mathscr{B}}(b) =$ *full-(r,q)-type*$^{\mathscr{A}}(a)$. Also, all the formulae $\theta_{(r,q,\mathscr{A},a)}$ are r-local and of quantifier rank at most $\tilde{q}$ (where $\tilde{q} \geq q$ only depends on r, q, and $\tau \cup \{X\}$). In the following, we often identify the types with these formulae. We denote the set of all full (r,q)-types by $\Theta_{(r,q)}$.
A type $\theta(x)$ is *realised* in a structure $\mathscr{A}$ if there is an element $a \in A$ such that $\mathscr{A} \models \theta(a)$. The element a is called a *realisation* of θ in $\mathscr{A}$.

Let $\mathscr{A}$ be a structure, let $C \subseteq A$, let $\theta \in \Theta_{(r,q)}$ be a full (r,q)-type, and let $R,K \geq 0$. We say that

θ is *R-covered* by C

if for all realisations a of θ in $\mathscr{A}$ we have $a \in N_R(C)$. We say that

θ is *(R,K)-free* over C

if there are realisations $a_1,\ldots,a_K$ of θ in $\mathscr{A}$ such that $a_i \notin N_R(C)$ for all $i \in \{1,..,K\}$ and $\text{dist}(a_i,a_j) > R$ for all $i,j \in \{1,..,K\}$ with $i \neq j$.

The next lemma analyses the spatial distribution of the types occurring in a structure.

Lemma 8. *For all $k,r,q \geq 0$ there are $\hat{K} \geq k$ and $\hat{R} \geq r$, such that for all $\tau \cup \{X\}$-structures $\mathscr{A}$ and $\mathscr{B}$ there are K,R with $k \leq K \leq \hat{K}$ and $r \leq R \leq \hat{R}$ and sets $C^{\mathscr{A}} \subseteq A$ and $C^{\mathscr{B}} \subseteq B$ such that for $\kappa := 2^{K^2-1}$ and each $\mathscr{D} \in \{\mathscr{A},\mathscr{B}\}$, the following properties are satisfied:*

(1) $|C^{\mathscr{D}}| \leq K$;

(2) $\text{dist}(c,c') > \kappa \cdot 10R$, *for all $c,c' \in C^{\mathscr{D}}$ with $c \neq c'$;*

(3) each $\theta \in \Theta_{(r,q)}$ realised in $\mathscr{D}$ is either R-covered by $C^{\mathscr{D}}$ or $(\kappa \cdot 10R, 10K)$-free over $C^{\mathscr{D}}$.

Due to lack of space, we defer the proof of Lemma 8 to the full version of the paper. For the proof of Lemma 7 we also need the notions of *positive* types and *negative* types of an element a in a $\tau \cup \{X\}$-structure $\mathscr{A}$. The *positive (r,q)-type* of a is the set

$$\textit{pos-}(r,q)\textit{-type}^{\mathscr{A}}(a) := \{\varphi^r(x) :$$
$$\varphi \in \text{FO}(\tau \cup \{X\}) \text{ positive in } X,\ \text{qr}(\varphi) \leq q,\ \mathscr{A} \models \varphi^r(a)\}.$$

Similarly, the *negative* (r,q)*-type* of a is the set

$$\begin{aligned}neg\text{-}(r,q)\text{-}type^{\mathscr{A}}(a) &:= \{\varphi^r(x) :\\ &\varphi \in \mathrm{FO}(\tau \cup \{X\}) \text{ negative in } X, \mathrm{qr}(\varphi) \leq q,\ \mathscr{A} \models \varphi^r(a)\}.\end{aligned}$$

Note that $pos\text{-}(r,q)\text{-}type^{\mathscr{A}}(a) \subseteq full\text{-}(r,q)\text{-}type^{\mathscr{A}}(a)$ and $neg\text{-}(r,q)\text{-}type^{\mathscr{A}}(a) \subseteq full\text{-}(r,q)\text{-}type^{\mathscr{A}}(a)$. The formula

$$\theta^{+}_{(r,q,\mathscr{A},a)}(x) \quad := \bigwedge_{\varphi \in pos\text{-}(r,q)\text{-}type^{\mathscr{A}}(a)} \varphi(x),$$

defines the positive (q,r)-type, in the sense that for all $(\tau \cup \{X\})$-structures $\mathscr{B}$ and all $b \in B$ with $\mathscr{B} \models \dot{\theta}^{+}_{(r,q,\mathscr{A},a)}(b)$ we have $pos\text{-}(r,q)\text{-}type^{\mathscr{B}}(b) \supseteq pos\text{-}(r,q)\text{-}type^{\mathscr{A}}(a)$. Analogously, one obtains a formula $\theta^{-}_{(r,q,\mathscr{A},a)}(x)$ that defines the negative (q,r)-type of a in $\mathscr{A}$. Note that the formulae $\theta^{+}_{(r,q,\mathscr{A},a)}$ and $\theta^{-}_{(r,q,\mathscr{A},a)}$ are r-local and of quantifier rank at most $\tilde{q}$ (where $\tilde{q} \geq q$ only depends on q, r, and $\tau \cup \{X\}$). Furthermore, $\theta^{+}_{(r,q,\mathscr{A},a)}(x)$ is positive in X, whereas $\theta^{-}_{(r,q,\mathscr{A},a)}(x)$ is negative in X. In the following, we often identify the types with these formulae.

We denote the set of all positive and negative (r,q)-types by $\Theta^{+}_{(r,q)}$ and $\Theta^{-}_{(r,q)}$, respectively. A (positive or negative) type $\theta(x)$ is *realised* in a structure $\mathscr{A}$ if there is an $a \in A$ such that $\mathscr{A} \models \theta(a)$. We call a a *realisation* of θ in $\mathscr{A}$.

Proof of Lemma 7:
We fix $q \geq 0$ and let $k := q$, $r := 3^q$, and $Q := \widetilde{q+1}$. Let $\hat{K}, \hat{R}$ be chosen according to Lemma 8. Now let $\mathscr{A}$ and $\mathscr{B}$ be $\tau \cup \{X\}$-structures such that

(∗) for every $\varphi \in \mathrm{BL}^{+}(\hat{K}, 2^{\hat{K}^2-1}\cdot 10\hat{R}, Q)$, $\mathscr{A} \models \varphi$ implies $\mathscr{B} \models \varphi$, and for every $\varphi \in \mathrm{BL}^{-}(\hat{K}, 2^{\hat{K}^2-1}\cdot 10\hat{R}, Q)$, $\mathscr{B} \models \varphi$ implies $\mathscr{A} \models \varphi$.

Before we can describe the duplicator's winning strategy in the q-round X-positive EF-game on $\mathscr{A}$ and $\mathscr{B}$, we first need to explore the "playing fields" $\mathscr{A}$ and $\mathscr{B}$. To this end, we first apply Lemma 8 to $\mathscr{A}$ and $\mathscr{B}$ (with k, r, q) to obtain numbers $K \leq \hat{K}, R \leq \hat{R}$ and sets $C := C^{\mathscr{A}} \subseteq A$ and $D := C^{\mathscr{B}} \subseteq B$ such that for $\kappa := 2^{K^2-1}$ and for each $\mathscr{D} \in \{\mathscr{A}, \mathscr{B}\}$ the properties (1)–(3) of Lemma 8 are satisfied.

Note that, since $K \leq \hat{K}$ and $R \leq \hat{R}$, (∗) in particular holds when replacing $\hat{K}$ with K and $\hat{R}$ with R. Thus, by applying Lemma 4 (both the X-positive and the X-negative version, while interchanging the roles of $\mathscr{A}$ and $\mathscr{B}$ when applying the X-negative version), we obtain

(∗∗) for every $\varphi \in \mathrm{ABL}^{+}(K, \kappa, 5R, Q)$, $\mathscr{A} \models \varphi$ implies $\mathscr{B} \models \varphi_{[1/\kappa]}$ and for every $\varphi \in \mathrm{ABL}^{-}(K, \kappa, 5R, Q)$, $\mathscr{B} \models \varphi$ implies $\mathscr{A} \models \varphi_{[1/\kappa]}$.

Let us proceed with fixing some more notation. We call a *full* (r,q)-type $\theta \in \Theta_{(r,q)}$ *rare in* $\mathscr{A}$ *(in* $\mathscr{B}$*)* if it is R-covered by C (by D, respectively); otherwise, we call θ *frequent*.

A *positive* (r,q)-type $\pi \in \Theta^{+}_{(r,q)}$ is called *saturated* if there is a *full* type $\theta \in \Theta_{(r,q)}$ that is frequent in $\mathscr{B}$ such that $\pi \subseteq \theta$. Similarly, a *negative* (r,q)-type $\nu \in \Theta^{-}_{(r,q)}$ is called *saturated* if there is a full type $\theta \in \Theta_{(r,q)}$ that is *frequent in* $\mathscr{A}$ such that $\nu \subseteq \theta$.

We define a bipartite Graph $\mathscr{G}$ on $C \cup D$ by drawing an edge from $c \in C$ to $d \in D$ if there are a $c' \in N_{2R}(c)$ and a $d' \in N_{2R}(d)$ such that the positive $(4R, q+1)$-type of c' is contained in the positive $(4R, q+1)$-type of d' and hence the negative $(4R, q+1)$-type of d' is contained in the negative $(4R, q+1)$-type of c'.

We call an element $c \in C$ *special* if there is an $a \in N_R(c)$ such that the positive (r,q)-type of a is *not saturated* (i.e., every *full* (r,q)-type $\theta \supseteq pos\text{-}(r,q)\text{-}type^{\mathscr{A}}(a)$ is *rare* in $\mathscr{B}$, i.e., realised only by elements in $N_R(D)$). Similarly, an element $d \in D$ is called *special* if there is a $b \in N_R(d)$ such that the negative (r,q)-type of b is *not saturated.*

Let $C_S \subseteq C$ and $D_S \subseteq D$ be the sets of all special vertices.

Claim 9. *The bipartite graph* $\mathscr{G}$ *has a matching* M *such that each special element of* C *and* D *is an endpoint of an edge in* M.

Proof of Claim 9: Let $\ell = |C_S|$ and $C_S = \{c_1, \ldots, c_\ell\}$. For every $i \in \{1,..,\ell\}$ let $\pi_i(x)$ be the positive $(4R, q+1)$-type of c_i. Then $\mathscr{A}$ satisfies the X-positive asymmetric basic local sentence $\varphi := \exists x_1 \ldots \exists x_\ell \Big(\bigwedge_{1 \leq i < j \leq \ell} d(x_i, x_j) > \kappa \cdot 10R \wedge \bigwedge_{i=1}^{\ell} \pi_i(x_i) \Big)$. Thus $\mathscr{B}$ satisfies the sentence $\varphi_{[1/\kappa]}$ (to see this, recall the assumption (∗∗) on $\mathscr{A}$ and $\mathscr{B}$ on the sentences in $\mathrm{ABL}^{+}(K, \kappa, 5R, Q)$, note that $\ell \leq K$ since $C_S \subseteq C$ and $|C| \leq K$, and recall from Lemma 8 that elements in C have pairwise distance $> \kappa \cdot 10R$). Hence we can find $b_1, \ldots, b_\ell \in B$ of pairwise distance greater than $10R$ such that $\mathscr{B} \models \pi_i(b_i)$ for every $i \in \{1,..,\ell\}$.

Let us next note that each of the b_i belongs to $N_{2R}(D)$. This can be seen as follows. Since c_i is special, there exists an $a_i \in N_R(c_i)$ whose positive (r,q)-type π' is not saturated, i.e., each full (r,q)-type that contains π' is realised in $\mathscr{B}$ only by elements in $N_R(D)$. Since the positive $(4R, q+1)$-type of b_i contains the positive $(4R, q+1)$-type π_i of c_i and $\mathscr{N}_{4R}(c_i)$ satisfies the X-positive formula $\exists y \big(\mathrm{dist}(c_i, y) \leq R \wedge \pi'(y)\big)$, we know that also $\mathscr{N}_{4R}(b_i)$ satisfies this formula, and thus there exists an element b'_i with $\mathrm{dist}(b_i, b'_i) \leq R$ whose full (r,q)-type contains π'. Since π' is not saturated, we conclude that $b'_i \in N_R(D)$ and hence $b_i \in N_{2R}(D)$.

Since each b_i belongs to $N_{2R}(D)$, there are $d_1, \ldots, d_\ell \in D$ such that $\mathrm{dist}(d_i, b_i) \leq 2R$, for every $i \in \{1,..,\ell\}$. The vertices $d_1, .., d_\ell$ are pairwise distinct, since $\mathrm{dist}(b_i, b_j) > 10R$ and thus $\mathrm{dist}(d_i, d_j) > 6R$, for all $i, j \in \{1,..,\ell\}$ with $i \neq j$. Furthermore, by the definition of the graph $\mathscr{G}$, there is an edge between c_i and d_i, for every $i \in \{1,..,\ell\}$ (to see this, note that $c'_i := c_i \in N_{2R}(c_i)$ has the positive $(4R, q+1)$-type π_i, and $d'_i := b_i \in N_{2R}(d_i)$ has a positive $(4R, q+1)$-type that contains π_i). It follows that each set $C' \subseteq C_S$ of special vertices has at least $|C'|$ neighbours in D.

Analogously, we can show that each set $D' \subseteq D_S$ of special vertices has at least $|D'|$ neighbours in C.

Now Claim 9 immediately follows from the following purely combinatorial lemma, which may be viewed as an extension of Hall's well known marriage theorem. Let us a say that a vertex is *covered* by a matching if it is an endpoint of an edge in the matching.

Lemma 10. *Let $\mathscr{G}$ be a bipartite graph with bipartition C, D of the vertex set. Let $C_S \subseteq C$ and $D_S \subseteq D$, and suppose that each $C' \subseteq C_S$ has at least $|C'|$ neighbours in D and each $D' \subseteq D_S$ has at least $|D'|$ neighbours in C. Then there is a matching M of $\mathscr{G}$ that covers each vertex in $C_S \cup D_S$.*

The proof of Lemma 10 can be found in the full version of this paper. To proceed with the proof of Lemma 7 let us now fix a matching M that covers all special vertices (such a matching exists by Claim 9). Let $c_1, \dots, c_m \in C$ and $d_1, \dots, d_m \in D$ be the vertices covered by M via an edge between c_i and d_i, for each $i \in \{1, .., m\}$. By the definition of the graph $\mathscr{G}$, for $i \in \{1, .., m\}$, there are vertices $c'_i \in N_{2R}(c_i)$ and $d'_i \in N_{2R}(d_i)$ such that the positive $(4R, q+1)$-type of d'_i contains the positive $(4R, q+1)$-type of c'_i. In particular, the duplicator has a winning strategy for the q-round X-positive EF-game on $\mathscr{N}_{4R}(c'_i)$ and $\mathscr{N}_{4R}(d'_i)$.

Recall that, by the definition of *special* vertices, every $a \in A$ whose positive (r, q)-type is not saturated is in the R-neighbourhood of some special vertex of C and hence, in particular, in $N_R(c_i) \subseteq N_{2R}(c'_i)$, for some $i \in \{1, .., m\}$ (to see this, note that (1) a has to belong to $N_R(C)$ due to Lemma 8, and (2) the vertex from C in whose R-neighbourhood a lies has to be special). Similarly, every $b \in B$ whose negative (r, q)-type is not saturated is in $N_R(d_i)$ and hence in $N_{2R}(d'_i)$ for some $i \in \{1, .., m\}$.

Now it is easy to define a winning strategy for the duplicator in the q-round X-positive EF-game on $\mathscr{A}$ and $\mathscr{B}$: If the spoiler plays near a vertex c'_i or d'_i, the duplicator answers according to the local strategy there. If the spoiler plays near a vertex played before, the duplicator answers according to the local strategy there. Otherwise, the spoiler plays a saturated vertex far away from everything, and the duplicator can always find an answer. The meaning of "near" varies with the number j of moves remaining in the game. The duplicator seeks to preserve neighbourhoods of radius 3^j around previously played elements or $2R + 3^j$ around c'_i or d'_i.

This finally completes the proof of Lemma 7 and thus, altogether, the proof of Theorem 2. □

4. Graph Decompositions

In this section we fix some notation and briefly present the basic notions from graph minor theory used later on. See the last chapter of [8] or the survey [24].

The vertex set of a graph $\mathscr{G}$ is denoted by $V^{\mathscr{G}}$ and its edge set is denoted by $E^{\mathscr{G}}$. For $U \subseteq V^{\mathscr{G}}$ we write $\langle U \rangle$ for the subgraph of $\mathscr{G}$ induced by V. A tree is an acyclic, connected graph. We usually use rooted directed trees where edges are directed from the root towards the leaves.

A *minor* of a graph $\mathscr{G}$ is a graph $\mathscr{H}$ that can be obtained from a subgraph of $\mathscr{G}$ by contracting edges. We write $\mathscr{H} \preceq \mathscr{G}$ to denote that $\mathscr{H}$ is a minor of $\mathscr{G}$. A class $\mathscr{C}$ of graphs is *minor closed* if, and only if, for all $\mathscr{G} \in \mathscr{C}$ and $\mathscr{H} \preceq \mathscr{G}$ also $\mathscr{H} \in \mathscr{C}$. A class $\mathscr{C}$ of graphs is *$\mathscr{H}$-free* if $\mathscr{H} \not\preceq \mathscr{G}$ for all $\mathscr{G} \in \mathscr{C}$. We then call $\mathscr{H}$ an *excluded minor* of $\mathscr{C}$.

A *tree-decomposition* of a graph $\mathscr{G}$ is a pair $(T, (B_t)_{t \in V^t})$, where T is a directed tree and $B_t \subseteq V^{\mathscr{G}}$ for all $t \in V^T$ such that $\bigcup_{t \in V^T} \langle B_t \rangle = \mathscr{G}$ and for every $v \in V^{\mathscr{G}}$ the set $\{t : v \in B_t\}$ is connected. The sets B_t are called *blocks* of the decomposition. The *width* of $(T, (B_t)_{t \in V^T})$ is $\max\{|B_t| : t \in V^T\} - 1$ and the *tree-width* $\text{tw}(\mathscr{G})$ of a graph $\mathscr{G}$ is the minimal width of any of its tree-decompositions. A class $\mathscr{C}$ of graphs has *bounded tree-width*, if there is a constant k bounding the tree-width of all members of $\mathscr{G}$.

For a tree-decomposition $(T, (B_t)_{t \in V^T})$ and $t \in V^T$ with parent $s \in V^T$ we let $A_t := B_t \cap B_s$. For the root r of T we let $A_t := \emptyset$. The *adhesion* of $(T, (B_t)_{t \in V^T})$ is the number $\text{ad}(T, (B_t)_{t \in V^T}) := \max\{|A_t| : t \in V^T\}$. The *torso* $[B_t]$ of $(T, (B_t)_{t \in V^T})$ at $t \in V^T$ is the graph with vertex set B_t and with an edge between $u, v \in B_t$ if $(u, v) \in E^{\mathscr{G}}$ or u, v both belong to a block B_s with $s \neq t$.

A tree-decomposition of a graph $\mathscr{G}$ *over* a class $\mathscr{B}$ of graphs is a tree-decomposition $(T, (B_t)_{t \in V^T})$ whose torsi $[B_t]$ are contained in $\mathscr{B}$.

We also need the following notion. The *local tree-width* of a graph $\mathscr{G}$ is the function $\text{ltw}^{\mathscr{G}} : \mathbb{N} \to \mathbb{N}$ defined as $\text{ltw}^{\mathscr{G}}(r) := \max\{\text{tw}(\langle N_r^{\mathscr{G}}(v) \rangle) : v \in V^{\mathscr{G}}\}$. A class $\mathscr{C}$ of graphs has *bounded local tree-width* if there is an $f : \mathbb{N} \to \mathbb{N}$ such that $\text{ltw}^G(r) \leq f(r)$ for all $\mathscr{G} \in \mathscr{C}$ and $r \in \mathbb{N}$.

5. First-order definable optimisation problems

In this section we present a proof of Theorem 1. Here, we only prove the minimisation version of the theorem. The maximisation version is proved similarly using techniques from [14]. We defer the details to the full version of the paper. We begin with a formal definition. Let $X_{\min}$ be an optimal solution for $\text{MIN}_{\varphi(X)}$ on input $\mathscr{G}$. For $\varepsilon > 0$ we call a solution X, i.e. a set X with $(\mathscr{G}, X) \models \varphi$, *$\varepsilon$-close* if $|X| \leq (1 + \varepsilon)|X_{\min}|$. A *polynomial-time approximation scheme* (PTAS) for $\text{MIN}_{\varphi(X)}$ is a uniform family $(A_\varepsilon)_{\varepsilon > 0}$ of algorithms, where A_ε, given an instance $\mathscr{G}$, computes an ε-close solution for $\mathscr{G}$ in polynomial time. Uniform here means that there is an algorithm that, given ε, generates A_ε. A PTAS is called *efficient*, (or, it is an EPTAS), if the degree of the polynomial bounding the running time of A_ε does not depend on ε. Our proof of Theorem 1 establishes an EPTAS for first-order definable optimisation problems.

Example 11. It is well known that the class of planar graphs excludes a minor. Thus, by Theorem 1, every optimisation problem definable by an X-positive or X-negative first-order formula has a PTAS on the class of planar graphs.

However, the result neither extends to monadic second-order logic (MSO) nor to first-order formulae which are not monotone in X. For this, note that 3-colourability is NP-complete even on the class of planar graphs (see [13]). As 3-colourability can easily be defined by a formula $\psi \in$ MSO, the minimisation problem defined by $\varphi(X) := \psi \rightarrow \forall x Xx$ cannot have a PTAS (unless P = NP). Similarly, a simple reduction shows that the 3-colourability problem on planar graphs can be reduced to a minimisation problem on planar graphs defined by a non-monotone first-order formula. □

To prove Theorem 1 we first need some preparation. Let φ be a first-order formula positive in X. By Theorem 2 we can assume that $\varphi := \bigvee_i \bigwedge_j \psi_{i,j}$, where each $\psi_{i,j}$ is X-positive and either basic local or the negation of a basic local formula. To compute a minimal set X satisfying the formula, it suffices to consider the disjuncts $\bigwedge_j \psi_{ij}$ separately. Thus we can assume that $\varphi := \bigwedge_j \psi_j$, where each ψ_j is either an existential basic local formula of the form $\exists x_1 \ldots \exists x_{r_j} \bigwedge_{s\neq t} \mathrm{dist}(a_s,a_t) > 2r \wedge \bigwedge_{s=1}^{r_j} \vartheta_j(x_s)$ or a *universal basic local formula* of the form $\forall x_1 \ldots \forall x_{r_j} \big(\bigwedge_{s\neq t} \mathrm{dist}(a_s,a_t) > 2r \rightarrow \bigvee_{s=1}^{r_j} \vartheta_j(x_s)\big)$. Here, the formulae ϑ_j are X-positive and restricted to the r-neighbourhoods of x_l. We will transform φ even further. For this, observe that for any fixed graph $\mathcal{G} := (V,E)$, the formula $\exists x_1 \ldots \exists x_k \bigwedge_{s\neq t} \mathrm{dist}(a_s,a_t) > 2r \wedge \bigwedge_{s=1}^{k} \vartheta(x_s)$ is equivalent to $\bigvee_{(a_1,\ldots,a_k)\in(V^{\mathcal{G}})^k} \big(\bigwedge_{s\neq t} \mathrm{dist}(a_s,a_t) > 2r \wedge \bigwedge_{s=1}^{k} \vartheta(a_s)\big)$ which can be simplified even further to

$$\bigvee\Big\{\bigwedge_{s=1}^{k} \vartheta(a_s) : (a_1,\ldots,a_k) \in (V^{\mathcal{G}})^k \text{ and } \bigwedge_{s\neq t} \mathrm{dist}(a_s,a_t) > 2r\Big\}. \tag{*}$$

Here, the elements a_i are used as constants in the formulae. A similar, although more complicated, translation can be given for the universal basic local sentences. Let $\mathcal{G}$ be a graph and $\psi(X) := \forall x_1 \ldots \forall x_k \big(\bigwedge_{s\neq t} \mathrm{dist}(x_s,x_t) > 2r \rightarrow \bigvee_{s=1}^{k} \vartheta(x_s)\big)$ be a universal basic local sentence. For every $0 \leq j \leq k-1$ let π_j be the set of functions $f : \{1,\ldots,j\} \rightarrow \mathbb{N}$ such that $\sum_{i=1}^{j} f(i) < k$. Let $\psi^*(X)$ be the formula

$$\bigvee_{j<k}\Big(\bigvee_{(a_1,\ldots,a_j)\in(V^{\mathcal{G}})^j}\big(\bigvee_{f\in\pi_j}\bigvee_{n=0}^{k-j}\chi_{j,\overline{a},f,n}\big)\Big) \tag{**}$$

where $\chi_{j,\overline{a},f,n} :=$

$$\bigwedge_{1\leq l<l'\leq j} \mathrm{dist}(a_l,a_{l'}) > 5^n\cdot 8r \wedge$$
$$\forall x\big(\bigwedge_{i=1}^{j} \mathrm{dist}(x,a_i) \geq 5^n\cdot 4r \rightarrow \vartheta(x)\big) \wedge$$
$$\bigwedge_{s=1}^{j} \forall x_1 \ldots \forall x_{f(s)+1}\Big(\bigwedge_{l=1}^{f(s)+1} \mathrm{dist}(x_l,a_s) < 5^n 4r \wedge \bigwedge_{1\leq l<l'\leq f(s)+1} \mathrm{dist}(x_l,x_l') > 2r\Big) \rightarrow \bigvee_{l=1}^{f(s)+1} \vartheta(x_l).$$

We claim that ψ and ψ^* are equivalent on $\mathcal{G}$ in the following sense. Due to lack of space, we defer the proof to the full version of the paper.

Lemma 12. *For every set $X \subseteq V^{\mathcal{G}}$, $(\mathcal{G},X) \models \psi$ if, and only if, $(\mathcal{G},X) \models \psi^*$.*

Lemma 12 implies that for a given graph $\mathcal{G}$ we can translate the formula $\varphi(X)$ into a conjunction of formulae of the form $(*)$ and $(**)$. By distributivity, we can translate this into a disjunction of conjunctions of formulae $\chi_{j,\overline{a},f,n}$ and formulae $\xi := \bigwedge_{s=1}^{k} \vartheta(b_l)$ for tuples of constants $\overline{a}_i, \overline{b}_i$, functions f and numbers j and n. As the arity of the tuples $\overline{a}, \overline{b}$ is bounded by a function of φ and the ranges of the variables j, n, and f also only depend on φ, the translation can be done in polynomial time in the size of $\mathcal{G}$.

Further, the first line of the formula $\chi_{j,\overline{a},f,n}$ only imposes conditions on the choice of the tuple $\overline{a}$. It follows that for computing an approximation of a set X satisfying φ in $\mathcal{G}$ it suffices to compute an approximation of a set X satisfying the conjunction of formulae

a) $\bigwedge_{s=1}^{k} \vartheta(a_l)$ for an r-local formula ϑ and a tuple of constants $(a_1,\ldots,a_k)$ with $\mathrm{dist}(a_s,a_t) > 2r$ for all $i \neq j$,

b) $\forall x\big(\bigwedge_{i=1}^{j} \mathrm{dist}(x,a_i) \geq q \rightarrow \vartheta(x)\big)$ for an r-local formula ϑ, some $q > 2r$ and a tuple of elements $(a_1,\ldots,a_j)$ of distance $\mathrm{dist}(a_s,a_t) > 2q$ for all $i \neq j$, and

c) $\forall x_1 \ldots \forall x_{f(s)+1}\Big(\bigwedge_{l=1}^{f(s)+1} \mathrm{dist}(x_l,a_s) < 5^n 4r \wedge \bigwedge_{1\leq l<l'\leq f(s)+1} \mathrm{dist}(x_l,x_l') > 2r\Big) \rightarrow \bigvee_{l=1}^{f(s)+1} \vartheta(x_l)$ which are q-local around a_s for some $q > 2r$ only depending on φ.

Note that the formulas in $c)$ are $5^n\cdot 4r$-local around a_s. Hence, Theorem 1 follows from the following lemma.

Lemma 13. *Let $\mathcal{C}'$ be a class of graphs with an excluded minor and let $\sigma := \{a_1,\ldots,a_k\}$ be a set of constant symbols. Let $q > 0$ and let $\varphi(X) \in$ FO be an X-positive conjunction of q-local formulae $\varphi_i(a)$ using only one constant symbol $a \in \sigma$ and formulae $\psi_t := \forall x(\bigwedge_{s=1}^{k_t} \mathrm{dist}(x,a_{s,t}) > q_t \rightarrow \vartheta(x))$, for an r-local formula ϑ with $q_t > 2r$, using constant symbols $\overline{a}_t \subseteq \sigma$.*

Let $\mathcal{C} := \{(\mathcal{G},\overline{a}) : \mathcal{G} \in \mathcal{C}'$ and $\overline{a} \subseteq V^{\mathcal{G}}\}$. Then $\mathrm{MIN}_{\varphi(X)}(\mathcal{C})$ *has a polynomial time approximation scheme.*

To prove the lemma we use a decomposition theorem for classes of graphs with an excluded minor that is due to [14]. We first introduce some notation.

For $\lambda, \mu \geq 0$ we let

$$\mathscr{L}(\lambda) := \left\{ \mathscr{G} : \begin{array}{l} \text{for all } \mathscr{H} \preceq \mathscr{G}, \text{for all } r \geq 0 \\ \text{ltw}^{\mathscr{H}}(r) \leq \lambda \cdot r \end{array} \right\}$$

$$\mathscr{L}(\lambda,\mu) := \left\{ \mathscr{G} : \begin{array}{l} \text{there is } X \subseteq V^{\mathscr{G}} \\ \text{s.th. } \big(|X| \leq \mu \wedge \mathscr{G} \backslash X \in \mathscr{L}(\lambda)\big) \end{array} \right\}$$

Note that $\mathscr{L}(\lambda, \mu)$ is minor closed. The proof of Lemma 13 is based on the following decomposition theorem for classes of graphs with an excluded minor.

Theorem 14 ([14]). *Let $\mathscr{C}$ be a class of graphs with an excluded minor. Then there exist $\lambda, \mu \in \mathbb{N}$ such that all $\mathscr{G} \in \mathscr{C}$ have a tree-decomposition over $\mathscr{L}(\lambda, \mu)$.*

For the approximation algorithms we want to show, we need an algorithmic version of this theorem.

Theorem 15 ([14]). *Let $\mathscr{C}$ be a minor closed class of graphs. Then there is a polynomial-time algorithm that computes for a given graph $\mathscr{G}$ a tree-decomposition of $\mathscr{G}$ over $\mathscr{C}$ or rejects $\mathscr{G}$ if no such decomposition exists.*

We apply this result to the minor closed classes $\mathscr{L}(\lambda, \mu)$. Let $\mathscr{G}$ be a graph. For every vertex $v \in V^{\mathscr{G}}$ and integers $j \geq i \geq 0$ we define

$$L_v^{\mathscr{G}}[i, j] := \{w \in V^{\mathscr{G}} : i \leq \text{dist}^{\mathscr{G}}(v, w) \leq j\},$$

where $\text{dist}^{\mathscr{G}}(v, w)$ denotes the distance between v and w in $\mathscr{G}$. To simplify notation, we will use $L_v^{\mathscr{G}}[i, j]$ for arbitrary integers i, j and set $L_v^{\mathscr{G}}[i, j] := \emptyset$ if $i > j$ and $L_v^{\mathscr{G}}[i, j] := L_v^{\mathscr{G}}[0, j]$ for $i \leq 0$. The following lemma follows easily.

Lemma 16. *Let $\lambda \in \mathbb{N}$. Then $\text{tw}(\langle L_v^{\mathscr{G}}[i, j]\rangle) \leq \lambda \cdot (j - i + 1)$ for all $\mathscr{G} \in \mathscr{L}(\lambda)$, $v \in V^{\mathscr{G}}$ and $i, j \in \mathbb{Z}$ with $i \leq j$.*

Now, let φ be as in the hypothesis of Lemma 13 and let $\mathscr{C}$ be a class of graphs with an excluded minor. By Theorem 14, we can choose $\lambda, \mu \in \mathbb{N}$ such that every graph $\mathscr{G} \in \mathscr{C}$ has a tree-decomposition over $\mathscr{L}(\lambda, \mu)$. Let $\varepsilon > 0$. We describe a polynomial time algorithm that, on input $\mathscr{G} \in \mathscr{C}$ and $\bar{a} \in V^{\mathscr{G}}$, computes an ε-close solution for $\text{MIN}_{\varphi(X)}(\mathscr{C})$ on $(\mathscr{G}, \bar{a})$. To ease notation we will consider the tuple $\bar{a}$ as part of the graph and use notation such as $\mathscr{G} \models \varphi$ for $(\mathscr{G}, \bar{a}) \models \varphi$.

The proof of Lemma 13 is split into two steps. In the first step, which we present in the next subsection, we prove the lemma for the classes $\mathscr{L}(\lambda)$ and $\mathscr{L}(\lambda, \mu)$ of graphs. Here, we use the corresponding result for graphs of bounded tree-width which essentially follows from [2].

Theorem 17 ([2]). *Let $\varphi(X)$ be an X-positive formula of* MSO. *Then $\text{MIN}_{\varphi(X)}(\mathscr{C})$ can be solved in linear time on any class $\mathscr{C}$ of graphs of bounded tree-width.*

In Section 5.3, we extend the proof to graphs which have a tree-decomposition over $\mathscr{L}(\lambda, \mu)$, i.e. to all graphs in $\mathscr{C}$.

5.1. The levels of graphs of bounded local tree-width.

In the first step of the proof of Lemma 13 we show that the restriction of $\text{MIN}_{\varphi(X)}(\mathscr{C})$ to instances in $\mathscr{L}(\lambda)$ has a PTAS. Let $\varphi := \bigwedge_{i \in I_e} \varphi_i(a_i) \wedge \bigwedge_{t \in I_u} \psi_t$, where the $\varphi_i(a_i)$ are r-local formulae and the $\psi_t := \forall x(\bigwedge_{s=1}^{k_t} \text{dist}(x, a_{s,t}) > r_t \rightarrow \vartheta_t(x))$, for a q-local formula ϑ_t with $r_t > 2q$, using constant symbols $\bar{a}_t \subseteq \sigma$. For simplicity we assume w.l.o.g. that $r_t = r_{t'}$ for all t, t'. Let $r := r_t$.

Let $k := \lceil \frac{2r}{\varepsilon} \rceil$. Note that $\frac{k+2r}{k} \leq (1 + \varepsilon)$. Let $\mathscr{G} \in \mathscr{L}(\lambda)$. Choose a node $v \in V^{\mathscr{G}}$ arbitrarily. For $1 \leq i \leq k$ and $j \geq 0$ let $L_{ij} := L_v^{\mathscr{G}}[(j-1) \cdot k - r + i, j \cdot k + r + i]$. By Lemma 16, $\text{tw}(\langle L_{ij}\rangle) \leq \lambda(k + 2r + 1)$.

For all $1 \leq i \leq k$, $j \geq 0$ let X_{ij} be a set of minimal cardinality such that

(1) $(\langle L_{ij}\rangle, X_{ij}) \models \varphi_l(a_l)$ for all $l \in I_e$ such that a_l and its r-neighbourhood is contained in L_{ij} and

(2) $(\langle L_{ij}\rangle, X_{ij}) \models \psi_t$ for all $i \in I_u$.

Note that as $\psi_t := \forall x(\bigwedge_{s=1}^{k_t} \text{dist}(x, a_{s,t}) > r_t \rightarrow \vartheta_t(x))$ also mentions constants interpreted by vertices outside of L_{ij}, this is, strictly speaking, not well defined. However, as the a_t are constants, we can easily check whether x is close to any constant interpreted by an element outside of L_{ij}. For instance, we could colour the r-neighbourhoods of $a_1, \ldots, a_{k_t}$ and then check in ψ_t that x is outside a coloured area. For ease of presentation we will therefore simply write $(\langle L_{ij}\rangle, X_{ij}) \models \psi_t$ even in cases where some or all of the constants are interpreted by elements outside of L_{ij}.

By Theorem 17 the sets X_{ij} can be computed in linear time. For $1 \leq i \leq s$ let $X_i := \bigcup_{j \geq 0} X_{ij}$. As φ is monotone in X, every X_i is a solution of $\text{MIN}_{\varphi(X)}(\mathscr{C})$ on $\mathscr{G}$.

Let $X_{\min}$ be an optimal solution of $\text{MIN}_{\varphi(X)}(\mathscr{C})$ for $\mathscr{G}$, i.e. a set of minimal cardinality such that $(\mathscr{G}, X_{\min}) \models \varphi$. Clearly, $X_{\min} \cap L_{ij}$ satisfies the conditions (1) and (2) above for all levels $L_{i,j}$. Hence,

$$\sum_{i=1}^{k} |X_i| \leq \sum_{i=1}^{k} \sum_{j \geq 0} |X_{ij}| \leq \sum_{i=1}^{k} \sum_{j \geq 0} |L_{ij} \cap X_{\min}| \leq (k + 2r)|X_{\min}|.$$

The last inequality follows as every node $v \in V^{\mathscr{G}}$ can be contained in at most $k + 2r$ levels L_{ij}. Choose m, $1 \leq m \leq k$ such that $|X_m| := \min\{|X_1|, \ldots, |X_k|\}$. Then

$$|X_m| \leq \frac{(k+2r)}{k} |X_{\min}| \leq (1 + \varepsilon)|X_{\min}|.$$

Hence, X_m is an ε-close solution of $\text{MIN}_{\varphi(X)}(\mathscr{C})$ on $\mathscr{G}$. As every set X_i can be computed in polynomial time, the set X_m can also be computed in polynomial time.

5.2. Extension to the classes $L(\lambda,\mu)$.

In a second step we show how this approximation algorithm can be extended to the classes $\mathscr{L}(\lambda,\mu)$ for constants $\lambda,\mu \geq 0$. Let $\mathscr{G} \in \mathscr{L}(\lambda,\mu)$ and let $U \subseteq V^{\mathscr{G}}$ be such that $|U| \leq \mu$ and $\mathscr{G} \setminus U \in L(\lambda)$. The following extension of Theorem 17 can easily be proved by dynamic programming.

Theorem 18. *For every $k \geq 0$ and every first-order formula $\varphi(X)$ which is positive in the set-variable X, the following problem can be solved in linear time. Given a graph $\mathscr{G}$, a set $U \subseteq V^{\mathscr{G}}$ so that* $\text{tw}(\mathscr{G} \setminus U) \leq k$ *and a subset $Y \subseteq U$, find a set $X \subseteq V^{\mathscr{G}} \setminus U$ of minimal cardinality such that $(\mathscr{G}, X \cup Y) \models \varphi$ or determine that no such set exists.*

Let again $\varphi(X)$ be an X-positive first-order formula. For every $Y \subseteq U$ let $X(Y)$ be a subset of $V^{\mathscr{G}} \setminus U$ such that $(\mathscr{G}, X(Y) \cup Y) \models \varphi$ and

$$|X(Y)| \leq (1+\varepsilon)\min\{|X| : X \subseteq V^{\mathscr{G}} \setminus U \text{ and } (\mathscr{G}, X \cup Y) \models \varphi\}$$

or $X(Y) := \perp$ if no such set exists. If $X(Y) = \perp$ for all $Y \subseteq U$ then $\text{MIN}_{\varphi(X)}(\mathscr{C})$ has no solution on $\mathscr{G}$ and we are done. Otherwise let $Y_0 \subseteq U$ be such that $|X(Y_0) \cup Y_0|$ is minimal among $\{|X(Y) \cup Y| : Y \subseteq U \text{ and } X(Y) \neq \perp\}$. Then clearly, $X(Y_0) \cup Y_0$ is an ε-close solution for $\text{MIN}_{\varphi(X)}(\mathscr{C})$.

Using Theorem 18 instead of Theorem 17, the sets $X(Y)$ can be computed in polynomial time analogously to the first step. As there are only 2^{μ} possible subsets of U – recall that μ is a constant only depending on the class $\mathscr{C}$ – and for each $Y \subseteq U$, $X(Y)$ can be computed in polynomial time, the solution $X(Y_0) \cup Y_0$ can be computed in polynomial time.

5.3. Excluded Minors.

In the last step, we show how the approximation algorithm can be extended to graphs that have a tree-decomposition over $\mathscr{L}(\lambda,\mu)$, i.e. to all graphs in $\mathscr{C}$.

Let $\mathscr{G} \in \mathscr{C}$. We first compute a tree-decomposition $(T,(B_t)_{t\in V^T})$ over $\mathscr{L}(\lambda,\mu)$. By Theorem 15, this can be done in polynomial time. Let r be the root of T and for every $t \in V^T$ with parent s let $A_t := B_t \cap B_s$. We set $A_r := \emptyset$. Further, for every node $t \in V^T$ let T_t be the subtree of T rooted at t and let $\mathscr{B}_t := \bigcup_{s\in T_t} B_s$.

In what follows we will construct for subgraphs $\mathscr{B}$ of $\mathscr{G}$ sets X such that $(\langle\mathscr{B}\rangle, X)$ satisfies

(1) $(\langle\mathscr{B}\rangle, X) \models \varphi_l(a_l)$ for all $l \in I_e$ such that a_l and its r-neighbourhood is contained in $\mathscr{B}$ and

(2) $(\langle\mathscr{B}\rangle, X) \models \psi_t$ for all $t \in I_u$.

(Here, we use the same convention as in Section 5.1 above.) To simplify the presentation we write $(\langle\mathscr{B}\rangle, X) \models \varphi$ to indicate that X satisfies the conditions (1) and (2) in $\mathscr{B}$. The notation is motivated by the fact that for $\mathscr{B} = \mathscr{G}$, $(\mathscr{G}, X) \models \varphi$ for any set satisfying condition (1) and (2) and vice versa.

Inductively, from the leaves to the root, we compute for every node $t \in V^T$ and for every subset $Y \subseteq A_t$ an $X(t,Y)$ such that $X(t,Y) \subseteq \mathscr{B}_t \setminus A_t$, $(\langle\mathscr{B}_t\rangle, X(t,Y) \cup Y) \models \varphi$ and

$$|X(t,Y)| \leq (1+\varepsilon)\min\{|X| : (\langle\mathscr{B}_t\rangle, X \cup Y) \models \varphi, X \subseteq \mathscr{B}_t \setminus A_t\}$$

or $X(Y) := \perp$ if no such set exists. As tree-decompositions over $\mathscr{L}(\lambda,\mu)$ have adhesion at most $\lambda+\mu+1$, we have $|A_t| \leq \lambda+\mu+1$. Hence, we only have to compute a constant number of sets $X(t,Y)$ for each t. Further, for the root r we have $A_t = \emptyset$ and $\langle\mathscr{B}_t\rangle = \mathscr{G}$. Hence, $X(r,\emptyset)$ is an ε-close solution for $\text{MIN}_{\varphi(X)}(\mathscr{C})$ or $\perp$ if no solution exists.

We show next how to compute the sets $X(t,Y)$. Suppose $t \in V^T$ and for every child t' of t we have already computed the family $X(t',\cdot)$. Let $U \subseteq B_t$ such that $|U| \leq \mu$ and $[B_t] \setminus U \in \mathscr{L}(\lambda)$. (Recall that $[B_t]$ denotes the torso of $(T,(B_t)_{t\in V^T})$ at t.) Let $W := U \cup A_t$.

For every $Z \subseteq W$, let $X_{\min}(Z)$ be a set of minimal cardinality such that $X_{\min}(Z) \subseteq \mathscr{B}_t \setminus W$ and $(\langle\mathscr{B}_t\rangle, X_{\min}(Z) \cup Z) \models \varphi$ or $X_{\min}(Z) := \perp$ if no such set exists.

Claim 19. *For every set $Z \subseteq W$ we can compute in polynomial time an $X(Z)$ such that $X(Z) \subseteq \mathscr{B}_t \setminus W$, $(\langle\mathscr{B}_t\rangle, X(Z) \cup Z) \models \varphi$, and $|X(Z)| \leq (1+\varepsilon)|X_{\min}(Z)|$ or $X(Z) := \perp$ if no such set exists.*

Before we prove Claim 19 let us show how the proof of Lemma 13 can be completed using the claim. For every $Y \subseteq A_t$ choose a $Z \subseteq W$ such that $Z \cap A_t = Y$ and $|X(Z) \cup (Z \setminus Y)| = \min\{|X(Z') \cup (Z' \setminus Y)| : Y \subseteq Z' \subseteq W \text{ and } Z' \cap A_t = Y\}$. Set $X(t,Y) := X(Z) \cup (Z \setminus Y)$. By our choice of Z it follows that $|X(t,Y)| \leq (1+\varepsilon)\min\{|X| : (\langle\mathscr{B}_t\rangle, X \cup Y) \models \varphi\}$ which concludes the proof.

So all that remains is to prove Claim 19. Fix a $Z \subseteq W$. We show how to compute $X(Z)$ in polynomial time. If $W = B_t$, i.e. $B_t := U \cup A_t$, then let $X(Z) := \bigcup_{(t,t')\in E^T} X(t', A_{t'} \cap Z)$.

Otherwise choose an arbitrary $v \in B_t \setminus W$. For $1 \leq i \leq k$ and $j \geq 0$ let $L_{ij} := L_v^{[B_t]\setminus W}[(j-1)\cdot k+i-r, j\cdot k+i+r]$. Then $\text{tw}(\langle L_{ij}\rangle) \leq \lambda(k+1+2r)$. For every child t' of t and every $1 \leq i \leq k$ there is at least one $j \geq 0$ such that $A_{t'} \setminus W \subseteq L_{ij}$. This follows from that fact that $A_{t'}$ induces a clique in $[B_t]$. Let $j_{\min}(i,t')$ be the least such j and let

$$L^*_{ij} := L_{ij} \cup \bigcup\{\mathscr{B}_{t'} \setminus A_{t'} : (t,t') \in E^T \text{ and } j_{\min}(i,t') = j\}.$$

Similarly, for every $X \subseteq L_{ij}$ let

$$X^* := X \cup \bigcup\{X(t', (X \cup Z) \cap A_{t'}) : (t,t') \in E^T, j_{\min}(i,t') = j\}.$$

We compute an $X_{ij} \subseteq L_{ij}$ with minimal $|X^*_{ij}|$ such that $(\langle L_{ij}\rangle, X_{ij} \cup Z) \models \varphi$ or set $X_{ij} := \perp$ if no such X exists. This can be done in polynomial time using the standard dynamic programming techniques on graphs of bounded tree-width, provided that the numbers $|X(t',Y)|$ for the children t' of t are given. It is important here that every $A_{t'} \setminus W$ is a clique in $\langle L_{ij} \rangle$, as this implies that it is contained in a single block of every tree-decomposition of $\langle L_{ij} \rangle$.

Let $X_i := \bigcup_{j \geq 0} X_{ij}$ and $X_i^* := \bigcup_{j \geq 0} X_{ij}^*$. Then, by monotonicity of φ in X, $(\langle \mathscr{B}_t \rangle, X_i^* \cup Z) \models \varphi$ or $X_i = \perp$ if no set satisfying φ in $\langle \mathscr{B}_t \rangle$ exists. Finally, choose an $i \in \{1, \dots, k\}$ such that $|X_i^*| := \min\{|X_1^*|, \dots, |X_k^*|\}$ and let $X(Z) := X_i^*$. It follows that $X(Z)$ can be computed in polynomial time.

Recall that we defined $X_{\min} := X_{\min}(Z) \subseteq \mathscr{B}_t \setminus W$ to be a set of minimal order such that $(\langle \mathscr{B}_t \rangle, X_{\min} \cup Z) \models \varphi$ or $X_{\min} := \perp$ if no such set exists. It remains to prove that $|X(Z)| \leq (1+\varepsilon)|X_{\min}|$.

By hypothesis of the algorithm we have for every child t' of t, $|X(t', (X_{\min} \cup Z) \cap A_{t'})| \leq (1+\varepsilon)|X_{\min} \cap \mathscr{B}_{t'} \setminus A_{t'})|$. Further, the construction of X_{ij} and X_{ij}^* guarantees that for $1 \leq i \leq k$ and $j \geq 0$

$$|X_{ij}^*| \leq |X_{\min} \cap L_{ij}| + \sum_{\substack{(t,t') \in E^T \\ j_{\min}(i,t') = j}} |X(t', (X_{\min} \cup Z) \cap A_{t'})|.$$

But then

$$\begin{aligned} k|X(Z)| &\leq \sum_{i=1}^{k} |X_i^*| \leq \sum_{i=1}^{k} \sum_{j \geq 0} |X_{ij}^*| \\ &\leq \sum_{i=1}^{k} \sum_{j \geq 0} \Big(|X_{\min} \cap L_{ij}| + \\ &\qquad \sum_{\substack{(t,t') \in E^T \\ j_{\min}(i,t') = j}} |X(t', (X_{\min} \cup Z) \cap A_{t'})| \Big) \\ &\leq \sum_{i=1}^{k} \sum_{j \geq 0} \Big(|X_{\min} \cap L_{ij}| + \\ &\qquad \sum_{\substack{(t,t') \in E^T \\ j_{\min}(i,t') = j}} (1+\varepsilon)|X_{\min} \cap \mathscr{B}_{t'} \setminus A_{t'})| \Big) \\ &\leq (k+2r)|X_{\min} \cap B_t| + k(1+\varepsilon)|X_{\min} \cap \mathscr{B}_t \setminus B_t| \end{aligned}$$

This implies $|X(Z)| \leq (1+\varepsilon)X_{\min}$ and concludes the proof of Lemma 13 and with it also the proof of Theorem 1.

References

[1] N. Alon, P. Seymour, and R. Thomas. A separator theorem for graphs with an excluded minor and its applications. In *Proc. of STOC'90*, pages 293–299, 1990.

[2] S. Arnborg, J. Lagergren, and D. Seese. Easy problems for tree-decomposable graphs. *Journal of Algorithms*, 12(2):308–340, 1991.

[3] A. Atserias, A. Dawar, and M. Grohe. Preservation under extensions on well-behaved finite structures. In *Proc. of ICALP'05*, volume 3580 of *LNCS*, pages 1437–1450. Springer-Verlag, 2005.

[4] B. Baker. Approximation algorithms for NP-complete problems on planar graphs. *J. ACM*, 41:153–180, 1994.

[5] L. Cai, M. Fellows, D. Juedes, and F. Rosamond. The complexity of polynomial-time approximation. *Theory of Computing Systems*. To appear.

[6] B. Courcelle. Graph rewriting: An algebraic and logic approach. In J. van Leeuwan, editor, *Handbook of Theoretical Computer Science, Volume B: Formal Models and Sematics*, pages 193–242. Elsevier, 1990.

[7] E. Demaine, M. Hajiaghayi, and K. Kawarabayashi. Algorithmic graph minor theory: Decomposition, approximation, and coloring. In *Proc. of FOCS'05*, pages 637–646, 2005.

[8] R. Diestel. *Graph Theory*. Springer-Verlag, 2nd edition, 2000.

[9] H.-D. Ebbinghaus and J. Flum. *Finite Model Theory*. Springer-Verlag, 2nd edition, 1999.

[10] D. Eppstein. Subgraph isomorphism in planar graphs and related problems. *Journal of Graph Algorithms and Applications*, 3:1–27, 1999.

[11] J. Flum and M. Grohe. *Parameterized Complexity Theory*. Springer Verlag, 2006.

[12] H. Gaifman. On local and non-local properties. In J. Stern, editor, *Proceedings of the Herbrand Symposium, Logic Colloquium '81*, pages 105–135. North Holland, 1982.

[13] M. R. Garey, D. S. Johnson, and L. Stockmeyer. Some simplified NP-complete graph problems. *Theoretical Computer Science*, 1:237 – 267, 1976.

[14] M. Grohe. Local tree-width, excluded minors, and approximation algorithms. *Combinatorica*, 23(4):613–632, 2003.

[15] M. Grohe and S. Wöhrle. An existential locality theorem. *Annals of Pure and Applied Logic*, 129:131–148, 2004.

[16] H. J. Keisler and W. B. Lotfallah. Shrinking games and local formulas. *Annals of Pure and Applied Logic*, 128:215–225, 2004.

[17] S. Khanna and R. Motwani. Towards a syntactic characterization of PTAS. In *Proc. of STOC'96*, pages 329–337, 1996.

[18] P. Kolaitis and M. Thakur. Logical definability of NP optimization problems. *Information and Computation*, 115(2):321–353, 1994.

[19] P. Kolaitis and M. Thakur. Approximation properties of NP minimization classes. *Journal of Computer and System Sciences*, 50:391–411, 1995.

[20] R. Lipton and R. Tarjan. A separator theorem for planar graphs. *SIAM J. on Applied Mathematics*, 36:177–189, 1979.

[21] D. Marx. Parameterized complexity and approximation algorithms, 2006.

[22] C. Papadimitriou and M. Yannakakis. Optimization, approximation, and complexity classes. *Journal of Computer and System Sciences*, 43:425–440, 1991.

[23] N. Robertson and P. Seymour. Graph minors I–XX. App. in *Journal of Combinatorial Theory, Series B* since 1982.

[24] R. Thomas. Recent excluded minor theorems. In *Surveys in Combinatorics*, LMS Lecture Note Series. Cambridge University Press, 1999.

Approximate Satisfiability and Equivalence*

Eldar Fischer[†] Frédéric Magniez[‡] Michel de Rougemont[§]

Abstract

Inspired by Property Testing, we relax the classical satisfiability $U \models F$ between a finite structure U of a class $\mathbf{K}$ and a formula F, to a notion of ε-satisfiability $U \models_\varepsilon F$, and the classical equivalence $F_1 \equiv F_2$ between two formulas F_1 and F_2, to ε-equivalence $F_1 \equiv_\varepsilon F_2$ for $\varepsilon > 0$. We consider the class of strings and trees with the edit distance with moves, and show that these approximate notions can be efficiently decided.

We use a statistical embedding of words (resp. trees) into ℓ_1, which generalizes the original Parikh mapping, obtained by sampling $O(f(\varepsilon))$ finite samples of the words (resp. trees). We give a tester for equality and membership in any regular language, in time independent of the size of the structure. Using our geometrical embedding, we can also test the equivalence between two regular properties on words, defined by Monadic Second Order formulas. Our equivalence tester has polynomial time complexity in the size of the automaton (or regular expression), for a fixed ε, whereas the exact version of the equivalence problem is PSPACE-complete.

Last, we extend the geometric embedding, and hence the tester algorithms, to infinite regular languages and to context-free languages. For context-free languages, the equivalence tester has an exponential time complexity, whereas the exact version is undecidable.

1 Introduction

Let $\mathbf{K}$ be a class of finite structures with a distance dist between structures. In the classical setting, satisfiability is the decision problem whether $U \models F$ for a structure $U \in \mathbf{K}$ and a formula F, and equivalence is the decision problem $F_1 \equiv F_2$, *i.e.* whether $U \models F_1$ iff $U \models F_2$ for all $U \in \mathbf{K}$, for two formulas F_1 and F_2. Equivalence is typically very hard as a function of the size of the formulas, and in some cases undecidable. For any $\varepsilon > 0$, two structures are *ε-close* if their normalized distance is at most ε, and otherwise they are *ε-far*. We introduce the notions $U \models_\varepsilon F$ and $F_1 \equiv_\varepsilon F_2$ based on Property Testing. $U \models_\varepsilon F$ if there exists a U' ε-close to U such that $U' \models F$, otherwise $U \not\models_\varepsilon F$. $F_1 \equiv_\varepsilon F_2$ if all but finitely many structures that satisfy $U \models F_1$ satisfy also $U \models_\varepsilon F_2$, and conversely.

An *ε-tester* for a property P defined by a formula F on $\mathbf{K}$, is a randomized algorithm which takes a finite structure $U \in \mathbf{K}$ of size n as input, and distinguishes with high probability between $U \models F$ and $U \not\models_\varepsilon F$. A property P is *testable* if there exists a randomized algorithm A such that, for every $\varepsilon > 0$ as input, $A(\varepsilon)$ is an ε-tester of P whose time complexity only depends on ε, *i.e.* is independent of the size n. An equivalence tester for a logic $\mathcal{L}$ is an algorithm that can distinguish between $F_1 \equiv F_2$ and $F_1 \not\equiv_\varepsilon F_2$, for any two formulas $F_1, F_2 \in \mathcal{L}$.

We consider the class of strings and trees with a specific distance, and show that these approximate notions can be efficiently decided for important properties. These decision methods are robust, in the sense that they are adaptable to noisy inputs. They are well adapted to environments such as XML data on the Web represented by unranked labelled trees or Genomics data represented by strings.

Property testing of regular languages was first considered in [2] for the Hamming distance, and then extended to languages recognizable by bounded width read-once branching programs [16], where the *Hamming distance* between two words is the minimal number of character substitutions required to transform one word into the other. The *edit distance* between two words (resp. trees) is the minimal number of insertions, deletions and substitutions of a letter (resp. node) required to transform one word (resp. tree) into the other. The *edit distance with moves* considers one additional operation: Moving one arbitrary substring (resp. subtree) to another position in one step. Our results depend on this last specific distance and in particular do not apply to the edit distance without moves.

We develop a statistical embedding of words (into ℓ_1) which has similarities with the Parikh mapping [17]. Based on this embedding, we develop an ε-tester (**Theorem 3.1**)

*Work supported in part by grants *ACI-SI: VERA* and *AlgoQP* of the French Ministry of research, and by an Israel Science Foundation grant number 55/03

[†]Faculty of Computer Science, Technion – Israel institute of technology, Haifa 32000, Israel, eldar@cs.technion.ac.il

[‡]CNRS–LRI, Université Paris–Sud, France, magniez@lri.fr

[§]LRI & Université Paris II, France, mdr@lri.fr

for the equality between two words whose complexity is $|\Sigma|^{O(1/\varepsilon)}$, where $|\Sigma|$ is the alphabet size. Our tester is also *tolerant*, that is it is not only an ε-tester, but it also accepts with high probability words that are ε^2-close. The notion of tolerance, initially present in self-testing, was firstly not considered in property testing. Recently, coming back to this notion, a relation between tolerant property testing and weak approximation was pointed out in [18]. Based on this observation and our tolerant tester, we directly get an approximation algorithm for the normalized edit distance with moves between two words (**Corollary 3.2**), whose complexity is $|\Sigma|^{O(1/\varepsilon)}$. To our knowledge this is the first such approximation algorithm whose complexity is independent of the size n.

Computing the edit distance with moves is NP-hard [21] but can be approximated within an $\tilde{O}(\ln n)$ factor only in near linear time [10]. It has been used in [13] for testing regular languages, where the tester is more efficient and simpler than the one of [2], and can be generalized to tree regular languages. We note that the edit distance without moves, whose value always lies between the Hamming distance (for which there is a trivial tolerant tester) and the edit distance with moves (for which we prove the existence of a tolerant tester), is in itself hard for tolerant testing [3].

Then we extend our embedding to languages. This leads us to an approximate geometrical description of regular languages by finite unions of polytopes, which is robust (**Theorem 3.2**). Discretizing this representation gives us a new ε-tester (**Theorem 3.3**) for regular languages whose query complexity is $|\Sigma|^{O(1/\varepsilon)}$ and time complexity is $2^{|\Sigma|^{O(1/\varepsilon)}}$. Whereas the complexity of previous testers for regular languages depended (exponentially) on the number of states m of the corresponding automaton (whether it is deterministic or non-deterministic), here the tester construction requires time $m^{|\Sigma|^{O(1/\varepsilon)}}$, which is polynomial in m for a fixed ε. In addition, the automaton here is only used in a preprocessing step to build the tester, which is independent of the size of the input.

Using again discretization, we construct an ε-equivalence tester (**Theorem 3.4**) for nondeterministic finite automata in deterministic polynomial time, that is $m^{|\Sigma|^{O(1/\varepsilon)}}$ (where the exact decision version of this problem is PSPACE-complete by [22]). We then extend this result to the ε-equivalence testing of Büchi automata (**Theorem 3.5**) (after generalizing our definitions to deal also with languages of infinite words), and a deterministic exponential time algorithm for the ε-equivalence testing of context-free grammars (**Theorem 3.6**) (for which the exact decision version is not even recursively computable). Equivalence testers decide if MSO (Monadic second-order) formulas on strings are ε-equivalent. Approximate Model-Checking could generalize this approach to other Logics in the future, when exact Model-Checking remains infeasible.

Last we consider 2-ranked ordered trees, but our results generalize to any ranked trees. When trees are interpreted as graphs, their edit distance with moves is closely related to the minimal number of edges one has to add or remove in order to get one tree from the other. This distance was highly used in the context of property testing in bounded-degree graphs [12]. We define a compression of trees by a relabeling of the tree. Basically, all small subtrees are removed and encoded into the labels of their ancestor nodes. Such a compression removes a large fraction of 2-degree nodes, and can therefore be used to encode any ranked tree T into a word $w(T)$. Since our ℓ_1-embedding of $w(T)$ can be approximately sampled from samples on T, some of our previous results on words can be extended to trees. Then the tree isomorphism problem is testable (**Theorem 4.1**). This is unlike the context of dense graphs where there is a negative result [1]. In addition, regular tree languages have an $(\varepsilon^4, O(\varepsilon))$-tolerant tester (**Theorem 4.2**) whose query complexity is $|\Sigma|^{O(1/\varepsilon^5)}$ and time complexity is $2^{|\Sigma|^{O(1/\varepsilon^5)}}$. Again, as opposed to previous testers for tree regular languages [13], here the automaton is only used in a preprocessing step to build the tester, in time exponential in the tree automaton size for fixed ε.

2 Preliminaries

Let **K** be a class of finite structures U, such as words or trees. A property P is a subset of **K**. A formula F in the language of **K** is defined in some Logic such as First-Order Logic or Monadic Second-Order Logic, and we use the logical characterization of regular properties of words (resp. trees) by Monadic Second Order Logic. We say that $U \in \mathbf{K}$ *satisfies* P, or $U \models P$, when $U \in P$. When P is defined by a formula F, we extend this notation to F. Instead of properties, we may speak of classes or languages, and in particular, regular languages of words and trees.

2.1 Distances on Words and Trees

An *elementary operation* on a word w is either an insertion, a deletion or a substitution of a letter, or the *move* of a subword of w into another position. The *edit distance with moves* $\mathrm{dist}(w, w')$ between w and w' is the minimal number of elementary operations performed on w to obtain w'.

The above distance is extended to trees by generalizing the elementary operations. An *elementary operation* (see Figure 1) on an unranked ordered tree T is either an insertion or a deletion of a node [23], the substitution of a label, or the move of an entire subtree [13]. More precisely, a *move* (u, v, i) moves in one step u (and the corresponding subtree rooted at u) to be the i-th successor of v, shifting all the j successors of v for $j \geq i$ by one. As a consequence, the new parent of u is now v. When trees are specified to be r-ranked, we will restrict ourselves only to deletions and moves that gives a r-ranked tree.

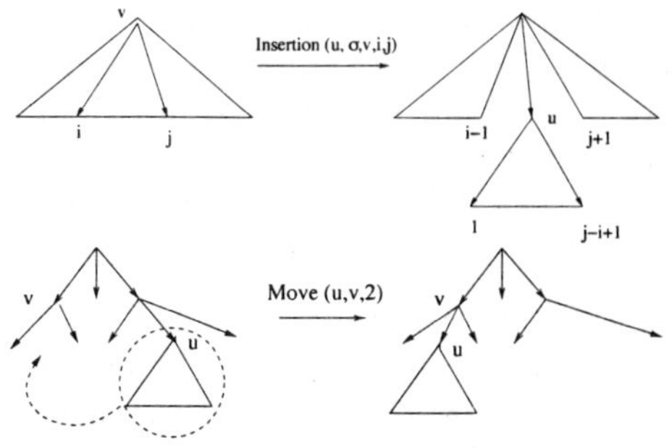

Figure 1. Elementary operations on trees.

2.2 Approximate Satisfiability and Equivalence

We define the notion of approximate satisfiability as in property testing [11]. Let $\mathbf{K}$ be a class of finite structures U with a distance dist between structures. Since property testing is an approximate notion of verification for dense instances, or equivalently for normalized distances, we first define a suitable notion of closeness for any distance dist. We say that $U, U' \in \mathbf{K}$ are *ε-close* if their distance is at most $\varepsilon \times M$, where M is a normalization factor, that is the maximum of $\mathsf{dist}(V, V')$ when V and V' range over $\mathbf{K}$ and have respectively same sizes as U and U'. They are *ε-far* if they are not ε-close. For words and trees, M is set to be the maximal size of the respective structures, since this is always the order of the maximum distance. (For dense graphs, M is the square of the maximal size of the respective structures.)

Definition 2.1. *Let P be a property on $\mathbf{K}$. A structure $U \in \mathbf{K}$* ε-satisfies *P, or $U \models_\varepsilon P$ for short, if U is ε-close to some $U' \in \mathbf{K}$ such that $U' \models P$.*

When P is defined by a formula F we extend this notation to F. Note that $U \not\models_\varepsilon P$ means that U is ε-far from every U' such that $U' \models P$.

Definition 2.2 (Tester [11])**.** *Let $\varepsilon > 0$. An* ε-tester *for a property $P \subseteq \mathbf{K}$ is a randomized algorithm A such that, for any structure $U \in \mathbf{K}$ as input:*
(1) If $U \models P$, then A accepts with probability at least $2/3$;
(2) If $U \not\models_\varepsilon P$, then A rejects with probability at least $2/3$.

If in addition the algorithm is guaranteed to always accept if $U \in P$, then we call it a *one-sided error ε-tester*. When (1) is amended as follows for some $0 < \varepsilon_0 < \varepsilon$:
(1') If $U \models_{\varepsilon_0} P$, then A accepts with prob. at least $2/3$;
then we say that the tester is a *(tolerant) $(\varepsilon_0, \varepsilon)$-tester* [18]. Approximation algorithms are related to tolerant testers [18]. Let $\alpha, \beta : \mathbb{R} \to \mathbb{R}$ and $f : \mathbf{K} \to \mathbb{R}$. An *$(\alpha, \beta)$-approximation* of f is a randomized algorithm that, for any input x, outputs a value z such that $\Pr[\alpha(f(x)) \leq z \leq \beta(f(x))] \geq 2/3$.

A *query* to a structure U depends on the model for accessing the structure. For a word w, a query is asking for the value of $w[i]$, for some i. For a tree T, a query is asking for the value of the label of i, for some i, and potentially for the index of its parent and its j-th successor, for some j. We also assume that the algorithm may query the input size. The *query complexity* is the number of queries made to the structure. The *time complexity* is the usual definition, where we assume that the following operations are performed in constant time: arithmetic operations, a uniform random choice of an integer from any finite range not larger than the input size, and a query to the input.

Definition 2.3. *A property $P \subseteq \mathbf{K}$ is* testable, *if there exists a randomized algorithm A such that, for every real $\varepsilon > 0$ as input, $A(\varepsilon)$ is an ε-tester of P, and the query and time complexities of the algorithm A depend only on ε.*

We extend these definitions to any formula F that defines P. We then introduce the new notion of equivalence testing for two properties P_1 and P_2 and in particular when the properties are definable by two formulas F_1 and F_2 over a logic $\mathcal{L}$.

Definition 2.4. *Let $\varepsilon > 0$. Let F_1 and F_2 be two formulas on $\mathbf{K}$. Then F_1 is* ε-equivalent *to F_2, or $F_1 \equiv_\varepsilon F_2$ for short, if all but finitely many structures $U \in \mathbf{K}$ that satisfy $U \models F_1$ satisfy also $U \models_\varepsilon F_2$, and conversely.*

Definition 2.5 (Equivalence tester)**.** *Let $\varepsilon > 0$. A (deterministic)* ε-equivalence tester *for $\mathcal{L}$ is a (deterministic) algorithm A such that, given as input $F_1, F_2 \in \mathcal{L}$:*
(1) If $F_1 \equiv F_2$, then A accepts;
(2) If $F_1 \not\equiv_\varepsilon F_2$, then A rejects.

The probabilistic version would require modifying the above conditions, to hold for A with probability $2/3$.

3 Words

We will define several statistics over words and study their robustness [19, 20] and soundness. Robustness means that far words have far statistics, and soundness means that close words have close statistics. Despite the difficulty of computing the edit distance with moves, one can efficiently approximate the statistics of a word. This will directly give us a tolerant tester and then an approximation algorithm for the normalized edit distance with moves.

We will first study the robustness of our first statistics, the block statistics. Then we will extend the robustness to the uniform statistics, which have the advantage of being also sound. Last we will see how to use these statistics to efficiently decide approximate satisfiability and equivalence.

3.1 Statistical Embeddings

Let k be an integer and $\varepsilon = 1/k$. For a word w over a finite alphabet Σ, we will define and study statistics of subwords of k consecutive letters of w for different probability distributions.

In this section, w and w' are two words of size n over Σ, such that k divides n. We implicitly decompose any word w into consecutive subwords of size k, $w = w[1]_b w[2]_b \ldots w[\varepsilon n]_b$, where $w[i]_b \in \Sigma^k$ is the *i-th block letter* of w. The *block statistics* $\mathsf{b\text{-}stat}(w)$ is the statistics of the block letters of w, that is, for every $u \in \Sigma^k$, the value $\mathsf{b\text{-}stat}(w)[u]$ is equal to the probability that for a uniformly random choice of $j \in \{1, \ldots, n/k\}$ we get $w[j]_b = u$.

The *block distribution* of w is the uniform distribution on block letters $w[1]_b, \ldots, w[\varepsilon n]_b$ (with some possible repetitions). Let X be the random vector of size $|\Sigma|^k$ whose coordinates are 0 except the u-coordinate which is 1, for a randomly chosen u according to the block distribution of w. The expectation of X satisfies $\mathrm{E}(X) = \mathsf{b\text{-}stat}(w)$.

We want to construct statistics that are both robust and sound. Since the block statistics will appear to be non robust, we define other statistics using variants of the block distribution. The *uniform distribution* $\mathsf{u\text{-}stat}(w)$ corresponds to a uniform and random choice of a subword of size k of w. This is very much related to the previous work of [8], where the subwords of length k were referred to by the term "shingles".

For example, for binary words, if $k = 2$ (and so $\varepsilon = 0.5$), there are 4 possible subwords of length 2, which we take in lexicographic order. For the binary word $w = 000111$, $\mathsf{b\text{-}stat}(w) = (1/3, 1/3, 0, 1/3)$, whereas $\mathsf{u\text{-}stat}(w) = (2/5, 1/5, 0, 2/5)$, as there are 2 blocks 00, 1 block 01, no block 10 and 2 blocks 11 among the possible 5 blocks.

The block uniform distribution, defined below, will be a link between block and uniform distributions. To define the *block uniform distribution* $\mathsf{bu\text{-}stat}(w)$ we first partition w into bigger consecutive blocks of size K, where $K = \lfloor \frac{\varepsilon^3 n}{8\ln(|\Sigma|)|\Sigma|^{2/\varepsilon}} \rfloor$. To simplify, we assume that k divides $(K - k - 1)$, that n is divisible by K, and that $n = \Omega(\frac{(\ln|\Sigma|)|\Sigma|^{2/\varepsilon}}{\varepsilon^5})$. We call the new blocks the *big blocks*. Now $\mathsf{bu\text{-}stat}(w)$ is defined by the following two-step procedure: First, in every big block choose uniformly a random $0 \le t \le k-1$, and delete the first t letters and the last $k - 1 - t$ letters; then take uniformly a random block letter in the remaining subword of the original word.

In order to construct an efficient algorithms based on those statistics, we need to efficiently approximate them. For this, we state a more general result that implies the approximability of our statistics. There are several methods which can be used to obtain a Chernoff-Hoeffding type bound on vectors. In our simple case, the use of Chernoff-Hoeffding bound together with a direct union bound is polynomially tight using an argument similar to the one of [4].

Lemma 3.1. *Let f be a function from $\{1, \ldots, M\}$ to $\mathbb{R}^D$, such that $f(x)$ has non-negative coordinates and has unit ℓ_1-norm, for every x. Let $\{Y_1, \ldots, Y_N\}$ be random variables over $\{1, \ldots, M\}$ independently distributed according to the same probabilistic distribution d. Then for every $t > 0$, $\Pr\left[|\mathrm{E}_d(f(Y)) - \frac{1}{N}\sum_{i=1}^N f(Y_i)| \ge D \times t\right] \le D \times 2e^{-2Nt^2}$.*

Proof. Let $\mu = \mathrm{E}_d(f(Y))$ and $\hat{\mu}_N = \frac{1}{N}\sum_{i=1}^N f(Y_i)$. For each coordinate $u \in \{1, \ldots, D\}$, $\Pr[|\mu[u] - \hat{\mu}_N[u]| \ge t] \le 2e^{-2Nt^2}$, by the Chernoff-Hoeffding bound for the random variables $X_i = f(Y_i)[u]$ which are between 0 and 1 and whose expectation is $\mu[u]$. We conclude using a union bound. □

As a corollary we can approximate both block and uniform statistics using a number of samples independent of n. The variables Y_i denote the position of the selected block letters u of w, and X_i denote the corresponding vectors of size $|\Sigma|^k$ whose u-coordinate is one and others are zero. Let stat denote either $\mathsf{b\text{-}stat}$ or $\mathsf{u\text{-}stat}$. Then we define $\widehat{\mathsf{stat}}_N(w) \stackrel{\text{def}}{=} \frac{1}{N}\sum_{i=1,\ldots,N} X_i$.

Corollary 3.1. *There exists $N \in O(\frac{(\ln|\Sigma|)|\Sigma|^{2/\varepsilon}}{\varepsilon^3})$ for which $\Pr[|\mathsf{stat}(w) - \widehat{\mathsf{stat}}_N(w)| \ge \varepsilon] \le \frac{1}{3}$, where stat denotes either $\mathsf{b\text{-}stat}$ or $\mathsf{u\text{-}stat}$.*

3.2 Robustness and Soundness

Note that $\mathsf{b\text{-}stat}(w) = \mathsf{b\text{-}stat}(w')$ iff w' can be obtained by a permutation of the block letters of w (since w and w' have same size). This can be extended when the equality is only approximate, by relating the distance between two words to the ℓ_1-distance of their respective block statistics.

Lemma 3.2 (Robustness)**.** $\mathsf{dist}(w, w') \le (\frac{1}{2}|\mathsf{b\text{-}stat}(w) - \mathsf{b\text{-}stat}(w')| + \varepsilon) \times n$.

Proof. If $\mathsf{b\text{-}stat}(w) = \mathsf{b\text{-}stat}(w')$, the distance $\mathsf{dist}(w, w')$ is at most εn as we only need to move εn block letters. Otherwise, we will construct a word w'' from w such that $\mathsf{b\text{-}stat}(w'') = \mathsf{b\text{-}stat}(w')$, using at most $\frac{n}{2}|\mathsf{b\text{-}stat}(w) - \mathsf{b\text{-}stat}(w')|$ substitutions. Applying the triangle inequality and the previous case, we obtain the desired result.

Collect in X_+ the positions i of block letters $w[i]_b$ such that $\mathsf{b\text{-}stat}(w)[w[i]_b] > \mathsf{b\text{-}stat}(w')[w[i]_b]$, and in X_- the positions j such that $\mathsf{b\text{-}stat}(w)[w'[j]_b] < \mathsf{b\text{-}stat}(w')[w'[j]_b]$. Note that X_+ and X_- have the same cardinality, which is $\frac{n}{2k}|\mathsf{b\text{-}stat}(w) - \mathsf{b\text{-}stat}(w')|$. Initially we let $w'' = w$. Until $X_+ \ne \emptyset$ repeat the following: take any $i \in X_+$ and $j \in X_-$; replace in w'' the letters of $w''[i]_b = w[i]_b$ with those of $w'[j]_b$ (using at most k substitutions); remove i from X_+ and j from X_-. The resulting word w'' satisfies the required conditions. □

We now prove that u-stat is both robust and sound, which leads to an estimator of the distance for far away instances, whereas b-stat is only robust. For instance, the words $(01)^n$ and $(10)^n$ are $\frac{1}{2n}$-close, whereas for an even k their block statistics are $\Omega(1)$-far. The proof of the robustness of u-stat will use in an intermediate step the robustness of the block uniform statistics bu-stat. For the soundness of u-stat, the proof is much simpler.

Lemma 3.3 (Soundness). *Let $n = \Omega(\frac{1}{\varepsilon})$. If $\mathsf{dist}(w, w') \le \varepsilon^2 n$ then $|\mathsf{u\text{-}stat}(w) - \mathsf{u\text{-}stat}(w')| \le 6.1\varepsilon$.*

Proof. First, remember that there are at most $n-k+1$ subwords of size k in w. Assume that $\mathsf{dist}(w, w') = 1$. In case of a simple edit operation (insertion, deletion, substitution) on a letter, $|\mathsf{u\text{-}stat}(w) - \mathsf{u\text{-}stat}(w')| \le 2 \times \frac{k}{n-k+1}$. For a move operation, if $w = ABCD$ and $w' = ACBD$ where a subword B has been moved, there are three border areas where we may choose a word of length k in w which does not exist in w'. Conversely, there are similar borders in w'. For each border, there are $k-1$ possible subwords that intersect it, hence $|\mathsf{u\text{-}stat}(w) - \mathsf{u\text{-}stat}(w')| \le 2 \times \frac{3(k-1)}{n-k+1}$.

If $\mathsf{dist}(w, w') \le \varepsilon^2 n$ and $n = \Omega(\frac{1}{\varepsilon})$, then by the triangle inequality $|\mathsf{u\text{-}stat}(w') - \mathsf{u\text{-}stat}(w')| \le \varepsilon^2 n \times \frac{6.1k}{n} = 6.1\varepsilon$, since $k = \frac{1}{\varepsilon}$. □

We now show that the robustness for $\mathsf{b\text{-}stat}(w)$ implies the robustness for $\mathsf{bu\text{-}stat}(w)$, which then will imply the robustness for $\mathsf{u\text{-}stat}(w)$. For a big block B_i, where $i = 1, \ldots, \frac{n}{K}$, we denote by v_{i,t_i} the subword of B_i after deleting the first t_i letters and the last $k-1-t_i$ letters of B_i. Let v be the concatenations of the words v_{i,t_i}. Then by the definition of $\mathsf{bu\text{-}stat}(w)$ we have $\mathsf{bu\text{-}stat}(w) = \frac{K}{n}\sum_{i=1}^{n/K} \mathrm{E}_{t_i=0,\ldots,k-1}(\mathsf{b\text{-}stat}(v_{i,t_i})) = \mathrm{E}_v(\mathsf{b\text{-}stat}(v))$.

Intuitively one would like to use this equation directly for extending the robustness of b-stat to bu-stat. However, this will not work since one would need to use a triangle inequality in the wrong direction. Instead we use a more elaborate proof using a Chernoff-Hoeffding bound argument.

Lemma 3.4. *There exists a word v obtained from w after deleting $O(\frac{(\ln|\Sigma|)|\Sigma|^{2/\varepsilon}}{\varepsilon^4})$ letters, so that $|\mathsf{bu\text{-}stat}(w) - \mathsf{b\text{-}stat}(v)| \le \frac{\varepsilon}{2}$.*

Proof. Fix a coordinate $u \in \Sigma^k$. For every $i = 1, \ldots, \frac{n}{K}$, let X_i be the random variable $X_i \stackrel{\text{def}}{=} \mathsf{b\text{-}stat}(v_{i,t_i})[u]$, where t_i is chosen uniformly in $\{0, \ldots, k-1\}$. We denote by v the random word obtained from the concatenation of the words v_{i,t_i}. Note that v is obtained from w after deleting $(k-1) \times \frac{n}{K} = O(\frac{(\ln|\Sigma|)|\Sigma|^{2/\varepsilon}}{\varepsilon^4})$ letters.

The variables $(X_i)_i$ are independent random variables such that $0 \le X_i \le 1$ and $\mathrm{E}_v(\mathsf{b\text{-}stat}(v)[u]) = \frac{K}{n}\sum_i \mathrm{E}(X_i) = \mathsf{bu\text{-}stat}(w)[u]$. By the Chernoff-Hoeffding bound we then get that, for any $t \ge 0$, $\Pr\left[|\mathsf{bu\text{-}stat}(w)[u] - \mathsf{b\text{-}stat}(v)[u]| \ge t\right] \le 2e^{-2(\frac{n}{K})t^2}$.

We repeat the same argument for every u-coordinate, and using a union bound, we conclude that: $\Pr\left[|\mathsf{bu\text{-}stat}(w) - \mathsf{b\text{-}stat}(v)| \ge |\Sigma|^k \times t\right] \le |\Sigma|^k \times 2e^{-2(\frac{n}{K})t^2}$. If we set $t = \frac{\varepsilon}{2|\Sigma|^k} = \frac{1}{2k|\Sigma|^k}$, and use the definition of K, we conclude that there exists with non-zero probability a word v that satisfies the required property about the statistics, completing the proof. □

Combining the robustness of block statistics, the previous lemma, and the next lemma, which easily relates bu-stat to u-stat, we get our robustness lemma.

Lemma 3.5. $|\mathsf{bu\text{-}stat}(w) - \mathsf{u\text{-}stat}(w)| = O(\frac{(\ln|\Sigma|)|\Sigma|^{2/\varepsilon}}{\varepsilon^4 n})$.

Lemma 3.6 (Robustness). *Let $n = \Omega(\frac{(\ln|\Sigma|)|\Sigma|^{2/\varepsilon}}{\varepsilon^5})$. If $\mathsf{dist}(w, w') \ge 5\varepsilon n$ then $|\mathsf{u\text{-}stat}_k(w) - \mathsf{u\text{-}stat}_k(w')| \ge 6.5\varepsilon$.*

Using the Soundness and Robustness Lemmas, we can construct a one-sided error tester for the equality of two words which is also $(\varepsilon^2, 5\varepsilon)$-tolerant:

Uniform Tester(w, w', ε)**:**
Let $N = \Theta(\frac{(\ln|\Sigma|)|\Sigma|^{2/\varepsilon}}{\varepsilon^3})$, and $k = \frac{1}{\varepsilon}$
Compute $\widehat{\mathsf{u\text{-}stat}}_N(w)$ and $\widehat{\mathsf{u\text{-}stat}}_N(w')$ using the same N uniformly random indices in $\{1, \ldots, n-k+1\}$
Accept if $|\widehat{\mathsf{u\text{-}stat}}_N(w) - \widehat{\mathsf{u\text{-}stat}}_N(w')| \le 6.25\varepsilon$
Reject otherwise

Theorem 3.1. *For any $\varepsilon > 0$, and two words w, w' of the same size of order $\Omega(\frac{(\ln|\Sigma|)|\Sigma|^{2/\varepsilon}}{\varepsilon^5})$, the above test:*
(1) accepts if $w = w'$ with probability 1;
(2) accepts if w and w' are ε^2-close with prob. at least 2/3;
(3) rejects if w and w' are 5ε-far with prob. at least 2/3.
Moreover its query and time complexities are in $O(\frac{(\ln|\Sigma|)|\Sigma|^{2/\varepsilon}}{\varepsilon^4})$.

From this $(\varepsilon^2, 5\varepsilon)$-tolerant tester, one can derive an $(\varepsilon^2, 5\varepsilon)$-approximation algorithm of the distance following the approach of [18].

Corollary 3.2. *There exists an $(\varepsilon^2, 5\varepsilon)$-approximation algorithm for computing the normalized distance $\varepsilon = \mathsf{dist}(w, w')/|w|$ between every words w, w' of the same size in $\Omega(\frac{\ln(|\Sigma|/\varepsilon)|\Sigma|^{2/\varepsilon}}{\varepsilon^4})$, and with query and time complexities in $O(\frac{(\ln(|\Sigma|/\varepsilon))|\Sigma|^{2/\varepsilon}}{\varepsilon^4})$.*

3.3 Geometric Embedding of a Language

3.3.1 General Observations

We want to use the notion of block statistics in order to efficiently characterize a language. We choose this statistics vector for the sake of clarity of the explanation since it is the simplest to manipulate. Nonetheless, this work can be extended to the uniform statistic, leading to tolerant testers, by following a more complex approach that will appear in a future journal version.

Using the previous section, we can embed a word w into its block statistics $\mathsf{b\text{-}stat}(w) \in \mathbb{R}^{|\Sigma|^{1/\varepsilon}}$. This characterization is approximately one-to-one from Lemma 3.2 if the size of the words is fixed. This means that given unlimited computational power we could test any language with a constant number of queries, by first precomputing the statistics of all possible words of length n in that language.

However, the block statistics do not characterize words of different lengths, as $\mathsf{b\text{-}stat}(w_0) = \mathsf{b\text{-}stat}(w_0^t)$ for every positive integer t, if w_0 is any word whose size is a multiple of k. This means that the set of block statistics $\mathsf{b\text{-}stat}(w)$ of all the elements $w \in L$ is not a good characterization of a general language L. For instance, the word $w_0^{3\times 2^{s-1}}$ is $(1 - 1/k^{2^{s-1}})$-far from the language $\{w_0^{2^t} : t \geq 1\}$, for every positive integer s. Moreover, it is not hard to construct using the appropriate powers a language whose testing algorithm requires arbitrarily intensive computations.

To construct a test that works for all n using only one preprocessing stage, one might consider only block statistics of loops of a language (as provided by an appropriate pumping lemma). This makes sense when any word of a language can be decomposed into loops up to a few remaining letters. Regular languages have this property, and context-free languages also share it when any permutation between block letters is allowed (see Section 3.6).

3.3.2 Regular Languages on strings

We fix a finite alphabet Σ, and an automaton A (possibly non-deterministic) on Σ with a set of states Q of size m, that recognizes a regular language L. Let k be a positive integer and $\varepsilon = \frac{1}{k}$. We consider only words whose size is divisible by k, as any word of length n of L, for n large enough, is close to such a word. Define A^k, the *k-th power of A*, as the automaton on Σ^k with set of states Q such that the transitions of A^k are exactly all sequences of k consecutive transitions of A. Then A and A^k recognize the same words. In the general case, one can modify A^k such that A^k recognizes the language of words of L where the last $(|w| - k\lfloor\frac{|w|}{k}\rfloor)$ letters are deleted.

We will characterize L by the block statistics of its loops on the block alphabet. We remark that the statistics of the A^k-loops basically only depend on L and k (the proof is omitted due to the lack of space).

Definition 3.1. *A word v over Σ^k is an A^k-*loop *if there exist two words u, w over Σ^k and an accepting path of A^k for uvw, such that the state of the automaton after reading u (following the above accepting path) is identical to the state after reading uv.*
*A finite set of A^k-loops is A^k-*compatible *if all the loops can occur one after the other (in any order) in one accepting path of A^k.*

We define the geometric embedding of L by the union of convex hulls of every compatible set of loops.

Definition 3.2. *Let $\mathcal{H}$ be the union of $\mathsf{Convex\text{-}Hull}(\mathsf{b\text{-}stat}(v_1), \ldots, \mathsf{b\text{-}stat}(v_t))$ when $v_1, \ldots, v_t$ range over A^k-compatible loops, for every $t \geq 0$.*

This definition is motivated by a standard result on finite automata: one can rearrange any word of a regular language into a sequence of small compatible loops. We formulate this fact in our context.

Proposition 3.1. *Let $w \in L$. Then there exists a permutation of the block letters of w into $w' = vu_1u_2\ldots u_l$, such that $|v|_b, |u_1|_b, \ldots, |u_l|_b \leq m$ and $\{u_1, u_2, \ldots, u_l\}$ is an A^k-compatible set of A^k-loops (not necessarily distinct).*

A consequence together with Caratheodory's theorem is that one can equivalently define $\mathcal{H}$ when the loop sizes and the number of compatible loops are bounded. Recall that even if this new characterization explicitly depends on A^k (that is on A and ε), the set $\mathcal{H}$ only depends on L and ε.

Proposition 3.2. *$\mathcal{H}$ equals the union of $\mathsf{Convex\text{-}Hull}(\mathsf{b\text{-}stat}(v_1), \ldots, \mathsf{b\text{-}stat}(v_t))$ when $v_1, \ldots, v_t$ range over A^k-compatible loops such that $|v_i|_b \leq m$ and $t = |\Sigma|^{1/\varepsilon} + 1$.*

Another consequence of this proposition is that if a word w belongs to L, then it has to satisfy approximately $\mathsf{b\text{-}stat}(w) \in \mathcal{H}$ (Lemma 3.7). This can be understood as an approximate Parikh classification of regular languages, whereas the original Parikh characterization was for context-free languages [17]. The converse is also approximately true (Theorem 3.2).

As an example, let $L = (010)^*0^*$ and $k = 2$. Let $s_1 = \mathsf{b\text{-}stat}((010)^2) = (1/3, 1/3, 1/3, 0)$, $s_2 = \mathsf{b\text{-}stat}(00) = (1, 0, 0, 0)$, then $\mathcal{H}_L = \mathsf{Convex\text{-}Hull}(s_1, s_2)$.

Lemma 3.7. *For every $w \in L$ there exists w', so that $0 \leq |w| - |w'| \leq \frac{m}{\varepsilon}$, $\mathsf{dist}(w, w') \leq \frac{m}{\varepsilon}$, $|\mathsf{b\text{-}stat}(w) - \mathsf{b\text{-}stat}(w')| \leq \frac{2m}{\varepsilon|w|}$, and $\mathsf{b\text{-}stat}(w') \in \mathcal{H}$.*

Lemma 3.8. *For every $X \in \mathcal{H}$ and every n there exists $w \in L$, such that $0 \leq |w| - n \leq (|\Sigma|^{1/\varepsilon} + 3)\frac{2m}{\varepsilon}$ and $|X - \mathsf{b\text{-}stat}(w)| \leq (|\Sigma|^{1/\varepsilon} + 2)\frac{3m}{\varepsilon n}$.*

Proof. Let $X \in \mathcal{H}$, that is $X = \sum_{i=1}^{l} \lambda_i \, \mathsf{b\text{-}stat}(u_i)$, where $l = |\Sigma|^k + 1$, $|u_i|_b \leq m$, $0 \leq \lambda_i \leq 1$ and $\sum_i \lambda_i = 1$. Fix any integer n. We choose non-negative integers $(r_i)_{i=1,2,\ldots,l}$ that respectively approximate $\lambda_i \frac{\varepsilon n}{|u_i|_b}$, that is satisfy $0 \leq |r_i - \lambda_i \frac{\varepsilon n}{|u_i|_b}| \leq 1$, and such that

$0 \leq \sum_i r_i|u_i|_b - \varepsilon n \leq m$. It is always possible to satisfy this last condition due to the degree of freedom on the choices of r_i and the upper bound $|u_i|_b \leq m$: We let $j \geq 0$ be the minimum integer so that $\sum_{i=1}^{j}\lceil\lambda_i\frac{\varepsilon n}{|u_i|_b}\rceil|u_i|_b + \sum_{i=j+1}^{l}\lfloor\lambda_i\frac{\varepsilon n}{|u_i|_b}\rfloor|u_i|_b \geq 0$, and set $r_i = \lceil\lambda_i\frac{\varepsilon n}{|u_i|_b}\rceil$ for $i \leq j$ and $r_i = \lfloor\lambda_i\frac{\varepsilon n}{|u_i|_b}\rfloor$ for $i > j$.

Define the word $w' = u_1^{r_1}u_2^{r_2}\dots u_l^{r_l}$. Then its block length is close to εn: $0 \leq |w'|_b - \varepsilon n \leq m$. Moreover its block statistics satisfies

$$
\begin{aligned}
&|\text{b-stat}(w') - X| \\
= \;& \left|\sum_i \left(r_i\frac{|u_i|_b}{|w'|_b} - \lambda_i\right)\text{b-stat}(u_i)\right| \leq \sum_i |r_i\frac{|u_i|_b}{|w'|_b} - \lambda_i| \\
\leq \;& \sum_i |r_i\frac{|u_i|_b}{|w'|_b} - r_i\frac{|u_i|_b}{\varepsilon n}| + \sum_i |r_i\frac{|u_i|_b}{\varepsilon n} - \lambda_i| \\
\leq \;& \sum_i r_i|u_i|_b \times |\tfrac{1}{|w'|_b} - \tfrac{1}{\varepsilon n}| + \sum_i \tfrac{m}{\varepsilon n} \\
\leq \;& (m+\varepsilon n) \times (\tfrac{1}{\varepsilon n} - \tfrac{1}{m+\varepsilon n}) + l\tfrac{m}{\varepsilon n} = \tfrac{m}{\varepsilon n} + l\tfrac{m}{\varepsilon n}.
\end{aligned}
$$

Using A^k-compatibility, we can get a word of L from w' by inserting few block letters. Let $v_0u_{i_1}v_1u_{i_2}v_2\dots u_{i_l}v_l \in L$ be the witness of the A^k-compatibility of the loops $u_1, \dots, u_l$, such that $|v_j|_b \leq m$ for every j, and where $(i_1, \dots, i_l)$ is a permutation of $(1, \dots, l)$. Then $w = v_0u_{i_1}^{r_{i_1}}v_1u_{i_2}^{r_{i_2}}v_2\dots u_{i_l}^{r_{i_l}}v_l \in L$ by construction. Moreover $0 \leq |w|_b - |w'|_b \leq (l+1)m$, and $|\text{b-stat}(w') - \text{b-stat}(w)| \leq \frac{2(l+1)m}{\varepsilon n}$, so we conclude. □

Theorem 3.2. *Let $w \in \Sigma^n$ and $X \in \mathcal{H}$ be such that $|\text{b-stat}(w) - X| \leq \delta$. Then*

$$\text{dist}(w, L) \leq \left(\frac{\delta}{2} + (1 + O(\tfrac{m|\Sigma|^{1/\varepsilon}}{\varepsilon^2 n}))\varepsilon\right)n.$$

3.3.3 Construction of $\mathcal{H}$

One of the remaining tasks is to efficiently construct $\mathcal{H}$ for a given automaton A with m states. One could try to enumerate all A^k-loops of size at most m over Σ^k. This is not efficient enough due to the possible large number of loops, $O(|\Sigma|^{km})$. Nevertheless, since we only care about block statistics of compatible loops one can enumerate them using a standard reduction to matrix multiplication over the appropriate algebra. The complexity is then just polynomial in the number of possible corresponding block statistics, $\binom{m+|\Sigma|^k}{|\Sigma|^k} = O(m^{|\Sigma|^k})$, since a block statistics of a word v of size at most m over Σ^k basically corresponds to a partition of m into $|\Sigma|^k$ parts.

Lemma 3.9. *Given A and ε, a set H of $(|\Sigma|^{1/\varepsilon}+1)$-tuples of vectors can be computed in time $m^{|\Sigma|^{O(1/\varepsilon)}}$ such that $|H| \leq m^{|\Sigma|^{O(1/\varepsilon)}}$ and $\mathcal{H} = \bigcup_{S\in H}\text{Convex-Hull}(S)$.*

For a regular language, the set $\mathcal{H}$ is a subset of the unit ball of $\mathbb{R}^{|\Sigma|^k}$ for the ℓ_1-norm. Let us consider the grid $\mathcal{G}_\varepsilon = \{0, \frac{\varepsilon}{|\Sigma|^k}, \frac{2\varepsilon}{|\Sigma|^k}, \dots, 1\}^{|\Sigma|^k}$ of the cube $[0,1]^{|\Sigma|^k}$ with step $\frac{\varepsilon}{|\Sigma|^k}$. Let $\mathcal{H}_\varepsilon$ be the set of points of $\mathcal{G}_\varepsilon$ that are at distance at most $\frac{\varepsilon}{2}$ from $\mathcal{H}$ (for the ℓ_1-distance). Since $|\mathcal{G}_\varepsilon| = (k|\Sigma|^k+1)^{|\Sigma|^k} = 2^{|\Sigma|^{O(1/\varepsilon)}}$, then $|\mathcal{H}_\varepsilon| = 2^{|\Sigma|^{O(1/\varepsilon)}}$. Moreover, one can easily construct it from H.

Proposition 3.3. *Given A and ε, the set $\mathcal{H}_\varepsilon$ can be computed in time $m^{|\Sigma|^{O(1/\varepsilon)}}$.*

3.4 Property and Equivalence Testers

Theorem 3.3. *For every real $\varepsilon > 0$ and regular language L over a finite alphabet Σ, there exists an ε-tester for L whose query complexity is in $O(\frac{(\ln|\Sigma|)|\Sigma|^{2/\varepsilon}}{\varepsilon^4})$ and whose time complexity is in $2^{|\Sigma|^{O(1/\varepsilon)}}$.*
Moreover, given an automaton with m states that recognizes L, the tester can be constructed in time $m^{|\Sigma|^{O(1/\varepsilon)}}$.

Proof. We fix $\varepsilon > 0$, and automaton A with m states that recognizes L. We construct a 3ε-tester for L whose correctness directly follows from the previous section. Let w be a word given as input. We assume that $|w|/(\frac{m|\Sigma|^{1/\varepsilon}}{\varepsilon^2})$ is large enough, otherwise we just run the automaton on w.

The tester is in two steps: a preprocessing step and the testing step itself. Given A and ε, one can compute $\mathcal{H}_\varepsilon$ in time $m^{|\Sigma|^{O(1/\varepsilon)}}$ from Proposition 3.3. Now the testing part consists of computing an estimation $\widehat{\text{b-stat}_N}(w)$ of $\text{b-stat}(w)$ as in Corollary 3.1, where $N = \Theta(\frac{(\ln|\Sigma|)|\Sigma|^{2/\varepsilon}}{\varepsilon^3})$, using $O(\frac{(\ln|\Sigma|)|\Sigma|^{2/\varepsilon}}{\varepsilon^4})$ queries to w. If $\widehat{\text{b-stat}_N}(w)$ is at distance at most 2ε from $\mathcal{H}_\varepsilon$, the tester accepts, and otherwise it rejects. □

Theorem 3.4. *There exists a deterministic algorithm T such that, for every $\varepsilon > 0$ as input, $T(\varepsilon)$ is an ε-equivalence tester for automata over a finite alphabet Σ. Moreover the running time complexity of T is in $m^{|\Sigma|^{O(1/\varepsilon)}}$, where m is the input automata size.*

Proof. Fix $\varepsilon > 0$. The algorithm simply computes the respective discrete approximations $\mathcal{H}_{A,\varepsilon/2}$ and $\mathcal{H}_{B,\varepsilon/2}$ of $\mathcal{H}_A$ and $\mathcal{H}_B$ corresponding to the automata A and B. If they are equal, the tester accepts, and otherwise it rejects. The correctness proof, omitted here, essentially follows from the previous section. □

3.5 Infinite Regular Languages

We now consider an application to infinite words over a finite alphabet Σ. In this section, all words are infinite unless we explicitly state otherwise. A *Büchi automaton* is a finite automaton A on which the notion of acceptance has been modified as follows. For a word $w \in \Sigma^\omega$ over Σ and a corresponding (infinite) path in A, we denote by $\mathrm{Inf}_A(w)$ the set of states of A which are reached infinitely many times by the path. We say that w is *accepted* by A if there exists a path for w such that $\mathrm{Inf}_A(w)$ contains an accepting state of A. We say that A *recognizes* the language of accepted infinite words. Such languages are called *ω-regular languages*.

For every integer n, we denote by w_n the prefix of w of size n. Two words w, w' are *ε-close* if the superior limit $\overline{\lim}_{n\to\infty} \mathsf{dist}(w_{|_n}, w'_{|_n})/n$ is at most ε. Last, the *block statistics* $\mathsf{b\text{-}stat}(w)$ of w is the set of accumulation points of the sequence $(\mathsf{b\text{-}stat}(w_{|_n}))_n$.

By adapting our geometric embedding for this distance, an equivalence tester for two Büchi automata follows from the one previously defined for regular languages (over finite words). In this tester, we modify the Definition 3.2 of $\mathcal{H}$, by simply restricting ourselves to the loops of (strongly) connected components of the accepting states of A^k (we could also extend Theorem 3.3 to lasso words as in [9]).

Definition 3.3. *For every connected component C of A^k, let $\mathcal{H}_C$ be the convex hull of the vector set $\{\mathsf{b\text{-}stat}(w) : w$ is a loop in C s.t. $|w|_b \leq m\}$. We denote by $\mathcal{H}'$ the union $\bigcup_C \mathcal{H}_C$ where C ranges over all connected components of A^k that contain an accepting state and are reachable from an initial state.*

Theorem 3.4 is then valid for nondeterministic Büchi automata, with $\mathcal{H}'$ taking the place of $\mathcal{H}$.

Theorem 3.5. *There exists a deterministic algorithm T such that, for every $\varepsilon > 0$ as input, $T(\varepsilon)$ is an ε-equivalence tester for Büchi automata over a finite alphabet Σ. Moreover the running time complexity of T is in $m^{|\Sigma|^{O(1/\varepsilon)}}$, where m is the input automata size.*

This result has a direct application for the Logic LTL, Linear Time Logic. A classical construction associates a Büchi automaton to an LTL formula, whose size can be exponential in the size of the formula. When exact Model Checking is infeasible, we can use our approximate Equivalence tester with a fixed small parameter ε.

3.6 Context-Free Languages

We can construct an exponential time test and an equivalence tester for context-free languages, given by their grammar, or by their push-down automaton (the two representations are polynomially equivalent so we can switch back and forth between them as convenient). In comparison, the exact decision problem of whether two context-free grammars define the same language is not decidable.

The proof uses the original Parikh theorem about spectra of context-free languages, that provides a formula defining a semi-linear set on the letter counts of all possible words. The exponential blow-up in the grammar size comes from this step. From the spectrum one can calculate the set $\mathcal{H}$ that approximates the block-statistics of all large enough words, and then construct an appropriate $\mathcal{H}_\varepsilon$.

Therefore we can design string testers for a context-free language (which are not possible for the usual edit distance without moves, as the counter example in [2] works for the edit distance as well as the Hamming distance), in analogy to Theorem 3.3. We explicitly state the equivalence testability for context-free grammars we get as in Theorem 3.4 .

Theorem 3.6. *There exists a deterministic algorithm T such that, for every $\varepsilon > 0$ as input, $T(\varepsilon)$ is an ε-equivalence tester for context-free grammars over a finite alphabet Σ. Moreover the running time complexity of T is exponential in $m^{|\Sigma|^{O(1/\varepsilon)}}$, where m is the input grammars size.*

We note a corollary for regular expressions with squaring. Although they recognize only regular languages, their (exact) equivalence problem is EXPSPACE-complete by [15], so the exponential time algorithm given here can be considered as a slight improvement. Applying the previous theorem, we can obtain an equivalence tester.

4 Trees

To simplify the discussion we will consider only 2-ranked labeled ordered, trees but our results can be extended to any ranked trees. Let Σ be the finite label alphabet. The *size of a tree* is the number of its nodes, which we will denote by n. The *degree of a node* is the number of its successors. Let k be an integer and $\varepsilon = 1/k$.

We define the k-compression of a tree T, which basically consists of removing every node whose subtree has size $\leq k$, and encoding the removed subtrees into the labels of their ancestor nodes. This compression leads naturally to a word $w(T)$ that encodes T such that $\mathsf{u\text{-}stat}(w(T))$ can be approximately sampled from samples on T. Then some of our previous results on words can be extended to trees.

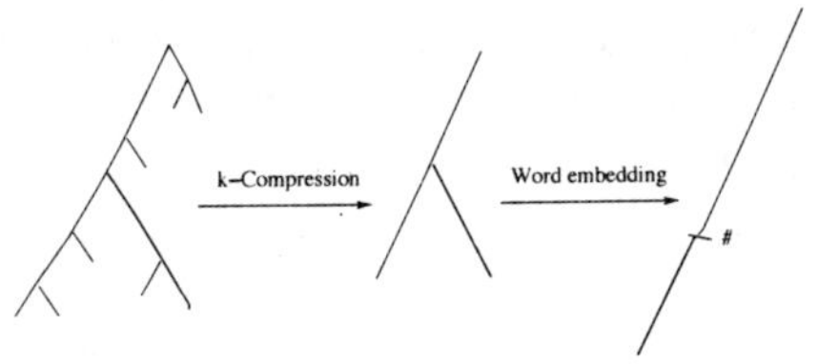

Figure 2. k-compression and word embedding.

4.1 Compression

Initial labels are named *simple labels*. We introduce new *tree labels* for leaves l whose purpose is to encode a subtree from l. We also interpret a simple label on a leaf as a tree label. A *mixed label* is an ordered pair of a simple label and a tree label, whose tree label encodes the subtree of the corresponding successor. Notice that an internal node might have either a simple label or a mixed label. Such a labeled tree *encodes* T when expanding the tree labels (from leaves and from the tree components of mixed labels) leads to the initial tree T.

The *size of a simple label* is 1. The *size of a tree label* is the size of the tree that it encodes. The *size of a mixed label* is the sum of the sizes of its labels, that is 1 plus the size of its tree label part.

Definition 4.1. *Let T be a tree and $k \geq 1$ be an integer. The* k-compression *T_k of T is the tree encoding of T such that each tree label has the minimal possible value in $[k, 2k-1]$.*

The *k-tree alphabet* (denoted $\Sigma^{(k)}$), is the set of any possible labels that come from a k-compression, that is when tree labels encode trees of size in $[k, 2k-1]$. Therefore $|\Sigma^{(k)}| = |\Sigma|^{O(k)}$. The new label of a node v can be computed using $O(k)$ queries to T by the following procedure that either computes its label on T_k, or rejects if v is not anymore in T_k.

Encode(T, v, k)
If the subtree from v in T has size $< k$ then Reject
Let u_1 and u_2 be the successors of v (or $u_1 = u_2$ if v has only one successor)
If the subtrees from u_1 and u_2 in T have both size $< k$ then return v and the encoding of the subtree from v in T
If no subtree from u_1 and u_2 in T has size $< k$ then return v and the simple label of v
If only the subtree from u_1 (resp. u_2) in T has size $< k$ then return v, and the pair of the simple label of v and the tree label of the subtree from u_1 (resp. u_2, but with opposite order) in T

In fact the k-compression of a tree T is almost a word, the number of remaining 2-degree nodes in T_k are small.

Lemma 4.1. *T_k has at most εn 2-degree nodes.*

Proof. In this proof the labels are the ones of T_k. Only nodes with simple labels can have degree 2 in T_k. Moreover, a node has degree 2 in T_k iff it has degree 2 in T and has a simple label. To every 2-degree node of T_k we will associate a distinct part of T of size $\geq k$. Then the lemma follows since T_k has $\leq n$ nodes.

The construction is bottom-up. We start with the tree $T' = T$ and continue until there are no more 2-degree nodes in T' with simple labels. We will maintain the following invariant of T', which T initially satisfies by assumption:

(*): Every 2-degree node of T' with a simple label (in T_k) has two successors whose subtrees in T' have size $\geq k$.

The iteration procedure is now described. Let v be a lowest node of T' with degree 2 and a simple label. By Property (*), the node v has two successors u_1 and u_2 whose subtrees in T' have size $\geq k$. We remove from T' the remaining subtree of u_1. Therefore v has now degree 1 in T'. Moreover since the subtree from u_2 is still in T', we guaranty that the new T' still satisfies Property (*). □

4.2 Word Embedding

From Lemma 4.1 we show that any tree T is 3ε-close to another tree T', such that T'_k has no 2-degree nodes and is 2ε-close to T_k. First let us fix a new symbol $\#$. To construct T'_k, we recursively eliminate each 2-degree node v with a simple label and successors (u_1, u_2), by moving u_2 to the rightmost leaf l of the subtree of u_1 in T_k and by changing the tree label σ of l to a mixed label $(\sigma, \#)$; equivalently on T we insert a new node u with label $\#$ between l and its parent, the left successor of u is l, its right sucessor is u_2.

Then we define $w(T)$ as the word over the k-tree alphabet which enumerates the labels of T'_k from its root. $w(T)$ is also the enumeration of the labels of T_k obtaining by a DFS from its root, where at most εn tree labels t have been modified to mixed labels $(t, \#)$.

We will perform the uniform statistics on $w(T)$ in order to apply the results of previous sections on words. Since each letter of $w(T)$ might encode a tree of size up to $O(1/\varepsilon)$ we need to apply an ε^2-tester on words, in order to get an $O(\varepsilon)$-tester on trees. An important fact is that u-stat$(w(T))$ (with block-size k^2) can be approximately sampled with additive error ε^2 by $O(1/\varepsilon^6)$ samples on T_k.

Statistics(T, k)
(*) Take a random v in T while **Encode**(T, v, k) rejects
Let $i = 1$ and $u_1 = v$; and iterate $k^2 - 1$ the following
  If u_i has at least one successor in T_k let be v the left one
  If u_i has no successor then
    Using a backtracking of depth k^4 in T_k, Search the first 2-degree node v in T_k such that u_i is on the left subtree of v
    If the search fails then go back to Step (*)
  Let $i = i + 1$ and $u_i = v$
Outputs the labels of $u_1 u_2 \ldots u_i$ using **Encode**$(T, \cdot, k)$

Lemma 4.2. ***Statistics**$(T, 1/\varepsilon)$ outputs a probabilistic distribution which is at ℓ_1-distance at most ε^2 from* u-stat$(w(T))$ *(with block-size $1/\varepsilon^2$). Moreover, its expected query and time complexities are in $O(1/\varepsilon^6)$.*

Proof. **Statistics**$(T, 1/\varepsilon)$ connects all but $\varepsilon^4 n$ leaves of T_k as in T'_k because of the backtracking. This means that only an ε^2 fraction of subwords is missing from $w(T)$. Then we can conclude. □

First our equality tester for words can be applied to trees as an isomorphism tester since any elementary operation on $w(T)$ corresponds to $O(1)$ elementary operations on T.

Theorem 4.1. *The tree isomorphism problem is tolerantly* $(\varepsilon^4, O(\varepsilon))$*-testable with query and time complexities in* $|\Sigma|^{O(1/\varepsilon^5)}$.

Then our regular language tester can also be extended since we also get that an automaton on trees T of size m corresponds to a push-down automaton on words $w(T)$ whose number of states and stack alphabet have both size m.

Theorem 4.2. *For every real* $\varepsilon > 0$ *and* 2*-tree regular language* L *over a finite alphabet* Σ*, there exists a tolerant* $(\varepsilon^4, O(\varepsilon))$*-tester for* L *whose query complexity is in* $|\Sigma|^{O(1/\varepsilon^5)}$ *and whose time complexity is in* $2^{|\Sigma|^{O(1/\varepsilon^5)}}$. *Moreover, given a* 2*-tree automaton with* m *states that recognizes* L*, the tester can be constructed in time exponential in* $m^{|\Sigma|^{O(1/\varepsilon^5)}}$.

Proof. The push-down automaton basically reads the tree as a word from the bottom up using the tree alphabet with a few modifications. When a label $(t, \#)$ is read, the current state is pushed on the stack and the state goes to an accessible state from reading t with an initial state, as a leaf. Then the symbol of the stack can be pulled while reading a simple label which corresponds to a branching between a previously evaluated branch of the tree and the current one. □

For the equivalence problem, there already exists a deterministic exponential time algorithm for the exact version of the problem. Therefore it seems that our current approach does not reduce the complexity. However, in the previous construction, if L is a tree language such that the number of $\#$ symbols in $w(T)$ for $T \in L$ is constant, then the set of $w(T)$ is regular. It is the case for the binary encoding for regular unranked tree of constant depth. We can then apply the equivalence tester for regular languages of words, and test the equivalence between such classes of tree languages in polynomial time. The general case remains an open problem.

References

[1] N. Alon, E. Fischer, M. Krivelevich, and M. Szegedy. Efficient testing of large graphs. *Combinatorica*, 20(4):451–476, 2000.

[2] N. Alon, M. Krivelevich, I. Newman, and M. Szegedy. Regular languages are testable with a constant number of queries. *SIAM J. Comp.*, 30(6):1842–1862, 2000.

[3] T. Batu, F. Ergun, J. Kilian, A. Magen, S. Raskhodnikova, R. Rubinfeld, and R. Sami. A sublinear algorithm for weakly approximating edit distance. In *Proc. STOC*, pp. 316–324, 2003.

[4] T. Batu, L. Fortnow, R. Rubinfeld, W. Smith, and P. White. Testing that distributions are close. In *Proc. FOCS*, pp. 259–269, 2000.

[5] M. Blum, M. Luby, and R. Rubinfeld. Self-testing/correcting with applications to numerical problems. *J. Comp. Syst. Sci.*, 47(3):549–595, 1993.

[6] M. Blum and S. Kannan. Designing programs that check their work. *J. ACM*, 42(1):269–291, 1995.

[7] N. Blum and R. Koch. Greibach normal form transformation revisited. *Information and Computation*, 150(1):112–118, 1999.

[8] A. Broder. On the resemblance and containment of documents. In *Proc. Compression and Complexity of Sequences*, pages 21–30, 1997.

[9] H. Chockler and O. Kupferman. ω-regular languages are testable with a constant number of queries. *Theor. Comp. Sci.*, 329:71–92, 2002.

[10] G. Cormode and S. Muthukrishnan. The string edit distance matching problem with moves. In *Proc. SODA*, pp. 667–676, 2002.

[11] O. Goldreich, S. Goldwasser, and D. Ron. Property testing and its connection to learning and approximation. *J. ACM*, 45(4):653–750, 1998.

[12] O. Goldreich, and D. Ron. Property Testing in Bounded Degree Graphs. *Algorithmica*, 32(2): 302–343, 2002.

[13] F. Magniez and M. de Rougemont. Property testing of regular tree languages. In *Proc. ICALP*, pp. 932–944, 2004.

[14] W. Masek and M. Paterson. A faster algorithm for computing string edit distance. *J. Comp. Syst. Sci.*, 20(1):18–31, 1980.

[15] A. Meyer and L. Stockmeyer. The equivalence problem for regular expressions with squaring requires exponential space. In *Proc. FOCS*, pp. 125–129, 1972.

[16] I. Newman. Testing membership in languages that have small width branching programs. *SIAM J. Comp.*, 3142(5):1557–1570, 2002.

[17] R. Parikh. On context-free languages. *J. ACM*, 13(4):570–581, 1966.

[18] M. Parnas, D. Ron, and R. Rubinfeld. Tolerant property testing and distance approximation. TR04-010, ECCC, 2004.

[19] R. Rubinfeld. On the robustness of functional equations. *SIAM J. Comp.*, 28(6):1972–1997, 1999.

[20] R. Rubinfeld and M. Sudan. Robust characterizations of polynomials with applications to program testing. *SIAM J. Comp.*, 25(2):23–32, 1996.

[21] D. Shapira and J. Storer. Edit distance with move operations. In *Proc. Symp. Combinatorial Pattern Matching*, pp. 85–98, 2002.

[22] L. Stockmeyer and A. Meyer. Word problems requiring exponential time. In *Proc. STOC*, pp. 1–9, 1973.

[23] K. C. Tai. The tree-to-tree correction problem. *J. ACM*, 26:422–433, 1979.

Author Index